FIGHTING SHIPS OF THE WORLD

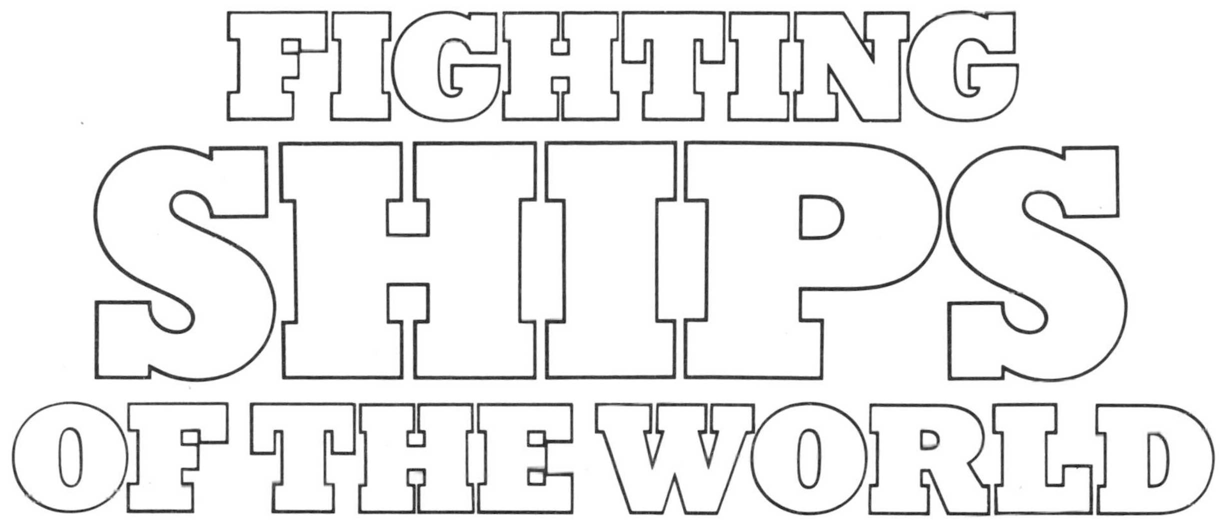

FIGHTING SHIPS OF THE WORLD

AN ILLUSTRATED ENCYCLOPEDIA OF MODERN SEA POWER

Consultant Editor Antony Preston

Exeter Books

NEW YORK

in association with Phoebus

Contributors: David Brown, Ian Buxton, Bernard Fitzsimons, Ian Friel, John Jordan, David Lyon, Hugh Lyon, Antony Preston, John A Roberts, Anthony J Watts, Michael R Wilson

Consultant editor: Antony Preston
Illustrator: John Batchelor

First published in USA 1980 by Exeter Books
Distributed by Bookthrift, Inc
New York, New York

ISBN 0-89673-074-3

This material first appeared in *Weapons and Warfare* © 1977/1980 Phoebus Publishing Company/BPC Publishing Limited, 52 Poland Street, London W1A 2JX

Made and printed in Hong Kong

During the 1920s and 1930s naval construction was limited by a series of international treaties restricting the number, size and armament of new warships. These were abandoned as the Second World War loomed, and by 1940 new construction programmes were under way, with different results for different navies. Germany's grandiose Plan Z for a powerful navy of surface ships gave way to concentration on U-Boat warfare; Japan persisted with such redundant concepts as aircraft-carrying submarines while neglecting more useful types; Britain, dependent on the Atlantic convoys, concentrated on providing escorts for them; and the United States, after standardizing on a number of basic designs, proceeded to build them by the dozen, and sometimes the hundred.

Tactically, the Second World War saw a number of profound changes in the use of sea power. Aircraft and submarines became the main enemy of surface ships, while the battleships and battle-cruisers that had been regarded as the king-pins of the fleets were eclipsed by the aircraft carrier, sea battles being fought at aircraft range without the opposing fleets ever sighting each other. Germany made startling progress in submarine design, though too late to have any influence on the outcome of the war; the necessity for aircraft protection of Allied convoys led first to merchant ships being equipped with a single catapult-launched fighter, then to the production of large numbers of comparatively inexpensive escort carriers; and Japan, her carrier force destroyed in a series of epic Pacific battles, managed to produce the most powerful battleship ever built, the ill-fated *Yamato*.

The postwar period brought new challenges. Nuclear power, first for submarines and then for surface ships, offered virtually unlimited range – at a price – and the combination of the nuclear-powered submarine and the long-range ballistic missile added a new dimension to sea power, while the radius of action of the aircraft carrier was extended greatly by new generations of jet-propelled aircraft.

Warships in the medium-size range have benefited from the introduction of gas turbines, allowing an increase in performance comparable to that produced by the first steam turbines 50 years earlier. In turn, the amount of equipment they are called on to carry has shown a dramatic increase, for although tactical missiles have to a large extent replaced heavy guns, the new weapons are dependent on extensive electronic systems for their effectiveness. Moreover, the raising of the stakes in underwater warfare, and the virtual silence of the nuclear submarine, have made helicopters and complex underwater sensors vital for effective anti-submarine warfare.

At the same time, however, there has been a renewed emphasis on the smaller types of vessel. Fast patrol boats can launch missiles such as Exocet, Otomat and Harpoon, able to deliver explosive power roughly equivalent to that of an 8-in. shell at anything up to radar range and with the probability of a first-round hit. This has given rise to the principle that the smaller a modern warship is, the heavier the punch per ton it can deliver. Of course, the corollary of this principle is that the smaller a warship is, the greater its need for back-up: only limited quantities of fuel, supplies and ammunition can be carried, so that virtually day-to-day support is required, and the more sophisticated electronic systems are precluded.

A particularly promising line of development in the field of small warships is that of the hydrofoil. Hydrofoils offer the advantages of high speed, great manoeuvrability and longer range than is possible with conventional craft of similar size, and modern missile and automatic gun systems enable them to carry a powerful armament.

Meanwhile, the conventional categories of warships – frigates, destroyers, cruisers and so on – have come to be applied to vessels which would have been unrecognizable as such 40 years ago. Frigates carry anti-submarine helicopters almost as a matter of course, destroyers retain their traditional escort function but have grown to the size of cruisers, and 'through-deck cruisers' such as the British *Invincible* and Soviet *Kiev* Classes have more than a passing resemblance to the traditional aircraft carrier. Their role, though, is crucially different: while retaining, to a limited extent, the ability to provide mobile air support, they also have anti-submarine warfare as a primary task, carrying out long-range anti-submarine patrols in response to the strategic submarine threat.

Perhaps the main common factor of the different types of major surface warships is their reliance on electronics. Their profiles are dominated by arrays of radar and other sensors, and their operation is automated to the extent that data from the sensors are analyzed by computer, and guns and missiles in turn are deployed by automatic fire-control systems.

IWM

IWM

Left: **The large mine decks and unusually high speed of the *Abdiel* class ships made them ideal for running supplies to Malta: here, *Welshman* unloads stores in July 1942. *Right:* HMS *Welshman* enters Grand Harbour, Malta, in 1942 disguised as a Vichy French destroyer with funnel caps and her sides painted to simulate a break in the deckline. The disguise twice succeeded in fooling enemy aircraft**

Abdiel

British fast minelayer class. These ships were among the most glamorous warships of the Second World War and also the most versatile. Although designed for the single purpose of laying mines in enemy waters, their high speed (for rapid transit to and from the laying area) and capacious decks made them useful for carrying stores and personnel. One of them spent her whole career carrying stores, and never laid a mine.

The most remarkable feature of the design was the provision of what amounted to a cruiser's horsepower in a hull little larger than that of a destroyer. The designed speed was 40 knots, and this, coupled with the reputation that the ships gained by their dramatic dashes through the Mediterranean to Malta, led to exaggerated accounts of their speed. In fact the ships were rather overweight, and in any case the forecasts of the engineers proved over-optimistic, so that none reached more than a fraction over 37 knots on trials, whereas speeds well in excess of 40 knots were claimed. Still, a sea speed of 35 knots or more was extremely creditable when it is remembered that destroyers were only capable of sea speeds of 30-31 knots. Another virtue of the design was the heavy antiaircraft armament, which gave the ships some chance of survival in the dangerous waters of the Mediterranean.

The first four ships—the *Abdiel, Manxman, Latona* and *Welshman*—were built under the 1938 Programme; all but one were war losses by 1943, but a repeat class of two—the *Apollo* and *Ariadne*—had been started in 1941. These ships differed from the earlier quartet in sacrificing a pair of 4-in AA guns in favour of a heavier and more efficient close-range armament. Both groups carried 156 mines on four sets of rails at main deck level, two of which extended as far as the forward superstructure. The mines were winched aft and discharged through stern doors.

The most outstanding achievements of the class were two runs made, one to lay mines in the Gulf of Leghorn and one to run desperately needed supplies to Malta, by *Manxman* and *Welshman* disguised as Vichy French destroyers. This was aided by the flush deck and three funnels, which were unique in

HMS *Abdiel* in early 1943 after her final refit. The original quad 0.5-in machine-gun mounts were replaced by seven single 20-mm Oerlikons in 1942. She is shown here painted in a 1943 Admiralty Disruptive camouflage scheme. The vessel was sunk by a mine in September 1943 while landing troops at Taranto

British ships of that size; a dark patch simulated a break in the deck level and caps on the funnels changed the appearance entirely. The ruse succeeded in deceiving the enemy on both occasions when the ships were sighted by German aircraft.

Displacement: 2650 tons (standard), 4000 tons (full load) *Dimensions:* 127.41 m (418 ft) oa×12.19 m (40 ft) ×4.88 m (16 ft) max *Machinery:* 2-shaft geared steam turbines, 72 000 shp=37 knots *Armament: (Abdiel, Latona, Manxman, Welshman)* 6×4-in (102-mm) AA (3×2), 4×2-pdr pom-poms (1×4), 8×.5-in (13-mm) machine-guns (2×4) later replaced by 20-mm (0.79-in) AA; *(Apollo, Ariadne)* 4×4-in AA (2×2), 4×40-mm (1.6-in) Bofors AA (2×2), 12×20-mm AA (6×2), 156 mines *Crew:* 246

Abercrombie

British monitor (1943). Britain had built no monitors between the wars, so when HMS *Terror* was lost off North Africa in February 1941, only two were left. A new monitor was therefore ordered from Vickers-Armstrong, to be named *Abercrombie.* She was similar to the nearly completed *Roberts* and was fitted with the twin 15-in turret built in 1917 as a spare for the battlecruiser *Furious*, should the latter's 18-in single mountings prove unsuccessful. Strong resistance to air attack was necessary operating close to enemy shores, so she was equipped with eight 4-in, 16 2-pdr and 20 20-mm AA guns, first class radar and 4-in deck armour, plus 5-in side armour and bulges.

HMS *Abercrombie* was completed in May 1943 in time for the Allied landings in Sicily in July, when the 29 250-m (32 000-yd) range of her guns was put to good use supporting the Americans. On September 9 she started bombarding at the Salerno landings, but had the misfortune to strike a mine, which put her out of action for 11 months. After repairs she was exercising off Malta when she had the bad luck to hit another mine. This time she was out of action until July 1945, when she set off for the Indian Ocean to support operations against the Japanese in Malaya. The war was over before she could see any action; she was scrapped in 1954.

Displacement: 7850 tons (standard), 9720 tons (full load) *Dimensions:* 113.77 m (373 ft 3 in) oa×227.13 m (89 ft)×4.27 m (14 ft) max *Machinery:* 2-shaft geared turbines, 4800 shp=12 knots *Armament:* 2.380-mm (15-in) (1×2); 8×4-in (102-mm) AA (4×2); 16 2-pdr AA (1×8, 2×4); 20 20-mm (0.79-in) AA (20×1) *Protection:* see above *Crew:* 350

Activity

British escort carrier. The *Activity* was built as a merchant ship and taken over for conversion to a small aircraft carrier for service with convoys. In most respects she resembled other British CVEs (CVE is the US Navy designation for escort carriers) in being larger than the American conversions, and her twin-screw diesel engines enabled top speed to be maintained more easily.

The ship was ordered in 1941 from the Caledon Shipbuilding company of Dundee as the fast refrigerated cargo carrier *Empire Activity.* She was launched on May 30, 1942 as the *Telemachus*, completed on September 29 the same year, and was operated by the Alfred Holt Line. In 1943 she was requisitioned by the British Admiralty from the Ministry of War Transport for conversion to an escort carrier, but did not come into service until February 1944. She escorted convoys to Gibraltar and northern Russia during 1944 and 1945 and her Swordfish aircraft sank *U 288* on April 3, 1944.

The Air Group embarked in HMS *Activity*, 819 Squadron, operated three Swordfish and seven Wildcats in February 1944. This was increased to nine Swordfish and three Wildcats when the ship switched to Arctic convoys, as there was more need for antisubmarine aircraft than fighters. In 1946 she returned to mercantile service.

Displacement: 11 800 tons (standard), 14 300 tons (full load) *Length:* 156.27 m (512 ft 9 in) oa *Beam:* 20.26 m (66 ft 6 in) *Draught:* 7.92 m (26 ft) max *Machinery:* 2-shaft Burmeister & Main 6-cylinder diesels, 12 000 bhp=18 knots *Aircraft:* 15 max *Armament:* 2 4-in (102-mm) AA (1×2); 28 20-mm (14×2); originally only 10 single 20-mm carried *Crew:* 700

Afridi

British destroyer class. During the 1930s several countries built large, fast destroyers with a heavy gun armament. The *Afridi* Class, which were more commonly known as the 'Tribals', were built to counter these foreign ships. Compared with earlier British destroyers they carried twice as many guns and were almost 500 tons heavier. It was, however, necessary to restrict their torpedo armament to four 21-in tubes (earlier ships carried eight or ten tubes) in order to reduce cost and keep them within the international treaty limit of 1850 tons. This limitation lapsed before the ships were completed and additions during construction increased their displacements by over 100 tons. They were the first British destroyer class to carry twin gun mountings and the last to be constructed on the transverse framing system. The 16 Royal Navy ships were completed between May 1938 and March 1939. The four Royal Canadian Navy vessels built in Britain were ordered in 1940-41 and completed in 1942-43. The four built in Canada were ordered in 1942 and laid down in the following year, but did not complete until after the war. Australia originally intended to build seven but in the event only laid down three. The first pair completed in 1942 and served in the Pacific, but *Bataan* did not complete until May 1945.

The 'Tribals' saw a considerable amount of action during the Second World War, serving in practically all the theatres of war from the Arctic to the Pacific. Of the 16 original Royal Navy ships 12 were lost in the early years of the war, and no fewer than seven were lost in 1942.

Probably the most famous of the 'Tribals' was the *Cossack* which, on February 17, 1940, violated Norwegian territorial waters by entering Jössing Fiord where the German supply ship *Altmark* lay hidden. This ship carried 299 British seamen from merchantmen captured by the *Graf Spee.* A boarding party from the destroyer seized the *Altmark* and, after a brief fight, released the captives who were transferred to the *Cossack* and brought home. Two months later, on April 13, she took part in the Second Battle of Narvik together with the *Eskimo, Bedouin* and *Punjabi.* During this battle *Cossack* was hit by eight 5-in shells from the damaged destroyer *Diether von Roeder* before she silenced her adversary, which later blew up. Badly damaged, the *Cossack* ran aground where she remained for 13 hours until she freed herself and made her way home. In the meantime the *Eskimo* had sunk the destroyer *Erich Köllner*, with the help of *Bedouin*, and torpedoed the destroyer *Hermann Künne* which had run aground. *Eskimo* was torpedoed by the *Georg Thiele*, her bows from B mounting forward being blown off, but she

Left: *Eskimo* in wartime configuration. The superimposed after 4.7-in mounting was replaced by a twin 4-in AA after the Norway campaign, the aft funnel shortened, and a variety of light AA guns added. The later Canadian Tribals were armed with 8 4-in guns. Right: *Tartar* off Iceland

survived and was repaired on the Clyde. Two other 'Tribals' did not survive the Norwegian campaign; on April 9 the *Gurkha* and on May 3 the *Afridi* were sunk by aircraft.

On the night of May 26/27, 1941 the *Cossack* was in action again when, with the *Maori*, *Sikh* and *Zulu*, she carried out several torpedo attacks against the *Bismarck*. Although the destroyers claimed hits on the German battleship they did not in fact score any. On May 28 the *Mashona*, returning home with *Tartar* after being involved in the search for *Bismarck*, was bombed and sunk by German aircraft. The *Cossack* was also lost before the end of the year. On October 23 she was torpedoed by *U 563* west of Gibraltar.

The Mediterranean proved a deadly battleground for destroyers during 1941-43 and among those lost were five of the 'Tribal' Class. The first was the *Mohawk*. On April 16, 1941 in company with the *Nubian*, *Janus* and *Jervis* she attacked an Italian convoy of five merchant ships. All the merchantmen and the three escorting destroyers were sunk by the British force, but the *Mohawk* was hit by two torpedoes from the sinking destroyer *Luca Tariago*. She was quickly abandoned and was later sunk by *Janus*. Better luck accompanied the *Maori* and *Sikh* on the night of December 12/13, 1941. With the destroyers *Legion* and *Isaac Sweers* (Dutch) they intercepted the Italian cruisers *Alberto di Giussano* and *Alberico da Barbiano* off Cape Bon. The *Barbiano* was hit by three torpedoes and sank almost immediately, the *Giussano* was hit by one torpedo amidships, caught fire and sank one hour later. Two months later, on February 12, the *Maori* was bombed and sunk in Grand Harbour, Malta, during an air raid.

On June 15, 1942 the *Bedouin* was damaged in action with Italian naval forces and was later torpedoed and sunk by an aircraft (which she shot down). On September 14, 1942 *Sikh*, *Zulu* and other warships were covering an unsuccessful commando raid on Tobruk. *Sikh* was hit by the shore batteries, disabled and eventually sank; the *Zulu* was bombed and sunk by German aircraft while returning to Alexandria.

Three 'Tribals' were lost in Arctic waters during 1942. The *Matabele* was torpedoed on January 17 by *U 454* in the Barents Sea while escorting PQ8; there were two survivors. On May 1 the *Punjabi* was covering PQ15 in a thick fog when she was accidentally rammed and cut in two by the battleship *King George V*. On September 20, while escorting QP14, the *Somali* was torpedoed by *U 743*. She was taken in tow by *Ashanti* but broke in two and sank four days later.

During 1942-43 the remaining Royal Navy 'Tribals' served in the Mediterranean, covering convoys and the seaborne invasions of North Africa, Sicily and Italy. During the same period the four newly completed Royal Canadian Navy ships served in the Arctic, mainly covering Russian convoys. In 1944 all except *Nubian* joined the 10th Destroyer Flotilla based at Plymouth for operations in the English Channel and Bay of Biscay. On April 27-28 the *Athabaskan (i)* was torpedoed and sunk by the German destroyer *T 24* off St Brieux. *Tartar*, *Eskimo* and *Nubian* ended the war in the Far East while the remainder of the class stayed in home waters.

The surviving Royal Navy ships were placed in reserve shortly after the war ended and were sold for scrap in 1948-49. The Australian and Canadian ships, being newer, survived much longer, and all except *Micmac* served in the Korean war. During the 1950s they were modified as A/S escorts. The *Bataan* was sold for scrap in 1958, and the *Warramunga* in 1963, while *Arunta* foundered in tow to the breakers in 1969. The Royal Canadian Navy vessels were sold for scrap between 1964 and 1970, except for *Haida*, now preserved as a naval museum.

Displacement: 1960 tons *Length:* 114.91 m (377 ft) oa *Beam:* 11.12 m (36 ft 6 in) *Draught:* 3.96 m (13 ft) *Machinery:* 2-shaft geared turbines, 44 000 shp=36 knots *Armament:* 8 4.7-in (120-mm) (4×2); 4 2-pdr pom-poms (1×4); 8 .5-in (12.7-mm) machine-guns (2×4) *Crew:* 190

HMS *Eskimo* in wartime. The 'Tribals' were designed to lend heavier gun support to existing flotillas and were influenced by similar contemporary German (Type 1934) Japanese (*Asashio* Class) and American (*Gridley* Class) destroyers

Agano

Japanese cruiser class. Shortly before the Second World War the Japanese navy drew up designs for light cruisers to replace the old vessels dating from the First World War. After several designs were studied it was decided to build a new type of high-speed scout to work with the Combined Fleet.

The four *Agano* Class were unusual in many ways. They were very lightly armoured to ensure maximum speed and carried quadruple 24-in torpedo tubes on the centreline, like destroyers. In addition they were fitted with Sonar and depth-charges, and in many ways they resembled large destroyer leaders more than fleet cruisers.

The fates of the four ships reflect the final destruction of Japanese naval power. The *Agano* was laid down in June 1940 and was completed in October 1942. She was torpedoed by the US submarine *Skate* north of Truk on February 16, 1944. The *Noshiro* was laid down in September 1941 and completed in June 1943, and was sunk by carrier planes from USS *Hornet* and *Wasp* off Panay on October 26, 1944. The *Yahagi* was begun in November 1941 and completed in December 1943. She escorted the giant battleship *Yamato* on her final sortie to Okinawa, but, like her consort, she was sunk by Task Force 58 aircraft 130 miles west-southwest of Kagoshima on April 7, 1945. The fourth ship, *Sakawa*, was laid down in November 1942 but material shortages and delays held up her completion until November 1944. She was surrendered in August 1945 and was expended as a target in the Bikini nuclear test on July 1, 1946.

The antiaircraft armament of all four ships was augmented during the war, increasing to 46 25-mm in 1943. *Yahagi* and *Noshiro* received this armament on completion, and in 1944 they received a further six single 25-mm (1-in) guns. By the July of that year they had 59 25-mm, in addition to two radar sets.

To assist in their scouting role, the *Agano* Class were fitted with a catapult for launching two floatplanes. No hangar was provided as the space was not available, and the floatplanes were stowed on a platform amidships.

Agano launched Sasebo dockyard October 22, 1941

Noshiro launched Yokosuka dockyard July 19, 1942
Sakawa launched Sasebo dockyard April 9, 1944
Yahagi launched Sasebo dockyard October 25, 1942

Displacement: 6652 tons (normal), 8534 tons (full load) *Length:* 176 m (572 ft 6 in) oa *Beam:* 15 m (49 ft 9 in) *Draught:* 5.5 m (18 ft 6 in) *Machinery:* 4-shaft geared steam turbines, 110 000 shp=35 knots *Protection:* 60 mm ($2\frac{1}{4}$ in) belt; 20 mm ($\frac{3}{4}$ in) deck; 25 mm (1 in) turrets; 50 mm (2 in) magazines *Armament:* 6 150-mm (5.9-in) (3×2); 4 76-mm (3-in) AA (2×2); 32 25-mm (1-in) AA (8×3, 8×1); 8 24-in (61-cm) torpedo tubes (2×4); 2 floatplanes *Crew:* 730

Agosta

French submarine class. In 1970 the Marine Nationale (French navy) announced the building of a new class of four high-speed conventionally powered submarines. Although claimed to be of the most advanced design, the details published by mid-1976 had failed to indicate any unusual features. They are presumably intended to maintain continuity of design, and are a logical improvement over the *Daphné* Class of 1958-70.

Published information indicates that there are only four forward torpedo tubes, and no stern tubes, but 20 torpedoes are carried. These are presumably homing torpedoes of the L5 type, which is a 55-cm (21.7-in) weapon with an active/passive head. Two sonar sets are carried, an active DUUA 1 set with transducers forward and aft, and a passive DSUV set with 36 hydrophones.

The class includes four units: the prototype *Agosta*, begun in February 1972 and completed in the spring of 1976; the *Bevéziers*, due for completion about three months later; and the *Ouessant* and *La Praya*. The names commemorate French submarines of the pre-Second World War period, and all four are being built by DCAN Cherbourg (a naval dockyard). Two are reported to be building in Spain at Cartagena, and more are on order for South Africa.

Displacement: 1200 tons (standard); 1450/1725 tons (surfaced/submerged) *Length:* 67.6 m (222 ft) *Beam:* 6.8 m (22 ft) *Draught:* 5.4 m (18 ft) *Machinery:* Single-shaft diesel-electric, 3600 bhp=12 knots (surfaced); single-shaft electric motor, 4600 hp=20 knots (submerged) *Torpedo tubes:* 4 55-cm (21.7-in), 20 torpedoes *Endurance:* 560 (350 miles) at $3\frac{1}{2}$ knots (dived); 14 500 km (9000 miles) at 9 knots (snorting) *Crew:* 50

Akitsuki

Japanese destroyer class. In the late 1930s the Imperial Japanese Navy gave serious thought to the problem of defending the fleet against air attack. The Type B destroyers evolved out of a requirement for a light cruiser, and in size they certainly approached the cruiser category.

The main element of the design was a new twin 100-mm/65-cal high-velocity antiaircraft gun mounting. With its high rate of fire and a range of 18 300 m (20 000 yds), it was more powerful than the contemporary 5-in/38-cal US Navy gun. To increase its effectiveness, the new design was given a second fire-control position aft. To add an offensive capability, the design was subsequently altered to include a bank of quadruple 24-in torpedo tubes amidships.

By re-arranging the boiler- and engine-rooms the uptakes were trunked into one large funnel. This made the ships look remarkably like the light cruiser *Yubari*, and for some months in 1942, when the first vessels appeared, American intelligence reported the *Yubari* appearing in several places at once. Six ships were ordered (Nos 104-109) under the 1939 Programme and a further ten under the 1941 Programme. (Nos 360-369). During the war Nos 366-369 were cancelled for lack of materials and additional units numbered 770-785 and 5061-5083 were cancelled before being laid down. The following ships were built:

Akitsuki, shown here in her original form, was the first of a class of destroyers completed from 1942 on, and designed to provide antiaircraft screening for carriers. It was then decided to equip them for the fleet escort as well as the AA role, and to their original main armament of twin quick-firing 100-mm high velocity AA guns were added a quadruple torpedo tube and six depth-charge throwers. Subsequently, the light antiaircraft armament was greatly increased. *Akitsuki* was sunk in October 1944 during the Battle of Leyte Gulf

Maizuru Dockyard
Akitsuki, Fuyutsuki, Hanatsuki, Hatsutsuki, Hazuki, Kiyotsuki

Sasebo Dockyard
Harutsuki, Michitsuki, Natsutsuki

Mitsubishi, Nagasaki
Niitsuki, Ootsuki, Shimotsuki, Suzutsuki, Terutsuki, Wakastsuki

Uraga Dock Co.
Yoitsuki

The lead ship, *Akitsuki*, was started in July 1940 and completed in June 1942, but the last of the class was not completed until April 1945 *(Hatsutsuki)*. The *Hatsuki, Kiyotsuki* and *Ootsuki* were never laid down and the *Michitsuki* was stopped in March 1945 and broken up to make way for suicide craft. Six were sunk in action or torpedoed, and the other six were surrendered, two of them badly damaged. The *Fuyutsuki* was taken over by the US Navy in 1947 and scrapped, the *Harutsuki* became the Soviet *Pospechny*, the *Hatsutsuki* went to Britain and the *Yoitsuki* became the Chinese *Fen Yang*.

Soon after completion the minesweeping gear was replaced by four depth-charge throwers and 54 depth-charges to cope with the growing menace of Allied submarines. Later the outfit was increased to 72 depth-charges. The light armament was soon increased to 15 25-mm AA guns and Type 21 and Type 22 radars were fitted. In June 1944 the typical armament was 29 25-mm guns and 4 13-mm, but the later ships were completed with 40 to 51 25-mm (5/7×3, 25/30×1).

Displacement: 2701 tons (normal) *Length:* 134.21 m (440 ft 4 in) oa *Beam:* 11.58 m (38 ft 0 in) *Draught:* 4.11 m (13 ft 6 in) mean *Machinery:* 2-shaft geared turbines, 52000 shp=33 knots *Armament:* 8 100-mm (4-in) dual-purpose (4×2); 4 25-mm (1-in) AA (2×2); 4 60-cm (24-in) torpedo tubes (8 torpedoes) *Crew:* 290

US Navy

Sixteen-inch gun practice on the *Alabama*, one of the smaller and better protected, but equally heavily armed—three triple 16-in turrets were mounted—derivatives of the *North Carolina* Class

Alabama

US battleship. *Alabama* was the last of the four *South Dakota* Class battleships to be completed. They were 15.25 m (50 ft) shorter and 0.9 m (3 ft) deeper than the preceding *North Carolinas*, which gave them better protection over a greater proportion of their length for virtually the same armament.

Legend credits the *South Dakotas* with 406-mm (16-in) armour, but in fact they were only moderately armoured by contemporary standards. The main belt amidships (which was recessed, giving a smooth-sided hull) was only 310 mm (12.2 in) thick.

Alabama was built very quickly. Laid down at Norfolk naval yard in February 1940, she was launched in February 1942, and commissioned in August of the same year at a cost of over $77 million.

In early 1943 she was attached to the British Home Fleet, escorting North Atlantic and Russian convoys. In August 1943 she was transferred to the Pacific, where she spent the rest of the war with the other fast American battleships acting as escorts to the fast carriers.

Alabama took part in most of the raids against the Japanese-held Pacific islands, and was present at the 'Battle of the Philippine Sea' in June 1944 and the battle for Leyte Gulf in October of that year. However, she took no part in any of the surface actions, her main function being that of heavy antiaircraft escort.

She went into reserve at Bremerton after

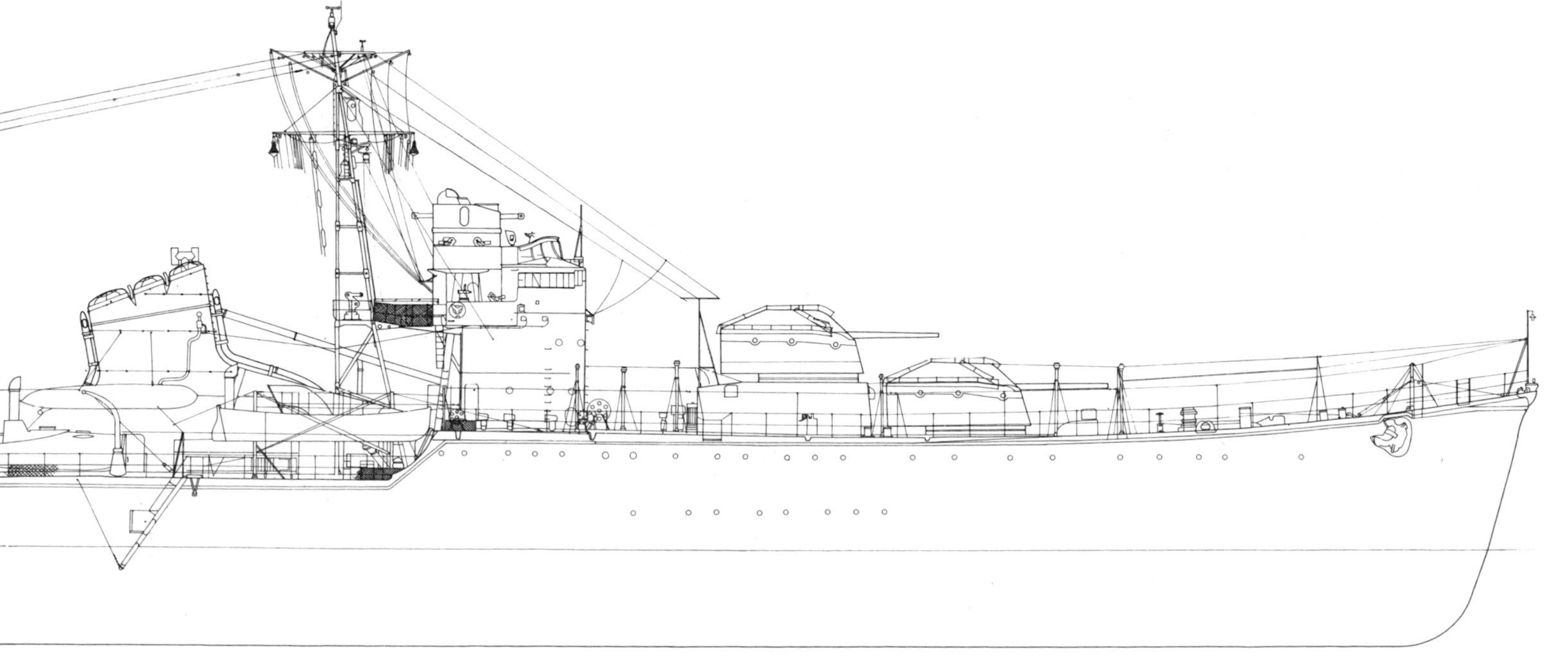

decommissioning in January 1947, and was handed over to the State of Alabama in June 1964. Since September 1964 she has been moored as a national memorial near Mobile.

Displacement: 39 000 tons (standard), 44 500 tons (full load) *Length:* 207.1 m (679 ft 5 in) oa *Beam:* 33.3 m (108 ft $1\frac{1}{2}$ in) *Draught:* 10.47 m (36 ft 2 in) *Machinery:* 4-shaft geared steam turbines, 130 000 shp=27.8 knots *Protection:* 310 mm (12.2 in) inclined belt; 146 mm (5.75 in) main deck; 457 mm (18 in) turret faces *Armament:* 9 16-in (406-mm); 20 5-in (127-mm); 48 40-mm; 56 20-mm; *Aircraft:* 2 *Crew:* 2332

Alaska

US battlecruiser class. Although always regarded as battlecruisers, the official designation of these unusual ships was 'CB' or large cruiser. The original class of six ships was conceived as a reply to the German 'pocket battleships' and the imaginary *Chichibu* Class which US Naval Intelligence then believed the Japanese to be building.

The ships that resulted were remarkable in many ways and, although hardly cost-effective, a great credit to the American shipbuilding industry. They were armed with a completely new mark of 12-in (304-mm) gun, and steamed at 31 knots. The armour was only 9 in (127 mm) on the belt, and the scheme of distribution stamped the design as a cruiser rather than a battleship. The machinery of the *Essex* Class fleet carriers was duplicated to save time, but unlike the carriers the *Alaska* Class were not economical steamers. The cost of the *Alaska* was $67 million, of which the hull and machinery cost $45.6 million.

The USS *Alaska* was launched at Camden, New Jersey on August 15, 1943 and commissioned on June 17, 1944. In January 1945 she left for Pearl Harbor, and joined Task Group 58.5 at Ulithi Atoll in the Western Carolines in February. She operated with the fast carriers *Saratoga* and *Enterprise*, screening them on the first night strikes against Tokyo and its airfields. In March she screened the forces attacking Iwo Jima, as part of Task Force 58. She shot down two *kamikaze* bombers on March 18 and the next day had to escort the badly damaged carrier *Franklin* clear of the battle zone. At the close of the

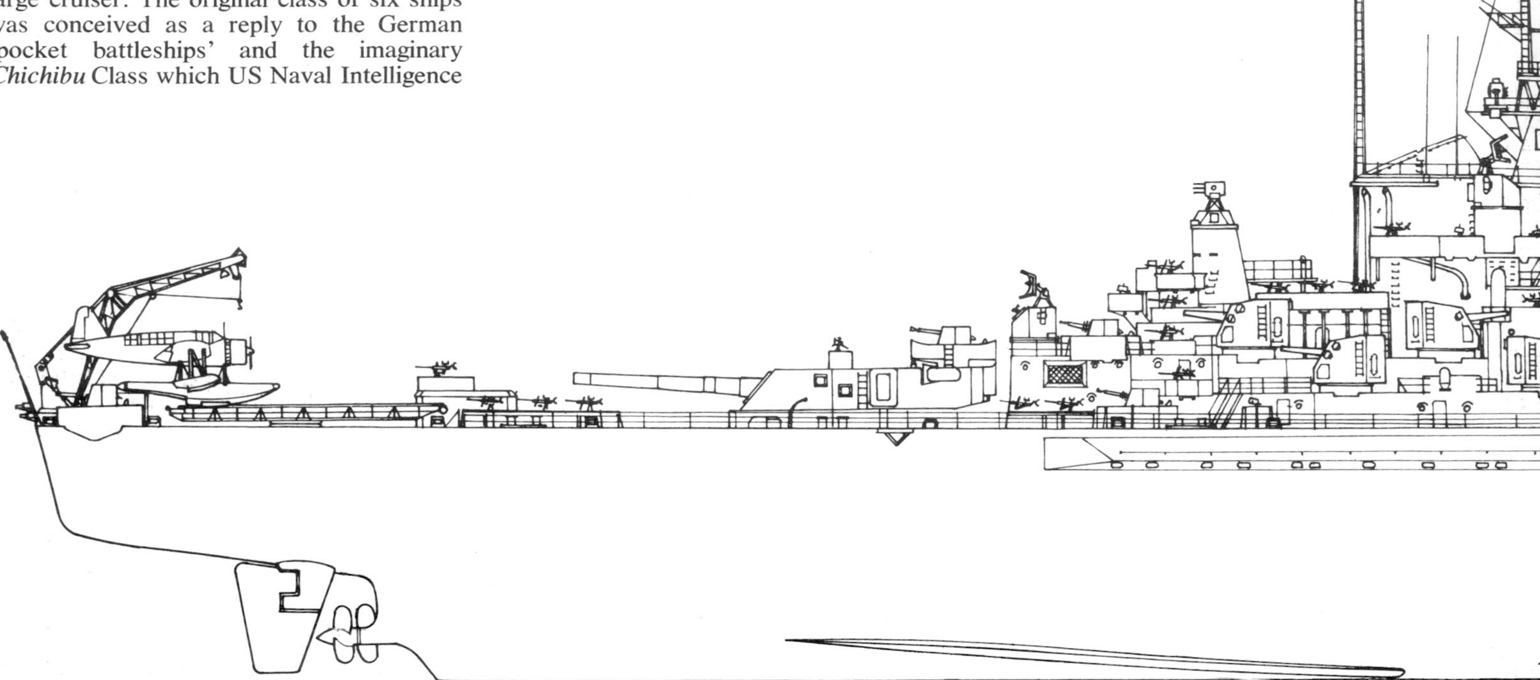

USS *Alabama*. The *South Dakota* Class battleships, of which *Alabama* was the fourth and last, were smaller versions of the preceding *North Carolina* Class. Reduced in length by some 50 ft, they were given much better protection while mounting virtually the same main armament. Large underwater bulges and internal bulkheads gave protection against torpedoes, and the main belt was $12\frac{1}{4}$ in thick. Note the extensive light AA armament of 48 40-mm and 56 20-mm guns

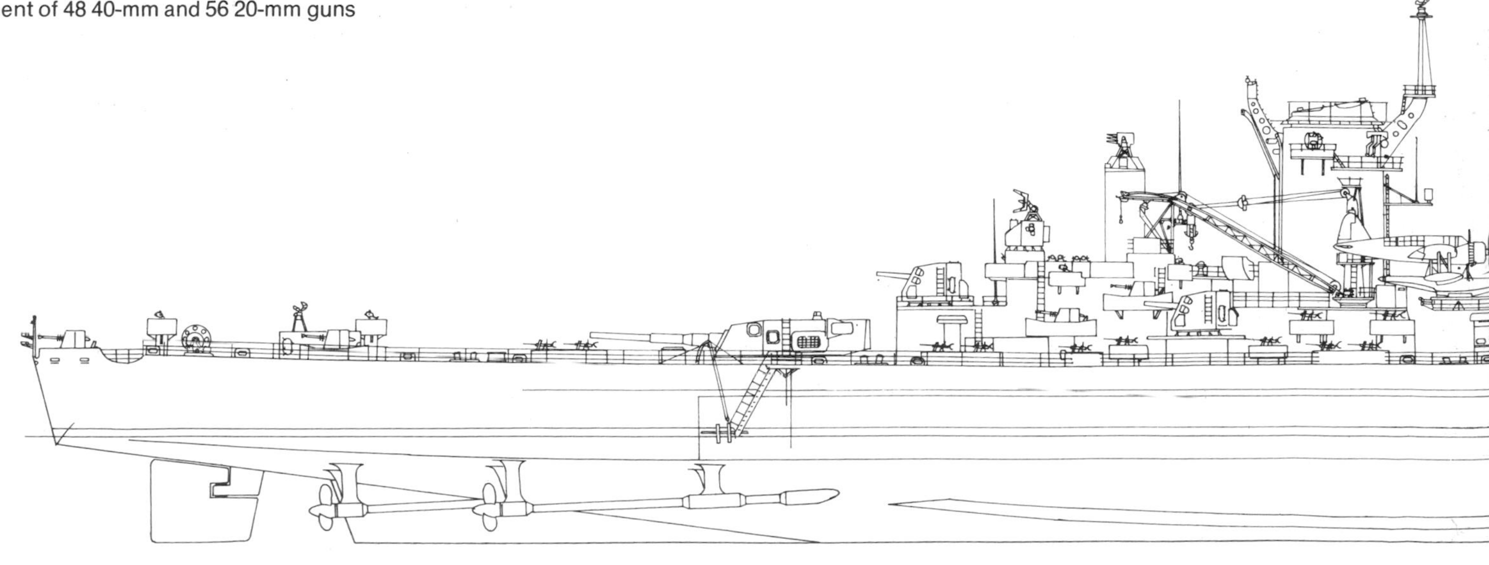

Okinawa campaign TF 58 attacked shipping in the East China Sea.

The *Alaska* returned home in November 1945 and was decommissioned in February 1947. Her sister *Guam* was launched on November 12, 1943 at Camden, New Jersey by the New York Shipbuilding corporation and commissioned in September 1944. She joined the *Alaska* at Ulithi in March 1945 and screened the fast carriers. She carried out various bombardments between March and June in the Okinawa campaign, and remained at sea for three months. In June 1945 she became the flagship of Cruiser Task Force 95, with the *Alaska*, four light cruisers and nine destroyers. The *Guam* returned to Bayonne, New Jersey in December 1945 and decommissioned there on February 17, 1947.

The third ship, *Hawaii* (CB 3), was not launched by the time the war ended. The launch was postponed several times, but she finally took the water on November 3, 1945 and was laid up in reserve. In 1952 she was reclassified as a large Tactical Command ship (CBC 1) but no work was done; subsequent discussions centred around her conversion to a guided missile cruiser but in September 1954 she reverted to CB 3. She was stricken in 1958 and sold a year later for scrapping.

The *Philippines, Puerto Rico* and *Samoa* (CB 4-6) were all authorized in July 1940 and ordered two months later, but the steel shortage of 1943 resulted in the contracts being cancelled in June 1943.

Neither *Alaska* nor *Guam* ever saw service again, as both were stricken from the Navy List in June 1960 and sold for scrapping. They had proved expensive hybrids which did not fit into the US Navy organization. They did very little that smaller cruisers could not have done just as well, and lacked the armour to face bigger ships.

Displacement: 31 700 tons (normal), 34 250 tons (full load) *Length:* 246.4 m (808 ft 6 in) *Beam:* 27.8 m (91 ft 1 in) *Draught:* 9.9 m (32 ft 4 in) max *Machinery:* 4-shaft double-reduction geared turbines, 150 000 shp=33 knots (designed) 31 knots (sea speed) *Protection:* 230 mm (9 in) belt; 80-120 mm ($3\frac{1}{4}$-$4\frac{3}{4}$ in) decks; 320 mm ($12\frac{3}{4}$ in) turret face *Armament:* 9 12-in (305-mm) (3× 3); 12 5-in (127-mm) dual-purpose (6× 2); 56 40-mm (1.6-in) Bofors AA (14× 4); 34 20-mm (0.79-in) Oerlikon AA (34× 1) *Crew:* 1773-2251

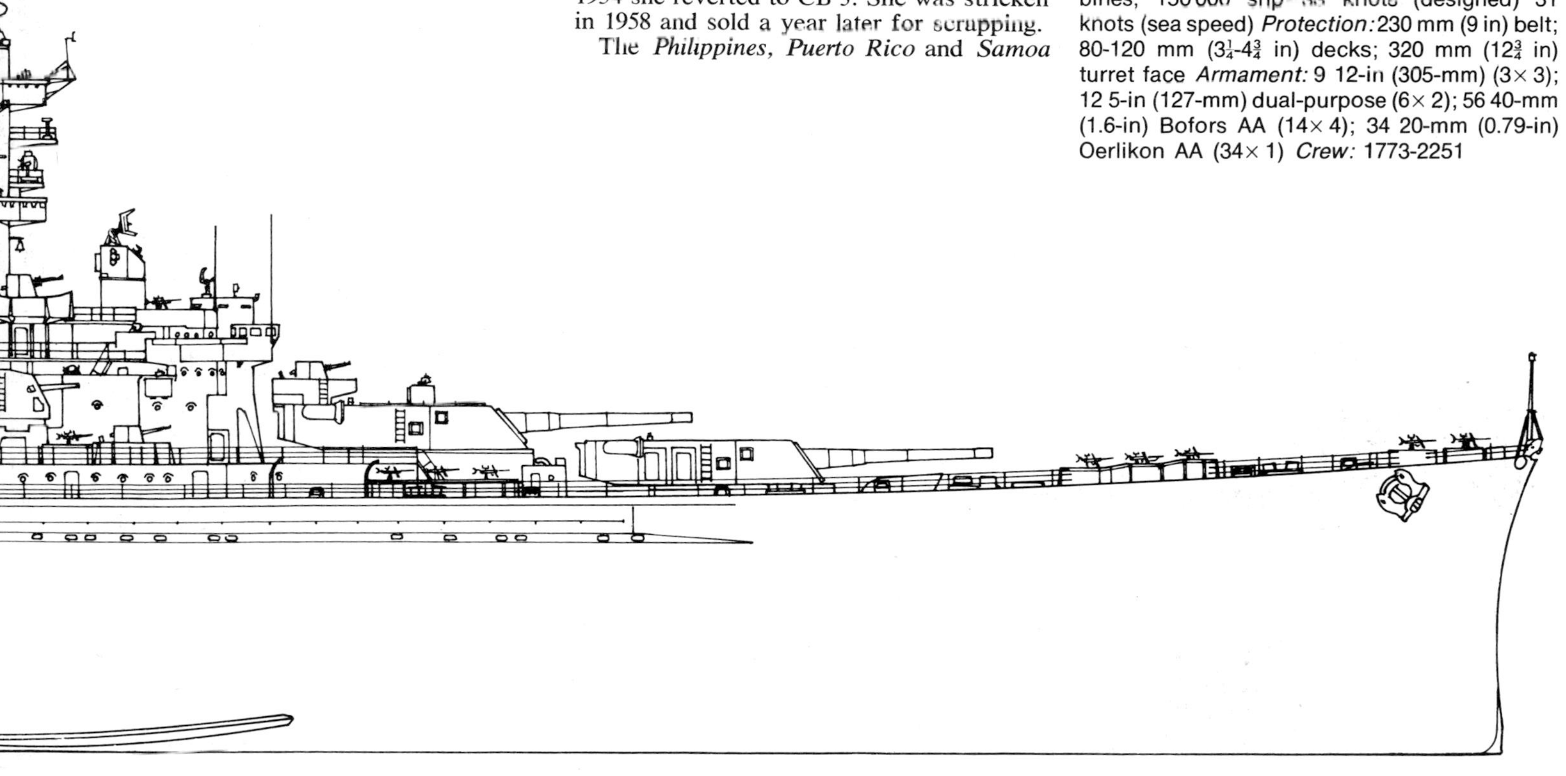

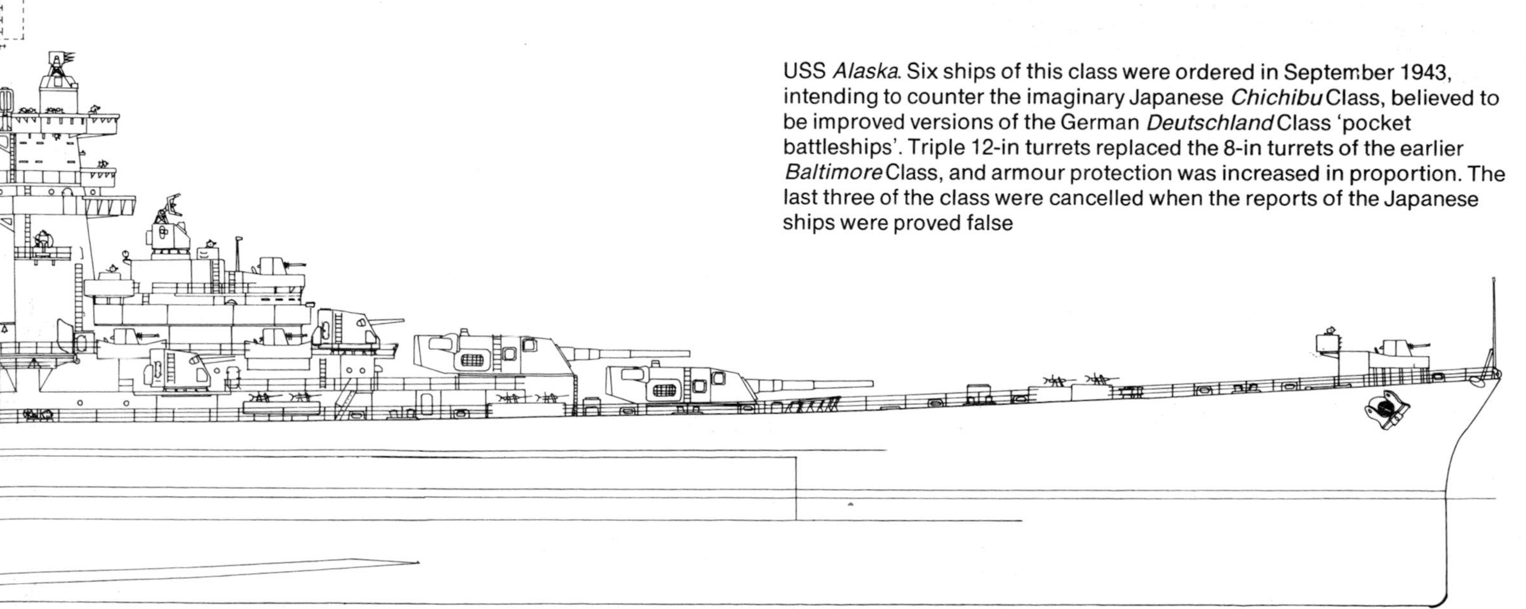

USS *Alaska*. Six ships of this class were ordered in September 1943, intending to counter the imaginary Japanese *Chichibu* Class, believed to be improved versions of the German *Deutschland* Class 'pocket battleships'. Triple 12-in turrets replaced the 8-in turrets of the earlier *Baltimore* Class, and armour protection was increased in proportion. The last three of the class were cancelled when the reports of the Japanese ships were proved false

Alava

Spanish destroyer class. In 1925 the Spanish started building the first of the *Churruca* Class destroyers, whose design had been inspired by the British *Scott* Class destroyer leaders of 1918. Nine were built to the original design, of which two were sold to Argentina. All survived the civil war, and the last was disposed of in 1966.

During the late 1920s and early 1930s a further seven, the *Almirante Antequera* Class, were built to a slightly modified design. One was sunk in 1937 but was salvaged and returned to service in 1939. Two survived into the 1970s.

In 1936 the Spanish navy decided to build two more, *Alava* and *Liniers*, to a further modification of the basic design. The civil war intervened, and construction was delayed. Work restarted in 1939, but stopped again in 1940. Building did not finally start in earnest until 1944. Even then, Spain's poor financial position meant that they were built very slowly.

	laid down	launched	completed	completed reconstruction
Alava	12/1944	5/1947	12/1950	1/1962
Liniers	1/1945	5/1946	1/1951	9/1962

As first completed, they had an armament of 4 4.7-in, 6 37-mm and 3 20-mm guns, and 6 21-in torpedo tubes in two triple mountings.

With the advent of American military aid, they were modernized in 1961/62, being rearmed as fast antisubmarine frigates. They were given two side-launching racks for antisubmarine torpedoes, and a completely new antiaircraft gun armament. A lattice mast with a prominent search radar was also fitted. They can easily be recognized because the break in the forecastle comes most unusually between the two funnels.

Displacement: 1842 tons (standard), 2287 tons (full load) *Length:* 102.5 m (336 ft 3 in) oa *Beam:* 9.6 m (31 ft 6 in) *Draught:* 6.0 m (19 ft 8 in) *Machinery:* 2-shaft geared steam turbines, 31 500 shp=29 knots *Armament:* 3 3-in (76-mm); 3 40-mm; 2 hedgehogs; 8 DC mortars; 6 DC racks; 6 torpedo launching racks (2×3 above water, beam) *Crew:* 224

Albany

US missile cruiser class. In the mid-1950s, two *Baltimore* Class heavy cruisers and six *Cleveland* Class light cruisers were converted by the US Navy to have antiaircraft missile launchers in place of the aft turrets. This was a temporary measure pending the introduction of purpose built missile ships, of which the first, the nuclear powered *Long Beach*, was laid down in December 1957.

It was obvious, however, that the new guided missile cruisers would not be available in sufficient numbers for many years, so three heavy cruisers were selected to be fully converted into guided missile cruisers. The three originally chosen were *Chicago* (CG II ex-CA 136) and *Fall River* (CA 131) of the *Baltimore* Class and *Albany* (CG 10 ex-CA 123) of the *Oregon City* Class, but *Fall River* was not suitable for conversion, so *Columbus* (CG 12 ex-CA 74), also of the *Baltimore* Class, was chosen to replace her.

The USN planned to convert two more *Baltimore* Class cruisers but the very high cost of conversion and the greater effective-

	laid down	launched	commissioned as CA	commissioned as CG
Albany	3/1944	6/1945	6/1946	11/1962
Chicago	7/1943	8/1944	2/1945	5/1964
Columbus	6/1943	11/1944	6/1945	12/1962

ness of the new purpose-built ships meant that this plan was dropped.

The hull and machinery of the two classes were identical and since all their original armament and superstructure was removed, the three ships as converted were almost indistinguishable. The new superstructure is mainly aluminium to save weight and improve stability, and instead of having separate masts and funnels, they are combined into two 'macks'. These have vents set at an

USS *Albany* after conversion in the late 1950s. She was fitted with two twin Talos, two twin Tartar and one Asroc launcher

US Navy

The USS *Albany* (CG 10), after conversion to a guided missile cruiser, firing two Talos (fore and aft) and one Tartar (amidships) missiles in salvo

US Navy

angle near the top to exhaust the steam away from the radar, and are covered with plastic in an attempt to reduce the changes in alignment of the mack-head radar caused by expansion and contraction from the varying heat of the exhaust steam.

Albany was converted in Boston naval yard from January 1959 to November 1962. She was fitted with a twin Talos long range surface-to-air missile launcher fore and aft with 92 missiles, and a twin Tartar medium range surface-to-air missile launcher on either side of the fore-bridge with 80 missiles. It was planned to mount 8 Polaris missile tubes amidships, and space was provided, but this requirement was cancelled in mid-1959.

She was given an extensive antisubmarine capability, including Sonar and an Asroc 8-tube launcher. Initially, no guns were fitted, but it was soon realized that the missiles were not suited for close low-level defence, nor for such tasks as stopping a small ship for examination. Therefore a single 5-in gun was added on either side of the after mack.

Albany's antiaircraft systems were extensively modified at Boston naval yard from February 1967 to August 1969. The refit gave *Albany* better radar and a faster and more reliable Talos fire control than the one with which *Chicago* shot down a MiG off North Vietnam at a range of 77 km (48 miles) in May 1972.

Chicago and *Columbus* were not modernized. The state of their aging hulls and the availability of new ships meant that they could soon be discarded. *Columbus* was decommissioned in January 1975. All conventionally powered cruisers are scheduled for replacement by the late 1970s, to be replaced by nuclear powered vessels.

Displacement: 13700 tons (standard), 17500 tons (full load) *Length:* 205.13 m (673 ft) *Beam:* 21.34 m (70 ft) *Draught:* 8.23 m (27 ft) *Machinery:* 4-shaft geared steam turbines, 120000 shp=33 knots *Armament:* 2 Twin Talos launchers, 2 Twin Tartar launchers, 2 5-in (127-mm), 1 Asroc 8-tube launcher, 2 triple torpedo launchers (beam) *Crew:* 1000

Albion

British aircraft/commando carrier. HMS *Albion* was the second unit of the *Hermes* Class of aircraft carriers laid down in 1944-45. She was launched on May 6, 1947 but as the design of the class was under review the hull was immediately laid up. Machinery had been installed but she was minus armament and equipment.

Work proceeded slowly, and the ship was finally completed by Swan, Hunter and Wigham Richardson at Wallsend-on-Tyne on May 26, 1954. On October 27 the same year she became flagship of the Aircraft Carrier Squadron in the Mediterranean, but transferred to the Home Fleet in March 1955. After a refit in May-September 1956 she left hurriedly for the Mediterranean to take part in the Suez operations.

Air strikes against Egyptian targets were begun by *Albion*'s Sea Hawk and Sea Venom aircraft at dawn on November 1, and included an attack on Al Naza field, six miles from Cairo and over 209 km (130 miles) from the Fleet. Numerous sorties were flown during the next two days, and the carrier's aircraft provided cover for the paratroops' attack on November 5. Her Skyraiders and helicopters landed medical supplies and evacuated wounded from Gamil Airport near Port Said. Before returning to Malta on November 29 the *Albion*'s air group had flown over 2000 sorties in two months.

After service in the Home Fleet, Far East and Mediterranean the *Albion* went into Portsmouth dockyard for conversion to a commando carrier, which took a year. She recommissioned in her new role in August 1962, and only a month after she had joined the Far East Fleet in November 1963 her Royal Marine Commandos had to quell a small and not too significant revolt in the Sultanate of Brunei.

She returned to England in April 1964 for a refit and so missed the start of the Indonesian confrontation, but she was sent out to the Far East as soon as her refit ended, and she was to remain there until the end of 1967. After a period in the Mediterranean in 1970 the *Albion* began her last Far East commission in March 1971, one which ended with the withdrawal from Singapore.

The last leg of *Albion*'s final commission began in April 1972 for she was now getting too old to warrant further modernization. When she paid off for the last time at Portsmouth on March 2, 1973 she had been in service almost continuously for 18 years. She was sold to a firm in July 1973 for conversion to a heavy lift ship to operate in the North Sea oilfields, but in November 1973 her new owners announced that the conversion would not be carried out, and the carrier was ultimately scrapped.

Displacement: 22000 tons (standard), 27000 tons (full load), 23300 tons (standard as commando carrier) *Length:* 224.8 m (737 ft 9 in) *Beam:* 27.4 m (90 ft), extreme width 37.5 m (123 ft) *Draught:* 8.2 m (27 ft) *Machinery:* 2-shaft geared turbines, 78000 shp=28 knots *Armament:* (As built) 32 40-mm (1.5-in) Bofors AA (2×6, 8×2, 4×1); (After refit with angled deck) 20 40-mm AA (1×6, 5×2, 4×1); (As Commando Ship) 8 40-mm AA (4×2) *Crew:* 1390 (originally) increased to 1035+733 commandos

Albrighton

British destroyer escort class. The *Albrighton* Class were laid down under the 1940 Programme and launched between 1941 and 1943. They were the third group of the 'Hunt' Class escort destroyers and are usually referred to as the 'Hunt' Class Type III. The Hunts were designed as general antisubmarine and antiaircraft escorts for convoys and were originally designated Fast Escort Vessels. They were very well armed for their size, the displacement having been restricted for cheapness and speed of construction, but as they were considered escort vessels the first two groups had no torpedo armament.

HMS *Aldenham*, an *Albrighton* or 'Hunt Type III' Class destroyer escort, was mined in the northern Adriatic in December 1944. The class proved very successful, but losses were heavy

In the *Albrighton* Class, however, it was decided to fit a bank of twin torpedo tubes so that they could be employed in offensive operations against enemy shipping. To compensate for the additional weight it was necessary to reduce the number of twin 4-in mountings from three, as in Type II, to two. Most of the 'Hunt' Class were fitted with stabilizers but these were not popular and were omitted from several of the ships of Type III, the space being used for stowage.

On completion several units were manned by Allied navies but remained under Admiralty control. The *Bolebroke, Border, Modbury* and *Hatherleigh* were transferred to Greece, being renamed *Pindos, Adrias, Miaoulis* and *Kanaris* respectively; the *Haldon* became the Free French *La Combattante* and the *Eskdale* and *Glaisdale* were transferred to the Norwegians.

The *Albrighton* Class served mainly in the English Channel and Mediterranean where they proved most effective in convoy escort, antisubmarine patrols and shipping strikes. Their losses were heavy; out of the 28 ships of the class 13 were lost, as compared with 11 losses out of 45 ships in the first two groups of the 'Hunt' Class.

Seven were lost in the Mediterranean. On June 15, 1942 the *Airedale* was bombed and heavily damaged by German aircraft while escorting the Malta convoy 'Vigorous' and had to be sunk by other ships of the escort. Six months later on December 11 the *Blean* was hit by two torpedoes from the *U 443* off Oran. The first blew off her stern, and the second exploded abreast her engine room and she quickly capsized and sank. The *Derwent* was torpedoed by German aircraft while in Tripoli harbour on March 19, 1943 and was written off as a constructive total loss. The Greek *Adrias* (ex-*Border*) and the *Rockwood* were also declared constructive total losses. The former vessel had her stern blown off by a mine near Kalymnos on October 22, 1943 and the latter was severely damaged by an Hs293 glider bomb in the Aegean Sea on November 11, 1943. All three of these vessels were sold for scrap in 1945/46. The *Holcombe* was torpedoed and sunk by *U 593* in the western Mediterranean, off Bougie, on

December 12, 1943 and the *Aldenham* was sunk by a mine in the Adriatic on December 14, 1944.

The remaining six casualties were lost in home waters. Two were torpedoed in the English Channel by German E-boats, the *Penylan* on December 3, 1942 and the *Eskdale* on April 14, 1943. The *Limbourne* was torpedoed by the German torpedo boat *T 22* off the coast of France on October 23, 1943 and, being heavily damaged, had to be sunk by the British. Two more were constructive total losses; the *Goathland*, mined off Normandy on July 24, 1944, and the *Wensleydale*, damaged in a collision in November of the same year. Both were sold for scrap in 1945. The last of the class to be lost was the Free French *La Combattante* (ex-*Haldon*) which was mined and sunk off the Humber during the night of February 22/23, 1945.

After the war several of the class served in foreign navies. Greece retained those she had manned during the war; they were officially returned to the Admiralty in 1959 and were scrapped in Greece. Greece also purchased the *Tanatside* and *Catterick* in 1946 and renamed them *Adrias* (after the vessel lost during the war) and *Hastings* respectively; both were scrapped in 1963. The *Glaisdale* was sold to Norway in 1946 and renamed *Narvik*; she was sold for scrap in 1961. The *Albrighton* and *Eggesford* were sold to the Federal German navy in 1959 and renamed *Raule* and *Brommy* respectively. The remaining ships of the class were sold for scrap between 1953 and 1961.

Albrighton, Airedale—built by J. Brown.
Aldenham, Belvoir, Eskdale, Glaisdale—built by Cammell Laird.
Blean—built by Hawthorn Leslie.
Bleasdale, Catterick, Derwent, Hatherleigh, Haydon, Penylan, Rockwood—built by Vickers-Armstrong.
Bolebroke, Border, Melbreak, Modbury—built by Swan Hunter.
Easton, Eggesford, Stevenstone, Talybont—built by White.
Goathland, Haldon—built by Fairfield.
Holcombe, Limbourne—built by Stephen.
Tanatside, Wensleydale—built by Yarrow.

Displacement: 1050 tons (standard) *Length:* 85.34 m (280 ft) oa *Beam:* 9.6 m (31 ft 6 in) *Draught:* 2.36 m (7 ft 9 in) *Machinery:* 2-shaft turbines, 19 000 shp=27 knots *Armament:* 4 4-in (102-mm) (2×2); 4 2-pdr pom-poms (1×4); 2 20-mm (2×1); 2 21-in (53-cm) torpedo tubes (1×2); 4 depth-charge throwers (110 depth-charges) *Crew:* 170

Allen M Sumner

US destroyer class. The US *Fletcher* Class destroyers were one of the most successful class of warships to be used in the Second World War, but by 1943 it was obvious that its design could be improved.

The most obvious requirement was for better antiaircraft armament and fire-control. The obvious way to do this was to fit the very successful twin 5-in/38 cal turret used as secondary armament in battleships and cruisers and as the main antiaircraft battery in fleet carriers, in place of the single 5-in/38 cal mounting used in the *Fletchers*.

Country	New name	Old name	Date transferred or sold
Argentina	*Bouchard*	*Borie*	7/1972
	Segui	*Hank*	7/1972
	for spares	*Mansfield*	6/1974
Brazil	*Mato Grosso*	*Compton*	9/1972
	Alagoas	*Buck*	7/1973
	Sergipe	*James C Owen*	7/1973
	Espirito Santo	*Lowry*	10/1973
	Rio Grande De	*Strong*	10/1972
Chile	*Bordales*	*Douglas H Fox*	1/1974
	Zenteno	*Charles S Sperry*	1/1974
Colombia	*Caldas*	*Willard Keith*	7/1972
	Santander	*Waldron*	10/1973
Greece	*Miaoulis*	*Ingram*	7/1971
Iran	*Babr*	*Zellars*	1972
	Palang	*Stormes*	1972
	for spares	*Gainard*	3/1971
South Korea	*Dae Gu*	*Wallace L Lind*	12/1973
	Iu Cheon	*De Haven*	12/1973
Taiwan	*Hsiang Yang*	*Brush*	2/1976
	Heng Yang	*Samuel N Moore*	2/1970
	Hua Yang	*Bristol*	2/1970
	Yueh Yang	*Haynsworth*	5/1970
	Po Yang	*Maddox*	5/1970
	Lo Yang	*Taussig*	5/1974
	Wu Yang	*John W Thomason*	5/1974
	Huei Yang	*English*	9/1970
Turkey	*Muavenet*	*Gwin*	10/1971
Venezuela	*Carabobo*	*Beatty*	7/1972
	Falcon	*Robert K Huntington*	10/1973

By increasing the beam by one foot, the basic *Fletcher* hull could carry three twin 5-in mounts (two forward and one aft) in place of the five single 5-in mounts (two forward and three aft). This gave more room abaft the funnels for a more concentrated and better arranged antiaircraft armament, as well as providing one extra 5-in barrel—although all other things being equal, a twin mounting fires more slowly than two single ones, due to interference between the guns.

This was the genesis of the *Allen M Sumner* Class, 70 of which were built between 1943 and 1945. They were succeeded on the stocks from 1945 to 1947 by the *Gearing* Class, which were basically the same as the *Allen M Sumners*, except that a 14-ft hull extension was inserted in the mid-section between the two funnels to accommodate extra fuel—the one major fault with the *Allen M Sumners* had been their relatively short range for Pacific warfare. The additional hull section also gave the *Gearings* a greater measure of stability.

The *Allen M Sumners* were all built at six yards, the Bethlehem Steel Corporation Staten Island yard, San Francisco yard and San Pedro yard, the Federal Ship Building and Dry Dock Company yard, the Bath Iron Works Corporation yard, and the Todd Pacific Shipyard. As built the class was divided into two groups, 58 being completed as ordinary destroyers, and 12 as light minelayers—identical with the other 58 except

The *Allen M Sumner* in April 1953 before the FRAM II conversion. The only wartime modification to the class had been to replace the after bank of torpedo tubes with an additional quadruple 40-mm AA mounting and director. The modernization in the early 1960s was not altogether successful because of the limited space available

US Navy

that they had provision to carry 80 mines.

Destroyers: *English* DD696, *Haynsworth* DD700, *John W Weeks* DD701, *Hank* DD702, *Compton* DD705, *Gainard* DD706, *Soley* DD707, *Harlan R Dickson* DD708, *Barton* DD722, *Maddox* DD731, *Hyman* DD732, *Purdy* DD734, *Brush* DD745, *Samuel N Moore* DD747, *Harry E Hubbard* DD748, *John R Pierce* DD753, *Beatty* DD756, *Henley* DD762, *Willard Keith* DD775, *Bristol* DD857, *Hugh W Hadley* DD774, *Cooper* DD695, *Meredith* DD726, *Mannert L Abele* DD733, *Drexler* DD741, *Allen M Sumner* DD692, *Moale* DD693, *Ingraham* DD694, *Charles S Sperry* DD697, *Ault* DD698, *Waldron* DD699, *Wallace L Lind* DD703, *Borie* DD704, *Hugh Purvis* DD709, *Walke* DD723, *Laffey* DD724, *O'Brien* DD725, *De Haven* DD727, *Mansfield* DD728, *Lyman K Swenson* DD729, *Collett* DD730, *Blue* DD744, *Taussig* DD746, *Alfred A Cunningham* DD752, *Frank E Evans* DD754, *John A Bole* DD755, *Putnam* DD757, *Strong* DD758, *Lofberg* DD759, *John W Thomason* DD760, *Buck* DD761, *Lowry* DD770, *James C Owen* DD776, *Zellars* DD777, *Massey* DD778, *Douglas H Fox* DD779, *Stormes* DD780, *Robert K Huntington* DD781.

Light Minelayers: *Adams* DM27, *Gwin* DM33, *Harry F Bauer* DM26, *Henry A Wiley* DM29, *Lindsey* DM32, *Robert H Smith* DM23, *Shannon* DM25, *Shea* DM30, *Thomas E Fraser* DM24, *Tolman* DM28, *J William Ditter* DM31, *Aaron Ward* DM34.

Of these, *Cooper, Meredith, Mannert L Abele* and *Drexler* were lost during the war, and *Hugh W Hadley* was so badly damaged by a kamikaze attack that she was scrapped soon after the war ended.

After the war most of the class except some of the light minelayers had their 40-mm and 20-mm guns replaced by 6 3-in and the pole mast was replaced by a tripod to carry the heavier radar. One of the two pentad 21-in torpedo tube mountings had already been removed on most to make way for a quadruple 40-mm gun mounting.

The majority were then mothballed in the

reserve fleet until the early 1960s, when 29 were given the FRAM II modernization. These were: *Allen M Sumner, Moale, Ingraham, Charles S Sperry, Ault, Waldron, Wallace L Lind, Borie, Hugh Purvis, Walke, Laffey, O'Brien, De Haven, Mansfield, Lyman K Swenson, Collett, Blue, Taussig, Alfred A Cunningham, Frank E Evans, John A Bole, Putnam, Lowry, James C Owen, Zellars, Massey, Douglas H Fox, Stormes* and *Robert K Huntington.*

This conversion was intended to make the destroyers suitable for modern antisubmarine warfare. All the old antiaircraft guns were removed and the space was used to fit a hangar and landing pad for two of the unsuccessful DASH drone helicopters. Modern antisubmarine weapons and electronic equipment, including a variable depth sonar, were fitted and living spaces rehabilitated.

The *Allen M Sumner* FRAM II conversions were not as successful as the *Gearings*, whose extra space and stability now came in useful. Despite this, the *Allen M Sumners* lasted virtually intact until the early 1970s, with none transferred to foreign navies. However, the rundown, when it came, was swift. The last of this class in US Naval service, *Laffey,* was stricken on March 1, 1975.

Twenty-nine were transferred or sold abroad, of which two were for spares: the above chart shows the purchasing countries, new names and date of transfer.

All in all, they were a successful class, but they have always been overshadowed by their famous predecessors and successors.

Displacement: 2200 tons (standard) 3320 tons (full load) *Length:* 114.76 m (376 ft 6 in) *Beam:* 12.44 m (40 ft 10 in) *Draught:* 5.79 m (19 ft) *Machinery:* 2-shaft geared steam turbines, 60 000 shp=34 knots *Armament:* 6 5-in (130-mm); 2 torpedo-launchers (triple) 2 torpedo tubes (fixed); 2 Hedgehogs *Aircraft:* 2 drone helicopters *Crew:* 274

Almirante Clemente

Venezuelan frigate class. In the early 1950s the Americans provided what was termed

Almirante Clemente as refitted in 1976 with an Oto-Melara 76-mm (3-in) bow gun and Plessey AWS-1 air warning and target acquisition radar. The water-cooled automatic gun is a dual-purpose weapon whose rate of fire is reported to be as high as 150 rds/min

Oto-Melara

'Offshore Aid' to a number of countries, under which warships were built in Europe for various 'free world' countries, but were paid for by the USA. Most of these ships were minesweepers, but they also included the very similar *Tritan, Albatros* and *Pattiniwa* Class corvettes for Denmark, Italy and Indonesia respectively. These were all designed and built by Ansaldo of Italy, who also designed a rather larger fast frigate, of which six were supplied to Venezuela and two to Indonesia.

Three of the Venezuelan vessels were ordered in 1953, and the other three in 1954; the two almost identical Indonesian vessels were ordered in 1956 (see chart).

These ships were really light destroyers, with geared turbines rather than diesels to give a high speed. They were designed for service in tropical waters, with large airy superstructures and air-conditioning throughout the living and command spaces. Aluminium alloys were extensively used in the superstructure to reduce topweight. They were all equipped with Denny-Brown active fin stabilizers and fully automatic radar-controlled 4-in guns.

Almirante Jose Garcia, Almirante Brion and *General Jose Trinidad Moran* were refitted by the Cammell Laird/Plessy group from April 1968, the former recommissioning in February 1975 and the latter in May 1975.

These frigates are a useful cheap addition to navies that do not need sophisticated vessels. In the late 1950s and early 1960s Indonesia acquired a large number of modern Russian warships, which she found difficult to operate even before political disagreements with Russia made spares impossible to obtain. The result is that the four Italian-built frigates and corvettes of the *Iman Bondjol* and *Pattimura* Classes continued to form the backbone of the Indonesian navy after the Russian built ships had been disposed of.

Displacement: 1300 tons (standard), 1500 tons (full load) *Length:* 99.1 m (325 ft) *Beam:* 10.8 m (35 ft 5 in) *Draught:* 3.7 m (12 ft 1 in) *Machinery:* 2-shaft geared steam turbines, 24 000 shp=32 knots *Armament:* 4 4-in (100-mm); 4 40-mm (1.5-in); 8 20-mm; 3 21-in (53-cm) torpedo tubes (above water triple) *Crew:* 162

Venezuelan vessels	laid down	launched	completed
Almirante Clemente	5/1954	12/1954	1956
Almirante Jose Garcia	12/1954	10/1956	1957
Almirante Brion	12/1954	9/1955	1957
General Jose de Austria	12/1954	7/1956	1956
General Jose Trinidad Moran	5/1954	12/1954	1956
General Juan Jose Flores	5/1954	2/1955	1956
Indonesian vessels			
Iman Bondjol	1/1956	5/1956	5/1958
Surapat	1/1956	5/1956	5/1958

Almirante Oquendo

Spanish antisubmarine destoyer class. The *Oquendos* were originally designed as conventional destroyers, and were intended to carry an armament of 8 105-mm, 6 37-mm and 4 20-mm guns, 7 torpedo tubes (2 double and 1 triple) and two depth-charge throwers. Then they were redesigned and classed as antisubmarine frigates in 1955. They were eventually rated as antisubmarine destroyers in 1961.

Nine of the class were ordered from Ferrol in 1947-48. Of these, *Blas de Lazo, Blasco de Gavery, Bonifaz, Gelmirez, Langare* and *Recalde* were cancelled in 1953. Only three were completed (see chart).

The length of time taken to complete these ships was partly due to Spain's precarious financial position in the 1950s, partly to uncertainties over the role these vessels should play and partly to the need to ensure that they were not obsolete before they even joined the navy.

When completed, they formed two entirely separate sub-groups, the *Almirante Oquendo* having a totally different weapons and electronics fit to the *Roger de Lauria* and the *Marques de la Ensenada.* The *Almirante Oquendo* was first completed in September 1960, and was then immediately taken in hand for modernization to make use of the American aid that had become available as a trade-off for the American use of two air-bases and the submarine base at Rota.

When finally completed, she had a British radar outfit, and had two twin 120-mm AA turrets, one forward and one aft.

The *Roger de Lauria* and *Marques de la Ensenada,* which were much less complete, were returned to Cartagena for a complete reconstruction. The beam was increased by two metres to cope with the extra top hamper and the forecastle was lengthened to leave only a short quarter deck. They were fitted with three twin 127-mm (5-in) turrets, two forward and one aft, two triple launchers for antisubmarine torpedoes, and a landing pad and hangar for an antisubmarine helicopter at the break of the forecastle. In addition to an extensive American radar fit, they also have variable depth sonar at the stern, and are the equivalent of the American *Allen M Sumner* FRAM II conversions. Only the machinery is now the same as that in the *Almirante Oquendo.*

(Almirante Oquendo) Displacement: 2050 tons (standard), 2765 tons (full load) *Length:* 116.4 m (381 ft 10 in) *Beam:* 11.0 m (36 ft) *Draught:* 3.85 m (12 ft 7 in) *Machinery:* 2-shaft geared steam turbines, 60 000 shp=38 knots *Armament:* 4 120-mm (4.7-in); 6 40-mm (1.5-in); 4 20-mm; 6 torpedo launchers (2 triple); 2 21-in (53-cm) torpedo tubes (fixed above water) *Crew:* 249

Vessel	laid down	launched	completed
Almirante Oquendo	6/1951	9/1956	4/1963
Roger de Lauria	9/1951	11/1958	5/1969
Marques de la Ensenada	9/1951	7/1959	9/1970

Alpha

Russian submarine class. The Russians have always had an interest in underwater warfare. They were the first to use mines on a large scale, and were early exponents of the submarine. Their submarine fleet at the start of the Second World War was the largest —though by no means the most effective—in the world.

After the end of that war they captured many advanced German submarine projects which they made good use of in building up a very large fleet of conventional submarines.

When the US produced the first nuclear submarines, Russia was quick to follow. Her first class of nuclear fleet submarines, the *Novembers*, began construction in 1958 and they first entered service in 1961. Fifteen *Novembers* were built, but they were very noisy. In 1970 one sank near the English Channel.

The next Russian class of fleet submarines, the *Victor* Class, commenced construction in 1966. They represent a great advance over the *November* Class. Both of these classes were built in batches, apparently without a prototype.

Then in 1970 a Russian submarine was spotted that was apparently nuclear powered, and by its size and shape it would appear to be a fleet submarine—that is, one that is equipped to hunt other submarines and surface vessels. It was assigned the NATO reporting name of *Alpha.*

By 1976 no other submarine of that class had appeared, and it differs significantly both from the *Victor* Class that preceded it and from the *Uniform* Class of fleet submarines, which first appeared in 1974. It is conceivable that the *Alpha* was a trials ship for a new type of reactor, since all other types of Russian fleet submarine have been built in substantial numbers, without prototypes having appeared before the production boats.

Displacement: 3500/4500 tons (surfaced/submerged) *Machinery:* probably nuclear

Alpino

Italian frigate class. The *Alpino* Class frigates had their origin in the provision for two frigates to be named *Circe* and *Climene* in the Italian 1959-60 naval programme. Alterations to both armament and machinery were made to the design in 1962, making them the first Italian warships to use gas turbine propulsion. Their names were changed in June 1965, *Circe* becoming *Alpino* and *Climene* becoming *Carabiniere*.

Name	laid down	launched	completed
Alpino	2/1963	6/1967	1/1968
Carabiniere	1/1965	9/1967	1968

Based on the preceding *Bergamini* and *Centauro* Classes, they resemble the *Bergaminis* in appearance apart from a much more prominent funnel, but are larger and more heavily armed. They carry two Agusta-Bell 204 antisubmarine helicopters and are fitted with variable depth sonar.

However, the main difference between the *Alpinos* and their predecessors lies not in their size or armament but in their machinery. In place of the *Centauro*'s steam turbines and the *Bergamini*'s diesels, the *Alpinos* were given a CODAG (Combined Diesel And Gas) turbine arrangement. This consists of four Tosi diesels developing a total of 16 800 shp, and two Tosi-Metrovick gas turbines giving 15 000 shp.

The diesels can be used on their own for cruising, and give a maximum speed of 22 knots. The gas turbines are used for quick starts and rapid acceleration, and boost the maximum speed by six knots.

Two more of the class were projected, but the *Lupo* Class, a slightly smaller improved version, was ordered instead.

Displacement: 2700 tons (full load) *Length:* 113.3 m (371 ft 7 in) *Beam:* 13.3 m (43 ft 7 in.) *Draught:* 3.9 m (12 ft 10 in) *Machinery:* 2-shaft diesels and gas turbines, 31 800 shp=28 knots *Armament:* 6 3-in (76-mm); 1 depth-charge mortar; 6 12-in (30.4-cm) torpedo tubes (2 triple) *Aircraft:* 2 helicopters *Crew:* 254

Below and bottom: **The frigate *Alpino*, the first Italian warship to have gas turbine propulsion. The auxiliary turbines are used to supplement the main diesels for rapid acceleration**

PPL

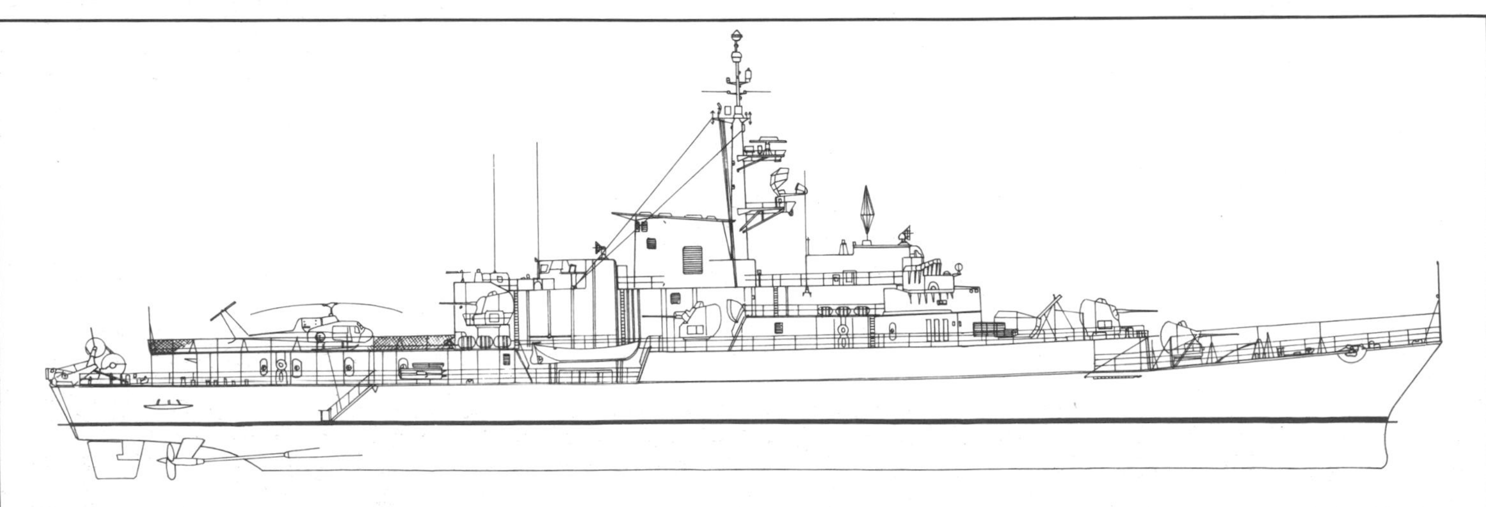

Amatsukaze

Japanese destroyer. In 1945 the Imperial Japanese Navy ceased to exist, and it was not until the Korean war that the Maritime Self Defence Force (MSDF), as the Japanese navy is now known, came into being.

The terms of the Japanese constitution preclude the use of ships designed for offensive purposes, and for many years this meant that the largest ships in the MSDF were destroyers and frigates of less than 3000 tons full load.

However, in 1960 a large antisubmarine escort named *Amatsukaze* (Heavenly Wind) was ordered. Laid down in November 1962 and launched in October 1963, she was completed in February 1965. Fitted with American weapons and electronic equipment (as are all MSDF warships) she was the first Japanese vessel to be fitted with guided missiles (a single Tartar medium range antiaircraft missile launcher aft) and also the first to carry and operate a helicopter for antisubmarine warfare.

When completed, she was the largest Japanese warship built since the war, displacing 1100 tons more than the next largest, the destroyers *Akizuki* and *Teruzuki*, though the considerably larger helicopter-cruiser *Haruna* (which has hangar space for several helicopters) was later taken into service.

Unlike the Americans, whose warships need to carry a large amount of fuel for operations overseas, MSDF vessels are only required to operate in home waters. The weight and space saved by the smaller amount of fuel carried was used to provide a heavier armament, *Amatsukaze* being no exception. As well as the single Tartar launcher aft she mounts two twin 3-in turrets and two Hedgehogs forward, and antisubmarine dropping gear amidships. In addition she can operate an antisubmarine helicopter.

However, no more ships of this type were constructed, the Japanese considering that *Haruna*, a considerably bigger ship with a large helicopter platform and on-board maintenance facilities, represents a better investment.

The present *Amatsukaze* is not the first ship of that name to introduce new concepts to the Japanese navy. The *Amatsukaze* of 1917 was the first Japanese destroyer to have longitudinal framing, and the *Kagero* Class destroyer *Amatsukaze* of 1939 was the first to have high pressure boilers.

Displacement: 3050 tons (standard), 4000 tons (full load) *Length:* 131 m (429 ft 8 in) *Beam:* 13.4 m (43 ft 11 in) *Draught:* 4.2 m (13 ft 9 in) *Machinery:* 2-shaft geared steam turbines, 60 000 shp=33 knots *Armament:* 1 single Tartar missile launcher; 4 3-in (76-mm); 2 Hedgehog; 2 torpedo dropping racks (one on each beam above water) *Aircraft:* 1 helicopter *Crew:* 290

Amazon

British frigate class. In the 1960s the Royal Navy planned to follow its very successful Improved Type 12 *Leander* Class general-purpose frigates with a new design carrying an antisubmarine helicopter and the Seawolf short-range antiaircraft missile. This new design evolved into the Type 22 *Broadsword* Class. However, by the late 1960s it had become obvious that the extended development of Seawolf and several other systems

Below: The Royal Navy frigate HMS *Antelope* (foreground) with her sister *Amazon* in the English Channel during Antelope's sea trials which took place in January 1975

Below: **The British Type 21 frigate HMS *Amazon*, the first of a class of eight built since 1969, based on a Vosper Thornycroft commercial design**

Amazon

Below: **The *Amazon* Class frigate HMS *Ambuscade*. *Bottom:* *Amazon* and *Antelope* in January 1975. The *Amazon* Class were built as a stopgap during the extended development of the *Broadsword* Class. Armed with an automatic quick-firing 4.5-in (114-mm) Vickers Mk 8 gun and a quadruple Seacat close-range antiaircraft and surface-to-surface missile launcher, and with accommodation for a Lynx ASW helicopter, the first four ships were to have Exocet launchers added, the remainder being equipped with Exocet as standard; two triple 21-in (53-cm) torpedo launchers were also to be added**

intended for the Type 22s meant that they could not be in service before the mid-1970s at the earliest.

The first *Leander* was laid down in 1959, and the basic design dated back to 1951, when the first *Whitby* was ordered. The hull could no longer accommodate all the weapons systems and electronic equipment that were desirable. Therefore the last of the 26 *Leanders* was completed in 1972, and a stopgap design had to be found to fill the gap before the Type 22s came into service.

Fortunately, a suitable design was at hand. The commercial shipbuilders Vosper Thornycroft had proposed a series of designs for vessels ranging in size from corvettes to large guided-missile destroyers, all of which shared the same basic layout, hull-form and appearance. Four variants of the Mark V design, the 1100-ton *Saams*, were already under construction for Iran.

Vosper Thornycroft was therefore given a contract on February 27, 1968, to design a patrol frigate in collaboration with Yarrow, based on the Vosper Thornycroft commercial frigate designs. This was the first time the British Admiralty had adopted a commercial design since the Thornycroft 'Hunt' Type IV

Name and Pendant No	laid down	launched	completed
Amazon F169	11/1969	4/1971	5/1974
Antelope F170	3/1971	3/1972	2/1975
Active F171	7/1971	11/1972	1975
Ambuscade F172	7/1971	1/1973	1975
Arrow F173	6/1972	2/1974	1975
Alacrity F174	2/1973	9/1974	1977
Ardent F175	2/1974	5/1975	1977
Avenger F176	10/1974		

MOD

escort destroyers *Brecon* and *Brissenden* of 1942. That the procedure was justified is shown by the fact that the first of the *Amazon* Class was laid down only 20 months after the design contract was placed.

There are eight in the class. The first three were built by Vosper Thornycroft, and the last five by Yarrow.

They are handsome ships, with a 4.5-in Vickers Mk 8 gun forward, a single 20-mm gun either side of the bridge for counter-insurgency work, a quadruple Seacat antiaircraft missile launcher over the hangar at the break of the quarterdeck, and a landing pad

MOD

for the Lynx ASW helicopter right aft.

Arrow was the first of the class to be fitted with four MN38 Exocet surface-to-surface missiles, mounted on the break of the forecastle, just under the bridge. The first four vessels were to be refitted with Exocet at a later date, and the entire class was also to have two triple 21-in torpedo launchers as they became available.

The *Amazons* were the first frigates to be designed and constructed with COGOG machinery (COmbined Gas Or Gas), an arrangement tried out in the Converted *Blackwood* frigate *Exmouth*, and also fitted in the Type 42 *Sheffield* Class missile destroyers. The machinery consists of two Tyne gas turbines for cruising and two Olympus for maximum speed.

Displacement: 2500 ton (full load) *Length:* 117 m (383 ft 10 in) *Beam:* 12.7 m (41 ft 8 in) *Draught:* 3.7 m (12 ft 2 in) *Machinery:* 2-shaft gas turbines (COGOG) 50 000 shp=30+ knots *Armament:* 1 4.5-in (115-mm); 2 20-mm; 4 Exocet; 1 Seacat quadruple launcher *Aircraft:* 1 Lynx antisubmarine helicopter *Crew:* 170

US Navy

USS *America* off Cannes, France. Originally planned as a nuclear-powered carrier, *America* was given oil-fired boilers after the excessive expense of building the *Enterprise*

America

US aircraft carrier. After the first two *Kitty Hawk* Class aircraft carriers had been laid down it was decided that all future American carriers would be powered by nuclear reactors. Next, USS *Enterprise* was given a nuclear powerplant, but she was so expensive to build that Secretary of Defense McNamara abandoned nuclear power for the next two, *America* (CVA66) and *John F Kennedy* (CVA67). These reverted to oil-fired boilers and were built to virtually the same design as the *Kitty Hawk* and *Constellation.*

America was built at Newport News, and was laid down in January 1961. Launched in February 1964, she was completed in January 1965 at a cost of $248 800 000, a fast building time for such a large and complicated ship.

She is fitted to carry between 70 and 90 aircraft, depending on the size of those embarked. Until recently she was rated as an Attack Aircraft Carrier (CVA) and carried only fighter and attack squadrons, their associated reconnaissance and early warning aircraft and rescue helicopters. Now that the wartime *Essex* Class carriers, which were modified for antisubmarine work, have been scrapped, the CVAs have had to embark antisubmarine aircraft. This has meant a diminution in the number of fighter and attack aircraft carried, and the carriers have been rerated as CVs.

The carrier herself is armed with two Mark 10 Twin Terrier medium range antiaircraft missile launchers—an updated version which can also accommodate Standard. She has a very extensive radar fit and the Naval Tactical Data System. *America* was the first American carrier to be fitted with sonar.

She saw active service off North Vietnam, and has also been in the US 6th Fleet. During the 1967 Arab-Israeli war, she launched her planes when Israeli aircraft and torpedo boats attacked the USS *Liberty.*

Displacement: 60 300 tons (standard) 78 250 tons (full load) *Length:* 319.3 m (1046 ft) oa *Beam:* 39.6 m (129 ft 11 in) (hull), 76.8 m (252 ft) (flight deck) *Draught:* 10.9 m (35 ft 9 in) *Machinery:* 4-shaft geared steam turbines, 280 000 shp=35 knots *Armament:* 2 twin Terrier launchers *Aircraft:* 70-90 *Crew:* 2700+2000 aircrew

Amphion

British submarine class. Intended to operate in the Far East and Pacific, these submarines were specifically designed for mass-production using prefabrication and welding techniques. These methods had been used in earlier submarines but could not be employed to their full advantage because the boats in question had not originally been designed for this type of construction. The *Amphion* or 'A' Class were the first British submarines designed to have a completely welded hull. The system gave considerable advantages in that the prefabricated sections could be built under cover in ideal conditions before being transferred to the building slip for assembly. The slip was, moreover, occupied for the shortest possible time, which allowed a higher rate of production.

The 'A' Class pressure hull was constructed from 10 main sections and the ballast tanks from 16. Welding also improved hull strength, which enabled the boats to dive to a greater depth and saved weight. Compared to the earlier 'T' Class the 'A' Class incorporated several improvements without a major increase in size. They had a range of 16 800 km (10 500 miles) at 11 knots and a surface speed of 18.5 knots compared with 12 800 km (8000 miles) at 10 knots and 15.25 knots for the 'T' Class. This high surface speed and radius of action were essential for their intended area of operations in the Pacific and Far East.

The gun armament was not always carried, being fitted or not according to operational requirements. Four of the ten torpedo tubes were fitted in the casing outside the pressure hull (two forward and two aft). The remainder were mounted in the pressure hull (four forward and two aft). To enable the diesels to be run while the boat was submerged they were fitted with a hinged 'snort', developed from the German *Schnorchel*, containing the engines' inlet and exhaust pipes. They were also fitted with two air-conditioning plants and an air-purification system, which war experience had demonstrated to be essential in areas of extreme climate such as the Far East, to keep the crew at peak efficiency.

Forty-six of the class were ordered between 1944 and 1945 but at the end of hostilities 30 were cancelled. Of these 30 only two, *Ace* and *Achates*, had been launched. The remaining 16 were completed between 1946 and 1948. Between 1955 and 1962 the class was modernized. The old casing, including the four external tubes, was removed and replaced by a modern streamlined casing with a sonar dome at the forward end. The conning tower was replaced by a tall streamlined 'dorsal fin' which enclosed the navigating position, snort, periscope standards, and radio and radar aerials (retracted), thereby eliminating the underwater resistance to propulsion caused by these items. This streamlining, together with the weight saved by the use of aluminium and the removal of the external torpedo tubes, provided a slight improvement in speed. No position was provided for the 20-mm gun but there was one for the 4-in gun, although this was seldom carried.

On April 16, 1951, the *Affray* disappeared while operating in the English Channel. A search was instituted and she was eventually found lying on the bottom of Hurd Deep, off Alderney, in 55 fathoms (100 m) of water.

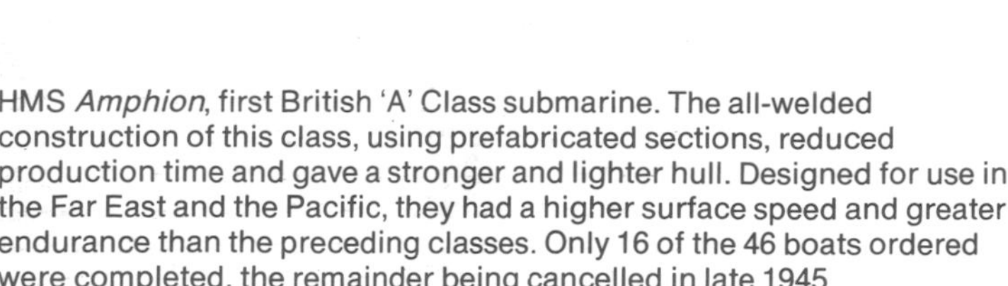

HMS *Amphion*, first British 'A' Class submarine. The all-welded construction of this class, using prefabricated sections, reduced production time and gave a stronger and lighter hull. Designed for use in the Far East and the Pacific, they had a higher surface speed and greater endurance than the preceding classes. Only 16 of the 46 boats ordered were completed, the remainder being cancelled in late 1945

There were no external signs of damage except for a broken 'snort' tube (unlikely by itself to cause her loss). No attempt was made at salvage for reasons of cost and the great depth, and her loss remains a mystery. The remainder of the class were scrapped between 1967 and 1975, starting with *Aurochs*, the only unconverted of the class.

Alcide, Alderney, Alliance, Ambush, Amphion, Anchorite, Andrew, Astute, Auriga, Aurochs—built by Vickers Armstrong.
Aeneas, Alaric, Affray—built by Cammell Laird.
Artemis, Artful—built by Scotts.
Acheron—built by Chatham dockyard.

Displacement: 1120/1620 tons (surfaced/submerged) *Length:* 85.8 m (281 ft 9 in) *Beam:* 6.78 m (22 ft 3 in) *Draught:* 5.18 m (17 ft) *Machinery:* 2-shaft 8-cylinder diesels, 4300 bhp=18½ knots (surfaced); 2-shaft electric motors, 1250 shp=8 knots (submerged) *Armament:* 10 21-in (53-cm) torpedo tubes; 1 4-in (102-mm) gun; 1 20-mm AA *Crew:* 61

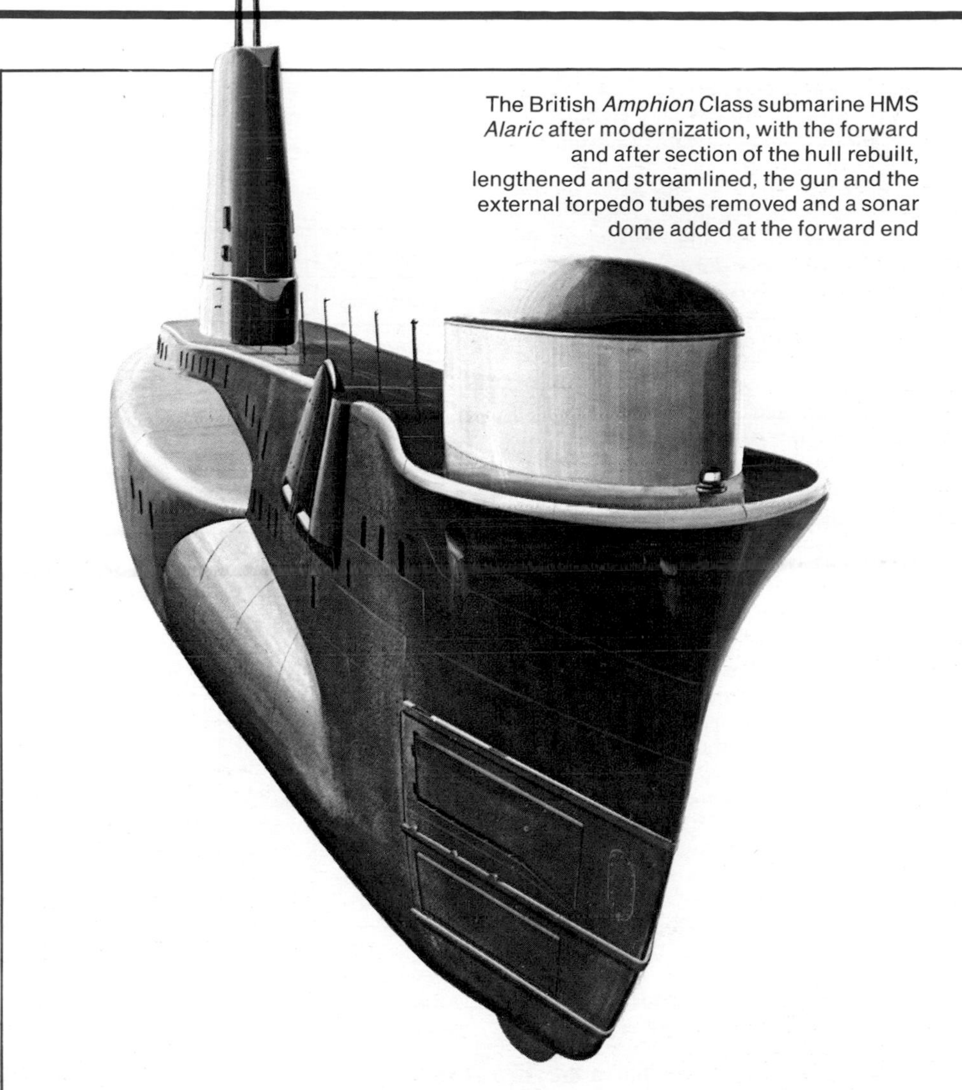

The British *Amphion* Class submarine HMS *Alaric* after modernization, with the forward and after section of the hull rebuilt, lengthened and streamlined, the gun and the external torpedo tubes removed and a sonar dome added at the forward end

Andrea Doria

Italian cruiser class. After the Second World War the Italians were faced with the problem of rebuilding their navy. At first they concentrated on destroyers and light escorts, and produced some very innovative designs. Then, in the mid-1950s, they turned their attention to the use of shipborne antisubmarine helicopters. Destroyers and frigates could be fitted to carry one or at most two small helicopters, but it would be much more effective to carry larger numbers, so that a greater area could be searched at one time and to allow for unserviceability.

The result was the two ships of the *Andrea Doria* Class (*Andrea Doria* was originally to be named *Enrico Dandolo*).

These were a completely new type of warship, and were designed to protect a convoy against both air and submarine attack. They were given a twin Terrier medium-range antiaircraft missile launcher forward, and eight 3-in fully automatic antiaircraft guns in single turrets arranged four on each side of the superstructure amidships.

The superstructure aft of the second funnel is a hangar for the four helicopters, which operate from a 30 m × 16 m landing pad right aft. The helicopters are two pairs of Agusta-Bell 204B antisubmarine helicopters. These work in tandem, one of each pair carrying sonar and the other carrying two Mk 44 antisubmarine torpedoes. They are to be replaced by more modern helicopters, each of which can carry sonar and torpedoes, thereby doubling the ships' striking force. The landing pad on *Andrea Doria* was also used in 1969 for landing trials by the British VTOL Harrier aircraft. At that time the *Andrea Doria* was the smallest ship that the Harrier had operated from.

The *Andrea Doria*s also have two triple 12.75-in torpedo tubes as close-range antisubmarine armament. They are both very beamy in relation to their length, which gives them a large landing pad for their size, and they are fitted with Gyrofin-Salmorraghi stabilizers.

They are a very sensible design for Mediterranean warfare, and the idea was soon copied by other countries. The one problem is the limited number of helicopters that can be carried, and other vessels of this type are considerably larger. The Italians have also built a larger version, *Vittorio Veneto*, which operates nine helicopters from a hull of 2000 tons greater displacement.

Displacement: 6000 tons (standard), 7500 tons (full load) *Length:* 149.3 m (489 ft 10 in) *Beam:* 17.2 m (56 ft 4 in) *Draught:* 5 m (16 ft 5 in) *Machinery:* 2-shaft geared steam turbines, 60 000 shp=30 knots *Armament:* 1 twin AA missile launcher; 8 3-in (76-mm) AA guns; 6 12.75-in (32.4-cm) torpedo tubes (two triple) *Aircraft:* 4 helicopters *Crew:* 478

Name	laid down	launched	completed
Andrea Doria	5/1958	2/1963	2/1964
Caio Duilio	5/1958	12/1962	11/1964

Animoso

Italian escort class. The Italian navy's major warships and submarines performed very badly in the Second World War, mainly due to the failings of Italian politicians and naval commanders. However, Italian convoy escorts and light craft were very successful.

Unfortunately, prewar Italian shipbuilding programmes had concentrated on major warships, with the result that when war came there was a great shortage of convoy escorts, indeed of all types of antisubmarine vessels. The success of British aircraft and naval units, mainly operating from Malta, meant that escorts were urgently needed to protect the North African supply routes.

In 1936 Italy had laid down the four *Orsa* Class destroyer escorts. These were basically small destroyers, with a good antisubmarine armament and no torpedoes, and were somewhat similar to the British *Kingfisher* Class. This design was repeated, with slight improvements, as the *Animoso* Class.

Name	laid down	launched	completed
Aliseo	9/1941	9/1942	2/1943
Animoso	4/1941	4/1942	8/1942
Ardente	4/1941	5/1942	9/1942
Ardimentoso	4/1941	6/1942	12/1942
Ardito	4/1941	3/1942	6/1942
Ciclone	5/1941	3/1942	5/1942
Fortunale	5/1941	3/1942	8/1942
Ghibli	8/1941	2/1943	7/1943
Groppo	6/1941	4/1942	8/1942
Impavido	8/1941	2/1943	4/1943
Impetuoso	8/1941	4/1943	6/1943
Indomito	1/1942	7/1943	8/1943
Intrepido	1/1942	9/1943	1/1944
Monsone	6/1941	6/1942	11/1942
Tifone	6/1941	3/1942	9/1942
Uragano	6/1941	5/1942	9/1942

There were a number of variations from the basic design. *Animoso, Ghibli, Impavido, Indomito, Intrepido* and *Monsone* had three instead of two 3.9-in guns, and the standard displacement varied from 1100 to 1200 tons. Like almost all Italian warships, they were fitted to carry mines, and unlike the *Orsas* they were fitted with torpedo tubes so that they had some chance of defending themselves against enemy surface ships.

They had short careers in the Italian navy. Six were sunk before the Italian surrender of September 1943: *Ciclone* and *Uragano* by mines, *Ardente* by collision with the Italian destroyer *Grecale, Groppo* and *Monsone* by Allied bombing, and *Tifone* was scuttled in Tunisia during the evacuation in May 1943. She had been hit and disabled so badly that she could not sail for Italy.

Two—*Ghibli* and *Impetuoso*—were scuttled in September 1943. *Ghibli* was salvaged by the Germans and towed to Genoa for repairs. These were never completed, and she was scuttled again by the Germans in April 1945.

Ardito, Impavido and *Intrepido* were all sunk in 1944 whilst being operated by the Germans. *Ardito* was sunk by British MTBs, *Impavido* by a mine, and *Intrepido* by a British submarine.

The survivors were all transferred to Yugoslavia or the USSR after the war. *Aliseo* and *Indomito* went to Yugoslavia, and were

The cruiser *Caio Duilio*, sister ship of the *Andrea Doria*, under way. Antiaircraft armament consists of a twin Terrier and eight automatic 76-mm guns, while two triple A/S torpedo tubes and four Agusta Bell 204B helicopters are provided for antisubmarine work

Italian Naval Attaché

HMS *Anson* in 1948. One of the *King George V* Class, she became flagship of the Training Squadron after the Second World War

renamed *Biokovo* and *Triglav* respectively: they remained in service in the 1970s. *Animoso*, *Ardimentoso*, and *Fortunale* went to Russia and were all discarded by 1960.

Displacement: 1200 tons (standard), 1700 tons (full load) *Length:* 89.5 m (293 ft 7½ in) *Beam:* 9.8 m (32 ft 2 in) *Draught:* 3.5 m (11 ft 6 in) *Machinery:* 2-shaft geared steam turbines, 16 000 shp=26 knots *Armament:* 2 3.9-in (99.05-mm); 12 20-mm; 6 depth-charge throwers; 20 mines; 4 17.7-in (45-cm) torpedo tubes *Crew:* 180

Annapolis

Canadian destroyer escort class. The success of the original *St Laurent* Class destroyer escorts (DDEs) built between 1950 to 1957 led to the building of seven *Restigouche* Class, four *Mackenzie* Class and finally two *Annapolis* Class. All have the same basic hull as the original *St Laurent* but each represents an important change in armament and role.

The most important difference in the *Annapolis* Class is the provision of a hangar for a CHSS-2 Sikorsky Sea King antisubmarine helicopter, the first time this large machine was taken to sea in a ship of frigate size. This necessitated a split funnel and the sacrifice of one 'Limbo' depth-charge mortar. As a further compensation for topweight the lighter US-pattern 3-in/50 cal Mk 22 gun mounting was chosen instead of the British-pattern 3-in/70 cal Mk 6 turret used in the *Mackenzies* and *Restigouches*. To distinguish them they were rerated as DDH.

The secret of the *Annapolis* Class' ability to handle the big Sea King is the 'Beartrap' device. This automatic hauldown device tethers the helicopter and winches it down to the deck, with self-tensioning to compensate for the roll of the ship. The Beartrap also manoeuvres the Sea King into the hangar. Between 1960 and 1966 the remaining six *St Laurent* Class were rebuilt along similar lines and were also rerated as DDHs.

Name	laid down	launched	completed
Annapolis (DDH.265)	7/1960	4/1963	12/1964
Nipigon (DDH.266)	4/1960	12/1961	5/1964

Three radar sets are carried, the USN-pattern Sylvania SPS-10 for surface search at the masthead, and the SPS-12 air warning, with its parabolic aerial on a lower platform. The 3-in guns have an on-mounting scanner as well, for the X-Band Mk 63 gunfire control system. Three sonars are carried, one hull-mounted, one 'dunking' set in the helicopter and a variable depth set (VDS) carried at the stern.

Displacement: 2400 tons (standard), 3000 (full load) *Length:* 113.1 m (371 ft 0 in) oa *Beam:* 12.8 m (42 ft 0 in) *Draught:* 4.4 m (14 ft 5 in) *Machinery:* 2-shaft geared steam turbines, 30 000 shp=28 knots *Armament:* 2 3-in (76-mm)/50 cal (1×2); 1 Limbo triple depth-charge mortar; 6 Mk 32 12.75-in (32.4-cm) torpedo tubes (2×3) *Crew:* 246 men

Anson

British battleship. The *Anson* was one of the five ships of the *King George V* Class constructed under the 1937 Programme. She was originally to have been named *Jellicoe* after the First World War admiral but the name was changed before she was launched. Laid down on July 20, 1937, at the Wallsend-on-Tyne shipyard of Swan Hunter and Wigham Richardson, she was launched on February 24, 1940. Her construction was suspended for three months in May 1940 because of the need to concentrate shipbuilding facilities on more urgent requirements and as delays of less drastic nature continued to affect her fitting-out she did not complete until June 22, 1942. While under construction some improvements were incorporated in her hull structure and fittings as a result of war experience and the loss of her sister ship *Prince of Wales*.

On completion she joined the Home Fleet and became the flagship of Vice-Admiral Sir Bruce Fraser (Second-in-Command, Home Fleet). In June 1943 she became the flagship of Vice-Admiral Sir Henry Moore who took over when Admiral Fraser became C-in-C Home Fleet. Between September 1942 and May 1944 she provided distant cover for Russian convoys and on several occasions covered carrier raids on the Norwegian coast, principally against the *Tirpitz*.

Between July 1944 and March 1945 she was refitted at Devonport preparatory to going to the Pacific. The more important modifications made during this refit were the removal of the aircraft catapult amidships and its associated equipment, and the replacement of her Mk IV high-angle/low-angle directors by Mk VI (she was the only battleship to carry this model); the close-range AA was also increased substantially.

She arrived in the Pacific in July 1945 where she became flagship of the 1st Battle Squadron of the British Pacific Fleet but the war ended before she became involved in any major operations. She was present at the reoccupation of Hong Kong in August and the Japanese surrender in Tokyo Bay in September. At the end of the war she mounted a close-range AA armament of 88 2-pdr pom-poms, 8 40-mm and 65 20-mm guns as against 48 2-pdrs and 18 20-mm at the time of her completion.

She served the remainder of her active career as a training ship for seamen before being placed in reserve in 1949 and was eventually sold for scrap.

Aragua

Venezuelan destroyer class. In 1950 the Armada Republica Venezuela ordered two destroyers from the British firm of Vickers, followed by a third ship two years later. The design was basically an enlargement of the contemporary British 'Battle' Class, but with improvements suggested by the *Daring* Class. When completed they were among the biggest and most powerful destroyers afloat.

The gun armament comprised six 4.5-in (114-mm) Mark 3 guns in dual-purpose BD Mk 4 mountings. This mounting had 80° elevation with remote power control (RPC) to allow it to follow the training and elevation of the Mk 6 fire-control director. In addition a set of triple 21-in (53-cm) torpedo tubes was mounted amidships, and eight twin 40-mm Mk 5 Bofors guns.

The ships entered service between 1953 and 1956, at a reported cost of £2.5 million each. In 1959 the *Nueva Esparta* and *Zulia* were refitted in Britain, and further improvements were made at New York Navy Yard the following year. A similar refit was given to the *Aragua* between 1964 and 1965. The *Nueva Esparta* was given a much bigger modernization between 1968 and 1969 by the British firms Plessey Radar and Cammell Laird. When she emerged in 1969 she had lost her torpedo tubes and six twin Bofors mountings. To improve her antiaircraft capability two Short Seacat short-range missile launchers were added amidships and Plessey AWS-1 and AWS-2 radars were installed. Other equipment fitted by Plessey's included operations room and bridge displays.

The three ships consequently became diffe-

The *Aragua* Class Venezuelan destroyer *Nueva Esparta* after her refit in 1968-69. Twelve 40-mm Bofors AA guns have been deleted, along with the torpedo tubes, and two twin Seacat launchers added amidships. New radar, fire control and communications equipment have been added

Plessey

rent in detail. The most noticeable external change was the removal of the original latticework aerial spreader mounted on the after side of the funnel, but in most other respects their appearance remained the same. The antisubmarine equipment varies. Hedgehog spigot mortars being fitted in *Aragua* and Squid triple depth-charge mortars in the other two. The two ships refitted at New York Navy Yard were given the Westinghouse/Bendix SPS-6 surveillance radar, but all three retained the venerable Type 275 fire-control tracker radar.

Displacement: 2600 tons (standard), 3670 tons (full load) *Length:* 122.5 m (402 ft) oa *Beam:* 13.1 m (43 ft) *Draught:* 5.8 m (19 ft) max *Machinery:* 2-shaft geared steam turbines 50 000 shp=34 knots (max), 31 knots sea speed *Armament:* 6 4.5-in (114-mm) DP (3×2); 16 40-mm AA (8×2) (reduced to 4 40-mm (2×2) in *Nueva Esparta*); 2 quadruple Seacat SAM-launchers (*Nueva Esparta* only); 3 21-in (53-cm) torpedo tubes (removed from *Nueva Esparta*); 2 depth-charge throwers and racks (replaced by Squid in *Nueva Esparta* and *Zulia*, and by Hedgehog in *Aragua*) *Crew:* 256

Archer

British escort carrier class. The first escort carrier, the British *Audacity* converted from a German merchant vessel, was used as the model for the US prototype *Long Island*, completed in 1941. However, this American mercantile conversion was much superior to the British original. A sister ship of the *Long Island* was transferred to the Royal Navy under the Lend-Lease agreement and named *Archer*, and to meet the Admiralty's order for five such vessels the American authorities acquired four more mercantile hulls for conversion. All five were built by the Sun Shipbuilding company, Chester. They were fitted with a large hangar served by a single lift to a full-length, wooden flight deck. *Archer* differed slightly from the later ships and was fitted with four, instead of two, diesel engines driving a single shaft. This arrangement was not entirely satisfactory and machinery troubles led to her early retirement.

The *Avenger* was the first to see action when during September 1942 she escorted the Russian convoy *PQ18*. Her aircraft proved invaluable in defence against air attack and on the 14th they assisted in the sinking of the submarine *U 589*. In November she joined the *Biter* and *Dasher* in support of the North African landings but on November 15 was torpedoed by *U 155* west of Gibraltar. The torpedo caused a petrol explosion and fire. The *Dasher* was also lost due to a petrol explosion and fire, but in this case by accident, in the River Clyde on March 27, 1943.

These two events cast considerable doubt on the arrangements for working and stowing of the aviation spirit, and the *Archer* and *Biter* were taken out of service to have their petrol systems modified. The *Archer* served as an Atlantic escort in mid-1943 and on May 23 her aircraft sank the submarine *U 752*. She was laid up in October 1943 and returned to the US Navy after the war, only to be sold into merchant service in 1946 and scrapped in 1962. The *Biter* served as an Atlantic escort from April 1943 until August 1944 and during that time her aircraft assisted in the sinking of the *U 203*, on April 25, 1943, and *U 89*, on May 12, 1943. In 1945 she was transferred to the French navy and renamed *Dixmude*, serving off Indo-China and in the Mediterranean before being returned to the US Navy in 1966 and subsequently sold for scrapping.

The fifth unit of the class, *Charger*, was retained in the United States and served as a Fleet Air Arm air crew training ship until the end of the war. In 1949 she was sold into mercantile service.

Displacement: 8200 tons (*Archer* 9000 tons) standard *Length:* 149.96 m (492 ft) oa, 134.72 m (442 ft) flight deck *Beam:* 21.18 m (69 ft 6 in) *Draught:* 7.01 m (23 ft), *Archer* 9.75 m (23 ft) *Machinery:* single-shaft diesel engines, 8500 bhp=17 knots *Armament:* 3 4-in (102-mm) (3×1); 15 20-mm (4×2, 7×1) *Crew:* 555

Aréthuse

French submarine class. The French navy, or Marine Nationale, took energetic steps to rebuild its submarine fleet after the Second World War, but this took time as French heavy industry also had to be rebuilt. Under the 1953 Programme two small submarines, *Aréthuse* and *Argonaute*, were ordered, followed by another pair in 1954, the *Amazone* and *Ariane*.

The design was the minimum consistent with efficiency, and the class is useful mainly for coast defence, but the boats are reported to be manoeuvrable and handy. The number of ballast tanks is small, for simplicity, but the hull is fully streamlined and capable of submerging to 200 metres. All four torpedo tubes are mounted in the bow and four reloads are carried.

The four boats were built in the Arsenal at Cherbourg between 1955 and 1960, and remained in service in the mid-1970s though probably scheduled for replacement by the new 1200-tonne *Agosta* Class, being rather too small to receive the latest sonar and weaponry.

The class is distinguished by its small but high conning tower 'fin' and a prominent sonar dome on the bow, faired into the hull. No details have been released about the sensors or type of torpedoes carried by this class, but it can be assumed that neither are the latest examples of their type. Similarly, nothing has been published about the deployment of the class, but it is believed that they are used in the Mediterranean, where conditions are better suited to small submarines.

Displacement: 400 tons (standard); 543 tons (surfaced); 669 tons (submerged) *Length:* 50 m (164 ft) *Beam:* 5.8 m (19 ft) *Draught:* 3.9 m (12 ft 10 in) *Machinery:* (surfaced) single-shaft 12-cylinder diesel, 1060 bhp=12½ knots; (submerged) electric motors, 1300 shp=16 knots *Armament:* 4 55-cm (21.7-in) torpedo tubes (8 torpedoes carried) *Crew:* 40

Ariete

Italian torpedo boat class. The Italians, as well as the Germans and the French, were firm believers in torpedo boats. These were basically very small destroyers, with a large torpedo armament and high speed. Between 1936 and 1938 they built 30 *Spica* Class and by 1942 they decided to build more of these ships. 42 ships of the consequent *Ariete* Class were projected, but only 16 were laid down.

Name	laid down	launched	completed
Alabarda	3/1943	5/1944	11/1944
Ariete	7/1942	3/1943	8/1943
Arturo	7/1942	3/1943	10/1943
Auriga	7/1942	4/1943	12/1943
Balestra	9/1942	1948	1949
Daga	1/1943	7/1943	3/1944
Dragone	7/1942	8/1943	4/1944
Eridano	7/1942	7/1943	3/1944
Fionda	8/1942	1948	—
Gladio	1/1943	6/1943	1/1944
Lancia	3/1943	5/1944	9/1944
Pugnale	1/1943	8/1943	7/1944
Rigel	7/1942	5/1943	1/1944
Spada	1/1943	7/1943	2/1944
Spica	1/1942	1/1944	9/1944
Stella Polare	3/1942	7/1943	1/1944

These were very similar to the destroyer escorts of the *Animoso* Class except that they concentrated on torpedo rather than antisubmarine armament.

Only *Ariete* was completed before the Italian surrender in September 1943, the rest were still building in north Italian yards, and when completed were used by the German navy except for *Balestra*, and *Fionda*. *Balestra* was finally completed by the Yugoslavs and named *Ucka*. *Fionda* was badly damaged by bombs in 1945, and although the Yugoslavs restarted construction as *Velebit*, they never completed her.

Alabarda, Arturo, Auriga, Daga, Dragone, Eridano, Gladio, Lancia, Pugnale, Rigel, Spada, Spica, and *Stella Polare* were sunk during the war.

Ariete was transferred to the Yugoslav navy under the terms of the Peace Treaty in April 1949, where she was renamed *Dumitor*.

Displacement: 797 tons (standard); 1120 tons (full load) *Length:* 82.3 m (270 ft) *Beam:* 8.6 m (28 ft 3 in) *Draught:* 2.8 m (9 ft 2 in) *Machinery:* 2-shaft geared steam turbines, 22 000 shp=31.5 knots *Armament:* 2 100-mm (3.9-in); 10 20-mm; 6 45-cm (17.7-in) torpedo tubes (2×3); 28 mines *Crew:* 158

Arkhangelsk

Russian battleship. When Italy surrendered in September 1943 the Soviet government immediately laid claim to one-third of the Italian fleet as reparations for the damage done by Italian units in the Black Sea. Although the Allies had little choice and no willingness to make this settlement, they compromised by transferring a number of their own ships on loan, until such time as the surrendered Italian fleet could be apportioned.

As part of this deal the Royal Navy made available the old battleship *Royal Sovereign*, which had been launched in 1915, together with four submarines and nine ex-US destroyers. The *Royal Sovereign* had recently been equipped with new radar and antiaircraft guns, but she was surplus to Royal Navy requirements except for shore bombardment tasks. A Soviet crew arrived in England early in 1944 and commissioned the ship formally as the *Arkhangelsk* on May 30, 1944. She left for the Kola Inlet with convoy JW59 in August 1944 and remained in the Arctic without firing a shot for the rest of the war. As a bizarre sidelight on the Russian character, when she was returned in February 1949 it was found that every gun on board was still loaded, from 15-in down to 2-pdr pom-poms. In addition the mess decks were covered in human excrement.

Displacement: 29 150 tons (normal), 32 500 tons (full load) *Length:* 190.95 m (620 ft 6 in) oa *Beam:* 30.94 m (101 ft 6 in) over bulges *Draught:* 9.76 m (28 ft 6 in) max *Machinery:* 4-shaft Parsons turbines, 40 000 shp=23 knots *Protection:* 330-102 mm (13-4 in) belt; 20-64 mm (¾-2½ in) decks; 330-280 mm (13-11 in) turrets; 280-152 mm (11-6 in) conning towers *Armament:* 8 15-in (381-mm) (4×2); 12 6-in (152-mm) (12×1); 8 4-in (102-mm) AA (4×2); 32 2-pdr (40-mm) AA (4×8); 17 20-mm AA (17×1) *Crew:* 1146

MOD

The battleship *Arkhangelsk* (ex-HMS *Royal Sovereign*) in June 1944, shortly after commissioning in the Soviet navy. She was returned to the Royal Navy in February 1949

Ark Royal

British aircraft carrier. The *Ark Royal* can easily lay claim to being the Royal Navy's most famous aircraft carrier for, in a very brief career, she achieved more than the majority of ships achieve in a lifetime. Ordered on April 17, 1935 under the 1934 Naval Estimates, she was laid down by Cammell Laird at Birkenhead on September 9, 1935 and launched on April 13, 1937. Her design benefited from the vast amount of experience gained from the six carriers, all but one converted vessels, commissioned between 1918 and 1930. For this reason, and because she had been designed as a Fleet Carrier from the start, she showed a considerable amount of improvement over these earlier vessels.

The flight deck, instead of being carried by the hull, was incorporated as part of its structure, the side plating being continued up to this deck, resulting in the fully enclosed bow that was to become a distinctive feature of later British carriers. This, together with the extensive use of welding, provided a light but very strong hull. The hangars were built on two levels and were intended to accommodate six squadrons (72 aircraft) but in practice this was found to be too large a number for efficient operation and in service she carried only five squadrons (60 aircraft). However, this was more aircraft than any of the other carriers could accommodate, the largest number otherwise being 48 in the *Courageous* and *Glorious*.

By providing a considerable overhang at the stern the flight deck was made much longer than in previous British carriers and this allowed aircraft to land on from the stern while others were being launched from the catapults fitted at the forward end of the

A Fairey Swordfish prepares to land on *Ark Royal*. The carrier's career was brief but glorious, escorting convoys to Malta and assisting in the destruction of *Bismarck*

Central Press

deck. The aircraft arrester gear was of an improved type and three lifts were provided to ensure the rapid transfer of aircraft from the hangar to the flight deck.

The *Ark Royal* was commissioned on November 16, 1938 and in January of the following year embarked her first aircraft. She worked up in the Mediterranean and then returned to Britain to join the Home Fleet. Within a month of the outbreak of the Second World War she was narrowly missed by two torpedoes from the submarine *U 39* (which was later sunk by the *Ark*'s escort) and by a 910-kg (2000-lb) bomb from a German aircraft. This last event was the first of many occasions on which the enemy claimed to have sunk the *Ark Royal.*

Between October 1939 and February 1940 she operated in the South Atlantic, and on her return home was refitted at Portsmouth. After taking part in the Norwegian campaign in April and May 1940, she sailed to Gibraltar where she joined Force H on June 23. During 1940 and 1941 she was constantly in action, mainly escorting Malta convoys and carrying out air strikes against the Italian mainland. In May 1941 she took part in the *Bismarck* action, her aircraft being responsible for two torpedo hits on the German battleship. One of these torpedoes damaged the *Bismarck*'s steering gear, prevented her escape, and ensured her ultimate destruction by the main units of the Home Fleet.

During the latter half of 1941 the *Ark Royal* escorted two Malta convoys and on four occasions flew off air reinforcements for the island. While returning from one of the latter operations of November 13, 1941 she was torpedoed by the submarine *U 81* when about 48 km (30 miles) from Gibraltar. She was hit on the starboard side below the bridge and almost immediately listed over 10°. All power failed but, after several hours, she was got under way with the aid of two tugs from Gibraltar. Progress was extremely slow and by 0400 on the morning of November 14 she was still 25 miles from Gibraltar, there was a fire in the boiler rooms and the list had increased to 27°. At 0613, nearly 13 hours after being torpedoed, she rolled over and sank. Only one of her crew was lost.

Displacement: 22 000 tons (standard) 27 840 tons (full load) *Length:* 219.91 m (721 ft 6 in) water line; 242.93 m (797 ft) flight deck *Beam:* 28.88 m (94 ft 9 in) *Draught:* 6.96 m (22 ft 10 in) *Machinery:* 3-shaft geared steam turbines, 102 000 shp=30.75 knots *Protection:* 115 mm ($4\frac{1}{2}$ in) belt, 76 mm (3 in) deck, 64 mm ($2\frac{1}{2}$ in) bulkheads *Armament:* 16 4.5-in (115-mm) (8×2); 48 2-pdr (6×8); 32 0.5-in (8×4) *Aircraft:* 60, 2 catapults *Crew:* 1860 (including air crew)

PPL

The aircraft carrier HMS *Eagle* as completed in 1951. She was accepted by the RN in 1952

Ark Royal/Eagle

British aircraft carrier class. As early as 1940 the British Admiralty drafted plans for a new class of aircraft carriers to follow the six authorized under the 1936-39 rearmament programmes. However, little could be done until 1942, by which time valuable knowledge had been gained from the war experience of the *Ark Royal* and the *Illustrious* Class.

The new carrier class was to be an expansion of the *Implacable* design, with a double-storied hangar with 14 ft 6 in headroom, thicker armour and high speed. But the growing size of aircraft, particularly the new US types being used by the Fleet Air Arm, made it necessary to increase the hangar height to 17 ft 6 in, resulting in a jump in displacement from 30 000 to 36 000 tons. The increase also allowed aircraft capacity to be increased from 78 to 100. The internal layout in other respects followed the *Implacable* closely, with separate boiler rooms and engine rooms on the unit system to minimize the risk of a single torpedo-hit knocking out the machinery. One important change was that the aviation fuel (avgas) was now stowed as in US carriers, in structural tanks surrounded by seawater.

The heavy armament typical of earlier British carriers was repeated, eight twin 4.5-in high-angle mountings disposed in four quadrants at the edge of the flight deck forward and aft, and lavish fire-control was provided. Two Mk 5 fire-control directors were mounted on the port side at deck-edge level, and one ahead and one abaft the island superstructure. Eight of the massive Mk 6 six-barrelled 40-mm Bofors mountings were provided, one at either end of the island, two on the starboard side aft and four on the port side. Each of these had its own Mk 37 US-pattern director with radar control, and there were a further nine single Bofors guns with gyro gunsights (six on the island and three on the port side). This meant that 64 guns controlled by 12 radar directors provided long-range and short-range defence, with a further nine guns in local control. Later two pairs of Bofors guns on Mk 5 mountings were provided under the overhang of the flight deck at the stern, with their own Simple Tachymetric Director (STD) control.

Four ships were laid down between 1942 and 1943, but in 1945, with the end of the Second World War, the *Africa* and *Eagle* were cancelled. On January 21, 1946 the former *Audacious* was renamed *Eagle* to commemorate the famous carrier of that name sunk in 1942. Although many references quote *Irresistible* as the original name for the *Ark Royal* there is no evidence that this name had been allocated to the hull; in any case the previous *Ark Royal* was sunk in 1941, a year-and-a-half before the new ship was begun, and it was unlikely that a chance

After the *Eagle* was paid off in January 1972 she was cannibalized to help keep her sister *Ark Royal* running. She is shown here in 1974, after being partially stripped

C & S Taylor

would be missed to revive her great name.

The original *Eagle* (Pendant No 94) was ordered from Swan Hunter, Wallsend-on-Tyne, in August 1942 but the order was transferred to Vickers-Armstrong in December. The *Africa* (Pendant No D.06) was ordered from Fairfield, Govan, in July 1943. The orders for both ships were subsequently cancelled.

The *Eagle* (ex-*Audacious*—Pendant No D.29) was ordered from Harland and Wolff, Belfast; was laid down in October 1942, launched on March 19, 1946 and completed in October 1951. The *Ark Royal* (Pendant No 91) was ordered from Cammell Laird, Birkenhead; was laid down in May 1943, launched on May 3, 1950 and completed in February 1955.

The renamed *Eagle* was formally accepted by the Royal Navy on March 1, 1952, with the new Pendant number R.05. She was fitted with an interim angled deck and mirror landing sight in 1956-57, but in 1959 she was taken in hand once more at Devonport for a full modernization along the lines of the reconstructed *Victorious*. This time she was given a proper $8\frac{1}{2}°$ angled deck, steam catapults and the Type 984 Comprehensive Radar Display

Although there were differences between the *Ark Royal* and the *Eagle* on completion, successive refits to both ships left them even less similar. In 1969 the flight deck of the *Ark Royal* was fully angled as part of a conversion to enable the ship to carry F-4K Phantom and Buccaneer Mk 2 aircraft. *Ark Royal* is seen below in 1973 with a Sea King helicopter about to land

system (CDS). This radar had a huge 'searchlight' aerial mounted above the island.

Other alterations included the replacement of the tripod masts with lattice masts, the forward one carrying a 'double bedstead' Type 965 M radar array. The two groups of 4.5-in guns forward were removed and a quadruple Seacat guided missile launcher and its director (GWS22) were installed on either side, with another in place of the starboard 40-mm guns and one on the stern.

In another refit at Devonport the *Eagle* was given more powerful catapults and arrester wires to allow her to operate the F-4 Phantom aircraft. She recommissioned in April 1967 but her future was uncertain as the British government had announced the year before that aircraft carriers were to be phased out. She was paid off at Portsmouth in January 1972 and de-stored; on August 9 the same year she was towed to Devonport to be laid up. By the end of 1976 she remained officially in reserve, but had been partially 'cannibalized' to keep her sister *Ark Royal* running.

Ark Royal began her contractor's sea trials on June 4, 1954, after her lengthy time of building had become a national joke—Liverpudlians began to think that her vast hull was part of the landscape. She was different in many ways from the *Eagle*, having a $5\frac{1}{2}°$ angled deck, a lattice foremast and a side lift giving access to the upper hangar—the first British carrier fitted with this American device. To enlarge the forward end of the angled deck the two port forward 4.5-in gun mountings had been blanked off, and were completely removed in 1956. The two starboard forward turrets were removed in 1959 and then in 1964 the foremost of the two pairs of after turrets were also suppressed.

The *Ark* has been constantly altered and

MOD

HMS *Ark Royal* passing her de-commissioned sister *Eagle* at Plymouth in October 1975

modified to suit changing needs. By 1959 it was clear that the deck edge lift was of limited use, and it was removed to allow the hangar to be enlarged. In 1961 the ship was given a mirror landing sight, more powerful steam catapults and the 'Hilo' long-range guidance system. Her biggest reconstruction started in March 1967, when she was converted to operate Phantom and Buccaneer Mk 2 aircraft. When she emerged in February 1970 she had a full $8\frac{1}{2}°$ angled deck, a bigger island and two 'double bedstead' Type 965M radar arrays on lattice masts forward and aft. The last 40-mm guns were also removed and replaced by four quadruple Seacat close-range missiles disposed one on either side aft, one on the island and one at the stern.

Both ships were fully employed throughout their active lives, *Eagle* in particular playing an important role in the Mediterranean during the Suez landings in 1956 and again during the confrontation with Indonesia in 1964, with *Ark Royal*. HMS *Eagle* established a peacetime record by remaining at sea for 78 days during the early days of the Beira patrol in 1965, and also made history by embarking the Royal Navy's first operational squadron of jet fighters (Attackers) early in her career. In 1976 the *Ark Royal* achieved stardom when a complete commission was filmed to make a TV series called *Sailor*. During the course of a routine helicopter operation the TV cameras recorded an heroic rescue of a crewman from a US nuclear submarine.

(Both ships—as designed) *Displacement:* 36 800 tons (normal), 45 720 tons (full load) *Length:* 244.96 m (803 ft 9 in) oa *Beam:* 34.21 m (112 ft 9 in) *Draught:* 10.97 m (36 ft 0 in) max *Armament:* 16 4.5-in (114-mm) Mk 6 DP (8×2); 61 40-mm AA Mk 6, Mk 5 & Mk 9 (8×6, 2×2, 9×1); 100 aircraft

(*Eagle*—as redesigned) *Displacement:* 43 060 tons (normal), 53 390 tons (full load) *Dimensions:* As designed, but 51.81 m (171 ft 0 in) across flight deck *Machinery:* 4-shaft geared steam turbines, 152 000 shp=$31\frac{1}{2}$ knots (deep load) *Protection:* 114 mm ($4\frac{1}{2}$ in) main belt, 38 mm ($1\frac{1}{2}$ in) hangar side, 102-38 mm (4-$1\frac{1}{2}$ in) flight deck, 64-25 mm ($2\frac{1}{2}$-1 in) hangar deck *Armament:* 16 4.5-in (114-mm) DP (8×2), reduced to 8 between 1959 and 1964; 58 40-mm AA (8×6, 2×2, 6×1), replaced by 6 Seacat GWS22 (6×4); 4 3-pdr saluting guns (4×1); 34 aircraft, 10 helicopters (in 1966) *Crew:* 2637 (including embarked air groups)

(*Ark Royal*—as redesigned) *Displacement:* 43 340 tons (normal) 53 340 tons (full load) *Dimensions:* As designed, but 49.98 m (164 ft 6 in) across flight deck *Protection:* As *Eagle* *Machinery:* As *Eagle* *Armament:* 12 4.5-in DP (6×2), reduced to 8 in 1959, 4 in 1964, removed altogether in 1969; 40 40-mm AA (5×6, 2×2, 6×1) reduced to 34 in 1956, 14 by 1965, all removed by 1970; 2 3-pdr saluting guns; 40 aircraft, 8 helicopters (1966), 30 aircraft, 6 helicopters (1972) according to types embarked *Crew:* 2640 (including air staff) while acting as flagship

Arromanches

French aircraft carrier. The *Arromanches* was a unit of the British *Colossus* Class light fleet carriers coming into service at the end of the Second World War. The French navy was very anxious to rebuild its naval air arm, and so the *Colossus* was borrowed for five years in August 1946, with an option to buy her at the end of the five-year loan. The option was taken up and the carrier, renamed *Arromanches*, was transferred permanently in 1951.

For many years *Arromanches* was the main strength of French naval airpower. She was extensively refitted in 1950-51, 1957-58 and again in 1968-69 but always retained her original appearance. She received a 4° angled flight deck and other improvements to allow her to operate new aircraft, and in 1969 all her guns were removed. She was reduced to an antisubmarine carrier in 1958 and in 1969

The aircraft carrier HMS *Eagle* at sea in July 1969. Several refits during her career have resulted in an $8\frac{1}{2}°$ angled flight deck, lattice masts with

C & S Taylor

became a helicopter and training carrier.

The *Arromanches* was equipped initially with Hellcat fighters and Helldiver dive-bombers, and could carry a maximum of 43 aircraft depending on type; the usual air group embarked had 24 aircraft. After 1958 she carried Breguet Alizé antisubmarine aircraft, but in 1969 these were replaced by Alouette III A/S helicopters.

For some years she retained her British radar and guns but the latter were eventually replaced by French-pattern 40-mm Bofors guns, 31 in 1957, but increased to 43 by 1969. When she became a helicopter-carrier all guns were removed and she was given a DRBV 22 air/surface surveillance radar. The *Arromanches* was striken in 1974 and sold for scrapping.

Displacement: 14 000 tons (normal); 18 500 tons (full load) *Length:* 211.7 m (694 ft 6 in) oa *Beam:* 36 m (118 ft) over angled deck sponson *Draught:* 7 m (23 ft) *Armament:* 43 40-mm AA (removed 1969) *Aircraft:* 40 max *Crew:* 1019 (200 aircrew)

Vosper-Thornycroft

The Iranian destroyer *Artemiz*, converted from the old destroyer HMS *Sluys*, on preliminary trials after her refit by Vosper-Thornycroft. The original twin 4.5-in guns forward were retained new radar, the removal of several of the guns and the fitting of Seacat missiles for antiaircraft defence

Artemiz

Iranian destroyer. In 1964 the growing navy of Iran decided to acquire a destroyer from the Royal Navy. As British shipyards were fully booked at the time and as the Iranians wished to train ratings as soon as possible they decided to buy and modernize an older ship for their purposes.

The 20-year-old destroyer HMS *Sluys* was bought and towed to Southampton to begin a three-year modernization by Vosper-Thornycroft. During this period she was completely altered, with a new bridge, an enclosed foremast and a new enclosed mainmast amidships. A long deckhouse extended from the funnel almost right aft, with a Seacat missile launcher at the after end.

The electronics outfit was remarkably cosmopolitan, reflecting the modern trend towards collaboration between firms in more than one country. The Italian firm Contraves supplied its Sea Hunter fire-control system but the air-warning and surveillance radar was the Plessey ASW-1, with its prominent aerial mounted on the new mainmast. Decca's RDL 1 radar interception set was installed, and Racal's direction-finder.

Some vestiges of the original armament remained, principally the two twin 4.5-in Mk 4 mountings mounted in A and B positions, and the 'Squid' triple depth-charge mortar on the quarterdeck. The hull and machinery were unaltered apart from the provision of new boilers. As the ship had seen only peacetime service her sea speed probably remained near the original 31 knots (34 knots maximum) provided by the twin Parsons geared turbines. Endurance is claimed to be 3000 miles at 20 knots.

HMS *Sluys* (D 60) was completed by Cammell Laird at Birkenhead on September 30, 1946 and after many years of active service in various destroyer squadrons was paid off in the early 1960s. Following her modernization she was formally handed over to the Imperial Iranian Navy at Portsmouth on January 26, 1967 and renamed *Artemiz*.

Subsequent reports have indicated that she may have been reconstructed once more, this time to take surface-to-surface missiles. As the Shah's navy has already bought the McDonnell Douglas Harpoon system it is unlikely that another missile would be chosen. The alterations would be limited to clearing sufficient deck space for the launching tubes, as these missiles are of the 'fire-and-forget' type requiring no additional guidance radar other than the normal target acquisition sets already fitted.

Displacement: 2325 tons (standard), 3360 tons (full load) *Length:* 115.5 m (379 ft 0 in) oa *Beam:* 12.3 m (40 ft 6 in) *Draught:* 5.2 m (17 ft 6 in) *Machinery:* 2-shaft geared steam turbines, 50 000 shp=34 knots (max) *Armament:* 4 4.5-in (114-mm) DP (2×2); 8 40-mm (1.5-in) Bofors AA (8×1); 1 quadruple Seacat missile launcher; 1 'Squid' depth-charge mortar *Crew:* 270

Ashanti

British frigate class. The prototype of the Royal Navy's Type 81 frigates was laid down in January 1958, launched in 1959 and completed in November 1961. The Type 81 frigates were a revolutionary design using the world's first COSAG (combined steam and gas turbine) machinery, with a single-shaft Metrovick steam turbine for cruising and a gas turbine coupled to the same shaft for high-speed boost.

The reason behind the Type 81 design was the growing complexity of the specialized antiaircraft, antisubmarine and aircraft-direction frigates built in the 1950s. By adopting COSAG machinery, with its high concentration of power by low weight, more tonnage could be devoted to armament, and the *Ashanti* could find room for two gun-mountings, a helicopter and hangar and a triple antisubmarine mortar. Another weight-saving expedient was to make the hull flush-decked, the first time this feature was seen in a British frigate or destroyer-sized ship.

Seven ships were built, specifically to

The *Ashanti* (or 'Tribal') Class frigates *Zulu* (below) and *Eskimo* (right). The first British flush-deck frigates or destroyer-sized ships, the *Ashantis* were also the first ships in the world to be fitted with COSAG (combined steam and gas) machinery, giving a high power:weight ratio and enabling a greater weight of armament to be fitted. This means the ships can be used for antiaircraft, antisubmarine and aircraft direction rather than having separate, specialized types for the various duties

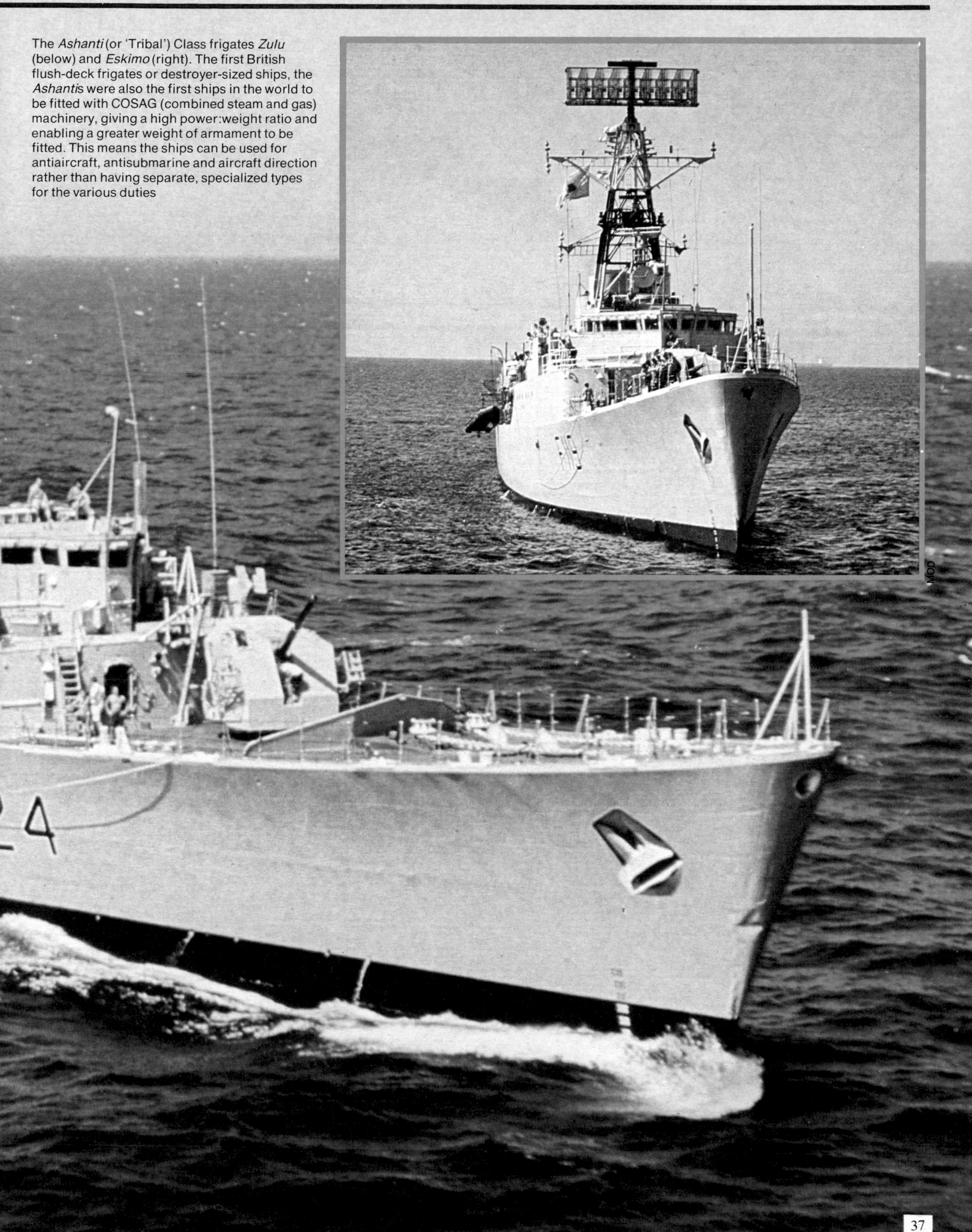

MOD

replace the nine old 'Loch' Class frigates used to patrol the Persian Gulf. They were *Ashanti* (F117), *Eskimo* (F119), *Gurkha* (F122), *Mohawk* (F125), *Nubian* (F131), *Tartar* (F133), and *Zulu* (F124). All were laid down in 1958-60 and the last, HMS *Zulu*, was completed in 1964. The cost of the *Ashanti* was £5 220 000, but this included the cost of modifications to her machinery during her lengthy trials.

The 'Tribal' Class, as they are popularly known, have an appearance quite distinct from other British frigates, with a flush deck, a tall lattice mast crowned by a Type 965 'bedstead' radar aerial and two funnels. HMS *Zulu* was the first of the class to have Seacat close-range guided missiles, and could be distinguished by her two large directors on platforms amidships, but her sisters are now similarly fitted. In 1970 two ships of the class were fitted with variable-depth sonar (VDS) on the stern.

Displacement: 2300 tons (standard), 2700 tons (full load) *Length:* 109.7 m (360 ft) oa *Beam:* 12.9 m (42.3 ft) *Draught:* 5.3 m (17.5 ft) max *Machinery:* Single-shaft COSAG, steam turbine 12 500 shp+gas turbine 7500 shp=28 knots *Armament:* 2 4.5-in (114-mm) DP (2×1); 2 40-mm Bofors AA (2×1) in first six ships; 2 quadruple Seacat missile launchers in place of 40-mm guns (four ships by 1976); 2 20-mm guns (2×1) in Seacat-fitted ships; 1 Limbo antisubmarine mortar; 1 Wasp antisubmarine helicopter *Crew.* 253 (13 officers, 240 ratings)

MOD

HMS *Zulu* (above) and *Tartar* (below) of the *Ashanti* Class. The heavy armament of this class includes a 4.5-in DP gun fore and aft, two quadruple Seacat launchers amidships, a Wasp ASW helicopter and a Limbo antisubmarine mortar forward of the helicopter platform

MOD

Asheville	PG-84
Gallup	PG-85
Antelope	PG-86
Ready	PG-87
Crockett	PG-88
Marathon	PG-89
Canon	PG-90
Tacoma	PG-92
Welch	PG-93
Chehalis	PG-94
Defiance	PG-95
Benecia	PG-96
Surprise	PG-97
Grand Rapids	PG-98
Beacon	PG-99
Douglas	PG-100
Green Bay	PG-101

US Navy

USS *Asheville*, first of a class of 17 general-purpose patrol gunboats ordered in 1963 for blockade, surveillance and support work

Asheville

US gunboat class. In 1963 the US Navy realized that it had no general-purpose patrol craft for blockade, surveillance and support missions, and so Congress authorized the building of 17 'patrol gunboats', PG-84–90 and PG-92–101 (formerly PGM, or Patrol Motor Gunboats). They were also the first American warships with CODAG (combined diesel and gas turbine) propulsion.

The hulls were all-aluminium, with an aluminium and fibreglass superstructure, and the gas turbine was an LM1500 adapted from the J79-8 used in the F-4 Phantom aircraft. PGs can reach 40 knots in one minute from a dead stop, and their controllable-pitch propellers give them great manoeuvrability.

Four ships, *Antelope, Ready, Grand Rapids* and *Douglas,* were armed with the Standard RIM-66 surface-to-air missile system, and the first two ships were equipped with the new Mark 87 weapon-control system for tracking fast-moving targets. The other ships have a single 40-mm Bofors gun aft in place of the single-arm Standard launcher, and all have a single 3-in/50-cal gun forward.

PG-84–92 and 94, 96, 98, 100 were built by Tacoma Boatbuilding, and PG-93, 95, 97, 99, 101 by Petersen Builders of Sturgeon Bay, Wisconsin. In 1971 the *Benecia* was transferred to South Korea and renamed *Paek Ku.* The *Surprise* and *Defiance* were transferred to Turkey in 1973 and renamed *Bora* and *Yildrim.*

Displacement: 225 tons (normal), 245 tons (full load) *Length:* 50.03 m (164 ft 6 in) oa *Beam:* 7.22 m (23 ft 9 in) *Draught:* 2.89 m (9 ft 6 in) *Machinery:* 2-shaft CODAG: 2 Commins diesels, 1450 bhp=16 knots; 1 General Electric gas turbine, 13 300 shp=40 knots *Armament:* 1 3-in/50-cal (76-mm) AA; 1 40-mm AA (not mounted in missile-armed ships); 4.5-in mgs (2×2); 1 Standard missile launcher (four ships) *Crew:* 27

Atherstone

British escort destroyer class. Constructed under the 1939 Programme the *Atherstone* Class were the first group, or Type I, of the famous 'Hunt' Class escort destroyers. They were designed to provide antisubmarine and antiaircraft defence for merchant ships and were originally described as 'fast escort vessels'. In essence they were small destroyers with the torpedo armament omitted and the speed reduced in order to keep their size and cost within moderate limits. They were, however, too small to take their designed armament of three twin 4-in gun mountings, and only two were mounted.

The first unit to complete, the *Atherstone,* was found to be seriously deficient in stability, a fact revealed rather forcibly by her heeling over whilst in dock. Drastic measures were taken to reduce topweight and the entire class had the 4-in gun mounting in X position removed and the funnel and rig cut down. In order to avoid a trim by the bow, the 4-in mounting was replaced by a quadruple 2-pdr pom-pom, originally to have been fitted abaft the funnel. All were fitted with Denny fin stabilizers in the hope of reducing the roll that such small ships would produce in a heavy sea. These were, however, only effective under limited conditions of wind and sea and were generally unpopular with sea officers as they occupied valuable space.

The 20 ships of the class were launched in 1939 and 1940, and entered service during 1941-42. They had insufficient endurance and sea-keeping qualities for ocean work and were mainly employed in the restricted waters of the North Sea, English Channel and Mediterranean. In home waters they were used extensively and very successfully as escorts for coastal convoys and in offensive operations against enemy shipping. In these operations they often encountered E-

HMS *Southdown,* one of the *Atherstone* or 'Hunt' Type I British escort destroyer class, in December 1942. Designed armament had to be reduced from six to four 4-in guns

MOD

Boats and, for use against such craft, a large number of the class were fitted with a single 2-pdr pom-pom in the bow.

Three of the class were lost in home waters. The *Exmoor* was torpedoed by the E-Boat *S 30* off Lowestoft on February 25, 1941, the *Berkeley* was sunk by the *Albrighton* after being bombed and heavily damaged by German aircraft during the raid on Dieppe on August 19, 1942 and the *Quorn* was hit and sunk by a German explosive motor boat off Normandy on the night of August 2/3, 1944. One of the class, the *Tynedale*, was lost in the Mediterranean; she was torpedoed by the German submarine *U 593* off Bougie on December 12, 1943.

All surviving ships served in the postwar fleet and the majority were eventually sold for scrap between 1956 and 1958. Four found their way into foreign navies. The *Mendip* and *Cottesmore* were transferred to Egypt in 1950 and the *Meynell* and *Quantock* to Ecuador in 1954.

Atherstone, Berkeley—built by Cammell Laird
Cattistock, Cleveland, Cotswold, Cottesmore—built by Yarrow
Eglinton, Exmoor—built by Vickers Armstrong and Parson
Fernie, Garth—built by John Brown
Hambledon, Holderness, Mendip, Meynell—built by Swan Hunter
Pytchley, Quantock—built by Scotts
Quorn, Southdown—built by White
Tynedale, Whaddon—built by Stephen

Displacement: 1000 tons *Length:* 85.34 m (280 ft) oa *Beam:* 8.84 m (29 ft) *Draught:* 2.44 m (8 ft) *Machinery:* 2-shaft Parsons turbines, 19000 shp=27.5 knots *Armament:* 4 4-in (102-mm) (2×2); 4 2-pdr (1×4); 2 20-mm (2×1); 2 DCT, 1 chute, 40 depth charges *Crew:* 146

The 'assault carrier' HMS *Stalker*, one of the *Attacker* or *Tracker* Class escort carriers

Atlanta

US light cruiser class. In 1940 the US Navy, having built no light cruisers since the end of the First World War, suddenly broke with tradition by ordering a radically new class of small cruiser. These ships were to be armed with dual-purpose surface/antiaircraft guns and have a speed of 38 knots to permit them to work with destroyers.

The resulting class was unique among US cruisers and carried the heavy armament of 16 5-in guns as well as eight torpedo tubes. But the *Atlantas* were something of a disappointment in service and were not as successful as other American cruisers of their day. With only two Mk 37 high-angle directors they could only engage two aircraft at a time, and would have been better off with fewer 5-in guns, more directors and more close-range AA guns. Their radius of action was considerably less than that of other cruisers, which limited their usefulness in the Pacific, and their speed was no better than that of contemporary foreign cruisers and about 5 knots below the designed speed.

The second group (CL.95 etc), known also as the *Oakland* Class, attempted to rectify some of the faults by omitting the pair of beam 5-in guns. And in the last three, the second and fifth 5-in turrets were mounted a deck lower to reduce topweight; the torpedo tubes were also omitted. CL.51-52 and 119-121 were built by Federal Shipbuilding, Kearny, CL.53-54 by Bethlehem at their Quincy yard, and CL.95-98 by Bethlehem's San Francisco yard. In 1949 the class were reclassified as antiaircraft cruisers (CLAA), and were sold for scrapping in 1962-66.

Atlanta (CL.51) was badly damaged by gunfire from Japanese battleships and cruisers during the Battle of Guadalcanal on November 13, 1942 and foundered off Lunga Point next day. The *Juneau* (CL.52) was torpedoed by the Japanese submarine *I.26* off San Cristobal during the same battle.

CL.53 *San Diego*
CL.98 *Tucson*
CL.54 *San Juan*
CL.95 *Oakland*
CL.96 *Reno*
CL.97 *Flint* (ex-*Spokane*)
CL.119 *Juneau* (ii)
CL.120 *Spokane* (ii)
CL.121 *Fresno*

Displacement: 6000 tons (standard), 8100 tons (full load) *Length:* 165.04 m (541 ft 6 in) oa *Beam:* 16.24 m (53 ft 3 in) *Draught:* 8.07 m (26 ft 6 in) max *Machinery:* 4-shaft Westinghouse geared steam turbines, 75000 shp=33 knots *Protection:* 88 mm (3½ in) belt, 50 mm (2 in) deck, 38 mm (1½ in) turrets *Armament:* 16 5-in (127-mm)/38-cal DP (8×2) (later ships 12 5-in DP

The *Atlanta* (CL.51) under way. She was damaged at the Battle of Guadalcanal in 1942

US Navy

[6×2]); 12/16 1.1-in AA (3/4×4) removed 1942; 8 40-mm AA (4×4) added 1942 (later ships had 32 40-mm AA [4×2, 6×4]); 8/20 20-mm AA (8/20×1) added 1942-45; 16 21-in (53-cm) torpedo tubes (2×4) (not in last three ships) *Crew:* 810-820

Attacker

British escort carrier class. The *Attacker* Class (also known as the *Tracker* Class) were the second batch of escort carriers built for the Royal Navy in the United States, the lead ship of the class, *Tracker*, originally having been intended to be one of the *Avenger* Class. They were also the first to be ordered after America joined the Second World War. Like their predecessors they were converted from mercantile hulls. Unlike them they were known by the new designation CVE1, and were briefly appropriated for the US Navy before delivery to Britain.

The USN kept the other 10 vessels (the *Bogue* Class) it had ordered at the same time.

The diesels of the earlier ships were replaced by steam turbines in the *Attacker* Class, which also had a larger hangar designed to take 20 aircraft. The problem of disposing of the boiler gases was solved by small uptakes exhausting on either side of the flight deck. The armament was altered, two 5-in guns being carried in sponsons either side of the stern (these were in some cases later replaced by British 4-in), with two twin 40-mm Bofors mountings, and 14 (later more) 20-mm Oerlikons. Speed was increased to 18½ knots, though displacement and size were much the same as the earlier class.

Although the first of the class was handed over to the Royal Navy in January 1943 none actually reached active service until August that year. This caused a lot of American criticism, but was largely caused by unavoidable delays in getting the ships to Britain, and by what the Royal Navy considered to be essential alterations in the aviation fuel systems, deck lengthening, adding permanent ballast and so on. The loss of two of the earlier ships in the *Avenger* Class had emphasized the importance of antifire precautions in a carrier laden with petrol and explosives.

Once these ships were ready for action they soon proved themselves. *Attacker, Hunter* and *Stalker* were converted to 'assault carriers', carrying fighters and equipped to support the army after a landing. They gave valuable service at Salerno, though the Seafires operating from their short decks with inexperienced pilots had a very high accident rate. *Pursuer* and *Searcher* specialized as fighter carriers, and *Ravager* in training; the other members of the class were mainly used for escort, their original purpose. They played an important part in assuring victory in the Battle of the Atlantic, operating Swordfish and later Avengers. Carriers of this class also backed up escort groups attacking U-Boats in the Bay of Biscay, and accompanied Arctic convoys. Some also served in Eastern waters against the Japanese.

At the end of the war all were handed back to the Americans, none having been lost. Most then were reconverted to merchant ships. They had proved to be useful and efficient conversions, and had, amongst other achievements, introduced the Royal Navy to the American system of cafeteria messing.

Displacement: 10 200 tons *Length:* 151 m (495 ft 9 in) *Beam:* 21.18 m (69 ft 6 in) *Draught:* 7 m (23 ft 3 in) *Machinery:* 1-shaft geared turbines, 9350 shp=17 knots *Armament:* 2 5-in (127-mm) AA (2×1); 8 40-mm AA (4×2); 15 20-mm AA (14×1); 20 aircraft *Crew:* 646

RN name	USN name	mercantile name	builder
Attacker	*Barnes*	*Steel Artisan*	Western Pipe & Steel
Battler	*Altahama*	*Mormactern*	Ingalls
Chaser	*Breton*	*Mormacgulf*	Ingalls
Fencer	*Croatan*	—	Western Pipe & Steel
Hunter (ex-*Trailer*)	*Block Island*	*Mormacpenn*	Ingalls
Pursuer	*St George*	*Mormacland*	Ingalls
Ravager (ex-*Charger*)	—	—	Seattle-Tacoma
Searcher	—	—	Seattle-Tacoma
Stalker	*Hamlin*	—	Western Pipe & Steel
Striker	*Prince William*	—	Western Pipe & Steel
Tracker	—	*Mormacmail*	Seattle-Tacoma

Below: The US-built British escort carrier HMS *Battler* was used for convoy escort duties, carrying Seafires and Swordfish

Attilio Regolo

Italian light cruiser class. In reply to the French *contre-torpilleurs* of the *Fantasque* Type, the Italian navy drew up plans for an ultra-fast light cruiser. The designers in charge of the project were Generals Umberto Pugliese and Ignazio Alfanó, and work began as early as 1937. Pugliese and Alfanó followed the lines developed in the original 'Condottieri' or *Alberto di Giussano* Class of 1928 but with different armament and even higher speed. The original light cruisers had been designed for a maximum speed of 37 knots, but this time a speed of 41 knots was specified.

A new dual-purpose 135-mm (5.3-in) gun was developed, capable of ranging 19 600 m (64 300 yds) with 45° elevation. Another new gun was the 65-mm/64-cal AA piece, but instead of carrying six of these the new cruisers eventually received 37-mm Breda guns. Despite the high speed asked for, the tonnage was to be limited to 3400 tons, and so protection was restricted to very thin armour over the vitals.

The first ships were laid down in the spring of 1939 and all 12 were in hand by the end of that year. Unfortunately, wartime shortages caught up with them and only three were completed by the time Italy decided to negotiate an armistice with the Allies. As they commemorated the Roman heroes so beloved of Mussolini, they were also known as the 'Capitani Romani' Class.

Name	launched	completed	builder
Attilio Regolo	8/1940	5/1942	Odero-Terni Orlando, Livorno
Caio Mario	8/1941	—	Odero-Terni Orlando, Livorno
Claudio Tiberio	—	—	Odero-Terni Orlando, Livorno
Scipione Africano	1/1941	4/1943	Odero-Terni, Orlando, Livorno
Claudio Druso	—	—	Cant. del Tirreno, Riva Trigoso
Vipsanio Agrippa	—	—	Cant. del Tirreno, Riva Trigoso
Cornelio Silla	6/1941	—	Ansaldo, Genoa
Paolo Emilio	—	—	Ansaldo, Genoa
Giulio Germanico	7/1941	—	Cant. di Castellammare di Stabia
Ottaviano Augusto	5/1941	—	Cant. Navali Riuniti, Ancona
Pompeo Magno	8/1941	6/1943	Cant. Navali Riuniti, Ancona
Ulpio Traiano	11/1942	—	Cant. Navali Riuniti, Palermo

Work on the *Claudio Druso, Claudio Tiberio, Paolo Emilio* and *Vipsanio Agrippa* was stopped in June 1940, and between July 1941 and August 1942 all four were demolished to clear the slips. The *Caio Mario* was delivered as a bare hull in January 1943 but had to be scuttled at La Spezia in September the same year to avoid capture by the Germans. The *Cornelio Silla* was 84% complete when her machinery was removed for the aircraft carrier *Aquila*. She fell into German hands at Genoa and was sunk by Allied bombs in July 1944. The *Ottaviano Augusto* was also captured and sunk by Allied aircraft, on November 1, 1943.

The *Ulpio Traiano* was completing in Palermo harbour when on January 3, 1943, 'chariots', or human torpedoes, blew her up. The *Giulio Germanico* was captured on September 11, 1943 by German troops while completing at Castellammare, but they had to scuttle her only 17 days later. However, she was later raised by Italian salvage teams. Thus when the time came to discuss the disposal of the Italian navy among the victors in 1945, only four of the 'Capitani Romani' Class were left: *Pompeo Magno* (designated *FV.1*), *Giulio Germanico (FV.2), Attilio Regolo (R.4)* and *Scipione Africano (S.7)*.

Under the peace treaty *R.4* and *S.7* were handed over to France as reparations. They were stricken in July and August 1948 respectively and were renamed *Chateaurenault* and *Guichen* on hoisting the French flag. They were then completely reconstructed at the Forges et Chantiers de la Méditerranée yard at Toulon between 1951 and 1954. With new armament and equipment they were now *escorteurs d'escadre* (large flotilla leaders). The *Guichen* was discarded by the French navy on April 1, 1961, and the *Chateaurenault* on October 1, 1962.

The other two ships, renamed *San Giorgio* (ex.-*FV.1*) and *San Marco* (ex.-*FV.2*), were retained by Italy and were used for much the same purpose. However, the reconstruction was not as comprehensive as in the French ships. They were given American 5-in guns and fire control and recommissioned in 1955-56 as *esploratori* (scouts). In 1958 they were rerated as *cacciatorpidiniere conduttori* (destroyer leaders). The *San Marco* was stricken in January 1971 but the *San Giorgio* underwent another rebuilding at La Spezia during 1963-65. She could now accommodate 130 cadets from the Accademia Navale as a training ship, and she was re-engined with diesels and gas turbines. Her armament was also changed, to 4 5-in and 3 76-mm AA guns, with two triple 2.75-in torpedo-tubes and triple depth-charge mortar. She remained in service in the mid-1970s.

As a class these cruisers lived up to their designers' expectations, being very fast and good seaboats. Their main weakness was lack of range but they certainly represented a better investment than the super-destroyers like the *Fantasque* or *Mogador* Classes, for they could not only chase and catch fast destroyers but also act as convoy escorts.

(As built) *Displacement:* 3745 tonnes (standard), 5035 tonnes (normal), 5420 tonnes (full load) *Length:* 142.9 m (457 ft 3 in) oa *Beam:* 14.4 m (47 ft 3 in) *Draught:* 4.9 m (16 ft 1 in) max *Machinery:* 2-shaft geared steam turbines, 110 000 shp=41 knots (sea speed 36 knots) *Protection:* Splinter-proof plating to bridge only *Armament:* 8 135-mm (5.3-in)/45 cal (4×2); 8 37-mm ($1\frac{1}{2}$-in)/54 cal AA (8×1); 8 20-mm AA (2×4); 8 53-cm (21-in) torpedo tubes *Crew:* 418

Audace

Italian guided-missile destroyer class. In April 1966 the Italian navy announced that it would be building two new destroyers armed with guided missiles. The new class was basically an improved version of the previous *Impavido* Class built during 1957-64, but with improved armament and a hangar for two helicopters.

The main armament is the American RIM-66A Standard surface-to-air missile, fired from a single-arm launcher sited above the after superstructure. A heavy gun armament is also mounted: two OTO-Melara 127-mm (5-in) lightweight automatic guns forward and four OTO-Melara 76-mm (3-in) guns amidships for close-range defence. In addition they have two sets of triple 12.75-in torpedo tubes for use against submarines and four fixed 21-in tubes for firing wire-guided torpedoes against submarine and surface targets.

The missile-guidance radar is the Hughes AN/SPS-52 for three-dimensional search and target acquisition, with two AN/SPG-51 tracker radars. For gun control three ELSAG NA 10 directors are provided, and for air-warning the AN/SPS-12. One hull-mounted sonar set is also provided.

The quarterdeck forms a helicopter landing pad big enough to take two Sea King SH3Ds or three of the smaller Agusta Bell 212 antisubmarine helicopters. For passive defence against missiles two Breda Meccanica SCLAR chaff-dispensing rocket-launchers are also carried. These fire salvoes of 20 105-mm rockets carrying flares and 'Window' metal chaff.

The hull is flush-decked with a graceful sheer and high freeboard. Double rudders are fitted for manoeuvrability and the twin-shaft double-reduction geared steam turbines are capable of developing 73 000 shp. Four Foster-Wheeler boilers provide high-pressure steam and six 800-kW and 400-kW generators provide electric power.

The Standard missile can be used against surface targets as well as aircraft. With the heavy gun armament and the helicopters this gives the *Audace* Class great flexibility in meeting the requirements of escort, attack and shore bombardment. They are the latest and most powerful major warships in the Italian navy. *Ardito* (Pendant No D 550) was built by Navalmeccanic, Castellammare, laid down in July 1968, launched in November 1971 and completed in March 1973. *Audace* (Pendant No D 551) was built by Cantieri del Tirreno, Riva Trigoso, laid down in April 1968, launched in October 1971 and completed in November 1972.

Displacement: 3600 tons (normal) 4554 tons (full load) *Length:* 143 m (469 ft 0 in) oa *Beam:* 14.6 m (48 ft 0 in) *Draught:* 4.6 m (15 ft 4 in) *Machinery:* 2-shaft geared turbines, 73 000 shp=35 knots *Armament:* 1 RIM-66A Standard SAM launcher; 2 5-in (127-mm)/54 cal (2×1); 4 3-in (76-mm)/62 cal (4×1); 6 12.75-in (32.5-cm) torpedo tubes (2×3); 4 21-in (53-cm) torpedo tubes (2×2) *Crew:* 395

Audacity

British escort carrier. Few ships with so short an operational career (she lasted only three months in service) have had such a great influence on naval history as the *Audacity*, the first of the escort carriers.

Before the outbreak of war in 1939 the Royal Navy had considered the conversion of merchant ships to carry aircraft, and the building of specially designed escort carriers, but other projects had higher priorities. The fall of France in 1940 altered matters, as the U-Boats were no longer forced to use the narrow exits of the North Sea, but instead could be based on the Atlantic shore itself. This meant that the surface escorts of British convoys were strained to the limit while shore-based aircraft could no longer control the danger area open to submarine attack. Worse still, Focke-Wulf Condors, a bomber type developed from an airliner design, could range virtually without opposition around the approaches to the British Isles. It was predominantly this last danger which produced the *Audacity.*

She had begun life in 1939 as the North German Lloyd's cargo and passenger liner *Hannover.* A motor vessel of 5537 tons gross, she was very similar to the ships converted by the Germans to disguised raiders like the *Atlantis.* She was caught outside home waters by the outbreak of war, and captured in 1940 whilst trying to run the blockade. She was originally scheduled for conversion to an ocean boarding vessel, a smaller equivalent of an armed merchant cruiser, but in January 1941 the conversion to an escort carrier began. At this stage she was known as *Empire Audacity* and this mercantile form of name was not dropped until after she was commissioned.

She was suited for conversion because she had a powerful two-shaft diesel installation giving her the respectable speed of 16 knots, and presenting less problems in trunking the exhaust over the side than did a steam installation. Her superstructure had been damaged during her capture so it was easier to cut down to take the simple wooden flight deck. Above all she was available and could be converted rapidly. She was given a 4-in gun aft and 6 20-mm Oerlikons for self-defence. There was neither time nor space to give her a hangar or lift, so her aircraft would have to be parked on deck. Three arrester wires and an open conning position on either side of the flight deck completed the conversion.

As the chief threat was conceived to be the Condors, the six aircraft carried were fighters. Hurricanes were proposed but were not available, while the excellent and robust Grumman Martlet (known in American service as the F4F Wildcat) was not only available but was specially designed for carrier use, and so was provided to *Audacity.*

Commissioned in June, the *Audacity*, after her work-up and having extra equipment such as 'Huff-Duff' (high-frequency direction finding) fitted, sailed with her first convoy, to Gibraltar, in September. Despite the difficulties of maintenance on the open flight deck, her Martlets proved themselves by shooting down a Condor, fending off a bombing attack, and forcing several U-Boats to leave the surface by strafing them. Two more convoys, and two more Condors shot down, found *Audacity* joining Commander Walker's escort to convoy *HG76*, homeward bound from Gibraltar, for what was to be one of the classic convoy actions of the war.

Audacity was torpedoed and sunk by *U 751* on December 21, 1941, but not before she had claimed two more Condors, assisted in the sinking of a U-Boat, and played a vital part in the defence of the convoy against large numbers of submarines, for whom she was a priority target. The concept was proven, and already improved types of escort carriers were commissioning from American yards.

Displacement: 5537 tons *Length:* 142.34 m (467 ft 0 in) *Beam:* 17.06 m (56 ft 0 in) *Draught:* 5.48 m (18 ft 0 in) *Machinery:* 2-shaft diesels, 4750 hp=16 knots *Armament:* 1 4-in (102-mm); 6 20-mm AA; 6 aircraft

The *Audace*'s 76-mm gun mounting showing in detail the turret and upper shell hoist. The smaller illustration shows the loaders, lower shell hoist and the captain of turret with the main distribution box. One of the feeders in the upper hoist automatically reloads one of the drums

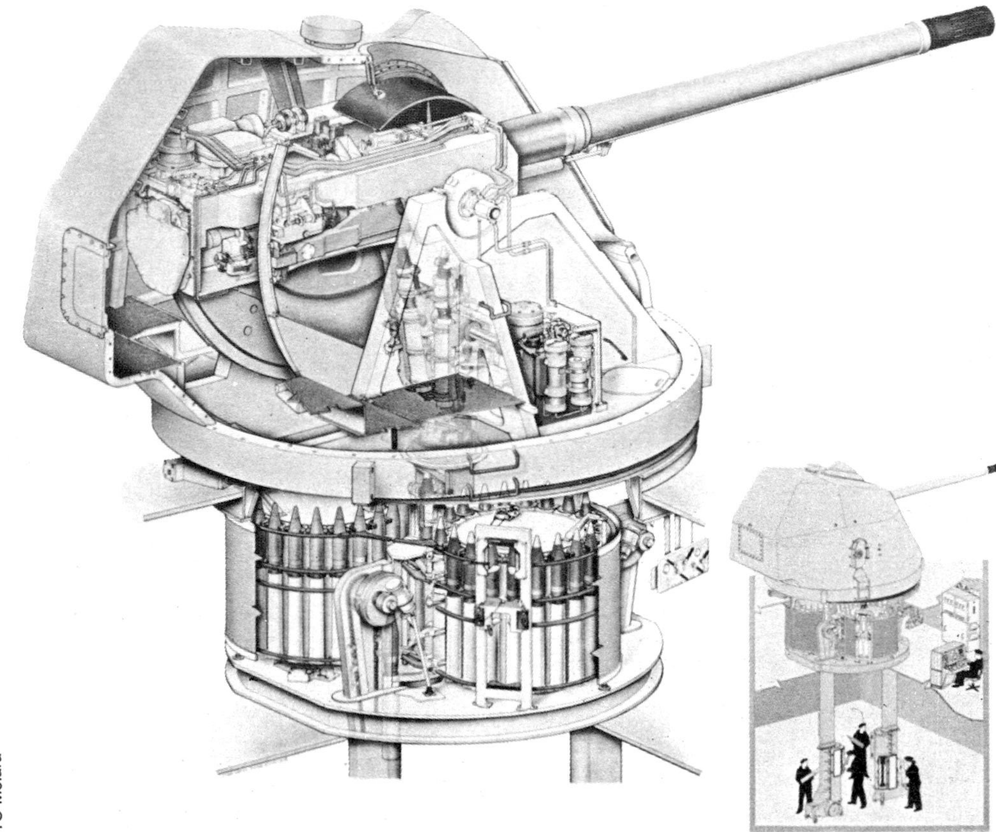

OTO-Melara

Audaz

Spanish destroyer class. The nine ships of the *Audaz* Class were originally intended to be conventional destroyers. Very few major Spanish warships of the twentieth century have been built to totally Spanish designs, and the *Audaz* Class was not one of the exceptions. The original design was very closely based on that of the French *Le Fier* light destroyers, which were laid down in France between 1939 and 1940, but never completed because of the Second World War.

The first five *Audaz* Class were completed very much to the *Le Fier* design, though they were rerated as fast frigates in 1955 and then as antisubmarine frigates in 1956. They were armed with three 4.1-in, four 37-mm AA and eight 20-mm AA. The 4.1-in had a maximum elevation of 90°. Forty mines could be carried and they had a crew of 28. As in the *Le Fier*s, all the main guns were carried aft—this was a common arrangement in European navies at that time. There was a very short forecastle, with a 37-mm AA mount before the bridge. This arrangement was not uncommon in contemporary European navies: the German *Möwe* Class torpedo boats had their armament mounted in a similar fashion.

The entire *Audaz* Class had been badly

delayed by Spain's poor economic position after 1945. However, the provision of US guns and antisubmarine and electronic equipment after 1960 enabled the completed ships to be modernized and the incomplete ones to be finished with more sophisticated American equipment. Ironically, considering the time some of the class were under construction, they were originally designed to permit rapid building in an emergency.

Meteoro was originally named *Atrevido*. They were all rerated as antisubmarine destroyers. Even after modernization, they retained the hull form and machinery of the *Le Fiers*. The modernization was confined to the upperworks, except for the provision of sonar. The armament was totally altered: the two single 76-mm guns replaced the aft two 4.1-in and one of the two single 40-mm was mounted before the bridge and the other just abaft of the second funnel. A lattice mast was fitted to carry the radar. The eventual fit was one MLA-lb, one SPS 5B and one SPG 34 fire-control radar.

The first of the class to go was *Ariete*, which grounded on the rocks at the entrance to the River Muros on February 25, 1966. She was so badly damaged that she was declared a total loss. The first ships to be completed were the first to be discarded: *Osado* was removed from the active list in 1972, followed by *Audaz, Meteoro, Furor* and *Rayo* in 1974. *Temerario* and *Relampago* were stricken in late 1975, having spent nearly 20 years under construction, to be followed by only ten years of service.

(Audaz) *Displacement:* 1227 tons (standard); 1550 tons (full load) *Length:* 93.92 m (308 ft 2 in) *Beam:* 9.29 m (30 ft 6 in) *Draught:* 5.20 m (17 ft 1 in) *Machinery:* 2-shaft geared steam turbines, 28 000 shp=31.6 knots *Armament:* 2 76-mm (3 in); 2 40-mm (1½-in); 2 side-launching torpedo tubes; 2 Hedgehogs; 8 DC throwers *Crew:* 191

Name	laid down	launched	completed	completed modernization
Audaz	9/1945	1/1951	6/1953	6/1961
Furor	8/1945	2/1955	9/1960	9/1960
Intrepido	7/1945	2/1961	3/1965	
Meteoro	8/1945	9/1951	11/1955	2/1963
Osado	8/1945	9/1951	1/1955	8/1961
Ariete	8/1945	2/1955	1961	
Rayo	8/1945	9/1951	1/1956	2/1963
Relampago	7/1945	9/1961	7/1965	
Temerario	7/1945	3/1960	3/1964	

Aurore

French submarines class. The first of a new class of seagoing or 2nd Class submarines was authorized for the French navy under the 1934 Programme. She was started at Toulon arsenal in December 1935 but not launched until July 1939. Under the 1937 Estimates four more (*Q-193* to *196*) were ordered and a further four (*Q-200* to *203*) under the 1938 Estimates. The acceleration of French rearmament after Munich led to a Supplementary Programme decreed on May 2, 1938 and under this *Q-206* and *207* were ordered; a further Supplementary Programme, known as 1938c and decreed on March 4, 1939, provided for another four (*Q-211* to *214*).

Only the name ship had been completed by the time France surrendered in 1940. One, *La Créole*, was 60% complete, and she was towed to England. Three others were captured by the Germans, *L'Africaine, La Favorite* and *L'Andromède*; they were renumbered *UF.1-3* but only *UF.2* was completed. She was finished in 1943 but was sunk by Allied bombs at Gdynia (Gotenhafen) on July 6, 1944. *L'Aurore* lay at Toulon with the rest of the French fleet until November 27, 1942, when she was scuttled to avoid capture by the Germans.

As designed, the class conformed to previous French ideas, with a small conning tower and a 100-mm deck gun. The armament comprised nine torpedo tubes, four forward, two aft and a triple training mount in the external casing. In this class the unsuccessful 40-cm slow-running torpedoes were dropped and the external tubes had conventional 55-cm weapons. The diving depth was 100 m (330 ft).

After the war the French navy decided to recast the design and completed the five hulls which had survived. In the case of *La Créole* this involved towing her back to France, replacing her on the slipway and then launching her a second time on May 8, 1946. Bunker capacity was increased to give better surface endurance and the gun armament was altered. *L'Astrée, L'Africaine* and *La Créole* were not greatly altered, but they had 20-mm antiaircraft guns on the conning tower. The last two, *L'Andromède* and *L'Artémis*, were restarted under the 1949 and 1950 Programmes respectively, by which time it was possible to incorporate more modern ideas. Both emerged in 1953 with streamlined hulls and conning tower fins. *L'Andromède* was used to test equipment designed for the forthcoming *Narval* Class.

The five submarines, now known as the *Créole* Class, served as front-line submarines for about ten years until new construction came forward from the shipyards. *La Créole* was paid off for scrapping in July 1961, *L'Africaine* in 1963, *L'Andromède* and L'Aurore in December 1965, and *L'Artémis* in 1967.

(As completed 1946-53) *Displacement:* 970 tons (surfaced), 1180 tons (submerged) *Dimensions:* as before *Machinery:* Sulzer diesels, except *L'Africaine*, which had Schneider; *L'Andromède*

Name	hull no	launched	builder
L'Aurore	*Q-192*	7/1939	Toulon Arsenal
La Créole	*Q-193*	6/1940	Normand, Le Havre
La Bayadère	*Q-194*	–	Normand, Le Havre
La Favorite	*Q-195*	11/1942	Ch Worms, Le Trait
L'Africaine	*Q-196*	12/1946	Ch Worms, Le Trait
L'Astrée	*Q-200*	5/1946	Ch Dubigeon, Nantes
L'Andromède	*Q-201*	11/1949	Ch Dubigeon, Nantes
L'Antigone	*Q-202*	–	Schneider, Chalon-sur-Saône
L'Andromaque	*Q-203*	–	Ch Worms, Le Trait
L'Artémis	*Q-206*	6/1942	Normand, Le Havre
L'Armide	*Q-207*	–	Ch Worms, Le Trait
L'Hermione	*Q-211*	–	Normand, Le Havre
La Gorgone	*Q-212*	–	Normand, Le Havre
La Clorinde	*Q-213*	–	Ch Dubigeon, Nantes
La Cornélie	*Q-214*	–	No contract awarded

The nuclear-powered frigate USS *Bainbridge* in September 1962, armed with two twin Terriers, Asroc launcher and 3-in guns

had 2000-hp electric motors, others as before *Armament:* 1 88-mm (3.5-in) in *La Créole, L'Astrée* and *L'Africaine*; 2 20-mm AA in *L'Astrée* and *L'Africaine*; 10 55-cm (21.7-in) torpedo tubes (6 internal forward, 2 aft and 2 external forward of the conning tower in last two; 4 forward, 2 aft and 4 external in older boats) *Crew:* 62

Bainbridge

US nuclear frigate. In Fiscal Year 1956 the US Navy was authorized to build its third nuclear-powered surface ship, as part of the programme to explore and develop the concept of an all-nuclear navy. The new ship was to be a 'destroyer-size' frigate armed with the latest surface-to-air missiles (DLGN) and was intended to act as an escort for the nuclear-powered carrier *Enterprise (CVAN-65)* and the cruiser *Long Beach (CGN-9).*

For a cost of $163 610 000 the US Navy got a 7600-ton ship armed with light guns, antiaircraft missiles and antisubmarine weapons. She is capable of almost indefinite cruising at high speed, and like the old sailing warships her endurance is limited only by the stores and fresh water carried. The D2G pressurized water-cooled nuclear plant was designed by the Atomic Energy Commission's Knolls Atomic Power Laboratory, and it comprises two reactors. They generate steam for twin-shaft geared turbines.

Armament is conventional, two twin Terrier RIM-2 SAM launchers, one forward and one aft, an Asroc RUR-5A eight-tube launcher behind the forward Terrier launcher and two twin 3-in/50 cal automatic guns abreast of the after superstructure at forecastle deck level. These were added as an afterthought when it dawned on the USN that a ship like the *Bainbridge* had no close-range defence against 'soft' targets. Mark 10 Terrier launchers are carried, a Mod 5 type forward and a Mod 6 aft. Unofficial reports credit the ship with 40 Terrier rounds in each magazine. Two triple Mk 32 torpedo tubes are carried just forward of the boats amidships, and they fire Mk 44 or Mk 46 antisubmarine homing torpedoes.

The SQS-23 sonar is mounted in a massive bulbous bow. The Hughes SPS-52 3-D search radar aerial is carried on the foremast, with an SPS-10 on a lower platform and an SPS-37 search antenna on the mainmast. In late 1976 the *Bainbridge* completed a comprehensive overhaul of her antiaircraft capability, at Puget Sound naval shipyard. Known as an Anti-Air Warfare (AAW) fit, it began in June 1974 and cost an estimated $103 million. She will probably have a mixture of Terrier and Standard missiles with improved guidance, and it is known that she will be equipped with the Naval Tactical Data System (NTDS).

The *Bainbridge* is basically an enlarged version of the conventional *Leahy* Class frigates, and looks similar apart from her heavy lattice masts. She was laid down on May 15, 1959, launched on April 15, 1961, commissioned on October 6, 1962 and allocated to the Pacific Fleet in 1965. She was built by Bethlehem Steel, Quincy, Mass.

Balao

US submarine class. No class better demonstrates the US Navy's rational policy of speeding up and simplifying wartime shipbuilding. Following the construction of the successful *Gato* Class (itself only a repetition of a sound pre-war design) through 73 units, the decision was taken to increase diving depth and incorporate improvements suggested by war experience. To achieve this it was not necessary to do more than strengthen the hull of the *Gato* design, and so no external change was made apart from shifting the anchor to the port side and mounting the deck gun forward of the conning tower.

In fact, the first of the *Balao* Class were laid down and launched in 1942 before the last of the *Gatos*. The lead ship, *Balao*, was launched on October 27, 1942 at Portsmouth navy yard and commissioned on April 2, 1943. In all 132 boats were ordered from five shipyards, and only ten contracts were cancelled at the end of the war. From the *Clamagore* (SS.343) onwards the diesel/electric drive was changed, reduction gearing was done away with and the motors were coupled directly to the shafts to reduce noise.

The five builders involved were Portsmouth navy yard (SS.285-291, SS.308-312 and SS.381-410); Wm Cramp Shipbuilding, Philadelphia (SS.292-303); Mare Island navy yard, California (SS.304-307 and SS.411-416); Electric Boat company, Groton (SS.313-352 and SS.370-378); and Manitowoc (SS.361-369). The *Dugong* (SS.353) *Eel* (SS.354) and *Espada* (SS.355) were cancelled on October 23, 1944. *Jawfish* (ex-*Fanegal*, SS.356), *Ono* (ex-*Friar*, SS.357), *Garlopa* (SS.358), *Garrupa* (SS.359), *Goldring* (SS.360), *Needlefish* (SS.379) and *Nerka* (SS.380) were cancelled on July 29, 1944.

The *Balao* Class had as impressive a war record as the *Gatos*, and included many of the most successful US submarines of the Second World War. Probably the most outstanding feat was that of the *Archerfish* which sank the giant Japanese aircraft carrier *Shinano* while she was being moved from Yokosuka to the Inland Sea to complete fitting out.

In 1947-48 the *Carbonero* (SS.337) and *Cusk* (SS.348) became the first operational submarines fitted to fire guided missiles.

US Navy

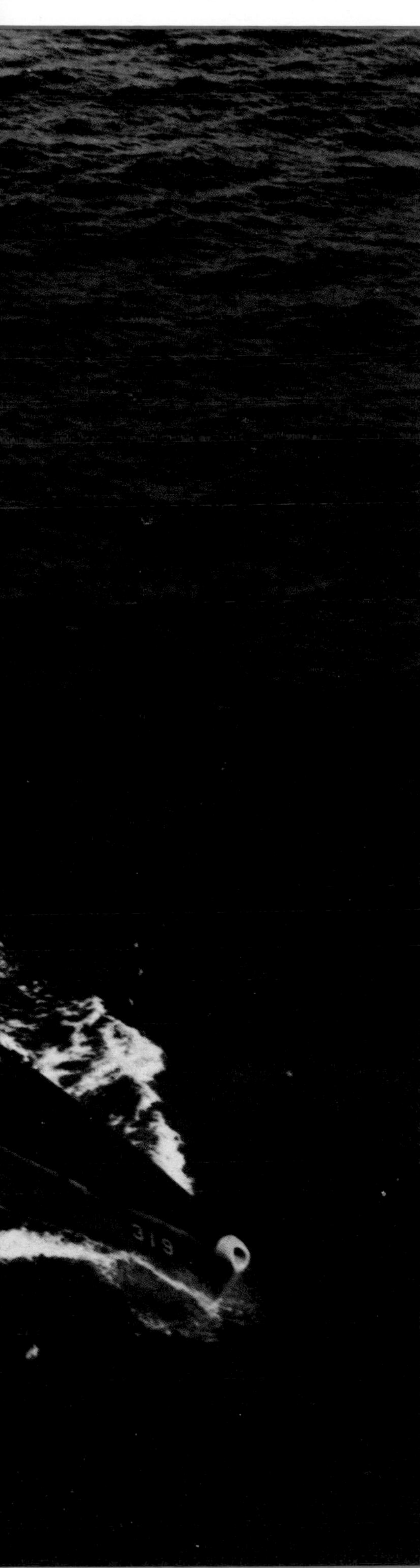

***Left:* The *Balao* Class submarine USS *Becuna* (SS.319) running on the surface**

They were fitted with a watertight hangar and a ramp for launching a 'Loon', the American copy of the V-1 flying bomb.

Many of the class were modernized under the Guppy (Greater Underwater Propulsive Power) programme initiated at the end of the 1940s. This resulted in a total confusion of the *Balao* Class with the later *Tench* Class. The conversion included lengthening the hull to accommodate larger batteries, removing all deck guns and rebuilding the bow and conning tower (now called the 'sail') to provide faster underwater speed and less noise. As time progressed further improvements were incorporated, so that there were Guppy I, IA, II, IIA and III types. The following *Balao*s were converted:

Guppy IA—SS.319, SS.322-324, SS.341-342, SS.403, SS.406-407
Guppy IIA—SS.340, SS.365, SS.368, SS.377, SS.382, SS.391, SS.394, SS.396, SS.402, SS.410
Guppy II—SS.339, SS.347, SS.349-350, SS.352
Guppy III—SS.343-344, SS.346, SS.351

By the end of 1976 only one *Balao* Class remained in service with the USN, the transport submarine *Sealion* (LPSS.315). Ironically she was unmodernized, apart from having a widened casing to allow the launching of inflatable assault boats. She has the distinction of being the last Second World War submarine in the US Navy.

See also *Gato*, Guppy.

Displacement: (later boats) 1526/2424 tons (surfaced/submerged); (earlier boats) 2391-2414 tons submerged *Length:* 95.02 m (311 ft 9 in) oa *Beam:* 8.31 m (27 ft 3 in) *Draught:* 4.65 m (15 ft 3 in) *Machinery:* (surfaced) 2-shaft diesel 5400 bhp=$20\frac{1}{4}$ knots; (submerged) 2-shaft electric, 2740 hp=$8\frac{3}{4}$ knots *Armament:* 1 5-in (127-mm)/25-cal or 1 4-in (102-mm)/50-cal or 1 3-in (76-mm)/50-cal; 1 40-mm AA (some); 1 20-mm AA (some); 2 .5-in or .3-in mg; 10 21-in (53-cm) torpedo tubes (6 forward, 4 aft, 24 torpedoes carried) *Diving Depth:* 122 m (400 ft); SS.361-364 only 91.4 m (300 ft) *Crew:* 80-85

Hull no and name	launched	fate
SS.285 *Balao*	10/1942	Used as target 1964
SS.286 *Billfish*	11/1942	Scrapped 1971
SS.287 *Bowfin*	12/1942	Stricken 1971 and preserved as memorial
SS.288 *Cabrilla*	12/1942	Scrapped 1972
SS.289 *Capelin*	1/1943	War loss Dec 1943
SS.290 *Cisco*	12/1942	War loss Sep 1943
SS.291 *Crevalle*	2/1943	Scrapped 1971
SS.292 *Devilfish*	5/1943	Sunk as target 1968
SS.293 *Dragonet*	4/1943	Sunk as target 1961
SS.294 *Escolar*	4/1943	War loss Oct 1944
SS.295 *Hackleback*	5/1943	Scrapped 1968
SS.296 *Lancetfish*	8/1943	Accidentally lost 1945, scrapped 1959
SS.297 *Ling*	8/1943	Stricken 1971
SS.298 *Lionfish*	11/1943	Stricken 1971
SS.299 *Manta*	11/1943	Sunk as target 1969
SS.300 *Moray*	5/1944	Sunk as target 1970
SS.301 *Roncador*	5/1944	Stricken 1971
SS.302 *Sabalo*	6/1944	Stricken 1971
SS.303 *Sablefish*	6/1944	Scrapped 1971
SS.304 *Seahorse*	1/1943	Scrapped 1968/69
SS.305 *Skate*	3/1943	Used as target at Bikini 1946

Hull no and name	launched	fate
SS.306 *Tang*	8/1943	Sunk by own torpedo Oct 1944
SS.307 *Tilefish*	10/1943	Venezuelan *Carite* 1960
SS.308 *Apogon* (ex-*Abadejo*)	3/1943	Used as target at Bikini 1946
SS.309 *Aspro* (ex-*Acedia*)	4/1943	Sunk as target 1963
SS.310 *Batfish* (ex-*Acoupa*)	5/1943	Stricken 1969 and preserved as memorial
SS.311 *Archerfish*	5/1943	Sunk as target 1968
SS.312 *Burrfish* (ex-*Arnillo*)	6/1943	Canadian *Grilse* 1961-69
SS.313 *Perch*	9/1943	Stricken 1971
SS.314 *Shark*	10/1943	War loss Oct 1944
SS.315 *Sealion*	10/1943	Transport submarine, still in service 1976
SS.316 *Barbel*	11/1943	War loss Feb 1945
SS.317 *Barbero*	12/1943	Sunk as target 1964
SS.318 *Baya*	1/1944	Stricken 1972
SS.319 *Becuna*	1/1944	Stricken 1973
SS.320 *Bergall*	2/1944	Turkish *Turgut Reis* 1958
SS.321 *Besugo*	2/1944	Italian *Francesco Morosini* 1966
SS.322 *Blackfish*	3/1944	Stricken 1972
SS.323 *Caiman* (ex-*Blanquilla*)	3/1944	Stricken 1972
SS.324 *Blenny*	4/1944	Stricken 1973
SS.325 *Blower*	4/1944	Turkish *Dumlupinar* 1950
SS.326 *Blueback*	5/1944	Turkish *Ikinci Inonu* 1948
SS.327 *Boarfish*	5/1944	Turkish *Sakarya* 1948
SS.328 *Charr* (ex-*Boccaccio*)	5/1944	Stricken 1971
SS.329 *Chub* (ex-*Chubb*, ex-*Bonaci*)	6/1944	Turkish *Gür* 1948
SS.330 *Brill*	6/1944	Turkish *Birinci Inonu* 1948
SS.331 *Bugara*	7/1944	Accidentally lost 1971
SS.332 *Bullhead*	7/1944	War loss Aug 1945
SS.333 *Bumper*	8/1944	Turkish *Cannakale* 1950

Hull no and name	launched	fate
SS.334 *Cabezon*	8/1944	Sold 1971 for scrapping
SS.335 *Dentuda* (ex-*Capidoli*)	9/1944	Sold 1969 for scrapping
SS.336 *Capitaine*	10/1944	Italian *Alfredo Cappellini* 1966
SS.337 *Carbonero*	10/1944	Stricken 1970
SS.338 *Carp*	11/1944	Stricken 1971
SS.339 *Catfish*	11/1944	Argentine *Santa Fe* 1971
SS.340 *Entemedor* (ex-*Chickwick*)	12/1944	Turkish *Preveze* 1972
SS.341 *Chivo*	1/1945	Argentine *Santiago del Estero* 1971
SS.342 *Chopper*	2/1945	Stricken 1971
SS.343 *Clamagore*	2/1945	Stricken 1974
SS.344 *Cobbler*	4/1945	Turkish *Canakkale* 1973
SS.345 *Cochino*	4/1945	Foundered off Norway 1949
SS.346 *Corporal*	6/1945	Turkish *Ikinci Inonu* 1973
SS.347 *Cubera*	6/1945	Venezuelan *Tiburay* 1972
SS.348 *Cusk*	7/1945	Stricken 1969
SS.349 *Diodan*	9/1945	Sold 1972 for scrapping
SS.350 *Dogfish*	10/1945	Brazilian *Guanabara* 1972
SS.351 *Greenfish* (ex-*Doncella*)	12/1945	Brazilian *Amazonas* 1973
SS.352 *Halfbeak* (ex-*Dory*)	2/1946	Stricken 1971
SS.361 *Golet*	8/1943	War loss Jun 1944
SS.362 *Guavina*	8/1943	Sunk as target 1967
SS.363 *Guitarro*	9/1943	Turkish *Preveze* 1954
SS.364 *Hammerhead*	10/1943	Turkish *Cerbe* 1954
SS.365 *Hardhead*	12/1943	Greek *Papanikolis* 1972
SS.366 *Hawkbill*	1/1944	*Zeeleeuw* 1954
SS.367 *Icefish*	2/1944	Netherlands *Walrus* 1953
SS.368 *Jallao*	3/1944	Stricken 1974
SS.369 *Kete*	4/1944	War loss Mar 1945
SS.370 *Kraken*	4/1944	Spanish *Almirante Garcia de los Reyes*

Hull no and name	launched	fate
SS.371 *Lagarto*	5/1944	War loss May 1945
SS.372 *Lamprey*	6/1944	Argentine *Santa Fe* 1960
SS.373 *Lizardfish*	7/1944	Italian *Evangelista Torricelli* 1960
SS.374 *Loggerhead*	8/1944	Sold 1969 for scrapping
SS.375 *Macabi*	9/1944	Argentine *Santiago del Estero* 1960
SS.376 *Mapiro*	11/1944	Turkish *Piri Reis* 1960
SS.377 *Menhaden*	12/1944	Stricken 1973
SS.378 *Mero*	1/1945	Turkish *Hizir Reis* 1960

USS *Sea Devil* (SS.400) on completion of a refit at Mare Island in mid-March 1946, looking forward (below) and aft (right). The ringed areas indicate equipment modified or added during the refit. A second 5-in/25-cal gun has been added forward of the conning tower and the sonar transducer on the forward casing is ringed (right), as are the hydroplane guards on the stern

US Navy

US Navy

Balao

Hull no and name	launched	fate
SS.381 ***Sandlance*** (ex-*Ojanca*, ex-*Orca*)	6/1943	Brazilian *Rio Grande do Sul* 1963
SS.382 ***Picuda*** (ex-*Obispo*)	7/1943	Spanish *Narciso* Monturiol 1972
SS.383 ***Pampanito***	7/1943	Stricken 1971
SS.384 ***Parche***	7/1943	Sold 1970 for scrapping
SS.385 ***Bang***	8/1943	Spanish *Cosme Garcia* 1972
SS.386 ***Pilotfish***	8/1943	Sunk as target 1948
SS.387 ***Pintado***	9/1943	Sold 1969 for scrapping
SS.388 ***Pipefish***	10/1943	Sold 1969 for scrapping
SS.389 ***Piranha***	10/1943	Sold 1970 for scrapping
SS.390 ***Plaice***	11/1943	Brazilian *Bahia* 1963
SS.391 ***Pomfret***	10/1943	Turkish *Oruc Reis* 1971
SS.392 ***Sterlet*** (ex-*Pudiano*)	10/1943	Sunk as target 1969
SS.393 ***Queenfish***	11/1943	Sunk as target 1963
SS.394 ***Razorback***	1/1944	Turkish *Murat Reis* 1970
SS.395 ***Redfish***	1/1944	Sunk as target 1969
SS.396 ***Ronquil***	1/1944	Spanish *Isaac Peral* 1971
SS.397 ***Scabbardfish***	1/1944	Greek *Traina* 1964
SS.398 ***Segundo***	2/1944	Stricken 1970
SS.399 ***Sea Cat***	2/1944	Sunk as target 1968
SS.400 ***Sea Devil***	2/1944	Sunk as target 1965
SS.401 ***Sea Dog***	3/1944	Stricken 1968 for trials
SS.402 ***Sea Fox***	3/1944	Turkish *Burak Reis* 1970
SS.403 ***Atule***	3/1944	Stricken 1974
SS.404 ***Spikefish***	4/1944	Sunk as target 1963
SS.405 ***Sea Owl***	5/1944	Sold 1971 for scrapping
SS.406 ***Sea Poacher***	5/1944	Stricken 1973
SS.407 ***Sea Robin***	5/1944	Sold 1971 for scrapping
SS.408 ***Sennet***	6/1944	Stricken 1968
SS.409 ***Piper*** (ex-*Awa*)	6/1944	Stricken 1970
SS.410 ***Threadfin***	6/1944	Turkish *Birina Inonu* 1973
SS.411 ***Spadefish***	1/1943	Sold 1969 for scrapping
SS.412 ***Trepang***	3/1944	Sunk as target 1969
SS.413 ***Spot***	5/1944	Chilean *Al Simpson* 1962
SS.414 ***Springer***	8/1944	Chilean *Captain Thomson* 1961
SS.415 ***Stickleback***	1/1945	Sunk in collision 1958
SS.416 ***Tiru***	9/1947	Ran aground 1966 but refloated and stricken

USS *Guitarro* (SS.363) at Mare Island, June 1954, looking aft. Her conning tower has been streamlined and the light AA guns removed

US Navy

US Navy

US Navy

USS *Cusk* (SS.348) in late September 1947, being equipped for launching the Loon guided missiles (above left), and under way (above right). Tracking radar has been fitted to the conning tower, while the cylindrical hangar with hemispherical door and launching ramp are positioned aft. *Below:* USS *Carbonero* (SS.337) launches a Republic JB-2 Loon copy of the German V-1 flying bomb during Exercise Miki, November 1949. JATO (jet-assisted takeoff) bottles were used to launch the missile and to give it sufficient speed for the pulse-jet to be able to function

Richard P Hallion Collection

Baltimore

US heavy cruiser class. On July 1, 1940 under the Two-Ocean Navy programme, the US Navy ordered four heavy (8-in gunned) cruisers as the first installment of a massive rebuilding of American naval strength. The new class was to be called the *Baltimore* Class and as the Washington Treaty limits had now lapsed the Bureau of Ships was able to build to what it considered the right displacement, ie 13 600 tons as opposed to 10 000. In fact the US Navy was only doing what the Japanese, German and Italian navies had already decided to do in secret, which is an interesting example of how different navies ultimately come to the same conclusions about optimum size.

The design followed closely the previous *Wichita* (1937) but copied the layout of the contemporary *Cleveland* Class light cruisers. They were extremely powerful-looking ships with high freeboard, two tall capped funnels and superstructure divided into two distinct blocks. With a beamy hull there was ample room for a heavy antiaircraft armament of 12 5-in guns, disposed hexagonally in twin turrets, and six quad 40-mm Bofors mountings amidships. The protection was heavy by cruiser standards, a 6-in belt extending between the turrets, and a 2-3-in deck. All living and working spaces were given air-conditioning, and as a result no side scuttles were provided. The great size also meant a big radius of action, important in a class intended for action in the Pacific.

The first group was quickly followed by an order for a further four placed on September 9, 1940, but the emphasis on other ship types led to a two-year gap. A further ten were ordered on August 7, 1942 but only six were completed by 1945; three were completed to a modified design (the *Oregon City* Class) and one was suspended for many years, and finally completed as a command ship. Because of steel shortages, and the urgent need for destroyers and escorts, work on the class was not pushed forward with as much urgency as might be expected, and the lead ship did not commission until April 15, 1943. CA.68-75 and CA.122-125 were built by Bethlehem Steel at Quincy, Massachusetts, and CA.130-135 by New York Shipbuilding at Camden.

Several were renamed to commemorate older cruisers sunk in the fighting around Guadalcanal, but in a quixotic gesture the *Pittsburgh* was renamed *Canberra* in honour of the Australian 'County' Class heavy cruiser sunk at Savo Island. This proved embarrassing to the Australians, for there was an inter-allied agreement not to duplicate major ships' names: as a result of the American decision the Australians could not bestow the name on their own replacement for their *Canberra.* The antiaircraft armament was increased before completion, and the first ships carried 48 Bofors guns, two extra quads on either side forward, one on the forecastle, two aft and one at the stern. In the later ships the guns on the stern were changed to two twin mounts because the massive aircraft cranes tended to mask the arcs of fire of one mount set to port. The total of 20-mm guns varied from 22 to 24, and late in the war some of the singles were exchanged for manually operated twins.

US Navy

USS *Baltimore* (CA.68) with two Vought OS2U-3 Kingfisher floatplanes on the catapult

One unfortunate feature was retained from the pre-war *Brooklyn* Class cruisers, the large hangar for floatplanes under the quarterdeck. In theory this could be used to house up to four OS2U-3 Kingfisher floatplanes and allow maintenance to be carried out under cover. The position proved to be a bad one, for the large resonant cavity above the propellers caused vibration and there was always a risk of the hatch being damaged in heavy

USS *Baltimore* off Boston, Mass, in September 1943. Heavily armed and having a large radius of action, the heavy cruisers of this class were, at the time of their completion, probably the finest of their type in the world

Hull No and name	laid down	launched	completed
CA.68 ***Baltimore***	5/1941	7/1942	4/1943
CA.69 ***Boston***	6/1941	8/1942	6/1943
CA.70 ***Canberra*** (ex-*Pittsburgh*)	9/1941	4/1943	10/1943
CA.71 ***Quincy*** (ex-*St Paul*)	10/1941	6/1943	12/1943
CA.72 ***Pittsburgh*** (ex-*Albany*)	2/1943	2/1944	10/1944
CA.73 ***Saint Paul*** (ex-*Rochester*)	2/1943	9/1944	2/1945
CA.74 ***Columbus***	6/1943	11/1944	6/1945
CA.75 ***Helena*** (ex-*Des Moines*)	9/1943	4/1945	9/1945
CA.122 ***Oregon City***	4/1944	6/1945	—
CA.123 ***Albany***	3/1944	6/1945	—
CA.124 ***Rochester***	5/1944	8/1945	—
CA.125 ***Northampton***	8/1944	—	—
CA.130 ***Bremerton***	2/1943	7/1944	4/1945
CA.131 ***Fall River***	4/1943	8/1944	7/1945
CA.132 ***Macon***	6/1943	10/1944	8/1945
CA.133 ***Toledo***	9/1943	5/1945	10/1946
CA.134 ***Los Angeles***	7/1943	8/1944	7/1945
CA.135 ***Chicago***	7/1943	8/1944	1/1945

US Navy

weather. As a result only two aircraft were carried, on the catapults.

The class performed very well in action and were involved in all the campaigns which took the US Navy across the Pacific, from the Gilbert Islands to Iwo Jima. *Canberra* was badly damaged by a torpedo off Formosa in October 1944, and on June 5, 1945 the *Pittsburgh* lost her bow in a typhoon. This caused some misgivings about the standards of wartime shipbuilding, especially as she held the record for the class, being built in only 20 months. The *Quincy* was at Normandy in June 1944, the only one of the class to see service in Europe. Several ships served with distinction in the Korean war as well, but they were somewhat out of date by the mid-1950s, as well as being expensive to run, with large crews.

Los Angeles, Helena, Macon and *Toledo* were converted to carry the Regulus surface-to-surface missile in the same period, but this involved merely siting a ramp on the stern in similar fashion to the now-discarded catapults. Another change which affected all the ships in commission was the stripping of all 20-mm AA guns and the replacement of quadruple 40-mm guns by the new twin 3-in/50-cal rapid-fire mounting. The after pair of gun 'buckets' were not used in peacetime, and so only ten 3-in mountings were installed.

In 1952 the *Boston* and *Canberra* were taken in hand by the New York Shipbuilding Corporation (the same firm which had built many of their sisters) for conversion to the world's first guided-missile-armed cruisers. The after 8-in turret, weighing 143 tons, was removed, along with the aftermost 5-in twin AA gun. The entire superstructure abaft the bridge was rebuilt, with a lattice foremast, a single funnel and two sets of twin launchers and directors for the Terrier RIM-2 beam-riding missile. The two ships recommissioned as CAG.1 and CAG.2 in November 1955 and June 1956 respectively.

A much more ambitious conversion was given to the *Chicago* and *Columbus*, involving complete rebuilding of the topsides which permitted a 'double-ended' missile armament. They and the former *Oregon City* Class *Albany* formed a new class when they commissioned in 1962-64, and are described under a separate heading (referred to below).

The *Macon* was stricken in 1969, *Baltimore* and *Fall River* in 1971, *Pittsburgh, Quincy* and *Bremerton* in 1973, and *Helena, Toledo* and *Los Angeles* in 1974. The *St Paul* was modified to serve as the flagship of the 7th Fleet in the Western Pacific, and was the last all-gun cruiser to be in commission. She was decommissioned in 1971 but was still on the Navy List in 1976.

Displacement: 13600 tons (standard), 17070 tons (full load) *Length:* (CA.68-71) 205.3 m (673 ft 6 in) oa; (CA.72 ff) 205.74 m (675 ft) oa *Beam:* 21.56 m (70 ft 9 in) *Draught:* 6.25 m (20 ft 6 in) normal, 7.92 m (26 ft) max *Machinery:* 4-shaft geared steam turbines, 120000 shp=33 knots *Protection:* 152 mm (6 in) belt; 50-76 mm (2-3 in) deck; 76-152 mm (3-6 in) turrets; 203 mm (8 in) conning tower *Armament:* (As built) 9 8-in (203-mm)/55-cal (3×3); 12 5-in (127-mm)/38-cal DP (6×2); 48 40-mm AA (11×4, 2×2 or 12×4); 22-28 single 20-mm AA; (After 1945) 9 8-in; 12 5-in DP; 20 3-in AA *Crew:* 1142 (peace), 1700 (war)

(*Boston* and *Canberra* as CAG.1 and CAG.2) *Displacement:* 13300 tons (standard), 17500 tons (full load) *Dimensions, Machinery* and *Protection:* Unchanged *Armament:* 6 8-in/55-cal (2×3); 10 5-in/38-cal DP (5×2); 8 3-in/50-cal Mk 33 (4×2); 2 twin Terrier *Crew:* 1273

Barbel

US submarine class. In Fiscal Year 1956 the US Navy was authorized to build three submarines. They were the last non-nuclear combatant boats to be ordered but they incorporated many advanced features. The hull is a 'tear drop' form, as tested in the experimental USS *Albacore.* For the first time the controls were located together in an 'attack centre', and this proved so successful that it is now standard in US Navy submarines.

The machinery arrangement is unusual, with three Fairbanks-Morse diesels driving two General Electric motors on one shaft. Mk 101 Mod 20 torpedo fire control is fitted and a BQS-4 bow sonar. When built all three had their diving planes mounted on the bow but later they were relocated on the forward side of the 'sail' or fin, as the conning tower is now known.

Displacement: 2145/2895 tons (surfaced/submerged) *Length:* 66.8 m (219 ft 6 in) oa *Beam:*

8.8 m (29 ft 0 in) *Draught:* 8.5 m (28 ft 0 in) *Machinery:* Diesel/electric, 4800 bhp/3150 shp=15/25 knots (surfaced/submerged) *Armament:* 6 21-in (53-cm) torpedo tubes (bpw) (at least 18 torpedoes carried) *Crew:* 78

Barfleur

British destroyer class. By 1941 it had become clear that British destroyers were ill-equipped to defend themselves against aircraft. The Admiralty therefore decided to produce an entirely new design for the fleet destroyers of the 1942 and 1943 construction programmes in which the principal feature was to be a substantial antiaircraft armament.

The result was the 'Battle' Class, each of which carried four 4.5-in guns in two twin dual-purpose mountings fitted forward of the bridge. The mountings were virtually small turrets, being fully enclosed, power operated, and capable of elevating the guns to 85° compared to 40° or 55° in early destroyer mountings. In addition the main armament was provided with a sophisticated fire-control system based on the new Mk VI HA/LA director with radar control and full stabilization. The remainder of the designed armament consisted of a single 4-in gun amidships, for starshell, four twin 40-mm Hazemeyer Bofors mountings, two sets of quadruple 21-in torpedo tubes, four 20-mm AA guns and a depth-charge armament.

All this, together with the speed necessary for a fleet destroyer, required a ship of comparatively large dimensions, and at over 2300 tons they were the biggest destroyers thus far designed for the Royal Navy. They were handsome ships which met most of the requirements of the Second World War but very few were completed prior to the end of hostilities. Wartime modifications to the design resulted in the substitution of single 40-mm guns for the 20-mm and the fitting of a lattice foremast.

The class fell into three distinct groups —the Early, Later and Australian 'Battles'. The Early 'Battles' were constructed under the 1942 Programme, 16 being laid down during 1942-44 and completed during 1944-46. The Later 'Battles' were constructed under the 1943 Programme, 24 being laid down during 1943-44 of which 16 were cancelled at the end of the war, the remainder completed during 1946-48. The Australian 'Battles' were improved versions of the Later 'Battles' of which two were built for the RAN during 1946-1951; two RAN vessels belonging to the same group were cancelled.

The Early 'Battles'

Only those ships completed during the war, *Barfleur, Camperdown, Armada, Hogue* and *Trafalgar,* carried the 4-in gun amidships which in later ships was replaced by two single 40-mm guns. The last to complete, *Cadiz, St James, Sluys, Saintes, Vigo* and *Gabbard,* mounted two twin STAAG (Stabilized Tachymetric Anti-Aircraft Gun) 40-mm AA guns in place of the 4 Hazemeyers and all the earlier units were eventually modified to this standard. By the end of the 1950s the majority carried two twin and five single 40-mm, the sixth single 40-mm on the quarterdeck having been displaced by the fitting of a 'Squid' A/S mortar. In the early 1960s the STAAGs were replaced by twin 40-mm Mk Vs in *Camperdown, Cadiz, Saintes* and *Gabbard.*

US Navy

The attack submarine USS *Barbel* (SS.580) undergoing maintenance work in dry dock

Name and number	laid down	launched	completed	builder
***Barbel* (SS.580)**	5/1956	7/1958	1/1959	Portsmouth Naval Shipyard
***Blueback* (SS.581)**	4/1957	5/1959	10/1959	Ingalls SB Corporation
***Bonefish* (SS.582)**	6/1957	11/1958	7/1959	New York SB Corporation

The *Barfleur* was the only one of the class to see any real war service; she took part in the final assault on Japan and was present at the Japanese surrender. In 1957 the *Cadiz* and *Gabbard* were sold to Pakistan and renamed *Khaibar* and *Badr* respectively. The *Sluys* was sold to Iran in 1966, being substantially modernized and renamed *Artemiz.* The remainder of the class were sold for scrap between 1960 and 1970. *Armada, Saintes* and *Solebay* were built by Hawthorn Leslie. *Barfleur, Gabbard, St Kitts* and *Trafalgar* were built by Swan Hunter. *Cadiz, Camperdown, Finisterre, St James* and *Vigo* were built by Fairfield. *Gravelines, Hogue, Lagos* and *Sluys* were built by Cammell Laird.

The Later 'Battles'

Although of the same basic design these ships differed in a number of particulars from the earlier class. To compensate for the lack of astern fire a single 4.5-in gun, controlled by the main fire-control system, was mounted abaft the funnel in place of the 4-in starshell gun, a US Mk 37 director was fitted instead of the original Mk VI director (owing to limited manufacturing capacity for the British equipment) and quintuple torpedo tubes were substituted for quadruple. To compensate for the additional topweight the beam was increased by 3 in, which with the other modifications increased the displacement by over 200 tons.

As completed they carried a Squid A/S mortar on the quarterdeck and the close-range AA armament of all units consisted of two twin STAAG 40-mm, one twin Mk V 40-mm and two single 40-mm. During 1959 the *Jutland* had her STAAG replaced by Mk V 40-mm.

In the early 1960s the *Agincourt, Aisne, Barrosa* and *Corunna* were converted into AD (Aircraft Direction) ships, also known as radar pickets. All the torpedo tubes and 40-mm guns were removed and additional deck houses were constructed amidships. A new lattice foremast carrying a large air warning radar scanner was fitted abaft the bridge and a small lattice mainmast was added aft. A quadruple Seacat guided-missile launcher was added on the after superstructure and occasionally the ships carried two single 20-mm AA guns. The *Corunna,* commissioned in February 1962, was the first ship to carry the Seacat operationally.

During 1971-73 the *Matapan* was converted into a Sonar trials ship, emerging with a markedly different profile. The hull and superstructure were substantially remodelled, the forecastle deck being extended aft to provide a flush deck. A new clipper bow with increased flair, a modern bridge, solid foremast and a second funnel (for generator exhausts) are among the more obvious changes. The hull structure was also modified and this included the provision of a large bulbous sonar dome at the fore-foot.

The unmodified ships were sold for scrap in 1965 and of the AD conversions during the early 1970s only *Matapan* still remained in service by 1977.

Agincourt and *Alamein* were built by Hawthorn Leslie; *Aisne* by Vickers Armstrong; *Barrosa* and *Matapan* by John Brown; *Corunna* by Swan Hunter; and *Dunkirk* and *Jutland* by Alexander Stephens.

The Australian 'Battles'

The two ships of this group were ordered in 1945-46 to a modified 'Battle' design and were constructed in Australia. They differ from the previous ships mainly in carrying Mk VI 4.5-

in twin turrets instead of the earlier Mk IV. This mounting, under development at the end of the war, was tested in the *Saintes* and was later fitted in the destroyers of the *Daring* Class. Like the Early 'Battles', the Australian ships were fitted with the Mk VI director. As completed they carried three twin STAAG 40-mm and five single 40-mm and unlike any other 'Battle' they carried funnel caps. In 1960 *Anzac* was converted into a training ship having all but A turret and four single 40-mm guns of her armament removed and a number of deck houses added. *Tobruk* was placed in reserve in 1960 and both vessels have since been scrapped.

Anzac was built by Williamstown dockyard and *Tobruk* by Cockatoo dockyard.

See also *Artemiz*.

Displacement: (Early) 2315 tons, (Later) 2550 tons (standard) *Length:* 115.52 m (379 ft 0 in) oa *Beam:* (E) 12.27 m (40 ft 3 in), (L) 12.34 m (40 ft 6 in), (A) 12.49 m (41 ft 0 in) *Draught:* 4.24 m (13 ft 11 in) *Machinery:* 2-shaft geared steam turbines, 50 000 shp=$35\frac{3}{4}$ knots (54 000 shp=34 knots in Australians) *Armament:* (E) 4 4.5-in (114-mm) (2×2); 1 4-in (102-mm); 14 or 10 40-mm (6×1, 4×2 or 2×2); 8 21-in (53-cm) torpedo tubes (2×4); (L) 5 4.5-in (2×2+1); 8 40-mm (3×2, 2×1); 10 21-in torpedo tubes (2×5); (A) 4 4.5-in (2×2); 11 40-mm (3×2, 5×1); 10 21-in torpedo tubes (2×5) *Crew:* 250-310

FPL

The *Barfleur* or 'Battle' Class destroyer HMS *Matapan* in June 1973 converted to a Sonar trials ship. A 24-ft diameter sonar—reputedly the most powerful in the world—is fitted below the bows, and the after funnel is an exhaust for the turbo-generator used to power the Sonar

Bathurst

Australian minesweeper class. The 60 vessels of this class were constructed in Australia between 1940 and 1944. Thirty-six were for the RAN, while 20, paid for by the Admiralty, were intended for the RN. These latter were, however, transferred to the RAN on completion. A further four units, *Bengal, Bombay, Madras* and *Punjab*, were built for the Royal Indian Navy and differed from their sisters in having a 3-in gun in place of the 4-in. Another three ships intended for the RIN were cancelled in March 1945.

The ships were of conventional fleet minesweeper type and they were generally similar in design to the RN *Bangor* Class of the emergency war programme. Although

HMS *St Kitts* (foreground) meets the cruiser HMS *Glasgow* in the Mediterranean to take on board First Sea Lord Sir Rhoderick McGrigor

MOD

intended for minesweeping, they were often employed as escorts and patrol vessels and were frequently equipped with a depth-charge armament. They also served as transports and some members of the class even carried out shore bombardments.

During the Second World War they served mainly in Australian and Far Eastern waters, where three were lost. The first was the *Armidale*, sunk by Japanese torpedo planes off Timor on December 1, 1942. The remaining pair were lost in more mundane circumstances, both being sunk as a result of accidental collisions with merchant vessels; the *Wallaroo* off Fremantle on June 11, 1943 and the *Geelong* off New Guinea on October 18, 1944. Another unit was lost after the war; on September 13, 1947 the *Warrnambool* was sunk by a mine off the coast of Queensland.

In 1946 the *Burnie, Lismore, Toowoomba, Tamworth, Cairns, Ipswich, Kalgoorlie* and *Wollongong* were sold to the Royal Netherlands Navy and renamed *Ceram, Bajam, Boeroe, Tidore, Ambon, Morotai, Ternate* and *Banda* respectively. In 1949 the latter four of these ships were transferred to Indonesia and renamed *Banteng, Hang Tuah, Patti Unis* and *Radjawali* respectively. The *Broome, Gawler, Geraldton, Launceston* and *Pirie* were sold to Turkey in 1946 and renamed *Alanya, Ayvalik, Antalya, Ayancik* and *Amasra* respectively. In 1952 the *Echuca, Inverell, Kiama* and *Stawell* were presented to the RNZN. The *Ballarat, Bendigo, Benita, Whyalla* and *Gladstone* were sold into merchant service, the first four in 1947 and the fifth in 1956.

The *Bathurst* was scrapped in 1948 and the majority of the remaining ships of the class suffered the same fate during the late 1950s and early 1960s but a few survived into the 1970s as training ships.

Ararat, Broome, Bunbury, Bundaberg, Fremantle, Gympie, Ipswich*, Kiama, Launceston*, Parkes, Townsville*—built by Evans Deakin; *Armidale, Burnie, Colac, Deloraine, Dubbo, Inverell, Latrobe, Lismore, Lithgow, Mildura, Wagga, Warrnambool, Bombay, Punjab*—built by Morts Dock; *Ballarat*, Benalla, Castlemaine, Echuca, Geelong, Horsham, Shepperton, Stawell*—built by Williamstown Dockyard; *Bathurst*, Bendigo*, Cessnock*, Glenelg, Gouldburn*, Wollongong*, Bengal, Madras*—built by Cockatoo Dockyard; *Bowen, Cairns*, Gladstone, Maryborough*, Rockhampton, Tamworth*, Toowoomba**—built by Walkers; *Cootamundra, Cowra, Geraldton*, Junee, Kapunda, Katoomba, Wallaroo*—built by Poole and Steele; *Gawler*, Kalgoorlie*, Pirie*, Whyalla**—built by Broken Hill; *Strahan*—built by Newcastle. * RN vessels

Displacement: 650 tons (standard) *Length:* 56.69 m (186 ft 0 in) oa *Beam:* 9.14 m (31 ft 0 in) *Draught:* 2.51 m (8 ft 3 in) *Machinery:* 2-shaft steam piston engines, 2000 ihp=16 knots *Armament:* 1 4-in (102-mm) (3-in in RIN vessels); 1 20-mm; 4 .303-in mg (2×2) *Crew:* 60

PPL

The Royal Australian Navy's *Bathurst* Class minesweepers *Ararat* (above) and *Bowen* (below), photographed in 1945. Like other minesweepers, the vessels of this class were allocated J pendant numbers in 1940—the *Ararat* being the exception with a K pendant. The *Bowen* has a 40-mm AA gun aft, and a 20-mm on each bridge wing; *Ararat* retains her original armament

PPL

Battleaxe

British destroyer class. The *Battleaxe*, or 'Weapon', Class were constructed under the 1944 Programme but work on their design began as early as 1942. The main requirement was for a fleet destroyer which had good AA and A/S capabilities. At the same time it was considered desirable to keep the dimensions within reasonable limits so that they could be constructed by shipyards whose slips were too small for the large destroyers of the 1942 and 1943 Programmes.

This size necessitated the adoption of the twin 4-in DP gun mounting since this was the only weapon available that would meet both the AA requirement and the weight limitation. The designed armament was six 4-in, with two twin mountings forward and one aft, two twin 40-mm Hazemeyer mountings, four 20-mm singles, two banks of quadruple torpedo tubes, four depth-charge throwers, two depth-charge chutes and 50 depth charges.

Unit machinery intended to minimize the effect of damage was adopted for the first time in a British destroyer and was arranged forward to aft in the order: boiler room—engine room—oil fuel compartment—boiler room—engine room. This arrangement required a return to two funnels, the foremost of which was led up through the centre of the lattice foremast. The result was considered by most to be very ugly and this, together with their light gun armament, led to much criticism of the design.

Orders were placed for 20 ships in April and May 1943 and the design was approved in June. Of these ships three were cancelled in December 1944 and 13 at the end of 1945. The remaining four were completed during 1947-48 to a slightly modified design. Two Squid A/S mortars replaced the 4-in mounting in B position in *Battleaxe* and *Broadsword* and in X position in *Crossbow*, while *Scorpion* was fitted with a single Limbo A/S mortar in place of X 4-in mounting. In addition all mounted two twin STAAG 40-mm AA mountings instead of Hazemeyers, and single 40-mm guns in the bridge wings instead of the designed 20-mm guns.

During 1958-59 all four were refitted as radar pickets, a large air warning radar scanner being mounted on a new lattice mast between the foremast and the after funnel. All the torpedo tubes were removed and in *Crossbow* and *Scorpion* the after 4-in mounting was moved forward and the A/S mortar(s) aft. Standard displacement had by this time risen to 2280 tons.

In 1962 the *Battleaxe* was badly damaged in a collision with the frigate *Ursa* in the Clyde. It was decided that her repair was not justified and in 1964 she was sold for scrap. The remaining three were sold for scrap between 1968 and 1971.

Battleaxe and *Broadsword* were both fitted as flotilla leaders and were built by Yarrow. *Crossbow* was built by Thornycroft, and *Scorpion* (ex-*Tomahawk*. ex-*Centaur*) was built by White.

Displacement: 1980 tons (standard) *Length:* 111.25 m (365 ft 0 in) oa *Beam:* 11.58 m (38 ft 0 in) *Draught:* 3.57 m (11 ft 9 in) *Machinery:* 2-shaft geared steam turbines, 40 000 shp=34 knots *Armament:* 4 4-in (102-mm) (2×2); 6 40-mm (1½-in) (2×2+2×1); 10 21-in (53-cm) torpedo tubes (2×5); 2 A/S mortars *Crew:* 234 (flotilla leaders 256)

Bayandor

Iranian corvette class. In 1961 the United States agreed to build two frigate or escort-type warships for the Imperial Iranian Navy under the Mutual Aid programme. They were given hull-designations PF.103-104 and the order was given to the Levingstone Shipbuilding company, Orange, Texas. Five years later another pair, PF.105 and 106, were ordered from the same builder.

They resemble the Venezuelan *Almirante Clemente* Class, although smaller and slower, as they have a flush-decked hull with a marked sheer. The armament comprises two single 3-in guns, two light guns, a Hedgehog antisubmarine mortar and depth-charge throwers. A US Navy-pattern SPS-6 air surveillance radar and a navigation radar are provided, in addition to radar-direction for the 3-in guns.

No and name	laid down	launched	completed
F25 *Bayandor*	8/1962	7/1963	5/1964
F26 *Naghdi*	9/1962	10/1963	6/1964
F27 *Milanian*	5/1967	1/1968	2/1969
F28 *Kahnamuie*	6/1967	4/1968	2/1969

Displacement: 900 tons (standard), 1135 tons (full load) *Length:* 83.8 m (275 ft 0 in) oa *Beam:* 10 m (33 ft 0 in) *Draught:* 3.1 m (10 ft 3 in) *Machinery:* 2-shaft diesels, 6000 bhp=20 knots *Armament:* 2 3-in (76-mm) AA (2×1); 2 40-mm AA (2×1); 1 Hedgehog; 4 depth-charge throwers *Crew:* 140

Bayntun

British frigate class. Late in 1940 the United States Bureau of Construction began work on the design of a small DE (destroyer escort) similar in concept to the British 'Hunt' Class. It was proposed to place an initial order for 50 ships, but the final design was considered unsatisfactory and the project was cancelled early in 1941. However, in June 1941 the British asked if they could place orders with US builders for escort vessels, of which the Royal Navy was chronically short. The US agreed to this request and 50 ships based on the previously abandoned DE design were ordered. This design was chosen because the use of standard US building methods and equipment was essential and because it closely matched the Admiralty's requirements for a North Atlantic escort vessel. Despite the similarity of the ships to the 'Hunt' Class escort destroyers, the British classified the DEs as frigates.

IWM

The *Bayntun* Class frigates *Inman* (above), with the original armament of three 3-in, twin 40-mm and five 20-mm guns, and *Lawford* (below), after conversion to a Landing Ship Headquarter ship

When the United States entered the war most of the ships ordered by the Admiralty were taken over by the US Navy, but the DE programme was greatly enlarged and eventually 76 were supplied to Britain under lend-lease. Thirty-two of these vessels belonged to the *Bayntun* Class (the RN DEs were collectively known as the 'Captain' Class, being named after captains of the Nelson period), which were provided with diesel-electric machinery.

The original design provided for the installation of turbine machinery providing 24 knots with 12 000 shp, but limited turbine construction capacity led to the substitution of diesel-electric drive. This consisted of eight diesel generator sets providing power to two electric motors for the same speed. However, even the manufacture of this machinery was limited, and in order to increase the number of power plants available the number of diesel generator sets per ship was halved to four. This halved output to 6000 hp, but the resulting loss of speed was only three knots. The equivalent vessels in the US Navy were known as the *Evarts* Class and, unlike the British ships, they were equipped with torpedo tubes.

All the *Bayntun* Class were constructed by the Boston navy yard except *Drury*, which was built by the Philadelphia navy yard. *Inglis* and *Inman* were commissioned in 1944 and the remainder of the class in 1943. The intended armament, with which some earlier units were completed, was three 3-in dual-purpose guns, five single 20-mm and one twin 40-mm. However, the twin 40-mm was in short supply and several vessels mounted two more 20-mm instead. Subsequently a further six 20-mm mountings were fitted in most. Despite the substantial AA armament, they served mainly as A/S escorts, and among the early modifications made by the British was increased depth-charge armament.

The class served mainly on the North Atlantic and Russian convoy routes, but three, the *Lawson*, *Dacres* and *Kingsmill*, were converted into HQ vessels for landing craft during 1943-44 and took part in the Normandy invasion. Designated LSH (S)—Landing Ship HQ (Small)—alterations included the removal of the after 3-in gun, an increase in the 20-mm armament to 16, the fitting of a mainmast and increasing radar and communication equipment.

Two of the class were damaged beyond reasonable repair, the *Goodson*, torpedoed by *U 984* on June 25, 1944, and the *Manners*, torpedoed by *U 1172* on January 1, 1945. Another four were torpedoed and sunk by enemy submarines, the *Gould* by *U 358* on March 1, 1944, the *Blackwood* by *U 764* on June 15, 1944, the *Capel* by *U 486* on December 12, 1944 and the *Goodall* by *U 968* on April 29, 1945. In addition the *Lawford* was bombed and sunk by German aircraft while operating off Normandy on June 8, 1944. The class did, however, redress the balance by sharing in the sinking of 16 U-Boats between 1943 and 1945.

During 1945 to 1947 all the *Bayntuns*, including those damaged, were officially returned to the United States, and were subsequently sold for scrap.

See also *Bentinck*, *Buckley*, *Evarts*.

Bayntun, Bazely, Berry, Blackwood, Burges, Capel, Cooke, Dacres, Domett, Foley, Gardiner, Garlies, Goodall, Goodson, Gore, Gould, Grindall, Hoste, Inglis, Inman, Keats, Kempthorne, Kingsmill, Lawford, Lawson, Loring, Louis, Manners, Moorsom, Mounsey, Pasley—built by Boston navy yard.
Drury—built by Philadelphia navy yard.

Displacement: 1140 tons (standard) *Length:* 88.24 m (289 ft 6 in) oa *Beam:* 10.66 m (35 ft 0 in) *Draught:* 2.51 m (8 ft 3 in) *Machinery:* 2-shaft diesel-electric drive, 6000 bhp=21 knots *Armament:* 3 3-in (76-mm) (3×1); 2 40-mm (1×2); 5 20-mm; 1 Hedgehog; 4 depth-charge throwers *Crew:* 156

MOD

MOD

HMS *Edinburgh* (above and top) in late 1941 and *Belfast* (right) in February 1953. *Edinburgh*'s wartime career ended with her sinking in the spring of 1942, but *Belfast*, although mined in 1939, was refitted, serving out the war and later seeing action off Korea

Belfast

British cruiser class. Constructed under the 1937 Programme, the *Belfast* and *Edinburgh* were modified versions of the *Southampton* Class cruisers. As originally designed, they would have differed from the earlier ships in having four quadruple 6-in gun turrets instead of triples. This would have placed them on equal terms with contemporary US and Japanese cruisers. The heavier armament necessitated a larger hull, resulting in an increase in the displacement to 10 000 tons. However, trials with the prototype quad 6-in mounting were not successful, and after considering the difficulties and delays involved in designing a satisfactory alternative it was decided to abandon the quad mounting and revert to the triple turrets of the earlier *Southampton* Class cruisers.

The design was modified accordingly, and as finally worked out they differed from the *Southampton* mainly in appearance. This was the result of moving the 4-in magazines from abaft the machinery to forward of it, which in turn necessitated moving the machinery further aft. Consequently there was a substantial increase in the distance between the fore funnel and the bridge. Other differences were less obvious, the most important being a general improvement in the armour protection, both in thickness and distribution, and an increase of the armament by the fitting of two more twin 4-in gun mountings.

Ordered and laid down in 1936, both vessels were launched in 1938 and completed in the following year. The *Edinburgh* was constructed by Swan Hunter on the Tyne and the *Belfast* by Harland and Wolff at Belfast.

The *Edinburgh*'s career was comparatively short. On April 30, 1942, while escorting the Russian convoy QP11, she was torpedoed by the *U 456*. Despite heavy damage she eventually worked up speed to 8 knots and headed for Kola Inlet, but two days later she was intercepted by a group of German destroyers off Bear Island. In the engagement which followed she was torpedoed again, and all chance of saving her having been lost, she was abandoned and subsequently sunk by a torpedo from the destroyer *Foresight*.

The *Belfast* came close to having an even shorter career. On November 21, 1939 she detonated a magnetic mine in the Firth of Forth. The resulting damage was extensive—the keel was broken, the hull distorted and strained, the machinery suffered severe shock damage and the centre section of the ship was flooded. Later in the war she would have been written off as a total loss, but after temporary repairs at Rosyth she was taken to Devonport for a two-year repair and refit which was completed in October 1942. The hull was straightened and, to strengthen the damaged portion of the ship and improve stability, a narrow bulge was added on each side increasing the beam to 21 m (69 ft). At the same time the 0.5-in guns were removed and 14 20-mm (5×2+4×1) guns added, together with the standard radar equipment of the time. By 1944 a further 12 20-mm (10×1+1×2) guns had been added.

She recommissioned in November 1942 and spent a large part of the next 18 months covering Russian convoys. During one of these operations, on December 26, 1942, she took part in the Battle of North Cape in which the battlecruiser *Scharnhorst* was sunk by the battleship *Duke of York* and other units of the Home Fleet. After serving as a bombardment ship during the invasion of Normandy she was taken in hand for a refit for service in the Pacific. Modifications included the removal of the aircraft equipment, two of her twin 4-in mountings and eight 20-mm (8×1) and the addition of 20 2-pdr pom-poms (4×4+4×1).

She arrived at Sydney in August 1945 where five 40-mm (5×1) guns were added to the armament and four 20-mm (2×2) removed. The war with Japan ended before she could become involved, but she spent the major part of the next eight years in the Far East and took an active part in the Korean war during 1950-52.

In 1953 she was placed in reserve and between 1956 and 1959 was extensively modernized at Devonport. Alterations included a new bridge, lattice masts, substitution of 12 40-mm (6×2) guns for the existing close-range armament, a substantial improvement in her fire control, radar and communication equipment and the removal of the torpedo tubes. On completion of this refit her displacement had risen to 11 550 tons standard and 14 930 tons full load. This made her Britain's largest 6-in-gun cruiser, but claims that she is the largest ever British cruiser are exaggerated. Some of Britain's 8-in-gun cruisers exceeded the full load of *Belfast* during the Second World War and certain 1st Class cruisers built around the turn of the century were also larger.

Despite the expensive modernization she served only four years before being placed in reserve and was subsequently listed for disposal. However, after a difficult battle to save her from the breakers the government agreed in 1971 to place the ship under the control of the HMS *Belfast* Trust. She now serves as a museum ship, being permanently moored in the Pool of London.

See also *Southampton* Class.

Displacement: 10 550 tons (standard) *Length:* 187 m (613 ft 6 in) oa *Beam:* 19.3 m (63 ft 4 in) *Draught:* 5.26 m (17 ft 3 in) *Machinery:* 4-shaft geared steam turbines, 80 000 shp=32.5 knots *Protection:* 114 mm (4½ in) side; 51-102 mm (2-4 in) turrets; 51-76 mm (2-3 in) decks *Armament:* 12 6-in (152-mm) (4×3); 12 4-in (102-mm) (6×2); 16 2-pdr (2×8); 8 0.5-in (12.7-mm) (2×4); 6 21-in (53-cm) torpedo tubes (2×3, above water) *Aircraft:* 2 *Crew:* 880

MOD

HMS *Belfast* during bombardments of enemy troop concentrations off the west coast of Korea

Belknap

US guided missile cruiser class. Three guided missile destroyers (DLG.26-28) were authorized for the US Navy in the Fiscal Year 1961 building programme, followed by DLG.29-34 in the FY 1962 programme, and they were built between 1962 and 1967.

The *Belknaps* are improved versions of the 'double-ended' *Leahy* Class DLGs, to which they have a general resemblance. But in this class there is only one missile launcher forward and a 5-in gun mounting aft. The reason for this is that more missiles can be stowed in the broader forward section of the hull and allow space aft for a helicopter hangar. The added space is needed as the launcher fires both Terrier (since replaced by Standard) and Asroc missiles, and the inclusion of the 5-in gun mounting is the result of experience in Vietnam, when shore bombardments were in frequent demand.

The dual-purpose Standard/Asroc launcher is a Mk 10 Mod 7, with a triple-ring rotating magazine capable of supplying either type of missile to either arm of the launcher. Two Mk 76 Mod 4 control systems are provided for air defence and the 5-in gun is controlled by a Mk 68 Mod 8 fire control system. The two single 3-in guns at the after end of the forecastle deck are controlled by Mk 51 and Mod 3 systems. When the ships were first commissioned they had two 21-in torpedo tubes for antisubmarine torpedoes installed at the break of the forecastle, angled out, but these were later removed.

The sonar is a bow-mounted SQS-26 set, linked to the Asroc system and the triple Mk 32 torpedo tubes amidships. Aerials for the SPS-48 3-D and SPS-10 search radars are mounted on the forward 'mack', while the array for SPS-37 (in DLG.26-28) or SPS-40 search radar is on the after 'mack' with a small tactical aircraft navigation (TACAN) aerial. The Mk 11 Mod 0 weapon direction system is installed, with SPG-53A and SPG-55B weapon control radars.

Number	name	laid down	launched	completed	built
CG.26 (ex-DLG.26)	*Belknap*	2/1962	7/1963	11/1964	Bath Iron Works, Maine
CG.27 (ex-DLG.27)	*Josephus Daniels*	4/1962	12/1963	5/1965	Bath Iron Works, Maine
CG.28 (ex-DLG.28)	*Wainwright*	7/1962	4/1964	1/1966	Bath Iron Works, Maine
CG.29 (ex-DLG.29)	*Jouett*	9/1962	6/1964	12/1966	Puget Sound Naval Shipyard
CG.30 (ex-DLG.30)	*Horne*	12/1962	10/1964	4/1967	San Francisco Naval Shipyard
CG.31 (ex-DLG.31)	*Sterett*	9/1962	6/1964	4/1967	Puget Sound Naval Shipyard
CG.32 (ex-DLG.32)	*William H Stanley*	7/1963	12/1964	7/1966	Bath Iron Works, Maine
CG.33 (ex-DLG.33)	*Fox*	1/1963	11/1964	5/1966	Todd Shipyard Corporation
CG.34 (ex-DLG.34)	*Biddle*	12/1963	7/1965	1/1967	Bath Iron Works, Maine

Mk 10 Mod 7 dual-purpose Asroc/Terrier launcher as fitted to the *Belknap* Class guided missile cruisers. Two drums of Asroc—one with torpedo and one with depth-charge warheads—and one of Terrier rotate to position the correct round on the loading rail, which then feeds the missile up to the launching arm. The launcher trains and elevates in the usual way

The guided missile cruiser USS *Belknap* (CG.26). The Asroc/Terrier launcher is positioned forward, and is seen here loaded with two Terriers

On June 30, 1975 the class were reclassified as guided missile cruisers (CG), but retained their hull numbers. On November 22, 1975 the *Belknap* was badly damaged in collision with the carrier *John F Kennedy* off Sicily. The cruiser was caught under the carrier's overhang, and the resulting fire destroyed her largely alloy superstructure almost completely. She was towed back to the US for repairs, and is not expected to return to service before 1978. She will probably be armed with the new Phalanx 20-mm 'Gatling' Close-in Weapon System (CIWS).

The *Belknaps* were the first US Navy cruisers equipped with an integral helicopter support facility, as they have a hangar for the Light Airborne Multi-Purpose System (LAMPS)—in this instance a Kaman SH-2D Seasprite. The *Belknap* was the first of the class to embark the LAMPS Seasprite in December 1971.

Displacement: 6570 tons (standard), 7930 tons (full load) *Length:* 166.7 m (547 ft 0 in) oa *Beam:* 16.7 m (54 ft 9½ in) *Draught:* 8.7 m (28 ft 9½ in) *Machinery:* 2-shaft geared steam turbines, 85 000 shp=34 knots *Protection:* nil *Armament:* 1 twin Terrier RIM-2/Asroc RUR-5A combined surface-to-air/surface-to-subsurface guided weapon systems (Terrier replaced by Standard ER RIM-67A); 1 5-in (127-mm)/54-cal Mk 42; 2 3-in (76-mm)/50-cal Mk 34 (2×1); 2 triple 12.75-in (32.4-cm) Mk 32 torpedo tubes for Mk 44/46 A/S torpedoes; 2 21-in (53-cm) torpedo tubes (removed) *Aircraft:* 1 SH-2D Seasprite helicopter *Crew:* 418 (436 as flagships)

Benjamin Franklin

US ballistic-missile submarine class. The *Benjamin Franklin* Class of 12 nuclear submarines are repeats of the *Lafayette* (SSBN.616) Class built in 1961-64. Although they have the same hull their machinery was redesigned to reduce running noise, and other minor improvements were made. They were initially armed with the A-3 Polaris ballistic missile, but since 1970 they have been converted to fire the C-3 Poseidon missile; the last boat completed conversion in February 1974. All boats were fitted with snorkels.

The conversion to Poseidon involved the replacement of the Mk 84 fire-control system with the Mk 88. The Mk 113 Mod 9 torpedo fire-control system is also fitted. It is possible that some of the class may be armed with the Trident I missile to give longer range—4828-6437 km (3000-4000 miles)—than the Poseidon's 4630 km (2875 miles).

Displacement: 7250 tons/8250 tons (surfaced/submerged) *Length:* 129.5 m (425 ft) oa *Beam:* 10.1 m (33 ft) *Draught:* 9.6 m (31 ft 6 in) *Machinery:* Single-shaft twin-geared steam turbines, pressurized water-cooled S5W nuclear reactor, 15 000 shp=20/30 knots (surfaced/submerged)+diesel/electric emergency propulsion unit *Armament:* 16 C-3 Poseidon ballistic missiles; 4 21-in (53-cm) torpedo tubes (forward) *Crew:* 145

Hull no and name	laid down	launched	completed	builder
SSBN.640 *Benjamin Franklin*	5/1963	12/1964	10/1965	General Dynamics
SSBN.641 *Simon Bolivar*	4/1963	8/1964	10/1965	Newport News shipbuilders
SSBN.642 *Kamehameha*	5/1963	1/1965	12/1965	Mare Island navy yard
SSBN.643 *George Bancroft*	8/1963	3/1965	1/1966	General Dynamics
SSBN.644 *Lewis and Clark*	7/1963	11/1964	12/1965	Newport News shipbuilders
SSBN.645 *James K Polk*	11/1963	5/1965	4/1966	General Dynamics
SSBN.654 *George C Marshall*	3/1964	5/1965	4/1966	Newport News shipbuilders
SSBN.655 *Henry L Stimson*	4/1964	11/1965	8/1966	General Dynamics
SSBN.656 *George Washington Carver*	8/1964	8/1965	6/1966	Newport News shipbuilders
SSBN.657 *Francis Scott Key*	12/1964	4/1966	12/1966	General Dynamics
SSBN.658 *Mariana G Vallejo*	7/1964	10/1965	12/1966	Mare Island navy yard
SSBN.659 *Will Rogers*	3/1965	7/1966	4/1967	General Dynamics

Hull no and name	laid down	launched	completed	builder
DD.421 *Benson*	5/1938	11/1939	7/1940	Bethlehem, Quincy
DD.422 *Mayo*	5/1938	3/1940	9/1940	Bethlehem, Quincy
DD.423 *Gleaves*	5/1938	12/1939	5/1940	Bath Iron Works
DD.424 *Niblack*	8/1938	5/1940	8/1940	Bath Iron Works
DD.425 *Madison*	12/1938	10/1939	12/1940	Boston navy yard
DD.426 *Lansdale*	12/1938	10/1939	12/1940	Boston navy yard
DD.427 *Hilary P Jones*	11/1938	12/1939	12/1940	Charleston navy yard
DD.428 *Charles F Hughes*	1/1939	5/1940	12/1940	Bremerton navy yard

Benson

US destroyer class. Experience with the single-funnelled *Gridley, Benham* and *Sims* Classes led to the design of a new type of general-purpose destroyer with two funnels. This was the result of adopting the 'unit' system of separating the boilers and turbines into two units, to reduce the risk of a single torpedo- or shell-hit putting all the machinery out of action. The adoption of longitudinal framing also gave greater hull strength.

The *Bensons* were basically similar to the *Livermore* Class, but incorporated minor differences because they were designed by Bethlehem. All except *Gleaves* and *Niblack* had the typical Bethlehem flat-sided funnels (cf British Thornycroft destroyers, which also adopted this Bethlehem 'trade mark').

Although the design specified quintuple banks of torpedo tubes, all except the *Hilary P Jones* and *Charles F Hughes* had quadruple tubes mounted temporarily. For the first time these were mounted on the centreline, a much better arrangement than the cumbersome broadside arrangement used in earlier classes. The guns on the after deckhouse were initially without shields, but were later given open-backed or closed shields.

The original antiaircraft armament was weak, as it was considered that five dual-purpose guns were sufficient. The 5-in gun at the forward end of the after deckhouse was replaced by two twin 40-mm gun-mountings late in the war, but the initial changes were restricted to increasing the .5-in machine-guns from four to 10 or 12, in single, twin and even quadruple mountings. The after bank of torpedo tubes was also removed, and by the end of the war the AA armament had been increased to two quadruple 40-mm mountings sponsoned aft, in addition to the two twins, which were shifted further forward, or seven single 20-mm.

Only one of the class was lost in the Second World War, the *Lansdale*, which was torpedoed off Cape Bengut, Algeria, while escorting convoy UGS-37 from Norfolk to Bizerta. In 1954 *Benson* and *Hilary P Jones* were transferred to Nationalist China (Taiwan) and renamed *Han Yang* (DD.15) and *Lo Yang* (DD.14). Both ships were stricken in 1975 but their names and numbers were given to later ex-US destroyers. The *Niblack, Charles F Hughes* and *Madison* were stricken for scrapping in 1968, but the *Niblack* was retained for floating dock trials at Davisville, Rhode Island, and the *Madison* was sunk as a target. The *Gleaves* was stricken in November 1969 but was earmarked for preservation as a memorial, while the *Mayo* was stricken in 1970. A projected conversion of the surviving vessels to 'corvettes' (DDC), involving the removal of half the boilers and the improvement of the antisubmarine outfit, was dropped.

See also *Livermore* Class, *Bristol* Class.

Displacement: 1620 tons (standard), 2515 tons (full load) *Length:* 106 m (348 ft 0 in) oa; (DD.423, 428) 106.13 m (348 ft 3 in) oa; (DD.421, 422) 105.13 m (347 ft 3 in) oa; (DD.424) 105.91 m (347 ft 6 in) oa *Beam:* 10.91 m (36 ft 0 in) *Draught:* 5.42 m (17 ft 9 in) max *Machinery:* 2-shaft Westinghouse single-reduction geared turbines, 50 000 shp=37½ knots (max), 33 knots (full load) *Armament:* (As completed) 5 5-in (127-mm)/38-cal DP (5×1), later reduced to 4; 6 0.5-in (13-mm) AA machine-guns (6×1), (DD.421, 422 had 10, DD.423, 426, 428 had 4), 10 21-in (53-cm) torpedo tubes (2×5); (After 1945) 4 5-in/38-cal (4×1); 12 40-mm AA (2×2, 2×4) or 7 20-mm AA (7×1); 5 21-in (53-cm) torpedo tubes; 4 DCT *Crew:* 191 (peacetime), 276 (wartime)

Bentinck

British frigate class. The 46 vessels of this class were all constructed in the US by the Bethlehem Steel company and supplied to Britain under the lend-lease programme. They were similar to the *Bayntun* Class but were provided with a larger hull to accommodate a turbo-electric, instead of diesel-electric, machinery installation. This allowed for a return to the original designed power of 12 000 shp, providing a speed of 24 knots compared with 6000 shp and 21 knots in the *Bayntun* Class.

The designed armament was three 3-in dual-purpose guns, four single 20-mm and one twin 40-mm, but several ships were completed without the latter, owing to a shortage of 40-mm mountings, and shipped two additional 20-mm instead. Later additions, both before and after completion, increased the 20-mm armament to ten or 12 singles. Early modifications carried out by the British included an increase in the depth-charge stowage to 200, while later several ships had a single 2-pdr pom-pom fitted as a bow-chaser for use against E-Boats. Wartime modifications resulted in a large number of variations in the light antiaircraft armament fitted: the data below gives the designed armament.

The class was commissioned during 1943-44 and served in the North Atlantic, English Channel and North Sea and with the Russian convoys. A large number were also employed as escorts for the Normandy invasion force. During 1944, 14 were converted into coastal forces control frigates for operations against enemy coastal shipping and E-Boats in conjunction with MTBs, MGBs etc. They operated exclusively in the English Channel and North Sea, being based either at Harwich or at Portsmouth.

They proved very successful in the antisubmarine role and ships of the class shared in the sinking of 25 U-Boats. The most successful were *Duckworth*, which sank two submarines and shared in the destruction of three more, and *Affleck*, which shared in the sinking of five. Two of the class were lost: the *Bickerton*, which was torpedoed by *U 354* in the Barents Sea on August 22, 1944, was so badly damaged that she had to be sunk by the destroyer *Vigilant*; and the *Bullen*, torpedoed by *U 775* northwest of Scotland on December 6, 1944. In addition no less than eight were damaged beyond reasonable repair—the *Duff*, *Dakins* and *Ekins* were damaged by mines, the *Affleck*, *Redmill* and *Whitaker* were torpedoed by submarines, the *Trollope* was torpedoed by an E-Boat and the *Halsted* was torpedoed by a German torpedo boat. However, the *Duff* was reprieved and subsequently repaired. Another, the *Affleck*, and an undamaged unit, the *Hotham*, were converted to floating power stations in 1945 for service in ports where electric power was short. The turbo/generator sets of these vessels made them ideal for this purpose.

All but one of the class, including those damaged, were officially returned to the US between 1945 and 1947. The only exception was *Hotham*, which remained in British service until 1956 when she was returned.

The class consisted of: *Affleck, Aylmer, Balfour, Bentinck, Bentley, Bickerton, Bligh, Braithwaite, Bullen, Byard, Byron, Calder, Conn, Cosby, Cotton, Cranston, Cubitt, Curzon, Dakins, Deane, Duckworth, Duff, Ekins, Essington, Fitzroy, Halsted, Hargood, Holmes, Hotham, Narbrough, Redmill, Retalick, Riou, Rowley, Rupert, Rutherford, Seymour, Stockham, Spragge, Stayner, Thornbrough, Torrington, Trollope, Tyler, Waldegrave, Whitaker.*

Displacement: 1347 tons *Length:* 93.27 m (306 ft) oa *Beam:* 11.22 m (36 ft 9 in) *Draught:* 2.80 m (9 ft 3 in) *Machinery:* 2-shaft turbo-electric drive, 12 000 shp=24 knots *Armament:* 3 3-in (76-mm) (3×1); 2 40-mm (1×2); 4 20-mm (4×1); 1 Hedgehog; 4 depth-charge throwers *Crew:* 186

The *Bentinck* Class frigate *Riou* in 1945. Armament was modified as required: *Riou* here has three 3-in DP, and eight single 20-mm AA guns

IWM

The *Bigbury Bay* Class frigate *St Bride's Bay*. The most obvious difference between the 'Bay' and earlier 'Loch' Classes was the substitution of twin 4-in (102-mm) DP gun mounts for the original singles

IWM

Biber

German midget submarine class. The Biber (beaver) was one of several 'special assault' craft, 'K-Craft' or *kleine Kampfmittel* produced for local defence during the Second World War. With the Molch (salamander) it was the smallest of the seven midgets put into production, being designed for one-man operation.

The Biber was inspired by the British Welman craft, one of which was captured after an abortive attack on Bergen in November 1943. Work began at the Flender yard, Lübeck, in March 1944 on a prototype nicknamed the 'Bunte' boat after the head of the shipyard; its code-name was 'Adam'. Between May and November, 324 Bibers were built, by various firms.

The first operational use of the Biber was on the night of August 29/30, 1944 against the Allied invasion fleet lying off the Normandy beaches, but it produced little result. Further attacks were made during the winter of 1944-45 in the Den Helder area. In the Scheldt Estuary they claimed to have damaged 95 000 tons of shipping between December 1944 and May 1945, but in fact they inflicted relatively little damage while sustaining heavy losses themselves. According to British records Biber and Molch craft made 102 sorties, sank no ships and damaged none, although their mines accounted for 7 ships sunk and 2 damaged, totalling only 16 000 tons in all. To achieve this 70 Bibers and Molchs were sunk.

On January 5, 1945 three Type VIIC U-Boats left Harstadt with Bibers on deck in an unsuccessful attempt to attack the Russian battleship *Arkhanghelsk* (formerly HMS *Royal Sovereign*), which had recently arrived at Murmansk.

When running on the surface the Biber was driven by a petrol motor at a speed of $6\frac{1}{2}$ knots, and could run for 13 hours. When submerged the electric motor drove it at $5\frac{1}{4}$ knots for $2\frac{1}{4}$ hours. The armament comprised two conventional G7e torpedoes slung below the hull.

Other designs were planned, Biber II and Biber III, with two operators and larger hulls, and Biber III in particular had a range of 1770 km (1100 miles) on the surface, which would have made it a more formidable weapon. Neither was built.

Displacement: 6.3 tons (surfaced/submerged) *Length:* 9 m (29 ft 6 in) *Beam:* 1.6 m (5 ft 3 in) *Draught:* 1.45 m (4 ft 9 in) *Machinery:* 1-shaft petrol/electric, 32 ihp/13 hp=$6\frac{1}{2}$/5.3 knots (surfaced/submerged) *Armament:* 2 53-cm (21-in) torpedoes or 2 mines *Crew:* 1

Bigbury Bay

British frigate class. During the latter part of the Second World War the need for antiaircraft vessels led to the modification, while under construction, of a number of 'Loch' Class antisubmarine frigates for antiaircraft service. To distinguish the two types the modified ships were given Bay names in place of the Loch names originally allotted.

The main design changes consisted of the fitting of two twin 4-in (102-mm) DP mountings instead of one single, the addition of an AA director on the bridge and the reduction of the A/S armament, the ships were otherwise basically similar. As completed the armament consisted of a 4-in twin mounting in B and X positions, two twin 40-mm (1.7-in) mountings amidships, two twin 20-mm (0.79-in) AA mountings in the upper bridge wings and a Hedgehog on the forecastle. The 20-mm mountings were later replaced by single 40-mm guns and a few ships had a Squid fitted in place of the Hedgehog.

All the ships of the class were laid down in 1944 and completed during 1945-46 except *Morecambe Bay* and *Mounts Bay* which were suspended at the end of the war and did not complete until 1949. Two, the *Hollesley Bay* and *Runswick Bay*, were cancelled in 1945. Four other suspended vessels, the *Cook* (ex-*Pegwell Bay*), *Dalrymple* (ex-*Luce Bay*), *Dampier* (ex-*Herne Bay*) and *Owen* (ex-*Thurso Bay*), were redesigned as survey vessels and transferred to royal dockyards for completion (first pair at Devonport, second pair at Chatham). They commissioned during 1948-50, carried no armament and displaced 1640 tons.

A further two, the *Alert* (ex-*Dundrum Bay*) and *Surprise* (ex-*Gerrans Bay*), were completed in 1946 as Admiralty yachts/despatch vessels with an armament of one twin 4-in and two 40-mm guns only. Both served as C-in-C's yachts, the *Alert* on the China Station and the *Surprise* in the Mediterranean. The latter vessel also served as the Royal Yacht during the Coronation Review at Spithead in 1953.

The *Bigbury Bay*, *Burghead Bay*, *Morecambe Bay* and *Mounts Bay* were sold to Portugal, the first pair in May 1959 and the second pair in May 1961, and renamed *Pacheco Pereira*, *Alvares Cabral*, *Don Francesco de Almeida* and *Vasco da Gama* respectively. The *Dalrymple* was also sold to Portugal, being renamed *Alfonso de Albuquerque*, while the *Porlock Bay* was sold to Finland and renamed *Matti Kurki*.

The remainder of the frigates were sold for scrap in the late 1950s and early 1960s while the survey vessels and yachts survived in subsidiary roles before being scrapped in the late 1960s and early 1970s.

Bigbury Bay, *Owen*—built by Hall Russell
Cardigan Bay, *Carnarvon Bay*, *Padstow Bay*—built by Henry Robb
Enard Bay, *Surprise*, *Dampier*—built by Smiths Dock
Largo Bay, *Morecambe Bay*, *Mounts Bay*, *Cook*, *Dalrymple*—built by Pickersgill
Veryan Bay, *Burghead Bay*, *Porlock Bay*—built by Charles Hill
Alert, *Cawsand Bay*—built by Blyth Dry Dock
St Austell Bay, *Whitsand Bay*, *Widemouth Bay*, *St Brides Bay*, *Start Bay*, *Tremadoc Bay*, *Wigtown Bay*—built by Harland and Wolff

Displacement: 1580 tons (standard), 1590 tons (*Alert* & *Surprise*) *Length:* 93.67 m (307 ft 4 in) oa *Beam:* 11.73 m (38 ft 6 in) *Draught:* 3.89 m (12 ft 9 in) *Machinery:* 2-shaft triple-expansion engines, 5500 ihp=19.5 knots *Armament:* 4 4-in (102-mm) (2×2); 4 40-mm (1.7-in) (2×2); 4 20-mm (0.79-in) (2×2); 1 Hedgehog ATW *Crew:* 157

Bismarck

German battleship. Under the terms of the Anglo-German Naval Treaty of 1935, Germany was permitted to build up her naval strength to 35% of that of the Royal Navy. Shortly afterwards the German government decided on the construction of two new battleships which under the terms of the Treaty were limited to a maximum displacement of 35 000 tons standard. The ships were to be armed with a twin 38-cm (15-in) gun mounting which had been under development by Krupp since 1934. Design work, based on studies started in 1933, began almost immediately and it soon became clear that the requirements for the new ships could not be accommodated within the specified 35 000 tons. The Treaty terms were therefore ignored and the final design was for ships exceeding 40 000 tons. In 1938 the Treaty limit was raised to 45 000 tons, which theoretically legalized the design, but by her action Germany had gained a two-year advantage.

Foto Druppel

The *Bismarck* seen from the *Prinz Eugen* at the beginning of her final cruise on May 20, 1941. She has camouflage stripes painted on her hull and superstructure to break up her silhouette

The design of the new ships, which became the *Bismarck* and *Tirpitz*, was a mixture of both advanced and dated features, for although the German steel and armament industries had made substantial progress since 1919, ideas on general battleship construction had changed little. The best features were the use of a new high-tensile steel in a hull that was 90% welded, which resulted in a substantial saving of weight, the fitting of a very advanced fire-control system and an excellent armament. The beam was comparatively wide, which theoretically allowed more space for underwater protection compartments abreast of the magazines and machinery, but this area was not utilized to its full advantage and the structural arrangements for torpedo defence differed little from those employed in the First World War. The distribution of the armour and the machinery layout was similarly reminiscent of First World War practice and did not compare well with the systems employed in the battleships of other naval powers. The machinery itself, although efficient, absorbed a large amount of space and weight, this being partly due to a substantial amount of auxiliary machinery which included one of the better features—a large generating capacity of 7910 kW. The oil fuel capacity was also high at 6500 tons (a figure exceeded only by the US battleships, designed to operate in the vast area of the Pacific) which gave an endurance of 9280 nautical miles at 16 knots.

Contracts for the two ships were placed in 1936, the *Bismarck* being laid down on July 1 of that year at the Blohm und Voss yard in

The *Bismarck* showing the profile, topsides and hold plan. The honeycomb of bulkheads enabled her to stay afloat despite severe shell damage, and she had finally to be sunk by torpedoes

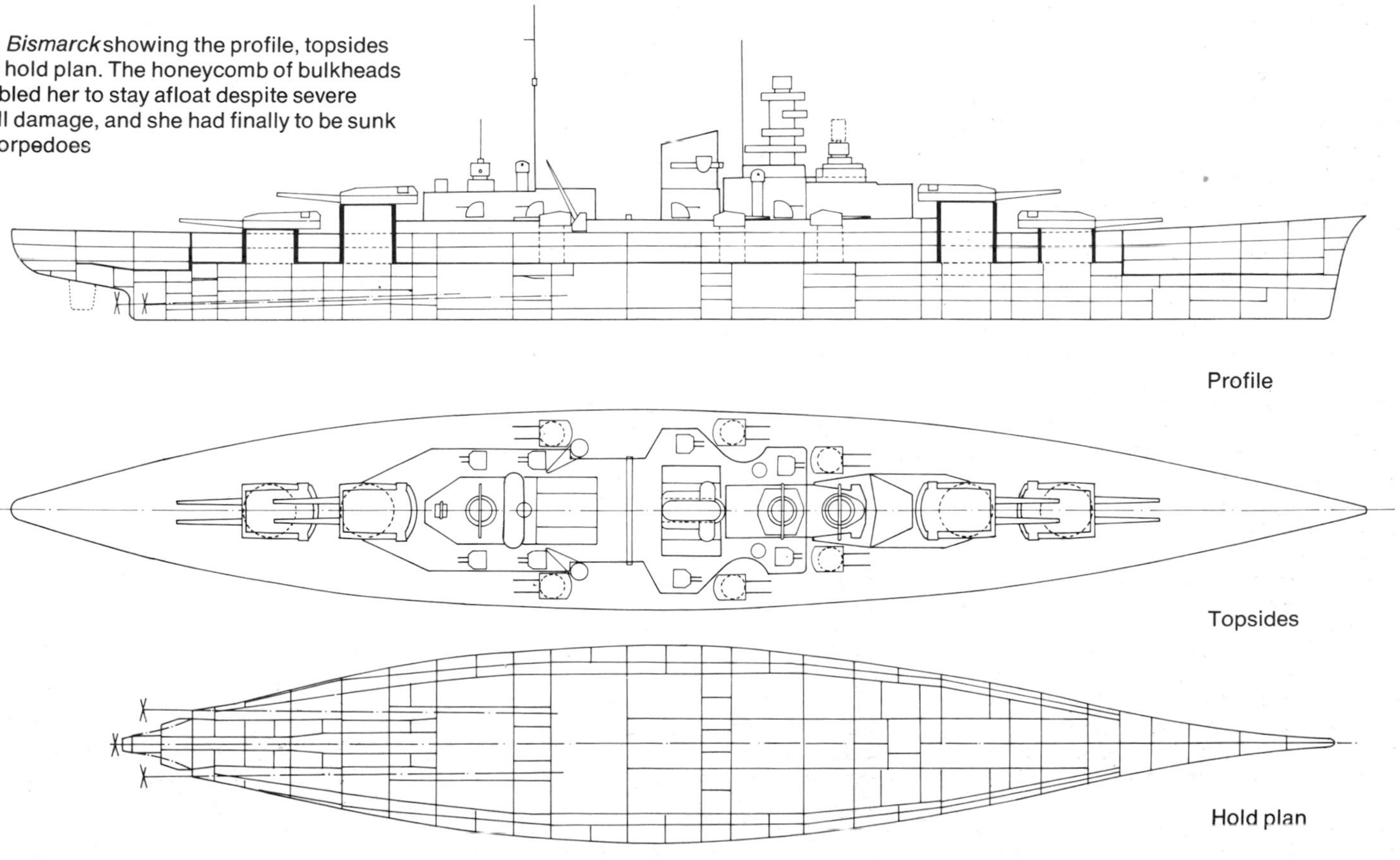

Profile

Topsides

Hold plan

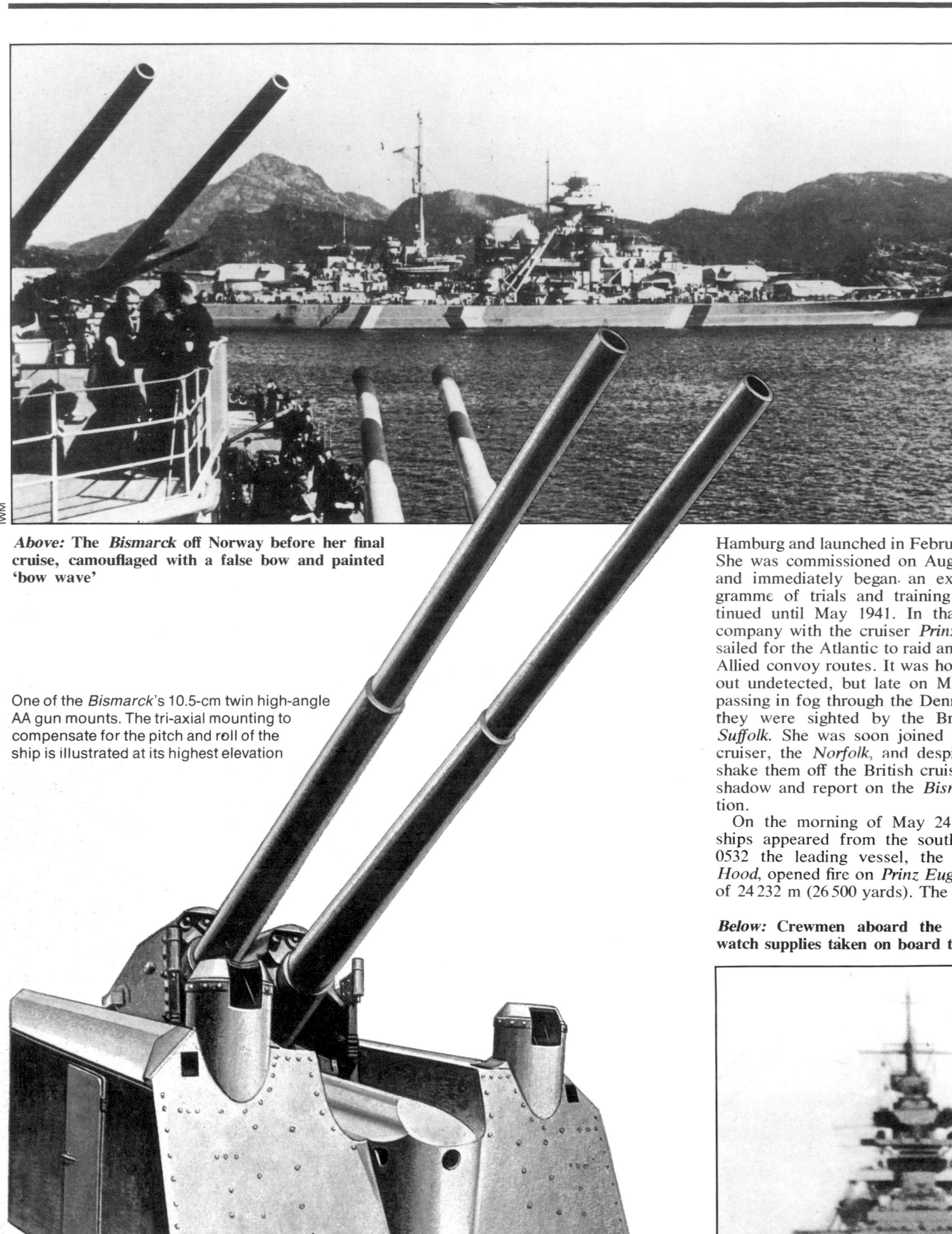

IWM

Above: **The *Bismarck* off Norway before her final cruise, camouflaged with a false bow and painted 'bow wave'**

One of the *Bismarck*'s 10.5-cm twin high-angle AA gun mounts. The tri-axial mounting to compensate for the pitch and roll of the ship is illustrated at its highest elevation

Hamburg and launched in February 14, 1939. She was commissioned on August 24, 1940 and immediately began an extensive programme of trials and training which continued until May 1941. In that month, in company with the cruiser *Prinz Eugen*, she sailed for the Atlantic to raid and disrupt the Allied convoy routes. It was hoped to break out undetected, but late on May 23, while passing in fog through the Denmark Straits, they were sighted by the British cruiser *Suffolk*. She was soon joined by a second cruiser, the *Norfolk*, and despite efforts to shake them off the British cruisers began to shadow and report on the *Bismarck*'s position.

On the morning of May 24, two heavy ships appeared from the southeast and at 0532 the leading vessel, the battlecruiser *Hood*, opened fire on *Prinz Eugen* at a range of 24 232 m (26 500 yards). The second ship,

Below: **Crewmen aboard the *Prinz Eugen* watch supplies taken on board the *Bismarck***

IWM

Above: The 10.5-cm Flak turret at its maximum angle of roll. The tri-axial mounting not only ensured that the gun remained on target when the ship was in a heavy sea, but also gave the gun crew a stable platform

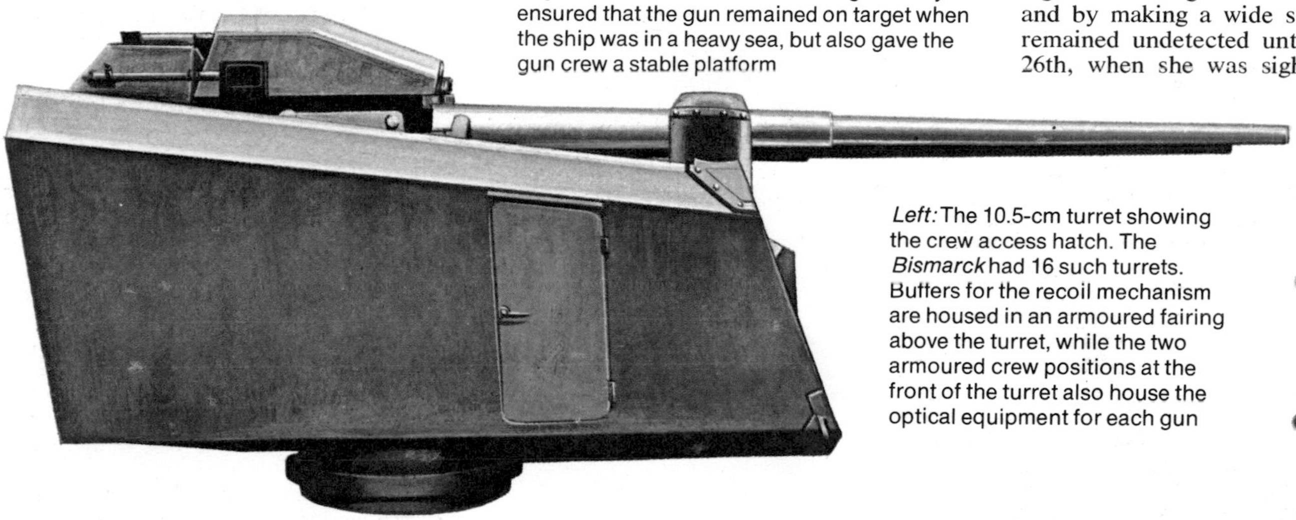

the battleship *Prince of Wales*, opened fire shortly afterwards while the *Bismarck* and *Prinz Eugen* replied at 0535 hrs, both firing on the *Hood*. The *Bismarck* straddled her target with her third and fifth salvos, the latter achieving one or two hits. At 0601 hrs the after magazines of the British flagship exploded. She broke in two and sank in three minutes, leaving only three survivors. Fire was shifted to *Prince of Wales* but after about ten minutes the British ship broke off the action and retired.

Bismarck had been hit by three 14-in (355-mm) shells from the *Prince of Wales*—one damaged and contaminated an oil fuel tank, another hit the side armour and caused a leak which later put one boiler-room and one dynamo out of action, while the third hit did no important damage. The contaminated oil reduced the ship's endurance and the loss of one boiler-room reduced the speed by 2 knots, so it was decided to call off the operation and make for St Nazaire for repairs. The *Prinz Eugen* was undamaged, and later that day she separated from the *Bismarck* and continued into the Atlantic.

On the evening of May 24, *Bismarck* was attacked by Swordfish aircraft from the carrier *Victorious* and was hit by one torpedo, but no serious damage was done. Later that night she managed to evade her shadowers, and by making a wide sweep to the west, remained undetected until 1030 hrs on the 26th, when she was sighted by a Catalina

Left: The 10.5-cm turret showing the crew access hatch. The *Bismarck* had 16 such turrets. Buffers for the recoil mechanism are housed in an armoured fairing above the turret, while the two armoured crew positions at the front of the turret also house the optical equipment for each gun

flying boat of Coastal Command. This aircraft had been directed into the area after signals from the *Bismarck* had been intercepted and decoded on an Enigma machine. That night she was again attacked by Swordfish aircraft, this time from the carrier *Ark Royal,* and was hit by two torpedoes. One hit

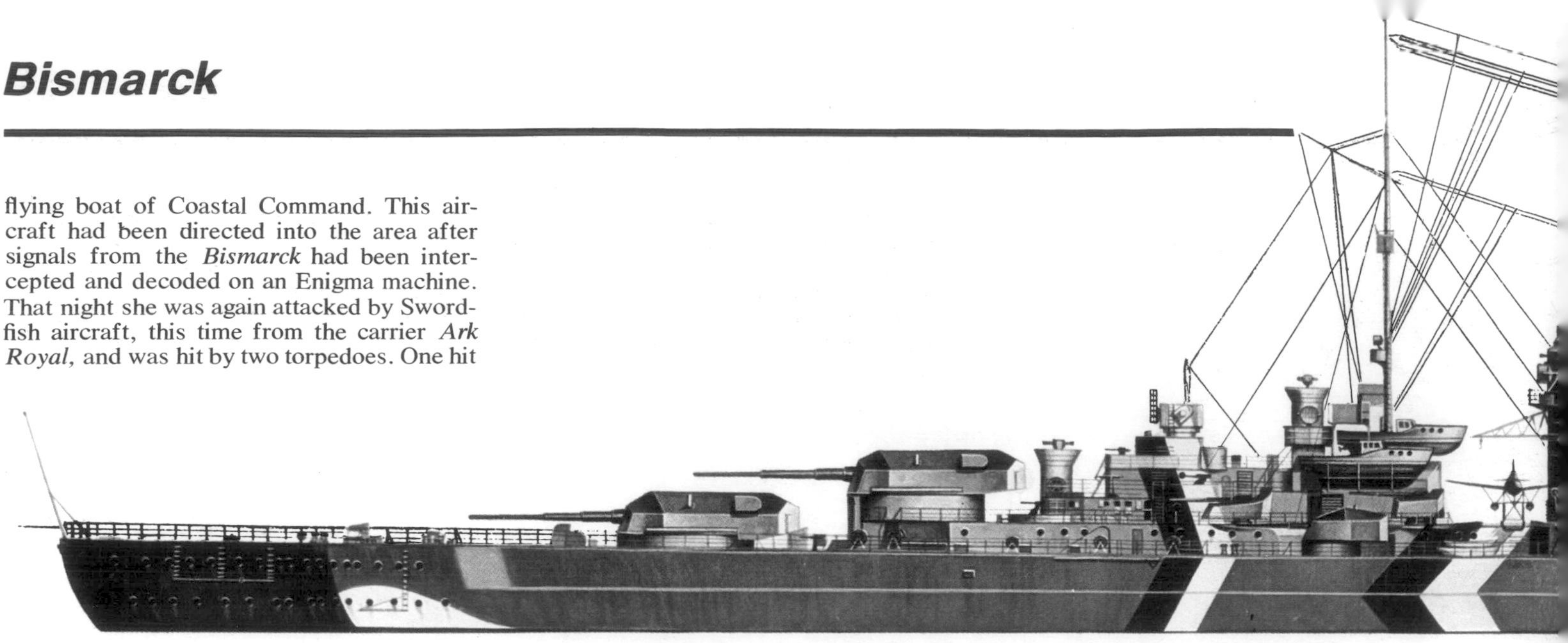

amidships caused only minor damage but the second hit the stern and seriously damaged the steering gear. With both rudders jammed 15° to port she began steaming in circles, and then, using her propeller revolutions, started steering an erratic course to the northwest—towards the oncoming enemy. During the night she was attacked by destroyers of the 4th Flotilla, but they achieved little apart from the disruption of attempts to repair the steering gear.

On the morning of May 27, 1941 two battleships appeared on the northern horizon, the *King George V* (Flag, Admiral Tovey, C-in-C, Home Fleet) and *Rodney.* The latter vessel opened fire at 0847 hrs, followed one minute later by the flagship. At 0849 *Bismarck* replied and straddled the *Rodney* with her second salvo. However, she was straddled herself by *Rodney*'s third and fourth salvos and a hit from the latter put A turret out of action. Five minutes later, at 0857, a direct hit put B turret out of action. Another hit destroyed the forward command post, killing most of the senior officers, and shortly afterwards the main fire-control positions, both forward and aft, were also destroyed.

By 0920 only X turret, under local control, remained in action and by 0940 the ship was silent. First *Rodney* and then *King George V* closed and fired on her at the point-blank range of 2743-3658 m (3000-4000 yards). When the British battleships finally ceased fire she was a floating wreck, very low in the water and on fire. At 1025 the cruiser *Dorsetshire* fired two torpedoes into her starboard side and, ten minutes later, a third into her port side. She heeled over and began to sink by the stern, and at 1040, her flag still flying, she capsized and sank in position 48°10′N, 16°12′W. There were 118 survivors.

See also *Tirpitz.*

Displacement: 41 700 tons *Length:* 251 m (823 ft 6 in) oa *Beam:* 36 m (118 ft) *Draught:* 9.3 m (30 ft 7 in) *Machinery:* 3-shaft, geared steam turbines, 150 000 shp=31 knots *Protection:* 322 mm (12.6 in) sides; 360 mm (14 in) turrets; 220 mm (9 in) barbettes; 51-120 mm (2-4.7 in) decks *Armament:* 8 38-cm (15-in) (4×2); 12 15-cm (5.9-in) (6×2); 16 10.5-cm (4.1-in) AA (8×2); 16 37-mm AA (8×2); 12 20-mm AA *Aircraft:* 6 *Crew:* 1962

The *Bismarck,* launched on February 14, 1939, is seen here during her extensive trials, which were carried out from Kiel, in the Baltic, between August 1940 and May 1941

Bismarck

The *Bismarck* was one of three *Schlachtschiffe* capital ships projected by the German navy before 1939. Two were built—the other was *Tirpitz*—and one was broken up on the stocks in 1948-57. They were the heaviest vessels built by the Germans but to comply with the Washington Treaty their weight was originally announced as 35 000 tons. In reality the *Bismarck* displaced 41 700 tons and the *Tirpitz* 42 900 tons. While the former had a brief but dramatic career during which she sank the battle cruiser *Hood*, the latter remained in Norwegian waters until she was sunk in 1944

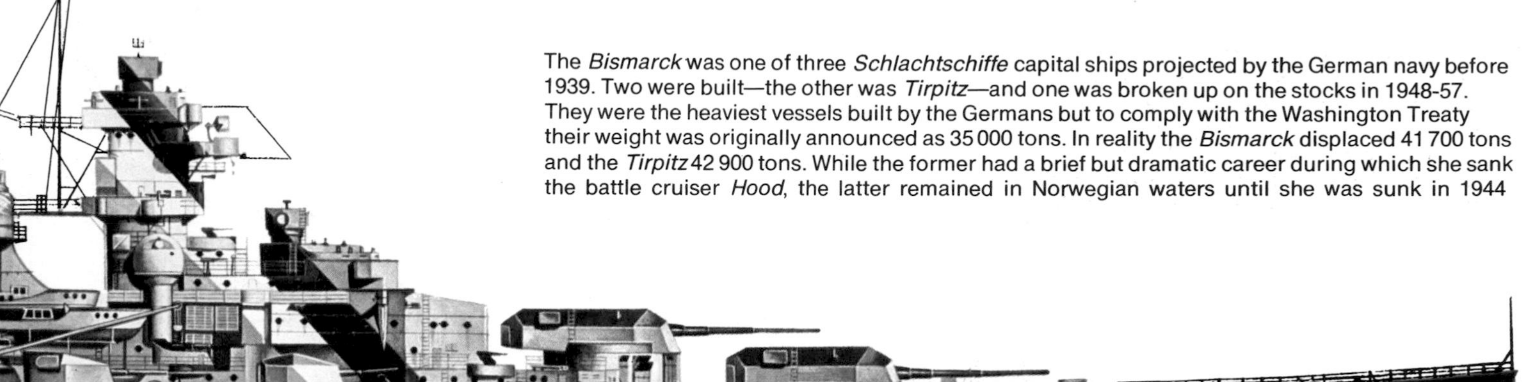

Foto Druppel

HMS *Narbada*, a Royal Indian Navy *Black Swan* Class sloop. Completed in 1943, she was transferred to the Pakistan navy in 1948 and renamed *Jhelm*

IWM

Black Swan

British sloop class. As originally designed, these ships were almost identical to the previous *Egret* Class except that the twin 4-in (102-mm) gun mounting in Y position was replaced by a quadruple 2-pdr pom-pom.

The class falls into two groups: the *Black Swan, Erne, Flamingo, Ibis, Jumna* and *Sutlej* were constructed under the 1938-39 Programmes and completed during 1940-41; the second group, the *Whimbrel, Wild Goose, Woodpecker, Wren, Godavari* and *Narbada* were constructed under the 1940 Programme and completed during 1943. The ships of the first group were completed to the original design, the only exception being the Indian vessels, which mounted a quadruple 0.5-in (13-mm) gun mounting in place of the quadruple pom-pom.

The RN ships of the second group were fitted with a heavier A/S armament and the pom-pom mounting was omitted to compensate for the additional weight. The light AA armament was modified progressively as the war continued and eventually all the RN vessels mounted six 20-mm (0.79-in) (2×2+2×1) and four 40-mm (1.57-in) (2×2).

The Indian vessels were similarly fitted but the 40-mm were not mounted in *Jumna* and *Sutlej*. The earlier ships were completed with a pole foremast which initially was replaced by a tripod and then a lattice mast. The ships of the second group were completed with lattice masts. All ships were fitted with air warning, surface warning and AA gunnery radar sets.

The ships proved very successful as antisubmarine escorts, the RN ships serving mainly in the North Atlantic, while those of the RIN operated in the Indian Ocean and Far East. Two of the class were lost: the *Ibis*, sunk in the Western Mediterranean on November 11, 1942, by Italian aircraft; and the *Woodpecker*, which foundered in tow on February 27, 1944, seven days after being torpedoed by *U 764* in the North Atlantic.

Four of the class were transferred to other navies: the *Whimbrel* was sold to Egypt in 1949 and renamed *El Malek Farouq*, the *Flamingo* was sold to West Germany in 1959

HMS *Cygnet*, a Modified *Black Swan* Class sloop which incorporated such additions as the ten 20-mm guns for close-range defence introduced on later *Black Swans*. The crew was increased from 180 to 192 and the displacement increased from 1250 to 1350 tons. *Cygnet* was scrapped at Rosyth in May 1956

IWM

and renamed *Graf Spee*, and the *Godavari* and *Narbada* were transferred to Pakistan in 1948, being renamed *Sind* and *Jhelm* respectively. The *Erne* became the RNVR drillship *Wessex* in 1952 and the remaining RN units were sold for scrap in 1956.

Black Swan, Flamingo, Whimbrel, Wild Goose—built by Yarrow
Erne, Ibis—built by Furness
Jumna, Sutlej*, Woodpecker, Wren*—built by Denny
Godavari, Narbada**—built by Thornycroft
*Royal Indian Navy vessels.

Displacement: 1250 tons, standard *Length:* 91.3 m (299 ft 6 in) oa *Beam:* 11.4 m (37 ft 6 in) *Draught:* 2.6 m (8 ft 6 in) *Machinery:* 2-shaft geared steam turbines, 4300 shp = 19.75 knots *Armament:* 6 4-in (102-mm) (3×2); 4 2-pdr (1×4) *Crew:* 180

Black Swan, modified

British sloop class. These ships differed very little from the *Black Swan* Class but incorporated in their original design all the modifications which had been made to the earlier ships. These included a uniform close-range armament of ten 20-mm (0.79-in) guns (4×2, 2×1), although in the event these were not always available and the earliest units completed during 1942-43 carried a variety of weapons. These ships were later modified to the designed armament, and it was fitted as standard in the ships completing during 1943-44. Towards the end of the war several vessels were fitted with two twin 40-mm (1.57-in) in place of the two twin 20-mm amidships, and after the war two single 40-mm were substituted for the remaining 20-mm, this becoming the standard postwar outfit. The *Snipe, Sparrow* and *Actaeon* were not completed until after the war, while a further five, which were still under construction in 1945, were cancelled.

Two of the class were lost during the war: the *Kite*, torpedoed by *U 344* in the Greenland Sea on August 21, 1944; and the *Lapwing*, torpedoed by *U 716* off the Kola Inlet on March 20, 1945. Two more were damaged beyond repair: the *Chanticleer*, torpedoed by *U 238* in the Atlantic on November 18, 1943; and the *Lark*, torpedoed by *U 968* in the Kola Inlet on February 17, 1945. *Chanticleer* was scrapped in 1946 but *Lark* was raised by the Russians and repaired, serving in the Soviet fleet as *Neptun* until scrapped in 1960. The class contained two famous ships: the *Starling*, which shared in the sinking of 16 German submarines while part of the 2nd Support Group during 1943-44; and the *Amethyst*, which escaped from the Yangtse River in very difficult circumstances in 1949, having come close to being trapped and destroyed by the Chinese Communist army artillery batteries on the banks of the river.

Three ships, the *Actaeon, Hart* and *Mermaid*, were sold to West Germany in 1958 and renamed *Hipper, Scheer* and *Scharnhorst* respectively. The remaining RN ships were sold for scrap between 1955 and 1963 while the German ships were sold for scrap during the late 1960s and early 1970s. The two RIN ships were still in service at the end of 1976.

Actaeon, Magpie, Peacock—built by Thornycroft
Alacrity, Chanticleer, Crane, Hind, Mermaid, Opossum, Snipe, Sparrow—built by Denny
Amethyst, Hart—built by Stephen
Cygnet, Kite—built by Cammell Laird
Lapwing, Lark—built by Scotts
Modeste, Nereide—built by Chatham dockyard
Pheasant, Redpole, Cauvery (RIN), *Kistna* (RIN)—built by Yarrow
Starling—built by Fairfield

Displacement: 1350 tons *Length:* 91.3 m (299 ft 6 in) oa *Beam:* 11.4 m (37 ft 6 in) *Draught:* 2.7 m (9 ft) *Machinery:* 2-shaft, geared steam turbines, 4300 shp – 19 knots *Armament:* 6 4-in (102-mm) (3×2); 10 20-mm (0.79-in) (4×2+2×1) *Crew:* 192

Blackwood

British frigate class. The 15 ships of the *Blackwood* Class were constructed between 1952 and 1959. Described as Type 14 2nd Class antisubmarine frigates, they were designed for a specialized role in order to provide a small vessel that could be built cheaply and in large numbers. The hull was of simple design using prefabricated construction, the majority of the useful load-carrying capacity being turned over to antisubmarine weapons. Their A/S qualities were therefore comparatively good whilst their usefulness in other roles was poor. The gun armament, in particular, was very weak and was the cause of much criticism, while the restrictive hull left little room for any additional equipment. Apart from the designed role, the ships proved useful as fishery-protection vessels and they have been used extensively for this purpose.

Modifications to the class have been few. In the late 1950s the hulls were strengthened after weaknesses were revealed in six vessels on fishery patrol off Iceland. Since then the ships have proved very seaworthy and able to stand up well to severe weather. The *Blackwood, Exmouth, Malcolm* and *Palliser* were completed with twin torpedo tubes on each side of the upper deck (for A/S torpedoes) but these were later removed. The single 40-mm (1.57-in) gun on the quarterdeck was removed from all ships, with the exception of those serving in the Royal Indian Navy.

During 1966-68 the *Exmouth* was re-engined at Chatham dockyard with gas turbine machinery, the intention being that she would serve as a test-bed for the propulsion plants of ships then being designed. Two Bristol Proteus cruising turbines, each of 3250 hp, were fitted in the engine room while the main plant, a Bristol Olympus gas turbine of 22 500 hp, was fitted in the former boiler room. Apart from a new squat funnel, fitted further aft of the original, and the addition of a large engine room vent amidships, her appearance was little altered. The ship was given an extended work-up period, to allow her engine room complement time to master the complexities. Trials during 1968-69 proved successful and led to the introduction of this type of machinery in the *Sheffield* and *Amazon* Classes.

A large number of the Class have recently been scrapped, and *Keppel* is in reserve. Only four (excluding *Exmouth*) now remain in service—the *Dundas, Hardy, Duncan* and *Keppel*.

Blackwood, Duncan—built by Thornycroft
Dundas, Exmouth, Grafton, Kuthar (RIN), *Khukri* (RIN)—built by White
Hardy, Keppel, Malcolm—built by Yarrow
Murry, Palliser, Kirpan (RIN)—built by Stephen
Pellew, Russell—built by Swan Hunter

Displacement: 1180 tons, standard *Length:* 94.49 m (310 ft) oa Beam: 10.05 m (33 ft) *Draught:* 3.04 m (10 ft) *Machinery:* 1-shaft, geared steam turbines, 15 000 shp × 27.8 knots *Armament:* 3 40-mm (1.57-in) (3×1); 2 Limbo A/S mortars *Crew:* 111

Blankney

British escort destroyers. Ordered under the Emergency War Programme, the *Blankney* Class were the second group, or Type II, of the 'Hunt' Class escort destroyers. The original design was the same as that for Type I, the *Atherstone* Class, but the beam was subsequently increased by 0.76 m (2 ft 6 in) to improve the level of stability which was deficient in the previous group. Thus while the *Atherstone* Class had to sacrifice a twin 4-in (102-mm) mounting to reduce topweight, the *Blankney* Class retained the designed armament of three twin 4-in mountings. The construction of three of the class, *Blencathra, Brocklesby* and *Liddesdale*, however, continued without the modification, and strictly speaking they belong to Type I although they number among the 36 ships of the second group.

The ships were launched during 1940-42 and completed during 1941-43. The *Bedale, Oakley* (1) and *Silverton* were commissioned by Polish crews and renamed *Slazak, Kujawiak* and *Krakowiak* respectively, but the name *Oakley* was retained in the Royal Navy by renaming the *Tickham*. The *Exmoor* (2) was originally named *Burton* but was renamed after the original *Exmoor* (of Type I) had been sunk. During 1943-44 the *Avon Vale, Bramham, Cowdray* and *Hursley* were transferred to Greece and renamed *Aegean, Themistoklis, Admiral Hastings* and *Kriti* respectively.

During the war the class served mainly in the Mediterranean, where their AA armament was of great value, but also where seven of the class were lost. The first was *Heythrop* which, torpedoed and badly damaged off Sollum by the German submarine *U 625*, had to be sunk by the escort destroyer *Eridge* on March 20, 1942. Four days later the *Southwold* was mined and sunk off Malta. On June 12, 1942 the *Grove* was torpedoed and sunk by the German submarine *U 77*. The *Kujawiak* (ex-*Oakley*) was mined off Malta on June 15 and foundered on the following day while in tow. The *Puckeridge* was torpedoed and sunk off Gibraltar by the German submarine *U 617* on September 6, 1943. On October 22, 1943, the *Harworth* was mined and sunk off Kalymnos, and on November 13, 1943 the *Silverton* was sunk by a glider bomb off Kos.

In addition to these war losses the *Eridge* became a constructive total loss after being torpedoed by a German MTB in the eastern Mediterranean in August 1942. She was subsequently used as an accommodation ship at Alexandria until scrapped in 1946. The *Cowdray* came close to a similar fate in November 1942 when she was bombed and beached in Algiers Bay, but she was later salvaged and towed home to Chatham for repair and refit.

In 1945 the two remaining Polish-manned ships were returned and reverted to their original names. The four taken over by Greece were retained by that country to be joined by a fifth unit, the *Lauderdale,* which was transferred in 1946 and renamed *Aigaion.* All five were officially returned during 1958-59 and sold for scrap shortly afterwards. Three were sold to Norway: the *Badsworth* (renamed *Arendal*) in 1946, the *Zetland* (renamed *Tromso*) in 1952 and the *Beaufort* (renamed *Haugesund*) in 1954. Another three, the *Blackmore, Exmoor* and *Calpe,* were sold to Denmark in 1952-53, being renamed *Esbern Snare, Valdemar Sejr* and *Rolf Krake* respectively. Three were transferred to the Royal Indian Navy in 1953, the *Bedale, Chiddingfold* and *Lamerton,* renamed *Godavari, Ganga* and *Gomati* respectively. The last unit to go abroad was the *Oakley,* which was sold to West Germany in 1958 and renamed *Gneisenau.*

Of the ships that remained in British service the *Liddesdale* was scrapped in 1948 and the majority of the remainder followed during 1955-59. However, the *Brocklesby* survived until 1968 as a trials ship. Most of the ships in other navies were scrapped during the 1960s, but the three in the Indian Navy were still in service at the end of 1976.

See also *Atherstone* Class and *Brecon* Class.

Avon Vale, Blankney—built by J. Brown
Badsworth, Beaufort, Blencathra, Brocklesby—built by Cammell Laird
Bedale, Bicester—built by Hawthorn Leslie
Blackmore, Bramham, Croome, Dulverton—built by Stephen
Calpe, Eridge, Exmoor, Farndale, Grove, Heythrop, Harsley, Lamerton—built by Swan Hunter
Chiddingfold, Cowdray—built by Scott's
Harworth, Liddesdale, Middleton, Oakley (1)—built by Vickers Armstrong (Tyne)
Lauderdale, Ledbury—built by Thornycroft
Puckeridge, Silverton, Southwold, Tetcott—built by White
Oakley (2), *Wheatland, Wilton, Zetland*—built by Yarrow

Note: Particulars of *Blencathra, Brocklesby* and *Liddesdale* as for the *Atherstone* Class.

Displacement: 1050 tons (standard) *Length:* 85.3 m (280 ft 0 in) oa *Beam:* 9.6 m (31 ft 6 in) *Draught:* 2.4 m (7 ft 9 in) *Machinery:* 2-shaft geared steam turbines, 19000 shp=27 knots *Armament:* 6 4-in (102-mm) (3×2); 4 2-pdr (1×4); 2 20-mm (0.79-in) (2×1) *Crew:* 168

Bogue

American escort carrier class. During the Battle of the Atlantic it rapidly became obvious that aircraft were vital for the struggle against the U-Boats. One way of providing air cover over a convoy was to convert a merchant ship into a small aircraft carrier. The Royal Navy proved how effective this could be with the *Audacity,* and before she was sunk the Americans were already building the *Long Island,* their first escort carrier, and accepting orders from the British for more (*Archer, Avenger* etc).

A large class of 21 improved versions of the *Avenger* were ordered in May 1942, but soon after the order 11 were transferred to the Royal Navy, becoming the *Attacker* and her sisters. The remainder served with the US Navy as the *Bogue* Class.

Though all the ships of this class utilized merchant ship hulls which had already been laid down, they were not very far advanced, and so a more satisfactory conversion was possible than with the original escort carriers. The hangar ran for most of the length of the vessel and was served by two lifts. *Bogue, Card* and *Core* had the luxury of two catapults.

A raised forecastle made for better seakeeping, and the amount and distribution of the armament was an improvement on the earlier ships. Radar was incorporated in the design from the start. The original two 5-in (127-mm), four twin Bofors 40-mm (1.57-in) and 12 single Oerlikon 20-mm (0.79-in) were later supplemented by the addition of four twin 40-mm and up to ten more 20-mm. With their bigger hangars these ships could operate 28 aircraft, or accommodate up to 90 when in use as aircraft transports.

Altamaha, Barnes, Breton, Copahee, and *Nassau* all spent their war service in the unglamorous but essential aircraft-ferry role in the Pacific, though most contributed aircraft to one or more of the raids in support of landings. *Breton,* for example, helped in the capture of Saipan, the Battle of the Philippine Sea, one of the raids on the Bonins, and the bombardment of Okinawa. However, she was the only one of her class to see any action in the Pacific, most of the close support to landings being supplied by the later classes of escort carrier.

Those ships of the class to serve in the Atlantic also did some ferrying of aircraft to Europe, but their main contribution to victory was a more active one. They made ideal centres for a hunter-killer group of escorts, and achieved a good score of U-Boats sunk, particularly in the Central Atlantic, aided by the decoding of German messages.

Aircraft from these carriers sank the following submarines (some of the claims were shared with surface escorts, who also sunk a number themselves):

Bogue—U 569, U 217, U 118, U 527, U 575, U 1229, U 152 (Japanese), *U 86, U 172, U 850.*
Card—U 177, U 664, U 525, U 847, U 460, U 422, U 402, U 584.
Core—U 487, U 67, U 84, U 185, U 378.
Block Island—U 220, U 1059, U 801, U 66.
Croatan—U 856, U 490, U 154.

Block Island was torpedoed and sunk in May 1944 by *U 549,* which was promptly sunk herself by the carriers' escorts. *Croatan* distinguished herself by initiating the first night flights from an escort carrier in late 1943. The Atlantic escort carriers were transferred to the Pacific in 1945, in time to take part in Operation Magic Carpet, the return of prisoners of war and troops to the US at the end of the war.

In 1955 the class was reclassified as escort helicopter carriers (CVHE). In 1960-61 five were scrapped, but the *Breton, Card, Core* and *Croatan* had already been converted to aircraft and cargo ferry ships (designation CVU, later AKV) equipped with large derricks for handling aircraft. In this role they were operated by the US MSTS transport service until the early 1970s, and then scrapped. The *Card* had been mined at Saigon by the Vietcong and sank, but was later raised and repaired.

Displacement: 11000 tons (standard), 15400 tons (full load), 7800 GRT *Length:* 151.12 m (495 ft 9 in) *Beam:* 21.12 m (69 ft 6 in) hull, 33.98 m (111 ft 6 in) flight deck *Draught:* 7.92 m (26 ft) max *Machinery:* 1-shaft geared steam turbines, 8500 shp=18 knots *Armament:* 2 5-in (127-mm)/38 cal DP (2×1); 8 40-mm AA (4×2); 12 20-mm AA (12×1); 28 aircraft (90 as ferry carrier) *Crew:* 890

Bonaventure

Canadian aircraft carrier. Originally laid down as the *Powerful* on November 27, 1943, this vessel was one of the Royal Navy's *Majestic* Class light fleet carriers of the 1942 Programme. She was launched at the Harland and Wolff yard in Belfast on February 27, 1945, but shortly after the end of the war her construction was suspended and her hull laid up at Belfast.

In 1952 she was purchased by Canada and renamed *Bonaventure,* construction, to a modified design, being resumed in July of that year. Alterations were mainly aimed at making her suitable for the operation of modern jet aircraft and included a $7\frac{1}{2}$°-angled flight deck, improved arrester gear, steam

HMS *Brocklesby* steaming at high speed. Although a member of the *Blankney* Class, the *Brocklesby,* along with *Blencathra* and *Liddlesdale,* was completed with the 'Hunt' Type I armament of only four 4-in (102-mm) guns. These three also had a smaller complement—146 against 168—and displaced 50 tons less than the other members of the *Blankney* Class

The USS *Bogue* (CVE.9), an escort carrier whose hull was laid down as the merchant ship *Steel Advocate*. She was launched January 15, 1942 after construction at the Seattle-Tacoma (Tacoma) and Allis-Chalmers yards. After service in the Atlantic, during which her aircraft assisted in the destruction of five U-Boats, she was scrapped in Japan in November 1960. Carriers of the *Bogue* Class served in the Atlantic and Pacific and subsequently as AKVs in Vietnam where *Card* was mined and sunk by the Vietcong

Hull no	name	launched	completed	builder
AVG.9	***Bogue*** (ex-*Steel Advocate*)	1/1942	9/1942	Seattle-Tacoma
AVG.11	***Card***	2/1942	11/1942	Seattle-Tacoma
AVG.12	***Copahee***	10/1941	6/1942	Seattle-Tacoma
AVG.13	***Core***	5/1942	12/1942	Seattle-Tacoma
AVG.16	***Nassau***	4/1942	8/1942	Seattle-Tacoma
AVG.18	***Altamaha***	5/1942	9/1942	Seattle-Tacoma
AVG.20	***Barnes***	5/1942	2/1943	Seattle-Tacoma
AVG.21	***Block Island***	6/1942	3/1943	Seattle-Tacoma
AVG.25	***Croatan***	8/1942	4/1943	Seattle-Tacoma

catapult and a mirror landing sight. In addition, her flight deck and elevators were strengthened so that she could operate heavier aircraft, the funnel and bridge were remodelled, lattice masts were fitted, and US-pattern fully-automatic twin 3-in (76-mm) dual-purpose guns were substituted for the designed armament.

To equip their new carrier the Canadians purchased 39 McDonnell F2H-3 Banshee fighters from the US. They also expanded their anti-submarine capability with the manufacture in Canada of 70 Grumman S2FI Tracker aircraft, some of which were intended to operate from the *Bonaventure*.

The ship completed on January 17, 1957, replacing the carrier *Magnificent* (which had been on loan from the RN since 1946), and her first aircraft joined her while on acceptance trials. In 1962 it was decided that Canada's maritime air force should turn over to antisubmarine work only. The Banshees

Royal Navy

were abandoned and the *Bonaventure* was re-equipped to operate as an A/S carrier with ten Tracker aircraft and ten helicopters. At about the same time two of her twin 3-in (76-mm) gun mountings were removed. She operated in this role for a few years before being placed in reserve and eventually was sold for scrap in 1971.

See also *Majestic* Class.

Displacement: 16 000 tons *Length:* 219.45 m (720 ft 0 in) *Beam:* 39.01 m (128 ft 0 in) max, flight deck; 24.44 m (80 ft 3 in) hull *Draught:* 7.62 m (25 ft 0 in) *Machinery:* 2-shaft geared steam turbines, 42 000 shp=24 knots *Armament:* 8 3-in (76-mm) AA (4×2); 3 6-pdr (3×1) saluting guns *Aircraft:* 34 max *Crew:* 1370

Bravo

Soviet patrol submarine class. The diesel-propelled *Bravo* Class patrol submarines made their first appearance in 1968. At least four were built at Soviet northern and Baltic yards between 1968 and 1974, with a possible two more reported as having been built since.

No photographs of the *Bravo* Class submarine have been released, but drawings giving an indication of the general shape which this class may be expected to take have appeared in a number of authoritative Western naval publications. These drawings show that the beam-to-length ratio is larger than normal for a conventionally-powered submarine, which, it is estimated, accounts in part for the large displacement for such a comparatively short hull length.

However, the role of the *Bravo* Class submarine is not clear. As one is attached to each of the main Soviet fleets, it is believed that these vessels are used as 'padded targets' for torpedo and antisubmarine weapon firings during manoeuvres.

Displacement: 2500/2800 (surfaced/submerged) *Length:* 70 m (229 ft 7 in) *Beam:* 7.5 m (24 ft 9 in) *Draught:* 4.5 m (14 ft 9 in) *Machinery:* Diesel/electric *Speed:* 16 knots submerged *Armament:* 6 21-in (53-cm) torpedo tubes

Brecon

British escort destroyer class. In 1938, at the request of the Admiralty, Thornycroft produced a design for an escort destroyer of similar type to the 'Hunt' Class, which was then in the early design stage. Thornycroft's design was rejected by the Admiralty, but in 1940, after being reworked several times to meet official requirements, a mutually acceptable design was produced. However, it was of a mildly innovatory nature, which is possibly why the conservative Admiralty ordered only two of what was to become Type IV of the 'Hunt' Class.

Constructed under the 1940 Programme, both vessels were laid down in February 1941 at the Thornycroft yard in Southampton and launched in 1941. The *Brecon* was completed

HMS *Brecon*, one of the Type IV 'Hunt' Class known as the *Brecon* Class. The *Brecon* served in the Mediterranean and covered the landings at Sicily, Anzio and the South of France and operations in the Aegean before ending the war in the East Indies. She was sold for scrap in 1962

PPL

PPL

The experimental guided-missile destroyer HMS *Bristol* entered service in 1973 as a testbed for a number of new weapon systems

in December 1942 and the *Brissenden* in February 1943.

The most marked departure from previous British design practice for destroyer-type vessels was the lengthening of the forecastle deck which extended as far aft as X gun mounting. This was intended to provide protection from the weather for men working on the upper deck and particularly to allow covered access to the armament for the gun crews. The arrangement had another advantage in that it eliminated the weak area produced by placing the forecastle-break abreast the main mast. Thus, with greater strength at forecastle deck level the hull stresses were considerably reduced and allowed for the use of mild instead of HT steel in the hull structure. This arrangement was used extensively in postwar ships in preference to the standard destroyer hull design with short forecastle.

The hull also included a new bow form, designed to reduce spray, which consisted of a double flare with a knuckle at upper-deck level. Another new feature was the pear-shaped funnel, which was specifically designed to keep smoke clear of the superstructure and in particular to prevent the funnel gases being drawn down into the bridge in a following wind. It contained a centre-division plate of spiral form, to prevent the glow of the boiler fires being observed from aircraft. The *Brecon* was fitted with stabilizers, but these were omitted from *Brissenden* and the space utilized for additional oil fuel storage.

Compared with the earlier 'Hunt' Classes they were more seaworthy and less prone to weather damage, but were more difficult to handle, with the new bow form causing bumping in heavy seas, resulting in additional stiffening being incorporated in the hull below the forward magazines.

Brecon was completed with two single 20-mm (0.79-in) guns in the bridge wings and two twin 20-mm abreast the searchlight platform, but *Brissenden* was completed with twin 20-mm in all four positions. *Brecon* had her twins replaced by single 40-mm (1.57-in) Bofors in 1945 and *Brissenden* mounted a single 2-pdr pom-pom at the forecastle head while operating in the Channel during 1943-45.

Both vessels took part in the invasion of Sicily in July 1943, after which *Brissenden* returned to home waters while *Brecon* remained in the Mediterranean. *Brecon* subsequently supported the landings at Anzio and in the South of France, covered the occupation of the Aegean Islands, and ended the war in the East Indies. *Brissenden* served mainly in the Channel and was part of the support force for the Normandy invasion; in 1945 she went to the Mediterranean. The *Brecon* and *Brissenden* were sold for scrap in 1962 and 1965 respectively.

See also *Albrighton, Atherstone* and *Blankney* Classes.

Displacement: 1170 tons (standard) *Length:* 90.22 m (296 ft) oa *Beam:* 10.13 m (33 ft 3 in) *Draught:* 2.74 m (9 ft) *Machinery:* 2-shaft, geared steam turbines, 19 000 shp = 27 knots *Armament:* 6 4-in (102-mm) (3×2); 4 2-pdr (1×4); 6 20-mm (0.79-in) (1×2, 2×2); 3 21-in (53-cm) torpedo tubes (1×3) *Crew:* 170

Bristol

British guided-missile destroyer. The *Bristol* was ordered on October 4, 1966 from the Swan Hunter Group (Associated Shipbuilders) of Wallsend as the first of a new class classified as Type 82 1st Rate general-purpose escorts. One of the primary functions of the class was to serve as escorts for the planned aircraft carrier CVAO1, which was subsequently cancelled. Combined with a change in Admiralty construction policy, this led to the cancellation of a plan to order a further three ships of the class. However, the building of *Bristol* went ahead despite her limited value as a single unit. This decision may well have been influenced by the fact that she would serve as a test bed for a number of new weapon systems which were also to be employed in other (projected) vessels.

The ship was laid down on November 15, 1967 and launched on June 30, 1969. She was completed in 1972 and, after builders' trials, was officially accepted for service on December 17. Early in 1973 she was fitted-out at Portsmouth with some of her more secret equipment and then proceeded to Portland for an extensive work-up and weapon and equipment trials. She was officially commissioned at Bristol in March 1973.

Bristol is a very sophisticated vessel, her design following the general lines of the earlier 'County' Class guided-missile destroyers. However, while the 'County' Class were mainly intended as AA escorts, the *Bristol* combines a formidable AA and A/S armament with an exceptionally advanced weapons-control system. The ship's antiaircraft armament consists of a single fully-automatic 4.5-in (114-mm) gun (compared with four 4.5-in in the 'County' Class) mounted on the forecastle and the GWS30 Sea Dart guided-missile system with its twin launcher mounted aft. Both weapons can be used against aircraft, missiles or surface targets, and the gun can also be used for shore support and for firing star shell. Antisubmarine weapons consist of the

Right: **The** ***Bristol*** **is the first Royal Navy vessel to be fitted with an ADAWS2 Action Data Automation System. This is connected to the inertial navigation system, various radar receivers and weapons sensors, plotting surface and subsurface movements in the cruiser's vicinity, and can control the fire of all the systems automatically, leaving only the initial decision to open fire in the crew's hands**

Australian Ikara A/S missile/torpedo, with a single launcher mounted forward of the bridge, and a three-barrelled Limbo A/S mortar mounted in a well aft. With the exception of the Limbo this was the first time that these weapons had been fitted in a seagoing RN ship. She carries 40 Sea Dart and 32 Ikara missiles.

As originally designed, *Bristol* was to have been fitted with the Anglo-Dutch 3D surveillance radar, but the UK withdrew from this project in 1968 and Type 965M radar (air search/target indication) was substituted, with the aerial on the short foremast. Other radar sets include two Type 909 for missile guidance, with aerials (covered by GRP domes) fore and aft, Type 992Q search radar, with the aerial on the mainmast head, and a Type 978 height-finder. The ship is also fitted with SINS (Ships' Inertial Navigation System) which provides instant information on the ship's position, course, speed etc, and a SCOT satellite terminal for worldwide communication via the Skynet 2 system.

The SINS, radar and weapon-sensing systems are generally connected to an ADAWS2 (Action Data Automation Weapon System Mk 2) which can control and fire all the weapons systems automatically—the decision to open fire being the only part left to human control. The *Bristol* was the first RN ship with such a sophisticated and complete computerized control system, based on two miniaturized Ferranti FM 1600 digital computers. These instruments supply several display consoles and two tactical plots (for surface and sub-surface situations respectively) positioned in a central operations room and give a complete picture of the tactical situation around and below the ship within the range of her sensors.

Other equipment includes two Corvus decoy (chaff) launchers as defence against homing missiles, three sonar sets and a helicopter landing space (but no hangar) aft.

The COSAG machinery arrangement is of similar type to that fitted in the 'County' Class, but with the power output of the gas turbine plant increased from 30000 to 44600 shp. All the machinery, including the auxiliaries and electrical supply, is controlled from a central control room and the main machinery compartments are virtually unmanned. *Bristol* is fitted with automatic steering gear, stabilizers and air conditioning, and is the last major RN warship to employ a steam power plant.

Displacement: 5650 tons (normal) *Length:* 154.53 mm (507 ft) oa *Beam:* 16.76 m (55 ft) *Draught:* 5.18 m (17 ft) *Machinery:* 2-shaft combined steam and gas turbines, 74600 shp (30000 steam+44600 gas)=32+ knots *Armament:* 1 4.5-in (114-mm) gun; 1 Sea Dart launcher (1×2); 1 Ikara launcher (1×1); 1 Limbo (1×3) *Crew:* 407

MOD

Bristol

US destroyer class. After the outbreak of war in Europe in September 1939 the US Navy wisely decided to accelerate its programme of destroyer construction. In 1940 two groups of destroyers, 72 ships in all, were ordered. One group was a repeat edition of the *Benson* Class and the other a repeat of the Bethlehem-designed *Livermore* Class variant. The new ships commissioned in 1941-43, and they differed from the prototypes in dropping the fifth 5-in (127-mm) gun aft in favour of additional light AA guns.

The *Bristol* was completed without shields to her guns, but these were added later. The after bank of torpedo tubes were soon replaced by four single 20-mm (0.79-in) Oerlikon guns, two forward of the bridge and two abreast the second funnel. The quadruple 1.1-in (28-mm) AA mounting was also replaced by a pair of single 20-mm at the forward end of the after shelter deck, and the after superstructure was removed to provide better arcs of fire. Subsequently, single and twin 40-mm (1.57-in) Bofors guns replaced the 20-mm guns, but a panic measure to replace the forward torpedo tubes by four single 40-mm was not carried out.

The first group had round funnels and carried the fire-control director on a prominent pedestal, while the Bethlehem-built ships of the second group had flat-sided funnels. Those built by Seattle-Tacoma had round funnels, but did not have the director on a pedestal, and had square-faced bridges.

The final light armament in 1945 was two pairs of 40-mm guns on the after shelter deck, sided, and six 20-mm guns sided in the bridge wings and waist, and a seventh 20-mm gun abaft B 5-in gun. In 1944-45, 24 were equipped as destroyer-mine-sweepers (DMS), with Y 5-in gun replaced by sweep gear:

DD.454 became DMS.19
DD.455 became DMS.20
DD.456 became DMS.21
DD.457 became DMS.22
DD.458 became DMS.23
DD.461 became DMS.24
DD.462 became DMS.25
DD.464 became DMS.26
DD.621 became DMS.27
DD.625 became DMS.28
DD.636 became DMS.29
DD.637 became DMS.30
DD.489 became DMS.31
DD.490 became DMS.32
DD.493 became DMS.33
DD.494 became DMS.34
DD.495 became DMS.35
DD.496 became DMS.36
DD.618 became DMS.37
DD.627 became DMS.38
DD.632 became DMS.39
DD.633 became DMS.40
DD.634 became DMS.41
DD.635 became DMS.42

As a class the *Bristols* bore the brunt of the early fighting in the Pacific and were also involved in the European theatre of operations. The *Bristol* (DD.453) was torpedoed by *U 371* off Oran on October 13, 1943. The *Laffey* (DD.459) was sunk by gunfire from the Japanese battleship *Hiei* off Savo Island during the Battle of Guadalcanal on the night of November 13, 1942; on the same night the *Barton* (DD.599) was torpedoed by the destroyer *Amatsukaze*. The *Duncan* (DD.485) was also sunk off Savo Island, on October 11, 1942, and the *Aaron Ward* sank after being bombed off Guadalcanal in April 1943. The *Maddox* was sunk by German aircraft off Licata in July 1943 and the *Glennon* was sunk off Normandy by shore batteries after being mined; the *Corry* was mined at about the same time. The *Beatty* was torpedoed by a German aircraft off Bougarouni in November 1943, and the *Turner* was sunk off the Ambrose light vessel in January 1944 after an internal explosion. The *Emmons, Forrest, Harding, Butler* and *Shubrick* were all hit by kamikazes off Okinawa in 1945, the *Emmons* being sunk by friendly forces and the others subsequently written off as beyond repair.

Six of the *Bristol* Class were transferred to other countries:
Ellyson became Japanese *Asakaze* (1954), thence to Taiwan for cannibalization (1970)
Woodworth became Italian *Artigliere* (1951)
Buchanan became Turkish *Gelibolu* (1949)
Lansdowne became Turkish *Gaziantep* (1949)
Lardner became Turkish *Gemlik* (1949)
McCalla became Turkish *Giresun* (1949)

On April 27, 1952 *Hobson* (DMS.26) collided with the carrier *Wasp* west of the Azores and sank with heavy loss of life. The *Baldwin* was wrecked while in tow off Montauk Point in April 1961. Scrappings started in 1966, the last of the class being stricken in 1971.

Builders were Federal Shipbuilding, Kearney (DD.453-456, DD.483-490, DD.645-648); Bath Ironworks (DD.457-458); Bethlehem, San Francisco (DD.459-460, DD.605-615, DD.617); Boston Navy Yard (DD.461-462, DD.632-635); Charleston Navy Yard (DD.463-464, DD.640-641); Bethlehem, Staten Island (DD.491-492, DD.602-604); Seattle-Tacoma (DD.493-497, DD.624-648); Bethlehem, Quincy (DD.598-601, DD.616); Philadelphia Navy Yard (DD.636-637) and Norfolk Navy Yard (DD.638-639).

The class consisted of (**First Group**): *Bristol* DD.453, *Ellyson* DD.454, *Hambleton* DD.455, *Rodman* DD.456, *Emmons* DD.457, *Macomb* DD.458, *Forrest* DD.461, *Fitch* DD.462, *Corry* DD.463, *Hobson* DD.464, *Aaron Ward* DD.483, *Buchanan* DD.484, *Duncan* DD.485, *Lansdowne* DD.486, *Lardner* DD.487, *McCalla* DD.488, *Mervine* DD.489, *Quick* DD.490, *Davison* DD.618, *Edwards* DD.619, *Glennon* DD.620, *Jeffers* DD.621, *Maddox* DD.622, *Nelson* DD.623, *Cowie* DD.632, *Knight* DD.633, *Doran* DD.634, *Earle* DD.635, *Butler* DD.636, *Gherhadi* DD.637, *Herndon* DD.638, *Shubrick* DD.639, *Beatty* DD.640, *Tillman* DD.641, *Stevenson* DD.645, *Stockton* DD.645, *Thorn* DD.647, *Turner* DD.648.
(**Second group**): *Laffey* DD.459, *Woodworth* DD.460, *Farenholt* DD.491, *Bailey* DD.492, *Carmick* DD.493, *Doyle* DD.494, *Endicott* DD.495, *McCook* DD.496, *Frankford* DD.497, *Bancroft* DD.498, *Barton* DD.599, *Boyle* DD.600, *Champlin* DD.601, *Meade* DD.602, *Murphy* DD.603, *Parker* DD.604, *Caldwell* DD.605, *Coghlan* DD.606, *Frazier* DD.607, *Gansevoort* DD.608, *Gillespie* DD.609, *Hobby* DD.610, *Kalk* DD.611, *Kendrick* DD.612, *Laub* DD.613, *MacKenzie* DD.614, *McLanahan* DD.615, *Nields* DD.616, *Ordronaux* DD.617, *Baldwin* DD.624, *Harding* DD.625, *Satterlee* DD.626, *Thompson* DD.627 *Welles* DD.628.

Displacement: 1620-1630 tons (standard), 2515-2525 tons (full load) *Length:* 106.01-106.13 m (347 ft 9 in-348 ft 3 in) oa *Beam:* 10.97-11.28 m (36-37 ft) *Draught:* 5.33 m (17 ft 6 in) max *Machinery:* 2-shaft geared steam turbines, 50 000 shp = $37\frac{1}{2}$ knots (max, light condition) *Armament:* (As completed) 4 5-in (127-mm)/38 cal DP (4×1); 4 1.1-in (28-mm)/75 cal AA (1×4); 6 0.5-in (12.7-mm) AA machine-guns (6×1); 10 21-in (53-cm) torpedo tubes (2×5); (As modified 1942-44) 4 5-in DP; 4 40-mm (1.57-in) AA (2×2); 4-8 20-mm (0.79-in) AA (4/8×1); 5 21-in torpedo tubes (1×5) *Crew:* 208 DD.453-464; 260 DD.598-615, 632-641, 645-648; 270 DD.616-628; 276 DD.483-497

Broadsword

British frigate class. Intended as successors to the *Leander* Class general-purpose frigates, the detailed design of this class began early in 1972. The first unit, *Broadsword*, was ordered from Yarrow in February 1975 and laid down in May of the same year. The second ship, *Battleaxe*, and a third unnamed unit, were ordered from the same company in September 1975 and September 1976 respectively; orders for a further nine vessels were expected. Yarrow were involved in the design at a very early stage, in order to obtain the maximum economy and efficiency in the ships' layout and construction, and the detailed design is the result of a high degree of cooperation between the Admiralty and the builders.

Broadswords are considerably larger than the *Leanders* and have abandoned the 4.5-in (114-mm) gun in favour of the RN's first all-missile armament (whilst retaining close-range AA). In appearance they show a similar general layout, but the *Broadsword* Class will have a larger funnel and the 01 (superstructure) deck has been extended well forward of the bridge and occupies the full width of the ship, which will add substantially to stability and seaworthiness.

For long-range A/S work the ships of the class will carry two Lynx helicopters equipped with A/S homing torpedoes. The quarterdeck serves as the flight deck, with the hangar positioned just forward of it. The Lynx can also carry missiles for use against surface targets. Two triple torpedo tubes (employing the same torpedoes as the helicopters) mounted abreast the main mast provide close-range A/S capability, and a new multi-frequency sonar, Type 2016, is to be fitted. The surface-to-surface armament consists of four launchers for the Exocet MM.38 missile fitted on the forecastle deck.

Defence against aircraft and missiles is to be provided by the Seawolf GWS25 surface-to-air missile system, housed in two six-cannister launchers, one before the bridge and the second on the hangar roof. No Exocet reloads are to be carried, but the Seawolf launchers will be supplied from two below-waterline magazines. The two 40-mm (1.57-in) Bofors, the only old weapon in the armament, are fitted for close-range AA defence, and two Corvus missile-decoy (chaff) launchers are mounted as passive defence against homing missiles.

Radar equipment includes two Type 910 for missile guidance, Type 967/968, back-to-back, for surface/air search and target indication, and Type 1006 for navigation. Type 1006 can also be employed for surface surveillance and direction of the A/S helicopters. Other electronic equipment includes a SCOT satellite communications terminal. Central data processing will be carried out by a Ferranti CAAIS (computer-aided action information system), which uses the Ferranti FM 1600B computer. Other FM 1600BS process radar information and supply guidance data to the Seawolf systems.

The COGOG machinery plant is similar to that fitted in the ships of the *Amazon* and *Sheffield* Classes. A Type RMIA gas turbine, for cruising, and an Olympus TM38 gas turbine, for high speed, are geared to each shaft to drive a five-bladed variable-pitch/reversible propeller. Cruising speed, using the two RMIAs, will be 18 knots, with a top speed of over 29 knots.

Displacement: 3860 tons (normal) *Length:* 131 m (429 ft 9 in) oa *Beam:* 14.75 m (48 ft 5 in) *Draught:* 4.27 m (14 ft) *Machinery:* 2-shaft gas turbines, 8200 shp (cruising)=18 knots+54 600 shp (boost)=29+ knots *Armament:* 4 Exocet launchers (4×1); 2 Seawolf launchers (2×6); 2 40-mm (1.57-in); 6 12.75-in (32.4-cm) torpedo tubes (2×3); 2 A/S helicopters *Crew:* 250 (approx)

Bronstein

US destroyer escort class. *Bronstein* and *McCloy* are the first of the American 'second-generation' postwar escorts. They mark a complete break from the preceeding *Dealey* Class escorts, and they introduced the hull shape, bow sonar and antisubmarine armament that has been used for all subsequent classes. They were authorized in Financial Year 1960, and both were built at the Avondale shipyard.

Like the earlier British frigates, the hull has a long, narrow bow to punch through waves and so maintain speed in rough weather. The bow has a considerable overhang so that the stem anchor will not foul the SQS 26 bow sonar. Active stabilization is fitted to ensure stability, and they are excellent sea boats. Unlike later US escorts, which are flush-decked, the *Bronstein* and *McCloy* have a break at the quarterdeck. They introduced a new profile with a large bridge structure and a mack (combined mast and stack).

They are mainly intended for antisubmarine work, their original antiaircraft armament being only a twin 3-in (76-mm) covered AA mount forward and a single open 3-in mount behind the helicopter deck on the quarterdeck. The antisubmarine armament is considerable and varied. Originally they carried one eight-tube Asroc 'pepperpot' launcher between the forward 3-in mount and the bridge, two triple 32.4-cm (12.75-in) Mk 32 torpedo launchers (one on either side of the funnel) and two DASH (Drone Anti-Submarine Helicopters) with a small hangar and operating pad just before the break of the quarterdeck. DASH proved to be an expensive failure, and the hangar was later enlarged to take a single LAMPS (Light Airborne Multi-Purpose System) SH-2 helicopter instead. In 1974-75 the aft single 3-in mount was removed and replaced by a towed sonar, thus depriving them of any antiaircraft capability aft.

The most controversial feature of the design was the adoption of a single shaft to simplify construction. While it does make the ships cheaper and slightly quicker to build, it also makes them very vulnerable to machinery breakdown or battle damage. However, in the Second World War the Americans found their chief bottleneck in escort production was the time it took to build engines, so they have decided to accept the limitations inherent in a single-shaft ship to avoid a recurrence of this problem. Two Foster Wheeler boilers drive a single 20 000-shp Westinghouse turbine, giving a maximum speed of 26 knots and a sea speed of nearer 24 knots.

On June 30, 1975 they were reclassified from ocean escorts (DE) to frigates (FF), and they were due to be transferred to the reserve fleet in the early 1980s. Much the same size as the later Second World War escorts, they are too small to take the weapons and electronics needed to equip vessels in a modern navy.

No and name	laid down	launched	completed
DE.1037 *Bronstein*	5/1961	3/1962	6/1963
DE.1038 *McCloy*	9/1961	6/1962	10/1963

Displacement: 2360 tons (standard), 2650 tons (full load) *Length:* 113 m (371 ft 6in) *Beam:* 12.3 m (40 ft 6 in) *Draught:* 7 m (23 ft) *Machinery:* 1-shaft geared steam turbines, 20 000 shp=26 knots *Armament:* 2 3-in (76-mm) AA; 1 8-tube Asroc; 6 32.4-cm (12.75-in) torpedo launchers *Aircraft:* 1 helicopter *Crew:* 220

Below: HMS *Broadsword* fitting out, and (bottom) as envisaged in the builders' model. She is the first of a new class of general purpose frigates to replace the well tried *Leander* Class

Yarrow Shipbuilding

Yarrow Shipbuilding

Brooke

US destroyer escort class. In the early 1960s, the US Navy realized that the *Bronstein* Class were not large enough to carry all the weapons and electronics necessary for a modern escort. They therefore introduced an enlarged flush-deck version, the *Garcia* Class, armed with a single 5-in (127-mm) mount fore and aft. They also decided to build a variant of the *Garcias* with an improved antiaircraft armament. These ships were the *Brooke* Class DEGs (rerated FFGs in June 1975).

The first three *Brookes* were authorized in the Fiscal Year 1962 and built by the Lockheed Shipbuilding and Construction company, Seattle, and the remaining three were authorized in the Fiscal Year 1963 and built by Bath Ironworks.

The class have the standard hull form of the modern American escort, with a sharply raked bow, an SQS 26 bow sonar, and a long superstructure, surmounted by a mack, extending to the hangar and helicopter deck right aft. The single 5-in/38-cal gun is mounted forward. It was originally intended to fit a much higher rate of fire but this would have cost too much. Between this and the bridge is the eight-tube Asroc launcher. *Talbot, Richard L Page* and *Julius A Furer* are fitted with an automatic reload system which alters the shape of the front of the bridge. The single Tartar Mk 22 lightweight launcher, with a 16-round magazine, is mounted on the superstructure just ahead of the hangar, and the associated SPG 51 radar, for target acquisition and tracking and missile guidance, is carried on the mack.

In addition to two triple Mk 32 torpedo launchers amidships, the *Brookes* carry two fixed Mk 25 wire-guided torpedo tubes at the stern, where the wires do not entangle the single propeller. The class was originally intended to carry two DASH helicopters, but recently the hangar has been enlarged and they now carry one LAMPS helicopter.

The machinery is very compact and works at the very high pressure of 1200 lb/sq in and a small auxiliary boiler is installed to provide steam when in port. Like all modern US escorts, the single screw renders them vulnerable to damage or breakdown.

Ten more *Brookes* were planned in Fiscal Year 1964, but although they only differed from the *Garcias* in having Tartar and the Mk 25 torpedoes, they cost $11 million more apiece, which made them too expensive for an expendable escort, and the idea was dropped. *Talbot* was fitted with an OTO Melara 76-mm (3-in) single mounting and other modifications in 1974-75 to act as a trials ship for *Oliver Hazard Perry* and *Pegasus. Glover* was built to a very similar design to the *Brookes* to test podded propulsion units, and the Spanish *Baleares* Class is an enlarged version with improved living conditions for the crew.

No and name	laid down	launched	completed
DEG. 1 *Brooke*	12/1962	7/1963	3/1966
DEG. 2 *Ramsey*	2/1963	10/1963	6/1967
DEG. 3 *Schofield*	4/1963	12/1963	4/1968
DEG. 4 *Talbot*	5/1964	1/1966	4/1967
DEG. 5 *Richard L Page*	1/1965	4/1966	8/1967
DEG. 6 *Julius A Furer*	7/1965	7/1966	11/1967

Displacement: 2643 tons (standard), 3425 tons (full load) *Length:* 1263m (414 ft 6 in) *Beam:* 13.4 m (44 ft) *Draught:* 7.3 m (24 ft) *Machinery:* 1-shaft geared steam turbines, 35 000 shp=26 knots *Armament:* 1 5-in (127-mm)/38 cal; 1 Tartar antiaircraft missile launcher; 1 8-tube Asroc launcher; 6 Mk 32 torpedo launchers; 2 Mk 25 wire-guided torpedo tubes *Aircraft:* 1 SH-2 LAMPS helicopter *Crew:* 241

Brooklyn

US light cruiser class. When the Japanese *Mogami* Class cruisers appeared in 1935 with their heavy armament of 15 6-in (152-mm) guns, the US Navy was forced to return to building light cruisers after a lapse of nearly 20 years. Although the Bureau of Construction and Repair favoured the 8-in (203-mm) gunned cruiser as the only type suitable for Pacific fighting, the US Navy had completed the quota permitted under the Washington Disarmament Treaty.

The *Brooklyn* Class adopted the same disposition of guns as the *Mogami*—five triple 6-in turrets, with two aft and three forward. The third turret was badly placed, with limited arcs of training, as in the British *Nelson* Class battleships, and was normally trained aft. A flush-decked hull was adopted, with a square stern. This was not a full transom stern but merely a convenient way of incorporating a large hangar under the fantail (quarterdeck) for the floatplanes launched from catapults.

The hangar was widely regarded as a good feature, for it was theoretically capable of accommodating six floatplanes as well as spare engines and other components. However, only four were normally carried, and it was revealed to the British in 1942, in answer to technical questions about hangar-design, that it 'would never be repeated in a future design'. There were three principal drawbacks: excessive vibration caused by having a large resonant cavity directly over the rudders and propellers; the risk of battle-damage or a wave damaging the hatch and causing flooding outside the main citadel; and the difficulty in recovering float-planes at the stern because of the greater rise and fall of the bows and stern of the ship in a seaway.

Despite these drawbacks the *Brooklyns* were successful and handsome cruisers, retaining many of the good features from the preceding heavy cruisers. They proved to have a low margin of stability, however, and *Brooklyn, Savannah* and *Honolulu* were given 'bulges' to compensate for extra equip-

Armada de Chile

The former *Brooklyn* Class light cruiser USS *Nashville* after her transfer to the Chilean navy, along with the *Brooklyn* (renamed *O'Higgins*) in 1951, when she was renamed *Capitan Prat*

No and name	laid down	launched	completed	builder
CL.40 *Brooklyn*	3/1935	11/1936	7/1938	New York navy yard
CL.41 *Philadelphia*	5/1935	11/1936	7/1938	Philadelphia navy yard
CL.42 *Savannah*	5/1934	5/1937	8/1938	New York shipbuilding corporation
CL.43 *Nashville*	1/1935	10/1937	11/1938	New York shipbuilding corporation
CL.46 *Phoenix*	4/1935	3/1938	3/1939	New York shipbuilding corporation
CL.47 *Boise*	4/1935	12/1936	2/1939	Newport News company
CL.48 *Honolulu*	9/1935	8/1937	9/1938	New York navy yard
CL.49 *St Louis*	12/1936	4/1938	12/1939	New York navy yard
CL.50 *Helena*	12/1936	8/1938	12/1939	Newport News company

ment. The last two of the class were given a better antiaircraft armament, with four twin 5-in (127-mm)/38 cal mountings in place of the inadequate four single 5-in (127-mm) guns in the waist on either side. During the war they were given four quadruple 40-mm (1.57-in) Bofors in place of the unreliable 1.1-in (30-mm) quads, and 20-28 20-mm (0.79-in) Oerlikons in single mountings. Another wartime alteration was to reduce the width of the bridge.

Three of the class, *Brooklyn, Philadelphia* and *Savannah,* served in the European theatre during the Second World War, being present at the Torch landings in North Africa, the landings at Salerno in 1943, and the liberation of southern France in 1944. The *Savannah* was badly damaged by glider-bombs at Salerno in 1943, and did not return to service until late in the war. The others all saw considerable action in the Pacific, notably in the fierce battles in the Solomon Islands in 1942-43. The *Helena* was damaged by a torpedo at Pearl Harbor, and was sunk in the Battle of Kula Gulf on July 6, 1943 by the Japanese destroyers *Suzukaze* and *Tanikaze. St. Louis* was damaged in the same action along with the *Honolulu,* which was torpedoed by an aircraft at Leyte in 1944. The *Nashville* was badly damaged by a kamikaze in December 1944.

The class was overshadowed by the wartime construction, and six were sold to the three major South American navies in 1951:
Phoenix became Argentine *Diecisiete de Octubre* (renamed *General Belgrano* in 1956)
Boise became Argentine *Nueve de Julio*
Philadelphia became Brazilian *Barroso*
St Louis became Brazilian *Tamadare*
Brooklyn became Chilean *O'Higgins*
Nashville became Chilean *Capitan Prat*

The terms to the three purchasers were identical, 10% of the original cost (average $18.5 million) plus the cost of reconditioning them, which amounted to an average cost of about $4 million.

The *Honolulu* was sold for scrapping in 1959, and the *Savannah* was sold early the following year. By 1977 Argentina retained her two ships, but they were expected to be scrapped to provide crews for new guided-missile destroyers. The Brazilian pair were stricken in 1973-75, and only the Chilean *Capitan Prat* remained operational, the *O'Higgins* having been laid up as an accommodation ship after running aground in 1974.

Displacement: 9475-10 000 tons (standard), 12 500-12 900 tons (full load) *Length:* 185.4 m (608 ft 3 in) oa *Beam:* 18.8 m (61 ft 9 in) *Draught:* 7.3 m (24 ft) max *Machinery:* 4-shaft geared steam turbines, 100 000 shp=32½ knots *Protection:* 38-128 mm (1½-5 in) belt; 63-77 mm (2½-3 in) decks; 76-127 mm (3-5 in) turrets *Armament:* 15 6-in (152-mm)/47 cal (5×3); 8 5-in (127-mm)/25 cal AA (8×1) OR 8 5-in/38 cal DP (4×2); 16 1.1-in (28-mm) AA (4×4), replaced by 40-mm (1.45-in) in 1942-42; 4 3-pdr (47-mm) saluting guns; 8 0.5-in (12.7-mm) machine-guns (8×1); 20-28 20-mm (0.79-in) AA (20-28×1) added *Aircraft:* 4 floatplanes, 2 catapults *Crew:* 868-888 (1200 wartime)

Buckley

US destroyer escort class. When the United States entered the Second World War, there was a critical shortage of antisubmarine escorts. The BDE or British destroyer escort was already in hand, but it had not been built to the original specification for want of suitable machinery.

The *Buckley* Class were given turbo-electric machinery to attain the desired 23-24 knots, and this resulted in a slightly longer hull than before. To reduce the risk of losing all power from a torpedo-hit, the boiler-rooms and engine-rooms were alternated, and the two uptakes were trunked into one slim funnel. In response to a request by the British, all the earlier units of the class were given torpedo tubes.

DE.51-98—built by Bethlehem, Hingham
DE.153-198—built by Norfolk navy yard
DE.199-213—built by Charleston navy yard
DE.214-223—built by Philadelphia navy yard
DE.563-578—built by Bethlehem, Hingham
DE.633-644—built by Bethlehem, San Francisco
DE.665-677—built by the Dravo corporation, Wilmington
DE.668-673—built by the Consolidated Steel corporation, Orange
DE.675-683—built by Bethlehem, Quincy
DE.693-705—built by Defoe Shipbuilding, Bay City
DE.789-800—built by Consolidated Steel corporation, Orange
DE.645-664, 801-1005, contracts not placed
DE.52, 55, 58, 61, 64, 67, 71-98 passed into Royal Navy, becoming members of *Bentinck* Class; DE.563-573 passed into Royal Navy, becoming members of *Bayntun* Class

The class comprised: DE.51 *Buckley*; DE.53 *Charles Lawrence*; DE.54 *Daniel T Griffin*; DE.56 *Donnell*; DE.57 *Fogg*; DE.59 *Foss*; DE.60 *Gantner*; DE.62 *George W Ingram*; DE.63 *Ira Jeffrey*; DE.65 *Lee Fox*; DE.66 *Amesbury*; DE.68 *Bates*; DE.69 *Blessman*; DE.70 *Joseph E Campbell*; DE.153 *Reuben James*; DE.154 *Sims*; DE.155 *Hopping*; DE.156 *Reeves*; DE.157 *Fechteler*; DE.158 *Chase*; DE.159 *Laning*; DE.160 *Loy*; DE.161 *Barber*; DE.198 *Lovelace*; DE.199 *Manning*; DE.200 *Neuendorf*; DE.201 *James E Craig*; DE.202 *Eichenberger*; DE.203 *Thomason*; DE.204 *Jordan*; DE.205 *Newman*; DE.206 *Liddle*; DE.207 *Kephart*; DE.208 *Cofer*; DE.209 *Lloyd*; DE.210 *Otter*; DE.211 *Joseph C Hubbard*; DE.212 *Hayter*; DE.213 *William T Powell*; DE.214 *Scott*; DE.215 *Burke*; DE.216 *Enright*; DE.217

The *Bentinck* Class frigate HMS *Bickerton,* originally a member of the US *Buckley* Class, after her transfer to the Royal Navy

IWM

Coolbaugh; DE.218 *Darby*; DE.219 *J Douglas Blackwood*; DE.220 *Frances M Robinson*; DE.221 *Solar*; DE.222 *Fowler*; DE.223 *Spangenberg*; DE.575 *Ahrens*; DE.576 *Barr*, DE.577 *Alexander J Luke; DE.578 Robert I Paine*; DE.633 *Foreman*; DE.634 *Whitehurst*; DE.635 *England*; DE.636 *Witter*; DE.637 *Bowers*; DE.638 *Willmarth*; DE.639 *Gendreau*; DE.640 *Fieberling*; DE.641 *William C Cole*; DE.642 *Paul G Baker*; DE.643 *Damon M Cummings*; DE.644 *Vammen*; DE.665 *Jenks*; DE.666 *Durik*; DE.667 *Wiseman*; DE.668 *Yokes*; DE.669 *Pavlic*; DE.670 *Odum*; DE.671 *Jack C Robinson*; DE.672 *Bassett*; DE.673 *John B Gray*; DE.675 *Weber*; DE.676 *Schmitt*; DE.677 *Frament*; DE.678 *Harmon*; DE.679 *Greenwood*; DE.680 *Loeser*; DE.681 *Gillette*; DE.682 *Underhill*; DE.683 *Henry R Denyon*; DE.693 *Bull*; DE.694 *Bunch*; DE.695 *Rich*; DE.696 *Spangler*; DE.697 *George*; DE.698 *Raby*; DE.699 *Marsh*; DE.700 *Currier*; DE.701 *Osmus*; DE.702 *Earl V Johnson*; DE.703 *Holton*; DE.704 *Cronin*; DE.705 *Frybarger*; DE.789 *Tatum*; DE.790 *Borum*; DE.791 *Maloy*; DE.792 *Haines*; DE.793 *Runels*; DE.794 *Hollis*; DE.795 *Gunason*; DE.796 *Major*; DE.797 *Weeden*; DE.798 *Varian*; DE.799 *Scroggins*; DE.800 *Jack C Wilke*.

Six of the Class, *Yokes, Pavlic, Odum, Jack C Robinson, Bassett* and *John B Gray* (DE.668-673), were altered while under construction as fast transports, and renumbered APD.69-74. This involved the adding of extra accommodation amidships at forecastle deck level, with davits for four landing craft assault (LCAs). They were armed with a 5-in (127-mm) DP gun forward and three twin 40-mm (1.57-in) guns, and could carry 162 troops. A further 40 of the class were similarly converted in 1944-45:

APD.37 ex-DE.53	APD.58 ex-DE.636
APD.38 ex-DE.54	APD.59 ex-DE.205
APD.39 ex-DE.576	APD.60 ex-DE.206
APD.40 ex-DE.637	APD.61 ex-DE.207
APD.42 ex-DE.60	APD.62 ex-DE.208
APD.43 ex-DE.62	APD.63 ex-DE.209
APD.44 ex-DE.63	APD.65 ex-DE.215
APD.45 ex-DE.65	APD.66 ex-DE.216
APD.46 ex-DE.66	APD.75 ex-DE.675
APD.47 ex-DE.68	APD.76 ex-DE.676
APD.48 ex-DE.69	APD.77 ex-DE.677
APD.49 ex-DE.70	APD.78 ex-DE.693
APD.50 ex-DE.154	APD.79 ex-DE.694
APD.51 ex-DE.155	APD.80 ex-DE.212
APD.52 ex-DE.156	APD.81 ex-DE.789
APD.53 ex-DE.211	APD.82 ex-DE.790
APD.54 ex-DE.158	APD.83 ex-DE.791
APD.55 ex-DE.159	APD.84 ex-DE.792
APD.56 ex-DE.160	APD.85 ex-DE.793
APD.57 ex-DE.161	APD.86 ex-DE.794

A further six, APDs 41, 64, 67-68 and 82-83 (ex-DEs 635, 213, 665-666 and 790-791) were not converted, although numbers were allocated. The later DEs mounted two single 5-in DP guns in place of the three 3-in (76-mm), and in 1944-45 some had the torpedo tubes removed and four single 40-mm Bofors guns added amidships, to cope with kamikaze attacks. Others were given a large tripod mast abaft the funnel to carry a large air-warning radar. These were later classified as Radar Pickets (DER) and they included *Buckley, Fogg, Reuben James, William T Powell, Spangenberg, Alexander J Luke* and *Robert I Paine*.

There is space only to give the briefest account of the class's war service, but worthy of mention is the *England* (DE.635), which holds the record for antisubmarine work. She sank six Japanese submarines (*RO 104-106, RO 108, RO 116* and *I 16*) between May 19 and 31, 1944. She intercepted a patrol line and picked off the submarines in succession, an achievement all the more remarkable as she was newly commissioned. The *Donnell* (DE.56) was written off as a total loss after being torpedoed north of Iceland on May 3, 1944. The *England* was also written off after being hit by a kamikaze off Okinawa on May 9, 1945. The *Underhill* (DE.682) was sunk by a Kaiten midget submarine off Cape Engaño on July 24, 1945, and the *Fechteler* (DE.157) was torpedoed by *U 967* off Oran on May 5, 1944.

The *Solar* (DE.221) was destroyed by an internal explosion in April 1946. Many were altered for subsidiary duties under various temporary classifications. Scrapping began in 1967 and the last was stricken in September 1973. Many of the APDs were transferred to other navies and are still in service.

Displacement: 1400 tons (standard), 1720 tons (full load) *Length:* 93 m (306 ft) oa *Beam:* 11.3-11.5 m (37 ft-37 ft 9 in) *Draught:* 4.1 m (13 ft 6 in) max *Machinery:* 2-shaft turbo-electric drive, 12 000 shp=23½-24 knots *Armament:* 3 3-in (76-mm)/50 cal DP (3×1) (some altered to 2 5-in [127-mm]/38 cal DP [2×1]); 4 1.1-in (28-mm)/75 cal AA (1×4) (some completed with 1×2 or 4×1 40-mm AA, others altered 1943-45); 6-10 20-mm (6/10×1) removed from all active units post-1945; 3 21-in (53.3-cm) torpedo tubes (1×3) later removed *Crew:* 220 (wartime)

Bunker Hill

US aircraft carrier. The *Bunker Hill* (CV.17) was launched on December 7, 1942, and commissioned on May 24, 1943. In two years she was to see more action than most other American fleet carriers, and her total of 11 battle stars was equalled only by *Essex*, *Hornet* and *Enterprise*.

She was one of the first group of *Essex* Class carriers, and one of the first to join the fleet in the Pacific. She was soon despatching her aircraft in strikes against Japanese-held islands, and in November 1943 she became the first carrier to operate the F6F Helldiver. Further strikes at the end of the year caused her crew to christen her the 'Holiday Inn'. Soon after this episode *Bunker Hill* formed part of the famous Task Force 58 under Vice-Admiral Mitscher.

On February 17, 1944 her aircraft joined the massive and devastating attack on Japanese shipping in Truk lagoon which sank over 30 ships. More raids on bases and operations in support of landings led in June 1944 to the Battle of the Philippine Sea, and the 'Marianas Turkey Shoot', in which her fighters shot down their share of the more than 400 Japanese aircraft destroyed. *Bunker Hill* was one of the few American ships damaged, a near-miss from a bomb causing splinter damage and casualties.

The series of strikes was interrupted by a refit from November 1944 to January 1945. Back with Task Force 58, her aircraft took part in the overwhelming air attack which sank the *Yamato*.

On May 11 the carrier was supporting the Okinawa landings when she was attacked by an A6M 'Zero' and a D4Y 'Judy.' Each aircraft dropped a bomb before its kamikaze crash. The Zero's bomb went through the flight deck and the ship's side before exploding in the air, while the Judy's penetrated to the gallery deck before exploding. The Judy dived into the base of the island and the Zero hit a group of fighters ranged to take off before going over the side. As a result of this attack the ship was soon on fire to a depth of three decks and over most of her length. *Bunker Hill*'s captain turned her violently off course, which threw most of the blazing wrecks off the deck into the sea, but it took over five hours to bring the fires under

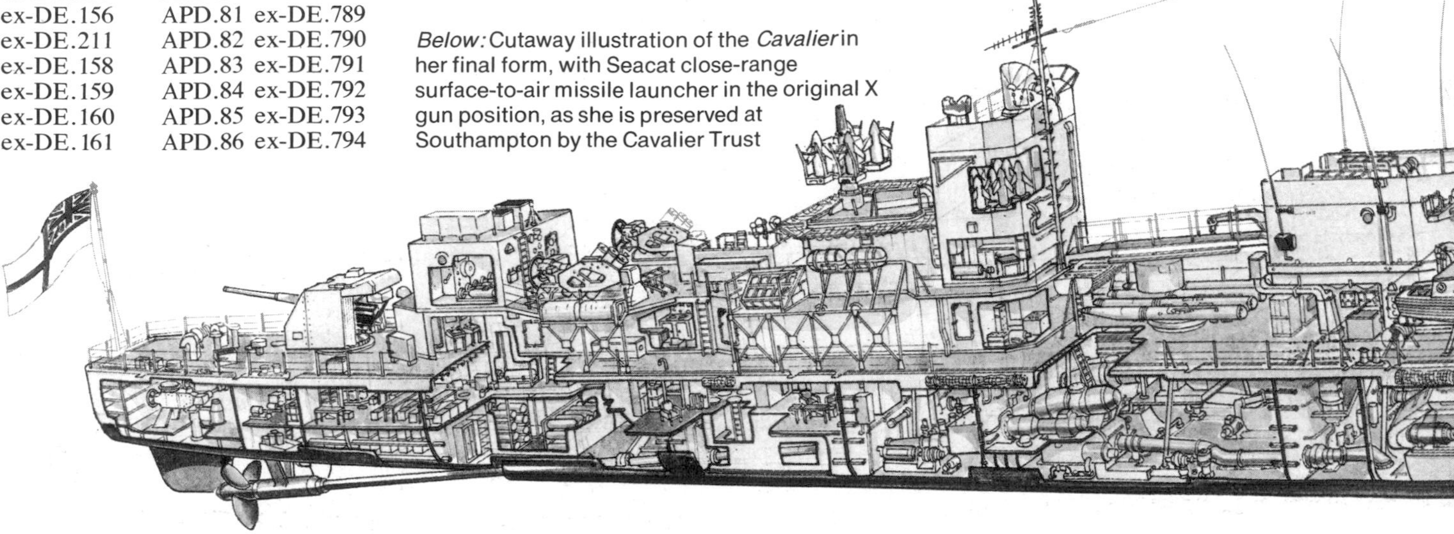

Below: Cutaway illustration of the *Cavalier* in her final form, with Seacat close-range surface-to-air missile launcher in the original X gun position, as she is preserved at Southampton by the Cavalier Trust

USS *Bunker Hill* moored off Point Loma, San Diego, after conversion to electronics test ship

control. The cruiser *Wilkes-Barre* and four destroyers helped to fight the fire and picked up crewmen forced to dive over the side to escape the flames.

No other American carrier except the *Franklin* went through such an ordeal and survived. Flames and smoke asphyxiation killed 396 men (some of whom were missing, their bodies never found) and 264 were injured. The carrier's survival was a tribute to her sturdy construction and excellent damage control. She was repaired, but only in time to repatriate troops after the end of the war, and soon afterwards went into mothballs. Despite being reclassified as an antisubmarine warfare support carrier (CVS-17) in August 1953 (from CVA-17) she remained unaltered, and was downgraded to an aviation transport (AVT-9) in May 1959. She was stricken on November 1, 1966, but was moored off Point Loma, near San Diego, California, as an electronics test-ship. She was finally sold for scrapping in 1972.

Displacement: 27 100 tons (normal), 33 000 tons (full load) *Length:* 267 m (876 ft) *Beam:* 28.34 m (93 ft) *Draught:* 7 m (23 ft) *Machinery:* 4-shaft geared turbines, 150 000 hp=32.7 knots *Armament:* 12 5-in (127-mm) DP (4×2, 4×1); 68 40-mm (1.57-in) AA (17×4); 52 20-mm AA (52×1) *Aircraft:* 80 (2 catapults) *Crew:* 3448

Caesar

British destroyer class. Ordered in February 1942, The *Caesar* Class was the 11th destroyer flotilla of the emergency war programme. They were of the same design as the earlier 'Emergency' flotillas and almost identical to the preceding 'Z' or *Zephyr* Class in which the traditional 4.7-in (120-mm) gun had been replaced by a new weapon of 4.5-in (114.3-mm) calibre. Having reached the end of the alphabet with the 10th Flotilla the new group were initially given names beginning with a variety of letters, but it was then decided to give them 'C' names as the original 'C' Class had been transferred to the RCN and renamed. The final three emergency flotillas were also given 'C' names, and to distinguish between them they were designated the 'Ca' (*Caesar*), 'Ch' (*Chequers*), 'Co' (*Cossack*) and 'Cr' (*Crescent*) Classes.

They were designed to carry a close-range armament of one twin 40-mm (1.57-in) Hazemeyer mounting amidships, two twin 20-mm (0.79-in) abaft the funnel and two single 20-mm in the bridge wings. However, the *Caprice* was completed with a quadruple 2-pdr pom-pom in place of the twin 40-mm and the *Cassandra* mounted twin 20-mm guns in her bridge wings instead of singles. In 1945 the majority had their 20-mm mountings replaced by four 2-pdr pom-poms but *Cassandra* was not altered, while *Caesar* mounted two 2-pdrs and one 40-mm gun and the *Cavendish* was fitted with three 2-pdrs only. These alterations were made to increase their firepower for defence against kamikaze attacks.

The class completed between April 1944 and February 1945, the *Caprice* being the first 4.5-in (114.3-mm) gunned destroyer to enter service, as the first of the 'Z' Class did not complete until July 1944. Initially they served with the Home Fleet as the 6th Destroyer Flotilla and operated mainly in northern waters where both *Cassandra* and *Cavalier* covered Russian convoys.

On December 11, 1944, while escorting RA62, the *Cassandra* was torpedoed by a U-Boat, about 7.62 m (25 ft) of her bow being blown away. She was towed to Murmansk, stern first, where temporary repairs were carried out by the Russians. She returned to the UK in June 1945 but was sent to Gibraltar for repairs as the home dockyards were full. The remainder of the class were transferred to the Far East and Pacific during 1945 but the majority arrived too late to take an active part in the war against Japan. All returned to Britain in 1946 and were placed in reserve until the 1950s.

In 1953 the *Carron* was taken in hand at Chatham dockyard for a two-year modernization. A new bridge, similar to that in the *Daring* Class, replaced the original structure and a new director and remote power control were provided for the main armament. The after bank of torpedo tubes was replaced by a deckhouse on which a twin Mk V Bofors was mounted and X 4.5-in (114.3-mm) mounting was supplanted by two 'Squid' antisubmarine mortars. All of the original close range AA weapons were removed. The rest of the class were modernized in the same manner bet-

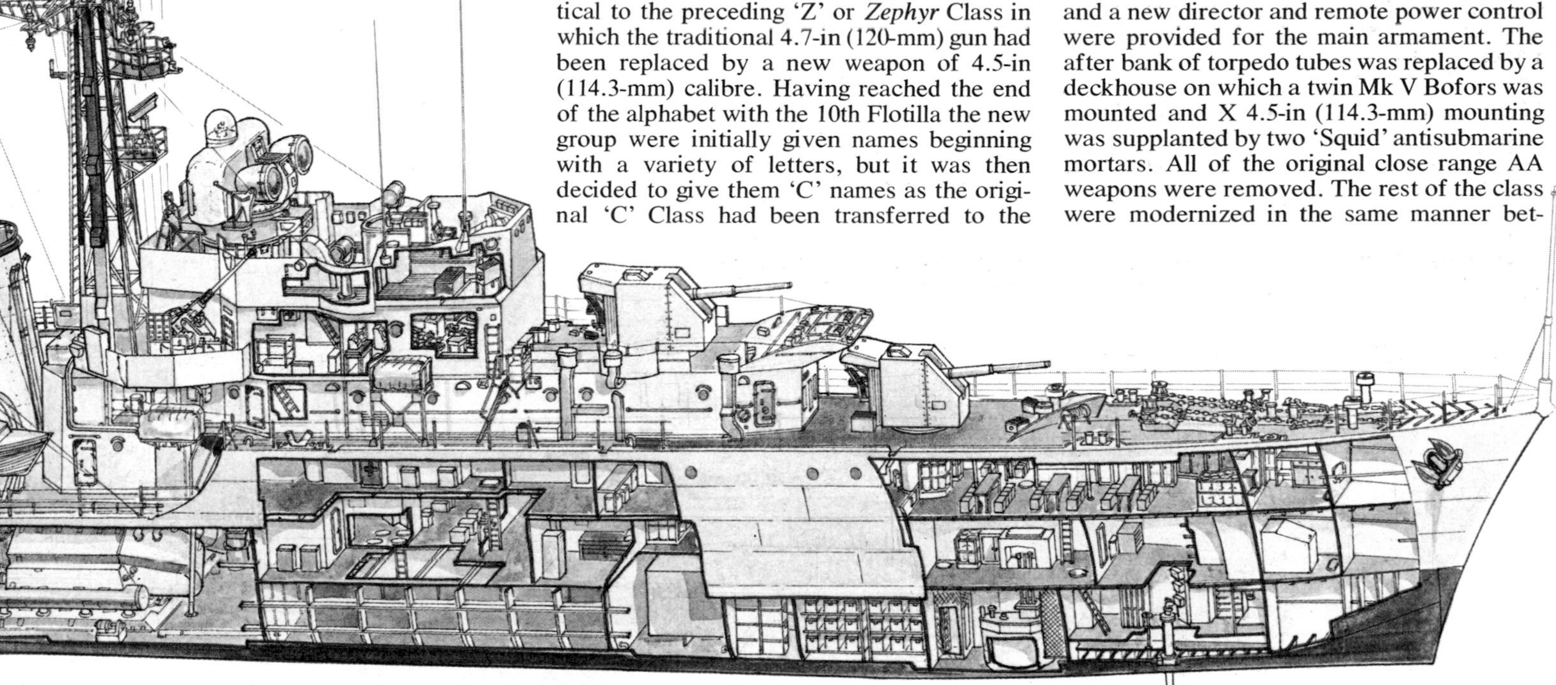

ween 1954 and 1963, the only major variation being in the last four (*Caesar, Cambrian, Caprice* and *Cassandra*) which were fitted with enclosed frigate-type bridges instead of the open destroyer type.

In 1963 the *Cavendish* became the first ship to be fitted with the 'Seacat' GWS which replaced the twin 40-mm (1.57-in) gun mounting. The *Cavalier* was similarly fitted in 1966. In 1971 a race was held between the *Cavalier* and the frigate *Rapid* to settle an argument over which was the fastest ship in the navy. The *Cavalier* won by a very narrow margin after averaging 31.8 knots over 64 miles.

Most of the class were sold for scrap between 1967 and 1975, but the *Cavalier* which is one of the last examples of her type, has been preserved and is permanently moored at Southampton.

Caesar, Cavendish (built by J Brown)
Cambrian, Carron (built by Scotts')
Caprice, Cassandra (built by Yarrow)
Carysfort, Cavalier (built by White).

Displacement: 1710 tons (standard), 2530 tons (full load) *Length:* 110.5 m (362 ft 9 in) *Beam:* 10.9 m (35 ft 9 in) *Draught:* 3.04 m (10 ft) mean *Machinery:* 2-shaft geared steam turbines, 40 000 shp=34 knots *Armament:* 4 4.5-in (114.3-mm) (4×1); 2 40-mm (1.57-in) (1×2); 6 20-mm (0.79-in) (2×2+2×1); 8 21-in (53-cm) torpedo tubes (2×4) *Crew:* 186

California

US nuclear-powered guided-missile cruiser class. The advantages of an all-nuclear-powered task force were demonstrated by Operation Sea Orbit in 1964, when the nuclear-powered carrier *Enterprise*, cruiser *Long Beach*, and frigate *Bainbridge* made a round the world voyage in 65 days without any form of replenishment. Although conventionally-powered vessels can be used to clear-powered carriers, they cannot maintain high speed for very long and have to refuel frequently, whereas an all-nuclear-powered task force can maintain full speed virtually indefinitely. This has many advantages, not least in hunting nuclear submarines. Therefore when the nuclear-powered carrier *Nimitz* was authorized in FY 1967, two nuclear-powered escorts were also authorized: *California* in FY 1967 and *South Carolina* in FY 1968.

They were both built by the Newport News Shipbuilding and Dry Dock company as nuclear guided-missile frigates (DLGN), but were reclassified as nuclear guided-missile cruisers (CGN) on June 30, 1975. They were developed from the earlier nuclear-powered *Bainbridge* and *Truxton*, but are larger and more sophisticated vessels. They are distinguishable from the earlier ships by their flush deck and their enclosed masts.

The *California*s' main function is to act as escorts to the nuclear-powered aircraft carriers, and they are armed primarily for antisubmarine and antiaircraft work. Although there is a helicopter landing pad aft, they have no facilities for maintaining helicopters, which would be operating from the accompanying carrier. The *California*s' primary A/S weapon in Asroc, and there is an eight-tube launcher just forward of the bridge, behind the bulky 'reload house'. Provision has been made aft to carry four Mk 32 torpedo tubes, and there is an SQS-26CX bow sonar.

The primary AA armament consists of two single Tartar-D Mk 13 Mod 3 launchers mounted well forward and aft. These fire Standard MR SAMs, and the forward and aft magazines can each carry about 40 missiles. These ships will eventually be refitted with

Name	No	laid down	launched	completed
California	(CGN-36)	1/1970	9/1971	2/1974
South Carolina	(CGN-37)	12/1970	7/1972	1/1975

The USS *South Carolina*, a nuclear-powered guided-missile cruiser of the *California* Class, launched in July 1972. Despite her modern power plant and weapons systems she still carries two 5-in (127-mm)/54-cal Mk 45 guns as a local deterrent in policing work

US Navy

US Navy

The *California* and *South Carolina* anchored at Pier 12, Norfolk, Virginia with the nuclear-powered attack carrier USS *Nimitz.* The submarine USS *Mendel Rivers* is at the end of the pier

Standard MR2 missiles. The missiles are controlled by two Mk 74 Mod 4 fire control systems, with four SPG 51 radars mounted two forward and two aft. A 5-in (127-mm) 54 cal Mk 45 gun is mounted forward between the Tartar and Asroc launchers, and another is superimposed aft. These are fitted to cope with low flying aircraft and fast patrol boats, and they also could be used for shore bombardment. They are controlled by a Mk 86 Mod 3 fire control system, and there is an SPG-60 radar. The *California*s also have an SPS-48 3-D radar on the foremast, and SPS-10 and SPS-40 search radars. They are fitted with NTDS.

At present the *California*s do not carry any surface-to-surface missiles, relying on the accompanying carrier's aircraft to deal with any major surface threat, but they may be refitted with Harpoon SSMs which would enable them to operate independently.

A third *California,* (DLGN-38), was authorized in FY 1968, but was deferred and eventually cancelled when the first of the improved *Virginia* Class CGNs was authorized in 1970. The *Virginia*s have improved electronics and combined standard/Asroc launchers. They can be distinguished from the *California*s because they have no Asroc launcher or 'reload house' forward, and the aft 5-in (127-mm) gun is mounted on the upper deck. They are 3.05 m (10 ft) shorter than the *California*s. The main problem with these nuclear escorts—and part of the reason why the third *California* was deferred—is the immense cost of these ships. The *California*s cost about $200 million each, and even the United States cannot afford to build very many of these extremely capable vessels.

Displacement: 10 150 tons (full load) *Length:* 181.66 m (596 ft) *Beam:* 18.59 m (61 ft) *Draught:* 9.6 m (31.5 ft) *Machinery:* 2 D2G reactors, 2 shafts, 100 000 shp=30+knots *Armament:* 2 Tartar SAM launchers; 2 5-in (127-mm) guns; 1 Asroc launcher; 4 12.7-in (32.25-cm) torpedo tubes *Crew:* 540

Campania

British escort carrier. The second *Campania* was originally laid down as a refrigerated merchant ship at Harland and Wolff's Belfast Yard on August 12, 1941. The Ministry of War Transport had already agreed in February 1941 to reserve ships being built for possible conversion into escort carriers, although they refused to release existing ships. The refrigerated cargo ships *Activity, Nairana, Vindex* and *Campania* were all completed as escort carriers, with a flight deck positioned well forward and the superstructure surmounted by a tall lattice mast.

Unlike the US escort carriers, which had short wooden flight decks, and many of which had open hangar sides and a single screw, these were all fast twin-screw vessels with closed hangar sides and relatively long steel flight decks. However, later US escort carriers had two lifts whereas these British ships only had one.

Nairana, Vindex and *Campania* were to have received identical conversions, but *Campania,* which was not launched until June 17, 1943 and completed until mid-1944, received several improvements not fitted in the first two ships, which were commissioned in December 1943. *Campania* received the first Action Information Organization fitted in a British escort carrier, and also had Type 277 radar, which gave good coverage at low level. Her modern Air Direction Room and radar proved invaluable for directing both her own and other carriers' aircraft.

In mid-1944 she served in home waters and was used to escort UK-Gibraltar convoys, but from September 1944 onward she was employed on the convoys to and from Russia. She normally embarked No 813 Squadron operating a mix of Swordfish III A/S aircraft and Wildcat VI fighters. In November 1944 she escorted two liners repatriating Soviet ex-prisoners of war to Russia, then returned with the crews for the Allied warships that had been loaned to Russia. In February 1945 *Campania* briefly embarked a Fulmar fitted with airborne radar which was intended to be used as a night fighter.

By 1950, *Activity, Nairana* and *Vindex* had all been reconverted into merchant ships, but *Campania* was used as the Festival of Britain exhibition ship, and made an extensive tour of Britain and Europe in 1951. Her unencumbered hangar and flight deck, which measured 157 m×21.64 m (515 ft×71 ft) made her ideal for this purpose. She was scrapped in 1955.

Displacement: 12 450 tons (standard), 16 000 tons (full load) *Length:* 164.59 m (540 ft) oa *Beam:* 21.34 m (70 ft) *Draught:* 5.79 m (19 ft) *Machinery:* 2-shaft diesel, 12 000 bhp=17 knots *Armament:* 2 4-in (102-mm); 16 2-pdr; 16 20-mm (0.79-in) *Aircraft:* 15 *Crew:* 700

A Hawker Hurricane IA is propelled down its launch ramp on the bow of a Catapult Armed Merchantman (CAM-Ship). After its mission the fighter ditched near the CAM-Ship

IWM

FIGHTER CATAPULT SHIPS

Name	fate
Pegasus	Accommodation ship (1944); stricken 1946
Springbank	Torpedoed September 27, 1941 by *U 201*
Ariguani	Accommodation ship from August 1942
Maplin	Returned to mercantile service December 1942
Patia	Sunk by air attack April 27, 1941

CATAPULT-ARMED MERCHANTMEN

Name	fate
Daghestan	returned to mercantile service
Daltonhall	returned to mercantile service
Eastern City	returned to mercantile service
Empire Barton	torpedoed September 20, 1941 by *U 74*
Empire Clive	returned to mercantile service
Empire Darwin	returned to mercantile service
Empire Day	returned to mercantile service
Empire Dell	torpedoed May 12, 1942 by *U 124*
Empire Eve	returned to mercantile service
Empire Faith	returned to mercantile service
Empire Flame	returned to mercantile service
Empire Foam	returned to mercantile service
Empire Franklin	returned to mercantile service
Empire Gale	returned to mercantile service
Empire Heath	torpedoed May 11, 1944 (returned earlier)
Empire Hudson	torpedoed September 10, 1941
Empire Lawrence	sunk by bombs May 27, 1942
Empire Moon	returned to mercantile service
Empire Morn	returned to mercantile service
Empire Ocean	wrecked August 5, 1942
Empire Rainbow	torpedoed July 26, 1942 by *U 607*
Empire Ray	returned to mercantile service
Empire Rowan	returned to mercantile service
Empire Shackleton	torpedoed December 28, 1942 by *U 225*
Empire Spray	returned to mercantile service
Empire Spring	torpedoed February 14, 1942 by *U 576*
Empire Stanley	returned to mercantile service
Empire Sun	torpedoed February 7, 1942 by *U 751*
Empire Tide	returned to mercantile service
Empire Wave	torpedoed October 2, 1941 by *U 562*
Helencrest	returned to mercantile service
Kafiristan	returned to mercantile service
Michael E	torpedoed June 2, 1941 by *U 108*
Novelist	returned to mercantile service
Primrose Hill	torpedoed October 29, 1942 by *UD 5*

CAM-Ships

British Catapult-Armed Merchantmen. After the German occupation of France in mid-1940 the Luftwaffe was able to establish air bases on the Atlantic coast. From here Focke-Wulf Condor four-engined bombers were able to harry British convoys, particularly those running to and from Gibraltar. Losses from air attack became so acute in 1941 that the British Admiralty was forced to take counter measures.

Although the idea of a 'mercantile' or 'trade protection' aircraft carrier was put forward (to emerge later as the escort carrier) the lack of suitable hulls caused the idea to be shelved. Instead, selected merchantmen were equipped with a single catapult mounted on the forecastle; by this means a single fighter aircraft could be launched at the right moment, to shoot down or drive off the Condor. If possible the pilot would land on an airfield, but normally he would have to 'ditch', and the aircraft would be lost. The aircraft used were mostly obsolescent marks of Hurricane, but fast enough to deal with a bomber, but all too often the pilot might be lost as well if an escorting warship did not get to him in time.

In all 35 merchant ships were fitted out as CAM-Ships, but in addition there were five Fighter Catapult Ships (FCS), which differed in being Royal Navy-manned and having naval fighter aircraft. Two of the FCSs were already serving as regular warships, the old seaplane carrier *Pegasus* and the auxiliary antiaircraft ship *Springbank* and the other three were Ocean Boarding Vessels. Unlike the FCSs, the CAM-Ships served as ordinary cargo-carriers and were mercantile-manned. Fifty RAF Hurricanes were allocated, and another 50 from Canada as reserves, but the first conversion, the *Michael E* had a naval Fulmar aircraft instead of a Hurricane.

The catapult ships suffered heavily. The *Patia* was sunk on April 27, 1941 off the Tyne, immediately after completion; the *Michael E* was torpedoed by *U 108* without ever launching her aircraft. Over a third were sunk, but they helped to provide air cover for convoys in the Western Approaches during the crucial period in 1941-42 before escort carriers appeared. The FCSs were ready in April 1941 and the first CAM-Ship sailed on May 27. The survivors were withdrawn in 1942-43 and converted to other uses or reverted to ordinary merchant ships.

Particulars: details of the *Pegasus* will be found under the entry for that ship, but as the others were an assorted variety of mercantile hulls it is impossible to give details. They varied in gross tonnage from 5100 tons to 9500 tons, and carried a variety of light antiaircraft weapons. The Fighter Catapult Ships could stow an additional aircraft, and were better armed than the CAM-Ships.

Cannon

US destroyer escort class. By the end of 1942 the US Navy had ordered over a thousand DEs to meet the needs of the Battle of the Atlantic. As with earlier destroyer escort designs the biggest problem was the supply of propulsion machinery, and this class was given a diesel-electric outfit. The decision had already been taken to avoid alterations to hull dimensions, and so the long hull of the *Buckley* Class was used. Unfortunately the demands for diesels for LSTs meant that only

CANNON CLASS TRANSFERS ON COMPLETION

Name	Transfer	Name	Transfer
Cannon	Brazilian *Baependi*	DE.110	French *Hova*
Christopher	Brazilian *Benavente*	DE.111	French *Somali*
Alger	Brazilian *Babitonga*	*Marts*	Brazilian *Bocaina*
Corbesier	French *Senegalais*	*Pennewill*	Brazilian *Bertioga*
Cronin	French *Algérien*	*Reybold*	Brazilian *Bauru*
Crosley	French *Tunisien*	*Herzog*	Brazilian *Beberibe*
DE.109	French *Marocain*	*McAnn*	Brazilian *Bracui*

half the engine-power could be provided. This was reflected in the tall funnel, which lacked the trunked uptakes of the *Buckley*, but had a similar height.

With US and British needs being met and the visible weakening of the U-Boat offensive in mid-1943 it was possible to give encouragements to Allied navies. Fifteen were transferred to France and Brazil on completion.

As the lead-ship was disposed of so early the class was frequently known as the *Bostwick* group. During the postwar years many more were transferred to friendly navies, either on loan or as outright purchases, usually under mutual aid programmes.

The class had the three 3-in (76-mm) guns of the earlier *Buckley* Class, and the triple 21-in (53-cm) torpedo tubes, although these were omitted from later units. To cope with kamikaze attacks many were rearmed with four single 40-mm (1.57-in) Bofors guns amidships in place of the torpedo tubes.

DE.99-128 were ordered from the Dravo Corporation, Wilmington; DE.162-193 from Federal Shipbuilding, Newark; DE.194-197 from Federal, Kearny; DE.739-762 from Western Pipe, San Pedro; and DE.763-788 from Tampa Shipbuilding. DE.114-128 (Dravo), DE.751-762 (Western Pipe) and DE.772-788 (Tampa) were all cancelled in 1943-44, when escort programmes were cut back to make room for landing craft.

The class comprised: DE.99 *Cannon;* DE.100 *Christopher;* DE.101 *Alger;* DE.102 *Thomas;* DE.103 *Bostwick;* DE.104 *Breeman;* DE.105 *Burrows;* DE.106 *Corbesier;* DE.107 *Cronin;* DE.108 *Crosley;* DE.109 unnamed; DE.110 unnamed; DE.111 unnamed; DE.112 *Carter;* DE.113 *Clarence L Evans;* DE.114-128 unnamed; DE.162 *Levy;* DE.163 *McConnell;* DE.164 *Osterhaus;* DE.165 *Parks;* DE.166 *Baron;* DE.167 *Acree;* DE.168 *Amick;* DE.169 *Atherton;* DE.170 *Booth;* DE.171 *Carroll;* DE.172 *Cooner;* DE.173 *Eldrige;* DE.174 *Marts;* DE.175 *Pennewill;* DE.176 *Micka;* DE.177 *Reybold;* DE.178 *Herzog;* DE.179 *McAnn;* DE.180 *Trumpeter;* DE.181 *Straub;* DE.182 *Gustafson;* DE.183 *Samuel S Miles;* DE.184 *Wesson;* DE.185 *Riddle;* DE.186 *Swearer;*

Name	Transfer	Name	Transfer
Thomas	Nationalist Chinese *Tai Ho* (1948)	*Bronstein*	Uruguayan *Artigas* (1952)
Bostwick	Nationalist Chinese *Tai Tsang* (1948)	*Baker*	French *Malagache* (1952)
Breeman	Nationalist Chinese *Tai Hu* (1948)	*Eisner*	Netherlands *De Zeeuw* (1951)
Burrows	Netherlands *Van Amstel* (1950)	*Garfield Thomas*	Greek *Panthir* (1951)
Carter	Nationalist Chinese *Tai Chao* (1948)	*Wingfield*	French *Sakalave* (1950)
Clarence L Evans	French *Bergère* (1952)	*Thornhill*	Italian *Aldebaran* (1951)
Baron	Uruguayan *Uruguay* (1952)	*Rinehart*	Netherlands *De Bitter* (1950)
Amick	Japanese *Asahi* (1955)	*Bangust*	Peruvian *Castilla* (1952)
Atherton	Japanese *Hatsuhi* (1955)	*Waterman*	Peruvian *Aguirre* (1952)
Booth	Filipino *Datu Kalantiaw* (1968)	*Weaver*	Peruvian *Rodriguez* (1951)
Eldridge	Greek *Leon* (1951)	*Hemminger*	Thai *Pin Klao* (1959)
Gustafson	Netherlands *Van Ewijck* (1950)	*Bright*	French *Touareg* (1950)
Samuel S Miles	French *Arabe* (1950)	*Cates*	French *Soudanais* (1950)
Wesson	Italian *Andromeda* (1951)	*Gandy*	Italian *Altair* (1951)
Riddle	French *Kabyle* (1950)	*Slater*	Greek *Aetos* (1951)
Swearer	French *Bambara* (1950)	*Ebert*	Greek *Zerax* (1951)
Stern	Netherlands *Van Zijl* (1951)	*Muir*	South Korean *Kyong Ki* (1956)
O'Neil	Netherlands *Dubois* (1951)	*Sutton*	South Korean *Kang Won* (1956)

DE.187 *Stern;* DE.188 *O'Neil;* DE.189 *Bronstein;* DE.190 *Baker;* DE.191 *Coffman;* DE.192 *Eisner;* DE.193 *Garfield Thomas;* DE.194 *Wingfield;* DE.195 *Thornhill;* DE.196 *Rinehart;* DE.197 *Roche;* DE.739 *Bangust;* DE.740 *Waterman;* DE.741 *Weaver;* DE.742 *Hilbert;* DE.743 *Lamons;* DE.744 *Kyne;* DE.745 *Synder;* DE.746 *Hemminger;* DE.747 *Bright;* DE.748 *Tills;* DE.749 *Roberts;* DE.750 *McClelland;* DE.751 *Gaynier;* DE.752 *Curtis W Howard;* DE.753 *John J Van Buren;* DE.754-755 unnamed; DE.756 *Damon M Cummings;* DE.757-762 unnamed; DE.763 *Cates;* DE.764 *Gandy;* DE.765 *Earl K Olsen;* DE.766 *Slater;* DE.767 *Oswald;* DE.768 *Ebert;* DE.769 *Neal A Scott;* DE.770 *Muir;* DE.771 *Sutton;* DE.772 *Milton Lewis;* DE.773 *George M Campbell;* DE.774 *Russell M Cox;* DE.775-788 unnamed.

Displacement: 1240 tons (standard), 1520 tons (full load) *Length:* 91.44 m (300 ft) wl *Beam:* 11.2 m (36 ft 9 in) *Draught:* 3.58 m (11 ft 9 in) max *Machinery:* 2-shaft diesel-electric, 6000 bhp=21 knots *Armament:* 3 3-in (76-mm)/50 cal (3×1); 2/6 40-mm (1.57-in) AA (1×2, 4×1); 8/10 20-mm (0.79-in) AA (8/10×1); 3 21-in (53-cm) torpedo tubes (removed from most); 1 Hedgehog antisubmarine mortar; 8 depth-charge throwers+2 racks *Crew:* 180 peacetime, 220 wartime

Carpenter

US destroyer class. *Carpenter* (DD.825) and her sister *Robert A Owens* (DD.827), built by the Consolidated Steel Corporation Orange shipyard and Bath Ironworks respectively, were originally designed as standard *Gearing* Class destroyers, with an armament of 6 5-in (127-mm)/38-cal guns in three twin turrets, 40-mm (1.57-in) and 20-mm (0.79-in) light AA guns and five 21-in (53-cm) torpedo tubes in a quintuple mounting. However, the *Carpenters* were still incomplete at the end of the Second World War, and were suspended until 1947 when they were transferred to the Newport News shipyard and completed as 'Hunter-Killer' destroyers (DDK).

On March 4, 1950 they were reclassified as DDE when the DDK and DDE classifications were combined. They were intended primarily as antisubmarine vessels and originally carried 3-in (76-mm) AA in twin mounts in place of the original 5-in (127-mm). At first *Carpenter* had four 3-in (76-mm) with a Hedgehog in B position, and *Robert A Owens* had six. They had powerful sonars and Weapon Able and Hedgehog A/S weapons were mounted.

They were to have acted in hunter-killer groups along with other converted Second World War destroyers, and were roughly comparable with the British Type 15 and Type 16 full and limited A/S destroyer conversions.

Both *Carpenter* and *Robert A Owens* were reclassified as DD on June 30, 1962 after they had undergone a FRAM I modernization. Their 3-in guns were removed and replaced by a single 5-in twin mount in A position.

US Navy

Her decks crammed with eight Catalina flying boats, naval fighters and vehicles USS *Thetis Bay*, a *Casablanca* Class escort carrier, steams through the Pacific. The *Casablancas* were used as 'jeep carriers' during island-hopping operations and deep penetration raids

They also have two triple Mk 32 A/S torpedo tube mountings in B position, an Asroc eight-tube launcher amidships, a tripod mainmast and extra superstructure forward of the aft funnel, and a hangar and landing pad aft for two Gyrodyne QH-50 DASH Drone A/S helicopters. They can be distinguished from other FRAM I *Gearing* conversions by the absence of an aft 5-in twin mounting.

Both are now used for Naval Reserve training, with a mixed regular and reserve crew.

Displacement: 2425 tons (standard), 3410 tons (full load) *Length:* 119.02 m (390 ft 6 in) oa *Beam:* 12.45 m (40 ft 10 in) *Draught:* 5.79 m (19 ft) *Machinery:* 2-shaft geared turbines, 60 000 shp=34 knots *Armament:* 2 5-in (127-mm) guns; 1 Asroc launcher; 6 12.7-in (32.25-cm) torpedo tubes (2×3) *Aircraft:* 2 DASH helicopters *Crew:* 282

Name	laid down	launched	completed
Carpenter	7/1945	12/1945	12/1949
Robert A Owens	10/1945	7/1946	11/1949

Casablanca

US escort carrier class. As with the preceding *Prince William* Class escort carriers (all except one of which were transferred to the Royal Navy), the *Casablanca* Class were built from the keel up as carriers, and were not converted mercantile hulls like the earlier *Bogue* and *Long Island* Classes. The *Casablancas*, however, were actually designed as escort carriers whereas the *Prince Williams* were a mercantile design with an added flight deck and hangar.

The *Casablancas* were built on what was basically a standard mercantile hull, and were designed more for ease of construction than for desirable operational characteristics.

The class comprised: CVE.55 *Casablanca* (ex-*Alazon Bay*, ex-*Ameer*); CVE.56 *Liscombe Bay*; CVE.57 *Coral Sea* (ex-*Alikula Bay*); CVE.58 *Corregidor* (ex-*Anguilla Bay*); CVE.59 *Mission Bay* (ex-*Atheling*); CVE.60 *Guadalcanal* (ex-*Astrolabe Bay*); CVE.61 *Manila Bay* (ex-*Bucareli Bay*); CVE.62 *Natoma Bay* (ex-*Begum*); CVE.63 *St. Lô* (ex-*Chapin Bay*); CVE.64 *Tripoli* (ex-*Didrickson Bay*); CVE.65 *Wake Island* (ex-*Dolomi Bay*); CVE.66 *White Plains* (ex-*Elbour Bay*); CVE.67 *Solomons* (ex-*Nassuk Bay*, ex-*Emperor*); CVE.68 *Kalinin Bay*; CVE.69 *Kasaan Bay*; CVE.70 *Fanshaw Bay*; CVE.71 *Kitkun Bay*; CVE.72 *Tulagi* (ex-*Fortalza Bay*); CVE.73 *Gambier Bay*; CVE.74 *Nehenta Bay* (ex-*Khedive*); CVE.75 *Hoggatt Bay*; CVE.76 *Kadashan Bay*; CVE.77 *Marcus Island* (ex-*Kanalku Bay*); CVE.78 *Savo Island* (ex-*Kaita Bay*); CVE.79 *Ommaney Bay*; CVE.80 *Petrof Bay*; CVE.81 *Rudyerd Bay*; CVE.82 *Saginaw Bay*; CVE.83 *Sargent Bay*; CVE.84 *Shamrock Bay*; CVE.85 *Shipley Bay*; CVE.86 *Sitkoh Bay*; CVE.87 *Steamer Bay*; CVE.88 *Cape Esperance* (ex-*Tananek Bay*); CVE.89 *Takanis Bay*; CVE.90 *Thetis Bay*; CVE.91 *Makassar Strait* (ex-*Ulitaka Bay*); CVE.92 *Windham Bay*; CVE.93 *Makin Island* (ex-*Woodcliff Bay*); CVE.94 *Lunga Point* (ex-*Alazon Bay*); CVE.95 *Bismarck Sea* (ex-*Alikula Bay*); CVE.96 *Salamaua* (ex-*Anguilla Bay*); CVE.97 *Hollandia* (ex-*Astrolabe Bay*); CVE.98 *Kwajalein* (ex-*Bucareli Bay*); CVE.99 *Admiralty Islands* (ex-*Chapin Bay*); CVE.100 *Bogainville* (ex-*Didrickson Bay*); CVE.101 *Matanikau* (ex-*Dolomi Bay*); CVE.102 *Attu* (ex-*Elbour Bay*); CVE.103 *Roi* (ex-*Alava Bay*); CVE.104 *Munda* (ex-*Tonowek Bay*).

They had a very short 152 m × 33 m (500 ft × 108 ft) flight deck. However, they did have two lifts and a catapult, and unlike earlier escort carriers they had two shafts which conferred much better manoeuvrability. To simplify production they had reciprocating machinery, but the twin-shaft arrangement enabled the speed to be raised by one knot, and they had better 'ship' characteristics than the earlier classes.

The forecastle was extended back to the forward end of the hangar and the *Casablancas* had a transom stern without sponsons, allowing room for only one 5-in (127-mm) AA

Aldo Fraccaroli

The *Canopo* entering port in March 1971 after her extensive modifications in 1968-69

gun in place of the previous two single mounts. The boiler uptakes were led into two ducts one on either side of the flight deck. These exhausted at the stern and there was a small island set forward on the starboard side surmounted by a lattice mast. The light AA guns were arranged in prominent sponsons on either side of the flight deck.

These ships entered service between July 1943 and July 1944, and were used in both the Atlantic and the Pacific. Some of the early members of the class were originally

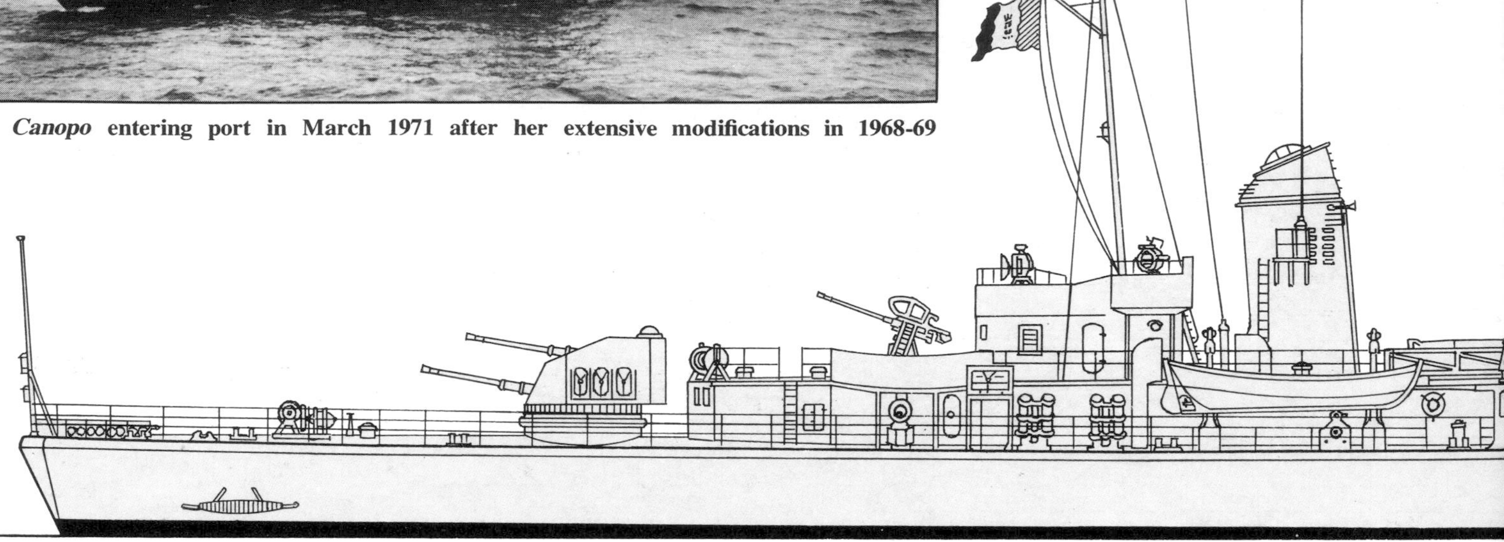

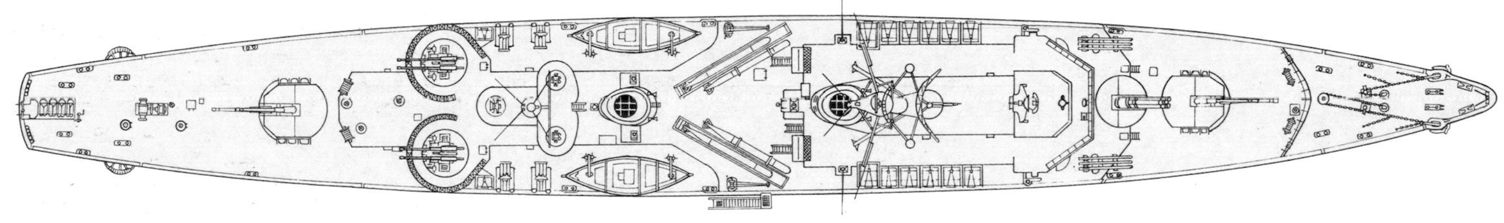

Deck plan and profile (above and top) of the *Centauro* Class light destroyer *Canopo,* as she appeared on her entry to the Italian navy in 1957, and profile of the *Castore* of the same class after her refit of 1966/67, with the F pennant number indicating the vessels' new rating as frigates. The *Castore* was the first of the *Centauros* to undergo the extensive modifications carried out to the class, the most noticeable of which is the replacement of the original main armament and the twin Breda 40-mm AA guns with the single 76-mm (3-in) 70-calibre guns in new OTO-Melara mounts. This replacement of the mountings after only ten years in service may well indicate that the original twin over-and-under mounting was unreliable. Other modifications included the replacement of the original single USN-pattern 21-in (53-cm) launchers for homing torpedoes between the funnels with triple Mk 32 torpedo tubes for acoustic homing torpedoes abaft the rear funnel

intended for the Royal Navy, including *Casablanca,* which was initially named HMS *Ameer,* but all were completed for the USN.

In the Atlantic they formed the nucleus of specialized hunter-killer groups consisting of one escort carrier and a number of destroyer escorts. These operated independently of the convoys, and went where they were most needed. Aided by cracking many German codes, they were highly successful. The most famous *Casablanca* Class carrier used for this purpose was *Guadalcanal* (CVE.60), whose hunter-killer group captured the German Type IXC submarine *U505* on June 4, 1944 off Dakar. *U505* became the USS *Nemo* and is now preserved at Chicago.

Most of the *Casablanca* Class went to the Pacific, where these 'jeep carriers' provided the close air support for the Pacific island-hopping campaign, whilst the faster fleet carriers made deep penetration raids or engaged the Japanese fleet. However, on October 25, 1944 a number of escort carriers providing air support for the landings at Leyte Gulf in the Philippines were attacked by the Japanese battleships *Yamato* and *Nagato,* together with several heavy cruisers. Admiral Halsey, whose battleships and fast carriers were supposed to protect the escort carriers and merchant ships, had been decoyed north out of range. The escort carriers were completely unarmoured and very weakly escorted, but despite this and the 10-knot speed advantage possessed by the Japanese, only the *Casablanca* Class *Gambier Bay* (CVE.73) was sunk, although several others were badly damaged. The Japanese ships had been held off by attacks from the carriers' own aircraft and by the escorting DDs and DEs. *St. Lô* (CVE.63) was sunk by Japanese aircraft the same day.

Two other *Casablancas* were sunk during the war. *Liscombe Bay* (CVE.56) was torpedoed by the Japanese submarine *I 175* on November 24, 1943, and *Ommaney Bay,* bombed by Japanese aircraft, was finally sunk by a torpedo from the US destroyer *Burns* on January 4, 1945. Some of the class, including *Casablanca,* were scrapped in 1947, but most survived in the mothball fleet until 1959-1960 when the remainder were disposed of. The *Casablanca* Class was succeeded in production by the improved and lengthened *Commencement Bay* Class.

Displacement: 7800 tons (standard), 10 400 tons (full load) *Length:* 156.13 m (512 ft 3 in) oa *Beam (hull):* 19.89 m (65 ft 3 in) *Draught:* 6.86 m (22 ft 6 in) *Machinery:* 2-shaft VTE reciprocating engines, 9000 ihp=19 knots. *Armament:* 1 5-in (127-mm); 16 40-mm (1.57-in); 24 20-mm (0.79-in) *Aircraft:* 28 *Crew:* 860

Centauro

Italian frigate/light destroyer class. Built in 1952-58, these were among the first Italian-designed ships built after the Second World War. They were originally rated as destroyers and had D-pendant numbers. The second pair, *Cigno* and *Castore* were built with US funds supplied under the Mutual Defence Aid Programme (MDAP) as *DE.1020* and *DE.1031,* and the class used USN sonar and radar.

The original armament comprised two twin 76-mm (3-in) gun mountings designed by OTO-Melara, La Spezia. These were a unique 'over-and-under' mounting with superimposed barrels, and they were credited with a rate of fire of 60 rounds per minute and 975 m/sec (3200 ft/sec) muzzle velocity. In 1966-67 the *Castore* underwent reconstruction, and the forward twin 76-mm (3-in), the after mounting and two twin Breda 40-mm (1.57-in)/70-cal guns were replaced by three single 76-mm (3-in) mountings in a new OTO-Melara mounting (one forward and two aft). Presumably the original mounting had proved unreliable, as it is a relatively rare occurrence for entire gun-mountings to be replaced only ten years after installation; it is more common for the fire-control system to be replaced.

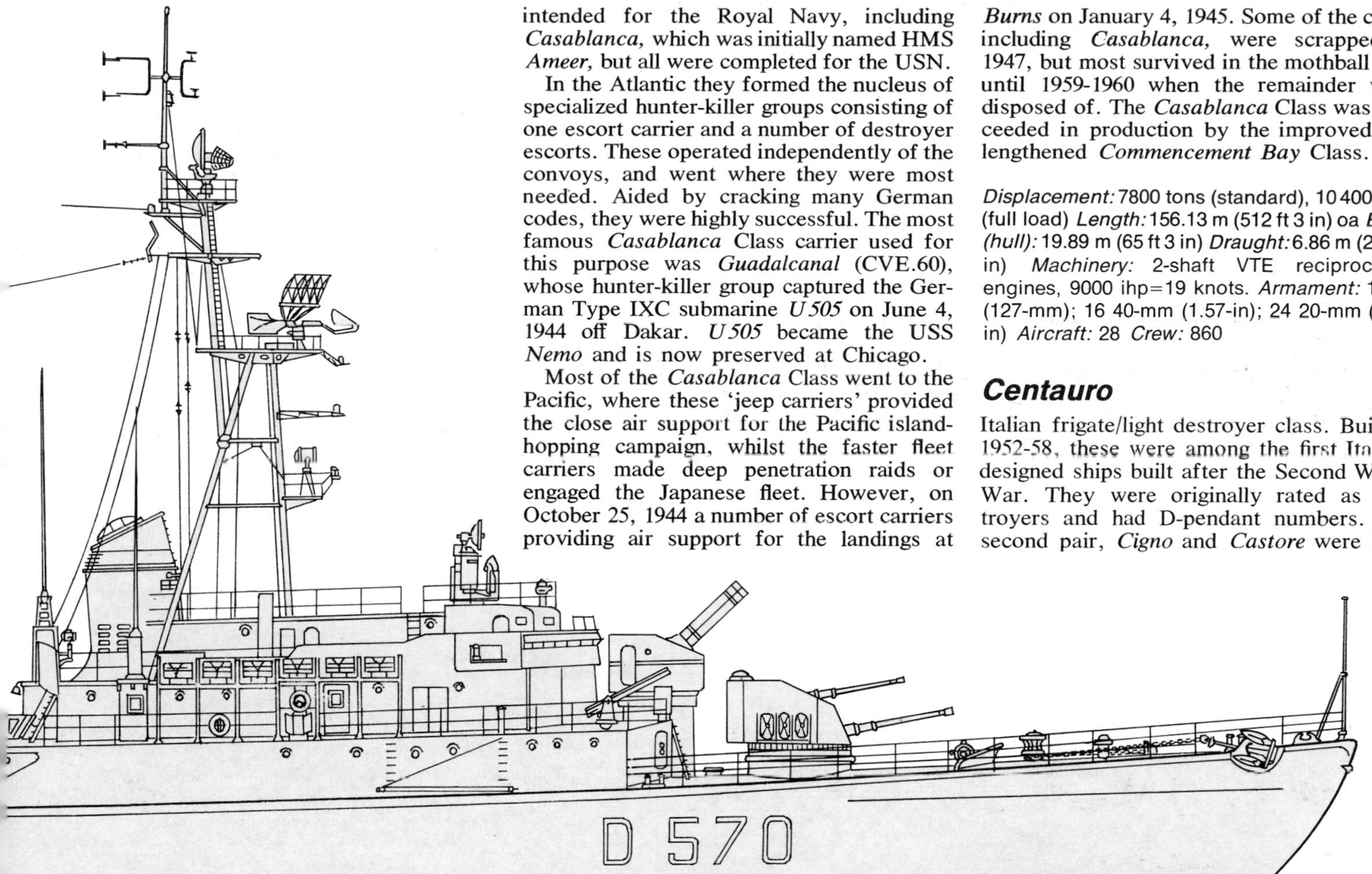

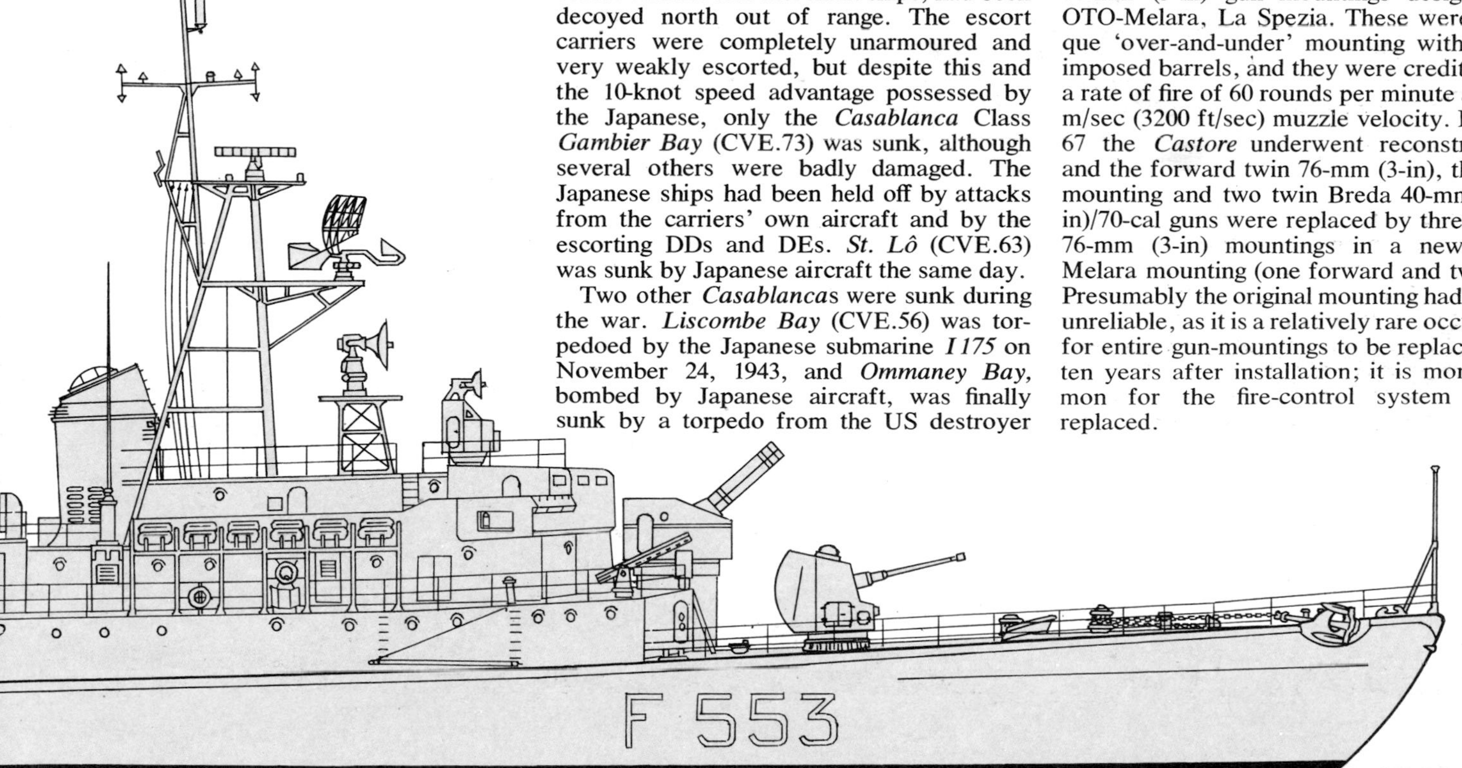

Ray Woodward

Museo Storico Navale

The Italian frigate/light destroyer *Centauro*, the first Italian-designed warship built after 1945

No and name	laid down	launched	completed	builder
D.570 *Canopo* (F.551)	5/1952	2/1955	4/1958	CN Taranto
D.571 *Centauro* (F.554)	5/1952	4/1954	5/1957	Ansaldo, Livorno
D.572 *Cigno* (F.555)	2/1954	3/1955	3/1957	CN Taranto
D.573 *Castore* (F.553)	3/1955	7/1956	7/1957	CN Taranto

In 1960 all four ships were rerated as frigates with F-numbers. The *Canopo* completed her conversion in 1968-69, followed by the *Centauro* in 1970-71 and the *Cigno* in 1972-73. The design emphasises anti-submarine armament, with two sonar sets and an Italian-designed Menon triple depth-charge mortar in B position. As built all four ships had USN-pattern single 21-in (53-cm) launchers for homing torpedoes between the funnels, but following reconstruction they have triple Mk 32 torpedo tubes for acoustic homing torpedoes (either US Mk 44s or Whitehead Motofides A-244s) abaft the second funnel.

Displacement: (As built) 1680 tonnes (standard), 2184 tonnes (full load); (After reconstruction) 1499 tonnes (standard), 2250 tons (full load) *Length:* 103.14 m (338 ft 5 in) oa *Beam:* 12 m (39 ft $4\frac{1}{2}$ in) *Draught:* 3.84 m (12 ft 7 in) *Machinery:* 2-shaft Tosi steam turbines, 22 000 shp=26 knots *Armament:* (As built) 4 76-mm (3-in)/62-cal (2×2) DP; 4 40-mm (1.57-in)/70-cal (2×2) AA; 2 21-in (53-cm) torpedo tubes; 1 triple A/S mortar; (After reconstruction) 3 76-mm (3-in)/62-cal (3×1) DP; 6 30.3-cm (12-in) torpedo tubes (2×3); 1 triple A/S mortar *Crew:* 235

Chapaev

Soviet cruiser class built 1938-1950, also known as the *Frunze* Class. After the construction of the *Kirov* Class heavy cruisers, the Soviet navy decided to revert to 6-in (152-mm) guns, but in greater numbers to provide increased rate of fire and weight of broadside. Another important change was to give the guns 50° elevation for antiaircraft capability.

As with the *Kirov* design, foreign aid was essential, for the Soviets had built so few large ships since 1916. The Italians provided the basic hull-design, while the Germans provided fire-control. Originally a catapult and triple torpedo tubes were to have been provided, the catapult between the funnels and two sets of torpedo tubes in wing positions. Six were ordered, three in Leningrad for the Baltic Fleet and three in Nikolaiev for the Black Sea Fleet. All work was suspended in mid-1941, started again in 1945, and they emerged looking very like prewar Italian heavy cruisers.

The layout resembled the British *Southampton*, with two pairs of triple 6-in (152-mm) turrets (two forward and two aft) and four twin AA mountings grouped around the second funnel. However, the superstructure was distinctly Italian, as was the style of the two funnels—capped and positioned widely apart.

As the first of the new generation of Soviet ships to appear after 1945, the *Chapaev* Class aroused considerable comment. To this day most reference books credit them with a combined steam-and-diesel propulsion system, but this is not correct. Since completion they have had progressive changes to their radar, but otherwise remain as they were completed.

The *Ordzhonikidze* was captured on the slip when German forces overran the Nikolaiev shipyard on August 18, 1941, and was so badly damaged that she had to be scrapped on the slip. The *Kuibishev* was towed to Poti in June 1941 and laid up there incomplete. Construction did not begin again until 1945. The *Frunze* was also towed to Poti, but in 1942 her stern was removed to repair the cruiser *Molotov*. She was also completed after the war. The three Baltic hulls were suspended from 1941-1945, but as they were still on the slips they were exposed to the risk of bombs and shells during the siege of Leningrad.

The *Chapaev* commissioned in 1949, followed by the *Zhelezniakov*, and both ships were transferred to the Arctic in 1950. The other four were completed in 1950, and

Ray Woodward

Inboard profile of the *Centauro* showing machinery details and mountings for the original main armament of two twin over-and-under Breda mountings for OTO-Melara 76-mm (3-in) 62-calibre guns

served until the 1960s. By the late 1970s only two of the class were left, the *Chkalov* (renamed *Komsomolets* in 1960) and the *Zhelezniakov*, both on training duties; the others were scrapped in the 1960s.

Displacement: 11 300 tons (normal) 15 000 tons (full load) *Length:* 202.8 m (665 ft) oa *Beam:* 18.9 m (62 ft) *Draught:* 7.3 m (24 ft) *Machinery:* 4-shaft geared steam turbines, 130 000 shp=32 knots *Protection:* 76 mm (3 in) belt; 51 mm (2 in) deck; 102 mm (4 in) turrets *Armament:* 12 150-mm (5.9-in)/50 cal (4×3); 8 100-mm (3.9-in)/50-cal (4×2) DP; 24 37-mm (1.46-in)/63-cal (12×2) AA; provision for laying 200 mines *Crew:* 840-900

Name	laid down	launched	completed	builder
Chapaev	1938	1940	1949	Ordzhonikidze yard, Leningrad
Zhelezniakov	1938	1940	1949	Marti yard, Leningrad
Chkalov	1939	1948	1950	Ordzhonikidze yard, Leningrad
Kuibishev	1939	1/1941	1950	Marti north yard, Nikolaiev
Frunze	1939	12/1940	1950	Marti south yard, Nikolaiev
Ordzhonikidze	1940	—	—	Marti south yard, Nikolaiev

Charles F Adams

US guided-missile destroyer class. Ordered in Fiscal Years 1957-61 and completed in 1960-64, they were the first DDGs designed from the keel up, and are basically an improved *Forrest Sherman* hull. A further three were built in US yards for the Royal Australian Navy, followed by three for the Federal German navy.

The first eight ships were allocated DD-numbers in the existing range, but were given DDG-numbers during construction, *DD.952-959* becoming *DDG.2-9.* The ships built for Australia and Germany were allocated numbers *DDG.25-30.*

The Australian ships differ in having a deckhouse amidships for the Anglo-Australian Ikara A/S missile system, and they were completed with a single-arm SAM-launcher instead of the twin type. The German ships are generally similar to USN ships but have square-topped 'macks' instead of conventional capped funnels.

The first 13 US ships had the Mk 11 twin launcher for Tartar missiles, whereas the later ships have the Mk 13 single-arm launcher. The Mk 13 weighs 60 129 kg (132 561 lb) as against 74 952 kg (165 241 lb) for the Mk 11, which allows 42 missiles to be stowed instead of 40, but the single type can fire just as fast (about 6 missiles per minute). Another difference between the groups is that the last five have a large SQS-23 bow sonar, which means that they have to have a single anchor housed in the stem to clear the dome.

The class is currently being modernized, with Standard-Medium Range (MR) missiles in place of the Tartar. It is believed that the additional topweight of new electronics may mean the removal of the Asroc launcher from between the funnels. The *Lawrence* and *Hoel* were fitted with launchers for Chaparral infrared short-range missiles in 1972-1973.

The *Biddle* was renamed *Claude V Ricketts* on July 28, 1964, in honour of the deceased vice-chief of naval operations, who had been a staunch supporter of NATO-manning of nuclear deterrent forces. The *Ricketts* then served for 18 months with a mixed NATO crew drawn from the Royal Navy, the Dutch, Italian, Greek, Turkish, Norwegian and Danish navies. The ship remained under USN control, with an American captain and part of her American crew, and the idea to prove the concept of mixed manning. Although the experiment was successful the project to build Polaris-armed surface ships for NATO was abandoned.

No	name	commissioned	builder
DDG.2	*Charles F Adams*	9/1960	Bath Ironworks
DDG.3	*John King*	2/1961	Bath Ironworks
DDG.4	*Lawrence*	1/1962	New York SB corporation
DDG.5	*Claude V Ricketts* (ex-*Biddle*)	1/1962	New York SB corporation
DDG.6	*Barney*	8/1962	New York SB corporation
DDG.7	*Henry B Wilson*	12/1960	Defoe SB company
DDG.8	*Lynde McCormick*	6/1961	Defoe SB company
DDG.9	*Towers*	6/1961	Todd Shipyards Inc
DDG.10	*Sampson*	6/1961	Bath Ironworks
DDG.11	*Sellers*	10/1961	Bath Ironworks
DDG.12	*Robison*	12/1961	Defoe SB company
DDG.13	*Hoel*	6/1962	Defoe SB company
DDG.14	*Buchanan*	2/1962	Todd Shipyards Inc
DDG.15	*Berkeley*	12/1962	New York SB corporation
DDG.16	*Joseph Strauss*	4/1963	New York SB corporation
DDG.17	*Conyngham*	7/1963	New York SB corporation
DDG.18	*Semmes*	12/1962	Avondale Marine Ways Inc
DDG.19	*Tattnall*	4/1963	Avondale Marine Ways Inc
DDG.20	*Goldsborough*	11/1963	Puget Sound B & DD company
DDG.21	*Cochrane*	3/1964	Puget Sound B & DD company
DDG.22	*Benjamin Stoddert*	9/1964	Puget Sound B & DD company
DDG.23	*Richard E Byrd*	3/1964	Todd Shipyards Inc
DDG.24	*Waddell*	8/1964	Todd Shipyards Inc
D.38	*Perth*	5/1965	Defoe SB company
D.39	*Hobart*	12/1965	Defoe SB company
D.41	*Brisbane*	1/1968	Defoe SB company
D.185	*Lütjens*	3/1969	Bath Ironworks
D.186	*Mölders*	8/1969	Bath Ironworks
D.187	*Rommel*	3/1970	Bath Ironworks

Below: **The USS *Tattnall*, a guided-missile destroyer of the *Charles F Adams* Class; she is armed with Tartar and Asroc missile systems**

C & S Taylor

Displacement: 3370 tons (standard), 4500 tons (full load) *Length:* 133.2 m (437 ft) oa *Beam:* 14.3 m (47 ft) *Draught:* 6.1 m (20 ft) *Machinery:* 2-shaft geared steam turbines, 70 000 shp=31 knots. *Armament:* 2 Tartar/Standard surface-to-air missile systems (twin- and single-arm launchers); 2 5-in (127-mm)/54-cal Mk 42 DP (2×1); 1 Asroc 8-barrelled antisubmarine missile system; 6 12.87-in (32.38-cm) Mk 32 torpedo tubes (2×3) *Crew:* 354

Charlie

Soviet cruise-missile submarine class. First seen in 1968, this group of 12 nuclear-propelled boats marked an important change in Soviet strategic thinking, for the *Charlie* 'C' Class is armed with vertical tubes for launching cruise missiles under water.

The missile is the SS-N-7 with a reported range of 48 km (30 miles), and it clearly gives a nuclear submarine a stand-off weapon with far greater range than any torpedo. It is believed to be intended for use against the US Navy's aircraft carriers, and it is significant that the *Charlie*s have been seen in the Mediterranean, the home of the 6th Fleet. The SS-N-7 can be fired underwater, to rise above the surface and then acquire its target and assume a cruising mode.

As far as is known all 12 were built at the Gorky yard on the River Volga, 480 km (300 miles) east of Moscow. The rate of construction was apparently three per year. They are all part of the Northern Fleet.

Displacement: 4000 tons/5100 tons (surfaced/submerged) *Length:* 94 m (308 ft 5 in) *Beam:* 10 m (32.8 ft) *Draught:* 7.5 m (24 ft 7 in) *Machinery:* 1-shaft nuclear reactor, steam turbines, 24 000 shp=20/30 knots (surfaced/submerged) *Armament:* 8 launchers for SS-N-7 subsurface-to-surface missiles; 8 21-in (53-cm) torpedo tubes

A German-crewed Sikorsky S-58 circles two destroyers of the *Hamburg* Class during joint exercises between the US Navy and Kriegsmarine, with a *Charles F Adams* Class destroyer in the foreground. Besides its surface-to-air and antisubmarine missiles the *Charles F Adams* mounts two 5-in (127-mm)/54 cal guns and two triple Mk 32 12.75-in (32.38-cm) torpedo tubes. Other ships of this class have been built in US yards, three for Australia and three for West Germany

Federal German Navy

Chequers

British destroyer class. The *Chequers* or *Ch* Class was the 12th Flotilla of the Emergency War Programme. Ordered in July 1942 they were of the same design as the 11th (*Caesar* Class) flotilla but incorporated new equipment under development in the later years of the war. Most important of this equipment was the Mk VI director which remotely controlled the main armament and utilized the latest type of gunnery radar which was capable of accurate 'blind fire'. This, together with additional close-range AA weapons, larger bridge, heavier masts and radar equipment, seriously increased topweight but some compensation was provided by the omission of the foremost bank of torpedo tubes.

All were laid down in 1943 but their construction was hampered by delays in the supply of equipment, particularly the new director, and none were completed before the end of the war. The last to complete was *Chivalrous* in May 1946. When they entered service they carried a close-range armament of one twin 40-mm (1.57-in) Bofors amidships, two single 2-pdr pom-poms on the platform abaft the funnel and one single 20-mm (0.79-in) in each of the bridge wings. However, the *Chevron* was completed with twin 20-mm (0.79-in) mountings in place of the 2-pdr guns and the *Chivalrous* with four single 40-mm (1.57-in) Bofors in place of the 2-pdr and 20-mm (0.79-in) guns. During the following years most of the remainder of the class were modified to the latter standard. During the 1950s X gun was removed to make way for the fitting of two 'Squid' antisubmarine mortars, and the two single 40-mm (1.57-in) guns abaft the funnel were removed. The *Chaplet* and *Chieftain* which were converted to minelayers, also had Y gun and the torpedo tubes removed.

Two of the class were sold to Pakistan; the *Chivalrous* (renamed *Taimur*) in 1954 and the *Charity* (renamed *Shah Jehen*) in 1958. All eight ships were sold for scrap between 1961 and 1971.

Chaplet, Charity (built by Thornycroft)
Chequers, Chieftain (built by Scott's)
Cheviot, Chevron (built by Stephen)
Childers, Chivalrous (built by Denny)

Displacement: 1900 tons (standard), 2535 tons (full load) *Length:* 110.57 m (362 ft 9 in) *Beam:* 10.90 m (35 ft 9 in) *Draught:* 3.20 m (10 ft 6 in) *Machinery:* 2-shaft geared steam turbines, 40 000 shp=34 knots *Armament:* 4 4.5-in (114.3-mm) (4×1); 2 40-mm (1.57-in) (1×2); 2 2-pdr (2×1); 2 20-mm (0.79-in) (2×1) *Crew:* 186

Chuyo

Japanese escort carrier class. Unlike other aircraft carriers converted from liners, *Chuyo* (ex-*Nitta Maru*) and her sisters *Taiyo* (ex-*Kasuga Maru*) and *Unyo* (ex-*Yawata Maru*) were built with spaces for lifts and hangars and other equipment so that they could easily be converted to aircraft carriers in an emergency; and the NYK shipping line, which operated from Japan to America, was paid a considerable subsidy for these ships by the Japanese navy.

All were built at Mitsubishi's Nagasaki yard, but only *Chuyo*, launched on May 20, 1939, and *Unyo*, launched on October 31, 1939 were completed as liners. *Taiyo*, launched on September 19, 1940, was completed in September 1941 at Sasebo dockyard as an aircraft carrier. *Unyo* was converted between January and May 1942 and *Chuyo* from May to November 1942 at Kure dockyard.

They were fitted with a 172 m by 23.5 m (564 ft 4in by 77 ft) flight deck, and were the first Japanese carriers to have a funnel on the island, which was quite large. The high freeboard forward meant that the bow plating extended almost up to the flight deck. They were fitted with two lifts, but not with catapults or arrester gear. This, combined with their slow speed and complete lack of protection, meant that they were unsuitable for use as fleet carriers, as had been intended. Instead they were mainly used as aircraft ferries and for training pilots in deck landing and carrier operations.

Taiyo differed from the other two by having only four 4.7-in (120-mm) AA, and a much smaller crew. The class originally had only eight 25-mm (1-in) AA guns, but by 1943 these had been increased to 24. By mid-1944 *Unyo* had had four 4.7-in (120-mm) removed, and both *Taiyo* and *Unyo's* light AA armament had been increased to 64 25-mm (1-in) and 10 13-mm (0.51-in) AA.

The lack of underwater protection made these ships very vulnerable to underwater damage, and all were sunk by American submarines. *Chuyo* was torpedoed by *Sailfish* off Honshu on December 4, 1943, *Taiyo* was torpedoed by *Rasher* off Cuzon on August 18, 1944, and *Unyo* by *Barb* in the South China Sea on September 16, 1944.

Displacement: 17 830 tons (standard) *Length:* 180.24 m (591 ft 4 in) oa *Beam:* 22.48 m (73 ft 9 in) *Machinery:* geared turbines, 25 200 shp=21 knots *Armament:* 8 4.7-in (120-mm); 8 25-mm (1-in) *Aircraft:* 27 *Crew:* 850

Claud Jones

US escort class, built 1957-1960. In Fiscal Year 1956 two diesel-engined escorts were authorized by Congress as successors to the *Dealey* and *Courtney* Classes, followed by a further two the following year. They were an attempt to provide the smallest and cheapest antisubmarine ships for mass production, but like their British Equivalents, the *Blackwood* Class, they proved too small to be re-equipped with modern sonar and weapons.

They were quite unlike any other DEs built for the US Navy, with diesel engines and a second diminutive funnel. The armament was light, two single 3-in (76-mm) guns, two triple A/S torpedo tubes and a depth-charge rack and two Hedgehogs. Between 1961 and 1964 *Charles Berry* and *McMorris* had the Norwegian Terne III antisubmarine rocket-launcher in place of the Hedgehogs, but later *Charles Berry* was fitted with variable-depth sonar equipment aft.

In February 1973 the *John R Perry* was transferred to Indonesia and was renamed *Samadikun*. The same navy then bought the rest of the class between January and December 1974. They were renamed *Martadinata* (ex-*Charles Berry*), *Mongisidi* (ex-*Claud Jones*) and *Ngurah Rai* (ex-*McMorris*).

Displacement: 1450 tons (standard), 1750 tons (full load) *Length:* 94.5 m (310 ft) oa *Beam:* 11.3 m (37 ft) *Draught:* 5.5 m (18 ft) *Machinery:* 1-shaft diesel, 9200 bhp=22 knots *Armament:* 2 3-in (76-mm)/50-cal AA (2×1); 6 12.75-in (32.38-cm) torpedo tubes Mk 32 (2×3); 2 Hedgehog mortars/Terne III rocket-launchers (removed) *Crew:* 175

No and name	launched	builder
DE.1033 ***Claud Jones***	5/1958	Avondale Marine Ways Inc
DE.1034 ***John R Perry***	7/1958	Avondale Marine Ways Inc
DE.1035 ***Charles Berry***	3/1959	Avondale Marine Ways Inc
DE.1036 ***McMorris***	5/1959	Avondale Marine Ways Inc

Clemenceau

French aircraft carrier class, built 1955-1963. Although aircraft carriers had been ordered for the Marine Nationale before the outbreak of the Second World War they had not made much progress, and so when the French Government authorized the construction of a fleet carrier (PA.54) in 1953 it marked the beginning of France's first aircraft carrier. A sister (PA.55) was authorized two years later.

As first envisaged they were to be 22 000-ton ships armed with 12 twin 57-mm (2.24-in) guns. An unusual feature was the positioning of the after end of the angled flight deck well to starboard of the centre-line. The theoretical advantage of this feature was the reduction of the port overhang, but on the advice of US and British carrier experts it was dropped, as turbulence from funnel-gas and the island super structure would have made landings hazardous. The armament was soon revised to 12 single 100-mm (3.9-in) guns and then to eight, disposed in four quadrants at the edge of the flight deck.

The *Clemenceau* was ordered in 1954 and work started at the end of 1955, while *Foch* was laid down in a special dry dock at St Nazaire in December 1956. After lengthy trials the first ship entered service in November 1961, and the second in July 1963.

The two carriers were fitted with the latest aids, including the Mitchell-Brown BS 5 steam catapult, a deck-edge lift on the starboard side, two mirror landing-sights and an 8° angled deck. The hangar measures 151.7 m×26.5 m×8.5 m (497 ft 8 in×87 ft×28 ft) and the flight deck is 165.5 m×29.5 m (543 ft×96 ft 9 in). The lifts are 16m×11m (52 ft 6 in×36 ft) in area. The only armour provided is in the form of crowns to the machinery spaces and magazines, and splinter-proof protection to the flight deck and bridges. As considerable topweight was added during the

USS *Cleveland* photographed in Cape Cod Bay in March 1946. She was the first of 27 light cruisers laid down between 1940 and 1944 and which saw action largely in the Pacific as fast escorts for carrier task forces. After the war six were equipped with Terrier or Talos guided missiles

design stage and building it is not surprising that the *Foch* needed the addition of bulges to give a greater margin of stability, and the *Clemenceau* was similarly altered during the first refit, increasing the beam by 1.8 m (6 ft).

The first air group comprised three flights of Etendard IV, Crusader and Alizé aircraft, 30 in all. Since then the ships have been modified to operate the Super-Etendard. The fuel capacity differs; the *Clemenceau* carries 1200 cu m (42 375 cu ft) of jet fuel and 400 cu m (14 125 cu ft) of avgas, while the *Foch* carries 1800 cu m, (63 566 cu ft) and 109 cu m (3848 cu ft) of each. As the French navy is showing considerable interest in V/STOL aircraft the two ships may end their days as 'Harrier carriers'.

Displacement: 27 307 tonnes (normal), 32 780 tonnes (full load) *Length:* 265 m (869 ft 5 in) oa *Beam:* 31.7 m (104 ft) over bulges; 51.2 m (167 ft 11 in) over flight deck *Draught:* 8.6 m (28 ft 2½ in) *Machinery:* 2-shaft geared steam turbines, 126 000 shp=32 knots *Protection:* Not published (see above) *Armament:* 8 100-mm (3.9-in) DP (8×1) *Aircraft:* 30 (normal), 40 (maximum) *Crew:* 1228

Cleveland

US light cruiser class. The 27 ships of this class were developed from the earlier *St Louis* Class (themselves modified *Brooklyns*, but they sacrificed one triple 6-in (152-mm) turret forward for an improved AA armament. This triple turret had only been carried by the *Brooklyns* and the *St Louis* Class to match the Japanese *Mogamis*, and the *Cleveland*'s main armament was more than adequate to cope with surface targets. They were a better-balanced design than the earlier US light cruisers, and they were at least the equal of any foreign contemporary.

The hull was slightly broader than that of the *St Louis* Class, and the main belt was shorter. There were no openings in the hull, which was mechanically ventilated throughout. It was excellently subdivided. Like the *St Louis* Class, the after superstructure was closed up to the second funnel, giving good sky arcs for most of the AA armament. The 5-in (127-mm) turrets were arranged in lozenge fashion about the superstructure, with the light AA guns fore and aft and on either side of the funnels. The seaplanes were carried in a hangar aft, with a catapult and prominent aircraft handling crane. The *Clevelands* were completed with gunnery control and air-search radar.

They were the largest class of cruiser ever built, despite nine being converted into *Independence* Class light fleet carriers and three being cancelled. Twenty-seven were completed to the original design, and they were built by only four firms.

Youngston (CL-94) was cancelled on August 11, 1945, and CL-84 and CL-88 were never commenced. The excellence of the design is shown by the fact that none were sunk, although *Birmingham* (CL-62) was severely damaged by the explosion aboard the carrier *Princeton* (CVL-23) in October 1944 and again by a Japanese kamikaze aircraft off Okinawa in May 1945, and *Houston* was very badly damaged by a torpedo from a Japanese aircraft off Formosa in October 1944.

By the time the Americans had worked out the correct methods of using radar fire control, the *Clevelands*, with the stream of fire from the power-worked triple 6-in (152-mm) turrets, were very formidable surface warships. They saw extensive action during the Second World War, and mostly served in the Pacific as escorts to the fast carrier Task Forces. Eleven more were redesigned as a result of wartime experience with a single funnel and a more compact superstructure to give better sky arcs for the AA guns. These were known as the *Fargo* Class, but only two were completed.

By the mid-1950s it was obvious that the all-gun armed cruiser was obsolete, and it was intended to convert 13 *Clevelands* into single-ended guided missile cruisers. However, these conversions took so long and were so expensive for the results achieved that only six were rebuilt in this way.

All had their aft superstructure completely rebuilt, and *Galveston* (CLG-3), *Little Rock* (CLG-4) and *Oklahoma City* (CLG-5) had a twin Talos SAM launcher fitted aft in place of the two triple 6-in (152-mm) turrets. *Providence* (CLG-6), *Springfield* (CLG-7) and *Topeka* (CLG-8) had a twin Terrier SAM instead. *Little Rock, Oklahoma City, Providence* and *Springfield* also had their forward bridge enlarged and the forward superfiring 6-

No and name	laid down	launched	completed
CL-55 *Cleveland*	7/1940	11/1941	6/1942
CL-56 *Columbia*	8/1940	12/1941	6/1942
CL-57 *Montpelier*	12/1940	2/1942	9/1942
CL-58 *Denver*	12/1940	1/1942	10/1942
CL-60 *Santa Fe*	6/1941	6/1942	11/1942
CL-62 *Birmingham*	2/1941	3/1942	1/1943
CL-63 *Mobile*	4/1941	5/1942	3/1943
CL-64 *Vincennes*	3/1942	7/1943	1/1944
CL-65 *Pasadena*	2/1943	12/1943	6/1944
CL-66 *Springfield*	2/1943	3/1944	9/1944
CL-67 *Topeka*	4/1943	8/1944	12/1944
CL-80 *Biloxi*	7/1941	2/1943	8/1943
CL-81 *Houston*	8/1941	6/1943	12/1943
CL-82 *Providence*	7/1943	12/1944	5/1945
CL-83 *Manchester*	9/1944	3/1946	10/1946
CL-86 *Vicksburg*	10/1942	12/1943	6/1944
CL-87 *Duluth*	11/1942	1/1944	9/1944
CL-89 *Miami*	8/1941	12/1942	12/1943
CL-90 *Astoria*	9/1941	3/1943	5/1944
CL-91 *Oklahoma City*	12/1942	2/1944	12/1944
CL-92 *Little Rock*	3/1943	8/1944	6/1945
CL-93 *Galveston*	2/1944	4/1945	5/1946
CL-101 *Amsterdam*	3/1943	4/1944	1/1945
CL-102 *Portsmouth*	6/1943	9/1944	6/1945
CL-103 *Wilkes-Barre*	12/1942	12/1943	7/1944
CL-104 *Atlanta*	1/1943	2/1944	12/1944
CL-105 *Dayton*	3/1943	3/1944	1/1945

in (152-mm) turret removed to provide sufficient office space, accommodation and communications facilities to enable them to be used as fleet flagships.

The two not fitted as flagships were discarded in the early 1970s, and the four flagships were also being phased out by the late 1970s. The unconverted *Clevelands* were scrapped from 1959 onwards. The USN had so many light cruisers after the Second World War that they had all been mothballed since 1950 with the exception of *Manchester* (CL-83), which was put in reserve in 1956.

CL-55-61, 76-79, 85, 99-100 and 103-105 were built by New York Shipbuilding; CL-62-63, 80-81, 86-87 and 101-102 by Newport News; CL-64-67 and 82-83 by Bethlehem (Quincy); and CL-89-94 by Cramp. Other numbers were cancelled.

Displacement: 10 000 tons (standard); 13 755 tons (full load) *Length:* 185.9 m (610 ft) *Beam:* 20.3 m (66 ft 6 in) *Draught:* 7.6 m (25 ft) *Machinery:* 4-shaft geared steam turbines, 100 000 shp=33 knots *Protection:* 38-127 mm (1.5-5 in) sides; 51-76 mm (2-3 in) decks; 76-127 mm (3-5 in) main turrets *Armament:* 12 6-in (152-mm); 12 5-in (127-mm); 8 40-mm (1.57-in); 10 20-mm (0.79-in) *Aircraft:* 4 *Crew:* 1200

Colbert

French cruiser, built 1953-59. Under the 1953 Programme a new antiaircraft cruiser was ordered, similar in design to the revised plans drawn up for the *de Grasse.* Nothing has been revealed about the system of armouring, but it has been officially stated that the new ship has a different scheme to the *de Grasse.*

As completed the *Colbert* has an extremely heavy armament of antiaircraft guns, eight twin 127-mm (5-in) guns and ten twin 57-mm (2.24-in) guns, disposed on four levels. The 127-mm (5-in) guns were French-designed, but chambered to take US-pattern 5-in (127 mm) ammunition; the 57-mm (2.24-in) guns were designed by Bofors.

The ship was laid down in a dry dock at Brest arsenal in December 1953, floated out on March 24, 1956, and began her trials the following year.

From April 1970 the ship was in dockyard hands for a complete reconstruction and conversion to a guided-missile cruiser. In the process she was rearmed with a twin Masurca SAM-system, with a double-arm launcher on the quarterdeck and a completely new radar array. At the same time the armament was revised, with all 127-mm (5-in) guns replaced by two of the new 100-mm (3.9-in) dual-purpose guns forward. Six of the original 57-mm (2.24-in) twins were retained, on two levels on either side of the superstructure. The bridge was rebuilt to accommodate new radar, fire control and command facilities.

The sketch design published in 1970 showed a more ambitious rearmament scheme, with six Exocet surface-to-surface missiles and six 100-mm (3.9-in) guns. However, it was later admitted that the scale of armament had been reduced, cutting 80 000 million francs from the estimated cost of 350 000 million francs. By late 1977 only the bedplates for four MM38 missiles had been installed, but the missiles were due to be fitted at the next refit. The Mk 2 Mod 3 Masurca is fitted, and 48 missiles similar to the US Terrier are carried in stowage.

Machinery and boilers are in separate compartments on the unit system, two boilers to each set of turbines. The port and starboard turbine rooms are divided by an 18 m (59 ft) watertight bulkhead.

Radar and fire control are entirely French, DRBV 51 guidance radars for the Masurca, DRBV 20 for long-range air warning and surveillance, DRBC 32C for gunnery, etc. The ship is also fitted with the British Knebworth Corvus chaff-rocket system and can operate a helicopter, although no hangar is provided. Extensive command and communications facilities enable her to act as a headquarters ship for combined operations.

Displacement: 8500 tonnes (standard), 11 300 tonnes (full load) *Length:* 180.8 m (593 ft 2 in) oa *Beam:* 18.9 m (62 ft) *Draught:* 7.7 m (25 ft 3 in) max *Machinery:* 2-shaft geared steam turbines, 86 000 shp=31½ knots *Protection:* 50-80 mm (1.97-3.1 in) belt; 50 mm (1.97 in) deck *Armament:* (As built) 16 127-mm (5-in)/54-cal (8×2); 20 57-mm (2.24-in)/60-cal (10×2); (After 1972) 2 100-mm (3.9-in) DP (2×1); 12 57-mm (2.24-in) AA (6×2); 1 twin Masurca surface-to-air missile system; 4 MM38 Exocet surface-to-surface missiles (to be fitted) *Aircraft:* 1 helicopter *Crew:* 777 as built, 560 after reconstruction

Colossus

British light fleet carrier. By the middle of the Second World War, it had become obvious to the British Admiralty that it was not possible to produce sufficient numbers of fleet aircraft carriers with their high speed, armoured flight deck and relatively large aircraft capacity,

ECP Armées

ECP Armées

Top: **The French cruiser *Colbert* prior to her conversion in 1972** ***Above:*** **The *Colbert* after 1972 fitted with twin Masurca SAM-system on the quarterdeck and a modernized radar array**

whilst the escort carriers were too small, too slow and could not carry sufficient aircraft to act as substitutes. What was needed was a design that could be built quickly by large numbers of shipyards, that could carry a reasonable number of aircraft and that had sufficient speed at least to keep up with the older battleships.

The result was the light fleet carriers. The first to be built were the ten *Colossus* Class. To fulfill the requirements a number of the qualities of the fleet carriers had to be sacrificed, and the *Colossus* Class was designed to mercantile specifications to enable them to be built by yards unaccustomed to building large warships. They were completely unprotected, though they were moderately well subdivided, and their machinery was arranged en echelon. A maximum speed of 23 knots at full load was accepted as adequate, and as a result they were able to use standard destroyer machinery. A single large hangar with sufficient headroom to accommodate the latest US carrier aircraft was served by two lifts. There was a shortage of twin 4.5-in (114-mm) turrets, and in any case long-range AA defence was seen as a job for the escort and carrier aircraft rather than for the carrier herself, so the *Colossus* Class only had close-range AA guns.

In the same way that a number of Japanese liners had been designed to be converted into aircraft carriers in time of war, the *Colossus* Class were intended to be converted easily into merchant ships at the end of hostilities. However, they proved to be far too valuable as warships, and none were ever converted in this way.

None were completed in time for active service during the Second World War. *Colossus* herself was loaned to the French in 1946 as *Arromanches*. She was used extensively in French Indo-China in the late 1940s, and in 1951 the French purchased her outright. She was rebuilt in 1957-58 with an angled deck and improved electronics, and like all surviving *Colossus* Class carriers had her deck

A de Havilland Sea Vampire makes a wheels-up landing on the specially designed flexible flight deck of HMS *Warrior* in 1948. These experiments with a deck of rubber-type material fixed 0.75 m above the flight deck were carried out to test the viability of using wheel-less aircraft

MOD

strengthened to operate the heavier modern aircraft. She survived until the early 1970s as a training and helicopter carrier.

Glory, *Ocean* and *Theseus* remained in service with the RN as light fleet carriers, taking part in the Korean War and the Suez campaign. They were discarded in 1960-61. *Perseus* and *Pioneer* were completed as aircraft maintenance carriers after the success of the purpose-built *Unicorn*. However, unlike the older ship they could not operate aircraft themselves because they had two large deckhouses on the flight deck. *Triumph*, after serving as a light fleet carrier, was converted into a heavy repair ship in 1964. She has large cranes and deckhouses on the flight deck, and she still exists in reserve.

Venerable became the Dutch *Karel Doorman* in 1948. She was completely rebuilt during 1955-58 with an angled deck and a revised superstructure with a tall lattice mast and capped funnel. She also received modern radars. After a small fire in 1968 she was sold to Argentina, where she remains as the *25 de Mayo*. *Vengeance* served in the Royal Australian Navy between 1952 and 1955, and was sold to Brazil in 1957. She was completely rebuilt in Holland during 1957-60 with a new lattice mast and funnel, new electronics and an angled deck. She is still in service, and is named *Minas Gerais*. *Warrior* served in the Royal Canadian Navy between 1946 and 1948. She was used for deck landing trials by the RN, and was sold to Argentina as *Independencia* in 1958. She was discarded in the early 1970s.

This excellent class and its successors was one of the most successful improvizations of the Second World War.

Displacement: 13 190-13 350 tons (standard), 18 000-18 200 tons (full load) *Length:* 211.7 m (694 ft 6 in) *Beam:* 24.5 m (80 ft 3 in) *Draught:* 7.2 m (23 ft 6 in) *Machinery:* 2-shaft steam geared turbines, 40 000 shp = 25 knots *Armament:* 24 2-pdr (40-mm); 21 20-mm (0.79-in) *Aircraft:* 48 *Crew:* 1076

Comandante Margottini

Italian destroyer class. This class of 18 vessels, otherwise known as the 'Comandanti Medaglie d'Oro' Class, were the last destroyers to be designed for the Italian navy before the Armistice in 1943. Only nine of the destroyers had been laid down by the time of the Armistice and they were taken over by the Germans and subsequently broken up on the slipways. The *Comandante Margottini*

Name	laid down	builder
Commandante Baroni	2/1943	Odero-Terni-Orlando, Leghorn
Comandante Borsini	4/1943	Odero-Terni-Orlando, Leghorn
Comandante Botti	8/1943	Cantieri Riuniti dell'Adriatico, Trieste
Comandante Casana	2/1943	Cantieri Navali Riuniti, Ancona
Comandante Corsi	N/A	Cantieri Riuniti dell'Adriatico, Trieste
Comandante de Cristofaro	2/1943	Cantieri del Tirreno, Riva Trigoso
Comandante Dell'Anno	2/1943	Cantieri Navali Riuniti, Ancona
Comandante Esposito	N/A	Cantieri Riuniti dell'Adriatico, Trieste
Comandante Fiorelli	N/A	Cantieri Riuniti dell'Adriatico, Trieste
Comandante Fontana	N/A	Oder-Terni-Orlando, Leghorn
Comandante Giannattasio	N/A	Cantieri Riuniti dell'Adriatico, Trieste
Comandante Giobbe	N/A	Cantieri del Tirreno, Riva Trigoso
Comandante Giorgis	N/A	Cantieri del Tirreno, Riva Trigoso
Comandante Margottini	3/1943	Oder-Terni-Orlando, Leghorn
Comandante Milano	N/A	Cantieri Riuniti dell'Adriatico, Trieste
Comandante Moccagatta	N/A	Odero-Terni-Orlando, Leghorn
Comandante Novaro	N/A	Cantieri Riuniti dell'Adriatico, Trieste
Comandante Rodocanacchi	N/A	Odero-Terni-Orlando, Leghorn
Comandante Ruta	8/1943	Cantieri Riuniti dell'Adriatico, Trieste
Comandante Toscano	12/1942	Cantieri del Tirreno, Riva Trigoso

A *Combattante II* French patrol boat of the Greek *Kimothoi* Class with her four Exocet MM.38 missile-launchers amidships. The MM.38 has a 32-km (20-mile) range which gives *Combattante* Class vessels the ability to deliver a considerable weight of fire from a useful range. Gun armament consists of a twin 35-mm fore and aft; two wire-guided torpedo tubes are positioned aft

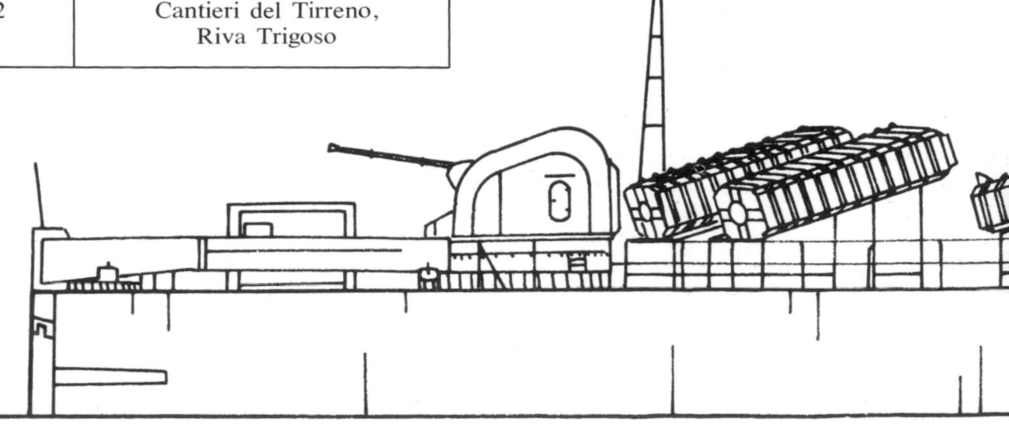

Name	laid down	launched	completed
Colossus	6/1942	9/1943	12/1944
Glory	8/1942	11/1943	2/1945
Ocean	11/1942	7/1944	6/1945
Perseus	6/1942	3/1944	10/1945
Pioneer	1942	5/1944	1946
Theseus	1/1943	7/1944	1/1946
Triumph	1/1943	10/1944	4/1946
Venerable	12/1942	12/1943	1/1945
Vengeance	11/1942	2/1944	1/1945
Warrior	12/1942	5/1944	1/1946

was in fact launched by the Germans and was found broken in two at La Spezia in 1945 when the Allies took over the port. None of the other ships had been laid down and four were neither named nor ordered. All built were named after late honoured officers.

In appearance the ships would have closely resembled the 'Soldati' Class but were much larger and differed in armament. A much more powerful gun was adopted for the main armament; it was originally planned to have five of these guns displaced as in the 'Soldati' Class. A twin mount in A and X positions and a single mount amidships were planned but it was found that the increased weight of the new mounting would have created stability problems, and so it was decided to mount four single 135-mm (5.3-in) in A, B, X and Y positions. The arrangement of the machinery would have been as in the 'Soldati' Class, with the two boiler rooms forward, exhausting into a single trunked funnel, and the engine rooms aft. *Comandante Esposito*, however, was to have associated boiler and engine rooms together, necessitating two separate funnels.

See also 'Soldati' Class.

Displacement: 2100 tons (standard) *Length:* 120.7 m (396 ft) oa *Beam:* 12.27 m (40 ft 3½ in) *Draught:* 3.58 m (11 ft 9½ in) *Machinery:* 2-shaft geared turbines, 60000 shp=35 knots (projected) *Armament:* 4 5.3-in (135-mm)/45-cal (4×1); 12 37-mm (1.46-in)/54-cal; 6 21-in (53-cm) torpedo tubes (2×3); 52 mines

Combattante

French patrol boat, built 1962 onwards. Under the 1960 Programme, an experimental patrol boat was authorized, and built by Constructions Mécaniques de Normandie in 1962-64. She was named *La Combattante*, thus commemorating a Free French destroyer (ex-HMS *Haldon*) sunk in the Second World War. She was built of laminated wood and plastic, and had a speed of only 23 knots.

The *Combattante* was used to test the feasibility of carrying and firing surface-to-surface missiles in minor warships, and fired Exocet MM.38 missiles. She was later fitted with a quadruple launcher for SS.11 missiles and an optical director, but the type has not been repeated.

The next step came in 1970, when the West German navy reached a decision to arm its Baltic forces with missile-armed patrol craft. The world-famous Lürssen firm of Vegesack, near Bremen, had produced a steel-hulled design capable of 35 knots for the Israeli navy, but for political reasons the contract was produced in France. A revised version was produced for the Federal German navy, to be armed with the Aerospatiale Exocet surface-to-surface missile. However, the French government was reluctant to give permission to the Germans to buy the weapon until French shipyards had been offered a fair chance to compete with the Germans for the hulls. By a very strange coincidence, the French shipyards produced a steel-hulled design called *La Combattante II*, and as it was 7 m (23 ft) longer than the original Lürssen design it fell outside the scope of any licensing agreement. To add to the Germans' discomfiture, the French government still refused to sell Exocet unless more than half the initial order was placed with a French yard, and the entire fitting out was done in France.

This has meant that Constructions Mécaniques de Normandie have been placed in the forefront of the fast patrol boat market, and since 1970 they have built the following:
20 *S.41* Class for West Germany (8 subcontracted in Germany);
4 *Kimothoi* Class for Greece;
4 *Perdana* Class for Malaysia;
12 *Kaman* Class for Iran.

The *Combattante II* is 47 m (154 ft) in length, has 4-shaft MTU diesels, and the usual armament is a 76-mm (3-in)/62 OTO-Melara Compact gun forward and four Exocet MM.38 launchers angled out amidships, though the Iranian, Greek and Malaysian boats have varying armament.

From this design was developed the 56-m (184-ft) *Combattante III*. The first of four for Greece, called *Antipliarchos Laskos*, ran her acceptance trials off Cherbourg in September 1976. She is armed with two 76-mm (3-in) OTO-Melara guns, four Exocets and two AEG T4 wire-guided torpedoes aft, plus two Emerlec twin 30-mm (1.18-in) guns, mounted on either side of the superstructure.

(Combattante II) Displacement: 234 tonnes (standard), 265 tonnes (full load) *Length:* 47 m (154 ft 2 in) oa *Beam:* 7 m (23 ft) *Draught:* 2 m (6 ft 6 in) *Machinery:* 4-shaft diesels, 12000

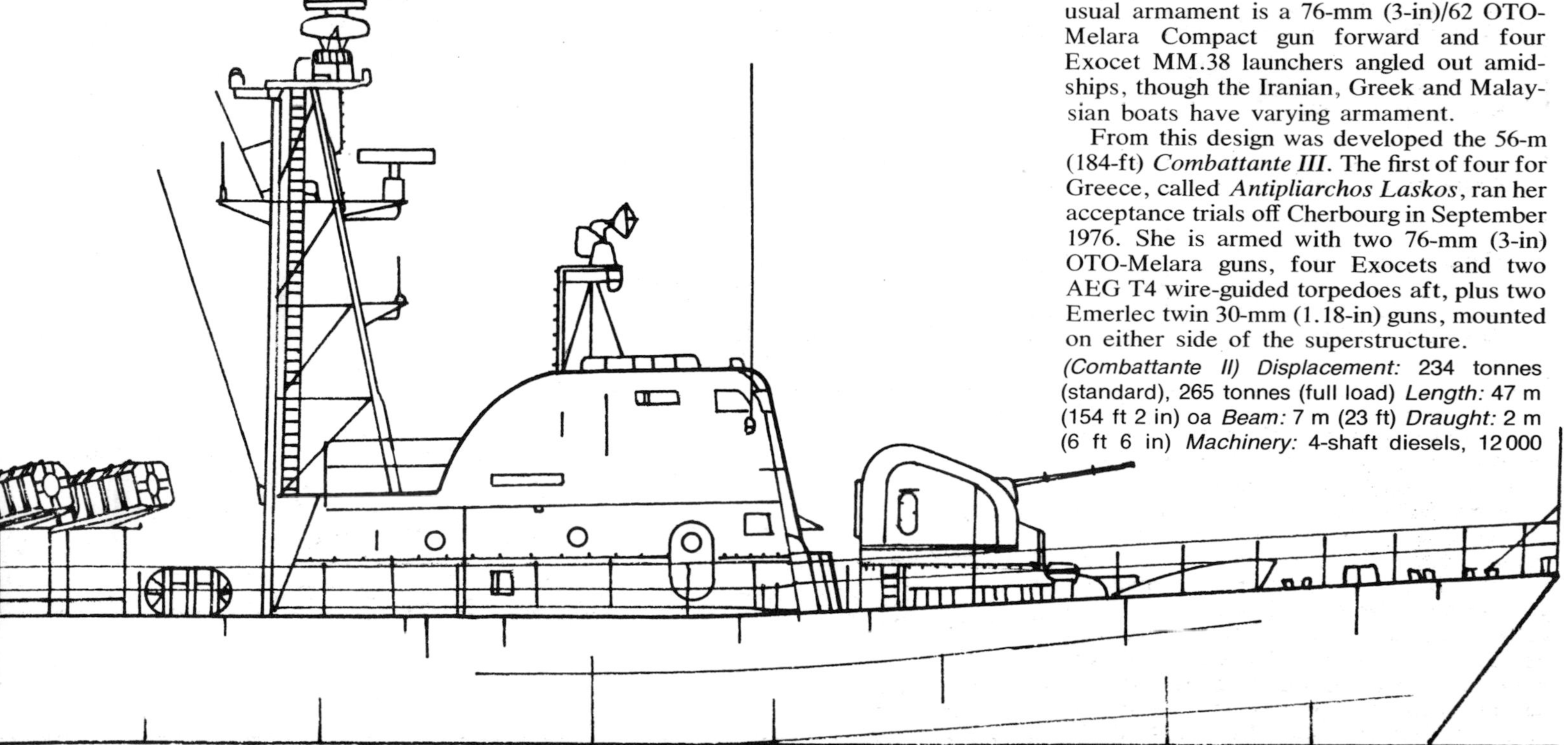

ECP Armées

La Combattante, the original vessel of this class mounting a quadruple SS.11 antiaircraft missile launcher and a rack for 14 flares. She can also carry a raiding force of 80 men, but only for short runs

bhp = 35½ knots *Armament:* 4 Exocet MM.38 missile-launchers (4 × 1), (2 in Malaysian *Perdana* Class); 1 76-mm (3-in); 1 40-mm (1.57-in) gun; (4 35-mm (1.38-in) (2 × 2) in Greek *Kimothoi* Class), (1 57-mm (2.24-in); 1 40-mm gun in *Perdana* Class)

(Combattante III) Displacement: 392 tonnes (mean), 425 tonnes (full load) *Length:* 56.15 m (184 ft 3 in) *Beam:* 8 m (26 ft 3 in) *Draught:* 2.5 m (8 ft 2 in) max *Machinery:* 4-shaft diesels, 20 000 bhp = 35.7 knots *Armament:* 3 MM.38 Exocet missiles; 2 76-mm (3-in) (2 × 1); 4 30-mm (1.18-in) (2 × 2); 2 53-cm (21-in) torpedo tubes

The Iranian fast attack craft *Kaman*, a *Combattante II* Class vessel built by Constructions Mécanique de Normandie. The egg-like fairing on her mast protects a Hollandse Signaalapparaten WM 28 tactical fire and control radar. She is to be armed with two twin Harpoon missile launchers (not at the time this photograph was taken) and has one 76-mm (3-in) OTO-Melara and one 40-mm (1.57-in) Bofors gun. Iran ordered 12 boats which were due to be delivered by April 1979. The *Kaman* Class boats differ considerably from the original *Combattante I*, and like the Greek *Calypso* Class are *Combattante IIs* with Thomson CSF Triton radar and Plessey IFF Mk 10. The complement of the original French boat was 25, the Iranian is 30, while the Greek boats have a crew of 40—though the French boat was slightly smaller and did not have the full armament of missiles and guns deployed on later versions of the class

CMN

The French sloop *Protet,* with her original armament. X 100-mm (3.9-in) gun was later replaced by a quadruple MM.38 Exocet launcher

Commandant Rivière

French sloop class, built 1957-1971. These handsome ships were designed as *avisos*, or colonials, with the dual role of escorts and patrol vessels for distant stations. For the latter role they have a modest speed with good endurance, but a reasonable antisubmarine armament is also included. All nine ships were built by Lorient arsenal (DCAN).

For their colonial role the ships can embark troops and two 9-m (29 ft 6 in) landing craft (LCPs). The *Commandant Bory* has had her 100-mm (3.9-in) gun in X position replaced by four launchers for MM.38 Exocet surface-to-surface missiles, a powerful increase in armament. In 1973 the after 100-mm (3.9-in) gun was removed from the *Commandant Bourdais* and *Enseigne de Vausseau Henry* to make way for a helicopter platform, but is due to be resited on the quarterdeck (Y position) when the ships receive Exocet.

The ships have been used as test-beds for new machinery. In particular the *Balny* spent nine years between launch and final acceptance as she tried out a new Combined Diesel And Gas Turbine (CODAG) system. The *Commandant Bory* had Sigma free-piston generators and gas turbines, but in 1974-75 she was given the same SEMT-Pielstick diesels as her sisters.

Four more were built for Portugal by Chantiers de Bretagne at Nantes in 1964-69: *Commandant Joao Belo, C Hermengildo Capelo, C Roberto Ivens* and *C Sacadura Cabral,* with a slightly wider beam and 40-mm Bofors instead of 30-mm guns.

Name and no	launched
***Commandant Rivière* E.733**	10/1958
***Victor Schoelcher* F.725**	10/1958
***Commandant Bory* F.726**	10/1958
***Amiral Charner* F.727**	3/1960
***Doudart de Lagrée* F.728**	4/1961
***Balny* F.729**	3/1962
***Commandant Bourdais* F.740**	4/1961
***Protet* F.748**	12/1962
***Enseigne de Vausseau Henry* F.749**	12/1963

Displacement: 1750 tonnes (standard), 2250 tonnes (full load) *Length:* 103 m (338 ft) oa *Beam:* 11.5 m (37 ft 9 in) *Draught:* 4.3 m (14 ft 1 in) *Machinery:* 2-shaft diesels (except *Balny),* 16 000 bhp=25 knots *(Balny* 2 diesels, 1 gas turbine) *Armament:* (as completed) 3 100-mm (3.9-in) DP; 2 30-mm (1.18-in) AA; 1 quad 305-mm (12-in) DC mortar; 6 550-mm (21.6-in) A/S torpedo tubes *Crew:* 167

Commencement Bay

US escort carrier class. The *Commencement Bay* Class were the last escort carriers to be built. Like the earlier *Casablanca* Class, they were specifically designed for their role and were not conversions from mercantile hulls. The *Commencement Bay* Class were longer than the *Casablanca*s and had a cruiser stern rather than the usual transom. Their Allis Chalmers steam turbines were more complicated than reciprocating machinery, and could only be built by a limited number of firms. However, besides the usual benefits of turbine propulsion, they also gave the carriers one extra knot of speed.

In the light of battle experience the AA armament was increased and two instead of one 5-in (127-mm) guns were mounted aft. Two catapults instead of one were fitted and the increased hangar space permitted an extra six aircraft to be carried. All these improvements took time and each carrier took about 15 months to complete. The earlier *Casablanca*s that had been designed primarily for ease of construction could be built in $3\frac{1}{2}$ months and 50 were put into service in a year.

Nineteen *Commencement Bay* Class carriers were built during 1943-46 by Todd Pacific shipyards at Tacoma: *Commencement Bay* (CVE-105), *Block Island* (CVE-106), *Gilbert Islands* (CVE-107), *Kula Gulf* (CVE-108), *Cape Gloucester* (CVE-109), *Salerno Bay* (CVE-110), *Vella Gulf* (CVE-111), *Siboney* (CVE-112), *Puget Sound* (CVE-113), *Rendova* (CVE-114), *Bairoko* (CVE-115), *Badoeng Strait* (CVE-116), *Saidor* (CVE-117), *Sicily* (CVE-118), *Point Cruz* (CVE-119), *Mindoro* (CVE-120), *Rabaul* (CVE-121), *Palau* (CVE-122), and *Tinian* (CVE-123). A further 16 were cancelled on August 8, 1945.

The carriers were intended for service in the Pacific, but only a few were completed before the end of the war. In 1946 they were mothballed because they were too small and

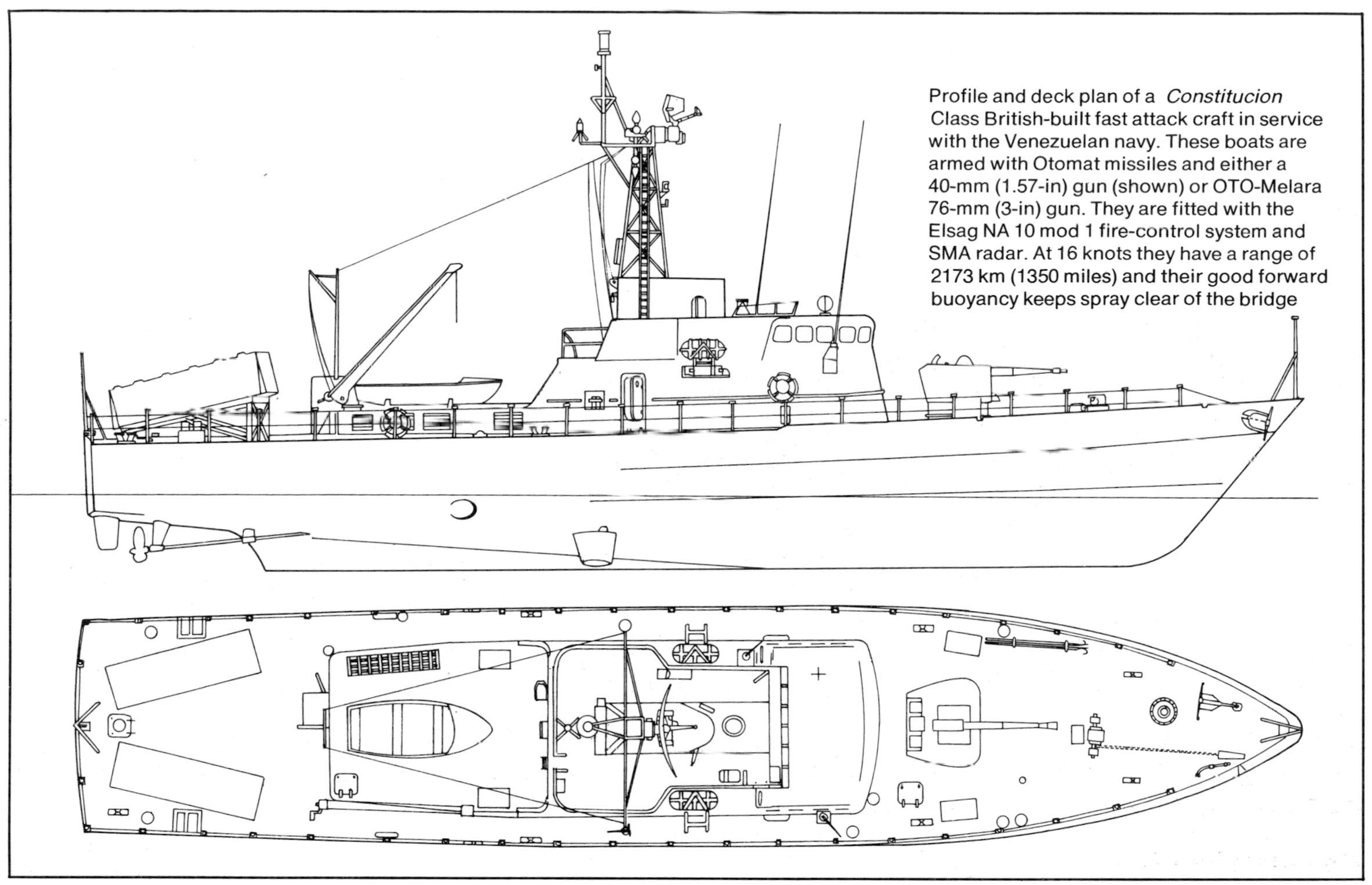

Profile and deck plan of a *Constitucion* Class British-built fast attack craft in service with the Venezuelan navy. These boats are armed with Otomat missiles and either a 40-mm (1.57-in) gun (shown) or OTO-Melara 76-mm (3-in) gun. They are fitted with the Elsag NA 10 mod 1 fire-control system and SMA radar. At 16 knots they have a range of 2173 km (1350 miles) and their good forward buoyancy keeps spray clear of the bridge

too slow for the new generation of US carrier aircraft. However, the rapid development of the helicopter in A/S and transport roles gave new life to these smaller carriers, and seven were brought back into service. The *Commencement Bay, Cape Gloucester, Vella Gulf, Puget Sound, Saidor, Rabaul* and *Tinian* were reclassified as escort helicopter aircraft carrier (CHVE) in 1955. In 1957 *Block Island* began conversion into a helicopter assault ship (CVHA later LPH). It was an elaborate process which involved removing the catapults, arrester gear and the aft end of the flight decks and adding extra quarters for the Marine complement. By 1958 escort carriers had become too small and slow to keep up with the new 20-knot amphibious assault ships and *Essex* Class fleet carriers were converted instead. The trial conversion of *Thetis Bay*—a *Casablanca* Class carrier—into a CVHA in 1955-56 had proved a slow and expensive business and so work was abandoned on the *Block Island*. *Block Island, Salerno Bay, Puget Sound, Bairoko, Sicily, Mindoro, Rabaul* and *Palau* were scrapped between 1960-62.

By 1959 the entire class had been reclassified as cargo and aircraft ferry ships (AKV) and some actually served in this role. During the Vietnam war some were reactivated as T-AKV and during 1962-64 *Gilbert Islands* was converted into a major communications relay ship (AGMR). All her aircraft handling equipment was removed and five large antenna towers, extensive electronics and a hurricane bow were fitted. Her guns were stripped out and replaced by eight 3-in (76-mm) guns in four twin mounts. Renamed *Annapolis* (AGMR-1) she was finally striken in 1975. The *Vella Gulf* was also to have been converted, but the larger, faster *Saipan* (CVL-48) was selected instead and she became the *Arlington* (AGMR-2).

Displacement: 11 373 tons (standard), 24 275 tons (full load) *Length:* 169.8 m (557 ft) *Beam:* 22.9 m (75 ft) *Draught:* 9.7 m (32 ft) *Machinery:* 2-shaft geared steam turbines, 16 000 shp=19 knots *Armament:* 2 5-in (127-mm), 36 40-mm (1.57-in), 30 20-mm (0.79-in) *Aircraft:* 34 *Crew:* 1066

Constitucion

Venezuelan fast patrol boat class. The contract for these vessels was placed in April 1972. They were specifically designed for Venezuela and completed with either a fully-automatic gun capable of engaging missiles, aircraft or ships, or Otomat surface-to-surface missiles, the first FPBs to use this weapon system. All six ships in this class were built by Vosper Thornycroft.

The main feature of the hull design is that it maintains a good reserve of buoyancy forward, deflecting the spray well clear of the forecastle deck where it would interfere with operation of the armament. This is achieved by use of modified round-bilge sections, a spray-deflecting knuckle forward just below the forecastle deck and a spray stake between this and the waterline. The all-welded steel hull is subdivided into seven watertight compartments while the aluminium alloy superstructure is partly welded and partly riveted. The ships are seaworthy both at high speed and in heavy following seas.

The diesel engines are remotely controlled, either from a noise-proof cubicle in the engine compartment, or from the enclosed bridge. The engine exhausts are sited at the ship's side, thus dispensing with the need for

Name	laid down	launched	completed
Constitucion	1/1973	6/1973	8/1974
Federacion	8/1973	2/1974	3/1975
Independencia	2/1973	7/1973	9/1974
Libertad	9/1973	3/1974	6/1975
Patria	3/1973	9/1973	1/1975
Victoria	3/1974	9/1974	9/1975

The *Constitucion* (right) with an OTO-Melara 76-mm (3-in) gun, and the missile-armed version, *Independencia* (below) armed with OTOMat missiles and Bofors 40-mm (1.57-in) gun on trials by Vospers before delivery

Vosper Thornycroft

Vosper Thornycroft

a funnel.

The vessels are equipped with a large operations room housing fire control, radar display, consoles etc, while a separate radio office is sited on the after part of the superstructure to starboard. A radar room is sited at the base of the mast. The ships are fully airconditioned throughout.

Displacement: 150 tons (standard) *Length:* 36.88 m (121 ft) oa *Beam:* 7.1 m (23 ft 3½ in) *Draught:* 1.7 m (5 ft 7¼ in) *Machinery:* 2-shaft MTU 16-cylinder diesels, 7080 bhp=27 knots *Armament:* 1 76-mm (3-in)/62-cal OTO-Melara DP gun; or 2 Otomat surface-to-surface missile launchers 1 40-mm (1.57-in) *Crew:* 18

Coontz

US guided-missile frigate class. The design of the *Coontz* Class of guided-missile frigates was evolved from that of the *Mitscher* Class guided-missile destroyers. The design displays the traditional American flush-deck destroyer hull form with pronounced sheer sweeping gracefully aft for two thirds of the hull. To keep weight down and overcome problems of stability the class was built with an aluminium superstructure.

The vessels were designed as AA frigates for screening high-speed carrier task forces and for independent operations, and original plans provided for two single 5-in (127-mm) guns in A and B positions. With the need for increased A/S capabilities, however, B gun was replaced by an 8-tube A/S rocket launcher. The ships were also provided with a helicopter landing pad at the stern, but no hangar was fitted and the ships have only limited facilities for servicing helicopters.

Between 1968 and 1975 the ships were considerably modernized when the twin 3-in (76-mm) guns amidships were removed and the superstructure considerably enlarged to house extra electronic, command and guidance equipment. This modernization substantially improved their AA capability and they were equipped with improved Terrier/ Standard missiles and associated equipment.

The *Farragut* had been equipped with an improved Asroc reload capability which incorporates a forward sloping extension in front of the bridge.

Displacement: 4770 tons (standard) *Length:* 156.2 m (512 ft 6 in) oa *Beam:* 16 m (52 ft 6 in) *Draught:* 7.62 m (25 ft) *Machinery:* 2-shaft geared turbines, 85 000 shp=34 knots *Armament:* 1 5-in (127-mm)/54 cal DP gun; 4 3-in (76-mm)/50 cal AA (2×2); 1 twin Terrier surface-to-air missile launcher; 6 21-in (53-cm) torpedo tubes (2×3); 1 8-tube Asroc launcher *Crew:* 370

Name	laid down	launched	completed	builder
Coontz	3/1957	12/1958	7/1960	Puget Sound navy yard
Dahlgren	3/1958	3/1960	4/1961	Philadelphia navy yard
Dewey	8/1957	11/1958	12/1959	Bath Ironworks
Farragut	6/1957	7/1958	12/1960	Bethlehem, Quincy
King	3/1957	12/1958	11/1960	Puget Sound navy yard
Luce	10/1957	12/1958	5/1961	Bethlehem, Quincy
Macdonough	4/1958	7/1959	11/1961	Bethlehem, Quincy
Mahan	7/1957	10/1959	8/1960	San Francisco navy yard
Preble	12/1957	5/1959	5/1960	Bath Ironworks
Wm V Pratt	3/1958	3/1960	11/1961	Philadelphia navy yard

Coronel

German auxiliary cruiser. The *Coronel* was originally built as the *Togo* for the Woermann Line of Hamburg. She was requisitioned for naval use in August 1940 and renamed *Coronel* in December 1942. Work on converting her to an auxiliary cruiser began at Wilton-Fijenoord, Schiedam, Holland and was completed by Oder-Werke, Stettin, and the naval yard at Gotenhafen.

She sailed (as *Schiff 14,* British designation *Raider K*) on January 31, 1943, but the breakout was constantly frustrated by air and sea surveillance. A final attempt was made on February 10, 1943. In the Straits of Dover the ship came under fire from the British heavy gun batteries and this was followed by an air attack by Whirlwind bombers of the RAF.

MOD

USS *Macdonough*, a guided-missile frigate of the *Coontz* Class, escorting HMS *Ark Royal* during joint NATO naval exercises in the autumn of 1977

The ship was damaged and put into Boulogne where further air attacks forced her back out to sea on February 14. The *Coronel* sailed east for Dunkerque, again coming under fire from the batteries at Dover. The next day she was ordered to return to Germany and arrived at Kiel on March 2. This was the last attempt by Germany to send an auxiliary raider to sea.

She was then converted into a fighter direction ship, renamed the *Togo*, and equipped with a Freya radar aerial forward and a Würzburg aft. The Freya FuMG A1 (Funkmessgerät Ausrüstung 1, or radar equipment 1) initially worked on a wavelength of 2.4 m, but this was subsequently reduced to 1.5 m. The range was between 40 and 75 km (25-47 miles) and the bearing accuracy ± 10°. The Würzburg (FuMG 65) worked on a wavelength of 53 cm with a range of 40-70 km (25-45 miles). The range accuracy was in the region of ± 40 m (131 ft) and the bearing accuracy between ± 9° and 16°. The aerial was 3 m (9 ft 10 in) across and weighed 1500 kg (3307 lb).

The *Togo* fell into British hands in August 1945 and was towed back to an English port for a detailed examination of her radar and fighter-direction gear, before being handed over to the United States for a similar examination in January 1946. After two months in US hands the ship was stripped and handed over to the Norwegian navy on March 15, 1946, for use as an auxiliary, and renamed *Svalbard* in 1947. In 1954 she became the mercantile *Tilthorn*, then *Stella Marina* a year later, and was passed back to

IWM

***Togo* (ex-*Coronel*) in her role as a fighter direction ship with an elaborate radar array**

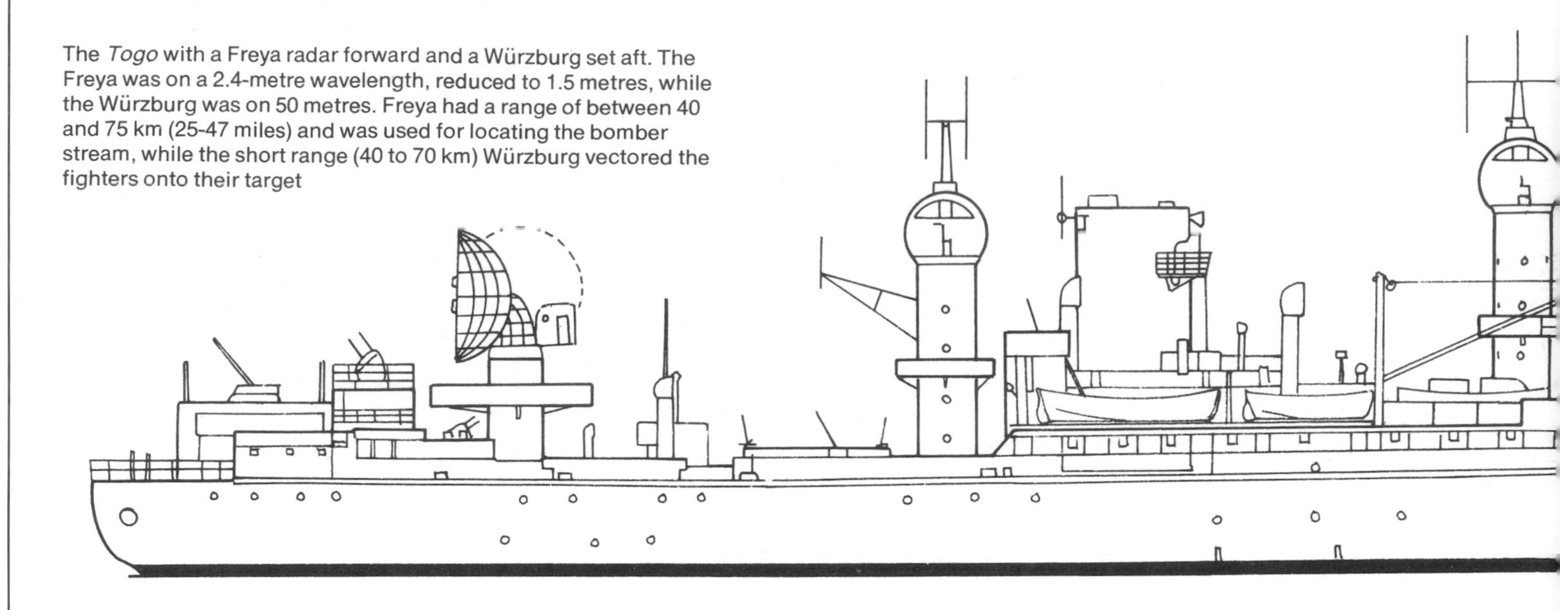

The *Togo* with a Freya radar forward and a Würzburg set aft. The Freya was on a 2.4-metre wavelength, reduced to 1.5 metres, while the Würzburg was on 50 metres. Freya had a range of between 40 and 75 km (25-47 miles) and was used for locating the bomber stream, while the short range (40 to 70 km) Würzburg vectored the fighters onto their target

Germany in 1956 reverting to the original name *Togo*.

Displacement: 11 000 tons (standard) *Length:* 134 m (439 ft 7 in) oa *Beam:* 17.9 m (58 ft 9 in) *Draught:* 6.47 m (21 ft 3 in) *Machinery:* single-shaft 8-cylinder diesel 5450 bhp=16 knots *Armament:* 6 5.9-in (150 mm)/55-cal (6×1); 6 40-mm (1.57-in) (6×1); 8 20-mm (0.79-in) (2×4); 2 21-in (53-cm) torpedo tubes (fixed and submerged); 4 aircraft *Crew:* 350

Le Corse

French frigate class. Before the Second World War the French navy built many excellent destroyers and torpedo boats, but these all suffered badly from their lack of endurance. Experience gained in the war showed the excellence of the US destroyer escort type, examples of which served in the French navy. It was therefore logical that when the French started to rebuild their much-reduced navy after the war. their new 'escorteurs rapides' (frigates) should be influenced by the Dealey Class, the latest examples of destroyer escort building for the US Navy.

ECP Armées

***Le Bordelais,* French frigate of the *Le Corse* Class, also known as the *Le Bordelais* Class**

No and name	laid down	launched	completed	builders
E50 Group				
F761 *Le Corse*	10/1951	8/1952	4/1955	Lorient dockyard
F762 *Le Brestois*	11/1951	8/1953	1/1956	Lorient dockyard
F763 *Le Boulonnais*	3/1952	5/1953	8/1955	A & Ch de la Loire
F764 *Le Bordelais*	5/1952	7/1953	4/1955	Forges & Ch de la Mediterranée

There were in fact to be two different French types, the E50 and E52, but as the only difference was in the arrangement of the armament they can be considered together. The first four built were of the E50 type, the *Le Corse* Class, in which the four sets of triple torpedo tubes for antisubmarine homing torpedoes were all forward, and the sextuple Bofors antisubmarine rocket projector aft.

The remaining ships, laid down somewhat later, were all of the E52 type, with the arrangement of torpedo tubes and projector reversed, and a different outfit of radar and sonar. The final three of this type were of the E52B variant with a new Strombos-Valensi funnel-cap, which had first been tried out in *Le Bordelais*.

Subsequent alterations included the fitting in the aftermost gun position of *Le Brestois* the new single 100-mm (3.9-in) gun mounting, developed jointly by France and Germany. This modification was retained but the twin Bofors 57-mm (2.24-in) mounting was never replaced. Some of the E52 Group also had one 57-mm (2.24-in) mounting removed and some were fitted with a four-barrelled rocket projector instead of the sextuple type.

Le Corse and *Le Bordelais* were removed from service in 1974 and *Le Brestois* in 1975. *Le Lorrain* was disarmed in 1975 and *Le Champenois* in 1976, and in the same year *Le Breton* and *Le Bourguignon* were placed in reserve. By early 1978 the *d'Estienne D'Orves* Class was entering service and it was thought that the remaining vessels in the *Le Corse* Class would be withdrawn.

Displacement: 1250 tons (standard), 1528 tons (normal), 1702 tons (full load) *Length:* 99.8 m (327 ft 5 in) oa *Beam:* 10.3 m (33 ft 9 in) *Draught:* 4.1 m (13 ft 5 in) maximum *Machinery:* 1-shaft geared turbine, 20 000 shp=28 knots *Armament:* 6 57-mm (2.24-in) (3×2); 1 6-barrelled 305-mm (12-in) A/S mortar, or 4-barrelled 375-mm (14.8-in); 12 53-cm (21-in) torpedo tubes (4×3), for K2 and L3 A/S torpedoes *Crew:* 171

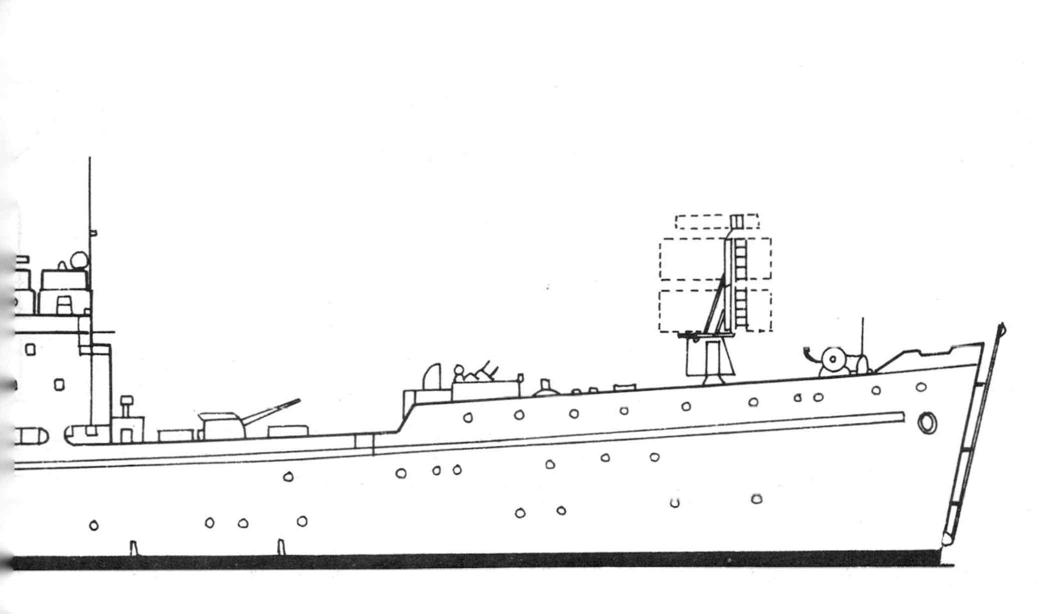

E52A Group				
F765 *Le Normand*	7/1953	2/1954	11/1956	Forges & Ch de la Mediterranée
F766 *Le Picard*	11/1953	5/1954	9/1956	A & Ch de la Loire
F767 *Le Gascon*	2/1954	10/1954	9/1956	A & Ch de la Loire
F768 *Le Lorrain*	2/1954	6/1954	1/1957	Forges & Ch de la Mediterranée
F769 *Le Bourguignon*	1/1954	1/1956	7/1957	Penhoët, St Nazaire
F770 *Le Champenois*	5/1954	3/1955	6/1957	A & Ch de la Loire
F771 *Le Savoyard*[3]	11/1953	5/1955	6/1956	Forges & Ch de la Mediterranée
F772 *Le Breton*[2,3]	6/1954	4/1955	8/1957	Lorient dockyard
F773 *Le Basque*[2,3]	12/1954	2/1956	10/1957	Lorient dockyard
F774 *L'Agenais*	8/1955	6/1956	5/1958	Lorient dockyard
F775 *Le Bearnais*[2]	12/1955	6/1956	10/1958	Lorient dockyard

E52B Group				
F776 *L'Alsacien*[1,2]	7/1956	1/1957	8/1960	Lorient dockyard
F777 *Le Provencal*[1,2]	2/1957	10/1957	11/1959	Lorient dockyard
F778 *Le Vendeen*[1,2]	3/1957	7/1957	10/1960	Forges & Ch de la Mediterranée

[1]quadruple rocket launcher [2]different bridge arrangement [3]two gun mountings only

Cossack

British destroyer class. These ships were the 13th Flotilla of the Emergency War Programme and the 3rd group of the 'C' Classes. Ordered in July 1942 and laid down in 1943, they were of all-welded construction but in almost every other respect were repeats of the *Chequers* Class.

The *Contest* was the first all-welded destroyer built for the Royal Navy and her construction was carefully monitored in order to gain data and experience. Many parts of her hull were prefabricated beside the slip before being placed in position. The *Cockade, Contest, Cossack, Comet* and *Constance*, completed in late 1945, were fitted with a close-range armament of one twin 40-mm (1.57-in) Hazemeyer Bofors amidships, two 2-pdr singles abaft the funnel and a single 20-mm (0.79-in) in each of the bridge wings. The remaining three, completed in 1946, mounted a twin Mk V in place of the Hazemeyer and single 40-mm (1.57-in) Bofors in place of the 2-pdrs.

The *Constance* and *Comus* were sold for scrap in the mid-1950s but the remainder were taken in hand for modernization. Those vessels completed in 1945 had their close-range weapons altered to that of the vessels completed in 1946. All had the 20-mm (0.79-in) guns removed and two 'Squid' antisubmarine mortars fitted in place of X 4.5-in (114-mm) gun. The *Comet* and *Contest* were fitted for minelaying and also had Y 4.5-in (114-mm) gun and the torpedo tubes removed. The last six of the group were sold for scrap between 1961 and 1964.

Cockade, Comet—built by Yarrow
Comus, Concord—built by Thornycroft
Consort—built by Stephen
Constance, Cossack (hull only)—built by Vickers
Contest—built by White

Displacement: 1870 tons (standard) 2500 tons (full load) *Length:* 110.57 m (362 ft 9 in) *Beam:* 10.9 m (35 ft 9 in) *Draught:* 3.2 m (10 ft 6 in) *Machinery:* 2-shaft geared steam turbines, 40 000 shp=34 knots *Armament:* 4 4.5-in (114-mm) (4×1); 2 40-mm (1.57-in) (1×2); 2 2-pdr (2×1); 2 20-mm (0.79-in) (2×1); 4 21-in (53-cm) torpedo tubes (1×4) *Crew:* 186

Crescent

British destroyer class. These ships were the last of the 'C' group and the final destroyer class of the Emergency War Programme, completing the 96 vessels (12 flotillas) whose design originated in the *Quilliam* Class ordered in 1940. They were laid down during 1943-44 and completed during 1945-47, none being finished in time to take part in the war. On completion the *Cromwell, Crown, Croziers* and *Crystal* were sold to Norway, and renamed *Bergen, Oslo, Trondheim* and *Stavanger* respectively. They were virtually unaltered until scrapped during the 1960s.

The *Crescent* and *Crusader* were transferred to the Royal Canadian Navy in 1945. In 1956, the *Crescent* was converted into a fast anti-submarine frigate at Esquimalt dockyard. This entailed rebuilding the superstructure, extending the forecastle deck and removing the original armament. A Limbo antisubmarine mortar was fitted aft, 2 3-in (76-mm) AA guns (1×2) added and 2 4-in guns (102-mm) (1×2) mounted on the forecastle. In 1960, the *Crusader* was fitted with an experimental variable depth sonar aft, Y gun being removed. Shortly afterwards this gear was transferred to the *Crescent*, which also had her Limbo removed and three homing torpedo launchers fitted. Both the Canadian vessels were scrapped in the early 1960s.

The only two to join the Royal Navy, *Creole* and *Crispin*, were converted to antisubmarine training ships during 1948-49, both having B gun replaced by a W/T cabin. In 1956, they were sold to Pakistan, but were refitted by Thornycroft before transfer in 1958; B gun was reinstated and X gun was

ECP Armées

Daphné, the first of a class of French submarines, was laid down in March 1958, launched on June 20, 1959, and commissioned on June 1, 1964. She was followed by ten more vessels but three were lost in accidents, the _Minerve_ and _Eurydice_ were lost at sea and the _Sirène_ at Derman, Lorient

replaced by two 'Squid' antisubmarine mortars.

Crispin, Creole—built by White
Cromwell, Crown—built by Scotts
Crescent, Crusader—built by J Brown
Croziers, Crystal—built by Yarrow

Displacement: 1870 tons (standard) 2500 tons (full load) *Length:* 110 m (362 ft 9 in) *Beam:* 10.9 m (35 ft 9 in) *Draught:* 3.2 m (10 ft 6 in) *Machinery:* 2-shaft geared steam turbines, 40 000 shp=34 knots *Armament:* 4 4.5-in (114-mm) (4×1); 6 1.57-in (40-mm) (1×2+2×1); 4 21-in (533-mm) torpedo tubes (1×4) *Crew:* 186

Daphné

French submarine class, built 1958-70. Ten of an improved *Arethuse* Class were ordered as Q 241-254 between 1958 and 1965, conventional hunter-killer submersibles with a diving depth of 300 m (984 ft). Although the class has not been without its problems, two having been lost in diving accidents, the French Government's policy of selling to all comers has made the *Daphné* design as successful an export item as the contemporary British *Oberon* design. Three were built for South Africa, three for Pakistan, four for Portugal and four were built for Spain in Spanish yards.

An unusual feature of the *Daphné* design is the heavy torpedo-salvo. Eight 55-cm (21.6-in) tubes are mounted forward and four aft, two in the stern casing, and two angled out midway between the conning tower fin and the stern. These are provided with wire-guidance but, apparently, no reload torpedoes are carried.

French *Daphné* Class

No and name	launched	builder
S.641 _Daphné_	6/1959	Dubigeon, Nantes
S.642 _Diane_	10/1960	Dubigeon, Nantes
S.643 _Doris_	5/1960	Cherbourg arsenal
S.644 _Eurydice_	6/1962	Cherbourg arsenal
S.645 _Flore_	12/1960	Cherbourg arsenal
S.646 _Galatée_	9/1961	Cherbourg arsenal
S.647 _Minerve_	5/1961	Dubigeon, Nantes
S.648 _Junon_	5/1964	Cherbourg arsenal
S.649 _Vénus_	9/1964	Cherbourg arsenal
S.650 _Psyche_	7/1969	Brest arsenal
S.651 _Sirène_	7/1969	Brest arsenal

Four Spanish *Daphné* Class (ordered 1965):

No and name	launched	builder
S.61 _Delfin_	3/1972	E N Bazan, Cartagena
S.62 _Tonina_	10/1972	E N Bazan, Cartagena
S.63 _Marsopa_	3/1974	E N Bazan, Cartagena
S.64 _Narval_	12/1974	E N Bazan, Cartagena

The first of the class, the *Daphné*, was commissioned in June 1964, and the last of the French boats, the *Sirène* in March 1970. The *Minerve* was lost by accident in the Western Mediterranean on January 27, 1968, followed by the *Eurydice* in the same area on March 4, 1970. The *Sirène* sank at Derman, Lorient, on October 11, 1972, after flooding through a faulty torpedo tube. She was raised 11 days later and refitted for further service.

Three South African *Daphné* Class (ordered 1967):

No and name	launched	builder
S.97 *Maria van Riebeeck*	3/1969	Dubigeon, Nantes
S.98 *Emily Hobhouse*	10/1969	Dubigeon, Nantes
S.99 *Johanna van der Merwe*	7/1970	Dubigeon, Nantes

Four Portuguese *Daphné* Class (ordered 1964):

No and name	launched	builder
S.163 *Albacora*	10/1966	Dubigeon, Nantes
S.164 *Barracuda*	4/1967	Dubigeon, Nantes
S.165 *Cachalote*	2/1968	Dubigeon, Nantes
S.166 *Delfim*	9/1968	Dubigeon, Nantes

Three Pakistani *Daphné* Class (ordered 1966):

No and name	launched	builder
S.131 *Hangor*	6/1969	Brest arsenal
S.132 *Shushuk*	7/1969	C N Ciotat, Le Trait
S.133 *Mangro*	2/1970	C N Ciotat, Le Trait

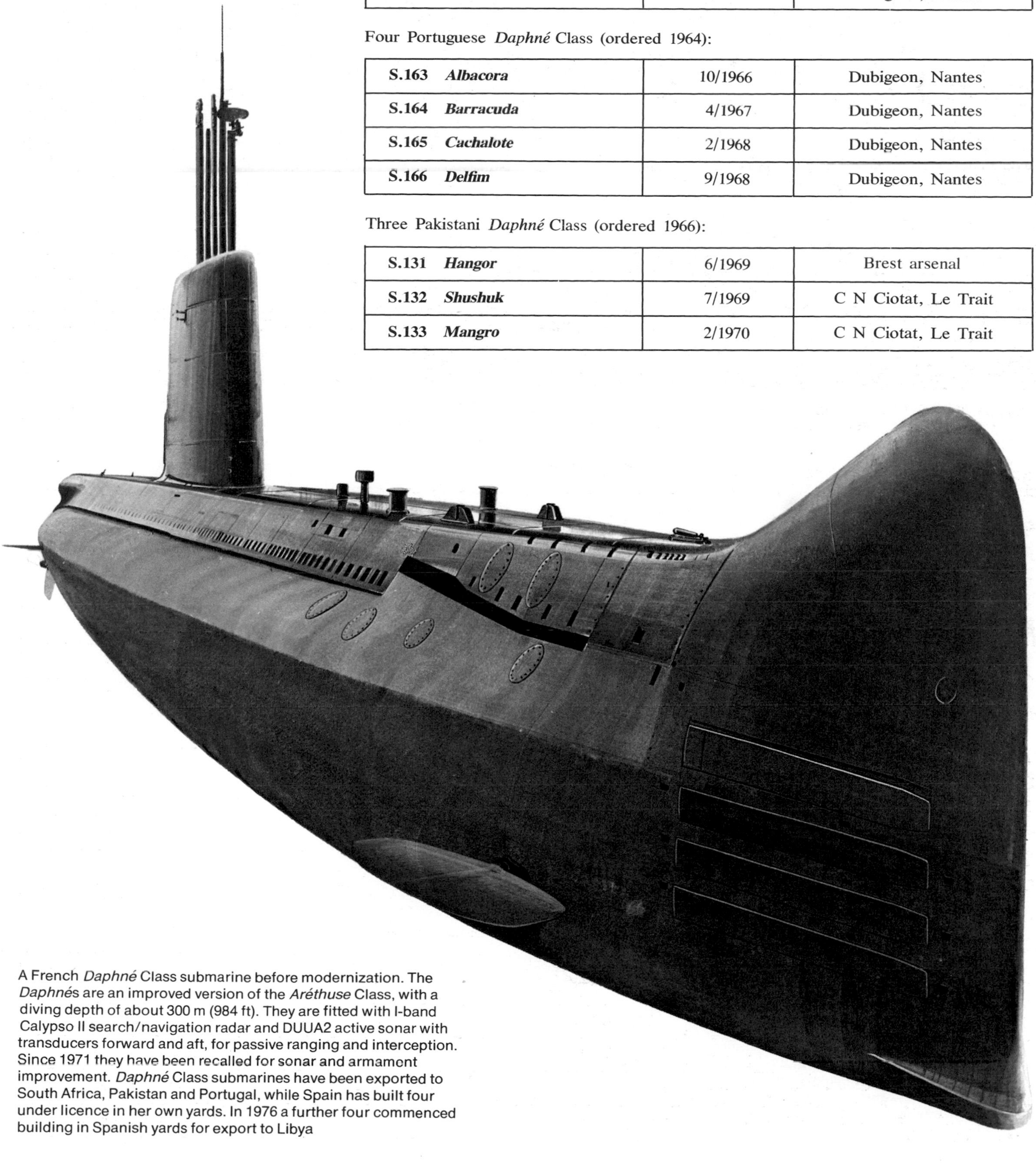

A French *Daphné* Class submarine before modernization. The *Daphnés* are an improved version of the *Aréthuse* Class, with a diving depth of about 300 m (984 ft). They are fitted with I-band Calypso II search/navigation radar and DUUA2 active sonar with transducers forward and aft, for passive ranging and interception. Since 1971 they have been recalled for sonar and armament improvement. *Daphné* Class submarines have been exported to South Africa, Pakistan and Portugal, while Spain has built four under licence in her own yards. In 1976 a further four commenced building in Spanish yards for export to Libya

COI

Above: **When launched on August 16, 1950, at Cowes, HMS *Dainty* was the most modern vessel in the Royal Navy.** ***Below:*** **HMS *Daring* which, along with *Dainty, Defender, Diana* and *Duchess*, was in the Suez Task Force in 1956.** ***Inset: Daring*'s name plate**

Another accident was reported to have happened to one of the South African boats during trials, but there has been no confirmation. The Pakistani *Hangor* sank the Indian frigate *Kukri* on December 9, 1971, during the Indo-Pakistan war. By early 1978 it was believed that the Portuguese *Cachalote* had been bought by the Pakistani navy, but her new name and pendant number had not been revealed.

Since 1971, the eight French boats have been undergoing modernization of sonar and fire-control, but the only external indication is a new, prominent sonar dome. CIT-Alcatel L5 Mod 3 torpedoes were expected to replace the E14 pattern believed to be carried.

Displacement: 869 tonnes/1043 tonnes (surfaced/submerged) *Length:* 57.5 m (188 ft $7\frac{3}{4}$ in) oa *Beam:* 6.76 m (22 ft 2 in) *Draught:* 4.62 m (15 ft $1\frac{3}{4}$ in) *Machinery:* 2-shaft diesel-electric, 1300/1600 hp=$13\frac{1}{2}$/16 knots (surfaced/submerged) *Armament:* 12 55-cm (21.6-in) torpedo-tubes (8 forward 2 aft, 12 torpedoes carried) *Crew:* 45

Gale & Polden

Daring

British destroyer class. The *Daring*s were the last and largest conventional British fleet destroyers. The design was evolved during 1943-44 and is a typical example of wartime requirements, leading to a substantial increase in size which in peacetime would have been financially unacceptable. This increase in size was largely due to the need to find space for the latest radar and communication equipment, together with a complex multi-function armament.

Their duties were to include attack on, and defence from, enemy destroyers and light craft, antisubmarine and antiaircraft defence and shore support. Because of their size they also went 'scouting', a function normally performed by cruisers. The main armament was fitted in three twin Mk VI mountings, two forward and one aft, with a fully-enclosed box-like gun house. These were dual purpose weapons with a rate of fire of 18 rounds per minute and fully automatic radar control from a Mk VI director mounted on the bridge. The close-range armament was to have consisted of three twin 40-mm (1.57-in) STAAG mountings fitted one each side of the bridge and one abaft the second funnel but prior to completion the latter was replaced by a twin Mk V 40-mm (1.57-in) mounting.

A great deal of attention was given to the machinery design, with a view to saving weight by the adoption of higher steam pressures and double reduction gearing. A unit machinery arrangement was employed with alternate engine and boiler rooms which necessitated two funnels, the foremost of which was led up through the centre of the lattice foremast.

Sixteen *Darings* were ordered during 1944-45 but in December 1945 eight were cancelled. Of the remainder, five were laid down during 1945-46 and three during 1948-49. Construction proceeded at a slow pace and they eventually entered service between 1952 and 1954. In 1946 a further four were ordered by Australia and laid down in that country in 1949-52. One was subsequently cancelled and the remaining three, *Vampire, Voyager* and *Vendetta*, were completed during 1957-59.

When completed the class was at first classified as *Daring* Type ships, but later reverted to the term destroyer. They were considered ugly, and to improve their appearance the cylindrical second funnel of the *Diana* and *Daring* was fitted with a streamlined aluminium casing, although this was removed in 1957 because it was judged to be a luxury. During 1958-60 preparations were made to fit the class with 'Seacat' GWS and all had the after bank of torpedo tubes replaced by a deckhouse, on which to mount the launcher, and a new director fitted on the bridge. However, only *Decoy* was fitted with this weapon which necessitated the removal of the twin 40-mm (1.57-in) mounting abaft the funnel. She also had her 40-mm (1.57-in) STAAG mountings replaced by single 40-mm (1.57-in) Bofors, a modification extended to the *Diamond, Diana* and *Duchess* during 1961-62. The remaining RN ships had their STAAGs replaced by twin 40-mm (1.57-in) Mk V mountings and their remaining torpedo tubes replaced by another deckhouse during 1963-64.

The three Australian ships, *Vampire, Voyager* and *Vendetta*, were completed with a deckhouse in place of the afterbank of torpedo tubes, and a Limbo antisubmarine mortar in place of the Squid. The *Voyager* was otherwise generally similar to the RN ships except that she mounted Mk V twins in the bridge wings from completion. The other pair mounted these latter weapons abreast the after shelter deck, carried single 40-mm (1.57-in) guns in the bridge wings and had a barrage director both before and abaft the funnel, instead of one on the after shelter deck as in the other ships.

The *Diamond, Defender, Daring, Diana* and *Duchess* were part of the Suez Task Force in 1956. The *Voyager* was sunk in collision with the aircraft carrier *Melbourne* during exercises on February 10, 1964. The *Duchess*, loaned to the Australians as a replacement, was purchased by them in 1971 and converted into a training ship in 1973, having her after 4.5-in (114.3-mm) turret and Squid removed. The *Vendetta* and *Vampire* were refitted during 1970-73 with a modified enclosed bridge, new masts and funnels and updated radar gear, B turret being removed from the *Vampire*. Most of the RN vessels were sold for scrap during 1968-72 but *Decoy* and *Diana* were sold to Peru and renamed *Ferre* and *Palacios*. These two and the Australian vessels were still in service with their respective navies in late 1977.

Dainty—built by White
Daring—built by Swan Hunter
Diamond—built by John Brown
Delight—built by Fairfield
Defender—built by Stephen
Decoy, Diana—built by Yarrow
Duchess—built by Thornycroft
Vampire, Voyager—built by Cockatoo dockyard
Vendetta—built by Williamstown dockyard

Displacement: 2950 tons (standard) 3580 tons (full load) *Length:* 118 m (387 ft) *Beam:* 13 m (42 ft 8 in) *Draught:* 3.9 m (12 ft 9 in) *Machinery:* 2-shaft geared steam turbines, 54 000 shp=34 knots *Armament:* 6 4.5-in (114-mm) (3×2); 6 40-mm (1.57-in) (3×2); 10 21-in (53-cm) torpedo tubes (2×5); 1 Squid A/S mortar (1×3) *Crew:* 290

Darter

American attack submarine. The *Darter* was one of the last conventional submersibles to be built for the US Navy. She was ordered under fiscal year 1954 as the first of three slightly improved *Tang* Class. Built by the Electric Boat division of General Dynamics, she was given the number SS.576 and launched in May 1956.

However, the realization of the potential of nuclear propulsion, with the commissioning of the *Nautilus* in 1954 and the high speeds obtained with the revolutionary 'tear-drop' hull of the *Albacore*, made it clear that the design was obsolescent. Accordingly only the *Darter* was completed, in order to test her exceptionally quiet Fairbanks-Morse diesels and Elliott electric motors. The funds for her sisters *Grayback* and *Growler* (SS.574 and 577) were diverted to convert the design to include Regulus surface-to-surface missiles.

The *Darter* resembles earlier conventional submersibles, with a streamlined bow, sail and fin-like domes for the Passive Underwater Fire-Control System (PUFFS) associated with her Mk 106 Mod II torpedo fire-control system and BQG-4 passive sonar. When completed in 1956 she was credited with 25 knots underwater, and was claimed to be the quietest submarine 'of all time'.

Displacement: 1720/2388 tons (surfaced/submerged) *Length:* 81.9 m (268.8 ft) oa *Beam:* 8.3 m (27.23 ft) *Draught:* 5.8 m (19 ft) *Machinery:* 2-shaft diesel-electric, 4500 bhp/5600 shp=19½/14 knots (surfaced/submerged) *Armament:* 8

The USS *Darter* (SS.576), the last of the US Navy's conventionally-powered submarines

US Navy

Dat Assawari

Libyan frigate, built 1968-73. The British firm of Vosper Thornycroft, formed from the amalgamation of the long-established destroyer-specialists, John I Thornycroft and the MTB-specialists, Vosper, had previously produced a range of designs for small, well-armed warships. Starting with the 440-ton Mk I corvette, sold to Ghana in 1963, the firm's designers produced larger versions, up to frigate size.

The *Dat Assawari* is the Vosper Thornycroft Mk 7 design, generally similar to the Iranian Mk 5 of *Saam* Class, but beamier to allow about 20 tons more armament to be carried. The speed is slightly lower, as the displacement has been increased without modifying the basic Combined Diesel Or Gas Turbine (CODOG) propulsion outfit.

The ship is powered by twin Rolls-Royce Olympus gas turbines and twin Paxman Ventura diesels, driving controllable-pitch propellers through common reduction gearboxes. The gas turbines are used for high-speed running, and the diesels for cruising. The armament comprises a single Vickers 4.5-in (114-mm) Mk 8 gun forward, a twin Oerlikon-Bührle 35-mm (1.38-in) gun right aft, two single 40-mm (1.57-in) Bofors Mk 9 on the after superstructure, and a triple Seacat close range missile system forward of the bridge. In addition a Limbo Mk 10 depth-charge mortar is mounted in a well in the quarterdeck.

Sensors include a Plessey AWS-1 air-warning and surveillance radar, with its array mounted on a stump mainmast forward of the funnel, a fire-control director on the foremast, Decca RDL-1 passive radar-detection equipment, and a hull-mounted sonar.

The ship was laid down in September 1968, was launched in September 1969, and commissioned in February 1973. After a work-up at Portland, she sailed for Tripoli later that year. She was due to be refitted by Vosper Thornycroft in 1978-79, and may receive new equipment.

Displacement: 1325 tons (standard), 1625 tons (full load) *Length:* 101.6 m (333 ft 4 in) oa *Beam:* 11.08 m (36 ft 4¼ in) *Draught:* 3.4 m (11.2 ft) *Machinery:* 2-shaft gas turbine or diesel, 46,500 shp+3500 bhp=36 knots (17 knots on diesels) *Armament:* 1 4.5-in (114-mm) Mk 8; 2 40-mm (1.57-in)/60-cal (2×1); 2 35-mm (1.38-in) DP (1×2); 1 triple Seacat SAM launcher; 1 triple Limbo mortar *Crew:* 132

Dealey

US destroyer escort class. Immediately after the Second World War the US Navy had a large surplus of brand-new wartime DEs, and it was not until the Korean war that it was decided to build a new class of DE incorporating all the latest improvements in weapons, machinery and shipbuilding techniques. Three *Dealeys* were built between 1952-55 by Bath Iron Works, and ten of the almost identical *Courtney* Class were built in various yards from 1955-1958.

The *Dealeys* were based on the Second World War DEs, having much the same layout and a similar but slightly longer hull. However, the main problem in producing the wartime ships had been the difficulty of manufacturing sufficient machinery, so the *Dealeys* were the first US DEs to adopt a single-shaft layout. The greater risk of total breakdown or of immobilization by battle damage was considered to be outweighed by the greater ease of production and the small size, simplicity and cheapness of the machinery.

Initially the *Dealeys* and the *Courtneys* were armed with a twin 3-in (76-mm)/50-cal mount fore and aft with a Weapon Able (Weapon Alpha) A/S rocket launcher between the forward gun mount and the bridge. *Dealey* herself ran trials for a time with the British Squid A/S launcher in its place. They also had fixed A/S torpedo tubes. The superstructure was aluminium to save topweight, and they had a lattice mast to carry the extensive electronic antennae.

The Portuguese *Almirante Pereira da Silva* Class frigates are virtual copies of the *Dealeys*, using US equipment and armament but with two Bofors four-barrelled A/S mortars replacing the Weapon Alpha forward. The Norwegian *Oslo* Class frigates are also based closely on the *Dealeys* but with a modified superstructure and new armament comprising an octuple NATO Sea Sparrow SAM launcher, six Penguin surface-to-surface missile launchers and a Terne six-barrelled A/S rocket launcher in addition to the two twin 3-in guns and two triple A/S torpedo tubes. The Portuguese vessels were built by Estaleiros Navais, Lisbon, and the Norwegians by Marinens Hovedverft, Horten.

Most of the *Dealeys* and *Courtneys* were modernized in the late 1960s. The aft 3-in (76-mm) mount was removed and a hangar and pad for two DASH helicopters was installed

Above: Stavanger, **one of five *Oslo* Class frigates (modified American *Dealey* Class) built in Norway by Marinens Hovedverft, Horten, and partly financed by the US Government**

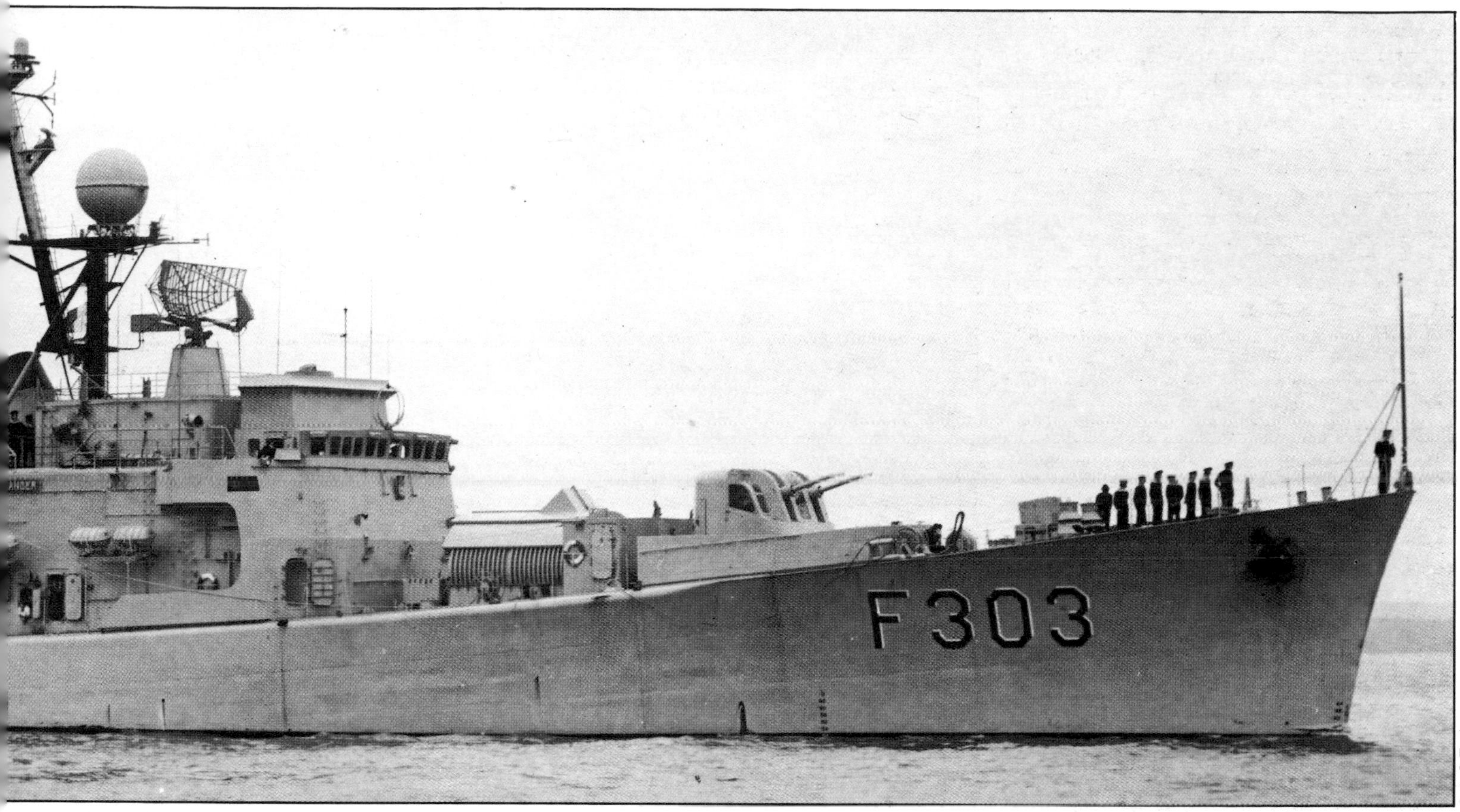
F303
C & S Taylor

Below: The Portuguese frigate *Almirante Magalhaes Correa,* a modified *Dealey* Class vessel built by Portugal in the mid-1960s. Though these ships were laid down in the early 1960s at yards in Lisbon and Viano do Castelo, parts had already been prefabricated a year earlier

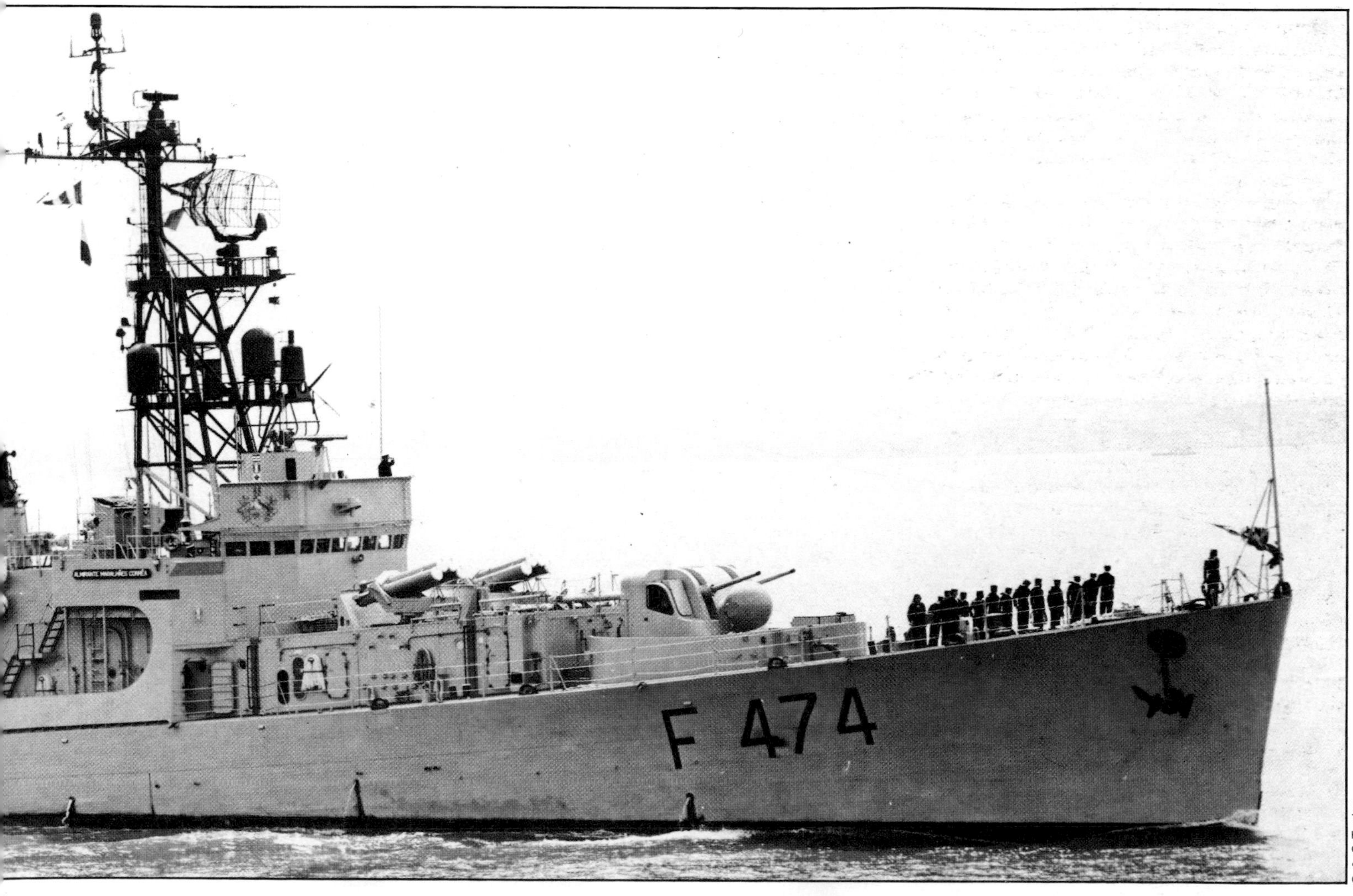
F 474
C & S Taylor

aft of the funnel. The electronics were updated and the fixed tubes were replaced by two triple Mk 32 A/S torpedo launchers amidships. However, DASH was a failure, and the *Dealeys* and *Courtneys* were too slow and too small for modern A/S warfare. As a result, the US Navy discarded or transferred all its early postwar DEs in the early 1970s. By 1977 none remained in service with the USN. *Dealey* herself was purchased by Uruguay in July 1972 and renamed *18 de Julio*.

Displacement: 1450 tons (standard), 1914 tons (full load) *Length:* 95.8 m (314 ft 6 in) oa *Beam:* 11.2 m (36 ft 10 in) *Draught:* 4.2 m (13 ft 8 in) *Machinery:* 1-shaft geared steam turbine, 20 000 shp=25 knots *Armament:* 2 3-in (76-mm); 1 Weapon Alpha; 2 triple 12.7-in (32.25-cm) torpedo tubes *Aircraft:* 2 DASH helicopters *Crew:* 149-170

Decatur

US guided-missile destroyer class. The four *Decatur* Class DDGs are guided-missile conversions of the *Forrest Sherman* Class destroyers. The *Forrest Sherman* Class were the first US post-Second World War destroyers, and were basically enlarged and improved *Gearings* with a single 5-in (127-mm)/54-cal gun forward and two, together with a twin 3-in (76-mm)/50-cal mount aft. They had aluminium upperworks and improved electronics. Eighteen *Forrest Shermans* were built between 1953-59. The later ships incorporated various improvements and from *Decatur* onwards they were completed with higher bows.

Between 1965-68 *Decatur* (DDG-31, ex-DD-936), *John Paul Jones* (DDG-32, ex-DD-932), *Parsons* (DDG-33, ex-DD-949) and *Somers* (DDG-34, ex-DD-947) were converted into guided-missile destroyers. The aft guns were removed and replaced by a new superstructure and a single Tartar Mk 13 Mod 1 SAM launcher, which has a magazine for about 40 missiles. It had originally been intended to fit these conversions with DASH helicopters for long range A/S work, but by the late 1960s it was apparent that DASH was a complete failure, so an 8-tube Asroc launcher was fitted aft of the second funnel instead. Two triple Mk 32 A/S torpedo launchers were mounted in front of the bridge for close-range A/S work. During the conversion the electronics were updated and two large lattice masts replaced the original tripods. They now carry the SPS-48 3-D search radar.

It had originally been intended to convert the *Forrest Sherman* Class into either specialist AA or A/S destroyers. *Turner Joy* (DD-951) was earmarked to be the next DDG conversion, but the cost and time taken to convert the first four into DDGs was such that it was not considered cost effective to convert any more in this way. However, the simpler and cheaper A/S conversion was more effective and eight were converted into specialist A/S destroyers between 1967-71.

Displacement: 4150 tons (full load) *Length:* 127.5 m (418 ft 4 in) oa *Beam:* 13.4 m (44 ft) *Draught:* 6.1 m (20 ft) *Machinery:* 2-shaft geared steam turbines, 70 000 shp=32.5 knots *Armament:* 1 Tartar SAM launcher; 1 5-in (127-mm) gun; 1 Asroc launcher; 2 Triple 12.7-in (32.26-cm) torpedo tubes *Crew:* 337-364

US *Dealey* Class

Name and No	launched
***Dealey* (DE.1006)**	11/1953
***Cromwell* (DE.1014)**	6/1954
***Hammerberg* (DE.1015)**	8/1954

US *Courtney* Class

Name and No	launched
***Courtney* (DE.1021)**	11/1955
***Lester* (DE.1022)**	1/1956
***Evans* (DE.1023)**	9/1955
***Bridget* (DE.1024)**	4/1956
***Baver* (DE.1025)**	6/1957
***Hooper* (DE.1026)**	8/1957
***John Willis* (DE.1027)**	2/1956
***Van Voorhis* (DE.1028)**	7/1956
***Hartley* (DE.1029)**	11/1956
***J K Taussig* (DE.1030)**	1/1957

Norwegian *Oslo* Class

Name and No	launched
***Oslo* (F 300)**	1/1964
***Bergen* (F 301)**	8/1965
***Trondheim* (F 302)**	9/1964
***Stavanger* (F 303)**	2/1966
***Narvik* (F 304)**	1/1965

Portuguese *Almirante Pereira da Silva* Class

Name and No	launched
***Almirante Pereira de Silva* (F 472)**	12/1963
***Almirante Gago Coutinho* (F 473)**	8/1965
***Almirante Magalhàes Correa* (F 474)**	4/1966

Dedalo

Spanish helicopter carrier. *Dedalo* (PH-01) was originally ordered by the US navy as the *Cleveland* Class light cruiser *Wilmington* (CL-79). In March 1942 she was reordered as one of the nine *Independence* Class carriers. She was laid down by the New York Shipbuilding Corporation as *Cabot* (CVL-28), launched on April 4, 1943 and completed on July 24, 1943. The *Cleveland* hull had large bulges added and a hangar and wooden flight deck with four small funnels to starboard replaced the cruiser upperworks. She took part in the Pacific island-hopping campaign and was damaged by a kamikaze aircraft off Luzon on November 25, 1944.

In the early 1950s *Cabot* was modified as an ASW carrier. Her flight deck and hangar deck were modified to take heavier aircraft, a large portside catapult was added, two funnels were removed, her AA armament was

The *John Paul Jones* (DDG-32), an ex-*Forrest Sherman* converted to a *Decatur* Class

reduced, her electronics were updated and her internal arrangements were modernized. However, she was really too small for this role and in May 1959 she was reclassified as an aircraft transport (AVT-3). *Cabot* was then put into reserve.

Spain asked the United States for the loan of an A/S helicopter carrier in the mid-1960s, and although the rebuilt escort carrier *Thetis Bay* was originally chosen, it was eventually decided to transfer *Cabot* instead. She was refitted, renamed *Dedalo*, and formally transferred on August 30, 1967 for five years. She was purchased by Spain in December 1973.

She operates Sea King A/S helicopters, but can embark other types for assault landings. A squadron of AV-8As (the US version of the Harrier) was formed in the late 1970s, and was due to operate from *Dedalo*. The AV-8A has been renamed the Matador by the Spanish. This will considerably upgrade the capabilities of the Spanish navy, and will make Spain the second Western country after the US to have a seaborne V/STOL strike force. *Dedalo* is the flagship of the fleet.

Displacement: 13 000 tons (standard), 16 416 tons (full load) *Length:* 189.9 m (623 ft) oa *Beam:* 33.2 m (109 ft) flight deck *Draught:* 7.92 m (26 ft) *Machinery:* 4-shaft geared steam turbines, 100 000 shp=32 knots *Protection:* 51-127 mm (2-5 in) sides; 51-76 mm (2-3 in) deck *Armament:* 26 40-mm (1.57-in) *Aircraft:* 7 Matadors; 20 helicopters *Crew:* 1112

De Grasse

French antiaircraft cruiser. Three improved *La Galissoniere* Class light cruisers were ordered for the French navy prior to the Second World War, but only one, *De Grasse*, had actually been laid down before the outbreak of hostilities. The other two, *Chateaurenault* and *Guichen*, were cancelled.

The *La Galissonieres* were a successful design, and the *De Grasse* Class were to have followed the same general layout, with three triple 6-in (152-mm)/50-cal turrets, three twin 3.5-in (90-mm), five single 25-mm (1-in), eight 13.2-mm (0.52-in), and two triple 21.7-in (55-cm) torpedo tubes. They were to have two rather than one catapult, for Loire Nieuport 130 seaplanes, similar protection and the slightly higher speed of 35 knots. The major difference was that whereas the *La Galissoniere* Class had two funnels and a relatively low bridge, the *De Grasse* Class were to have a large single funnel and a tall piled-up bridge.

De Grasse was ordered under the 1937 Estimates and was laid down in November 1938 at Lorient dockyard. Work continued on her until May 1940, by which time her hull was quite well advanced. Work was suspended during the German occupation, but it was restarted in 1946 and the hull was launched on September 11 of that year to clear the slip. Work was then once again suspended whilst the French navy decided what to do with her. The original design was obsolete, France had a number of gun-armed cruisers that had survived the war and it was already obvious that aircraft were a more important threat than surface vessels.

Work was therefore recommenced on *De Grasse* on January 19, 1951 to complete her as an all-gun armed antiaircraft cruiser. Although the US was beginning to convert some of her cruisers to missile-armed vessels, France lacked the technology and in any case the French did not consider that missiles were as yet developed sufficiently to be a ship's main armament.

De Grasse was completed at Brest dockyard, and was commissioned on September 3, 1956. Her main armament of eight twin 5-in (127-mm) mounts was arranged symmetrically, with two turrets forward, two aft, and two on either side of the superstructure fore and aft. Her secondary armament of six twin 57-mm (2.24-in) mounts was grouped round the superstructure at a higher level. She was comprehensively equipped with radar and was intended to act as a fleet flagship and to control air strikes and the air defence of the fleet. When she was completed she was a powerful and effective AA vessel, well equipped to operate with the French light carrier force.

However, new AA missiles were developed which could provide a reliable defence at much longer ranges than *De Grasse*'s guns. *Colbert*, whose design had been developed from that of *De Grasse*, had been built with the idea of fitting missiles at a later stage, but *De Grasse* herself was too thoroughly compartmented for it to be easy or cost effective to fit a missile system with its large magazine into her hull. In 1966, therefore, she was refitted at Brest to act as the flagship of the French Pacific Experimental Nuclear Centre.

The aft 5-in (127-mm) and the 57-mm (2.24-in) mounts were removed, the bridge was enlarged, and a large lattice mast and radars were added aft. Extra accommodation was fitted and the communication facilities were increased. She served in this role for a number of years, and was also used in the periods between the tests as a fleet flagship for operations in the French colonies. She was discarded in 1973.

Displacement: 9000 tons (standard), 12 350 tons (full load) *Length:* 188.3 m (617 ft 9 in) oa *Beam:* 21.3 m (69 ft 10½ in) *Draught:* 6.5 m (21 ft 4 in) *Machinery:* 2-shaft geared steam turbines, 105 000 shp=33 knots *Protection:* 102 mm (4 in) sides; 76 mm (3 in) deck *Crew:* 560

Delfinen

Danish submarine class, built 1954-64. These were the first submarines to be built to a Danish design after the Second World War, and in many ways they resemble the ex-British 'U' and 'V' Class boats handed over in 1946. They are of modest displacement, but are streamlined for good underwater speed, and have a snorkel mast, radar and sonar. All four boats were built by the Royal dockyard, Copenhagen.

They are conventional in appearance, with a streamlined fin and a sonar dome on the bow. The four torpedo tubes are all mounted in the bow.

Originally *Springeren* was to be built in 1959-60 with funds provided under the Mutual Defense Aid Programme (MDAP), but the contract was deferred for four years. The average cost was 17 million kroner.

Pennant no and name	launched
S.326 *Delfinen*	5/1956
S.327 *Spaekhuggeren*	2/1957
S.328 *Tumleren*	5/1958
S.329 *Springeren*	4/1963

Displacement: 576/643 tons (surfaced/submerged) *Length:* 54 m (177 ft 2 in) pp *Beam:* 4.7 m (15 ft 5 in) *Draught:* 4 m (13 ft 1½ in) *Machinery:* 2-shaft diesel-electric, 2600 bhp/1200 shp=13/12 knots (surfaced/submerged) *Armament:* 4 53-cm (21-in) torpedo tubes (probably 8 torpedoes carried) *Crew:* 33

Delhi

Indian cruiser. The *Delhi* was originally HMS

MOD

A Soviet *Delta* Class ballistic missile submarine, with a displacement of 9000 tons and the ability to carry and launch 12 SS-N-8 missiles

Achilles, one of the *Leander* Class cruisers of the 1929 Programme. She was laid down by Cammell Laird at Birkenhead on June 11, 1931, launched on September 1, 1932, and completed on October 10, 1933. She was manned by the Royal New Zealand Navy

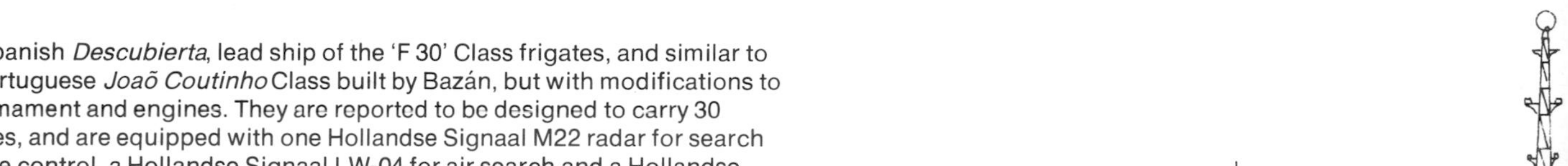

The Spanish *Descubierta*, lead ship of the 'F 30' Class frigates, and similar to the Portuguese *Joaõ Coutinho* Class built by Bazán, but with modifications to the armament and engines. They are reported to be designed to carry 30 marines, and are equipped with one Hollandse Signaal M22 radar for search and fire control, a Hollandse Signaal LW-04 for air search and a Hollandse Signaal M25 for navigation

from 1936 to 1943 during which period she became famous for her part in the Battle of the River Plate. In the Second World War one twin 6-in (152-mm) turret was removed reducing her main armament from eight to six 6-in (152-mm) guns.

On July 5, 1948, she was purchased by the Indian government and transferred to the Indian navy in October, when she was renamed *Delhi*. Her close range antiaircraft armament was modernized to provide a uniform battery of 14 40-mm (1.57-in) Bofors guns (4×2+6×1) but the remaining guns, six 6-in (152-mm) (3×2) and eight 4-in (102-mm) (4×2) remained as before. In 1958 her two triple 21-in (53-cm) torpedo tube mountings were removed and the forecastle side and deck plating was extended to fill the space that they had occupied. These were the only alterations made since the ship was transferred. She was flagship of the Indian navy until 1957 when she was relieved by the cruiser *Mysore* (ex-HMS *Nigeria*).

Although one of the oldest cruisers in existence she still has a limited level of usefulness for subsidiary service, such as shore support and patrol work and is at present largely employed on training duties.

See also *Leander* Class.

Displacement: 7114 tons (standard), 9740 tons (full load) *Length:* 158.8 m (521 ft) pp, 166 m (544 ft) oa *Beam:* 16.8 m (55 ft 1 in) *Draught:* 6.1 m (20 ft) *Machinery:* 4-shaft Parsons geared turbines, 72 000 shp=32 knots *Protection:* 51-102 mm (2-4 in) sides; 25 mm (1 in) turrets; 25 mm (1 in) bridge; 51 mm (2 in) deck *Armament:* 6 6-in (152-mm) (3×2); 8 4-in (102-mm) (4×2); 14 40-mm (1.57-in) (4×2, 6×1); 3-pdr saluting guns *Crew:* 800

Delta

Russian nuclear submarine class code-name. The existence of these Soviet ballistic missile-firing nuclear submarines (SSBNs) was announced at the end of 1972. In general they follow the pattern of the US Navy's Polaris submarines, but they have only 12 tubes for launching the 6437-km (4000-mile) SS-N-8 missile.

The *Delta* Class are built at Severodvinsk (formerly Molotovsk), north-west of Arkhangelsk, and first estimates suggested that ten or 12 could be turned out each year. However, later observations suggest that this would put an unbearable strain on Soviet resources of material and manpower, and the figure has been whittled down to six-eight boats per year. Even so, only ten *Deltas* have been reported. Since November 1973, the type has been followed by the bigger *Delta II*.

The *Delta II* can carry 16 of the big and bulky SS-N-8s, and is reputed to displace 16 000 tons. This makes it the biggest submarine ever built: a reflection on the Russian inability to keep the size of their rocket motors down, rather than proof of any advance in striking power. In 1976, two of these boats were reported, with another two building.

The future of the *Delta II* programme depends on the final outcome of the Strategic Arms Limitation Talks (SALT), but the existence of these boats has a direct bearing on the US Navy's decision to continue the *Trident* SSBN programme.

(Delta I) *Displacement:* 9000/10 000 tons (surfaced/submerged) *Length:* 137.2 m (450 ft 1½ in) oa *Beam:* 10.6 m (34 ft 9¼ in) *Draught:* 10 m (32 ft 9¾ in) *Machinery:* 2-shaft nuclear reactor+steam turbines, 24 000 shp=25 knots (surfaced/submerged) *Armament:* 12 SS-N-8 underwater-launched IRBMs; 8 53-cm (21-in) torpedo tubes *Crew:* 120 approx

(Delta II) *Displacement:* 16 000 tons (approx) *Length:* 152 m (498 ft 8¼ in) *Beam:* 11 m (36 ft 1½ in) *Draught:* 10 m (32 ft 9½ in) *Machinery:* Probably identical to Delta I *Armament:* 16 SS-N-8 underwater-launched IRBMs; 8 53-cm (21-in) torpedo tubes *Crew:* 40 approx

Descubierta

Spanish frigate class. Under the 5-Year Naval Programme of 1974 the Spanish navy was voted funds for the construction of eight 1270-tonne frigates to replace the elderly sloops of the *Pizarro* and *Atrevida* Classes dating from 1944. The design chosen was an adaptation of the *Joaõ Coutinho* Class built in German and Spanish yards for the Portuguese in 1970-75, with a much heavier and more effective armament.

Pendant no and name	launched	builder
F.31 *Descubierta*	7/1975	Bazán, Cartagena
F.32 *Diana*	1/1976	Bazán, Cartagena
F.33 *Infanta Elena*	9/1976	Bazán, Cartagena
F.34 *Infanta Cristina*	building	Bazán, Cartagena
F.35 unnamed	building	Bazán, El Ferrol
F.36 unnamed	building	Bazán, El Ferrol
F.37 unnamed	building	Bazán, El Ferrol
F.38 unnamed	building	Bazán, El Ferrol

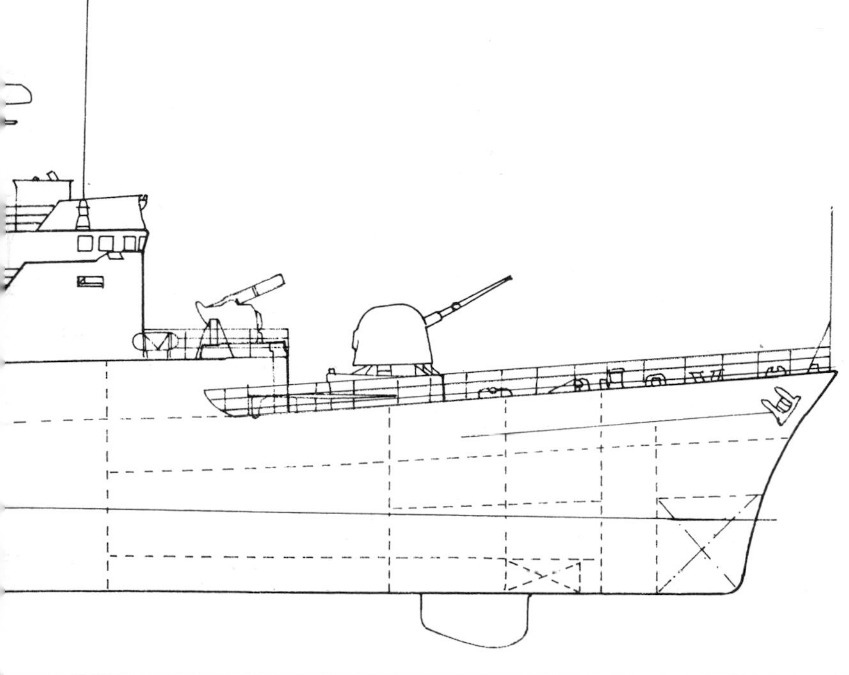

The hull is flush-decked, with a transom stern, and subdivided into 12 compartments. The armament comprises an OTO-Melara 76-mm (3-in) dual-purpose gun forward, two single Breda Bofors 40-mm (1.57-in) guns aft, a NATO Sea Sparrow launcher on the quarterdeck, antisubmarine torpedo tubes and a twin Bofors 375-mm (14.75-in) antisubmarine rocket-launcher in 'B' position. There is also provision for two 12-barrelled 20-mm (0.79-in) Meroka Close-In Weapon Systems (CIWS). This home-grown equivalent of the US Navy's Vulcan Phalanx system uses two rows of six barrels in a non-rotating mounting, with its own on-board radar control. The 20-mm (0.79-in)/120-cal gun is based on the Oerlikon 5TG, and is designed and manufactured by Empresa Naçional Bazán, the shipyard and arsenal at Cadiz.

There is also provision for two McDonnell Douglas Harpoon surface missile systems, which will make them the first Spanish warships so armed. The launchers angled at 90° to the centreline. Sixteen reloads are carried for the Sea Sparrow launcher.

The outfit of sensors is elaborate for the size of ship: Hollandse Signaalapparaten DA-05 E/F-bank surveillance radar at the head of the mainmast, HSA WM-25 I/J-band search and target-tracking radar at the head of the foremast, HSA WO-06 X-bank tactical radar on the foremast, and an ELT-715 active ECM and passive ESM outfit, also on the foremast. A Raytheon DE-1160B (also known as the AN/SWS-56) sonar set is mounted in the hull,

ECP Armées

Right: The _d'Estienne d'Orves_ after launching in 1973. _Below:_ In contrast to the clean lines of the newly-constructed vessel, an operational Type A69 with radar array, life rafts and the discolouration to the paintwork due to service

ECP Armées

and Aerojet AN/SLQ-25 antitorpedo ECM gear is provided.

The propulsion units are four MTU 16-cylinder diesels, built by Bazán under licence, giving a maximum speed of 27 knots. The exhausts are led to a split uptake, angled in a 'Y' shape to carry the fumes clear of the foremast and aerials.

The last four vessels were ordered on May 23, 1976, and will complete in 1979-80.

Displacement: 1270 tonnes (standard), 1520 tonnes (full load) *Length:* 88.88 m (291 ft 8 in) oa *Beam:* 10.4 m (34 ft 1 in) *Draught:* 6.2 m (12 ft 2 in) max *Machinery:* 2-shaft diesels, 16 000 bhp=27 knots *Armament:* 1 76-mm (3-in)/62-cal DP; 2 40-mm (1.57-in)/70-cal AA (2×1); 2 Harpoon SSMs (to be installed); 1 8-cell NATO Sea Sparrow SAM; 6 12.75-in (32.4-cm)/Mk 32 A/S torpedo tubes (2×3); 2 Meroka CIWS (to be installed) *Crew:* 100

Des Moines

US heavy cruiser class, built 1945-49. This was the last group of heavy cruisers ordered for the US Navy during the Second World War, and marks the ultimate in size and power reached by the cruiser-type.

Only two of the class, *CA.134* and *CA.139*, were laid down before the end of the war. Four units, *CA.150-153*, were cancelled in March 1945 without being laid down, another four, *CA.141-143* and *CA.149* were cancelled in August, but two, *CA.140* and *CA.148* were laid down in October 1945. The name *Dallas* had been allocated to *CA.150* and when that unit was cancelled it was given to *CA.140*, but she too was finally cancelled and the material on the slipway was broken up.

The basis of the design was the single-funnelled development of the *Baltimore* Class, known as the *Oregon City* Class, but the opportunity was taken to add 18 m (60 ft) to the length and 1.7 m (5 ft 6 in) to the beam to permit automatic loading gear for the 8-in (203-mm) guns, as well as extending the waterline belt armour to include the barbettes of the 8-in (203-mm) turrets. Automatic loading was a slight misnomer, in that all 8-in (203-mm) guns of that vintage had power-loading but the rate of fire was speeded up considerably by providing cased charges. The rate of fire of the new Mk XVI was about 10 rounds per minute, as against about 2½ rounds per minute for the Mk XV and older marks of 8-in (203-mm), which meant that the *Des Moines* Class could fire in the space of a minute a total of 15 tons of explosive at a range of 22.5 km (14 miles).

The secondary and tertiary armament reflected all the lessons of the Pacific War. The standard 'lozenge' disposition of twelve 5-in (127-mm)/38-cal dual-purpose guns was retained, but 12 of the new 3-in (76-mm)/50-cal twin automatic weapons were mounted in place of the quadruple 40-mm (1.57-in) Bofors, although a further 12 of the less effective 20-mm (0.79-in) Oerlikons were also provided in single mountings. These light AA guns were removed from all three ships soon after completion.

Since 1949 the number of 3-in (76-mm) twins has been reduced to make way for increased radar, communications and even accommodation; by 1973 the *Newport News* had lost her last two mountings. All three ships were designed to have floatplanes, two catapults and a handling crane on the stern, but only the *Des Moines* had them for a while. In all three the space was used to handle boats and later helicopters.

As a result of the slowing down of construction after the end of hostilities the *Des Moines* did not commission until November 1948, and *Newport News* and *Salem* joined the Fleet in January and May 1949 respec-

No and name	launched	builder
CA.134 _Des Moines_	9/1946	Bethlehem, Quincy, Mass
CA.139 _Salem_	3/1947	Bethlehem, Quincy, Mass
CA.140 _Dallas_	—	Bethlehem, Quincy, Mass
CA.148 _Newport News_	3/1947	Newport News Shipbuilding

PPL

Stages in the construction of *d'Estienne d'Orves* Class antisubmarine escorts. The prefabricated sections are assembled in covered building berths (top), and the photographs below show the *d'Estienne d'Orves* on the 16th day of building (left), the *Jean Moulin* on the 284th day (centre) and the *Detroyat* on the 287th day (right). Average time from laying down to launch is around one year

PPL

PPL

PPL

tively. For many years all three were active, and the *Salem* played the part of the *Admiral Graf Spee* in the film 'The Battle of the River Plate' in the 1950s.

The *Newport News* was the last of the three to remain active. Since 1949 she has been the flagship of the 2nd Fleet in the Atlantic. On October 9, 1967 she fired her guns in anger for the first time, in Operation 'Seadragon' off the coast of Vietnam. When she left the 'gun line' in April 1968 she had fired over 59 000 rounds of ammunition. On October 1, 1972, during a third tour of duty, she suffered a serious explosion in 'B' or No 2 turret, when a shell burst prematurely in the centre barrel. The barrel was completely detached from the turret, and was supported only by its liner; 20 men were killed and 36 injured, many of them by inhaling the smoke and fumes which engulfed the forward part of the ship.

In view of the age of the ship, and the need to keep her on the 'gun line', her defective gun was not replaced when she was repaired at Subic Bay in the Philippines. In fact the whole turret was wrecked by the explosion, and was no longer capable of firing. She was decommissioned on June 27, 1975, the last all-gun armed cruiser in the US Navy in service.

See also *Baltimore, Oregon City.*

Displacement: 17 000 tons (standard), 21 500 tons (full load) *Length:* 218.34 m (716 ft 3 in) oa *Beam:* 23.24 m (76 ft 3 in) *Draught:* 7.92 m (26 ft) *Machinery:* 4-shaft geared steam turbines, 1200 shp=33 knots *Protection:* 203-152-mm (8-6 in) belt; 152 mm (6 in) bulkheads; 76-51 mm (3-2 in) decks; 152 mm (6 in) turrets and barbettes; 203 mm (8 in) conning tower *Armament:* 9 8-in (203-mm)/55-cal Mk XVL (3×3); 12 5-in (127-mm)/38-cal DP (6×2); 24 3-in (76-mm)/50-cal AA (12×2); 12 20-mm (0.79-in) AA (12×1), removed 1948-49 *Crew:* 1860 (wartime) 271 in *Newport News* as Atlantic Fleet flagship

d'Estienne d'Orves

French escort class or *avisos.* Fourteen Type A69 *avisos* were authorized under the 1971 Programme, to replace the ageing E50 and E52 type *escorteurs rapides* built during 1952-60.

The class is intended for coastal antisubmarine escort, but the ships can operate overseas and for this purpose they can embark an extra detachment of an officer and 17 men. The units destined for the Mediterranean are armed with two MM38 Exocet surface-to-surface missile systems abaft the

The West German training cruiser *Deutschland*, the first postwar warship to exceed 3000 tons. She has a varied armament designed for instructional purposes and her machinery, two Daimler-Benz and two Maybach diesels, is also deliberately different for training purposes. Her full complement of 554 comprises 33 officers, 271 men and 250 cadets. A wide variety of radar equipment is carried for sea-going instruction, three navigation and surface warning sets, SGR 103, 105 and 114, one LW-02/3 air warning set, one DA 02 target designation set and two M45 fire control sets, an M2/2 and an M4. All the radar equipment is built by Hollandse Signaalapparaten. The *Deutschland* was ordered in 1956 when her name was to have been *Berlin*

Die Bildstelle der Marine

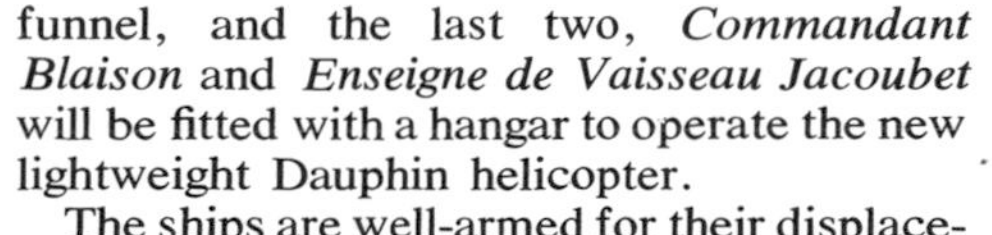

funnel, and the last two, *Commandant Blaison* and *Enseigne de Vaisseau Jacoubet* will be fitted with a hangar to operate the new lightweight Dauphin helicopter.

The ships are well-armed for their displacement, with a single 100-mm (3.9-in) dual-purpose gun forward, a six-barrelled 375-mm (14.76-in) antisubmarine rocket-launcher aft, and four fixed torpedo tubes for L3 homing torpedoes in the after superstructure. In addition two single 20-mm (0.79-in) Oerlikons are mounted at the after end of the superstructure. Two SEMT-Pielstick PC2V diesels drive two controllable-pitch propellers.

All fourteen ships were ordered from Lorient arsenal, and were to have been followed by the similar A70 type from the same yard. But in 1975 the French government announced that financial cuts had made it necessary to delay the commencement of the last of the class until April 1979, and to defer the A70 class indefinitely.

The class comprises *d'Estienne d'Orves* (No F.781); *Amyot d'Inville* (F.782); *Drogou* (F.783); *Detroyat* (F.784); *Jean Moulin* (F.785); *Quartier Maitre Anquetil* (F.786); *Commandant de Pimodan* (F.787); *Second Maitre le Bihan* (F.788); *Lieutenant de Vaisseau le Henaff* (F.789); *Lieutenant de Vaisseau Lavallée* (F.790); *Commandant l'Herminier* (F.791); *Premier Maitre l'Her* (F.792), projected; *Commandant Blaison* (F.793), projected; *Enseigne de Vaisseau Jacoubet* (F.794), projected.

The ships are prefabricated in a covered building berth, and work proceeds on two or more hulls at once, allowing double launches.

Two more ships, *Good Hope* and *Transvaal*, were ordered by South Africa about 1975, although to avoid international repercussions the date of the order was not announced. They are reported to be very similar to the French ships, but with a slightly different silhouette, and they would have had triple Mk 32 antisubmarine torpedoes but no Exocet missiles. However in November 1977 the French government suddenly announced the cancellation of the order, in deference to pressure from African countries. In all probability the ships will be taken back into the French navy's programme in place of two vessels not yet laid down. The *Good Hope* had been completed and was running trials at Lorient with a South African crew standing by, and the *Transvaal* was to be completed in May 1978. The last two French ships will be equipped to operate a Dauphin helicopter.

Displacement: 950 tonnes (standard), 1170 tonnes (full load) *Length:* 80 m (262 ft 6 in) oa *Beam:* 10.3 m (33 ft 9 in) *Draught:* 3 m (9.8 ft) *Machinery:* 2-shaft diesels, 11 000 bhp=24 knots *Armament:* 2 Exocet MM38 SSMs (in four ships); 1 100-mm (3.9-in) 1968 DP gun; 2 20-mm (0.79-in) (2×1); 1 Mk 54 A/S rocket launcher; 4 torpedo tubes for A/S torpedoes *Crew:* 79

Deutschland

German training ship, built 1959-63. *Deutschland* was the first ship of the new Federal German Navy to exceed the limit of 3000 tons placed on the West Germans under the Washington Treaty, and she is an enlarged frigate equipped with a variety of weapons and machinery for training purposes. She was ordered in 1956 and was originally to be named *Berlin*. She was launched at the Nobiskrug shipyard at Rendsburg on November 5, 1960 and started sea trials in January 1963, her NATO pendant number being A.59.

The armament comprises four French 100-mm (3.9-in) dual-purpose guns, six Breda 40-mm (1.57-in) Bofors guns (two twins and two singles), two quadruple 375-mm (4.8-in) Bofors antisubmarine rocket launchers behind B gun, and six torpedo launchers. The machinery plant is a combination of Daimler-Benz and Maybach diesels, and MAN geared steam turbines. A full outfit of Dutch radar and fire control, plus hull-mounted sonar is carried.

The ship embarks 250 cadets for a series of four-month voyages to various parts of the world. In 1978 she was due to be rearmed with more up-to-date hardware.

Displacement: 4880 tons (normal), 5400 tons (full load) *Length:* 145 m (475 ft 8¾ in) oa *Beam:* 18 m (59 ft) *Draught:* 4.8 m (15 ft 8 in) *Machinery:* 3-shaft diesel, 6800 bhp+geared steam turbines, 8000 shp=22 knots (max) *Armament:* 4 100-mm (3.9-in) (4×1); 6 40-mm (1.57-in) (2×2, 2×1); 2 375-mm (14.8-in) A/S rocket-launchers; 6 53-cm (21-in) torpedo-launchers (can also lay mines) *Crew:* 304, plus 250 cadets

MOD

HMS *Kent*, a *Devonshire* Class destroyer, passes through the English Channel. Her crew are drawn up on deck with a guard by B turret

Devonshire

British destroyer class, built 1959-70. Two 'fleet escorts' or large destroyers were projected under the 1955-56 Naval Estimates, followed by another two the following year. Originally intended to be a 'super-*Daring*', the design underwent no fewer than 64 changes. The original concept was a 4000-ton destroyer capable of 38 knots and armed with three single 5-in (127-mm) guns, each firing 80 rds/min, whose role was to destroy *Sverdlov* Class cruisers with gunfire and homing torpedoes. However, the new First Sea Lord, Admiral of the Fleet Earl Mountbatten, rejected the design as it had no guided-missile defence against air attack. Finally, after many vicissitudes, only the machinery was left of the original design, and it had been recast to include a Seaslug missile system and two Limbo antisubmarine mortars aft.

What finally emerged in 1962 was a handsome and unusually powerful-looking class of ships with high freeboard and two widely spaced funnels. They are generally known as the 'County' Class and because of their size were soon uprated from destroyers to destroyer-leaders (DLGs) to correspond with the similar regrading in the US Navy.

In the year that HMS *Devonshire* joined the Fleet a further pair were laid down, followed by another pair four years later. It had always been recognized that their traditional cruiser-names indicate that the RN regards them as light cruisers, and that 'destroyer' was a fiction to secure Parliamentary approval.

The 'Counties' had a Combined Steam and Gas Turbine (COSAG) propulsion system similar to, but double that in the 'Tribal' Class frigates. Two sets steam turbines and four G.6 gas turbines were geared to two shafts. The gas turbines could start from cold within a few minutes, allowing the ships to get underway without waiting for steam, or providing high-speed boost. The steam plant was forward, while the gas turbines vented through the fat after funnel.

The ships were built around the Armstrong-Whitworth Seaslug Guided Weapon System No 1 (GWS1), and were the first RN ships armed with guided missiles. As procurement was under the control of the old Ministry of Supply there were many unusual features, notably the very large and bulky twin-ramp launcher. Horizontal stowage was adopted on account of Seaslug's bulk, and the magazine was positioned below the waterline just abaft the forward funnel and engine room. From here the missiles were taken up to shelter deck level, and then travelled aft for fitting fins, warm-up, check-out etc, through the split gas turbine exhausts, and then out to the launcher on the quarterdeck. The normal stowage is 16 missiles, and fresh rounds can be embarked while underway.

When completed the eight ships were basically similar, but the last four had a thinner formast and a twin Type 965 AKE or 'double bedstead' air-warning radar aerial on the mainmast. They were also armed with the more powerful Seaslug Mk 2, which has a limited surface-to-surface capability, but no external difference can be detected. In 1973

Aérospatiale

HMS *Norfolk* fires an MM.38 Exocet from one of the launchers replacing B turret

Norfolk underwent conversion to carry four Exocet MM.38 surface-to-surface missiles, and lost B gun-mounting. She carried out firing trials in the French Mediterranean in April 1974, and since then *Glamorgan*, *Fife* and *Antrim* have been similarly fitted.

The first four ships saw active service during the confrontation with Indonesia in 1964, where it was belatedly realized that these large and expensive ships could be knocked out with relative ease by a man in a sampan armed with a bazooka. As a tempor-

No and name	launched	builder
D.02 *Devonshire*	6/1960	Cammell Laird, Birkenhead
D.06 *Hampshire*	5/1961	John Brown, Clydeside
D.12 *Kent*	9/1961	Harland & Wolff, Belfast
D.16 *London*	12/1961	Swan Hunter, Wallsend
D.19 *Glamorgan*	7/1964	Vickers-Armstrongs, Tyne
D.20 *Fife*	7/1964	Fairfield Shipbuilding, Govan
D.18 *Antrim*	10/1967	Fairfield Shipbuilding, Govan
D.21 *Norfolk*	11/1967	Swan Hunter, Wallsend

ary expedient old 20-mm (0.79-in) Oerlikon guns were fitted on either side of the bridge, but these have been retained ever since as a useful Cold War weapon.

HMS *Hampshire* paid off in April 1976, about seven years before the expected end of her operational life. The Seaslug beam-rider is not suited to modern aerial engagements, and can only engage a maximum of four targets. The COSAG propulsion system is complex, and the ships require large crews, but their command facilities make them very useful as flagships for task groups. The *Devonshire, Kent* and *London* were expected to be scrapped by 1980.

See also *Ashanti, Daring.*

Displacement: 5440 tons (standard), 6200 tons (full load) *Length:* 158.6 m (520 ft 6 in) oa *Beam:* 16.4 m (54 ft) *Draught:* 6.1 m (20 ft) *Machinery:* 2-shaft geared steam turbines, 15000 shp+gas turbines, 15000 shp=32½ knots *Armament:* 1 Seaslug GWS1 SAM launcher; 2 Seacat GWS22 quadruple SAM launchers; 4 4.5-in (114-mm) Mk 6 (2×2), or 2 4.5-in (114-mm) (1×2); 4 Exocet MM.38 SSM launchers; 2 20-mm (0.79-in) Oerlikon guns (2×1) *Aircraft:* 1 Westland Wessex helicopter *Crew:* 471

De Zeven Provincien

Dutch light cruiser class, built 1939-53. Two cruisers, to be known as *De Zeven Provincien* and *Kijkduin*, were ordered in 1937-38 to replace the elderly *Java* and *Sumatra*. The design was developed from the *De Ruyter*, but with considerably more gunpower and better protection.

The designed armament was to be ten 150-mm (5.9-in) guns in two triple and two twin turrets, six twin 40-mm (1.57-in) Bofors antiaircraft guns and two triple 21-in (53-cm) torpedo tubes. A catapult and two aircraft were to be provided, and a relatively high horsepower, 78000, was installed with only two shafts, to give 32 knots. The guns were to be provided by Bofors AB and the estimated cost was to be 20 million guilders each.

The keel of the first cruiser, the *Kijkduin*, was laid on May 19, 1939, at Rotterdam, but the name was soon changed to *Eendracht*; her sister's keel was laid on September 5 at Schiedam, only two days after the outbreak of the Second World War. The invasion of the Netherlands by German troops in May 1940 gave little enough time for much work to be done on the ships, and in any case a shortage of skilled workers had delayed them. There was no time to destroy the material on the slips, and the German administration rescinded the Dutch government's order to cancel the contracts, hoping that the ships could be completed for the Kriegsmarine. Work proceeded very slowly as the Dutch Resistance did its best to delay essential materials, but apart from giving *De Zeven Provincien* a lengthened 'Atlantic' bow, no changes were made to the design. She was ready for launching by November 1944, but with a view to using her as a blockship. Fortunately the hull remained in the Wilton shipyard at Rotterdam, and fell into Allied hands.

The main armament had not been delivered from Sweden before the fall of the Low Countries in May 1940, but Bofors AB was able to sell the two triple turrets and four twins to the Royal Swedish Navy. These were then used to arm the new cruisers *Göta Lejon* and *Tre Kronor*, which were started during the war.

Although the Dutch navy was anxious to rebuild the fleet it was aware that the design of the two undamaged hulls was now quite outdated, and would need considerable redesign to bring it into line with modern requirements. Under the aegis of the original designer, G't Hooft and using technical assistance from the Royal Navy, the armament was reduced to four twin 6-in (152-mm) guns of a new Bofors design and four twin 57-mm (2.24-in) mountings, but no torpedo tubes.

The new 6-in (152-mm) guns were dual-purpose, with 60° elevation and a rate of fire of 15 rds/min, while the 57-mm (2.24-in) guns were in tri-axially stabilized turrets. Six twin 40-mm (1.57-in) Bofors AA mountings of British Mk V pattern were also to be mounted, but finally eight single 40-mm (1.57-in) were chosen.

The radically different armament meant the redistribution of magazines and shell-rooms in the hull, but an even bigger change was the adoption of the 'unit' system of machinery. The original three-shaft arrangement, with six boilers in three boiler-rooms and three turbine-rooms, was replaced by a two-shaft arrangement, with four boilers and two engine rooms in two groups. Because the double boiler-rooms were now widely separated it was necessary to provide two funnels.

The original silhouette, with a single funnel and fairly light bridgework was replaced by two short upright funnels and a very big bridge. However, the need to keep fumes clear of radar and control-stations led to the funnels being raked and made much taller, and to save space the forward tripod mast was stepped over the forefunnel. When completed both ships had a lattice tripod mainmast abaft the second funnel, but this was soon shifted, and was stepped in similar fashion over the funnel, keeping gas clear of the radar arrays.

Plans were ready in 1947, and immediately work began on the cruisers once more. When the time came to launch the second ship in 1950 it was decided to transfer the name *De Zeven Provincien* to her, and to give the illustrious name *De Ruyter* to the other one.

The armament was partly provided by Bofors AB and partly built under licence in Holland, and installation was carried out in 1951. The *De Ruyter* sailed on her acceptance trials in the spring of 1953, followed by *De Zeven Provincien* in the summer. Both ships took part in a number of NATO exercises, including 'Fair Wind' in July 1956 and 'Shipshape' in September 1958.

The need for enhanced antiaircraft defence led to plans being drawn in the early 1960s to convert both cruisers to guided missile-ships, but the enormous cost and the fact that the hulls would be over 40 years old by the end of their effective lives led the Naval Staff to order the conversion of *De Zeven Provincien* only. She was taken in hand by the Rotterdam Dry Dock company. In April 1962 for conversion, and reemerged in August 1964.

The quarterdeck was built up flush with the forecastle deck and the after turrets were removed to provide space for Terrier missile magazines. The after funnel and mast were replaced by a 'mack' carrying the LW01 air-surveillance radar antenna, and a new mast was stepped further aft to carry the SPS-34 air-surveillance radar antenna. Two stumpy towers for the SPG-55 directors for Terrier guidance were also installed at the after end of the superstructure, and to compensate for all this top weight a twin 57-mm (2.24-in) turret and four single 40-mm (1.57-in) guns had to be removed.

On January 26, 1973, the unmodernized *De Ruyter* was stricken, but instead of being scrapped she was immediately sold to Peru and became the *Almirante Grau*. In August 1975 the Netherlands navy announced that *De Zeven Provincien* was to be laid up as an

Name	launched	builder
De Zeven Provincien (ex-*Eendracht*, ex-*Kijkduin*)	8/1950	Rotterdam Dry Dock company
De Zeven Provincien (ex-*Eendracht*, ex-*Kijkduin*)	12/1944	Wilt-Fijenoord, Schiedam

***Argonaut* steaming with her ten 5.25-in (133-mm) guns traversed to starboard in an AA role. She was damaged by air attacks in 1942 and 1943**

economy measure, but a year later she was also purchased for the Peruvian navy, under the name *Aguirre.*

See also *Tre Kronor.*

(As designed 1939) *Displacement:* 8350 tons (standard), 9820 tons (full load) *Length:* 188.7 m (619 ft) oa *Beam:* 17.3 m (56 ft 9 in) *Draught:* 5.64 m (18 ft 6 in) max *Machinery:* 3-shaft geared steam turbines, 78 000 shp=32 knots *Protection:* 76-102 mm (3-4 in) belt; 51-102 mm (2-4 in) turrets *Armament:* 10 150-mm (5.9-in)/53-cal DP (2×3, 2×2); 12 40-mm (1.57-in) AA (6×2); 8 12.7-mm (0.5-in) machine-guns (4×2); 6 53-cm (21-in) torpedo tubes (2×3) *Crew:* 700

(As completed 1953) *Displacement:* 9529 tons (standard), 11 850 tons (full load) *Length:* De *Zeven Provincien* 118.7 m (389 ft 5¼ in) oa, *De Ruyter* 190.3 m (624 ft 4 in) oa *Beam:* 17.3 m (56 ft 9 in) *Draught:* 6.7 m (22 ft) *Machinery:* 2-shaft geared steam turbines, 85 000 shp=32 knots *Armament:* 8 6-in (152-mm) DP (4×2); 8 57-mm (2.24-in) AA (4×2); 8 40-mm (1.57-in) AA (8×1); (*De Zeven Provincien* 1964) 4 6-in (152-mm) DP (2×2); 6 57-mm (2.24-in) AA (3×2); 4 40-mm (1.57-in) AA (4×1); 1 twin Terrier RIM-2 SAM system *Crew:* 700

Dido

British cruiser class. The *Dido* Class were designed primarily as Fleet antiaircraft escorts, for which purpose they were fitted with a uniform armament of ten 5.25-in (133.3-mm) Mk I guns of new design. These were mounted in five twin-dual purpose turrets so that the ships were also capable of engaging surface targets. However, this double requirement complicated both the gun mounting and the fire control gear and they were not as efficient in the antiaircraft role as they would have been with a pure high-angle armament. It was also required that they be 'small cruisers' so that larger numbers could be constructed to help make up for the deficiency of cruisers in the fleet. The hull and machinery were the same as those of the earlier *Arethusa* Class with such modifications as required by the new armament. In particular, this meant a rearrangement of the magazine spaces and superstructure, and a higher bridge to clear the third 5.25-in (133.3-mm) turret.

A total of 16 *Dido*s were constructed, 13 under the peacetime naval estimates of 1936 to 1939 and three under the Emergency War Programme. The last six of these ships were altered while under construction to incorporate the lessons of the war and were known as the *Modified Dido* Class. They had vertical, instead of raked, masts and funnels and had a lower bridge as Q turret was omitted and replaced by a third 4-barrel pom-pom mounting. The *Dido* Class completed between 1940 and 1942 and the Modified vessels during 1943-44. They proved to be good sea boats but structural weaknesses were revealed during heavy weather in the first units to complete, and all had their hulls strengthened.

Manufacture of the 5.25-in (133.3-mm) gun mounting did not keep pace with the construction of the ships and the *Phoebe* and *Dido* completed without Q turret and the *Bonaventure* without X turret. All three

The *Dido* Class cruiser *Scylla*, which saw action on the Arctic convoy route to Russia. She was mined off Norway on June 23, 1944 while supporting the D-Day landings, and was laid up until 1950 when she was scrapped

C & S Taylor

The Nigerian *Dorina* Class corvette *Otobo* (F.82) on trials in 1976 after her refit by Vosper Thornycroft at their Camber yard in Portsmouth

mounted a single 4-in (102-mm) gun in place of the missing weapon which was eventually fitted in the first two only, the *Bonaventure* having been sunk. No 5.25-in (133.3-mm) mountings were available for the *Scylla* and *Charybdis*, which completed with 8 4.5-in (114-mm) (4×2) dual purpose guns instead and neither ship ever received her intended armament.

During 1943-44 Q turret was removed from *Phoebe*, *Cleopatra*, *Argonaut* and *Euryalus* in order to reduce topweight. The turret was replaced by a third 2-pdr mounting (1×4) in the latter pair and by a quadruple 40-mm (1.57-in) Bofors mounting in the former pair which also had their two pom-pom mountings replaced by quadruple 40-mm (1.57-in) Bofors. The *Royalist*, in 1943, and the *Scylla* (1944) were refitted to serve as escort carrier squadron flagships and were equipped with the radar, communication equipment and accommodation necessary for this role for which the escort carriers themselves had insufficient space.

The *Dido*s served mainly in the Mediterranean during the war where they saw much front-line service including Malta convoys, the battles for Greece and Crete and the actions in the Gulf of Sirte. In the latter years of the war, the bulk of the class transferred to home waters but some joined the Eastern and Pacific fleets. Of the five ships lost, three were sunk by submarine torpedoes in the Western Mediterranean, the *Bonaventure* by the Italian *Ambra* on March 31, 1941, the *Naiad* by *U 565* on March 11, 1942, and the *Hermione* by *U 205* on June 16, 1942. The *Charybdis* was torpedoed twice and sunk by the German U-Boats *T23* and *T27* during a night action in the English Channel on October 23, 1943.

The only *Modified Dido* to be lost was *Spartan* which was hit and sunk by an HS293 glider bomb off Anzio on January 29, 1944. In addition to the above, the *Phoebe* and *Cleopatra* were extensively damaged by submarine torpedoes and the *Argonaut* by aircraft torpedoes during 1942-43 and all three were under repair in the US for long periods. The *Scylla* was damaged by a mine off Normandy on June 23, 1944, and was laid up until scrapped in 1950.

In 1948 the *Bellona* and *Black Prince* were transferred to the Royal New Zealand Navy. In 1956 the former vessel was returned and replaced by *Royalist* which had been refitted with an enclosed bridge, lattice masts, new fire control and radar gear and a uniform close-range armament of 40-mm (1.57-in) guns. The *Diadem* was sold to Pakistan in 1956 and renamed *Babur*, and the *Black Prince* were also given a uniform 40-mm (1.57-in) armament. The Royal Navy ships were sold for scrap during 1955-59 and the New Zealand vessels in 1962 and 1968. The *Babur* was still in service in 1978.

Dido, *Charybdis*, *Argonaut*—built by Cammell Laird

Euralus—built by Chatham dockyard
*Naiad, Cleopatra, Diadem**—built by Hawthorn Leslie
*Phoebe, Bellona**—built by Fairfield
Sirius—built by Portsmouth dockyard
Bonaventure, Scylla, Royalist—built by Scotts
Hermione—built by Stephen
*Black Prince**—built by Harland and Wolff
*Spartan**—built by Vickers Armstrong.
* *Modified Dido* Class

Displacement: 5600 tons (standard), 7000 tons (full load) *Length:* 156 m (512 ft) *Beam:* 15.4 m (50 ft 6 in) *Draught:* 4.3 m (14 ft) *Machinery:* 4-shaft geared steam turbines, 62000 shp=32 knots *Protection:* 76 mm (3 in) sides; 50.8 mm (2 in) deck *Armament:* 10 5.25-in (133.3-mm) (5×2); 8 2-pdr pom-poms (2×4); 8 0.5-in (12.7-mm) (2×4); 6 21-in (53-cm) torpedo tubes (2×3) *Crew:* 480

Dolfijn

Dutch submarine class, built 1954-66. In 1949 funds were voted for four submarines to be built for the Dutch navy. Design proved a protracted affair, and took five years to incorporate the latest developments, by which time the money could only cover two boats; the other pair were deferred for another eight years.

The design is unique in having three separate hulls, arranged in a triangle; the upper cylinder houses the crew, navigational equipment and the torpedo tubes, and the lower two contain the batteries and propulsion unit. The later pair, *Potvis* and *Tonijn*, incorporated several improvements, and were treated as a separate class, but the first pair *Dolfijn* and *Zeehond*, were later brought up to the same standard, and all four are virtually identical.

The design was drawn up by the distinguished Dutch ship designer M T Gunning, and although it is claimed to give increased strength for deep diving it has not been repeated in subsequent boats. The maximum diving depth is reported to be 300 m (984 ft). All four have had a prominent sonar dome added on the bow to house the Hollandse Signaalapparaten M8 fire-control sonar.

Displacement: 1494/1826 tons (surfaced/submerged) *Length:* 79.5 m (260 ft 9¾ in) oa *Beam:* 7.8 m (25 ft 7 in) *Draught:* 4.8 m (15 ft 9 in) *Machinery:* 2-shaft diesel/electric, 3100 bhp/4400 shp=14½/17 knots (surfaced/submerged) *Armament:* 8 53-cm (21-in) torpedo tubes (4 bow, 4 stern) *Crew:* 64

No and name	launched	builder
S.808 *Dolfijn*	5/1959	Rotterdam Dry Dock company
S.809 *Zeehond*	2/1960	Rotterdam Dry Dock company
S.804 *Potvis*	1/1965	Wilton-Fijenoord, Schiedam
S.805 *Tonijn*	6/1965	Wilton-Fijenoord, Schiedam

Dolphin

US submarine, built 1962-68. In Fiscal Year 1961 Congress authorized the construction of an experimental submarine for research into deep diving and oceanography. Although not intended for operational service she was armed with a single 21-in (53-cm) torpedo tube for firing experimental torpedoes, but this was removed in 1970.

The *Dolphin* has been elaborately equipped for her role, with three computer-aided systems, one for safety, one for hovering, and one for an undisclosed purpose. On November 24, 1968, three months after commissioning, she descended to a greater depth than any previously recorded by a true submarine. The cylindrical hull is about 4.6 m (15 ft) in diameter, and is constructed of HY-80 steel; fibreglass and aluminium is used in the conning tower (sail) and other non-vital positions to keep weight down.

The configuration of the *Dolphin* has changed; a prominent sonar dome was added on the bow-casing, and the height of the sail was increased. Her hull-number SS.555 was originally allocated to a *Tench* Class boat cancelled in 1945 before being laid down. The additional AG letter-designators indicate her auxiliary and experimental status, but she is nevertheless in normal commission, and is assigned to the Submarine Development Group 1 at San Diego. She was launched at Portsmouth naval shipyard on June 8, 1968, some two years later than planned.

Displacement: 800 tons (standard), 930 tons (full load) *Length:* 46.3 m (152 ft) *Beam:* 5.9 m (19 ft 3 in) *Draught:* 5.5 m (18 ft) *Machinery:* 1-shaft diesel/electric, 1500 bhp=12 knots (submerged) *Armament:* 1 21-in (53-cm) torpedo tube (later removed) *Crew:* 24

Dorina

Nigerian corvette class, built 1970-72. Following the success of their Mk 1 corvette design sold to Ghana, Vosper Thornycroft produced a Mk 3 design for Nigeria, 7.6 m (25 ft) longer, 0.76 m (2ft 6in) wider and 3 knots faster. The armament was also heavier, with a twin 4-in (102-mm) Mk 16 antiaircraft gun forward, two single 40-mm (1.57-in) Bofors AA and two 20-mm (0.79-in) Oerlikons.

The design is compact, and follows the lines of other Vosper Thornycroft ships, with a single fat funnel set well back from the bridge. The emphasis is on simplicity of operation and maintenance, but at the same time a weight of armament which makes the ship a useful coastal escort. The main air-warning and surveillance radar is the Plessey AWS-1 and a Hollandse Signaalapparaten M20 fire control outfit is provided.

Dorina (F.81) was laid down in January 1970 and completed in June 1972. Her sister *Otobo* (F.82) was laid down nine months later and was completed in November 1972. Both ships were refitted by the original builders at their Camber yard in Portsmouth in 1975-76. The names mean 'hippopotamus' in two of the main tribal languages used in the Federation of Nigeria.

See also *Kromantse, Erin'mi.*

Displacement: 500 tons (standard), 650 tons (full load) *Length:* 61.6 m (202 ft) oa *Beam:* 9.45 m (31 ft) *Draught:* 3.46 m (11 ft 4 in) *Machinery:* 2-shaft diesels, 3400 bhp= 23 knots *Armament:* 2 4-in (102-mm) Mk 16 AA (1×2); 2 40-mm (1.57-in) AA (2×1); 2 20-mm (0.79-in) (2×1) *Crew:* 66

Draken

Swedish submarine class, built 1958-62. Six Improved *Hajen* Class boats were ordered during 1958-60, four from Kockums and two from Karlskrona dockyard: *Draken, Vargen, Nordkaparen, Springaren, Gripen* and *Delfinen.*

These boats resemble the *Hajen* Class, with the same beam and a 10-ft (3-m) longer hull, but in place of the *Hajen*'s two-shafts the SEMT-Pielstick diesels drive a single five-bladed propeller through a single shaft. The armament is as before, four 53.3-cm (21-in) bow-tubes, firing FFV TP61 peroxide-driven homing torpedoes. The improved efficiency of the propulsion system gives 20 knots underwater.

The new-style recognition letters on the streamlined fin are: *Del (Delfinen), Dra (Draken), Gri (Gripen), Nor (Nordkaparen), Spr (Springaren)* and *Vgn (Vargen).*

The first in service was the *Vargen* in November 1961, and the last was *Springaren* a year later. There is no external difference between this group and the earlier *Hajens*, but they are likely to be retained longer than the older boats as they are more efficient.

Displacement: 835/1110 tons (surfaced/submerged) *Length:* 69 m (226 ft 4 in) pp *Beam:* 5.1 m (16 ft 7 in) *Draught:* 5.3 m (17 ft 4 in) *Machinery:* 1-shaft diesel-electric, 1660 bhp= 17/20 knots (surfaced/submerged) *Armament:* 4 53.3-cm (21-in) torpedoes *Crew:* 36

Dreadnought

British nuclear submarine, built 1959-63. The building of the Royal Navy's first nuclear submarine was authorized in 1956, and the original intention was to power her by a reactor designed jointly by Vickers-Armstrong, Rolls-Royce and Foster-Wheeler. However, the development of the reactor at the Dounreay establishment ran into a number of delays, and in 1958 the decision was made to buy a reactor from the United States. As a result the *Dreadnought* was given a Westinghouse S5W pressurized water-cooled reactor, although the installation and maintenance was still entrusted to Rolls-Royce.

As the machinery is identical to that in the US *Skipjack* Class the hull lines abaft the fin are very similar to the American boats, whereas the forward end conforms to the original British design. However the British design draws heavily on the US *Skipjack* and *Albacore* designs, apart from the decision not to adopt diving planes on the fin. When the *Dreadnought* first commissioned in 1963 she was reputed to have a notice outside the reactor compartment which read, 'Checkpoint Charlie – you are now entering the American Zone'.

As a prototype the *Dreadnought* has spent much of her career evaluating tactics and equipment. She has a ship's inertial navigation system (SINS) and in 1970 became the first British submarine to surface at the North Pole. She has two sonars, the big Type 2001 in the 'chin' position, and a Type 2007 passive set, and has an I-Band radar on a telescopic mast.

The *Dreadnought* was laid down in June 1959 at Vickers-Armstrongs, Barrow, launched in October 1960 and commissioned in April 1963. The name of the epoch-making battleship (which had commissioned on the same day as the submarine was launched) was chosen deliberately to emphasize the power and importance of the nuclear attack submarine in modern naval warfare. She was given a major refit during 1968-70.

Displacement: 3500/4000 tons (surfaced/submerged) *Length:* 81 m (265 ft 9 in) *Beam:* 9.8 m (32 ft 2 in) *Draught:* 7.9 m (26 ft) *Machinery:* 1-shaft nuclear reactor/geared steam turbines,

HMS *Duke of York*, one of the five *King George V* Class battleships completed in the opening years of the Second World War. Her ten 14-in (355.6-mm) guns were used with devastating effect against the German battlecruiser *Scharnhorst* in the Battle of the North Cape on December 26, 1943. The gun duel was almost one-sided, the *Duke of York* taking only two hits, but closing the range from 18 300 m (20 000 yards) to 15 550 m (17 000 yards) and finally shooting at 9500 m (10 400 yards). She opened fire at 1650 hours and three hours later the *Scharnhorst* sank, having suffered 11 torpedo hits and taking with her all but 36 of her complement of 2000

Two views of HMS *Dreadnought* at Faslane, Scotland. She was Britain's first nuclear-powered submarine and in 1970 became the first British submarine to surface at the North Pole

15 000 shp=25 knots (surfaced/submerged) Note: an electric motor is provided for emergency power *Armament:* 6 21-in (53-cm) torpedo tubes (forward) *Crew:* 88

Duke of York

British battleship. The *Duke of York* was one of the five 35 000-ton battleships of the *King George V* Class. She was laid down by J Brown at Clydebank on May 5, 1937, with the provisional name of *Anson* but this was changed to *Duke of York* in 1938. She was launched on February 28, 1940, and completed on November 4, 1941, when she joined the Home Fleet at Scapa Flow. At this time she carried air warning, surface warning and gunnery radar sets and was armed with ten 14-in (356-mm) (2×4+1×2), 16 5.25-in (133-mm) (8×2), 48 2-pdr pom-poms (6×8) and 6 20-mm (0.79-in) (6×1) guns. By early 1942, a further eight single 20-mm (0.79-in) guns had been added to the ship.

In December 1941, she was detached from the Home Fleet to carry the prime minister to the US which was followed by a shakedown cruise to Bermuda, prior to her return home at the end of January 1942. Between March and July, she provided distant cover for five outward and five homeward bound Russian convoys, including the disastrous PQ17, and during May and July served temporarily as flagship of the C-in-C Home Fleet. In October 1942, she went to the Mediterranean as part of the covering force for the North African landings and acted as flagship of the C-in-C Force H until her return in November. Between December 1942 and March 1943, she was refitted at Rosyth, during which time 14 single 20-mm (0.79-in) guns were added to her armament. In May 1943, she became flagship of Admiral Sir Bruce Fraser, C-in-C Home Fleet, and during the remainder of the year took part in several minor operations off the Norwegian coast.

On December 26, 1943, the battlecruiser *Scharnhorst* attempted to attack the Russian convoy JW55A but was frustrated by the cruisers of the Home Fleet. Covering this convoy to the south was the *Duke of York*, which intercepted the enemy ship as she returned to her Norwegian base. The resulting action, which later became known as the battle of North Cape, took place in a gale at night and was the last battleship engagement in which no aircraft took part. The battle lasted three hours, during which the *Scharnhorst* was pounded into a floating wreck by the *Duke of York* and cruisers and destroyers

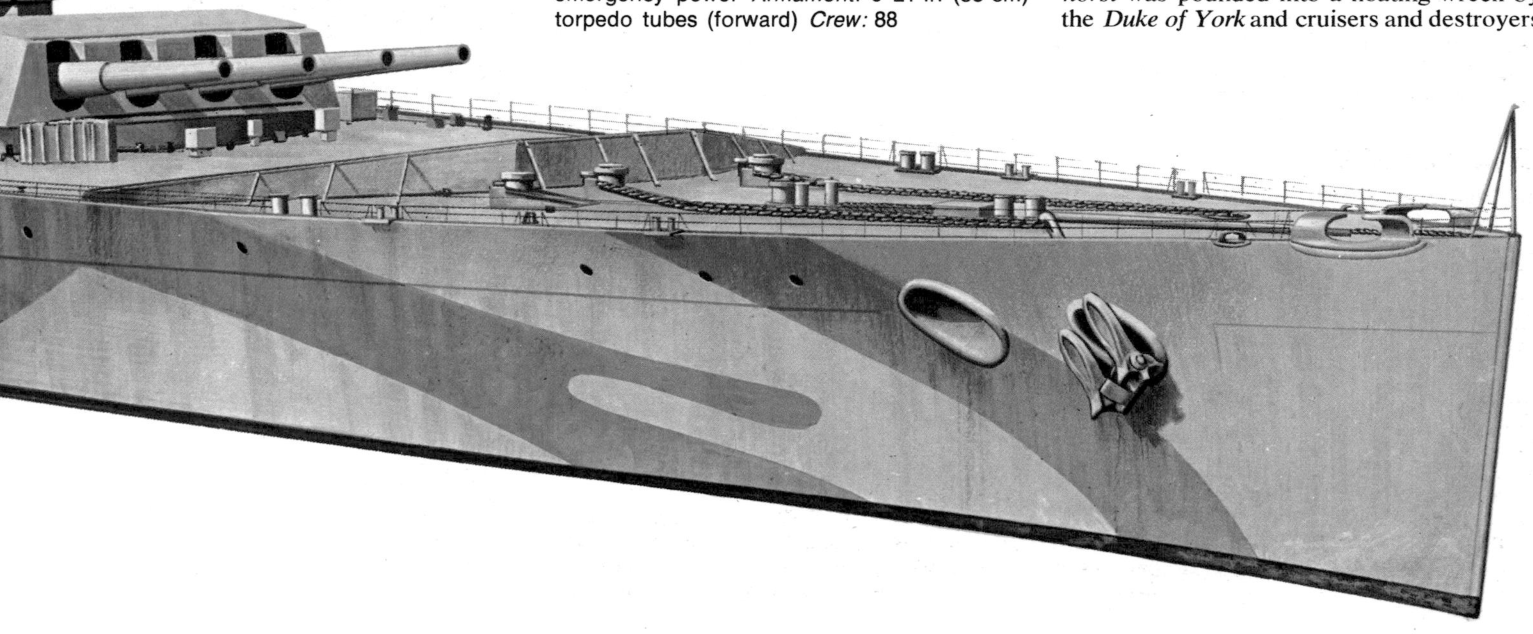

of the covering force. Having suffered four torpedo hits during the action and a further seven in the final stages, the German ship's magazines exploded and she sank taking all but 36 of her crew with her. During the battle, the *Duke of York*'s gunnery proved exceptionally good; she straddled *Scharnhorst* with her first salvo and continued to do so throughout the engagement. This performance was largely due to the use of her Type 284 gunnery radar set which provided sufficiently accurate fire control information for blind fire to be used when the *Scharnhorst* could not be seen.

The *Duke of York* provided cover for Russian convoys again in March and August 1944. In about June 1944 she had two of her single 20-mm (0.79-in) guns replaced by twin mountings of the same calibre. Between September 1944 and March 1945, she underwent a major refit at Liverpool to make her ready for transfer to the Pacific. This involved removing her aircraft equipment, constructing a new boat deck amidships, adding substantially to her close-range antiaircraft armament and modernizing her radar equipment. At the completion of this refit, she displaced 39450 tons standard (44794 tons full load) and carried 88 2-pdr pom-poms (8×8, 6×4), 8 40-mm (1.57-in) Bofors (2×4) and 55 20-mm (0.79-in) (39×1, 8×2) guns.

In April 1945, she sailed to join the British Pacific Fleet going via Suez, Ceylon and Australia. She arrived at Manus in July and was still there when Japan surrendered in the following month. She remained as flagship of the British Pacific Fleet until June 1946 and then returned home. She arrived at Devonport in July and was taken in hand for refit, having two of her four-barrel pom-pom mountings and 25 of her single 20-mm (0.79-in) guns removed. Until July 1949 she served as flagship of the C-in-C Home Fleet and then spent two years as flagship of the reserve fleet. She was finally sold for scrap in 1957.

Displacement: 35000 tons (standard) *Length:* 213.36 m (700 ft) pp; 227.07 m (745 ft) oa *Beam:* 31.39 m (103 ft) *Draught:* 8.46 m (27 ft 9 in) *Machinery:* 4-shaft geared turbines, 110000 shp= 29 knots *Protection:* 114-380 mm (4½-15 in) main belt; 25-152 mm (1-6 in) decks; 230-406 mm (9-16 in) turrets *Armament:* 10 14-in (355.6-mm)(2×4, 1×2); 16 5.25-in (133-mm) DP (8×2); 48 2-pdr AA guns (6×8); 16-in (406-mm) depth-charge throwers *Aircraft:* 4 *Crew:* 1553-1558

Dunkerque

French battlecruiser class, built 1932-38. The need to replace the ageing Dreadnought battleships of the *Courbet* type was discussed as early as 1926, for under the terms of the Washington Treaty, France could begin the construction of a new capital ship in 1927. The naval staff of the day favoured a *croiseur de combat* (light battlecruiser) and in January 1927 submitted a paper outlining a proposal for a ship somewhat like the later German pocket battleships, capable of attacking merchant shipping but fast enough to elude contemporary battleships.

The appearance of the *Deutschland* pocket battleship meant a reconsideration of the initial decision, and as the British were in favour of reducing battleship displacement to 25000 tons there was a wide divergence of official opinion about the right size of ship to build. Informal agreement was reached with the Italians to build not more than two 35000-tonners each, leaving a further 70000 tons available to each navy, out of which three or even four small capital ships could be built.

In the light of these factors the *Conseil Supérieur de la Marine* (naval board) produced drawings for a 25000-ton battlecruiser to be armed with four 330-mm (13-in) guns, armoured to withstand the 280-mm (11-in) shells of the *Deutschland* Class. To save weight the eight heavy guns were to be grouped in two quadruple turrets forward, an arrangement copied from the British *Nelson* but in fact proposed as early as 1914 in the cancelled *Normandie* Class.

By the end of April 1932 final plans were approved for a single ship known as a *batiment de ligne* (battleship), not *croiseur de combat* (battlecruiser). When it was learned that Mussolini had ordered two new large battleships for the Italian navy, funds were voted for a further ship in July 1934.

The two ships had a good turn of speed but their side armour consigned them to the second rank, as was proved at Mers-el-Kebir, when the *Dunkerque* was riddled by British

ECP Armées

The battlecruisers *Dunkerque* (above) and *Strasbourg* were modelled on the *Nelson* Class

Name	launched	builder
Dunkerque	12/1932	Brest arsenal
Strasbourg	12/1936	Ch de St Nazaire-Penhoët

The elegant lines of the *Dunkerque* emphasize her powerful armament of eight 330-mm (13-in) guns in two turrets forward. One of her four Loire Nieuport 130 seaplanes is in position on the launch ramp on the stern. The crane by the hangar has been raised for the recovery and inboard stowage of seaplanes. *Dunkerque*'s career was brief: launched in 1932 she sustained heavy damage during attacks by the Allied Force H in July 1940 which put her out of action for the rest of the war

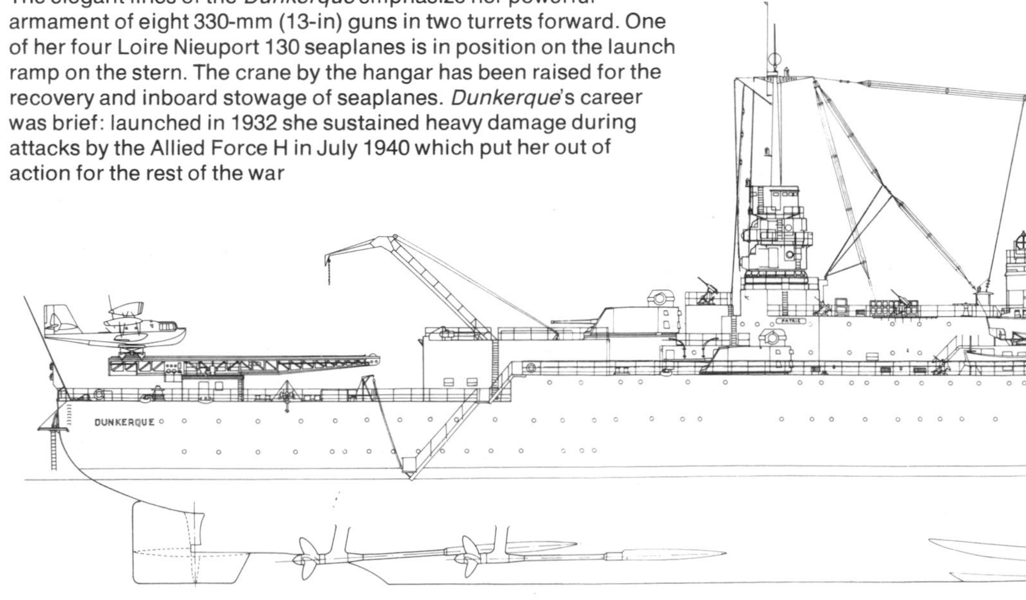

15-in (381-mm) shells. The theoretical advantage of the dual-purpose secondary armament was reduced by the innate weakness of the 130-mm (5.1-in) mounting, and the light antiaircraft armament was particularly weak. On the other hand the underwater protection was good, and *Dunkerque* withstood the explosion of a British 18-in (46-cm) aerial torpedo well, in addition to the detonation of several depth-charges when an armed trawler blew up alongside. The armour was angled inboard at 21°, with an internal 'bulge' and a layer filled with *ebonite mousée*, a thick black gum resembling the old cellulose layer used in French ships in the 1890s.

The 330-mm (13-in) Model 1933 had a muzzle velocity of 800 m/sec (2625 ft/sec) and could fire a 540-kg (1190-lb) shell 20 000 m (21 872 yards). The 130-mm (5.1-in) Model 1935 guns were in three quadruple mountings and two twins; they had the same muzzle velocity as the 330-mm (13-in) guns and could fire a 32.1-kg (71-lb) shell a distance of 19 800 m (21 653 yards). Each barrel was theoretically capable of firing 14 or 15 rounds per minute.

The ships were impressive steamers. *Dunkerque* made 30.57 knots on trials with 114 050 shp for eight hours, and for two hours she steamed at just over 31 knots with 135 585 shp. Her sister achieved slightly higher speeds on her trials, and both could maintain 20½ knots with 25 000 shp or 28 knots with 28 000 shp.

The two ships were lying at Mers-el-Kebir near Oran on July 3, 1940, when the French fleet was attacked by the British Force H under Admiral Somerville at 1656 hours. The *Dunkerque* was hit while trying to slip her moorings, and was stopped by four 15-in (381-mm) shells. Although she fired 40 rounds at HMS *Hood* her gunnery was not accurate enough to hit her opponent and eventually all power failed. Finally she was able to creep under the lee of Santon. Two days later Swordfish bombers from HMS *Ark Royal* attacked and hit her with a torpedo, while the *Terre Neuve* blew up alongside and inflicted further damage. In all the battleship suffered 150 dead and 797 men wounded.

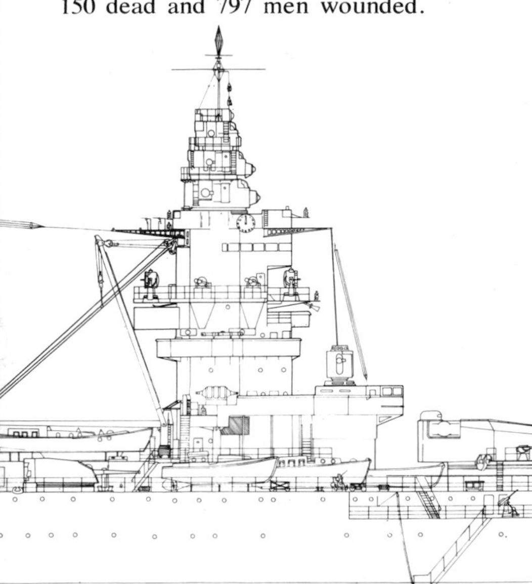

The *Strasbourg* was luckier, for she managed to get clear under a smokescreen and was protected by the guns of Santon until she got clear of the harbour. Once under way her high speed enabled her to avoid three further attacks by torpedo-bombers. She reached Toulon, and was later joined by her damaged sister, but both had to be scuttled on November 27, 1942, when German troops stormed the arsenal in an attempt to seize the fleet. The hull of the *Strasbourg* was salved by an Italian team under Ing Generale O Giannelli and was nominally taken over by the Italian navy in July 1943, but in August 1944 she was sunk once more by Allied bombing. When the French navy reoccupied Toulon in 1945 she was raised for the second time and used for various experiments with explosives and projectiles until scrapped in 1955.

Displacement: 30 750 tons (normal), 31 400 tons (full load) *Length:* 214.50 m (703 ft 9 in) oa *Beam:* 31.08 m (101 ft 11 in) *Draught:* 9.60 m (31 ft 6 in) max *Machinery:* 4-shaft geared steam turbines, 112 500 shp=29½ knots *Protection:* 241-141 mm (9½-5½ in) belt; 38-198 mm (1½-7¾ in) decks; 330 mm (13 in) turrets; 270 mm (10½ in) conning tower *Armament:* 8 330-mm (13-in)/52-cal (2×4); 16 130-mm (5.1-in)/45-cal DP (3×4, 2×2); 8 37-mm (1.46-in) AA (4×2); 32 13.2-mm (0.52-in) AA (8×4) *Aircraft:* 4 Loire Nieuport 130 seaplanes, 1 catapult *Crew:* 1381 (as flagships)

Echo

Soviet nuclear submarine class, built 1960-67. The prototype of this class was sighted in 1963, and appeared to be a nuclear-propelled development of the diesel-electric Juliet type, also armed with SS-N-3 Shaddock missiles. According to published sources, only five of the *Echo* type were built, and then an improved type, known as *Echo II*, was started in 1964.

The difference between *Echo I* and *Echo II* was the extra 3.05 m (10 ft) of hull of the *Echo II*, which allowed an extra pair of launching tubes to be installed abreast of the fin. The two groups used the same launching tubes for the SS-N-3 Shaddock missile as the *Juliet* Class, with the missile stowed horizontally, and then raised for firing at an angle of about 30°. The guidance radar, known in NATO parlance as 'Snoop Slab' or 'Snoop Tray', is housed in the forward section of the fin, which opens to allow it to function.

Sources conflict about how many of each type were built; originally it was believed that five *Echo I*s were built, followed by 28 *Echo II*s. In 1973-74 the last of the *Echo I* group had its missiles removed, and reverted to the status of a fleet or attack submarine, proof of the growing realization in the Soviet navy that surface-launching of Shaddocks was too risky in modern warfare.

There is, however, no similar report of the *Echo II* group being regraded in similar fashion, and in June 1972 three of them were part of a mixed task force operating in the South China Sea. The defensive armament is believed to consist of six 53-cm (21-in) torpedo tubes forward and four 40.6-cm (16-in) tubes for short-range antisubmarine torpedoes in the after part of the hull.

No names are known, apart from a rumour that one was named *Frunze*. All were built in Komsomolsk, on the Amur River. All boats were originally deployed in the Pacific, but since 1970 about half the *Echo II*s are believed to be with the Northern Fleet.

(Echo I) *Displacement:* 4600/5000 tons (surfaced/submerged) *Length:* 116 m (380 ft 7 in) oa *Beam:* 8.68 m (28 ft 5 in) *Draught:* 7.9 m (25 ft 10¾ in) *Machinery:* 2-shaft steam turbines/nuclear reactor, 22 500 shp=20 knots (surfaced/submerged) *Armament:* 6 SS-N-3 SSMs (removed by 1974); 6 53-cm (21-in) torpedo tubes (forward); 4 40.6-cm (16-in) torpedo tubes (aft) *Crew:* 92

(Echo II) *Displacement:* 4800/5600 tons (surfaced/submerged) *Length:* 119 m (390 ft 5 in) oa *Beam:* 8.68 m (28 ft 5 in) *Draught:* 7.9 m (25 ft 10¾ in) *Machinery:* As above *Armament:* 8 SS-N-3 SSMs; 6 53-cm (21-in) torpedo tubes (forward); 4 40.6-cm (16-in) torpedo tubes (aft) *Crew:* 100

Edsall

US destroyer escort class, built 1942-44. The endless problems with the supply of machinery for the vast DE programme started by the US Navy in 1942 finally forced the Bureau of Ships to accept half the designed power for future construction. As gear-cutting was no longer a problem, and as the higher-rated Fairbanks-Morse diesel was now available, it was decided to adopt a geared drive for a new class. This had the advantage of giving higher endurance and simplicity of operation.

The class was built entirely by two shipyards. Those built by the Consolidated Steel corporation, Orange, Texas, comprised: *Edsall* (DE.129); *Jacob Jones* (DE.130); *Hammann* (ex-*Langley*) (DE.131); *Robert E Peary* (DE.132); *Pillsbury* (DE.133); *Pope* (DE.134); *Flaherty* (DE.135); *Frederick C Davis* (DE.136); *Herbert C Jones* (DE.137); *Douglas L Howard* (DE.138); *Farquar* (DE.139); *J R Y Blakely* (DE.140); *Hill* (DE.141); *Fessenden* (DE.142); *Fiske* (DE.143); *Frost* (DE.144); *Huse* (DE.145); *Inch* (DE.146); *Blair* (DE.147); *Brough* (DE.148); *Chatelain* (DE.149); *Neunzer* (DE.150); *Poole* (DE.151); *Peterson*

(DE.152); *Harveson* (DE.316); *Joyce* (DE.317); *Kirkpatrick* (DE.318); *Leopold* (DE.319); *Menges* (DE.320); *Mosley* (DE.321); *Newell* (DE.322); *Pride* (DE.323); *Falgout* (DE.324); *Lowe* (DE.325); *Thomas J Gary* (ex-*Gary*) (DE.326); *Brister* (DE.327); *Finch* (DE.328); *Kretchmer* (DE.329); *O'Reilly* (DE.330); *Koiner* (DE.331); *Price* (DE.332); *Strickland* (DE.333); *Forster* (DE.334); *Daniel* (DE.335); *Roy O Hale* (DE.336); *Dale W Peterson* (DE.337) and *Martin H Ray* (DE.338).

Those built by Brown Shipbuilding, Houston, comprised: *Stewart* (DE.238); *Sturtevant* (DE.239); *Moore* (DE.240); *Keith* (ex-*Scott*) (DE.241); *Tomich* (DE.242); *J Richard Ward* (ex-*James R Ward*) (DE.243); *Otterstetter* (DE.244); *Sloat* (DE.245); *Snowden* (DE.246); *Stanton* (DE.247); *Swasey* (DE.248); *Marchand* (DE.249); *Hurst* (DE.250); *Camp* (DE.251); *Howard D Crow* (DE.252); *Pettit* (DE.253); *Ricketts* (DE.254); *Sellstrom* (DE.255); *Ramsden* (DE.382); *Mills* (DE.383); *Rhodes Richey* (DE.385); *Savage* (DE.386); *Vance* (DE.387); *Lansing* (DE.388); *Durant* (DE.389); *Calcaterra* (DE.390); *Chambers* (DE.391); *Merrill* (DE.392); *Haverfield* (DE.393); *Swenning* (DE.394); *Willis* (DE.395); *Jansen* (DE.396); *Wilhoite* (DE.397); *Cockrill* (DE.398); *Stockdale* (DE.399); *Hissem* (DE.400) and *Holder* (DE.401).

A total of 21 units (DE.316-325 and 382-392) were manned by the US Coastguard, and 12 of these were retained and renumbered: WDE.422 (ex-DE.322); WDE 424 (ex-DE.324); WDE.425 (ex-DE.324); WDE.428 (ex-DE.328); WDE.431 (ex-DE.331); WDE.434 (ex-DE.334); WDE.482 (ex-DE.382); WDE.485 (ex-DE.385); WDE.487 (ex-DE.387); WDE.488 (ex-388); WDE.489 (ex-DE.389) and WDE.491 (ex-DE.391).

Four ships were sunk in the Battle of the Atlantic: *Frederick C Davis* was torpedoed by *U 546* on April 24, 1945, *Fiske* was torpedoed by *U 804* on August 2, 1944, *Leopold* was torpedoed by *U 225* on March 9, 1944, and *Holder* was torpedoed by German aircraft on April 11, 1944. The *Menges* was also torpedoed by *U 371* in the Mediterranean in May 1944, but she was repaired with the stern of the *Holder*, which had been written off as a total loss.

In the mid-1950s the obsession with the Russian bomber threat led to the creation of the DEW Line of radar early warning stations in Canada and Alaska, and to extend this chain to cover the seaborne flanks of the North American continent 34 of the *Edsall* Class were converted to radar pickets. This involved a new aluminium superstructure amidships to provide better conditions for the crew during their monotonous patrols, and two tripod masts to carry the comprehensive array of aerials. The ships were rerated as DER, or destroyer escort, radar picket.

In appearance the *Edsall* Class was similar to the first diesel-engined DEs, the *Evarts* Class, with a single upright funnel, but they were armed with triple 21-in (53-cm) torpedo tubes. In 1945 the *Camp* was rearmed with 5-in (127-mm) guns, and in many the torpedo tubes were replaced by single 40-mm (1.57-in) Bofors guns and 20-mm (0.79-in) Oerlikons. The DERs looked very different, with single 3-in (76-mm) automatic guns forward and aft, and a massive rotating antenna on the after deckhouse.

US Navy

USS *Sloat*, an *Edsall* Class destroyer, mounting a Hedgehog A/S mortar on the forecastle

Scrapping of the class started in 1965 and the last was stricken in 1975. Only two survived at the end of the 1970s, the *Camp* (DER.251) which was transferred to the South Vietnam navy in 1971, and then given to the Philippines in 1976, and the *Thomas J Gary* (DER.326) which became the Tunisian *President Bourguiba* in 1973.

Displacement: 1200 tons (standard), 1490 tons (full load) *Length:* 93.27 m (306 ft) oa *Beam:* 11.12 m (36 ft 6 in) *Draught:* 3.73 m (12 ft 3 in) maximum *Machinery:* 2-shaft diesel, 6000 bhp=21 knots *Armament:* (As built) 3 3-in (76-mm)/50-cal DP (3×1); 2 40-mm (1.57-in)/60-cal AA (1×2); 8 20-mm (0.79-in) AA (8×1); 3 21-in (53-cm) torpedo tubes (1×3); Hedgehog mortar; 8 depth charge throwers *Crew:* 200

Enrico Toti

Italian submarine class, built 1965-69. Two submarines were authorized in 1964, followed by another pair in 1966, the first submarines to be designed or built in Italy since the end of the Second World War.

The design was revised several times, as the Italian navy was by no means certain about the best size for operations in the Mediterranean. Finally a coastal type was chosen, with the emphasis on antisubmarine qualities.

The hull layout is conventional, with four bow tubes, diesel-electric drive and a single shaft driving a five-bladed propeller. No information has been released about the type of torpedoes, but as it has been admitted that the boats have a computer-aided fire-control system, the torpedoes are probably the Whithead Moto Fides A.184 type. This is a 53-cm (21-in) wire-guided swim-out torpedo, equipped with active and passive homing.

Displacement: 524/584 tons (surfaced/submerged) *Length:* 46.17 m (151 ft 6 in) pp *Beam:* 4.72 m (15 ft 5 in) *Draught:* 4 m (13 ft $1\frac{1}{2}$ in) *Machinery:* 1-shaft diesel-electric, 2200 bhp=14/15 knots (surfaced/submerged) *Armament:* 4 53-cm (21-in) torpedo tubes (8 torpedoes carried) *Crew:* 26

Pendant no and name	launched	builder
S.505 *Attilio Bagnolini*	8/1967	CRDA, Monfalcone
S.506 *Enrico Toti*	3/1967	CRDA, Monfalcone
S.513 *Enrico Dandolo*	12/1967	CRDA, Monfalcone
S.514 *Lazaro Mocenigo*	4/1968	CRDA, Monfalcone

Enterprise

US aircraft carrier. The world's first nuclear-powered aircraft carrier, *Enterprise* (CVAN-65) was also the largest warship built, at the time of her launch and for nine years after.

Although the US Pacific Fleet's carrier forces had roamed at will throughout the ocean between 1943 and 1945, and had remained on station for long periods during the Korean War, these feats of endurance and mobility had been achieved only by the deployment of large numbers of auxiliaries whose sole purpose was to bring fuel to the carriers, and the aircraft. The adoption of nuclear-fuelled propulsion for the ship reduced her dependence upon the replenishment groups and released internal space which in 'fossil-fuelled' ships would have held up to 10 000 tons of 'black oil' for use as additional aviation fuel stowage, aviation and victualling stores. This allowed the carriage of more ordnance than a 'fossil-fuel' carrier of similar dimensions. Refuelling of the reactors could be undertaken during long refits. *Enterprise*'s first set of cores were sufficient for more than 96 560 km (60 000 miles) and more than 40 000 launches from the four steam catapults.

A further advantage of nuclear propulsion

was its 'closed-cycle' system, eliminating the vulnerable and space-consuming boiler intake and exhaust (uptake) ducting. Internally this gave up more stowage space, externally it halved the length of the island superstructure (by comparison with that of the contemporary oil-fuelled *Constellation).* No longer was funnel smoke and its turbulence an annoyance to pilots on final approach, and electronics antennae could be mounted in optimum locations, without regard to the corrosive effects of exhaust gases.

Enterprise was built in an astonishingly short time. Congress approved the programme in 1956, the contract was given in August 1957, and the keel was laid on February 4, 1958, at the Newport News shipbuilding yard. Launched on September 24, 1960, she was completed for trials 13 months later. The four ships of the conventionally-powered *Kitty Hawk* Class took between 47 and 52 months to build.

Apart from the use of nuclear power, *Enterprise* is essentially an enlargement of the *Kitty Hawk* design, itself an improved *Forrestal* type. All four deck-edge aircraft are located clear of the landing area and the four 76.2-m (250-ft) steam catapults, so that aircraft can be transferred between the single hangar deck and the flight deck without interfering with flying operations. The catapults, two forward and two in the waist position, amidships to port, can launch aircraft up to 38 555 kg (85 000 lb) in weight at ends speeds (relative to the deck) of up to 140 knots. With the ship capable of over 30 knots, aircraft can be launched at air speeds in excess of 170 knots even in light wind conditions. The accuracy of the pilot-interpreted visual landing aid—a stacked array of narrow beams of light—is such that only four arrester wires are needed, located far enough down the 'runway' to overcome the worst effects of any pitching of the 342.2-m (1123-ft) flight deck.

When completed, *Enterprise* was fitted with no built-in defensive weapons, depending entirely upon her aircraft and her surface escorts. Control of the aircraft, and the gun and missile armament of her screen, was coordinated by the carrier's threat evaluation computer and data communications system (Naval Tactical Data System), which can 'talk' to the computers in other ships so fitted

***Lazaro Mocenigo*, an *Enrico Toti* Class submarine. These were the first such vessels to be built in Italy since the end of the Second World War**

PPL

by means of a data link, correlating the inputs from various radar, sonar and electronic intercepter (ESM) equipment to analyze the threat and provide a solution. Unfortunately, the NTDS was not sufficiently widely fitted to ensure that *Enterprise*'s consorts would all be so equipped. In 1966, two eight-shot Sea Sparrow launchers were fitted, one on each quarter, with the associated electronics and handling gear which made up the Basic Point Defence Missile System and gave the carrier a fast-reaction short-range self-defence weapon.

The elimination of the funnel in the island permitted the installation of the SPS 32/33 search and tracking radars, the antennae of which consisted of fixed arrays on each face of the island. By replacing the conventional rotating antenna with electronic scanning in azimuth and elevation, reliability and accuracy were improved. A conventional outfit of SPS 10 and 12 air search and navigation radars was also installed.

The four-shaft propulsion machinery has four pairs of nuclear reactors, each pair providing steam to a set of geared turbines by means of eight heat exchangers. The system develops over 280 000 shp and gives a sea speed of more than 30 knots in deep load conditions.

Enterprise commissioned on November 25, 1961, and embarked her first air group early in February 1962. She became operational towards the end of June and was then deployed to the Sixth Fleet in the Mediterranean until October, when she joined the blockade forces off Cuba. Two further Sixth Fleet deployments occupied the 'Big E' until July 31, 1964, when she left the Mediterranean with the nuclear-powered cruiser *Long Beach* and destroyer *Bainbridge* for a 48 280-km (30 000-mile) nine-week unreplenished world cruise, returning to Newport News in October for her first refit and refuelling.

She became operational once again a year later and sailed east, via the Cape of Good Hope, to join the Pacific Fleet. On December 2, 1965, *Enterprise* commenced operations off Vietnam, going on to launch 13 020 combat sorties during the six months that followed. A short refit at San Francisco occupied her until December 1966, when she returned to the Gulf of Tonkin for another six months of operations. This pattern was repeated in 1967 and 1968. In January 1969, while she was working-up after a refit, she suffered a serious fire on the flight deck, the deck being holed by the explosion of nine bombs which had detonated in the heat. Repairs at Pearl Harbor took only two months and *Enterprise* was on station again by the end of March, remaining until July, when she set off westbound for Newport News for her second long refit and refuelling.

It was not until June 1971 that she reached Vietnamese waters for her fifth tour. This was followed in 1972 by a sixth and final deployment in this war, lasting until January 1973. She was still in service in the late 1970s.

Displacement: 75 500 tons (standard), 89 600 tons (full load) *Length:* 342.29 m (1123 ft) oa; 317 m (1040 ft) wl *Beam:* 40.53 m (133 ft) hull; 78.33 m (257 ft) flight deck *Draught:* 11.58 m (38 ft) mean *Machinery:* 4 pairs of nuclear reactors, providing steam to 4-shaft geared steam turbines, 280 000 shp=35 knots (approx) *Aircraft:* 85-100, dependent on types embarked *Armament:* (from 1966) 2×8 Sea Sparrow SAM launchers *Crew:* 5500

Erin'mi

Nigerian corvette class. In 1975 the Nigerian navy ordered two Mk 9 corvettes from Vosper-Thornycroft, to be built at Portchester. They are 71.6-m (235-ft) general-purpose escorts, basically an enlarged version of the builder's Mk 3 design already in service as the *Dorina* Class.

The surface armament comprises a single OTO-Melara 76-mm (3-in) gun forward, two 20-mm (0.79-in) Oerlikon guns amidships, a single 40-mm (1.57-in) Bofors gun on the after deckhouse, and a triple lightweight Seacat missile launcher on the quarterdeck. The antisubmarine armament comprises a twin 375-mm (14.8-in) Bofors rocket-launcher in B position and a hull-mounted Plessey/PMS26 sonar. Fire-control is provided by the Dutch HSA M22, and air-warning and surveillance by the Plessey AWS-1 radars. Two German MTU 20-cylinder diesels give a maximum speed of 27 knots and an endurance of 7081 km (4400 miles) at 14 knots.

The ships are tailored to meet the requirements of smaller navies, with a modern armament and good performance on a relatively cheap hull which is also easy to maintain. The *Erin'mi* was launched on January 20, 1977, and was expected to enter service in 1979. Her sister ship, *Enyimiri*, was launched on February 7, 1978, and will go into service

USS *Enterprise* (CVAN-65), the world's first nuclear-powered aircraft carrier, underway off Point Loma, California on June 21, 1976

US Navy

USS *Wasp* (CV-18), an *Essex* Class carrier commissioned in 1943. She was to have been called *Oriskany* but was named after CV-7 lost in 1942

in 1980.

See also *Dorina, Kromantse.*

Displacement: 740 tons *Length:* 67.06 m (220 ft) oa *Beam:* 10.51 m (34 ft 6 in) *Draught:* 3.35 m (11 ft) *Machinery:* 2-shaft diesels, 20 000 bhp=27 knots *Armament:* 76-mm (3-in) OTO-Melara DP; 1 40-mm (1.57-in)/60-cal; 2 20-mm (0.79-in) (2× 1); 1 triple Seacat SAM; 1 twin 375-mm (14.8-in) A/S rocket-launcher *Crew:* 67

Essex

US aircraft carrier class. The specification for what was to become the largest single class of fleet carriers was first issued in June 1939. The original concept was that of a modified *Yorktown* Class, but while the design, finalized early in 1940, followed the same general outlines, it was for a much larger ship, with a standard displacement equal to the full load tonnage of the *Yorktown* Class.

The additional weight was contributed to by the increase of the 5-in (127-mm) dual-purpose armament from eight to 12 barrels, in four single mounts and four twin turrets—the latter mounted fore and aft of the island —on the flight deck, thicker deck armour, more powerful propulsive machinery and the installation of flight deck machinery capable of handling heavier aircraft. More than 6300 tons of fuel oil and 690 tons of aviation gasoline gave a range of over 27 360 km (17 000 miles) at 20 knots. About 220 tons of ammunition and aviation ordnance brought the full load tonnage up to between 34 200 and 36 000 tons. Aircraft complement, at 82, was the same as that of *Yorktown*, but in practice the specified figure was always exceeded. Ninety were carried when the first ships entered combat in 1943 and 18 months later the total had reached 108, all larger and heavier than those carried by *Yorktown.*

Eleven 'CV-9' Class carriers were ordered in 1940 and subsequent programmes added another 21 ships; six were cancelled in 1945 before they had been laid down and two others were cancelled prior to launch. The name-ship, *Essex*, was laid down on April 28, 1941, launched on July 31, 1942, and completed exactly five months later—15 months ahead of the contracted schedule. The shipyard concerned, Newport News, built eight of the 17 ships of the class completed before the end of the war, and one of the seven completed after 1945. The average building time of the eight wartime ships was 17½ months—*Franklin* (CV-13) was built in just 14 months. One other civilian firm and three navy yards built the remaining 13 ships, only one of which, *Hancock* (CV-19), was built in less than 20 months.

Fourteen *Essex* Class carriers saw action between August 31, 1943, and August 15, 1945. They formed the main fighting strength of the Fast Carrier Task Force in the Pacific, supported by *Saratoga* (CV-3), *Enterprise* (CV-6) and the nine *Independence* Class light carriers.

Essex was withdrawn from the front line for a refit for three months in the spring of 1944, and for three weeks after being hit by a kamikaze in late November 1944. None of the other ships missed a scheduled mission due to machinery breakdown. During the first 14 months of combat, only three ships were damaged by enemy action, but the advent of the kamikazes brought a dramatic change and 14 kamikazes and seven conventional bombers scored hits during the next seven months, forcing the damaged carriers to return for repairs on ten occasions.

Six more *Essex* Class were completed between August 1945 and November 1946, by which time many of the ships had been decommissioned and laid up in reserve. In the same year, the US Navy began to plan a modernization scheme to enable a class of ships designed for 6803-kg (15 000-lb) piston-engined aircraft to operate jets of up to 20411-kg (45 000-lb); at the same time, the opportunity was taken to correct the more important defects in the design. The inevitable increase in weight was countered by the removal of the four 5-in (127-mm) twin turrets (and the compensatory addition of four single mountings) and the bulging of the hull, increasing the beam by 2.43 m (8 ft). The first ship to appear in service with all the modifications was the 'new' *Oriskany* (CV-34), launched in October 1945, but not completed until September 25, 1950. After this another 14 ships were modernized under Project 27A and Project 125.

In 1951, the Royal Navy began experiments to assess the potential of angled flight decks, with the increase of landing speeds and weights tending to extend the pull-out of the arrester wires and the safety barriers further and further up the deck until nearly two-thirds of the deck had to be left empty, free for landings, so that the deck park was shrinking and with it the size of the embarked air group. Safety was also marginal—once committed to a landing, jet aircraft had no chance of going around again and a barrier engagement frequently meant severe damage to an expensive aircraft. By angling the landing area to port, the need for barriers was eliminated, aircraft could miss the wires, open up the throttles and go round again; after landing they could park in an enlarged safe area forward and to starboard of the angled deck. Such a deck was painted on to HMS *Triumph* early in 1952 and the successful evaluation trials were witnessed by US Navy observers. So impressed were they that USS *Antietam* was immediately taken in hand and modified in a far more ambitious fashion. The port deck edge lift was extended outboard and a fillet added in the angle between the after edge of the lift and the flight deck edge. This triangular extension allowed the landing area to be angled by 8°, instead of the 4° which was all that could be contrived on the unmodified *Triumph.*

Antietam's experimental deck was completed on December 19, 1952, and trials in 1953 resulted in a decision to modify 14 *Essex* Class carriers to an even more advanced standard. Project 125 added the angled deck (canted deck in US Navy parlance), removed the after centreline lift to the starboard deck

US Navy

US Navy

Above: USS *Yorktown* (CV-10) burning after a Japanese air attack during the battle of Midway. Below: Helicopters and Douglas A-1 Skyraiders of MAG-26 aboard the *Antietam* in July 1958

US Navy

edge abaft the island, enclosed the open bows to improve sea-keeping in heavy seas, strengthened the lifts and provided up-dated electronics. The ships selected for modernization were those already modified by Project 27, with the exception of *Lake Champlain*, and the programme was not completed until 1960; *Antietam* had not been one of the up-dated 27s and was not converted. Most of the modernized ships were subsequently fitted with steam catapults in place of the hydraulic units, *Hancock* being the first to receive this British development, in 1954.

The Korean War was fought mainly by the unmodified ships, operating piston-engined attack aircraft and jet fighters off the east coast of the peninsula to supplement the efforts of the land-based Allied air forces in Korea and to implement the blockade of the Communist coast.

The war ended in July 1953, and in the following month the US Navy recategorized its large carriers as Attack (CVA) or Support (CVS) carriers, the latter being tasked with antisubmarine warfare duties. In practice, CVAs were those carriers fitted with steam catapults; a notable exception to the later categorization was the name-ship, *Essex*, which was classified as a CVA as late as 1960, in spite of her hydraulic catapults. In January 1959, *Boxer* (CV-21) was recategorized as a helicopter assault carrier (CVH), followed in the next month by *Princeton* (CVH-37) and two years later by *Valley Forge* (CVH-45); later designated Landing Platform, Helicopter (LPH). This minimal conversion of three narrow-beam *Essex* craft filled a gap in the US Navy's amphibious capability until purpose-built vessels were commissioned in the late 1960s. The three CVHs and seven of the angled-deck CVSs were equipped with improved antisubmarine gear between 1961 and 1966, as part of the Fleet Rehabilitation and Modernization (FRAM) programme.

The *Essex* Class was again in action in 1964, when on August 2 Vought F-8s from *Ticonderoga* strafed North Vietnamése MTBs in the Gulf of Tonkin. Three days

later, F-8s and Douglas A-4s from 'Tico' joined aircraft from *Constellation* in the first strikes north of the 17th Parallel. The war got underway in earnest, as far as the carriers were concerned, in February 1965, when *Hancock* was the class representative in the Gulf. During the next three years, these first two ships and later *Intrepid, Bon Homme Richard* and *Oriskany* joined the larger *Midway, Forrestal* and *Kitty Hawk* Class ships in striking at targets in both North and South Vietnam, using Crusaders and Skyhawks while the larger ships used F-4 Phantoms, A-6 Intruders and A-7 Corsairs as well as Skyhawks. The biggest and heaviest aircraft embarked was the Douglas A-3 Skywarrior airborne tanker and electronic support aircraft. The maximum all-up weight of the EKA-3B variant was 36741 kg (81000 lb). Twenty-one years before, *Intrepid*'s heaviest aircraft had been the 3703-kg (8164-lb) Gruman TBF-1 Avenger. One other *Essex* Class ship, *Shangri-La*, was used for offensive operations off South Vietnam and several of the CVSs provided ASW support for the striking forces.

Intrepid, Hancock, Oriskany and *Lexington* were still in service when the US Navy's direct involvement in the Vietnam War ended in January 1973. The evacuation of US nationals from Cambodia in the spring of 1975 was assisted by *Hancock* and covered by *Oriskany*—the final operational task for the *Essex* Class. *Hancock* was finally decommissioned in January 1976, 32 years after she had been launched; *Oriskany* was a mere 26 years old when she went in May of that year, but *Lexington* was still soldiering on as a deck-landing carrier a year later, nearly 35 years after entering the water. It is improbable whether there has ever been, or will ever be, a more cost-effective warship design.

In such a large class there were many variations in tonnage, armament, complement etc. The figures given below are for typical ships of the class at each stage.

Displacement: (1943, CV-17) 27 100 tons (standard), 35 700 tons (full load); (1953, CV-10) 33 100 tons (standard), 40 000 tons (full load);

Name and No	commissioned	laid up	builder
Essex (CV-9)	12/1942	6/1969	Newport News
Lexington (CV-16)	3/1943	1977	Bethlehem Steel
Yorktown (CV-10)	5/1943	6/1970	Newport News
Bunker Hill (CV-17)	5/1943	1947	Bethlehem Steel
Intrepid (CV-11)	8/1943	3/1974	Newport News
Wasp (CV-18)	11/1943	1/1972	Bethlehem Steel
Hornet (CV-12)	11/1943	6/1970	Newport News
Franklin (CV-13)	1/1944	1947	Newport News
Hancock (CV-19)	4/1944	1/1976	Bethlehem Steel
Ticonderoga (CV-14)	5/1944	1/1973	Newport News
Bennington (CV-20)	8/1944	1/1970	New York navy yard
Shangri-La (CV-38)	9/1944	7/1971	Norfolk navy yard
Randolph (CV-15)	10/1944	2/1969	Newport News
Bon Homme Richard (CV-31)	11/1944	7/1971	New York navy yard
Antietam (CV-36)	1/1945	5/1963	Philadelphia navy yard
Boxer (CV-21)	4/1945	12/1969	Newport News
Lake Champlain (CV-39)	6/1945	1/1966	Norfolk navy yard
Princeton (CV-37)	11/1945	1/1970	Philadelphia navy yard
Tarawa (CV-40)	12/1945	5/1960	Norfolk navy yard
Kearsarge (CV-33)	3/1946	2/1970	New York navy yard
Leyte (CV-32)	4/1946	5/1959	Newport News
Philippine Sea (CV-47)	5/1946	12/1958	Bethlehem Steel
Valley Forge (CV-45)	11/1946	1/1970	Philadelphia navy yard
Oriskany (CV-34)	9/1950	5/1976	New York navy yard

USS *Essex* (CV-9), in postwar service, her flight deck lined with McDonnell A-4 Skyhawks

R M Scott

Newport News Shipbuilding

USS *Sam Houston* (SSBN.609), the first of the *Ethan Allen* Class fleet ballistic missile submarines

(1973, CV-34) 33 250 tons (standard), 44 700 tons (full load) *Length:* (CV-17) 267.91 m (879 ft); (CV-10) 274.01 m (899 ft); (CV-34) 271.27 m (890 ft) oa; *Beam:* (CV-17) 28.34 m (93 ft); (CV-10) 30.78 m (101 ft); (CV-34) 32.46 m (106 ft 6 in) *Draught:* (CV-17) 8.83 m (29 ft); (CV-10) 8.91 m (29 ft 3 in); (CV-34) 9.44 m (31 ft) *Machinery:* 4-shaft Westinghouse geared turbines, 150 000 shp=32.5 knots (CV-17); 32.2 knots (CV-10); 30.7 knots (CV-34) *Aircraft:* 90-108 *Armament:* 12 5-in (127-mm); 8 5-in (127-mm); 4 5-in (127-mm); 68 40-mm (1.57-in) (17×4); 14 3-in (76-mm); 46-72 20-mm (0.79-in) *Crew:* 3448 (CV-17); 3300 (CV-10); 3630 (CV-34)

Ethan Allen

US fleet ballistic missile submarine class, built 1959-63. Although basically similar to the *George Washington* Class FBMs (SSBN 598-602), the following five were specifically designed to fire the Polaris intermediate-range ballistic missile, and were larger and better arranged internally. Four were authorized under fiscal year 1959, and the fifth under 1961.

The use of HY-80 steel enabled these submarines to have a diving depth comparable to the *Thresher* Class attack submarines. When first commissioned they were armed with the A-2 Polaris, with a range of 2400 km (1491 land miles). The *Ethan Allen* made the first launching on October 23, 1961, and on May 6 the following year she fired the first live A-2 round, including detonation of the nuclear warhead. This was the first complete test of a ballistic missile in the US.

All five ships were converted to fire the A-3 Polaris, with a range of 4630 km (2877 land miles). This involved replacing the Mk 80 fire control system and the compressed-air missile ejectors with the Mk 84 system and gas-steam missile ejectors. It has been confirmed that they will not be converted to launch the Poseidon missile, as they are too near the end of their effective lives, and would not be worth the expense.

Displacement: 6955/7900 tons (surfaced/submerged) *Length:* 125.12 m (410 ft 6 in) oa *Beam:* 10.05 m (33 ft) *Draught:* 9.14 m (30 ft) *Machinery:* 1-shaft S5W nuclear reactor/geared steam turbines, 15 000 shp=20/25 knots (surfaced/submerged) *Armament:* 16 Polaris ULBMs; 4 21-in (53-cm) torpedo tubes (bow, probably 8 torpedoes carried) *Crew:* 140

No and name	launched	builder
SSBN 608 *Ethan Allen*	11/1960	General Dynamics
SSBN 609 *Sam Houston*	2/1961	Newport News
SSBN 610 *Thomas A Edison*	6/1961	General Dynamics
SSBN 611 *John Marshall*	7/1961	Newport News
SSBN 618 *Thomas Jefferson*	2/1962	Newport News

Etorofu

Japanese escort class, built 1942-44. Under the War Programme of 1941 there was provision for 30 escorts, with hulls numbered 310 to 339. However, when the time came to order them in 1942, escort-building was only fifth in order of priority, and material could be provided for only 14 ships.

The design was an adaptation of the *Shimushu* or Type A escorts built in 1938-41, using the same machinery but with some rearrangement internally. A bulbous bow was adopted, and the bow itself was simplified, with more rake than before. The bulbous top to the funnel was also discarded.

The 4.7-in (120-mm) guns were from old destroyers. After December 1943 the depth charge outfit was raised to 60, and an army-pattern 3-in (76-mm) mortar was installed forward of the bridge, for use against submarines. In 1944 the survivors had their twin 25-mm (1-in) antiaircraft mountings replaced by triples. In all, five triples were mounted, but *Kanju* had two twins and two singles added in place of X 4.7-in (120-mm) gun. A Type 13 radar antenna was also fitted on the mainmast. Both *Oki* and *Tsushima* were modified following damage, the former receiving a new raked straight bow, and the latter getting a flat stern.

Deck plan and profile of the *Evarts* Class destroyer escort *Reynolds* (DE.42) before the modification which replaced the quadruple 1.1-in AA mounting in X position with a twin 40-mm Bofors

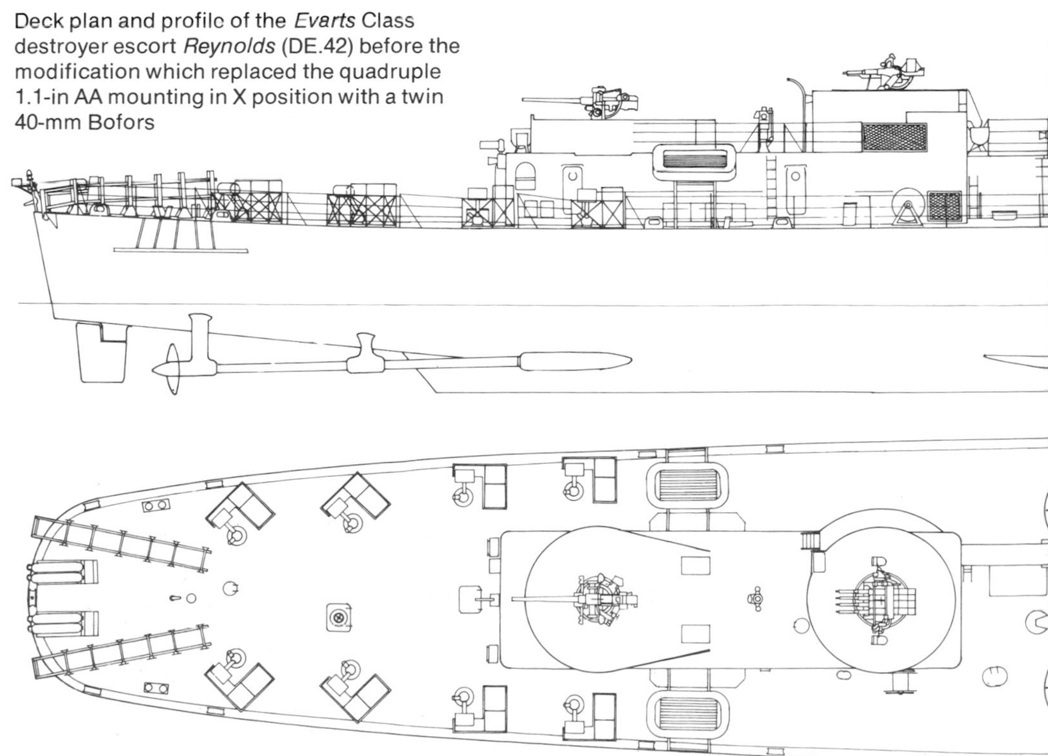

The class suffered heavily from the depredations of US submarines and aircraft. The *Mutsure* was torpedoed on September 2, 1943, only two weeks after completion, by the *Snapper* north-northwest of Truk. The *Wakamiya* survived for only two months before being torpedoed by the *Gudgeon* south of Chusan on November 23. On May 24, 1944, the month-old *Iki* was torpedoed by the *Raton* 385 km (240 miles) west of Singapore. The *Matsuwa* went down to a torpedo from the *Harder* off Manila on August 22, while on the same day only 30 km (19 miles) away her sister *Sado* fell victim to the *Haddo*. The *Hirado* was torpedoed by the *Growler* 400 km (250 miles) from Hainan on September 12, the sixth to be sunk by a submarine in a year. The *Amakusa* was sunk in the last days of the war, on August 9, 1945, by aircraft of Task Force 38 in Onagawa harbour. The *Kanju* was one of the few Japanese ships to fall to the Russians, being sunk by aircraft off Korea near Wonsan on August 15.

The six survivors were surrendered to the Allies, and four, *Etorofu, Oki, Fukue* and *Tsushima,* were used to repatriate Japanese soldiers from the outlying Pacific islands, which had been bypassed during the 'island-hopping' campaign, and from the mainland. The *Manju* had been badly damaged in an air raid on Hong Kong in April 1945, and had been only partially repaired. She was scrapped in 1946. The *Kasado* was damaged in a raid by TF 38 in July, but was towed to Ominato for temporary repairs and then reached Sasebo under her own steam. She too was scrapped. The four on repatriation duty were allocated to the Allies as reparations in 1947, *Etorofu* to the US, *Fukue* to Britain, and *Oki* and *Tsushima* to China. The first two were scrapped in Japan as neither the British nor the Americans were interested in acquiring more warships, but the *Oki* and *Tsushima* became the Chinese *Ku An* and *Lin An* respectively in August 1947. The *Ku An* was renamed *Ch'ang Pai* after falling into Communist hands in 1949, but her sister remained in Nationalist hands. She was discarded in 1963, but in 1976 *Jane's Fighting Ships* reported that the *Ch'ang Pai* was not a hulk, and had been refitted with three 100-mm (3.9-in) and two 37-mm (1.46-in) AA guns.

Name	builder
Etorofu	Hitachi, Sakurajima
Oki	Uraga dock, Tokyo
Sado	Asano, Tsurumi
Matsuwa	Mitsui, Tamano
Fukue	Uraga dock, Tokyo
Tsushima	Asano, Tsurumi
Mutsure	Hitachi, Sakurajima
Wakamiya	Mitsui, Tamano
Kanju	Uraga dock, Tokyo
Hirado	Hitachi, Sakurajima
Amakusa	Hitachi, Sakurajima
Manju	Mitsui, Tamano
Kasado	Uraga dock, Tokyo
Iki	Mitsui, Tamano

Displacement: 1556 tons/2128 tons (surfaced/submerged) *Length:* 83.97 m (275 ft 6 in) oa *Beam:* 8.3 m (27 ft 3 in) *Draught:* 5.02 m (16 ft 6 in) *Machinery:* 2-shaft Tosi diesel engines/electric motors, 5200 bhp/2000 ehp= 15/8 knots (surfaced/submerged) *Armament:* 1 4.7-in (120-mm)/45-cal; 4 0.5-in (12.7-mm); 8 53-cm (21-in) torpedo tubes (14 torpedoes) *Crew:* 78

Evarts

US destroyer escort class built 1942-44. Designs for utility destroyer-type escorts had been prepared by the US Navy's Bureau of Construction and Repair (later Bureau of

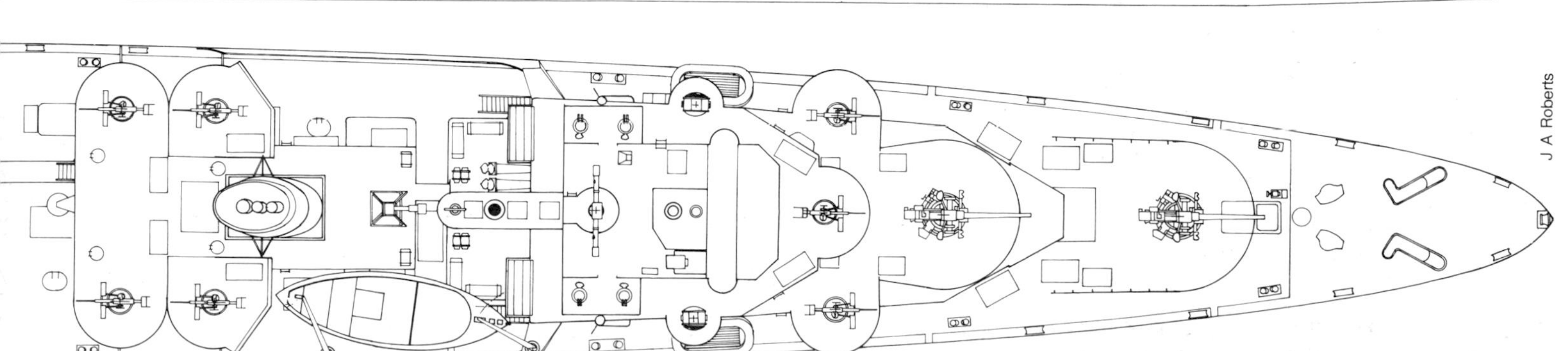

Ships) as early as 1940, but priority was given to more urgently needed warships and the plans were shelved. As a result, when the British Admiralty asked early in 1941 for 50 antisubmarine escorts to be built in US yards, the US Navy was able to offer a design with minimal delay.

The design chosen suited British requirements for a North Atlantic escort, a length of about 90 m (300 ft) for weatherliness, 20 knots' speed and long endurance. But in other respects the design followed contemporary US destroyer practice closely, with a flush deck, welded hull and a pole mast. Although the US Navy was assured of adequate supplies of General Motors diesels, there were many calls on them, and the original requirement for 12 000 bhp and 24 knots had to be dropped. The best arrangement would have been a direct-drive system, with four diesels coupled to two shafts, but this would have needed a complicated gear train, and facilities for cutting gear-teeth were already stretched. The decision was therefore made to have diesel-electric drive, with electric motors driven by diesel generators.

The plans for the Royal Navy were overtaken by events, as the first of the class were not ready until long after Pearl Harbor. By mid-1942, the US Navy found itself in desperate need of antisubmarine escorts, a requirement not foreseen by the planners. As a result, the order for 50 was expanded to 105 and only 32 units (DE 1-4, 12, 46, 266-280 and 516-526) were transferred to the RN as the *Bayntun* Class.

The class comprised: *Evarts* (DE.5); *Wyffels* (DE.6); *Griswold* (DE.7); *Steele* (DE.8); *Carlson* (DE.9); *Bebas* (DE.10); *Crouter* (DE.11); *Brennan* (ex-HMS *Bentinck)* (DE.13); *Doherty* (ex-HMS *Berry)* (DE.14); *Austin* (ex-HMS *Blackwood)* (DE.15); *Edgar G Chase* (ex-HMS *Burges)* (DE.16); *Edward C Daly* (ex-HMS *Byard)* (DE.17); *Gilmore* (ex-HMS *Calder)* (DE.18); *Durden R Hastings* (ex-HMS *Duckworth)* (DE.19); *Le Hardy* (ex-HMS *Duff)* (DE.19); *Harold C Thomas* (ex-HMS *Essington)* (DE.21); *Wileman* (ex-HMS *Foley)* (DE.22); *Charles R Greer* (DE.23); *Whitman* (DE.24); *Wintle* (DE.25); *Dempsey* (DE.26); *Duffey* (DE.27); *Emery* (ex-*Eisner*) (DE.28); *Stadtfeld* (DE.29); *Martin* (DE.30); *Sederstrom* (ex-*Gillette*) (DE.31); *Fleming* (DE.32); *Tisdale* (DE.33); *Eisele* (DE.34); *Fair* (DE.35); *Manlove* (DE.36); *Greiner* (DE.37); *Wyman* (DE.38); *Lovering* (DE.39); *Sanders* (DE.40); *Brackett* (DE.41); *Reynolds* (DE.42); *Mitchell* (DE.43); *Donaldson* (DE.44); *Andres* (ex-HMS *Capel*) (DE.45); *Decker* (DE.47); *Doubler* (DE.48); *Doneff* (DE.49); *Engstrom* (DE.50); *Seid* (DE.256); *Smart* (DE.257); *Walter S Brown* (DE.258); *William C Miller* (DE.259); *Cabana* (DE.260); *Dionne* (DE.261); *Canfield* (DE.262); *Deede* (DE.263); *Elden* (DE.264); *Cloues* (DE.265); *Lake* (DE.301); *Lyman* (DE.302); *Crawley* (DE.303); *Rall* (DE.304); *Halloran* (DE.305); *Connolly* (DE.306); *Finnegan* (ex-HMS *Calder*) (DE.307); *O'Toole* (DE.527); *John J Powers* (DE.528); *Mason* (DE.529); *John M Bermingham* (DE.530).

DE.5-DE.11, DE.256-DE.265 and DE.527-DE.530 were built by Boston navy yard; DE.13-DE.36 and DE.301-DE.307 were built by Mare Island navy yard; DE.37-DE.44 were built by Puget Sound navy yard; and DE.45-DE.50 were built by Philadelphia navy yard.

The ships shown as 'ex-HMS' were allocated RN names during construction, and had British Destroyer Escort numbers, but never served in the Royal Navy. On March 13, 1944, five of the Mare Island hulls were cancelled and broken up on the slipways: *Keppler, Lloyd Thomas, William C Lawe, Willard Keith* (DE.311-314) and the unnamed DE.315. Three more, *Creamer, Ely* and *Delbert W Halsey* (DE.307-309) were cancelled on September 5, 1944, and also scrapped before launch.

Building times varied considerably, the fastest being for ships built in Boston—as low as five months—whereas some of the West Coast ships took over a year, probably because the yards were occupied with repairs to battle-damaged ships after Pearl Harbor.

There is no space for details of war service, but the class was employed in both the Pacific and Atlantic on escort duty. Because so many later and more powerful DEs were built the *Evarts* Class were quickly removed from the US Navy strength after 1945. Only *Wyffels* (DE.6) and *Decker* (DE.47) survived, as they were given to China as the *Tai Kang* and *Tai Ping* in 1945. The latter was torpedoed and sunk by Chinese Communist MTBs off the Tachen on November 14, 1954. The rest were sold for scrapping between February 1946 and January 1948. The armament remained fairly standard, and they were the only class of DEs not to mount torpedo tubes. The quadruple 1.1-in (28-mm) AA mounting was soon replaced by a twin 40-mm (1.57-in) Bofors in most ships, although some were still around in the summer of 1944.

See also *Bayntun, Buckley.*

Displacement: 1140 tons (standard), 1360 tons (full load) *Length:* 88.23 m (289 ft 6 in) oa *Beam:* 10.66 m (35 ft) *Draught:* 3.35 m (11 ft) full load *Machinery:* 2-shaft diesel-electric, 600 bhp= 21 knots *Armament:* 3 3-in (76-mm)/50-cal AA (3×1); 4 1.1-in (28-mm) or 2 40-mm (1.57-in) AA (1×4 or 1×2); 9 20-mm (0.79-in) Oerlikon AA (9×1); 1 Hedgehog A/S mortar; 8 depth charge throwers *Crew:* 198

Explorer

British submarine class, built 1951-58. Following trials with HMS *Meteorite*, the ex-German Walther-turbine *U 1407*, in 1947-49 the Royal Navy went ahead with plans for two vessels of an improved type. *Explorer* (S.30) was launched by Vickers at Barrow in March 1954, and her sister *Excalibur* (S.40) was launched at Barrow in February 1955.

Being driven by high-test hydrogen peroxide (HTP) the two boats were known as the 'Blondes', but to their crews they were less affectionately known as HMS 'Exploder' and HMS 'Excruciator'. The main machinery comprised two-shaft turbines supplied with a mixture of steam and CO_2 produced by burning diesel fuel and HTP, which produced speeds of 20-25 knots in spurts; conventional diesel-electric drive was also provided for underwater cruising and surface running. Because of the cramped accommodation their crews lived aboard two tenders.

The two boats were, as their nicknames suggest, never a total success, but they provided valuable experience as fast underwater targets for ASW forces until the first nuclear submarines were commissioned. The inherent faults of the Walther HTP turbine were never eliminated, and they mark the last attempt to produce a closed-cycle before the change to nuclear propulsion. It is believed that similar submarines built in the Soviet Union were equally unsuccessful.

Excalibur was put on the disposal list in 1963 and *Explorer* was sold two years later.

Displacement: 780/1000 tons (surfaced/submerged) *Length:* 68.73 m (225 ft 6 in) oa *Beam:* 4.77 m (15 ft 8 in) *Draught:* 3.35 m (11 ft) *Machinery:* 2-shaft Walther turbine/diesel-electric= 20 knots (surfaced/submerged) *Armament:* None *Crew:* 42-49

Fantasque

French destroyer class, built 1931-35. Between 1925 and 1931, the French navy laid down 24 super-destroyers or *contre-torpilleurs.* These were inspired by the big Italian destroyers or scouts of the *Carlo Mirabello* and *Leone* types, but took the idea even further. Although armed with a conventional destroyer-scale armament, five 138.6-mm (5.4-in) guns and torpedo tubes, the requirement for maximum speed was raised in each class, from 35 knots in the *Guepard* Class to 37 in the *Fantasque* Class, and 39 in the *Mogador* Class. The *Fantasques*, however, by some mysterious process, proved to be capable of 27% more power than the contract required and this enabled them to average over 40 knots on trials. They were in fact the fastest destroyers ever built, and could operate as a division at speeds in excess of 37 knots, a feat unparalleled by any other class.

The six *Fantasques* were ordered under the 1930 Programme, and were all laid down in the last months of 1931. *Le Triomphant* was the first to start her trials, in July 1934, but *l'Audacieux* was the first to become operational.

The design was a logical refinement of the previous *Guepard, Jaguar* and *Vauquelin,* but with more attention paid to a compact silhouette. Admiral Drujon, when reporting to the standing trials committee on the *Guepard* Class, insisted that the four tall funnels made the *contre-torpilleurs* too easy to identify at a distance. His recommendations were followed, and the original four funnels of the *Fantasque* design were trunked into a pair of short, wide funnels widely separated. Rounding the bridge-face and putting the pole mast on top of the range finder position helped by making it much harder to estimate the ship's angle of bearing.

The armament remained the same as before, five single 138.6-mm (5.4-in) guns disposed forward in A and B positions, and aft on two levels. However, the guns were the new 1929 Model, 45 cal in length instead of 40 cal. With a muzzle velocity of 800 m/sec (2624 ft/sec), they had a range of 20 000 m (65 617 ft) at 30° elevation and could fire 12 rounds a minute. The torpedo armament was increased to nine 55-cm (21.6-in) tubes, two triples abreast between the funnels and a third on the centreline abaft the second funnel. The torpedo was the standard 1929 Model DT, with an all-up weight of 2105 kg

Name	launched	built
Le Fantasque	3/1934	Lorient arsenal
L'Audacieux	3/1934	Lorient arsenal
Le Malin	8/1933	Forge et Chantiers de la Méditerranée, La Syne
L'Indomptable	12/1933	Forge et Chantiers de la Méditerranée, La Syne
Le Terrible	11/1933	Chantiers Navals Francais, Caen
Le Triomphant	4/1934	Atelier et Chantiers de France, Dunkerque

(4641 lb) and a charge of 415 kg (915 lb). At 39 knots it had a range of 10 000 m (32 808 ft), but at 35 knots this could be increased to 14 000 m (45 932 ft).

The machinery showed the most startling improvements. Following a bold departure in the *Milan* and *Epervier*, but without waiting for the results of their trials, the French navy adopted a new boiler developed by Chantiers et Ateliers de St Nazaire-Penhoët, with 325° superheat and a pressure of 37 kg/sq cm (526.26 lb/sq in). For comparison, one of the class, *le Terrible*, was given the same Yarrow-Loire boilers as the *Milan* and *Epervier*. *Le Malin*, *l'Indomptabie* and *le Triomphant* had Parsons geared turbines, but the others had French-designed Rateau turbines. The designed horsepower has 74 000 shp, with 81 400 shp maximum output, but on her trials *le Terrible* reached the incredible speed of 45.029 knots with 94 240 shp, and established a world speed record not broken until 1961.

It was rumoured at the time, doubtless by the builders, that *le Terrible*'s hull-form had been modified. In fact, she differed only in not having the propeller shaft-brackets specially designed for the class, and had to use the type used for the previous *Vauquelin* Class which may account for her better performance. The others, however, also had superb trials results.

The only questions which have never been answered are whether any realistic cost-limit was stipulated when the contracts were put out to tender, and whether the machinery specification laid down strict rules on output. In any other navy, but particularly the RN or USN, the extraordinary rise in the installed power would have been questioned, unless the builders were specifically permitted to ignore competitive costing and to go for maximum power. The effectiveness of the *contre-torpilleurs* must therefore be judged against their cost, and the comparative figures are not available. Their high speed was a mixed blessing, for it only allowed a range of 1126 km (700 miles), although at 25 knots this rose to 4667 km (2900 miles), with 4828 km (3000 miles) at 14 knots. By comparison, a war-built British destroyer of half the displacement could steam 7523 km (4674 miles) at 20 knots, and an American destroyer on two-thirds the displacement steamed 9656 km (6000 miles) at 15 knots.

Name	1-hour trial	8-hour trial
Le Fantasque	42.71	40.48
L'Audacieux	43.18	41.41
Le Malin	43.11	41.49
Le Terrible	45.02	42.92
Le Triomphant	43.24	42.18
L'Indomptable	43.02	40.99

The war record of the class was outstanding. All six, with the two later ships of the *Mogador* Class, formed part of the 2nd Light Squadron of the Raiding Force. They operated in the Atlantic in 1939-40, and in April 1940 *l'Indomptable*, *le Malin* and *le Triomphant* carried out a spectacular raid in the Skagerrak. They returned to the Mediterranean, and *l'Audacieux* ended her active career at Dakar in September 1940, when an 8 in (203-mm) salvo from the cruiser *Australia* demolished the forward guns and machinery. *L'Indomptable* was a victim of the scuttling of the fleet when the German army stormed Toulon arsenal in November 1942, and was never repaired, although her bow was used to repair *le Malin* in 1946.

After the fall of Toulon, the French forces overseas joined the Allies, and so *le Fantasque* and *le Terrible* went from Dakar to the US for modernization, as did the damaged *le Malin*, which had been shattered by a 16-in (406-mm) shell from the US battleship *Massachusetts* while lying at Casablanca. The refits rectified the ships' most glaring weakness by substituting one quadruple and two twin 40-mm (1.57-in) Bofors and 10 Oerlikon 20-mm (0.79-in) AA guns for the outdated 37-mm (1.46-in) and 8-mm (0.315-in) machine-guns. The ships were also given more fuel, and radar and Asdic, but to compensate for these additions they sacrificed the after set of triple torpedo tubes. As they now displaced nearly 4000 tons in full load condition they were re-rated as light cruisers.

The fourth ship, *le Triomphant*, had a very different career, for she had nearly been caught in Lorient undergoing machinery repairs when the Germans overran France in June 1940. She reached Plymouth with only one shaft working, and after being seized on July 3, was returned to Free French control on August 28. It was necessary to rearm her with a British 4-in (102-mm) AA gun in place of the fourth 138.6-mm (5.4-in) gun aft and two 2-pdr (40-mm) pom-poms. For the time being, her remaining French weapons were retained but she was fitted with Asdic, being based on the Clyde as a convoy escort.

At the end of 1940, *le Triomphant* was sent to 'show the flag' in the Pacific, but here her short endurance was a crippling handicap. Apart from helping to evacuate Nauru Island when it was attacked by a German surface raider in December 1940, she spent her time escorting convoys. In December 1942, she completed a major overhaul at Sydney, and proved to be good for 40.4 knots at 3800 tons, only two knots less than she had achieved on her trials seven years earlier. A year later she was sent to the US to have the same modernization as her sisters, but while *en route* she was nearly overwhelmed by a cyclone and ran out of fuel. Eventually she made port in tow of a tanker, and went into Boston navy yard until March 1945.

The other three operated as the 10th Light Cruiser Division in the Mediterranean, and with conspicuous success in the Aegean. Here they were in their element, for the distances were short and the targets were ex-Italian and German light forces. In February 1944 they began a series of sweeps up the Adriatic, during which they sank a German cargo ship

The French destroyer *Fantasque*, name-ship of the fastest class of destroyers ever built

Musée de la Marine

and the patrol vessel *Uj 201* and severely damaged the ex-Italian destroyers *TA.36* and *TA.37* and *Uj 205*. In 40 days the division steamed 12 874 km (8000 miles), and *le Fantasque* claimed to have dropped and weighed anchor 79 times. In September 1944 they were earmarked for the Pacific and began to refit, but finally it was only *le Fantasque* that went out, to arrive in Indo-China at the end of hostilities.

There she was reunited with her sister *le Triomphant*, which had been operating with the battleship *Richelieu* and the British Eastern Fleet. In 'Operation Bentre' *le Triomphant* led the reoccupation of Haiphong, and suffered considerable damage to her upperworks from Communist fire.

The ships continued in service for some years. *Le Triomphant* was the first to go, in December 1954, followed by *le Fantasque* in May 1957, but *le Terrible* and *le Malin* became harbour hulks in 1957, the former as a training ship for engineer-cadets and the latter as a mooring hulk for minesweepers. They were scrapped in 1962 and 1964.

Displacement: (As built) 2727-2800 tons (normal), 3200-3400 tons (full load); (After modernization) 3300 tons (normal), 4300 tons (full load) *Length:* 132.4 m (434 ft 4½ in) oa *Beam:* 12.25 m (40 ft 2½ in) *Draught:* 5.01 m (16 ft 5½ in) *Machinery:* 2-shaft geared steam turbines, 74 000-94 000 shp= 37-42 knots *Armament:* (As built) 5 138.6-mm (5.4-in)/45-cal Model 1929 (5×1); 4 37-mm (1.46-in) AA Model 1925 (4×1); 4 13.2-mm (0.52-in) machine-guns (4×1); 9 55-cm (21.7-in) torpedo tubes (3×3); (*le Triomphant*, 1940) 4 138.6 mm (5.4-in)/45-cal (4×1); 1 4-in (102-mm) AA; 2 2-pdr (40-mm) AA (2×1); 4 37-mm (1.46-in) AA Model 1925 (2×2); 7 13.2-mm (0.52-in) AA machine-guns (1×4, 1×2, 1×1); 9 55-cm (21.7-in) torpedo tubes (3×3) (*as modernized*) 5 138.6-mm (5.4-in)/45-cal (5×1) 8 40-mm (1.57-in)/60-cal AA (1×4, 2×2) 10 20-mm (0.79-in) Oerlikon AA (10×1) 6 55-cm (21.7-in) torpedo tubes (2×3)

C & S Taylor

The British assault ship *Fearless* (L.10). She carries both landing craft and helicopters

C & S Taylor

Fearless can carry four LCM(9) (Landing Craft, Mechanized) in dock and four LCVP (Landing Craft, Vehicle or Personnel) on davits, with a flight deck for five Wessex helicopters above the stern dock. In an assault the stern dock is flooded to allow the LCMs to float out under their own power. She has a capacity for 380-400 troops or 700 marines for short periods

C & S Taylor

HMS *Fearless* showing her flooded stern dock which allows the landing craft to be floated out. Only a light close-range antiaircraft armament is carried, consisting of four Seacat missile launchers and two single 40-mm Bofors guns

Fearless

British assault ship class, built 1962-67. By 1946, the original Landing Ships, Dock (LSD) built in 1943-44 had all been returned to the US, and when the British Ministry of Defence decided to expand the amphibious capability of the Army and Navy in the late 1950s it was decided to build two expanded and up-to-date versions of this unusual type.

The *Fearless* was launched by Harland and Wolff, Belfast, in December 1963 and her sister *Intrepid* was launched six months later by John Brown on the Clyde. They are basically self-propelled floating docks, with a large well-deck and a stern gate; the ship can be flooded down, and when the stern gate is open landing craft can ferry men and vehicles to the beach-head. The main advantage of these big and complex ships over LSTs (Landing Ships, Tank) and LCTs (Landing Craft, Tank) is their seaworthiness, speed and range and the fact that a large number of assault troops can be accommodated in reasonable comfort. There is also room for the HQ and staff as well as tanks and vehicles.

The ships carry only a light close-range defence against air attack: four Seacat missile-launchers and two single 40-mm (1.57 in) Bofors guns. The pendant members were originally *L.3004* and *L.3005*, but they are now *L.10* and *L.11*. Each ship carries four LCM (9) ramped landing craft in davits. Both ships are fitted with helicopter landing-platforms and *Fearless* has tested the Harrier V/STOL aircraft. In 1969 *Intrepid* was fitted with the Skynet satellite communications system but this has since been removed.

In 1976 *Intrepid* went into reserve, leaving *Fearless* as a training ship attached to the Royal Naval College, Dartmouth. The *Intrepid* was due to relieve *Fearless* in 1979.

Displacement: 11 060 tons (standard), 12 120 tons (full load), 16 950 tons (ballasted) *Length:* 158.5 m (520 ft) oa *Beam:* 24.4 m (80 ft) *Draught:* 6.2 m (20 ft 6 in) *Machinery:* 2-shaft geared steam turbines, 22 000 shp=21 knots *Armament:* 2 40-mm (1.57-in) AA (2×1); 4 Seacat GWS 22 quadruples SAM-launchers *Crew:* 580 (including 400 troops)+700 troops for short periods

Le Fier

French torpedo boat. The 14 vessels which were to have made up this class were the last destroyer type to be designed for the French navy until after the Second World War. They were a much improved design of the earlier 600-tonne type whose design had suffered from the tonnage limitation imposed by the London Naval Treaty. The new design provided for a much greater displacement (1400 tonnes full load as against 914 tonnes full load for the 600-tonne type) with corresponding increase in dimensions. Installed power was increased to 30 800 hp from 22 000 hp which it was hoped would provide a top speed of about 34 knots, the same as the smaller 600-tonne type. Increased bunkerage was provided raising the radius of action by 1609 km (1000 miles) at 20 knots as designed.

The layout of the armament showed a radical departure from normal practice where it was usually sited fore and aft, with the light AA amidships. In *Le Fier* the main armament was sited aft in twin turrets and the light AA concentrated forward. Amidships two sets of twin torpedo tubes were to be installed.

Seven vessels were laid down in 1939 and by June when France surrendered, three had been launched and it was hoped to be able to tow them to a free port: none of the other vessels were ever laid down, although material for their construction had been assembled. All seven vessels laid down were captured by the Germans, but lack of French cooperation prevented their completion for the German navy, and they were either scuttled in harbour by the Germans in 1944 or sunk during air raids.

The Germans had planned to rearm the vessels with three 105-mm (4.1-in) guns in single mountings aft with two single 37-mm (1.46-in) and nine 20-mm (0.79-in) guns in a quadruple and single mounting forward.

The Spanish *Audaz* Class light frigates built with French assistance between 1945 and 1964 were closely modelled on the original design of the *Le Fier* Class.

Displacement: (1026 tonnes) (standard) *Length:* 95 m (311 ft 8 in) oa *Beam:* 9.37 m (30 ft 9 in) *Draught:* 3.25 m (10 ft 8 in) *Machinery:* 2-shaft geared turbines, 30 800 shp=33 knots *Armament:* 4 100-mm (3.9-in) (2×2); 8 13.2-mm (0.52-in) (4×2) guns; 4 55-cm (21.6-in) torpedo tubes (2×2); 2 A/S mortars *Crew:* 136

Fiji

British cruiser class. The 11 ships of the *Fiji* Class were constructed under the Estimates for 1937 *(Fiji, Mauritius, Kenya, Nigeria* and *Trinidad)*; 1938 *(Bermuda, Gambia, Jamaica* and *Ceylon)*; and 1939 *(Newfoundland* and *Uganda)*. The first group were laid down in 1938 and completed during 1940-41, the remainder were laid down in 1939 and com-

HMS *Mauritius,* a *Fiji* Class cruiser. Her 6-in (152-mm) guns supported the landings at Sicily, Salerno and Anzio and the Normandy landings

pleted during 1942-43. They were the first and only British cruisers designed within the 8000 tons maximum standard displacement specified under the terms of the London Naval Treaty of 1936. This replaced the earlier 10 000-ton limit, but at the same time restrictions on numbers of cruisers were abandoned, an object that the Admiralty had been trying to achieve for some years.

The ships were designed with the same armament as the 9000-ton *Southampton* Class, weight being saved by a reduction in protection and machinery which allowed for a smaller hull, producing the greatest saving at 450 tons. The magazine box protection of the *Southampton* Class was abandoned in favour of a thinner belt and a thicker protective deck, both of which were extended to cover the magazines and shell rooms as well as machinery spaces. The engine power was reduced to 72 500 shp which, because the ship was smaller, gave a slightly greater designed speed. The hull was 10.9 m (36 ft) shorter overall than that of *Southampton*, but only 6 m (20 ft) shorter between perpendiculars, the difference being largely due to the adoption of a transom stern (which also improved speed and saved weight). The actual design weights were slightly greater than the specified limit, but it was assumed that close attention to detail during construction and improvements in machinery design would bring them within 8000 tons. In the event, holding the displacement down proved unnecessary as the outbreak of the Second World War automatically ended the treaty limitations. A combination of wartime additions and the difficulty of maintaining strict weight controls under wartime conditions, led to the entire class exceeding 8500 tons standard displacement at the time of completion.

Although the class proved of great value during the war, their restricted size resulted in the ships being cramped and overcrowded when additional wartime crew and equipment became necessary The fitting of radar and AA weapons also produced a serious increase in topweight which necessitated limiting the number of AA guns added. In the last three ships to complete *(Newfoundland, Uganda* and *Ceylon)* the aircraft equipment and X triple 6-in (152-mm) turret were omitted to provide additional space and weight for these weapons. The aircraft equipment was removed from the remainder of the class during 1943-44 and X turret from all except *Nigeria* and *Gambia* during 1944-45. By the end of the war, three 4-barrelled 2-pdr pom-pom mountings had been added to most of the class the exceptions being *Nigeria* and *Gambia*, which retained X turret, *Kenya* which mounted a uniform close-range armament of 28 40-mm (1.57-in) Bofors (5×4+8×1), *Uganda* and *Newfoundland* which mounted one 4-barrel pom-pom and two 4-barrel Bofors. They were also fitted with between 12 and 28 20-mm (0.79-in) AA guns (removed from *Kenya* 1945).

All served initially with the Home Fleet; *Jamaica* serving with this force until the end of the war and becoming famous for her part in the sinking of *Scharnhorst* on December 26, 1943. *Fiji* transferred to the Mediterranean in 1941, where she was bombed and sunk during the battle for Crete on May 22, 1941. *Kenya* was temporarily transferred to the Mediterranean to cover Malta convoys during 1941 and 1942 and in the 'Pedestal' convoy of August 1942, was joined by *Nigeria*, both vessels being torpedoed and damaged by Italian submarines during the operation. In March 1942, *Trinidad* was struck by one of her own torpedoes (which had failed to run true because its gyroscope had frozen) during an action with German destroyers while covering the Russian Convoy PQ13. Temporary repairs were carried out at Murmansk, but during her return journey on May 14, she was attacked by German aircraft in the Barents Sea and so seriously damaged that she had to be abandoned. She was torpedoed and sunk on the following day by the British destroyer *Matchless*. *Mauritius* was transferred to the Eastern Fleet in 1942, and then to the Mediterranean in 1943, where she covered the landings at Sicily, Salerno and Anzio before returning to the Home Fleet to cover the Normandy landings in 1944. *Newfoundland* and *Uganda* also served in the Mediterranean in 1943, where the former was damaged by a submarine torpedo while covering the Sicily landings. *Uganda* was damaged by a glider bomb while covering the Salerno landings. After repairs, *Uganda* was transferred to Canada and renamed *Quebec*.

During 1943-44, *Gambia* (manned by the Royal New Zealand Navy until 1946), *Kenya, Ceylon* and *Nigeria* joined the Eastern Fleet but *Gambia* returned to the Home Fleet in 1944. In 1945 *Ceylon, Newfoundland, Quebec, Bermuda* and *Gambia* transferred to the British Pacific Fleet.

In 1957, *Nigeria* was transferred to India and renamed *Mysore.* In 1959, *Ceylon* and *Newfoundland* were sold to Peru, being renamed *Coronel Bolognesi* and *Almirante Grau* respectively. The remaining ships of the class were sold for scrap from 1961-68.

Fiji, Bermuda—built by John Brown
Kenya, Ceylon—built by Stephen
Mauritius, Gambia, Newfoundland—built by Swan Hunter
Nigeria, Jamaica, Uganda—built by Vickers Armstrong
Trinidad—built by Devonport dockyard

Displacement: 8500-8800 tons (standard), 10 350-10 850 tons (full load) *Length:* 169.31 m (555 ft 6 in) *Beam:* 18.9 m (62 ft) *Draught:* 5.03 m (16 ft 6 in) *Machinery:* 4-shaft geared steam turbines, 72 500 shp=33 knots *Protection:* 88.9 mm (3½ in) sides, 51 mm (2 in) deck *Armament:* 12 6-in (152-mm) (4×3); 8 4-in (102-mm) (4×2); 8 2-pdr (2×4); 16 0.5-in (12.7-mm) (4×4) guns; 6 21-in (53 cm) (2×3) torpedo tubes *Aircraft:* 2 *Crew:* 730

Bildstelle der Marine

Destroyer *Z.4*, the ex-US *Fletcher* Class destroyer *Claxton* (DD.571). Six of these ships were transferred to the Federal German Navy in 1958-60

Fletcher

US destroyer class, built 1940-45. Under the provisions of the disarmament treaties, the US Navy was inhibited from designing to maximum dimensions to match the Japanese 'Special type', the *Fubuki* Class, and so the original basis for the design of the *Fletcher* was a 1500-ton ship with the same armament as the previous *Benson* and *Bristol* Classes. The emphasis on endurance led to an addition of some 500 tons, but this extra displacement was used to enhance the antiaircraft battery, and not the surface armament.

Only 24 of the class were in hand at the time of Pearl Harbor, but another 100 were immediately ordered, plus two experimental variants.

The Class comprised: DD.445 *Fletcher*; DD.446 *Radford*; DD.447 *Jenkins*; DD.448 *La Vallette*; DD.449 *Nicholas*; DD.450 *O'Bannon*; DD.451 *Chevalier* (ex-*Pringle*); DD.452 *Percival*; DD.465 *Saufley*; DD.466 *Waller*; DD.467 *Strong*; DD.468 *Taylor*; DD.469 *De Haven*; DD.470 *Bache*; DD.471 *Beale*; DD.472 *Guest*; DD.473 *Bennett*; DD.474 *Fullam*; DD.475 *Hudson*; DD.476 *Hutchins*; DD.477 *Pringle*; DD.478 *Stanly*; DD.480 *Stevens*; DD.481 *Leutze*; DD.482 *Watson*; DD.498 *Philip*; DD.499 *Renshaw*; DD.500 *Ringgold*; DD.501 *Schroeder*; DD.502 *Sigsbee*; DD.503 *Stevenson*; DD.504 *Stockton*; DD.505 *Thorn*; DD.506 *Turner*; DD.507 *Conway*; DD.508 *Cony*; DD.509 *Converse*; DD.510 *Eaton*; DD.511 *Foote*; DD.512 *Spence*; DD.513 *Thatcher*; DD.515 *Anthony*; DD.516 *Wadsworth*; DD.517 *Walker*; DD.518 *Brownson*; DD.519 *Daly*; DD.520 *Isherwood*; DD.521 *Kimberly*; DD.522 *Luce*; DD.523 unnamed; DD.524 unnamed; DD.525 unnamed; DD.526 *Abner Read*; DD.527 *Ammen*; DD.528 *Mullany* (ex-*Beatty*); DD.529 *Bush*; DD.530 *Trathen*; DD.531 *Hazelwood*; DD.532 *Heermann*; DD.533 *Hoel*; DD.534 *McCord*; DD.535 *Miller*; DD.536 *Owen*; DD.537 *The Sullivans* (ex-*Putnam*); DD.538 *Stephen Potter*; DD.539 *Tingey*; DD.540 *Twining*; DD.541 *Yarnell*; DD.542 unnamed; DD.543 unnamed; DD.544 *Boyd*; DD.545 *Bradford*; DD.546 *Brown*; DD.547 *Cowell*; DD.548 unnamed; DD.549 unnamed; DD.550 *Capps*; DD.551 *David W Taylor*; DD.552 *Evans*; DD.553 *John D Henley*; DD.554 *Franks*; DD.555 *Haggard*; DD.556 *Hailey*; DD.557 *Johnston*; DD.558 *Laws*; DD.559 *Longshaw*; DD.560 *Morrison*; DD.561 *Prichett*; DD.562 *Robinson*; DD.563 *Ross*; DD.564 *Rowe*; DD.565 *Smalley*; DD.566 *Stoddard*; DD.567 *Watts*; DD.568 *Wern*; DD.569 *Aulick*; DD.570 *Charles Ausburn*; DD.571 *Claxton*; DD.572 *Dyson*; DD.573 *Harrison*; DD.574 *John Rodgers*; DD. 575 *McKee*; DD.576 *Murray*; DD.577 *Sproston*; DD.578 *Wickes*; DD.579 *William D Porter*; DD.580 *Young*; DD.581 *Charrette*; DD.582 *Conner*; DD.583 *Hall*; DD.584 *Halligan*; DD.585 *Haraden*; DD.586 *Newcomb*; DD.587 *Bell*; DD.588 *Burns*; DD.589 *Izard*; DD.590 *Paul Hamilton*; DD.591 *Twiggs*; DD.592 *Howorth*; DD.593 *Killen*; DD.594 *Hart* (ex-*Mansfield*); DD.595 *Metcalf*; DD.596 *Shields*; DD. 597 *Wiley*.

DD.445-448, DD.465-466 and DD.498-502 were ordered from Federal shipbuilding, Kearny; DD.449-451 and DD.507-517 from Bath Ironworks; DD.470-471 and DD.518-522 from Bethlehem, Staten Island; DD.472-476 and DD.581-586 from Boston navy yard; DD.477-481 and DD.587-591 from Charleston navy yard; DD.523-541 from Bethlehem, San Francisco; DD.544-549 from Bethlehem, San Pedro; DD.550-553 from Gulf shipbuilding, Chickasaw; DD.554-568 from Seattle-Tacoma shipbuilding; DD.569-580 from Consolidated Steel corporation, Orange; DD.592-597 from Puget Sound navy yard, Bremerton. DD.503-506 and DD.542-543 were not allocated.

Several ships were cancelled. Five unnamed vessels, DD.523-525 and DD.542-543, were cancelled in December 1940 before being awarded to individual yards, and *Stevenson, Stockton, Thorn* and *Turner* (DD.503-506) were cancelled in February 1941. The *Percival* (DD.452) and *Watson* (DD.482) were basically similar to the general design, but were experimental prototypes to test advanced machinery. The *Percival* was to have high-pressure boilers, while the *Watson* was to have 32-cylinder General Motors diesels; neither unit was laid down, and they were suspended for the duration of the war, and finally cancelled in January 1946.

Six units, *Hutchins, Pringle, Stanly, Stevens, Halford* and *Leutze* (DD.476-481), were earmarked to carry a floatplane and catapult in place of the after bank of torpedo tubes—an attempt to copy the Dutch practice of extending the range of destroyers beyond the horizon. The Kingfisher floatplane was to be handled by a derrick stepped from a samson post abaft the second funnel. Trials with the first three, *Halford, Pringle* and *Stevens*, showed that operating a floatplane was not feasible in a small warship, and they reverted to the standard armament. The other three, *Hutchins, Stanly* and *Leutze*, were not converted.

The antiaircraft armament was soon

Armada de Chile

Blanco Encalada, **ex-USS *Wadleigh* (DD.689), one of two *Fletcher* Class destroyers transferred to the Chilean navy in 1963**

Name	transfer
Taylor	Italy *Lanciere* (1951)
Walker	Italy *Fante* (1969)
Prichett	Italy *Geniere* (1969)
Guest	Brazil *Para* (1959)
Bennett	Brazil *Paraiba* (1959)
Hailey	Brazil *Pernambuco* (1961)
Lewis Hancock	Brazil *Piaui* (1967)
Irwin	Brazil *Santa Catarina* (1968)
Cushing	Brazil *Parana* (1961)
Ringgold	West Germany *Z.2* (1959)
Anthony	West Germany *Z.1* (1958)
Wadsworth	West Germany *Z.3* (1959)
Charles Ausburn	West Germany *Z.6* (1960)
Claxton	West Germany *Z.4* (1959)
Dyson	West Germany *Z.5* (1960)
Jarvis	Spain *Alcala Galiano* (1960)
McGowan	Spain *Jorge Juan* (1960)
Converse	Spain *Almirante Valdez* (1959)
Capps	Spain *Lepanto* (1957)
David W Taylor	Spain *Almirante Ferrandiz* (1957)
Isherwood	Peru *Guise* (1960)
Benham	Peru *Villar* (1961)
Kimberly	Taiwan *An Yang* (1967)
Yarnall	Taiwan *Kun Yang* (1968)
Heerman	Argentina *Brown* (1961)

Name	transfer
Stembel	Argentina *Rosales* (1961)
Dortch	Argentina *Espora* (1961)
Boyd	Turkey *Iskenderun* (1969)
Cogswell	Turkey *Izmit* (1967)
Van Valkenburgh	Turkey *Izmir* (1967)
Clarence K Bronson	Turkey *Istanbul* (1967)
Preston	Turkey *Icel* (1969)
Bradford	Greece *Thyella* (1962)
Brown	Greece *Navarinon* (1962)
Aulick	Greece *Sfendoni* (1959)
Charrette	Greece *Velos* (1959)
Conner	Greece *Aspis* (1959)
Hall	Greece *Lonchi* (1960)
Erben	South Korea *Chung Ma* (1963)
Wickox	South Korea *Pusan* (1968)
Halsey Powell	South Korea *Seoul* (1968)
Hale	Colombia *Antioquia* (1960)
Heywood L Edwards	Japan *Ariake* (1959)
Richard P Leary	Japan *Yugure* (1959)
Wadleigh	Chile *Blanco Encalada* (1963)
Rooks	Chile *Cochrane* (1962)
John Rodgers	Mexico *Cuitlahauc* (1970)
Harrison	Mexico *Cauahtemoc* (1970)

Brazilian Navy

***Para* (D.27), ex-USS *Guest* (DD.472), one of six *Fletcher* Class destroyers transferred on loan to the Brazilian navy between 1959-61**

augmented, and the quadruple 1.1-in (28-mm) mounting between No 3 and No 4 5-in (127-mm) guns was replaced by a twin 40-mm (1.57-in) Bofors, while the 20-mm (0.79-in) Oerlikons were in some cases reduced to four, or increased to a maximum of 11 singles. As more Bofors guns became available a second twin mounting was added aft, with a total of four or six 20-mm (0.79-in) guns. The fourth configuration, towards the end of the war, was three twin 40-mm (1.57-in) mountings and 10 or 11 Oerlikons, but under the threat of kamikaze attacks many finished the war with no fewer than five twin 40-mm (1.57-in), backed up by seven 20-mm (0.79-in) singles. This was achieved without sacrificing torpedo tubes, a remarkable testimony to the margin of stability of the original design. The flush-decked hull proved to be very tough, and a great improvement over the previous *Bristol* design, and the *Fletchers* can claim to be the finest all-round class of destroyers to serve in the Second World War.

Orders were placed in 1942 for a further 56, known as the 'Later *Fletchers*'. They were identical in design, but had a lower bridge and director control tower. Most were completed with heavy AA armament approved for the original *Fletchers* by 1943-44—five twin 40-mm (1.57-in) and 7 20-mm (0.79-in) guns although some had fewer 40-mm (1.57-in) guns.

The 'Later *Fletchers*' comprised: DD.629 *Abbot*; DD.630 *Braine*; DD.631 *Erben*; DD.642 *Hale*; DD.643 *Sigourney*; DD.644 *Stembel*; DD.649 *Albert W Grant*; DD.650 *Caperton*; DD.651 *Cogswell*; DD.652 *Ingersoll*; DD.653 *Knapp*; DD.654 *Bearss*; DD.655 *John Hood*; DD.656 *Van Valkenburgh*; DD.657 *Charles J Badger*; DD.658 *Colaham*; DD.659 *Dashiel*; DD.660 *Bullard*; DD.661 *Kidd*; DD.662 *Bennion*; DD.663 *Heywood L Edwards*; DD.664 *Richard P Leary*; DD.665 *Bryant*; DD.666 *Black*; DD.667 *Chauncey*; DD.668 *Clarence K Bronson*; DD.669 *Cotton*; DD.670 *Dortch*; DD.671 *Gatling*; DD.672 *Healy*; DD.673 *Hickox*; DD.674 *Hunt*; DD.675 *Lewis Hancock*; DD.676 *Marshall*; DD.677 *McDermut*; DD.678 *McGowan*; DD.679 *McNair*; DD.680 *Melvin*; DD.681 *Hopewell*; DD.682 *Porterfield*; DD.683 *Stockham*; DD.684 *Wedderburn*; DD.685 *Picking*; DD.686 *Halsey Powell*; DD.687 *Uhlmann*; DD.688 *Remey*; DD.689 *Wadleigh*; DD.690 *Mertz*; DD.792 *Callaghan*; DD.793 *Cassin Young*; DD.794 *Irwin*; DD.795 *Preston*; DD.796 *Benham*; DD.797 *Cushing*; DD.798 *Monssen*; DD.799 *Jarvis*; DD.800 *Porter*; DD.801 *Colhoun*; DD.802 *Gregory*; DD.803 *Little*; DD.804 *Rooks*.

DD.629-644, DD.650-653 and DD.688-690 were ordered from Bath Ironworks; DD.649-653 and DD.665 from Charleston navy yard; DD.654-656 from Gulf shipbuilding, Chickasaw; DD.657-658, DD.685-687 and DD.796-798 from Bethlehem, Staten Island; DD.659-661 and DD.666-680 from Federal shipbuilding, Kearny; DD.662-664 from Boston navy yard; DD.681-682 and DD.792-795 from Bethlehem, San Pedro; DD.683-684 from Bethlehem, San Francisco; DD.799-804 from Todd Pacific, Seattle.

The *Fletcher* Class received its baptism of fire in the Solomons, and *Chevalier*, *Strong*, *De Haven* and *Brownson* were lost in the confused actions which followed the landings on Guadalcanal. Two, the *Hoel* and *Johnston*, were sunk during the tremendous fight against heavy odds between Admiral Sprague's escort carriers and the Japanese fleet off Samar in October 1944, while the *Spence* and *Abner Read* were sunk by air attack during the landings in Leyte Gulf. The worst losses were suffered during the assault on Okinawa, when kamikazes and gunfire accounted for the *Hutchins*, *Pringle*, *Leutze*, *Thatcher*, *Luce*, *Bush*, *Evans*, *Haggard*, *Longshaw*, *Morrison*, *William D Porter*, *Bell*, *Twiggs*, *Callaghan*, *Halligan*, *Colhoun* and *Little*. The majority of these were not sunk outright, but were so badly damaged that they were written off as not worth repair.

The *Fletchers* formed the backbone of the postwar destroyer-strength of the US Navy, although more than half remained in mothballs. Those on the active list were gradually modernized in the 1950s, with a heavy tripod foremast to carry new radar arrays, the forward bank of 21-in (53-cm) torpedo tubes removed, and the third 5-in (127-mm) gun removed. This allowed the provision of three twin 3-in (76-mm) automatic gun-mountings, one firing over the after 5-in (127-mm) and two sponsoned between the funnels.

Under the 1948 Programme, nine were converted to escort destroyers (DDEs), with a view to improving their antisubmarine armament for use as convoy escorts. All torpedo tubes were removed and the antisubmarine rocket-projector known as Weapon Able/Alfa was installed in B position in some, although others had two trainable Hedgehogs. Three more were converted under the 1949 Programme, and six under the 1950 Programme, but the conversion of *Anthony* (DD.515) and *Charles Ausburn* (DD.570) were cancelled. *Saufley* was rerated as EDDE.465 but the others became DDE.445, 446, 447, 449, 450, 466, 468, 470,

IWM

HMS *Formidable* with the battleship *Nelson* in the western Mediterranean covering operations in North Africa during the Second World War

471, 498, 499, 507, 508, 510, 517, 576, and 577. In 1962 they all reverted to DDs.

Over the years many were transferred to allied navies.

The massive Fleet Rehabilitation and Modernization (FRAM) programme resulted in the reconstruction of many of the *Fletchers*, and details will be found elsewhere. The remainder started to be stricken for disposal from 1965 onwards, and by 1975 the last of these magnificent destroyers had gone, although strenuous efforts have been made to preserve the *Sullivans* as a destroyer-museum. Several were expended as targets. The *Ammen* was badly damaged in collision with the *Collett* off Newport Beach in 1960 and was subsequently scrapped, while the *Monssen* was wrecked while on tow off Beach Haven Inlet in 1962.

See also FRAM.

Displacement: 2050-2100 tons (standard), 2940 tons (full load) *Length:* 114.6 m to 114.76 m (376 ft to 376 ft 6 in) *Beam:* 11.96 m-12.19 m (39 ft 3 in-40 ft) *Draught:* 5.41 m (17 ft 9 in) maximum *Machinery:* 2-shaft geared steam turbines, 60 000 shp=37 knots (maximum on standard displacement), 31 knots (sea speed) *Armament:* (As built) 5 5-in (127-mm)/38-cal DP (5×1); 4 1.1-in (28-mm) AA (1×4); 6 20-mm (0.79-in) AA (6×1); 10 21-in (53-cm) torpedo tubes (2×5); (As modernized) 4 5-in (127-mm)/38-cal (4×1); 6 3-in (76-mm)/50-cal AA (3×2); 5 21-in (53-cm) torpedo tubes (1×5) *Crew:* 319-336

Formidable

British aircraft carrier, completed 1940. She was the sixth ship to be called *Formidable* and was ordered in 1938 as the third member of the *Illustrious* Class of 23 000-ton armoured fleet carriers. She was, in fact, the second to be completed, being accepted from the builders, Harland and Wolff, on November 24, 1940, 41 months after she had been laid down.

After a very brief workup, *Formidable* left the Clyde in company with a convoy bound for Capetown on December 18. *Illustrious* was badly damaged in the Mediterranean on January 10, 1941, and *Formidable* was allocated to replace her, arriving at Alexandria on March 9. En route, her Fairey Albacore torpedo bombers had attacked Italian harbours at Mogadishu and Massawa.

Formidable took part in four major operations with the Mediterranean Fleet between March 26 and May 25, 1941. The first saw her aircraft scoring hits on the battleship *Vittorio Veneto* and the cruiser *Pola* off Cape Matapan—British battleships finished off the cruiser and two sister-ships. The fleet then covered convoys and bombarded Tripoli, between April 18 and 23, before fighting a convoy through from Malta to Alexandria, between May 6 and 12. The carrier was extremely short of Fairey Fulmar fighters and not until May 25 did she have sufficient to enable her to sail to attack Axis airfields supporting the Crete invasion. On May 26, she was found and attacked by Junkers Ju 88 dive-bombers which scored a direct hit with an 1100-lb (500-kg) bomb and inflicted extensive damage, obliging her withdrawal to the US for repairs.

Formidable returned to the United Kingdom in December 1941 and embarked her aircraft in February 1942. She was deployed in the Indian Ocean, where she remained from March 10 to August 24, encountering the enemy only once, in July, when her Grumman Martlet fighters destroyed a Japanese reconnaissance aircraft to the east of Ceylon.

Returning to the UK on September 18, she remained for only a month before sailing again with *Victorious* to support the Allied landings in Algeria—Operation Torch. The carriers operated off Oran and Bone between November 8 and 13, when shore-based aircraft took over the task. *Formidable* remained in the Western Mediterranean, based on Gibraltar and Oran, until early October 1943. During this time, she took part in only two major operations, the invasion of Sicily in July and the Salerno invasion in September. Her Martlets shot down an Italian seaplane during the latter operation—her first victim since the previous November.

Formidable undertook one convoy support mission in the Arctic in October 1943 before commencing a six-month refit. In early July 1944, she embarked 24 Barracudas and 16 Vought F4U Corsairs which, on July 17, took part in an unsuccessful attack on the battleship *Tirpitz*, lying in a northern Norwegian

Aircraft complements:	**(Squadron Nos in parentheses)**
December 1940:	12 Fulmars, 12 Albacores (803, 826, 829)
April 1941:	16 Fulmars, 9 Albacores, 9 Swordfish (803, 806, 826, 829)
April 1942:	16 Martlets, 21 Albacores (888 & 820)
November 1942:	24 Martlets, 6 Seafires, 12 Albacores (885, 888, 893, 820)
September 1943:	32 Martlets, 5 Seafires, 12 Albacores (as November 1942)
August 1944:	30 Corsairs, 24 Barracudas (1841, 1842, 826, 828)
May 1945:	36 Corsairs, 18 Avengers (1841, 1842, 848)
July 1945:	36 Corsairs, 6 Hellcats, 12 Avengers (1841, 1842, 1844, 848)

***Formidable* at sea with Seafires and Martlets on deck, one of which is on the forward elevator**

fjord. On August 22, 24 and 29, a further 103 sorties were flown against *Tirpitz*, the target's smoke screens again preventing the dive-bombers from scoring hits.

Sailing for the Far East on September 16, 1944, *Formidable* suffered from a machinery breakdown which kept her at Gibraltar until January 15, 1945, and it was not until April 16 that she saw action again, joining the British Pacific Fleet in place of the damaged and defective *Illustrious.* She flew strike missions against targets in the Sakishima Gunto (archipelago), south-west of Okinawa, on 13 days up to May 22. Hit by kamikazes on May 4 and 9, she was able to operate aircraft within hours of each attack, thanks to her 3-in (76-mm) armoured flight deck, and sustained only 55 casualties.

The carriers of the joint US Navy-Royal Navy fleet struck at the Japanese home islands between July 17 and August 10, most of the British ships withdrawing on the latter date. *Formidable*'s Corsairs of No 6 Naval Fighter Wing were particularly effective, claiming over 60 aircraft destroyed or damaged on the ground and several escort vessels sunk or damaged. It was during a shipping strike on August 9 that Lieutenant R H Gray DSC RCNVR, flying a Corsair of 1941 Squadron, lost his life in earning the Fleet Air Arm's second Victoria Cross of the war.

After her return to Sydney on August 23, *Formidable* was employed as a personnel transport, returning Allied prisoners of war from Japan to Australia and subsequently plying as a troopship between the United Kingdom and the Far East. Her last trooping voyage ended in November 1946, and she was reduced to reserve at Rosyth in March 1947. Although plans were drawn up for her modernization, these were never implemented and she was scrapped in November 1953.

Displacement: 23 000 tons *Length:* 205.13 m (673 ft) pp *Beam:* 29.18 m (95 ft 9 in) *Draught:* 7.31 m (24 ft) *Machinery:* 3-shaft geared turbines, 110 000 shp=31 knots *Protection:* 114 mm (4.5 in) main belt; 114 mm (4.5 in) hangar side; 76-63.5 mm (3-2.5 in) deck *Armament:* 16 4.5-in (114-mm) dual purpose (8×2); 48 2-pdr AA (6×8); 8 20-mm (0.79-in) (8×1) *Aircraft:* 72 *Crew:* 1392

Forrestal

US aircraft carrier class. The first entirely new carrier design to be ordered and built after the Second World War, the *Forrestal* Class represented a major advance in all those aspects affecting aircraft operation at sea. Intended from the outset to operate jets and strategic bombing aircraft, they were large ships, displacing about 60 000 tons when light and little less than 80 000 tons at full load, and boasting a flight-deck area of nearly 2 hectares ($4\frac{1}{2}$ acres) in order to be able to stow and operate the 100 aircraft which 1943-45 Pacific operations had shown to be the ideal air group.

The name-ship of the class was authorized as CVB-59 (battle carrier) on March 10, 1951, during the Korean war. The general re-designation of large carriers in October 1952 placed her in the attack carrier (CVA) category, where the class was to remain for the next 20 years. The building time was remarkably short for such a huge ship—laid down in July 1952, *Forrestal* was launched on December 11, 1954, and was commissioned on October 1, 1955. The other three ships of the class, *Saratoga* (CVA-60), *Ranger* (CVA-61) and *Independence* (CVA-62) were completed in 1956, 1957 and 1959, respectively.

The recent British developments of the angled deck, steam catapult and mirror landing-aid were all incorporated, the length of the unobstructed landing area being 187 m (613 ft)—greater than the full length of the 1943 *Independence* Class light carrier's flight deck. Four catapults, capable of launching 36 290-kg (80 000-lb) aircraft at over 100 knots, were fitted: two in the conventional bow position and two amidships on the port side of the flight deck, in what became known as the 'waist' position. All four of the aircraft lifts were installed at the deck edge, three to starboard and one to port, all but the last being clear of the landing area and catapult tracks. Initially, the ships were able to carry their full intended complement of over 100 fighter and attack aircraft, but as the size of aircraft increased this figure was progressively reduced, until by the mid-1970s the normal air group embarked consisted of about 85 aircraft. Jets being thirsty aircraft, no less than 2 840 000 litres (625 000 Imp gal; 750 000 US gal) of aviation fuel were provided in *Forrestal*— more than four times as much as in the *Essex* Class.

In keeping with previous US Navy practice, the ships were powerful and very fast: the name-ship was fitted with machinery of a type dating from the Second World War, but her sisters had higher-pressure boilers which produced an additional 20 000 shp and made them the most powerful ships afloat. The high-speed seakeeping was improved by the extension of the bow plating up to flight-deck level, all US carriers after the first *Saratoga* having been built with bow gun-sponsons.

Conventional gun armament was reduced to just eight single 5-in (127-mm)/45-cal dual-purpose mountings, disposed in pairs—fore and aft, to port and starboard—below the level of the flight deck. Even though they were set well back from the bows, the forward sponsons were subject to slamming and they and their guns were removed in all the ships but *Ranger. Forrestal* lost her four after guns during repairs following the serious fire in 1967 and she appeared next with a close-range self-defence Sea Sparrow missile system, later to be known as the Basic Point Defence Missile System (BPDMS). A second BPDMS was fitted in *Forrestal* in 1972 and during the next two years *Saratoga* and *Independence* were each fitted with a pair of BPDMS and their guns removed. *Ranger,* however, retained her guns, reduced to two 5-in (127-mm), until 1976 before replacing them with the Sea Sparrow missile system.

Forrestal, like *Saratoga* and *Independence,* served in the Atlantic and Mediterranean until the mid-1960s. From the autumn of 1965, however, *Independence* joined Task Force 77 in the Gulf of Tonkin, attacking targets in North and South Vietnam. *Ranger,* deployed with the Pacific Fleet since commissioning, had been involved since February 1965, when regular attacks on the North had begun. *Forrestal* joined TF 77 in 1967, but on July 29 a mishap on deck started fires which raged on the flight and hangar decks for 13 hours and caused 194 casualties and the loss of 21 aircraft; repairs took seven months to complete.

Saratoga, which had never left the Atlantic Fleet, was redesignated as a CVS in 1972, following a refit to install antisubmarine command and control facilities. The addition of the ASW role to the continuing attack task marked a new departure in US Navy carrier policy but was made necessary by the withdrawal of the *Essex* Class CVS-designated ASW carriers. By June 1975, all four ships of the class had been fitted for ASW and were operating one fixed-wing and one helicopter squadron each, in addition to their three attack and two fighter squadrons.

The heaviest aircraft operated by the class

No and name	commissioned	builder
(CVA-59) *Forrestal*	1/10/55	Newport News
(CVA-60) *Saratoga*	14/4/56	New York navy yard
(CVA-61) *Ranger*	10/8/57	Newport News
(CVA-62) *Independence*	10/1/59	New York navy yard

was the 36 290-kg (80 000-lb) North American RA-5C Vigilante, embarked in 4-6 aircraft detachments up to the mid-1970s. Subsequently the Grumman F-14 Tomcat interceptor has been the heaviest aircraft aboard, grossing 32 885 kg (72 500 lb), and is not likely to be overtaken during the remaining life of the ships.

By 1978 the *Forrestal*s were between 20 and 23 years old and were expected to require replacement some time towards the end of the 1980s.

Displacement: 60 000 tons (standard) (*Forrestal* 59 650 tons), approx 78 000 tons (full load) *Length:* 316.7 m (1039 ft) oa (*Independence* 319 m [1046 ft 6 in]); 301.8 m (990 ft) wl *Beam:* 76.8 m (252 ft) flight deck (*Ranger* 79.2 m [260 ft]), 39.5 m (129 ft 6 in) wl *Draught:* 11.3 m (37 ft) *Machinery:* 4-shaft Westinghouse General Electric geared turbines 280 000 shp=34 knots. (*Forrestal* 260 000 shp=33 knots) *Armament:* (As designed) 8 5-in (127-mm)/54-cal DP (4×2); 18 3-in (76-mm)/50-cal AA (*Forrestal* only); (As modernized) 2 or 3 Sea Sparrow BPMS; 4 5-in (127-mm)/54-cal DP (2×2) (*Ranger* only) *Aircraft:* 85-100 *Crew:* 4950 approx

Forrest Sherman

US destroyer class built 1953-59. These were the first new destroyers designed for the US Navy after the Second World War, and were authorized under the FY 1952-56 programmes. Although basically similar to the *Gearing* design they differed from conventional destroyers in several ways. Apart from being nearly 50% larger, they had aluminium superstructures to reduce topweight; the only torpedo armament carried was four fixed antisubmarine tubes amidships, and more guns were mounted after than forward.

Twin 5-in (127-mm)/38-cal guns were dropped in favour of a new 5-in (127-mm)/54-cal Mk 42 in a single mounting, one forward and two aft. The close-range AA armament comprised two pairs of 3-in (76-mm)/70-cal—later replaced by 3-in (76-mm)/50-cal—one in B position and one between the after fire-control director and the superimposed 5-in (127-mm) gun. The antisubmarine armament comprised two Hedgehogs on B gundeck and four fixed Mk 25 21-in (53-cm) torpedo tubes amidships.

Forrest Sherman (DD.931), *John Paul Jones* (DD.932), *Barry* (DD.933), *Manley* (DD.940), *Du Pont* (DD.941), *Bigelow* (DD.942), *Hull* (DD.945), *Edson* (DD.946) and *Somers* (DD.947) were built by Bath Iron Works, Maine.

Decatur (DD.936), *Davis* (DD.937), *Jonas Ingram* (DD.938), *Blandy* (DD.943) and *Mullinnix* (DD.944) were built by Bethlehem Steel, Quincy; *Morton* (DD.948) and *Parsons* (DD.949) by Ingalls shipbuilding, Pascagoula; *Richard S Edwards* (DD.950) and *Turner Joy* (DD.951) by Puget Sound Bridge and Dry Dock, Bremerton.

Note that the 'missing numbers' in the sequence belonged to earlier destroyers, DD.934 was ex-Japanese *Hanazuki*, DD.935 was ex-German *T.35* and DD.939 was ex-German *Z.39*.

The ships have all lost their forward 3-in (76-mm) AA mountings (and in many cases both) and the Hedgehogs, while the Mk 25 torpedo tubes have been replaced by triple Mk 32 tubes. In 1965-68 the *Decatur, John Paul Jones, Parsons* and *Somers* underwent major modernization to guided missile-armed destroyers, and are now rated as DDG.31-34. Two massive lattice masts have replaced the tripods and a single-arm Tartar missile-launcher and a hangar for a DASH helicopter were built on the extended after gundeck. However, when the DASH system failed, an Asroc launcher was added between the after funnel and hangar. The two after 5-in (127-mm) guns were suppressed, leaving only one gun, in A position, while the triple torpedo tubes were moved forward to the former B gundeck.

Eight of the unconverted ships were given a major overhaul of their antisubmarine capability in 1967-71; *Barry, Davis, Du Pont, Jonas Ingram, Manley, Blandy, Morton* and *Richard S Edwards.* They were given an Asroc missile-launcher in place of the after superimposed 5-in (127-mm) gun, and variable depth sonar, and the after deckhouse was extended to full width of the upper deck. A big square lattice mast replaced the tall tripod foremast. In 1974-75 *Hull* was given the prototype 8-in (203-mm) Mk 71 Major Calibre Lightweight Gun (MCLWG) in place of her forward 5-in (127-mm) gun, to test the feasibility of a destroyer firing such a heavy projectile. The tests proved successful, even

USS *Parsons* (DDG.33), *Forrest Sherman* Class destroyer, off Hong Kong in 1975. The hangar for the DASH helicopter can be seen on the extended after gundeck with the Tartar launcher

US Navy

with standard cruiser-ammunition instead of the laser-guided shells planned for the production version. In 1976 *Bigelow* appeared with the second example of the Vulcan Phalanx 20-mm (0.79-in) Close-In Weapon System (CIWS) mounted on the after superstructure.

There are a number of minor differences between individual ships. For example, the later ships have slightly higher bows, and *Barry* has a stem anchor to clear her bow sonar, the first SQS-23 set fitted in a US navy ship. *Edson* was reduced to reserve status in 1977 for training duties, and it is expected that her unmodernized sisters will all be downgraded in a similar manner. The DDGs will probably be equipped with a LAMPS multi-purpose helicopter in the near future.

Displacement: 2800 tons (standard), 4050 tons (full load) DDG conversions about 100 tons more *Length:* 127.41 m (418 ft) oa *Beam:* 13.71 m-13.77 m (45 ft-45 ft 2 in) *Draught:* 6.09 m (20 ft) *Machinery:* 2-shaft geared steam turbines, 70 000 shp= 32.5 knots *Armament:* (as built) 3 5-in (127-mm)/54-cal Mk 42 DP (3×1); 4 3-in (76-mm)/50-cal Mk 33 (2×2); 4 21-in (53-cm) torpedo tubes (4×1) (DDG conversions) 1 5-in (127-mm)/54-cal Mk 42 (Mod) DP; 1 single Tartar Mk 13 SAM system; 1 8-barrelled Asroc A/S missile system; 6 12.75-in (32.4-cm) Mk 32 torpedo tubes (2×3) *Crew:* 292-364

Foxtrot

Soviet submarine class, built 1956-68. The Soviet navy started production of a conventional (diesel-electric) class in the mid-1950s to follow the *Zulu* type, and even when the first nuclear submarines were built their enormous cost led the Russians to continue the conventional programme to boost numbers.

The *Foxtrot* is believed to have the same propulsion as the interim missile-firing *Golf* type, and it is thought of as a very successful design. Western sources claim that 60 are in service, and they are certainly the most frequently sighted. The Indian navy has eight: *Kalvari* (S.121), *Kanderi* (S.122), *Karanj* (S.123), *Kursura* (S.124), *Vela* (S.40), *Vaqir* (S.41), *Vagli* (S.42) and *Vagsheer* (S.43). They were delivered between 1968 and 1975, and Libya took delivery of the *Babr*, first of seven, in 1977. It is not clear if these are new construction or serving boats from the total of 60 mentioned above, but it seems unlikely that the Russians would restart production of what is now a somewhat dated design. It is likely that *Foxtrots* will replace the ageing *Whiskeys* in Eastern bloc navies in the next few years.

All *Foxtrots* were built at the Sudomech yard in Leningrad, and the first was sighted in 1958. Three names have been reported: *Pskovskii Komsomolets, Jaroslavskii Komsomolets* and *Vladimirskii Komsomolets.*

Displacement: 2000/2300 tons (surfaced/submerged) *Length:* 90.5 m (296 ft 11 in) oa *Beam:* 8.3 m (27 ft 2¾ in) *Draught:* 5.8 m (19 ft) *Machinery:* 2-shaft diesel-electric, 6000 shp= 20/15 knots (surfaced/submerged) *Armament:* 10 53.3-cm (21-in) torpedo tubes (6 forward, 4 aft, 20 torpedoes carried) *Crew:* 70

FRAM

Acronym for Fleet Rehabilitation and Modernization, a massive effort to overhaul ageing ships of the US Navy in the fiscal years 1960-64. The modernization of the destroyers of the *Fletcher, Gearing* and *Allen M Sumner* Classes was so drastic that the ships formed new classes thereafter.

The reason for initiating the FRAM programme was primarily to offset the block obsolescence overtaking ships built in 1941-45 and to provide more effective antisubmarine ships by making use of the 15-17-year-old destroyers which no longer had any useful role to play, being designed for surface torpedo attack. Three new weapon systems were available, and it was hoped to incorporate all of them: the Mk 44 acoustic antisubmarine torpedo, the Asroc long-range antisubmarine (A/S) missile system and the DASH drone A/S helicopter.

The conversion of the destroyers was divided into two parts, the first being FRAM I, to extend the life of the hull by at least eight to ten years. FRAM II was to be less extensive, and would add at least five years to the ship's life. The long-hulled *Gearing* Class destroyers were the most suitable choice for FRAM I conversions and 79 hulls were earmarked. The work was to be done over a five-year period, eight ships under FY'60, 14 ships under FY'61, 14 ships under FY'62, 24 ships under FY'63 and 19 ships under FY'64. A further 16 *Gearings* were to be given the FRAM II conversion, with 33 *Allen M Sumners* and three *Fletchers*. It was hoped to extend the programme to include a further 17 *Fletchers* and *Sumners* in the FRAM II programme under FY'65 but this was subsequently cancelled.

Eleven shipyards took part in the programme, and all but eight of the destroyers were finished by December 1964. The cost worked out at about $11 million for a FRAM I conversion, and some $7 million for a FRAM II, making a total of $1100 million on the destroyers alone.

Other categories of ships were to be given FRAM II modernizations: 35 conventional submarines, six *Essex* Class antisubmarine carriers, 11 destroyer- and submarine-tenders

A *Foxtrot* in the Mediterranean, shadowing the USS *Jonas Ingram* in 1973. *Foxtrots* are the main Soviet submarine in the Mediterranean

US Navy

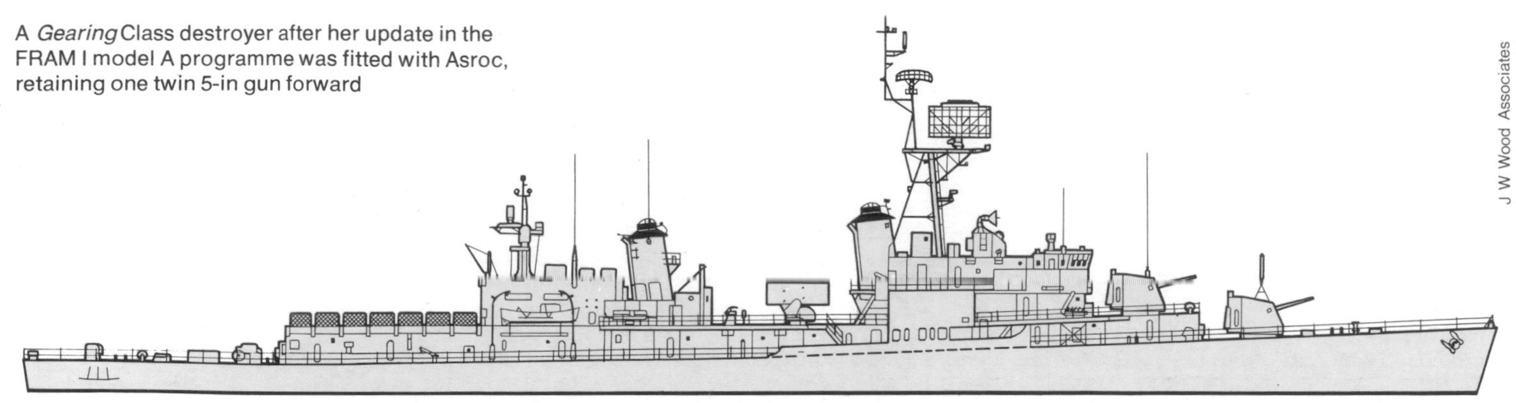

A *Gearing* Class destroyer after her update in the FRAM I model A programme was fitted with Asroc, retaining one twin 5-in gun forward

No and name		recom-missioned	disposal
DD.710	***Gearing***	10/1962	Stricken 7/1973
DD.711	***Eugene A Green***	10/1963	To Spain 8/1972 as *Churruca*
DD.714	***William R Rush***	4/1965	Serving 1978
DD.715	***William M Wood***	3/1965	Stricken 12/1976
DD.716	***Wiltsie***	9/1962	To Pakistan 1977
DD.717	***Theodore E Chandler***	1/1962	Sold 12/1975
DD.718	***Hamner***	11/1962	Serving 1978
DD.719	***Epperson***	12/1964	To Pakistan 1977
DD.743	***Southerland***	10/1964	Serving 1978
DD.763	***William C Lawe***	11/1961	Serving 1978
DD.782	***Rowan***	5/1964	To Taiwan 1977
DD.783	***Gurke***	5/1964	To Greece 1976
DD.784	***McKean***	11/1964	Serving 1978
DD.785	***Henderson***	4/1962	Serving 1978
DD.786	***Richard B Anderson***	7/1961	To Taiwan 1977
DD.787	***James E Kyes***	1/1963	To Taiwan 4/1973 as *Chien Yang*
DD.788	***Hollister***	12/1961	Serving 1978
DD.789	***Eversole***	2/1963	To Turkey 7/1973 as *Gayret*
DD.790	***Shelton***	6/1961	To Taiwan 4/1973 as *Lao Yang*
DD.806	***Higbee***	2/1964	Serving 1978
DD.808	***Dennis J Buckley***	10/1964	Serving 1978
DD.817	***Corry***	9/1964	Serving 1978
DD.818	***New***	12/1963	To South Korea 1977
DD.819	***Holder***	10/1963	Stricken 10/1976
DD.820	***Rich***	11/1963	Serving 1978
DD.821	***Johnston***	11/1962	Serving 1978
DD.822	***Robert H McCard***	12/1962	Serving 1978
DD.823	***Samuel B Roberts***	12/1962	Stricken 11/1970
DD.824	***Basilone***	4/1964	Serving 1978
DD.825	***Carpenter***	3/1965	Stricken 1977
DD.826	***Agerholm***	3/1961	Serving 1978
DD.827	***Robert A Owens***	11/1964	Stricken 1977
DD.829	***Myles C Fox***	10/1964	Serving 1978
DD.832	***Hanson***	12/1964	To Taiwan 4/1973 as *Liao Yang*
DD.833	***Herbert J Thomas***	8/1965	To Taiwan 5/1974 as *Han Yang*
DD.835	***Charles P Cecil***	5/1964	Serving 1978
DD.836	***George K Mackenzie***	12/1964	Stricken 10/1976

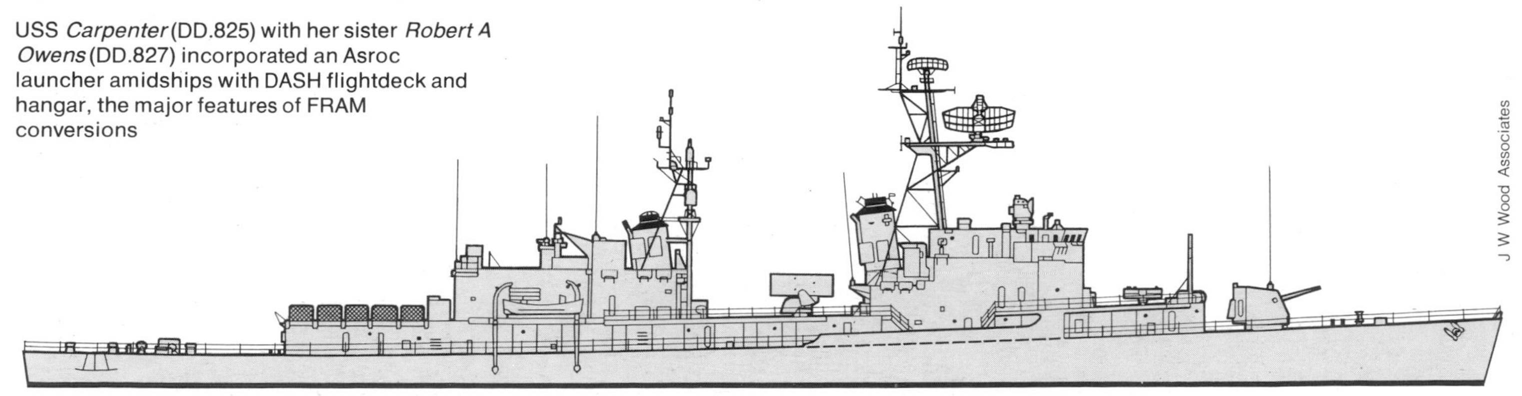

USS *Carpenter* (DD.825) with her sister *Robert A Owens* (DD.827) incorporated an Asroc launcher amidships with DASH flightdeck and hangar, the major features of FRAM conversions

DD.837	*Sarsfield*	5/1963	To Taiwan 1977
DD.839	*Power*	1/1962	To Taiwan 1977-78
DD.840	*Glennon*	7/1963	Stricken 10/1976
DD.841	*Noa*	5/1961	To Spain 10/1973 as *Blas de Lezo*
DD.842	*Fiske*	1/1965	Serving 1978
DD.843	*Warrington*	5/1962	Stricken 10/1972
DD.844	*Perry*	5/1960	Stricken 7/1973
DD.845	*Baussell*	6/1961	Serving 1978
DD.846	*Ozbourn*	12/1961	Stricken 5/1975
DD.847	*Robert L Wilson*	11/1963	Stricken 9/1974
DD.849	*Richard E Kraus*	5/1964	To South Korea 1977
DD.850	*Joseph P Kennedy Jr*	5/1962	Stricken 7/1973 (museum ship)
DD.851	*Rupertus*	11/1963	To Greece 7/1973 as *Kountouriotis*
DD.852	*Leonard F Mason*	1/1964	Stricken 11/1976
DD.853	*Charles H Roan*	6/1962	To Turkey 9/1973 as *Cakmak*
DD.862	*Vogelgesang*	1/1963	Serving 1978
DD.863	*Steinaker*	3/1965	Serving 1978
DD.864	*Harold J Ellison*	1/1963	Serving 1978
DD.865	*Charles R Ware*	1/1962	Stricken 12/1974
DD.866	*Cone*	1/1963	Serving 1978
DD.867	*Stribling*	5/1961	Stricken 7/1976
DD.868	*Brownson*	5/1964	Stricken 9/1976

DD.869	*Arnold J Isbell*	5/1962	To Greece 12/1973 as *Sachtouris*
DD.870	*Fechteler*	12/1963	Stricken 9/1970
DD.871	*Damato*	2/1964	Serving 1978
DD.872	*Forrest Royal*	4/1962	To Turkey 3/1971 as *Adatepe*
DD.873	*Hawkins*	1/1965	Serving 1978
DD.875	*Henry W Tucker*	12/1963	To Brazil 12/1973 as *Marcilio Dias*
DD.876	*Rogers*	6/1964	Serving 1978
DD.878	*Vesole*	10/1964	Stricken 12/1976
DD.879	*Leary*	1/1965	To Spain 10/1973 as *Langara*
DD.880	*Dyess*	2/1965	Serving 1978
DD.881	*Bordelon*	12/1963	Stricken 2/1977
DD.882	*Furse*	10/1963	To Spain 8/1972 as *Gravina*
DD.883	*Newman K Perry*	2/1965	Serving 1978
DD.884	*Floyd B Parkes*	5/1963	Stricken 7/1973
DD.885	*John R Craig*	2/1963	Serving 1978
DD.886	*Orleck*	11/1963	Serving 1978
DD.887	*Brinkley Bass*	5/1962	To Brazil 12/1973 as *Mariz é Barros*
DD.888	*Stickel*	3/1964	To Greece 7/1972 as *Kanaris*
DD.889	*O'Hare*	12/1963	To Spain 10/1973 as *Mendez Nunez*
DD.890	*Meredith*	6/1961	Serving 1978

***Gurke*, one of the US Navy destroyers given an extended operational career by a FRAM I update**

PPL

and 40 amphibious ships. This was a less drastic overhaul than the one given to the FRAM II destroyers, and involved such items as renewing boiler-tubes, rewiring etc, as well as the updating of radar and sonar, all important items in larger ships but not resulting in major change to the ships' appearance.

The appearance of the ships was changed completely, with new funnel caps and the big Asroc 'Pepperbox' launcher amidships. The Model A group retained the twin 5-in (127-mm) in B position, but had the after mounting removed; Model B ships had the 5-in (127-mm) aft but not in B position, the Model C group had only one 5-in (127-mm) mount, in A position. All had a hangar and flight deck aft for the two QH-50A DASH drone helicopters. The triple Mk 32 torpedo tubes were mounted in various positions, on B gun deck, abreast of the after funnel, or, in one case, on the quarterdeck.

Most of the modernized *Gearing* Class destroyers were given the FRAM I conversions, and these are listed above and opposite, though the 16 listed overleaf, along with 33 *Alan M Sumners* and three *Fletchers*, received the FRAM II modifications.

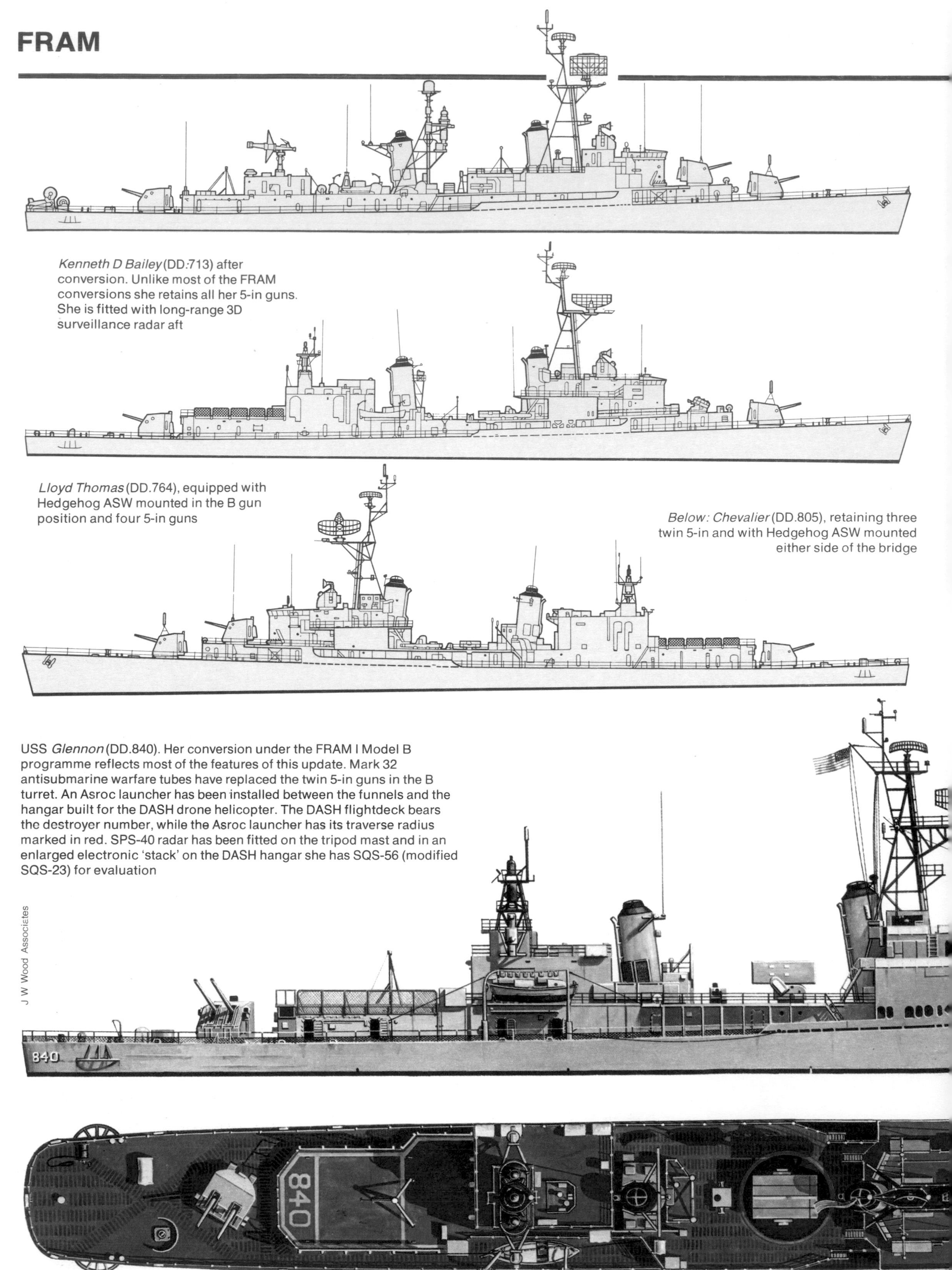

Kenneth D Bailey (DD:713) after conversion. Unlike most of the FRAM conversions she retains all her 5-in guns. She is fitted with long-range 3D surveillance radar aft

Lloyd Thomas (DD.764), equipped with Hedgehog ASW mounted in the B gun position and four 5-in guns

Below: Chevalier (DD.805), retaining three twin 5-in and with Hedgehog ASW mounted either side of the bridge

USS *Glennon* (DD.840). Her conversion under the FRAM I Model B programme reflects most of the features of this update. Mark 32 antisubmarine warfare tubes have replaced the twin 5-in guns in the B turret. An Asroc launcher has been installed between the funnels and the hangar built for the DASH drone helicopter. The DASH flightdeck bears the destroyer number, while the Asroc launcher has its traverse radius marked in red. SPS-40 radar has been fitted on the tripod mast and in an enlarged electronic 'stack' on the DASH hangar she has SQS-56 (modified SQS-23) for evaluation

J W Wood Associates

No and name	recom-missioned	disposal
DD.713 ***Kenneth D Bailey***	10/1960	Stricken 2/1974
DD.742 ***Frank Knox***	5/1961	To Greece 1/1971 as *Themistokles*
DD.764 ***Lloyd Thomas***	11/1961	To Taiwan 10/1972 as *Dang Yang*
DD.765 ***Keppler***	9/1961	To Turkey 6/1972 as *Tinaztepe*
DD.805 ***Chevalier***	8/1962	To South Korea 7/1972
DD.807 ***Benner***	2/1963	Stricken 2/1974
DD.830 ***Everett F Larson***	1/1963	To South Korea 10/1972 as *Jeong Buk*
DD.831 ***Goodrich***	9/1960	Stricken 2/1974
DD.834 ***Turner***	8/1960	Stricken 9/1969
DD.838 ***Ernest G Small***	8/1961	To Taiwan 2/1971 as *Fu Yang*
DD.858 ***Fred T Berry***	10/1961	Stricken 9/1970
DD.859 ***Norris***	10/1961	To Turkey 1975 as *Kocatepe I*
DD.860 ***McCaffery***	11/1961	Stricken 9/1973
DD.861 ***Harwood***	12/1961	To Turkey 12/1971 as *Kocatepe II*
DD.847 ***Duncan***	6/1961	Stricken 9/1973
DD.877 ***Perkins***	11/1962	To Argentina 1/1973 as *Py*

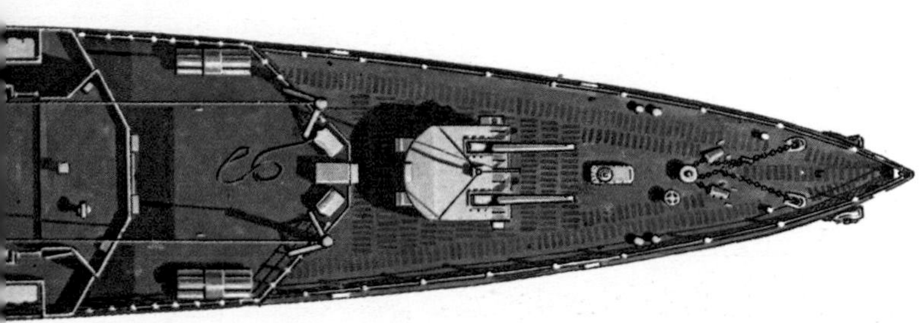

ex-*Allen M Sumner* Class

No and name	recommissioned	disposal
DD.692 ***Allen M Sumner***	12/1961	Stricken 8/1973
DD.693 ***Moale***	12/1961	Stricken 7/1973
DD.694 ***Ingraham***	12/1961	To Greece 7/1971 as *Miaoulis*
DD.697 ***Charles S Sperry***	6/1960	To Chile 1/1974 as *Ministro Zenteno*
DD.698 ***Ault***	12/1962	Stricken 7/1973
DD.699 ***Waldron***	12/1962	To Colombia 10/1973 as *Santander*
DD.703 ***Wallace L Lind***	7/1962	To South Korea 12/1973 as *Dae Gu*
DD.704 ***Borie***	7/1962	To Argentina 7/1972 as *Bouchard*
DD.709 ***Hugh Purvis***	10/1960	To Turkey 7/1972 as *Zafer*
DD.723 ***Walke***	10/1961	Stricken 2/1974
DD.724 ***Laffey***	9/1962	Stricken 3/1975
DD.725 ***O'Brien***	10/1961	Stricken 2/1972
DD.727 ***De Haven***	8/1960	To South Korea 12/1973 as *Inchon*
DD.728 ***Mansfield***	9/1960	Stricken 2/1974
DD.729 ***Lyman K Swenson***	1/1961	Stricken 2/1974
DD.730 ***Collett***	8/1960	Stricken 2/1974
DD.744 ***Blue***	1/1961	Stricken 2/1974
DD.746 ***Taussig***	9/1962	To Taiwan 5/1974 as *Lo Yang*
DD.752 ***Alfred A Cunningham***	9/1961	Stricken 2/1974
DD.754 ***Frank E Evans***	10/1961	Stricken 1969 (See below)
DD.755 ***John A Bole***	8/1962	Stricken 4/1974
DD.757 ***Putnam***	3/1963	Stricken 8/1973
DD.758 ***Strong***	11/1962	To Brazil 10/1973 as *Rio Grande do Norte*
DD.759 ***Lofberg***	7/1962	Stricken 4/1974
DD.760 ***John W Thomason***	1/1960	To Taiwan 5/1974 as *Nan Yang*
DD.761 ***Buck***	7/1962	To Brazil 7/1973 as *Alagoas*
DD.770 ***Lowry***	12/1960	To Brazil 10/1973 as *Espiritu*
DD.776 ***James C Owen***	10/1962	To Brazil 7/1973 as *Sergipe*
DD.777 ***Zellars***	5/1960	To Iran 3/1971 as *Babr*

No and name	recom-missioned	disposal
DD.778 *Massey*	7/1960	Stricken 9/1973
DD.779 *Douglas H Fox*	10/1962	To Chile 1/1974 as *Ministro Portales*
DD.780 *Stormes*	1/1961	To Iran 2/1972 as *Palang*
DD.781 *Robert K Huntington*	9/1960	To Venezuela as *Falcon*

ex-*Fletcher* Class

No and name	recom-missioned	disposal
DD.446 *Radford*	11/1960	Stricken 11/1969
DD.447 *Jenkins*	1/1961	Stricken 7/1969
DD.449 *Nicholas*	7/1960	Stricken 1/1970

The ex-*Allen M Sumner* Class destroyer *Charles S Sperry* after FRAM II conversion and transferred to Chile as the *Ministro Zenteno*

Allen M Sumner as she appeared after her conversion in 1965. She retained three of her twin 5-in 38s and had variable-depth sonar fitted aft. Mark 32 torpedo tubes are positioned between the stacks with Mk 25 tubes forward. Hedgehogs are mounted either side of the bridge. *Allen M Sumner* Class destroyers proved too small for Asroc and with the failure of the DASH programme they were not regarded as fully effective antisubmarine vessels. Remaining ships were either stricken or transferred and they remain in service with Argentina, Brazil, Chile, Colombia, Greece, Iran, South Korea, Taiwan, Turkey and Venezuela

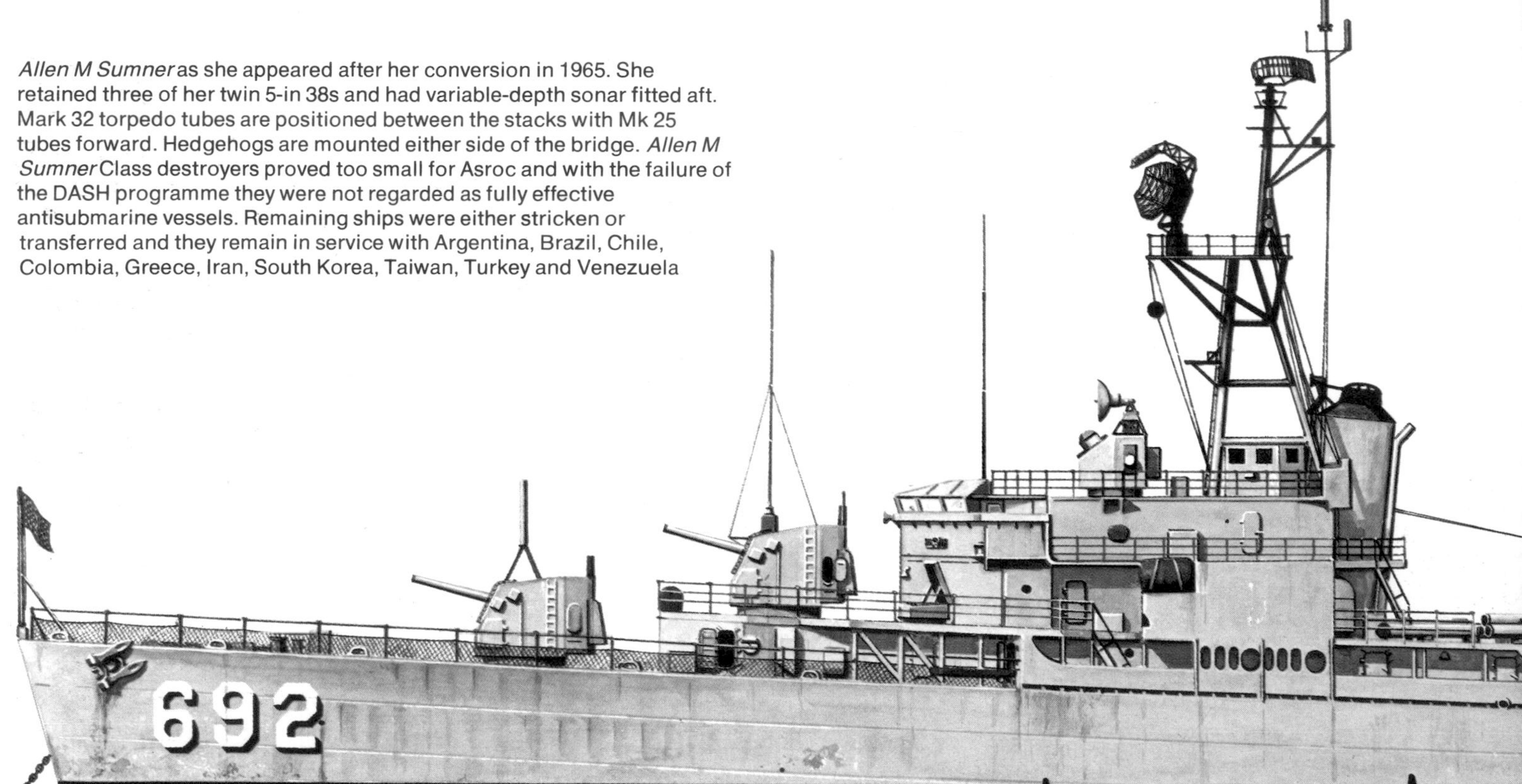

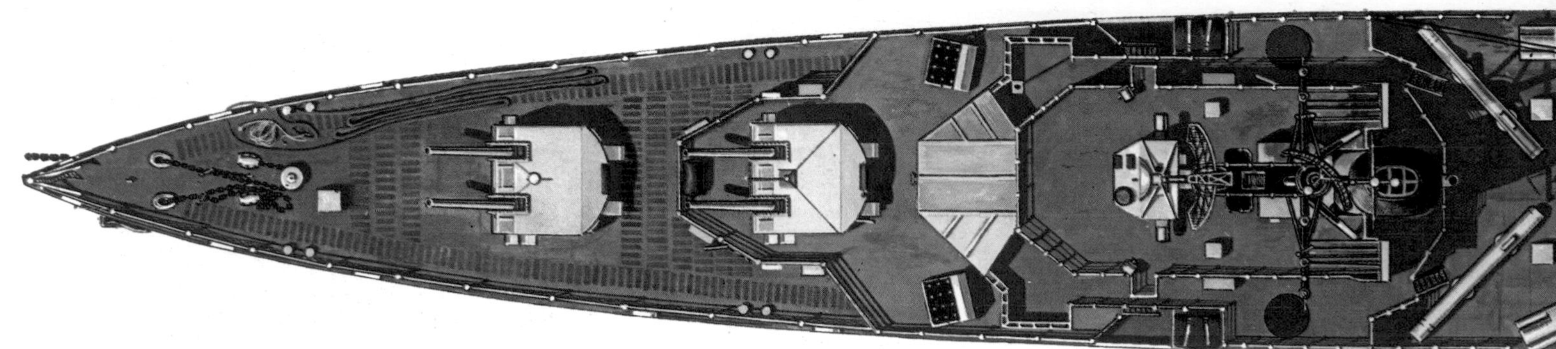

USS *Radford* (ex-*Fletcher* Class). She retained single 5-in guns and an A/S rocket launcher in B position. Hedgehog launchers are located forward of the bridge, but she carries no Asroc

J W Wood Associates

The three ex-*Fletchers* were given a DASH hangar and flight deck aft and Mk 32 torpedo tubes amidships, but retained the Weapon Alfa rocket-launcher and Hedgehog mortars in B position which they had had as DDEs. However, they had the same funnels as the other FRAM ships. The *Sumners* and *Gearings* differed widely, some retaining all three 5-in (127-mm) twin mountings, others having only two. None had Asroc, and two did not have a DASH hangar and flight deck.

The FRAM programme was widely criticized as a waste of money, but as the lists show in all cases the life of the ships exceeded the planned extension. The ships were at least suited for front-line service, whereas before they were of little fighting value for modern warfare. The biggest criticism had, in fact, nothing to do with the ships, but affected the value of the FRAM Is. This was the decision to install the DASH drone system before the concept had been fully proven. When the DASH programme collapsed in 1969, after 416 drones out of 746 delivered had crashed, there was a bitter wrangle over who was to blame. To make matters worse the flight decks were not strong enough to take a manned helicopter, so there was no hope of providing any replacement. Thus in the decade when the Royal Navy and others were proving that antisubmarine escorts had to have a helicopter to function effectively, the escorts of the US Navy could not operate any type at all.

One of the group, *Frank E Evans* was cut in half by the Australian carrier *Melbourne* during an exercise on the night of June 2, 1969, in the South China Sea. The forward half sank but the after portion was towed to safety; it was written off and sunk as a target. *Bordelon* was scrapped after being in collision with the carrier *John F Kennedy*. The Turkish *Kocatepe* (ex-*Harwood*) was sunk in error by Turkish aircraft on July 22, 1974, during the attack on Cyprus. The ex-*Norris*, which had been transferred for spares, was commissioned in her place and renamed *Kocatepe*.

The specifications given below are for the ships following their FRAM conversions. For original specifications see entries under class names.

See also *Allen M Sumner*, *Fletcher* and *Gearing*.

(FRAM I—*Gearings*) *Displacement:* 2425 tons (normal), 3512 tons (full load) *Dimensions and Machinery:* As built *Armament:* 2/4 5-in (127-mm)/38-cal dual purpose (1×2/2×2); 1 Asroc 8-barrelled missile launcher; 2 Hedgehogs; 6 12.75-in (32.4-cm) torpedo tubes (2×3) *Aircraft:* 2 DASH helicopters *Crew:* 274

(FRAM II—*Sumners* and *Fletchers*) *Displacement:* 2425 tons (normal), 3512 tons (full load) *Dimensions and Machinery:* As built *Armament:* 4/6 5-in (127-mm)/38-cal dual purpose (2×2/3×2); 2 Hedgehogs; 2 21-in (53-cm) Mk 25 torpedo tubes (not in all); 6 12.75-in (32.4-cm) Mk 32 torpedo tubes (2×3) *Aircraft:* 2 DASH helicopters (not in all)

(FRAM II—ex-*Allen M Sumner*) *Displacement:* 2200 tons (normal), 3300 tons (full load) *Dimensions and Machinery:* As built *Armament:* as FRAM II *Gearings*

(FRAM II—ex-*Fletcher*) *Displacement:* 2060 tons (normal), 2980 tons (full load) *Dimensions and Machinery:* As built *Armament:* 2 5-in (127-mm)/38-cal dual purpose; 1 Mk 108 A/S rocket-launcher; 2 Hedgehogs; 6 12.75-in (32.4-cm) torpedo tubes (2×3)

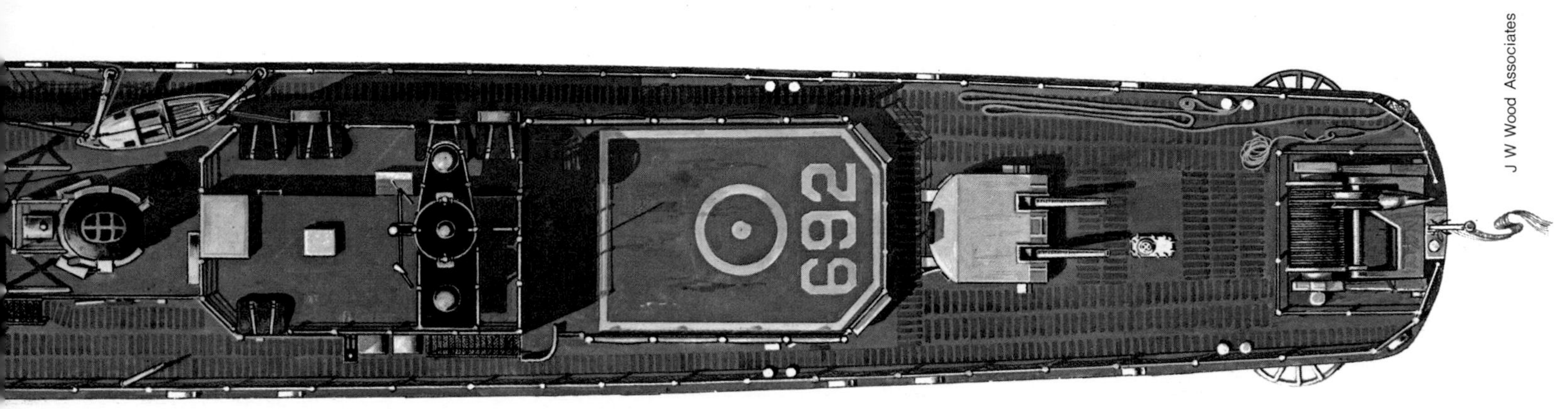

J W Wood Associates

Koninklijke Marine

The Dutch destroyer *Drenthe*, a *Friesland* Class vessel launched in March 1955 at Amsterdam

Friesland

Dutch destroyer class, built 1951-58. Eight ships of an enlarged 'Holland' design or 47B type were authorized between 1951 and 1955. They resembled the British *Daring* Class (the Netherlands Corps of Constructors was receiving considerable technical assistance from the British at the time) in having the forefunnel incorporated in a lattice mast. They also resembled the British *Daring* Class in layout, with a twin gun-mounting forward and aft, but had two antisubmarine rocket-launchers in B position.

The main difference between these ships and the earlier Type 47A *Holland* Class is in the armament. The two twin 120-mm (4.7-in) Bofors dual-purpose gun mountings and the 375-mm (14.76-in) rocket-launchers were as before, but the secondary armament was increased to six single 40-mm (1.57-in) AA guns, two on B deck, two between the funnels and two between the mainmast and the after 120-mm (4.7-in) gunhouse. Eight antisubmarine torpedo tubes were also to be mounted, four single tubes on either side amidships. The basic outfit of radar remained the same, a big air-warning search antenna on a short lattice mast aft, a tactical (surface and target-indication) one on the foremast and fire-control sets for the 120-mm (4.7-in) and 40-mm (1.57-in) guns.

The ships changed little in the course of 20 years, but the torpedo tubes were only mounted in *Overijssel* and *Utrecht* in 1960-61; after a year or two in service they were removed, and were never mounted in the rest of the class. The two 40-mm (1.57-in) guns in B position were also removed. The class are reported to have armour, but considering the displacement this cannot mean more than splinterproof plating, and is probably on the waterline and deck over the machinery, to prevent splinters from putting the turbines out of action. Plating thick enough to keep out even a 76-mm (3-in) shell would not be feasible without a severe reduction of speed. By the late 1970s the class was nearing the end of its effective life, and the ships had proved expensive to man. They were planned to be replaced by the 'Standard' or *Kortenaer* Class frigates, due to enter service from late 1978.

See also *Holland*.

Displacement: 2500 tons (standard), 3100 tons (full load) *Length:* 116 m (380 ft 7 in) oa *Beam:* 11.7 m (38 ft 4¾ in) *Draught:* 5.2 m (17 ft) max *Protection:* Splinterproof plating (see above) *Machinery:* 2-shaft geared steam turbines, 60 000 shp=36 knots *Armament:* 4 120-mm (4.7-in)/50-cal Bofors (2×2); 6 40-mm (1.57-in)/70-cal Bofors (6×1); 8 53-cm (21-in) torpedo tubes (only in two ships) *Crew:* 284

No	name	launched	builder
D.812	*Friesland*	2/1953	Nederlandse Dok, Amsterdam
D.813	*Groningen*	1/1954	Nederlandse Dok, Amsterdam
D.814	*Limburg*	9/1955	Royal de Schelde, Flushing
D.815	*Overijssel*	8/1955	Wilton-Fijenoord, Schiedam
D.816	*Drenthe*	3/1955	Nederlandse Dok, Amsterdam
D.817	*Utrecht*	6/1956	Royal de Schelde, Flushing
D.818	*Rotterdam*	1/1956	Rotterdam Dry Dock Co
D.819	*Amsterdam*	8/1956	Nederlandse Dok, Amsterdam

Gabbiano

Italian corvette class, first laid down 1942. The activities of British submarines operating

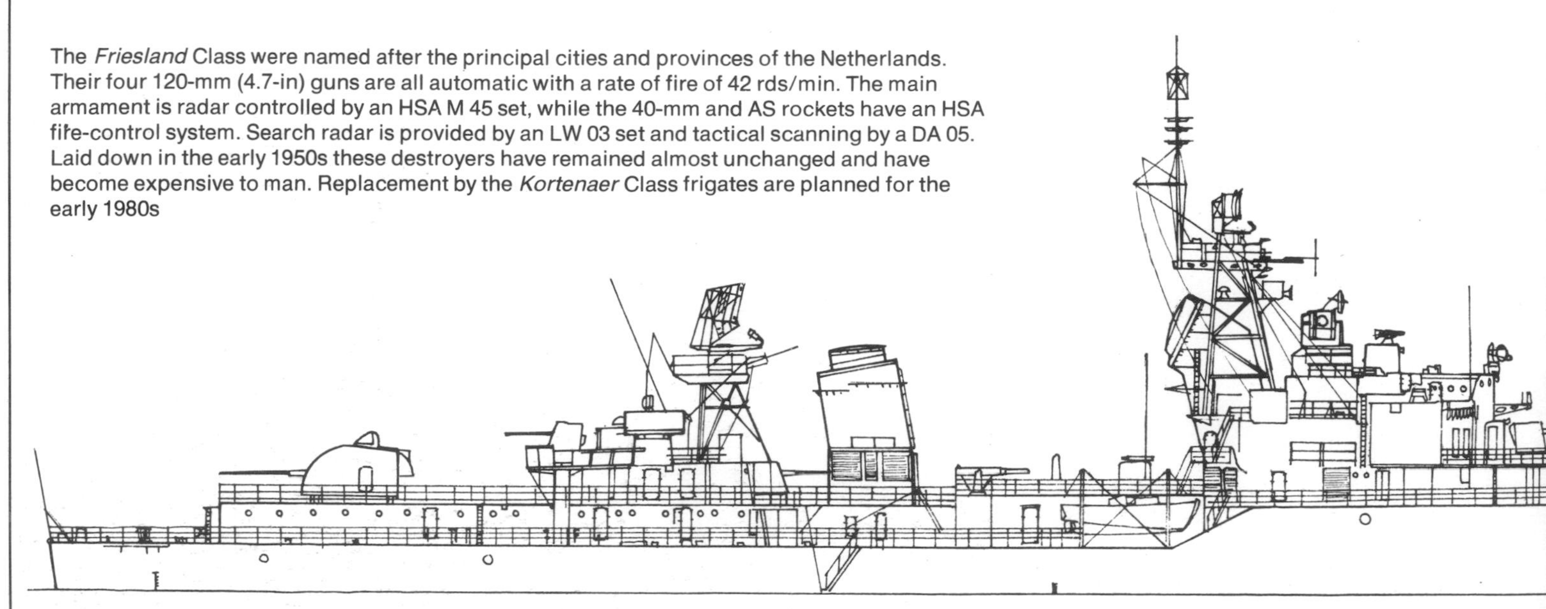

The *Friesland* Class were named after the principal cities and provinces of the Netherlands. Their four 120-mm (4.7-in) guns are all automatic with a rate of fire of 42 rds/min. The main armament is radar controlled by an HSA M 45 set, while the 40-mm and AS rockets have an HSA fire-control system. Search radar is provided by an LW 03 set and tactical scanning by a DA 05. Laid down in the early 1950s these destroyers have remained almost unchanged and have become expensive to man. Replacement by the *Kortenaer* Class frigates are planned for the early 1980s

out of Gibraltar, Malta and Alexandria during the early days of the war led to heavy losses among Italy's merchant fleet. The large Italian destroyers were unsuitable for convoy duties covering the small two- to six-ship slow convoys in the Adriatic, Aegean and across to North Africa. Because of this and because insufficient numbers of torpedo boats—which were inadequately armed for A/S (antisubmarine warfare) operations—were available, the Italian navy drew up a design for an A/S corvette. A large class of 60 vessels was ordered, the first being laid down in January 1942. Of the 60 ordered only 48 were completed.

Gabbiano (C.11); *Procellaria* (C.12); *Cormorano* (C.13); and *Pellicano* (C.14)—built by Cerusa, Voltri

Cicogna (C.15); *Folaga* (C.16); *Ibis* (C.17); *Gru* (C.18); *Tuffetto* (C.51); *Marangone* (C.52); *Strolaga* (C.53); and *Ardrea* (C.54)—built by Ansaldo, Genoa

Antilope (C.19); *Gazzella* (C.20); *Camoscio* (C.21); *Capriolo* (C.22); *Alce* (C.23); *Renna* (C.24); *Daino* (C.55); *Cervo* (C.56); and *Stambecco* (C.57)—built by Odero-Terni-Orlando, Livorno

Ape (C.25); *Vespa* (C.26); *Lucciola* (C.27); *Grillo* (C.28); *Cicala* (C.29); *Calabrone* (C.30); *Cavaletta* (C.31); *Libellula* (C.32); *Crisalide* (C.58); *Farfalla* (C.59); *Maggiolino* (C.60); and *Cocciniglia* (C.61)—built by Navalmeccanica, Castellammare di Stabia

Scimitarra (C.33); *Baionetta* (ex-*Parigiana*, C.34); *Colubrina* (C.35); *Springarda* (C.36); *Carabina* (C.37); *Bombarda* (C.38); *Scure* (C.62); *Clava* (C.63); and *Zagaglia* (C.64)—built by Breda, Porto Marghera

Artemide (C.39); *Persefone* (C.40); *Euterpe* (C.41); *Minerva* (C.42); *Urania* (C.65); *Berenice* (C.66); *Egeria* (C.67); *Melpomene* (C.68); *Tersicore* (C.69); and *Euridici* (C.70)—built by Cantieri Riuniti dell'Adriatico, Monfalcone

Driade (C.43); *Danaide* (C.44); *Pomana* (C.45); *Flora* (C.46); *Sfinge* (C.47); *Chimera* (C.48); *Sibilla* (C.49); and *Fenice* (C.50)—built by Cantieri Riuniti dell'Adriatico, Trieste

Construction of the vessels was given high priority and by the time of Italy's surrender in September 1943 a total of 29 had been completed. The remaining 31 ships had all been laid down and were in various stages of completion, many of them launched. Of these ten were completed by the Germans and either lost in action or scuttled on Germany's surrender. The remainder of the uncompleted vessels were either scuttled or damaged beyond repair in air raids. Of the 29 completed ships, three were lost as a result of enemy action while six were lost in action or scuttled at the end of the war.

In all 22 served in the postwar Marina Militare, rated as frigates with the pendant numbers F.547-549, 561-579. The armament was changed to 20-mm (0.79-in) and 40-mm (1.57-in) guns and antisubmarine weapons, while eight attached to the Command Training School had single 45-cm (17.7-in) torpedo tubes at the break of the forecastle. The *Pomona* (F.573), *Folaga* and *Fenice* (F.576-577) were stricken in 1965; the *Driade* (F.568) in 1966; the *Danaide* (F.563) in 1968; *Minerva* (F.562) in 1969; *Gru* (F.566), *Flora* (F.572) and *Pellicano* (F.574) in 1970; and the *Crisalide* and *Farfalla* (F.547-548), *Ibis* (F.651), *Scimitarra* and *Sibilla* (F.564-565), *Urania* and *Gabbiano* (F.571-572) in 1972. In 1978 there were still four of these hard-worked ships on the strength, the *Ape* (now a support ship for frogmen), and the *Bombarda*, *Chimera* and *Sfinge*, which were used as targets.

These corvettes were the first ships in the Italian navy to be completed with a navigating bridge. Because of a shortage of guns the first units to be completed were to have had 76-mm (3-in) guns, but sufficient 100-mm (3.9-in) weapons were found to arm all units when completed. Their appearance was distinctive, with a short funnel close to the bridge.

Displacement: 670-673 tons (standard), 737-743 tons (full load) *Length:* 64.3 m (211 ft), 64.4 m (211 ft 3¼ in) oa *Beam:* 8.71 m (28 ft 6 in) *Draught:* 2.53 m (8 ft 3½ in) *Machinery:* 2-shaft Fiat diesel, 3500 bhp (as designed)= 18-19.47 knots; 2 150-hp electric motors for silent running *Armament:* 1 100-mm (3.9-in)/47-cal; 7 20-mm (0.79-in)/65-70-cal; 2 40-mm (1.57-in)/56-cal AA; 2 45-cm (17.7-in) torpedo tubes; 10 depth charge throwers and 2 sets of chutes *Crew:* 110 (approx)

Galveston

US guided missile cruiser class. Of the 27 *Cleveland* Class light cruisers that were completed to the original design, six were converted into single-ended guided missile cruisers between 1956-60. It had originally been intended to convert seven more, but the initial conversions were so difficult and so expensive for the limited results achieved that the remaining ships were left in their original condition, and new guided missile frigates built instead. All the unconverted *Clevelands* were discarded between 1959-70.

The Italian *Gabbiano* Class corvette *Antilope* built for convoy escort work in 1942

Foto Drüppel

***Euterpe*, a *Gabbiano* Class corvette captured by the Germans in 1943 and designated UJ 2228**

Aldo Fraccaroli

PPL

USS *Oklahoma City*, a *Galveston* Class light guided missile cruiser recommissioned in 1960

Name	laid down	launched	completed
Galveston	20/2/1944	22/4/1945	24/5/1946
Little Rock	6/3/1943	27/8/1944	17/6/1945
Oklahoma City	8/3/1942	20/2/1944	22/12/1944

The three *Cleveland* conversions that were fitted with the Terrier medium-range SAM (surface-to-air missile) were reclassified as the *Providence* Class, whilst the three fitted with the larger Talos long-range SAM were reclassified as the *Galveston* Class.

The *Galvestons* were originally armed with 12 6-in (152-mm)/47-cal guns arranged in two triple turrets superimposed fore and aft, six twin 5-in (127-mm)/38-cal mounts (one superimposed fore and aft and one on either side of the fore and aft superstructure), and 28 40-mm (1.57-in) AA. They had a catapult and hangar aft and carried four seaplanes. *Galveston* had her after 6-in (152-mm) and 5-in (127-mm) mounts removed and a new enlarged superstructure was fitted where the after superimposed 5-in (127-mm) mount had been. This was surmounted by a platform carrying the SPS-30 long-range 3-D radar; the after superstructure also carried two SPG-49 missile control radars. The twin Talos Mk 7 Mod O SAM launcher was mounted on the quarterdeck, with a magazine capacity of 46 missiles. There was a helicopter pad at the extreme stern, but no hangar or maintenance facilities were fitted. A lattice foremast was fitted to carry the SPS-43 long-range search radar, and a very tall lattice mainmast was added immediately abaft the second funnel, with an SPS-39 3-D air-surveillance radar mounted at the masthead out of the way of the hot funnel gases. Her forebridge was also remodelled and enclosed. *Little Rock* and *Oklahoma City* were similarly rebuilt, except that their forward superstructures were totally altered to provide much greater space for offices and communications facilities so that they could act as flagships. The forward superstructure was therefore greatly enlarged and extended, necessitating the removal of the original forward 5-in (127-mm) mounts, and the replacement of B 6-in (152-mm) turret by a twin 5-in (127-mm)/38-cal mount.

All three were built by William Cramp at Philadelphia. *Galveston* (CL-93) began her conversion at Philadelphia naval yard in August 1956 and completed it in September 1958, though she was recommissioned on May 28, 1958. She was reclassified first as CLG-93 and then on May 23, 1957 as CLG-3. When she recommissioned as a guided missile cruiser she was the first operational ship to mount the Talos SAM. She was finally decommissioned on December 21, 1973. *Little Rock* was converted by the New York Shipbuilding Corporation at their Camden yard, New Jersey, between January 1957 and June 1960. She was reclassified as CLG-4 and recommissioned on June 3, 1960. She acted as flagship either of the Sixth Fleet (in the Mediterranean) or the Seventh Fleet (in the Western Pacific) in rotation with *Oklahoma City* and with *Providence* and *Springfield* of the *Providence* Class. She was stricken on November 22, 1976, to undergo refitting as a museum at Boston navy yard. *Oklahoma City* was converted at the Bethlehem Steel shipyard at San Francisco between May 1957 and September 1960. She was reclassified as CLG-5 and recommissioned on September 7, 1960. Her last commission was a flagship of the Seventh Fleet. The *Galvestons* can be distinguished from the *Providence* Class because the *Providences* have a much lower mainmast, and instead of having a platform on the after superstructure they have a third lattice mast.

Displacement: 10670 tons (standard), 14400 tons (full load) *Length:* 185.9 m (610 ft) oa *Beam:* 20.2 m (66 ft 4 in) *Draught:* 7.6 m (25 ft) *Machinery:* 4-shaft geared steam turbines 100000 shp=31.6 knots *Protection:* 127-38 mm (5-1½ in) belt; 76-51 mm (3-2 in) deck; 127-76 mm (5-3 in) turrets *Armament:* 1 twin Talos SAM launcher; 6 6-in (152-mm); 6 5-in (127-mm) *Crew:* 1350 approx

Garcia

US frigate class. This class of ten vessels was originally ordered in the 1961-63 programmes as destroyer escorts DE.1040-1051. The design is a development of the earlier *Bronstein* Class and, although the *Garcia* Class are larger and have a better ASW (antisubmarine warfare) capability than many destroyers, they have, since June 1975, been classified as frigates (FF). This is because the ships have only a single propeller shaft which limits their speed. The ships are fitted with an advanced pressure-fired steam-generating plant developing 70% more power than previous steam plants of similar weight and size. The two boilers are each fitted with an integrated supercharger and control system providing automatic regulation of fuel, air and water. The boilers use Naval Distillate (ND) fuel which simplifies boiler cleaning and maintenance and facilitates the ballasting of the fuel tanks with sea water. The simplified boiler maintenance and fully automatic control system means that the machinery requires far fewer engineers to control it.

The original design provided for the ships to mount the 5-in (127-mm)/54-cal gun. However, to keep costs down, it was decided to mount the older 5-in (127-mm)/38-cal weapon which has a slower rate of fire and a shorter range. Unfortunately, this reduces the effectiveness of this otherwise all-missile armed A/S (antisubmarine) ship. The 5-in (127-mm) guns provide the only self-defence armament of these vessels, and so they were designed to operate in conjunction with the very similar *Brooke* Class equipped with an AA missile armament. The design is flush-decked with a distinctive 'mack' (combined mast and stack, or funnel) amidships. The stem is acutely raked with a bow anchor. A second anchor is carried just forward of the 5-in (127-mm) gun on the port side and the ships are fitted with gyrostabilizers.

In the original design, plans were made for the ships to operate DASH (drone antisubmarine helicopter). Owing to the cutback in the DASH programme, only the *Bradley* operated a DASH for a short while. The *Bradley* was also equipped with a Sea Sparrow BPDMS (basic point defence missile system) between the after 5-in (127-mm) mount and the mack in 1968-69. This was subsequently removed for installation in the carrier *Forrestal*. Originally the ships were fitted with two Mk 25 torpedo tubes for wire-guided torpedoes in the transom stern. This was removed from early units and later units were never equipped with the tubes. During the early 1970s the hangar on all but the *Albert David* and *Sample* was modified to operate the LAMPS SH-2D helicopter.

Displacement: 2620 tons (standard), 3043 tons (full load) *Length:* 126.33 m (414 ft 6 in) oa *Beam:* 13.5 m (44 ft 3 in) *Draught:* 7.31 m (24 ft)

No and name	commissioned
FF1040 *Garcia*	12/1964
FF1041 *Bradley*	5/1965
FF1043 *Edward McDonnell*	2/1965
FF1044 *Brumby*	8/1965
FF1045 *Davidson*	12/1965
FF1047 *Voge*	11/1966
FF1048 *Sample*	3/1968
FF1049 *Koelsch*	6/1967
FF1050 *Albert David*	10/1968
FF1051 *O'Callahan*	7/1968

Machinery: 1-shaft geared steam turbine 35 000 shp=27 knots *Armament:* 2 5-in (127-mm)/38-cal (2×1); 2 triple Mk 32 torpedo tubes; 1 ASROC 8-tube launcher; 1 LAMPS SH-2D helicopter *Crew:* 239-247

James W Goss

USS *Voge* (FF1047), one of the ten *Garcia* Class frigates constructed for A/S and escort duties

Gato

US submarine class. This was the last submarine class to be designed for the US Navy before the Second World War, and embodied all the experience gained from the *Porpoise, Salmon* and *Tambor* Classes. So successful was the design that, apart from minor modifications required as a result of war experience, it was extended to the following *Ballao* and *Tench* Classes. More than 200 submarines were ordered.

By adopting the same basic and well-proven design for subsequent classes, the Americans were able to embark on a massive submarine construction programme. Less than half a dozen American shipyards were involved in building these classes and by adopting the same design utilizing the fully-welded hull and prefabrication construction techniques, large numbers were completed in a very short time. The average time of construction was about 12-14 months and keels were often laid down in the same yards at the rate of one every month. *Gato*, the first submarine in the class, was laid down in October 1940 and commissioned in December 1941. *Croaker*, the last boat in the class, was laid down in April 1943 and commissioned a year later in April 1944.

Both were built by the Electric Boat company at Groton, Connecticut. Four shipyards built the *Gato* Class: Electric Boat company, Groton (SS.212-227, SS.240-264); Manitowoc Shipbuilding company (SS.265-274); Mare Island navy yard, California (SS.236-239, SS.281-284); and Portsmouth navy yard (SS.228-235, SS.275-280).

The *Gato* Class was 1.2 m (4 ft) longer than the preceding *Tambor* Class which it closely resembled. The extra length arose from dividing the engine room into two compartments. Propulsion was provided by a diesel electric reduction gearing system which war experience soon showed to be too noisy for carrying out operations with any degree of safety in enemy-infested waters. Subsequent classes had a direct drive system (see *Ballao*).

US Navy

The *Gato* Class submarine USS *Flying Fish* shortly after her launch on July 9, 1941

The original design provided for the 3-in (76-mm) gun to be mounted abaft the conning tower, which some of the early units carried.

Later vessels, however, carried a 5-in (127-mm) gun forward of the conning tower and 20-mm (0.79-in) on extensions fore and aft of the conning tower. To accommodate these extensions the conning tower was built to a slightly smaller design. There were a number of variations in the armament mountings, a few units being fitted with a 4-in (102-mm) gun in place of the 3-in (76-mm) or 5-in (127-mm) and some carried a 40-mm (1.57-in) in place of the 20-mm (0.79-in) on the forward extension of the conning tower. Positions were also reversed on some units, the heavy gun being sited abaft the conning tower.

The *Gato* Class served with distinction throughout the war. *Flasher* (SS.249) achieved the highest score in the Pacific sinking 21 Japanese merchant ships totalling 1 123 000 grt (gross registered tonnage). Altogether the *Gato* Class were credited with sinking large numbers of Japanese merchant ships as well as a large number of warships. Among the most notable achievements were the sinking of the carrier *Taiho* by *Albacore* (SS.218) in June 1944—*Albacore* also sank the light cruiser *Tenryu* and two destroyers—and the escort carrier *Unyo* by *Barb* (SS.220) in September 1944. *Darter* (SS.227) and *Dace* (SS.247) achieved the greatest distinction, being responsible for locating and reporting the position of the main Japanese force heading to attack the American landings in the Philippines on October 23, 1944. This sighting led directly to the last great battle, Leyte Gulf. During their shadowing of the Japanese fleet, *Darter* sank the heavy cruiser *Atago* and damaged the heavy cruiser *Takao* while *Dace* sank the heavy cruiser *Maya*.

After the war, a number of the class were converted to hunter/killer submarines, the gun armament being removed and the conning tower rebuilt to a streamlined design. Boats so converted were: *Angler, Bashaw, Bluegill, Bream, Cavalla, Croaker, Grouper.* Other units were converted to radar picket vessels with a variety of aerials on short masts fore and aft of the conning tower. They were: *Pompon, Rasher, Raton, Ray, Redfin* and *Rock*.

Tunny was fitted to launch the Regulus guided missile, being equipped with a watertight hangar aft of the conning tower and a launching cradle. The conning tower was rebuilt to a streamlined design and all guns were removed.

USS *Drum* (SS.228). Launched in May 1941 she was stricken in 1968 but preserved as a memorial. *Gato*s were the standard US submarine during the Second World War. Notable members of the class were the *Flasher* which sank 100 231 tons (21 ships) and the *Rasher, Barb, Tang* and *Silversides* which sank over 90 000 tons

Displacement: 1526/2424 tons (surfaced/submerged) (SS.228-235 and SS.275-280 2410 tons submerged) *Length:* 95.02 m (311 ft 9 in) oa *Beam:* 8.30 m (27 ft 3 in) *Draught:* 4.65 m (15 ft 3 in) *Machinery:* 2-shaft diesel/electric, 5400 bhp=20.25 knots/2740 hp=8.75 knots (surfaced/submerged) *Armament:* 1 3-in (76-mm)/50-cal; 2 0.30-in (7.62-mm) mg; 10 21-in (53-

***Below:* USS *Peto* in 1944. *Gato* Class submarines like the *Peto* waged an eminently successful campaign against the Japanese**

US Navy

USS *Gato* in profile and plan. She was the first vessel in a class of over 200 boats launched between 1941 and 1945. *Gatos* carried 24 21-in (53-cm) torpedoes and a crew of 80

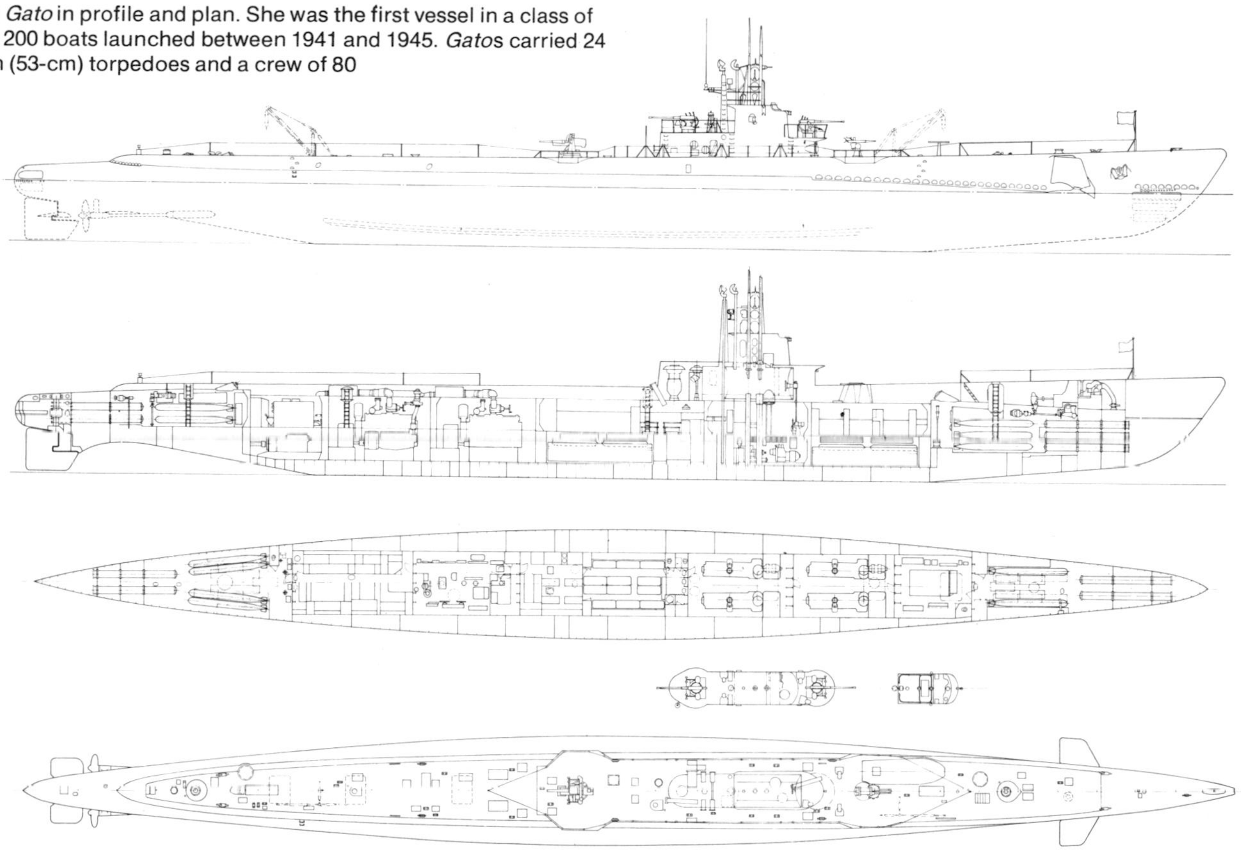

cm) torpedo tubes (6 forward, 4 aft, 24 torpedoes carried) *Diving depth:* 91.4 m (300 ft) *Crew:* 80-85

No and name	launched	fate
SS.212 ***Gato***	8/1941	Sold for scrapping 1960
SS.213 ***Greenling***	9/1941	Sold for scrapping 1960
SS.214 ***Grouper***	10/1941	Sold for scrapping 1970
SS.215 ***Growler***	11/1941	Sunk by own torpedo 11/1944
SS.216 ***Grunion***	12/1941	War loss 7/1942
SS.217 ***Guardfish***	1/1942	Sunk as target 10/1961
SS.218 ***Albacore***	2/1942	War loss 11/1944
SS.219 ***Amberjack***	3/1942	War loss 2/1943
SS.220 ***Barb***	4/1942	Italian *Enrico Tazzoli* 1955
SS.221 ***Blackfish***	8/1942	Stricken 1959
SS.222 ***Bluefish***	2/1943	Sold for scrapping 1959
SS.223 ***Bonefish***	3/1943	War loss 6/1945
SS.224 ***Cod***	3/1943	Stricken 1971
SS.225 ***Cero***	4/1943	Stricken 1967 preserved as memorial
SS.226 ***Corvina***	5/1943	War loss 11/1943
SS.227 ***Darter***	6/1943	Ran aground wrecked 10/1944
SS.228 ***Drum***	5/1941	Stricken 1968 preserved as memorial
SS.229 ***Flying Fish***	7/1941	Sold for scrapping 1959
SS.230 ***Finback***	8/1941	Sold for scrapping 1959
SS.231 ***Haddock***	10/1941	Sold for scrapping 1960
SS.232 ***Halibut***	12/1941	War loss 1/1944, scrapped 1947
SS.233 ***Herring***	1/1942	War loss 6/1944
SS.234 ***Kingfish***	3/1942	Sold for scrapping 1960
SS.235 ***Shad***	4/1942	Sold for scrapping 1960
SS.236 ***Silversides***	8/1941	Stricken 1969
SS.237 ***Trigger***	10/1941	War loss 3/1945
SS.238 ***Wahoo***	2/1942	War loss 10/1943
SS.239 ***Whale***	3/1942	Sold for scrapping 1960
SS.240 ***Angler***	7/1943	Stricken 1971
SS.241 ***Bashaw***	7/1943	Used as target 1969
SS.242 ***Bluegill***	8/1943	Scuttled for training 1970
SS.244 ***Bream***	10/1943	Used as target 1969
SS.244 ***Cavalla***	11/1943	Stricken 1969 preserved as memorial
SS.245 ***Cobia***	11/1943	Stricken 1970 preserved as memorial
SS.246 ***Croaker***	12/1943	Stricken 1971
SS.247 ***Dace***	4/1943	Italian *Leonardo da Vinci* 1955
SS.248 ***Dorado***	5/1943	Bombed in error 1943
SS.249 ***Flasher***	6/1943	Sold for scrapping 1963
SS.250 ***Flier***	7/1943	War loss 8/1944
SS.251 ***Flounder***	8/1943	Sold for scrapping 1959
SS.252 ***Gabilan***	9/1943	Sold for scrapping 1959
SS.253 ***Gunnel***	5/1942	Sold for scrapping 1959
SS.254 ***Gurnard***	6/1942	Sold for scrapping 1961
SS.255 ***Haddo***	6/1942	Sold for scrapping 1961
SS.256 ***Hake***	7/1942	Stricken 1967
SS.257 ***Harder***	8/1942	War loss 8/1944
SS.258 ***Hoe***	9/1942	Sold for scrapping 1960
SS.259 ***Jack***	10/1942	Greek *Amfitriti* 1958
SS.260 ***Lapon***	10/1942	Greek *Poseidon* 1957
SS.261 ***Mingo***	11/1942	Japanese *Kuroshio* 1955
SS.262 ***Muskallunge***	12/1942	Brazilian *Humaita* 1957
SS.263 ***Paddle***	12/1942	Brazilian *Riachuelo* 1957
SS.264 ***Pargo***	1/1943	Sold for scrapping 1961
SS.265 ***Peto***	4/1942	Sold for scrapping 1961
SS.266 ***Pogy***	6/1942	Sold for scrapping 1951
SS.267 ***Pompon***	8/1942	Sold for scrapping 1960
SS.268 ***Puffer***	11/1942	Sold for scrapping 1960
SS.269 ***Rasher***	12/1942	Stricken 1971
SS.270 ***Raton***	1/1943	Used as target 1969
SS.271 ***Ray***	2/1943	Sold for scrapping 1960
SS.272 ***Redfish***	4/1943	Sold for scrapping 1971
SS.273 ***Robalo***	5/1943	War loss 7/1944
SS.274 ***Rock***	6/1943	Used as target 1969
SS.275 ***Runner***	5/1942	War loss 6/1943
SS.276 ***Sawfish***	6/1942	Sold for scrapping 1960
SS.277 ***Scamp***	7/1942	War loss 11/1944
SS.278 ***Scorpion***	7/1942	War loss 2/1944
SS.279 ***Snook***	8/1942	War loss 4/1945
SS.280 ***Steelhead***	9/1942	Sold for scrapping 1961
SS.281 ***Sunfish***	5/1942	Sold for scrapping 1960
SS.282 ***Tunny***	6/1942	Used as target 1969
SS.283 ***Tinosa***	10/1942	Foundered 1961
SS.284 ***Tullibee***	11/1942	Sunk by own torpedo 3/1944

US Navy

The *Gato* Class submarine USS *Cavalla* (SS.244) which was stricken in 1969 but preserved as a memorial like her sisters *Cobia, Drum* and *Cero*

Gearing

US destroyer class, launched between 1944 and 1951. Experience with the *Allen M Sumner* Class had shown that for the Pacific they were unable to develop their full potential owing to a limited radius of action. However the basic design had shown itself to be a success and it was decided to repeat the class with an extra 4.26-m (14-ft) section added amidships between the two funnels to provide extra bunkerage. A beneficial side effect of the increased length was that the stability of the *Gearings* was much improved.

A total of 157 *Gearing* Class destroyers were ordered from seven builders, but owing to the end of the war and the run down of the fleet only 92 of these were completed. Yards involved in the construction of the *Gearings* were: Bethlehem (San Pedro, Staten Island, San Francisco and Quincy yards), Charleston navy yard (all the orders placed with this yard were subsequently cancelled), Bath Iron Works, Boston navy yard (like Charleston all orders were cancelled), Federal Shipbuilding yard of Kearny, the Consolidated Steel corporation at Orange, Maine, and the Todd Pacific yard at Seattle.

The main armament remained as in the *Allen M Sumner* Class, but light AA varied considerably between units, and was concentrated amidships around the after funnel and just abaft it. Shortly after completion, some units had the second quintuple torpedo tube bank replaced by extra AA and improved A/S weapons (being reclassed as destroyer escorts) while others had the forward torpedo tube bank replaced by a long-range radar aerial and were reclassed as radar pickets.

Destroyers: DD710 *Gearing*, DD711 *Eugene A Greene*, DD712 *Gyatt*, DD713 *Kenneth D Bailey*, DD714 *William R Rush*, DD715 *William M Wood*, DD716 *Wiltsie*, DD717 *Theodore E Chandler*, DD718 *Hammer*, DD719 *Epperson*, DD742 *Frank Knox*, DD743 *Southerland*, DD763 *William C Lawe*, DD764 *Lloyd Thomas*, DD765 *Keppler*, DD782 *Rowan*, DD783 *Gurke*, DD784 *McKean*, DD785 *Henderson*, DD786 *Richard B Anderson*, DD787 *James E Kyes*, DD788 *Hollister*, DD789 *Eversole*, DD790 *Shelton*, DD791 *Seaman*, DD805 *Chevalier*, DD806 *Higbee*, DD807 *Benner*, DD808 *Dennis J Buckley*, DD817 *Corry*, DD818 *New*, DD819 *Holder*, DD820 *Rich*, DD821 *Johnston*, DD822 *Robert H McCard*, DD823 *Samuel B Roberts*, DD824 *Basilone*, DD825 *Carpenter*, DD826 *Agerholm*, DD827 *Robert A Owens*, DD828 *Timmerman*, DD829 *Myles C Fox*, DD830 *Everett F Larson*, DD831 *Goodrich*, DD832 *Hanson*, DD833 *Herbert J Thomas*, DD834 *Turner*, DD835 *Charles P Cecil*, DD836 *George K MacKenzie*, DD837 *Sarsfield*, DD838 *Ernest G Small*, DD839 *Power*, DD840 *Glennoh*, DD841 *Noa*, DD842 *Fiske*, DD843 *Warrington*, DD844 *Perry*, DD845 *Baussell*, DD846 *Ozbourn*, DD847 *Robert L Wilson*, DD848 *Witek*, DD849 *Richard E Kraus*, DD850 *Joseph P Kennedy Jr*, DD851 *Rupertus*, DD852 *Leonard F Mason*, DD853 *Charles H Roan*, DD858 *Fred T Berry*, DD859 *Norris*, DD860 *McCaffery*, DD861 *Harwood*, DD862 *Vogelgesang*, DD863 *Steinaker*, DD864 *Harold J Ellison*, DD865 *Charles R Ware*, DD866 *Cone*, DD867 *Stribling*, DD868 *Brownson*, DD869 *Arnold J Isbell*, DD870 *Fechteler*, DD871 *Damato*,

USS *Gurke*, a *Gearing* Class destroyer, at San Diego on August 18, 1967, after FRAM conversion

George F Dale

Giorgio Arra

The Turkish destroyer *Adatepe* in 1973. She was formerly USS *Forrest Royal* and was transferred to Turkey in 1971 after FRAM 1 conversion

DD872 *Forrest Royal*, DD873 *Hawkins*, DD874 *Duncan*, DD875 *Henry W Tucker*, DD876 *Rogers*, DD877 *Perkins*, DD878 *Vesole*, DD879 *Leary*, DD880 *Dyess*, DD881 *Bordelon*, DD882 *Furse*, DD883 *Newman K Perry*, DD884 *Floyd B Parkes*, DD885 *John R Craig*, DD886 *Orleck*, DD887 *Brinkley Bass*, DD888 *Stickel*, DD889 *O'Hare*, DD890 *Meredith*.

The following units (some of which had been named, laid down and even launched in one or two cases) were eventually cancelled: DD720-721, 766-767 (all launched), DD768-769 (both laid down), DD791 (completed, but never commissioned), DD809-816, 854-856, 891-930, DD927-30 were eventually built as DL2-5 of the *Mitscher* Class. Of those completed the following were reclassed as radar pickets (DDR) in 1949-53: 711, 713-715, 742-743, 784, 805-808, 817, 829-835, 838, 842, 863, 870, 873-883, 888-889. The following were reclassed A/S escorts (DDE): 719, 764-765, 818-820, 824-825, 827, 847-848, 858-861, 871.

During the 1960s the class underwent the FRAM modernization which with the increased length and improved stability of the *Gearings* proved a far better proposition than the FRAM project of the *Allen M Sumner*.

Timmerman (DD828) was used as an experimental ship to test high pressure lightweight machinery; she was sold for scrap in 1959. *Witek* (DD848) was also used as an experimental ship, being fitted with two water-jet propulsion systems in place of the propellers. She was scrapped in 1969. *Gyatt* (DD712) was armed with a twin Terrier surface-to-air missile system aft in 1955-56. This was the first time a destroyer had been armed with guided missiles and she was used to test the suitability of the Terrier missiles as an installation on small ships. She retained A and B gun mounts and two twin 3-in (76-mm) amidships. She was equipped with two small rotating missile magazines in a deck house aft on the main deck holding 14 missiles. The Terrier was found to be unsuitable for small ship operation and a new smaller missile, the Tartar, was developed for use on destroyers. The Terrier installation on *Gyatt* was removed in 1962.

Like the *Allen M Sumner* Class, the *Gearings* remained in service until the early 1970s by which time they were no longer capable of meeting the high technical and performance standards required by modern warships. The class was rapidly run down and sold or stricken for scrap.

Gearing Class destroyers stricken: 834 (9/1969); 870, 858 (9/1970); 823 (11/1970); 843 (10/1972); 710, 808, 844, 850, 884 (7/1973); 860, 874 (9/1973); 859 (1/1974); 807, 713, 831 (2/1974); 883 (4/1974); 847 (9/1974); 865 (12/1974); 717 (4/1975); 846 (6/1975); 867 (7/1976); 868 (9/1976); 819, 836, 840 (10/1976); 715, 878 (12/1976).

See also FRAM.

Displacement: 2425 tons (standard), 3479 tons (full load) *Length:* 119 m (390 ft 6 in) oa *Beam:* 15 m (49 ft) *Draught:* 5.79 m (19 ft) maximum *Machinery:* 2-shaft geared steam turbines, 60 000 shp=34 knots *Armament:* 6 5-in (127-mm)/38-cal (3×2); 4-6 3-in (76-mm)/50-cal (2-3×2); 4-16 40-mm (1.57-in) quad and twin mounts; 8-15 20-mm (0.79-in); 5-10 21-in (53-cm) torpedo tubes (1-2×5) *Crew:* 336-367

George Washington

US fleet ballistic missile submarines, completed between 1959-61. These submarines were the first in the non-communist world to be armed with strategic missiles. The first three ballistic missile armed submarines were ordered under a supplementary estimate to the 1958 construction programme, with two more provided in the 1959 programme. The first, *George Washington*, was originally laid down on November 1, 1957, as *Scorpion* of the *Skipjack* Class, but was reordered as a

Below: USS *Glennon*, a *Gearing* Class destroyer having undergone FRAM conversion

PPL

ballistic missile submarine on December 31, 1957. The second ship in the class, *Patrick Henry*, was also originally ordered as a *Skipjack* Class submarine. Although the material had been assembled, she had not actually been laid down. This order too was converted on December 31, 1957, to a ballistic missile armed submarine.

The hull is whale-shaped and, in addition to the nuclear reactor, the boats are fitted with an auxiliary conventional diesel/electric propulsion plant for use in emergency. The submarines are also equipped with the then newly-developed SINS (Ships Inertial Navigation System) and the latest electronic and stabilizing equipment.

The design is a modified version of the *Skipjack* with an extra section 39.6 m (130 ft) long added abaft the sail (conning tower) for the 16 missile launching tubes and the associated fire control and navigating equipment. The missile tubes are arranged in two parallel rows of eight and were originally fitted for firing the solid-fuelled Polaris A-1 missile. The missile was fired with a compressed air ejection system, from either a surfaced or submerged position. The complete outfit of 16 missiles can be launched within 15 minutes.

On July 20, 1960, *George Washington* carried out America's first successful submerged firing of a strategic missile off Cape Kennedy.

George Washington

She sailed on her first patrol on November 15, 1960, setting up a world record for a continuous submerged patrol of 66 days and 10 hours. This was subsequently bettered in 1961 by her sister ship *Patrick Henry* which set the record with 66 days and 22 hours.

The ships systematically underwent a refit, the first nuclear reactor refuelling beginning in June 1964. The refit included modernizing the missile tubes to take the updated A-3 Polaris missile with increased range of 4630 km (2880 miles).

The fire-control equipment was also updated and a new gas-steam ejector system fitted to the missile tubes. The last ship to complete her refit was *Abraham Lincoln* in June 1967. The class will not be modernized to fire the improved Poseidon ballistic missile.

Displacement: 6019/6888 tons (surfaced/submerged), *Length:* 116.34 m (381 ft 8½ ins) oa *Beam:* 10.06 m (33 ft) *Draught:* 8.84 m (29 ft) *Machinery:* 1-shaft, 1 pressurized water-cooled nuclear reactor, 2 geared turbines, 15000 shp=20/30 plus knots (surfaced/submerged) *Armament:* 16 Polaris ballistic missiles; 6 (bow) 21-in (53-cm) torpedo tubes (which can also launch SUBROC missiles) *Crew:* 112 (2 crews are provided)

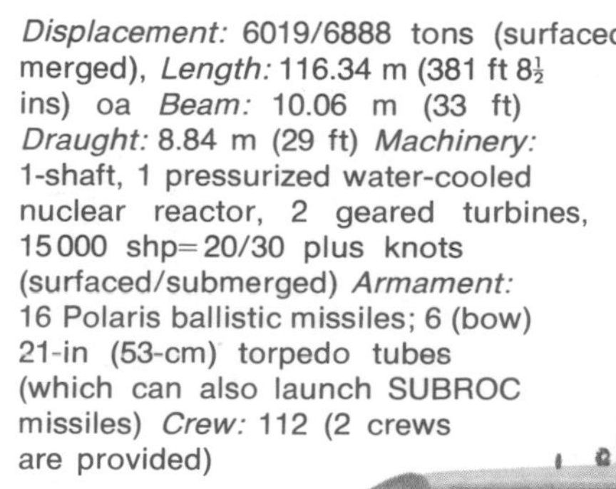

USS *George Washington*, armed not only with 16 Polaris missiles but six 21-in (53-cm) torpedo tubes. She fired two of her missiles for the first time in July 1960

No and name	builder	completed
SSBN598 ***George Washington***	General Dynamics, Groton	12/1959
SSBN599 ***Patrick Henry***	General Dynamics, Groton	4/1960
SSBN600 ***Theodore Roosevelt***	Mare Island navy yard	2/1961
SSBN601 ***Robert E Lee***	Newport News Shipbuilding	9/1960
SSBN602 ***Abraham Lincoln***	Portsmouth navy yard	3/1961

General Dynamics

To test one of the 16 missile tubes of the *George Washington*, a cylinder called a 'sabot' is forced out of a flooded missile cylinder

Georges Leygues

French corvette or frigate class, built 1974. With the *Surcouf* Class destroyers nearing the end of their useful lives the Marine Nationale (French navy) planned a new fleet escort as a standard type to be built for the early 1980s. The design chosen was the C70 (=Corvette 1970), midway between the *Aconit* and *Tourville* designs and incorporating the new Crotale antiaircraft missile.

One important change was in propulsion, for the *Georges Leygues* Class are not only the first large French ships with a CODOG (combined diesel or gas turbine) propulsion system but also the first French ships to use the British Rolls-Royce Olympus gas turbine. Two Olympus are used to provide high-speed running, while SEMT-Pielstick diesels provide economical cruising.

The armament comprises a standard 100-mm (3.9-in) Model '68 dual-purpose gun forward, four Exocet MM38 surface-to-surface missiles amidships and an eight-barrelled Crotale missile-launcher on the after deckhouse. In addition there is a big hangar housing two WG13 Lynx helicopters and both a bow sonar and a variable-depth sonar on the quarterdeck, and launchers for antisubmarine homing torpedoes behind the bridge.

The *Georges Leygues* Class was intended to comprise 24 ships, but at the beginning of 1978 only four firm orders had been placed, *Georges Leygues* (D.640)—already completed—*Dupleix* (D.641), *Montcalm* (D.643) and No 4, as yet unnamed. Building is being undertaken at Brest arsenal. *Georges Leygues* started preliminary trials in November 1977 and will become operational by March 1979. *Dupleix* is to join the fleet in October 1980 and *Montcalm* a year later. An air defence version is planned, with Standard SM-1 area-defence missiles in place of the short-range Crotale.

In appearance and dimensions *Georges Leygues* bears a resemblance to the British *Broadsword* or Type 22, apart from the gun and the big variable-depth sonar. She is

Georges Leygues

Above: Georges Leygues **(DD.640), a French antisubmarine frigate in Brest harbour during preliminary trials in December 1977**

The *Georges Leygues* showing her bow sonar, DRBV 51, 26 and DRBC 32E radar array, the Exocet missiles amidships, Crotale AA missiles, the diesel gas machinery, and Westland/Aérospatiale Lynx helicopter. She has a 100-mm (3.9-in) Model 68 dual-purpose gun in the bows which is capable of 60 rds/min with a maximum AA range of 8000 m (8750 yards) and surface range of 17 000 m (18 600 yards) typical of the big fleet escorts being built and has a good balance of antisurface and antisubmarine armament, in addition to being capable of defending herself against air attack. The design of the hull and propulsion emphasize simplicity and economy, and the type forms a basis for future variants. The two Lynx helicopters can be used for the antisubmarine or antisurface role.

Displacement: 3800 tonnes (mean for trials), 4170 tonnes (full load) *Length:* 139 m (456 ft) oa *Beam:* 14 m (45 ft 11 in) *Draught:* 5.73 m (18 ft 9½ in) (full load) *Machinery:* 2-shaft gas turbines, 42 000 shp plus diesels, 10 000 bhp= 29.75 knots *Armament:* 1 100-mm (3.9-in)/60-cal dual purpose; 2 20-mm (0.79-in) (2×1); 4 MM38 Exocet SSMs (4×1); 8 Crotale SAMs (1×8); 2 53.3-cm (21-in) A/S torpedo tubes (2×1) *Aircraft:* 2 Lynx helicopters *Crew:* 250

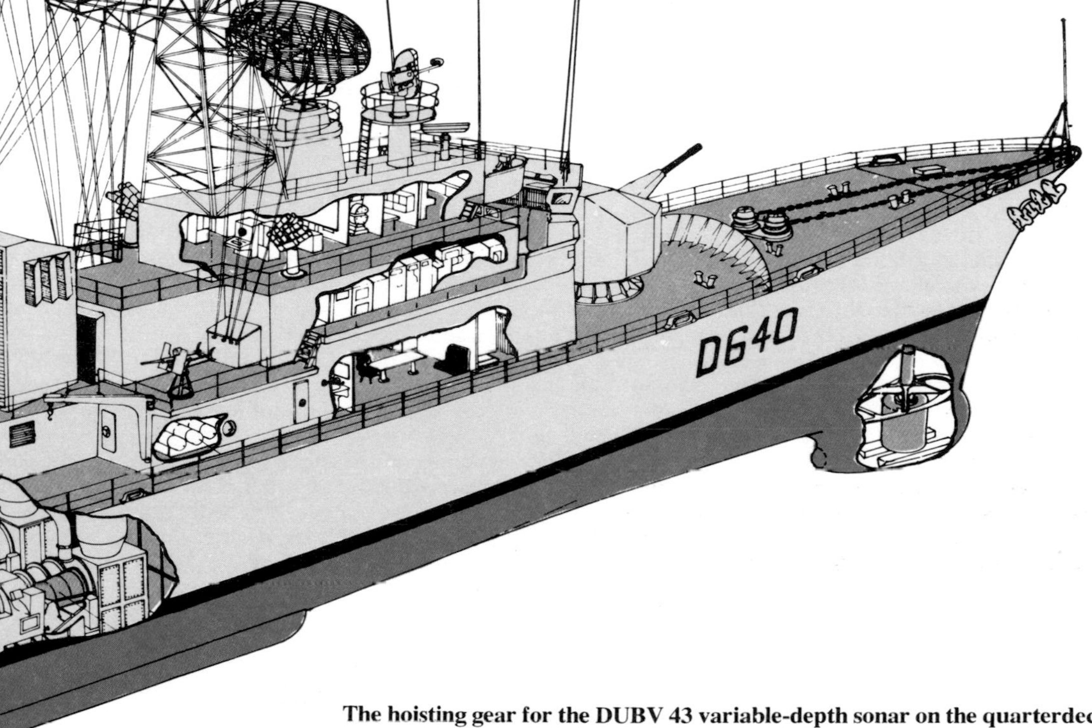

Gerard Callenburgh

Dutch destroyer class, built 1938-42. As with the preceding *van Ghent* Class, design was entrusted to the British firm of Yarrow, when a big expansion of the fleet was planned in the mid-30s. A total of 12 1600-ton destroyers was planned, basically similar to the earlier boats and to the British 'A to I' Classes, but considerably bigger to allow heavier armament and a seaplane to be carried.

The original appearance was broadly similar to British destroyers, with two funnels and two sets of quadruple torpedo tubes aft, but with the guns in twin shields forward and aft, a fifth single mounting aft and a seaplane stowed on a platform between the funnels. The AA armament comprised two Hazemeyer 1.57-in (40-mm) twin mountings, one in B position and one between the tubes. The seaplane was intended for reconnaissance in the East Indies, and was to be handled by two derricks on samson posts stepped on either side of the forefunnel.

Only the first four of the programme had been funded, *Gerard Callenburgh* and *Tjerk Hiddes* from Rotterdam dry dock and *Isaac Sweers* and *Philips van Almonde* from de

The hoisting gear for the DUBV 43 variable-depth sonar on the quarterdeck

D.C.A.N. Brest

Schelde yard, Flushing. *Isaac Sweers* was launched on March 16, 1940, followed by *Gerard Callenburgh* on May 9, 1940; the other two were still under construction when German forces overran the country in May.

Gerard Callenburgh was scuttled near Rotterdam on May 15, but her sister was towed from Flushing to England. *Tjerk Hiddes* was launched and scuttled, while her sister was blown up on the slipway.

Isaac Sweers was sent to the Woolston yard of John I Thornycroft and emerged considerably altered. The seaplane platform and derricks were not mounted, and three twin 4-in (102-mm) Mk XVI AA guns replaced the twin and single 4.7-in (120-mm) guns. A British-pattern high-angle director was mounted on the bridge wings. She was given a tripod mast to carry an air-warning radar aerial, and the director was fitted with Type 285 radar. Later the machine-guns were replaced by single 0.79-in (20-mm) guns. After a distinguished career in the Mediterranean, including the classic action which sank the cruisers *Alberico de Barbiano* and *Alberto di Giussano* off Cape Bon, she was torpedoed by *U 341* off Algiers on November 13, 1942.

Gerard Callenburgh, on the other hand, was salved in July 1940 and towed to Hamburg for completion as the German *ZH.1* in 1942. In her case the main armament was retained, but the secondary armament was replaced with two twin 1.46-in (37-mm) AA and four single 0.79-in (20-mm) guns. The funnels were fitted with distinctive German-style caps, giving her an entirely different appearance to *Isaac Sweers*. On June 9, 1944, she was sunk by gunfire and torpedoes from the British destroyers *Ashanti* and *Tartar* in a running fight in the English Channel.

The turbines for the incomplete sisters were earmarked by the German occupation forces for the *T.61* Class of torpedo boats ordered in Dutch shipyards, and further sets were ordered from the manufacturers. Four sets of machinery were recovered by the Dutch after the liberation of the Netherlands in July 1944, and were used to engine the postwar *Holland* Class.

See also *Holland*.

Displacement: 1992 tons (standard), 2228 tons (full load) *Length:* 106.30 m (348 ft 9 in) oa *Beam:* 10.30 m (33 ft 9 in) *Draught:* 3.5 m (11 ft 6 in) max *Machinery:* 2-shaft geared steam turbines, 45 000 shp=36 knots *Armament:* (Original) 5 4.7-in (120-mm) (3×2; 1×1); 4 1.57-in (40-mm) AA (2×2); 4 0.5-in (12.7-mm) AA machine-guns (4×1); 8 21-in (53-cm) torpedo tubes (2×4) *(Isaac Sweers)* 6 4-in (102-mm) AA (3×2); 4 1.57-in (40-mm) AA (2×2); 8 0.5-in (12.7-mm) AA machine-guns (2×4); 8 21-in (53-cm) torpedo tubes (*ZH.1*) 5 4.7-in (120-mm) (2×2, 1×1); 4 1.46-in (37-mm) AA (2×2); 4 0.79-in (20-mm) AA (4×1); 8 21-in (53-cm) torpedo tubes (2×4) *Aircraft:* 1 floatplane (as designed) *Crew:* 157 (*ZH.1*, 230)

Giuseppe Garibaldi

Italian guided-missile cruiser, converted 1957-61. In 1954 *Giuseppe Garibaldi*, the sister of *Luigi di Savoia Duca degli Abruzzi*, was disarmed at La Spezia while plans were drawn up for her conversion to Italy's first guided missile cruiser. She was stripped to the bare hull and rebuilt to a completely different design, the idea being to incorporate many new items of equipment in order to pave the way for a new generation of ships and weapon systems. In other words, she was a floating testbed for guns and equipment.

The first change was in machinery, for the original eight boilers were replaced by six delivering the same power. The 152-mm (6-in) guns were replaced by twin 135-mm (5.3-in)/45-cal guns but these were again replaced in 1968 by a 53-cal model of a new experimental type. These fired at a rate of 80 rds/min and had a range of 22 000 m (24 100 yards). The shell weighed 33.5 kg (73.85 lb) and had a muzzle velocity of 870 m/sec (2860 ft/sec). The secondary armament of OTO-Melara 76-mm (3-in)/62-cal guns fired a 6 kg (13.2 lb) shell to a range of 10 000 m (10 936 yards) and had a muzzle velocity of 950 m/sec (3120 ft/sec).

The missile battery at the after end of the superstructure comprised a Terrier RIM-2 twin-arm launcher and two Sperry AN/SPG-55 G/H-band guidance radars, and four vertical launching tubes for Polaris intermediate-range ballistic missiles. At the time NATO and the United States were discussing the possibility of a multinational nuclear deterrent force of surface ships, and the Italian navy took the lead in testing its feasibility. She launched dummy Terrier and Polaris missiles off La Spezia in late 1961 and early 1962, and her first live launching of Terrier was done on the missile range in the Caribbean on November 8, 1962. As far as is known she never fired a live Polaris and as the mixed-manning Polaris fleet was subsequently abandoned the launchers were never used again.

The radar outfit was comprehensive, with a big Selenia long-range air-warning radar on the mainmast, an American AN/SPS-39 Frescan medium-range 3-D radar on the foremast and an AN/SPS-6 below it.

The appearance of the ship was completely altered. She emerged from her four-year reconstruction in November 1961 with a big single funnel surmounted by a large cowl, new superstructure and two wide lattice masts. The two twin 135-mm (5.3-in) mountings were forward and the 76-mm (3-in) singles were abreast of the bridge and funnel. The Polaris launching tubes were housed in a low extension of the platform supporting the Terrier launcher and director towers aft. She was given the new NATO pendant number C.551.

After conclusion of her trials and workup in February 1963, she became the flagship of the commander-in-chief. During the second lease of life which followed she took part in many NATO exercises, culminating in 'Quick Draw' in November 1969. At one stage it was planned to modernize her and convert her to an Antisubmarine Warfare Command Ship, but the scheme was abandoned through lack of funds. After a career which spanned 33 years she was decommissioned in February 1971 and disarmed, and was later scrapped.

Displacement: 9802 tonnes (standard), 11 335 tonnes (full load) *Length:* 187 m (613 ft 6 in) oa *Beam:* 18.8 m (61 ft 8 in) *Draught:* 6.7 m (22 ft) *Protection:* 130 mm (5.1 in) sides; 60 mm (2.36 in) main deck; 140 mm (5.5 in) conning tower; 135 mm (5.31 in) turrets *Machinery:* 2-shaft geared steam turbines, 100 000 shp=30 knots *Armament:* 4 135-mm (5.3-in)/45-cal (2×2); 8 76-mm (3-in)/62-cal (8×1); 1 twin Terrier RIM-2 launcher (44 missiles); 4 Polaris IRBM launchers (experimental only) *Crew:* 665

Gladiolus

British corvette class, built between 1940 and 1944. These vessels, more commonly known as the 'Flower' Class corvettes, were among the most famous escort vessels of the Second World War. Their fame stemmed not from the excellence of their design—for they were of very simple construction—but from the fact that they formed a substantial part of the escort force which prevented the U-Boats from gaining victory during the early years of the battle of the Atlantic.

The class originated in 1938 when the Admiralty prepared an outline requirement for a small coastal escort vessel which could be constructed quickly in large numbers. The biggest problem was the shortage of capacity in those shipyards which specialized in warship construction. This was, however, solved by adopting a design based on mercantile practice, using shipyards not normally involved in warship production. In addition, reciprocating machinery and cylindrical boilers, which British firms could produce in large numbers, were to be employed in place of the more sophisticated turbines and water tube boilers normally fitted in warships. With these ideas in mind, the Admiralty approached Smiths Dock, an established merchant shipbuilder of Middlesbrough which had constructed similar vessels for the Royal Navy during the First World War. The subsequent discussions resulted in the selection of a Smiths Dock design for a whalecatcher (*Southern Pride*) as that upon which the new design was to be based.

The final design called for a 940-ton vessel with a maximum speed of 16 knots, an endurance of 6440 km (4000 miles) at 12 knots, armed with one 4-in (102-mm) gun forward, two twin 0.303-in (7.7-mm) Lewis guns and one 2-pdr pom-pom amidships, two depth-charge throwers and 25 depth charges. As with the rest of the design, this armament was very basic, reflecting the 'quantity in place of quality' requirement of the Admiralty. However, one sophisticated piece of equipment essential to an antisubmarine vessel was included—an Asdic set.

Orders were placed by the Admiralty for 56 'Flowers' under the estimates for 1931. Following the outbreak of war, further orders were placed at regular intervals until 1942. In all 300 corvettes were ordered (a few of which were cancelled), 164 in Britain, 130 in Canada and six in France. The six French vessels were ordered for the French navy which also placed orders for 16 in British yards. Only one, the British built *La Bastiase*, was completed for French service, but she was mined and sunk while running trials in June 1940. The remaining ships in British yards were taken over by the Admiralty after the fall of France. Of those under construction in France, four were completed for the Germans as PA1, PA2, PA3 and PA4. Two

HMS *Tamerisk*, a *Gladiolus* Class corvette, after modifications which included raising the bridge and platforms for the 4-in (102-mm) guns and the installation of radar. She was loaned to Greece during the war and named *Tompazis*

Royal Navy

Original name	new name	transferred	returned
To United States (Modified 'Flower' Class)			
Comfrey	*Action*	1942	retained
Cornel	*Alacrity*	1942	retained
Flax	*Brisk*	1942	retained
Mandrake	*Hasty*	1942	retained
Milfoil	*Intensity*	1942	retained
Musk	*Might*	1942	retained
Nepeta	*Pert*	1943	retained
Privet	*Prudent*	1943	retained
To Free French/France			
Aconite	*Aconit*	1941	1947
Alyssum	*Alysse*	1941	lost
Chrysanthemum	*Commandant Drogou*	1942	1947
Coriander	*Commandant Detroyat*	1941	1947
Lobelia	same	1941	1947
Lotus	*Commandante D'Estienne D'Orves*	1942	1947
Mimosa	same	1941	lost
Ranunculus	*Renoncule*	1941	1946
Sundew	*Roselys*	1942	1947
To Holland			
Carnation	*Frisio*	1943	1945
To Belgium			
Godetia	same	1943	1944

Original name	new name	transferred	returned
To United States ('Flower' Class)			
Arabis	*Saucy*	1942	1945
Veronica	*Temptress*	1942	1945
Begonia	*Impulse*	1942	1945
Calendula	*Ready*	1942	1945
Candytuft	*Tenacity*	1942	1945
Heliotrope	*Surprise*	1942	1945
Hibiscus	*Spry*	1942	1945
Larkspur	*Fury*	1942	1945
Heartsease	*Courage*	1942	1945
Periwinkle	*Restless*	1942	1945
To Greece			
Peony	*Sakhuouris*	1943	1951
Coreopsis	*Kriezis*	1943	1952
Hyacinth	*Aspostolis*	1943	1961
Tamarisk	*Tompazis*	1943	1952
To Norway			
Acanthus	*Andenes*	1941	1946
Buttercup	*Nordkyn*	1942	retained
Eglantine	*Soroy*	1941	retained
Montbretia	same	1941	lost
Potentilla	same	1942	1944
Rose	same	1941	lost
To Yugoslavia			
Mallow	*Nada*	1944	retained

Name	fate
La Bastiase	Mined off Hartlepool 6/1940
Snapdragon	Bombed by German aircraft in Mediterranean 9/1940
Godetia	Collision with merchantman off Ireland 9/1940
Picotee	Torpedoed by *U 568* off Iceland 8/1941
Zinnia	Torpedoed by *U 564* off Portugal 8/1941
Levis	Torpedoed by *U 74* off Greenland 9/1941
Fleur-de-Lys	Torpedoed by *U 206* off Gibraltar 10/1941
Gladiolus	Torpedoed by *U 558* in North Atlantic 10/1941
Windflower	Collision with merchantman off Newfoundland 12/1941
Salvia	Torpedoed by *U 568* in Mediterranean 12/1941
Arbutus	Torpedoed by *U 136* in North Atlantic 2/1942
Alysse	Torpedoed by *U 564* in North Atlantic 2/1942
Spikenard	Torpedoed by *U 136* in North Atlantic 2/1942
Hollyhock	Bombed by Japanese aircraft off Ceylon 4/1942
Auricula	Mined off Madagascar and sank on 5/1942
Mimosa	Torpedoed by *U 124* in North Atlantic 6/1942
Charlottetown	Torpedoed by *U 517* in Gulf of St Lawrence 9/1942
Gardenia	Collision with trawler off Oran 11/1942
Montbretia	Torpedoed by *U 624* in North Atlantic 11/1942
Marigold	Torpedoed by Italian aircraft off Algiers 12/1942
Snapdragon	Bombed by German aircraft in Mediterranean 12/1942
Samphire	Torpedoed by Italian submarine *Platino* off Bougie 1/1943
Louisburg	Torpedoed by Italian aircraft off Oran 2/1943
Erica	Mined off Benghazi 2/1943
Weyburn	Mined off Gibraltar 2/1943
Polyanthus	Torpedoed by *U 992* off Greenland 9/1943
Asphodel	Torpedoed by *U 575* off Spain 3/1944
Pink	Torpedoed by *U 988* off Normandy (constructive total loss) 6/1944
Regina	Torpedoed by *U 667* in English Channel 8/1944
Alberni	Torpedoed by *U 480* in English Channel 8/1944
Orchis	Torpedoed by *U 992* off Normandy (constructive total loss) 8/1944
Rose	Collision with merchantman in North Atlantic 10/1944
Shawinigan	Torpedoed by *U 1228* in Cabot Strait 11/1944
Bluebell	Torpedoed by *U 711* in Arctic 2/1945
Vervain	Torpedoed by *U 1208* south of Ireland 2/1945
Trentonian	Torpedoed by *U 1004* off Falmouth 2/1945

were cancelled.

The first of the class to complete was *Gladiolus*, in January 1940, while the last entered service in 1944. Initially, they were employed in their intended role of coastal escort, except for some fitted for minesweeping, but from mid-1940 they were used in increasing numbers for ocean escort duty because of the shortage of suitable vessels for this work.

Although they proved to be very seaworthy vessels, they were not suited to the deep Atlantic swell. They rolled excessively and the short forecastle which ended just before the bridge made them very wet amidships. In addition, they were very cramped and uncomfortable for the crew, the accommodation having been designed for short-range coastal work. The situation was worsened by wartime additions to the complement. To relieve this, it was decided to extend the forecastle to just abaft the funnel, which made the ships drier and provided additional crew space. The bilge keels were also deepened to reduce the roll. The first units to complete with this modification appeared in 1941, while the earlier units were altered when they came in for refit. During 1942-43, a further improvement was affected by providing increased sheer and flare to the forecastle. This also necessitated raising the 4-in (102-mm) gun platform to give the weapon a clear field of fire ahead. In turn, the wheelhouse and bridge had to be raised by one deck to allow a clear view over the gun. The alteration was made in all vessels still under construction, but not in all those completed.

Other important war modifications included increasing depth charge stowage to 40 and, from 1940, the number of depth charge throwers to four. Type 271 radar, the world's first microwave set, was fitted and this played a vital part in mastering the U-Boats. The radar office was accommodated at the rear of the bridge with the aerial on its roof. The first ship to carry this radar was the corvette *Orchis* in May 1941. Two 20-mm (0.79-in) (2× 1) AA guns were added in bridge wings and, later, two or four more 20-mm (0.79-in) abreast the after superstructure. Some vessels mounted a twin 20-mm (0.79-in) in place of the 2-pdr gun abaft the funnel and many others varied from the standard armament usually because of shortage of suitable weapons. During 1942-43 a Hedgehog A/S mortar was added in the forecastle.

In 1942, the design was recast to incorporate all the above modifications plus water tube boilers (which provided more power than the original cylindrical boilers), an increase in oil fuel stowage from 232 tons to 340 tons, which increased their endurance from 7242 to 11 265 km (4500 to 7000 miles) at 10 knots, and a slight increase in dimensions. The ships constructed to this design were known as the Modified 'Flower' Class, but there was very little difference between these and the original fully modified units.

All the vessels of the original 'Flower' Class constructed in Canada served in the Royal Canadian Navy. Many of the UK-built vessels were transferred to foreign navies—although in most cases they were still under Admiralty control—but the majority served in the RN. Of the Modified 'Flower' Class vessels constructed in

Royal Navy

HMS *Tenacity*. Her armament includes Hedgehog A/S mortars starboard of the 4-in gun

Canada, nine *(Burnett, Charlock, Dittany, Honesty, Linaria, Rosebay, Smilax, Statice* and *Willowherb)* joined the Royal Navy, eight were transferred to the US and the remainder joined the RCN. Of the modified vessels constructed in the UK, three *(Giffard, Mimico* and *Longbranch)* were transferred to the RCN and two *(Arabis* and *Arbutus)* to the Royal New Zealand Navy, while the rest joined the Royal Navy. Six of the original class and seven Modified 'Flowers' were cancelled.

The majority of the class served in the Atlantic, but they also operated in the Arctic, North Sea, Mediterranean and Far East. Thirty-five were lost during the war, but the class sank or helped to sink four Italian and 47 German submarines. After the war many were sold into merchant service and a few to other navies, while those that remain in British service: *Snowflake, Marguerite, Thyme* and *Genista*, were transferred to the RAF and converted to weather ships. They served in this role until the late 1950s.

'Flower' Class, UK-built: *Abelia*, Alisma*, Anchusa, Arabis, Armeria*, Aster*, Bergamot*, Bryony, Buttercup, Calendula, Camellia, Chrysanthemum, Clarkia, Cowslip, Eglantine, Erica, Freesia, Fritillary, Genista, Gentian, Gloxinia, Heather, Hibiscus, Hyacinth, Kingcup, Mallow, Orchis, Peony, Periwinkle, Picotee, Pimpernel, Rhododendron, Vervain, Heartsease* (built by Harland and Wolff, Belfast); *Acanthus, Aconite* (built by Ailsa, Troon); *Alyssum, Asphodel, Aubrietia, Auricula, Balsam, Bellwort, Borage* (built by G Brown, Greenock); *Amaranthus, Bluebell, Campanula, Clover, Jonquil, Larkspur, Monkshood, Montbretia, Tamarisk* (built by Fleming & Ferguson, Paisley); *Anemone, Arbutus* (built by Blyth, Blyth); *Azalea, Begonia* (built by Cook, Melton & Gemmell, Beverley); *Burdock, Campion, Godetia* (2nd) *Heliotrope, Hollyhock* (built by Crown, Sunderland); *Candytuft, Carnation, Celandine* (built by Grangemouth dockyard); *Clematis, Columbine, Convolvulus, Lotus, Meadowsweet, Mimosa, Rockrose, Saxifrage, Hyderabad* (built by C. Hill, Bristol); *Coltsfoot, Lavender, Lobelia, Poppy* (built by A Hall, Aberdeen); *Coreopsis, Crocus, Spiraea, Starwort, Oxlip, Pennywort* (built by A & Inglis, Pointhouse); *Cyclamen, Dahlia, Myosotis, Narcissus, Sundew, Dianella* (built by J Lewis, Aberdeen); *Delphinium, Dianthus, Petunia, Pink, Polyanthus, Lotus* (2nd) (built by H Robb, Leith); *Gardenia, Geranium, Potentilla, Primrose, Primula, Ranunculus, Rose, Salvia, Snapdragon, Violet, Woodruff* (built by W Simons, Renfrew); *Gladiolus, Godetia, Samphire, Snowdrop, Stonecrop, Sunflower, Sweetbriar, Thyme, Tulip, Verbena, Veronica, Vetch, Wallflower, Zinnia, Fleur-de-Lys*, La Malouine*, Snowflake, La Bastiaise** (built by Smiths Dock, Middlesbrough); *Honeysuckle, Hydrangea, Jasmine* (built by Ferguson, Port Glasgow); *Loosestrife, Marguerite, Marigold, Mignonette, Coriander* (built by Hall Russell, Aberdeen); *Nigella, Pentstemon* (built by Philip, Dartmouth). *=ordered for France originally.

'Flower' Class, Canadian-built: *Agassiz, Banff, Chilliwack, Trail* (built by Burrard, Vancouver); *Alberni, Edmundston, Nanaimo, Timmins, Vancouver* (built by Yarrow, Esquimalt); *Algoma, Cobalt, Kamsack, Kenogami, Morden, Oakville, Port Arthur, Rosthern, Weyburn* (built by Port Arthur); *Amherst, Sackville, Moncton* (built by St John); *Arrowhead, Bittersweet, Calgary, Camrose, Dunvegan, Fennel, Fredericton, Regina, Sherbrooke, Sorel* (built by Marine Industries, Sorel); *Arvida, Louisburg, Matapedia, Summerside, Ville de Quebec* (built by Morton, Quebec); *Baddeck, Brandon, Buctouche, Hepatica, Levis, Lunenburg, Pictou, Rimouski, Shawinigan, Shediac, Snowberry, Spikenard, Windflower, Kitchener* (built by Davie, Lauzon); *Barrie, Battleford, Collingwood, Drumheller, Galt, Halifax, Moosejaw, Orillia, The Pas, Woodstock* (built by Collingwood); *Brantford, Midland* (built by Midland); *Chambly, Chicoutimi, Dauphin, Eyebright, Lethbridge, Mayflower, Saskatoon, Trillium* (built by Canadian Vickers, Montreal); *Charlottetown, Napanee, Prescott, Sudbury, La Malbaie* (built by Kingston); *Dawson, Dundas, Kamloops, New Westminster, Quesnell* (built by Victoria).

Modified 'Flower' Class, UK-built: *Arabis* (2nd) *Arbutus* (2nd) (built by G Brown, Greenock); *Betony, Giffard* (built by A Hall, Aberdeen); *Bugloss, Mimico* (built by Crown, Sunderland); *Longbranch* (built by A & Inglis, Pointhouse).

Modified 'Flower' Class, Canadian-built: *Burnet, Charlock, Forest Hill* (built by Ferguson, Port Glasgow); *Ashestos, Atholl, Beauharnois, Hawkesbury, Lachute, Louisburg, Mandrake, Milfoil, Musk, Nepta, Norsyd, Privet, Riviere de Loup, St Lambert, Stellarton, Merrottonia* (built by Morton, Quebec); *Belleville, Flax, Frontenac, Honesty, Peterborough, Rosebay, Smiths Falls, Trentonian* (built by Kingston); *Coburg, Linaria, Lindsay, Parry Sound, Strathroy, Thorlock, West York, Whitby, Willowherb* (built by Midland); *Comfrey, Cornel, Dittany, Fergis, North Bay, Owen Sound, Guelph, Smilax, Statice* (built by Collingwood).

('Flower' Class) *Displacement:* 940 tons (standard), 1170 tons (full load) *Length:* 62.48 m (205 ft) *Beam:* 10.06 m (33 ft) *Draught:* 3.12 m (10 ft 3 in) *Machinery:* 1-shaft, 4-cylinder triple expansion engine, 2750 ihp=16 knots *Armament:* 1 4-in (102-mm); 1 2-pdr; 4 0.303-in (7.7-mm) MG (2×2); 2 depth charge throwers; 2 chutes; 25 depth charges *Crew:* 47

(Modified 'Flower' Class) *Displacement:* 980 tons (standard), 1350 tons (full load) *Length:* 63.47 m (208 ft 3 in) *Beam:* 10.13 m (33 ft 3 in) *Draught:* 3.35 m (11 ft) *Machinery:* as before except 2880 ihp=16 knots *Armament:* 1 4-in (102-mm); 8 20-mm (0.79-in) (6×1, 1×2); 1 Hedgehog; 4 depth charge throwers; 2 chutes; 40 depth charges *Crew:* 109

Glenard P Lipscomb

US nuclear submarine, launched 1973. Design studies on a silent running submarine began in October 1964. Approval for the construction was revoked on at least one occasion in an effort to combine extra features into the design. Final approval was given in October 1968, and the submarine was eventually ordered in October 1970, six years after work on the project had begun.

The project was designed to evaluate various items of equipment and machinery under operational conditions with a view to countering advanced ASW (antisubmarine warfare) techniques then being developed in the West, by reducing the noise level as much as possible. Noise created by a submarine, both from its movement through the water and from its machinery, is one of the most important factors in submarine detection. In particular the sounds made by the propulsion transmission system, known as a submarine's signature, are very distinctive and can identify a submarine type clearly.

Glenard P Lipscomb was designed as a test

The Soviet *Golf* Class ballistic missile submarines house their missiles in the extended conning tower. Since 1977 they have been deployed in the Baltic with missiles targeted for European military and industrial centres

platform for 'silent' machinery and a turbine electric drive system was installed as a far quieter piece of machinery than the normal steam turbine powerplant. The disadvantage of the turbo-electric drive is that it is far larger and heavier than a conventional steam turbine powerplant. With nuclear submarines having more or less reached an optimum size as regards combat efficiency and countering ASW techniques, the size of the turbo-electric system does not seem to make it a really practical proposition. Being an experimental submarine, *Glenard P Lipscomb* did not require a high underwater speed and she is somewhat slower than other nuclear submarines.

It was decided not to build a large class of submarines based on this design, but rather to design a new class incorporating the best features and most effective 'silent' equipment tested in *Glenard P Lipscomb. Glenard P Lipscomb* was built by the Electric Boat division of General Dynamics and laid down on June 5, 1971, launched on August 4, 1973, and completed on December 21, 1974.

Displacement: 5813 tons (standard), 6480 tons (submerged) *Length:* 111.25 m (365 ft) oa *Beam:* 9.7 m (31 ft 10 in) *Machinery:* 1-shaft, 1 pressurized water-cooled nuclear reactor, turbo-electric drive, 25+ knots *Armament:* 4 21-in (53-cm) amidships torpedo tubes, Asroc and A/S torpedoes *Crew:* 120

Golf

Soviet ballistic missile submarine class. Twenty-two conventionally-powered *Golf* Class ballistic missile submarines were built by the Soviet Union at Komsomolsk and Severodvinsk between 1958-61. They were intended to supplement the nuclear-powered *Hotel* Class which were being built at the same time and which were also armed with three tubes for the SSN-4 Sark SLBM. Although this missile is larger than the American Polaris SLBM (surface launched ballistic missile) it only has a range of about 300 nautical miles, and cannot be launched submerged. As with the *Hotel*s the missiles are housed not in the hull but in a casing integral with and behind the fin (sail or streamlined conning tower).

The very short range of the missile, combined with the need to surface to fire it, and the enormous size of the fin made these *Golf Is* very vulnerable to counterattack on the surface, whilst the noisiness of this generation of Soviet submarines made them relatively easy to find submerged. A longer-ranged SLBM, the SSN-5 'Serb', was therefore developed, and although this only has a range of about 700 nautical miles, this at least gives the submarines a slightly greater chance of surviving until they have fired their missiles. After the *Hotel*s had finished refitting with Serb SLBMs in 1967, 13 *Golf Is* were fitted with them. These have been redesignated *Golf IIs*. One of these sank in the Pacific in 1968 and was raised by the Hughes Corporation for the US government in the early 1970s.

These submarines have a range of over 35 400 km (22 000 miles) on the surface, and in the 1960s and 1970s were mainly deployed in the Atlantic, Pacific and the Caribbean. Since 1977 most of the surviving members of the class have been redeployed in the Baltic, where their missiles directly threaten the European NATO nations. Because of the short range of their missiles, these submarines are not counted in the SALT agreements.

One *Golf* Class submarine was built at Darien in China in 1964. It was built with missile tubes, but no missiles seem to have been supplied by the Soviet Union, nor has China yet developed her own SLBM.

Displacement: 2350/2800 tons (surfaced/submerged) *Length:* 90 m (295 ft 3 in) *Beam:* 8.2 m (27 ft) *Draught:* 4.8 m (15 ft 9 in) *Machinery:* 3-shaft diesel/electric motors, 6000 bhp=17.6/17 knots (surfaced/submerged) *Armament:* 3 SSN-5 Serb SLBM; 10 53-cm (21-in) torpedo tubes (6 bow, 4 stern) *Crew:* 86

Grayback

Class of US submarines built 1954-58, the first American submarines to be specifically built with a guided missile capability, previous submarines being conversions. *Grayback,* funded in the 1953 fiscal programme, was originally ordered on June 19, 1952, as an attack submarine. After construction had begun, however, it was announced (on February 27, 1956) that the requirement was altered, and the design was recast so that *Grayback* could operate the 1600-km (1000-mile) range Regulus I missile. The original plan provided for *Grayback* and her sister *Growler* to operate the Regulus II missile, but the missile was cancelled for economic reasons and only the Regulus I fitted. To provide the missile capability the submarines were cut in half on the slipway and a 15.2-m (50-ft) section built in amidships.

The basic hull configuration was similar,

Name and no	laid down	launched	completed
Grayback (SSG.574)	1/7/54	2/7/57	31/7/58
Growler (SSG.577)	15/2/55	5/4/58	15/12/58

The Brazilian *Rio Grande do Sul,* formerly USS *Grampus,* followed GUPPY conversion

Brazilian Navy

but much improved, to that of the previous *Darter* (an improved *Tang* Class high-speed attack submarine), and streamlined for high underwater speed with the now familiar sail (conning tower) housing the snorkel and periscopes.

Unlike earlier submarines converted with missile hangars on top of the deck casing, *Grayback* and *Growler* have the twin cylindrical hangars faired into the upper hull forward of the sail. The hangars are 21.3 m (70 ft) long and 3.4 m (11 ft) high. Between the hangars and the sail is the missile-launching platform. The missiles can only be launched when the submarine is surfaced, and loading the missile onto the launcher and firing takes only a short time. These submarines also have the ability to make very rapid crash dives after firing. The missile is now no longer in service, having been withdrawn in 1964 when the two submarines were put in reserve. *Grayback* was subsequently converted in 1967 to an underwater amphibious transport carrying 67 troops in addition to her crew, while *Growler* although initially due to undergo a similar conversion, which was deferred in 1968 due to rising conversion costs, has remained in reserve. The conversion involved increasing the length by 3.7 m (12 ft) to provide extra accommodation for the troops and their gear and two of the bow torpedo tubes were removed.

The submarines are powered by conventional diesel-electric propulsion system of improved design with high capacity batteries which gave the vessels, at that time, the relatively high underwater speed of 18 knots.

In addition to the missile capacity the two submarines are also equipped with extensive ASW equipment.

Grayback was built at Mare Island navy yard and *Growler* at Portsmouth navy yard.

Displacement: 2287 tons (surfaced) (*Growler* 2174 tons), 3638 tons (submerged) (*Growler* 3387 tons) *Length:* 98.3 m (322 ft 6 in) oa (*Growler* 96.8 m [317 ft 7 in]) (*Grayback* 101.8 m [334 ft] oa as a transport) *Beam:* 9 m (29 ft 6 in) (*Growler* 8.2 m [26 ft 11 in]) *Draught:* 5.2 m (17 ft) *Machinery:* 2-shaft diesels (3 engines), 4500 shp=20 knots, 2 electric motors, 5600 hp=18 knots *Armament:* 2 Regulus missiles; 8 21-in (53-cm) (6 bow, 2 stern) torpedo tubes *Crew:* 8 (*Growler* 96)

GUPPY

Acronym for Greater Underwater Propulsive Power programme to modernize US Navy submarines after the Second World War. The lessons of the war, particularly from examination of the German Type XXI and other advanced designs showed that the standard US Navy submarines, which had been designed for surface operations in the Pacific, would be quite outclassed in underwater performance.

The basic GUPPY conversion involved cutting the boat in two and inserting an extra section to give much greater battery capacity for high underwater speed. At the same time the conning tower with its AA platforms was replaced by a streamlined slender 'sail' or fin, which enclosed the snorkel- and radar-masts. The bow and stern were remodelled to give higher underwater speed and greater manoeuvrability.

10 GUPPY 1 Conversions (1951)

Name	no	fate
Becuna	(SS.319)	Stricken 1973
Blackfin	(SS.322)	Stricken 1972
Calman	(SS.323)	To Turkey June 1972 as *Dumlupinar*
Blenny	(SS.324)	Stricken 1973 (sunk as target)
Chivo	(SS.341)	To Argentina July 1971 as *Santiago del Estero*
Chopper	(SS.342)	Stricken 1971
Atule	(SS.403)	To Peru July 1974 as *Pacocha*
Sea Poacher	(SS.406)	To Peru July 1974 as *La Pedrera*
Sea Robin	(SS.407)	Stricken 1970
Tench	(SS.417)	Stricken 1973

15 GUPPY II Conversions (1948-50)

Name	no	fate
Catfish	(SS.339)	To Argentina July 1971 as *Santa Fe*
Cochino	(SS.345)	Lost by fire August 26, 1949
Cubera	(SS.347)	To Venezuela January 1972 as *Tiburon*
Diodon	(SS.349)	Stricken 1971
Dogfish	(SS.350)	To Brazil July 1972 as *Guanabara*
Halfbeak	(SS.352)	Stricken 1971
Tusk	(SS.426)	To Taiwan October 1973 as *Hai Po*
Cutlass	(SS.478)	To Taiwan April 1973 as *Hai Shih*
Sea Leopard	(SS.483)	To Brazil March 1973 as *Babia*
*Odax**	(SS.484)	To Brazil July 1972 as *Rio de Janeiro*
Sirago	(SS.485)	Stricken 1972
*Pomodon**	(SS.486)	Stricken 1970
Amberjack	(SS.522)	To Brazil May 1972 as *Ceara*
Grampus	(SS.523)	To Brazil May 1972 as *Rio Grande do Sul*
Grenadier	(SS.525)	To Venezuela May 1973 as *Picuda*

*Originally GUPPY Is, updated to GUPPY IIs.

16 GUPPY IIA Conversions (1952-54)

Name	no	fate
Entemedor	(SS.340)	To Turkey July 1972 as *Preveze*
Hardhead	(SS.365)	To Greece July 1972 as *Papanikolis*
Jallao	(SS.368)	Stricken June 1974
Menhaden	(SS.377)	Stricken August 1973

Only the welded-hull *Balao* and *Tench* Classes were chosen for the conversion.

There were many minor differences between the different groups, and when the more efficient 126-cell batteries were retrofitted the GUPPY Is became IAs. On February 11, 1969, *Chopper* accidentally dived to 305 m (1000 ft) in the Caribbean (her safe diving depth is 126 m [412 ft]). She recovered from the dive but on her return to Key West she was decommissioned.

See also *Gato, Tench.*

(GUPPY IA and IIA) *Displacement:* 1840-1870/2400-2420 tons (surfaced/submerged) *Length:* (GUPPY IA and IIA) 93.88 m (308 ft) oa (GUPPY III) 99.52 m (326 ft 6 in) oa *Beam:* 8.3 m (27 ft 3 in) *Draught:* 5.03 to 5.49 m (16 ft 6 in to 18 ft) *Machinery:* 2-shaft diesel/electric, 4800 bhp/5400 shp= 18-20/15 knots (surfaced/submerged) *Armament:* 10 21-in (53-cm) torpedo tubes (6 forward, 4 aft) *Crew:* 82-86

Gymnote

French submarine, built 1958-66. In 1958 the keel was laid at Cherbourg arsenal of hull No Q.244, France's first nuclear submarine, but the order was cancelled a year later on grounds of cost. Five years later work started again to a different design, a conventionally driven test-bed for the Mer-Sol-Ballistique-Strategique (MSBS), France's version of the Polaris submarine-launched ballistic missile.

Gymnote is large for a conventional submersible, and has two launching tubes for MSBS missiles abaft the fin (modified conning tower) in a large, wide platform built on the casing. Originally she tested the M-1 missile in 1967, then the M-2, and in 1977 she began a refit to alter her launching tubes for the larger M-4 missile. She also tests equipment and weapons for the *Redoutable* Class missile submarines.

See *Le Redoutable.*

Displacement: 3000/3250 tonnes (surfaced/submerged) *Length:* 84 m (275 ft 7 in) oa *Beam:* 10.6 m (34 ft 9 in) *Draught:* 7.6 m (24 ft 11 in) *Machinery:* 2-shaft diesel-electric, 2600 bhp= 11/10 knots (surfaced/submerged) *Armament:* 4 launching tubes for IRBMS (experimental only) *Crew:* 78

Ha 53

Japanese midget submarine. By the spring of 1942 it was becoming apparent that the *Ha 1* Class midget submarines were obsolete. In addition a number had been lost, including those used in the attack on Pearl Harbor on December 7, 1941, and it was possible that they had fallen intact into the hands of the Americans (as in fact they had). As a result a new, improved design was prepared, the major requirement being a dual propulsion system to overcome the limitations forced on the *Ha 1* Class by the electric motor.

Known as the Type B, a new experimental submarine, *Ha 53,* was built to the new design embodying various refinements found necessary in the light of operational experience with the Type A. The most important feature was the fitting of a diesel motor for surface propulsion and which was also used for recharging the batteries. The disadvantage of the 40 Kw diesel generator was that it took 18 hours to charge the batteries.

Displacement: 50 tons (submerged) *Length:* 24.92 m (81 ft 9 in) *Beam:* 2.59 m (8 ft 6 in) *Draught:* 0.76 m (2 ft 6 in) *Machinery:* 1-shaft diesel/electric motor, 40 bhp/600 hp=6.5/18.5 knots (surfaced/submerged) *Armament:* 2 46-cm (18-in) torpedoes *Crew:* 3

Ha 62

Japanese midget submarine class, completed 1942-44. It was immediately apparent that the Type B midget submarine, *Ha 53,* was a far superior design to the Type A. With the urgent need for large numbers of midget submarines for use in defending the numerous small Japanese-held islands in the southwest Pacific it was decided to put the Type B into quantity production with the minimum of alterations to the design. Known as the Type C a total of 15 midget submarines were completed to the new design between 1942-44 before it was superseded by another design. Bunkerage was increased in the Type C to give them a surfaced radius of action of 350 nautical miles at 6 knots compared to the 300 miles at 6 knots of the *Ha 53*: submerged, the vessels had a radius of action of 120 nautical miles at 4 knots. In addition the time taken to charge the batteries was reduced. Among the other design refinements of the Type C were attachments permitting them to be transported and launched from No 1 Class transports. The Type C replaced the Type A midgets which were relegated to training.

Displacement: 50 tons (submerged) *Length:* 24.92 m (81 ft 9 in) *Beam:* 2.59 m (8 ft 6 in) *Draught:* 0.76 m (2 ft 6 in) *Machinery:* 1 diesel motor/1 electric motor, 40 hp/600 hp=6.5/18.5 knots (surfaced/submerged) *Armament:* 2 46-cm (18-in) torpedoes *Crew:* 3

Ha 101

Japanese transport submarine class, built between 1944-45. Finding that the large submarines being used as transports to break the American naval blockade of their numerous island bases were unsatisfactory, the Japanese developed a small specifically designed

Picuda	(SS.382)	To Spain October 1972 as *Narciso Monturiol*
Bang	(SS.385)	To Spain October 1972 as *Cosme Garcia*
Pomfret	(SS.391)	To Turkey July 1971 as *Oruc Reis*
Razorback	(SS.394)	To Turkey November 1970 as *Murat Reis*
Ronquil	(SS.396)	To Spain July 1971 as *Isaac Peral*
Sea Fox	(SS.402)	To Turkey December 1970 as *Burak Reis*
Threadfin	(SS.410)	To Turkey August 1972 as *Birinci Inonü*
Stickleback	(SS.415)	Renamed—sunk May 29, 1958, by USS *Silverstein*
Thornback	(SS.418)	To Turkey July 1971 as *Uluc Ali Reis*
Tirante	(SS.420)	Stricken October 1973
Trutta	(SS.421)	To Turkey July 1972 as *Cerbe*
Quillback	(SS.424)	Stricken March 1973

9 GUPPY III Conversions (1960-62)

Name	no	fate
Clamagore	(SS.343)	Stricken 1975
Cobbler	(SS.344)	To Turkey November 1973
Corporal	(SS.346)	To Turkey November 1973
Greenfish	(SS.351)	To Brazil November 1973 as *Amazones*
Tiru	(SS.416)	Stricken 1975
Trumpetfish	(SS.425)	To Brazil October 1973 as *Goias*
Remora	(SS.487)	To Greece October 1973 as *Katsonis*
Volador	(SS.490)	To Italy August 1972 as *Gianfranco Gazzana Priaroggia*
Pickerel	(SS.524)	To Italy August 1972 as *Primo Longobardo*

Gymnote, an experimental French submarine used to test submarine-launched missiles

transport submarine. The design was prepared for rapid mass production techniques, being fully welded, and fittings and equipment were kept to the barest minimum essential for the operation of the craft. The submarines were built in sections and assembled on the slipways, construction taking about five to six months.

Displacement was deliberately kept low for by the time the vessels were laid down any hope of maintaining the outer defence circle of islands had been abandoned and therefore the submarines would operate from Japan. A large radius of action for overseas operation was not essential and the endurance was only 15 days. The surface radius at 10 knots was 3000 nautical miles and while submerged the vessels could steam for 46 nautical miles at 2.5 knots. Being transport submarines, machinery requirements were of a low order and speed was not considered of importance as the boats carried no defensive or offensive armament. Contact with the enemy was to be avoided. To help foil enemy radar, the conning towers were coated with a substance to reduce the echoes. A total of 100 submarines were planned, but only 12 were laid down of which ten were completed.

Displacement: 429 tons/493 tons (surfaced/submerged) *Length:* 44.50 m (146 ft) oa *Beam:* 6.09 m (20 ft) *Draught:* 4.04 m (13 ft 3 in) *Machinery:* 1-shaft diesel motor/1 electric motor, 400 hp/150 hp=10/5 knots (surfaced/submerged) *Armament:* 1 machine-gun *Cargo:* 60 tons *Crew:* 21

Ha 201

Japanese submarine class. The *Ha 201* Class was one of the largest ever to be ordered, comprising some 89 units. They were small high underwater speed craft developed for the defence of Japan. The design was evolved from trials conducted with the experimental submarine *No 71* and were comparable to the German Type XXIII submarines.

The hull and conning tower were very streamlined and of all welded construction specifically designed for mass production. The craft were planned to be completed at the rate of 13 a month. Being small boats of a fairly basic design with conventional machinery it was a fairly simple task to prefabricate sections in workshops and weld them together on the stocks. Endurance was 15 days and the submerged radius of action was 100 nautical miles at 2 knots with a designed surface radius of action of 3000 nautical miles at 10 knots. In practice, however, the surfaced radius of action was exceeded by some units, *Ha 201* achieving a radius of 5000 nautical miles at a surfaced speed of ten knots. The maximum safe diving depth was 76 m (250 ft).

The boats proved to be extremely manoeuvrable submerged with a maximum speed of 13 knots and from experience gained with the ten vessels completed it was undoubtedly a successful design, although limited by the conventional machinery. Completed units were equipped with Type 22 air warning radar and a primitive form of snorkel.

Displacement: 429 tons/493 tons (surfaced/submerged) *Length:* 52.96 m (173 ft 9 in) oa *Beam:* 3.96 m (13 ft) *Draught:* 3.43 m (11 ft 3 in) *Machinery:* 1-shaft diesel/1 electric motor, 400 bhp/1250 hp=10.5/13 knots (surfaced/submerged) *Armament:* 1 machine-gun, 2 bow 53-cm (21-in) torpedo tubes, 2 torpedoes *Crew:* 22

Hai Dau

Chinese fast patrol boat class. A new class of gas turbine-powered missile-armed craft has been seen in Chinese waters. The hull is conventional, apparently a round bilge-form, built of steel, with a prominent 'knuckle' forward to deflect spray. Three gas turbine exhausts can be seen in the transom stern, and the air-intake is on the rear of a 6-m (20-ft) 'mack' or combined mast and funnel.

The armament is six surface-to-surface missiles in individual weathertight containers, fixed at an angle of 20° elevation. These containers are not like those for the Soviet-designed SS-N-2 'Styx', and are about 6 m (20 ft) long and 1 m (3 ft 3 in) square. There are also two twin gun-mountings of new design, and the likeliest size is a 57-mm (2.24-in)/60-cal weapon; on either side of the turret is a ventilator similar to that on the T34/85 tank-turret.

The fire control is in a distinctive 2.4-m (7 ft 10½-in) radome, and it is probably a tri-axially stabilized track-while-scan (TWS) radar system, backed up by an optical range-finder. There is also a navigation radar aerial on the horizontal wing over the 'mack', two ECM 'pots' and an aerial for what may be an IFF/SID set. The bridge is spacious, and may house a small Combat Information Centre (CIC).

The colour scheme is dark blue overall, with the name-character painted in white on the bow.

(Estimated data) *Displacement:* 260-300 tons *Length:* 47.5 m (155 ft 10 in) oa *Beam:* 7.2 m (23 ft 7½ in) *Draught:* 1.88 m (6 ft 2 in) *Machinery:* 3-shaft gas turbine, 40 knots *Armament:* 6 SSMs (type unknown) (6×1); 4 57-mm (2.24-in)/60-cal (2×2) *Crew:* 3-40

Hajen

Swedish submarine class, built 1952-60. The Royal Swedish Navy ordered six submarines to take advantage of the new ideas generated after the end of the Second World War: five from Kochums of Malmö and one from the dockyard at Karlskrona. They were *Hajen*, *Sälen* (seal), *Valen* (whale), *Bävern* (beaver), *Illern* (polecat) and *Uttern* (otter). From their own resources, and with technical advice from the British and Americans, all the latest ideas were incorporated by the Swedish designers, such as the snorkel, streamlining and fast underwater running.

Like all Swedish submarines they carried recognition letters on the fin: Bä=*Bävern*, Ha=*Hajen*, In=*Illern*, Sä=*Sälen*, Ut=*Uttern* and Va=*Valen*. Later these were changed to Bav, Haj, Iln, Sal, Utn and Val. Torpedoes are the FFV TP 61 type, with wire-guidance.

The propulsion is diesel-electric, with two electric motors driven by SEMT-Pielstick diesels on the surface, or by batteries when submerged. These submarines are now rather elderly and will probably be replaced by the new *Näcken* Class.

Displacement: 785/1000 tons (surfaced/submerged) *Length:* 66 m (216 ft 6 in) pp *Beam:* 5.1 m (16 ft 9 in) *Draught:* 5 m (16 ft 5 in) *Machinery:* 2-shaft diesel-electric, 1660 bhp=16/17 knots (surfaced/submerged) *Armament:* 4 53.3-cm (21-in) torpedo tubes (bow, 8 torpedoes) *Crew:* 4

Halland

Swedish destroyer class, built 1951-56. In 1948 work began on a new class of large destroyer to incorporate the lessons of the Second World War. Two were laid down, *Halland* and *Småland*, and were launched in July and October 1952. Two more, *Lappland* and *Varmland*, were ordered subsequently, but in 1958, as a result of a stringent cutback in defence spending, they were cancelled.

The ships were the first Swedish destroyers with a raised forecastle, and had an armament of dual-purpose 120-mm (4.7-in) and 57-mm (2.24-in) guns, torpedoes and antisubmarine rocket-launchers. Shortly after completion both ships had the after bank of tubes replaced by a single launcher for the Rb.08A surface-to-surface missile. As the missile is reported to have become operational only in 1967 the ships were presumably not equipped with actual missiles until that date.

As built the two ships had a pole foremast and a short stump mainmast, but in 1962 both were modernized with a big Dutch air-warning radar on a short lattice tower aft, a French Saturn fire-control director on the bridge and a prominent surveillance radar at the masthead. The close-range armament, six single 40-mm (1.57-in) Bofors AA guns on the broadside, remained unaltered.

In 1954 the Colombian navy ordered two vessels of this class from Gotaverken and Kockums. *Siete de Agosto* (ex-*Trece de Junio*) and *Viente de Julio* were built in 1955-58.

Instead of the mixed armament of the Swedish pair, the Colombians have three twin 120-mm (4.7-in) gun-mountings, only one 375-mm (14.76-in) rocket-launcher forward, one set of torpedo tubes, four 40-mm (1.57-in) guns and different internal arrangements. They were given the Dutch air-warning radar and French surveillance radar from the outset, and had air-conditioning.

According to an official statement the highest sustained speed is now only 25 knots. *Siete de Agosto* had an extensive machinery

PPL

The Swedish destroyer *Halland* armed with two Bofors AA weapons and an A/S rocket launcher

overhaul in the US in 1975 and it is possible that her sister may be scrapped soon.

This class introduced three important Bofors weapons. The 120-mm (4.7-in)/50-cal twin mounting was introduced in 1950, and is fully automatic, radar-controlled and water-cooled. The mounting weighs 67 tons and can fire 40 rds/min per barrel. The shell weighs 23.5 kg (51 lb 13 oz) and can reach an altitude of 12 500 m (41 000 ft). In the same year the 57-mm (2.24-in)/60-cal antiaircraft twin mounting was announced. It weighs about 24 tons and can fire 130 rds/min from each barrel. The shell weighs 2.6 kg (5 lb 12 oz) and can reach a maximum altitude of 9000 m (29 530 ft). The 120-mm (4.7-in) guns are in service with the Netherlands navy and the 57-mm (2.24-in) mounting was adapted by the French for their destroyers and the cruisers *de Grasse* and *Colbert*.

The 375-mm (14.76-in) antisubmarine rocket-launcher was developed in the early 1950s, and is widely used by a number of navies. It fires a variety of rockets fuzed to burst at a preset depth, like a depth-charge. In its original form the M/50 rocket had a range of 300-830 m (984-2723 ft), but subsequent developments have doubled and quadrupled these figures.

Displacement: 2800 tons (standard), 3400 tons (full load) *Length:* 121 m (397 ft) oa *Beam:* 12.6 m (41 ft 4 in) *Draught:* 4.5 m (14 ft 9 in) *Machinery:* 2-shaft geared steam turbines, 58 000 shp=35 knots *Armament:* (Swedish ships) 4 120-mm (4.7-in)/50-cal DP (2×2); 2 57-mm (2.24-in)/60-cal AA (1×2); 6 40-mm (1.57-in)/70-cal AA (6×1); 8 53.3-cm (21-in) torpedo tubes (2×4); 2 375-mm (14.76-in) quadruple rocket-launchers (Colombian ships) 6 120-mm (4.7-in)/50-cal DP (3×2); 4 40-mm (1.57-in)/70-cal AA (4×1); 1 375-mm (14.76-in) quadruple rocket-launcher; 4 53.3-cm (21-in) torpedo tubes (1×4) *Crew:* 210/260

Hamburg

German destroyer class, built 1964-68, the first to be designed by Germany for the navy since the end of the Second World War. It had originally been hoped to order 12 of these

Hamburg, a West German destroyer, one of four ships commissioned between 1964-68. The *Hamburg* Class were the first destroyers designed and built by Germany after the Second World War. Modernization started in 1975, replacing the Bofors guns with Bredas and the 100-mm (3.9-in) with MM.38 Exocet missiles; in addition two extra 30.5-cm (12-in) A/S torpedo tubes have been installed. Gunnery, navigation and early warning radar is by Hollandse Signaalapparaten

destroyers, but as the need for so many large vessels was questioned, the Bundestag (parliament) in the end only granted funds for the construction of four destroyers.

The design was based on the conception of a multirole vessel, and the ships were to be equipped with a wide variety of weapons including A/S (antisubmarine), AA, light guns and minelaying facilities. Although the design was indigenous, the equipment was selected from a variety of foreign manufacturers. Thus the main gun armament was of French make and although a light weapon it was the only single mount available at the time. It was, however, capable of delivering 70 rds/min. The A/S rocket system was supplied by Bofors and the radar from the Dutch firm of Hollandse Signaalapparaten.

PPL

***Schleswig-Holstein*, a *Hamburg* Class destroyer, one of the most powerful in the German navy**

The design was highly complex and at the time German shipyards felt unequal to the task of embarking on the construction of such large warships. After 17 months of debate the firm of H C Stülcken Sohn at Hamburg finally agreed to construct the vessels. The vessels were ordered during the late 1950s for completion in 1960-61: *Hamburg*, *Schleswig-Holstein*, *Bayern* and *Hessen*. Completion, however, was further delayed while new technical improvements were incorporated into the design. The ships finally entered service between 1964-68 and at that time were the largest and most powerful vessels in the new German navy.

Plans were made in the design to replace the two after 100-mm (3.9-in) mounts with surface-to-air missiles, but when the vessels were ordered, in 1957, it was too early to reach a decision on this aspect. However, the technical department did suggest that a naval version of the Hawk missile might be fitted, but nothing came of the idea.

By the early 1970s the ships no longer met modern requirements and plans were put in hand to convert and modernize them between 1975-77. Certain items of equipment were to be renewed but the major alteration concerned the replacement of the after guns with four French Exocet missile launchers. In addition the 40-mm (1.57-in) guns were to be replaced by a Breda AA gun and two extra A/S torpedo tubes added. Work on converting *Hessen* started in 1975 and all four had been modernized by the end of 1978, the work being carried out by Blohm & Voss of Hamburg.

Displacement: 3400 tons (standard), 4400 tons (full load) *Length:* 134 m (439 ft 7½ in) oa *Beam:* 13.4 m (43 ft 11½ in) *Draught:* 5.2 m (17 ft) *Machinery:* 2-shaft geared turbines, 68 000 shp=35.5 knots *Armament:* 4 100-mm (3.9-in) (4×1), 8 40-mm (1.57-in) (4×2), 8 Bofors A/S rocket launchers (2×4), 4 30.5-cm (12-in) A/S torpedo tubes *Crew:* 280

***Hessen* in dry dock with a second destroyer of the same class, possibly the *Hamburg*, during conversion work at the Blohm & Voss yards**

Blohm & Voss

C&S Taylor

Bayern in 1969. Her four-barrelled Bofors A/S launchers can be seen in front of the bridge

Le Hardi

French destroyer class, built 1936-41. (Also known as the '1772-tonne' type.) In 1932 the French navy decided that future fleet destroyers must have a speed of 37 knots to give them an adequate margin over the new 30-knot capital ships under construction. It took two more years for a design to be approved and another two years before the first ships were laid down. Two more ships were authorized under the 1937 Estimates, three under the 1938 Estimates, and one under the 1938*bis* supplementary programme decreed on May 2, 1938; a further three were approved in April 1940.

Casque, Le Corsaire, Epée, Le Flibustier, Fleuret, L'Intrepide and *Le Temeraire* were ordered from Forges et Chantiers de la Méditerranée, La Seyne, *Le Hardi* and *Mameluck* from Ateliers et Chantiers de la Loire, Nantes, *Lansquenet, L'Aventurier* and *L'Opiniatre* from Forges et Chantiers de la Gironde, Bordeaux. The first eight had three twin 130-mm (5.1-in)/45-cal Model 1935 guns in low-angle mountings, but in 1938 it was realized that a big increase in AA armament was needed, and the last four ships were large enough to carry 130-mm (5.1-in) Model 130 dual-purpose mountings (as fitted in *Dunkerque* and *Strasbourg*). Nevertheless it was later planned to give *L'Opiniatre* the same low-angle armament as the earlier ships, in order to allow the ships to operate in the usual French manner of three-ship flotillas, although she was also allocated two twin 100-mm (3.9-in) AA guns, similar to the British twin 4-in (102-mm) Mk XIX.

On an eight hour trial *Le Hardi* reached 38.69 knots with just over 61 000 shp, and maintained 39 knots for an hour. In 1941 the vessels in service all received an additional pair of twin 13.2-mm (0.519-in) machine-guns and eight single 8-mm (0.315-in).

Le Corsaire was renamed *Sirocco* in 1941, *Epée* became *L'Adroit, Le Flibustier* became *Bison*, and *Fleuret* became *Foudroyant*, all commemorating destroyers sunk in 1939-40. With *Casque, Lansquenet, Mameluck* and *Le Hardi*, they were scuttled at Toulon on November 27, 1942, to avoid capture by the Germans. The last four were never completed, although *L'Intrepide* and *Le Temeraire* were launched in 1941. An Italian salvage team refloated *Sirocco* as *FR.32*, *L'Adroit* as *FR.33*, *Lansquenet* as *FR.34*, *Bison* as *FR.35*, *Foudroyant* as *FR.36*, and *Le Hardi* as *FR.37*. Of these only *FR.34* survived the vicissitudes of Allied bombing, German capture and scuttling, and although she returned to France as *Cyclone* she never recommissioned and was later scrapped. *FR.35* was seized by the Germans in September 1943 and converted into a smoke-making platform for use in Toulon, where she was torpedoed in June 1944. The four later ships were never completed, although the Germans did rename *L'Opiniatre* as *ZF.2*.

(*Le Hardi* type) *Displacement:* 1982 tonnes (normal), 2577 tonnes (full load) *Length:* 111.6 m (366 ft 3 in) pp *Beam:* 11.1 m (36 ft 6 in) *Draught:* 4.2 m (13 ft 9 in) *Machinery:* 2-shaft geared steam turbines, 58 000 shp=37 knots *Armament:* (As designed) 6 130-mm (5.1-in)/45-cal (1930 model) (3×2); 2 37-mm (1.46-in) AA (1925 model) (2×1); 4 13.2-mm (0.519-in) machine-guns (2×2); 7 55-cm (21.7-in) torpedo tubes (1×3+2×2) *Crew:* 187

(*L'Opiniatre* type) *Displacement:* 2562 tonnes (normal), 2929 tonnes (full load) *Length:* 118.6 m (389 ft 3 in) *Beam:* 11.89 m (39 ft) *Draught:* not known *Machinery:* 2-shaft geared steam turbines, 62 000 shp=35 knots *Armament:* 6 130-mm (5.1-in)/45-cal DP (3×2); 4 100-mm (3.9-in) AA (2×2) (*L'Opiniatre* only); 8 13.2-mm (0.519-in) machine-guns (4×2); 6 55-cm (21.7-in) torpedo tubes (2×3) *Crew:* not known

Harukaze

Japanese destroyer class. The two destroyers of this class, *Harukaze* (Spring Wind) and

Yukikaze (Snow Wind) were the first destroyers to be laid down in Japan after the Second World War, and were ordered under the 1953 Programme. The funds for the construction of the vessels were provided by the US government as part of the Military Aid Programme (MAP) designed partly to build up the Japanese Defence Forces.

Under the MAP, Japan was responsible for her own defence and was to be allowed enough armed forces to ward off any initial attack until American assistance could be provided. At that time, the naval arm of the Japanese Self Defence Forces (the Maritime Self Defence Force) was forbidden to possess warships with a high offensive capability and therefore the two 'Wind' Class destroyers were designed as high-speed escorts. The vessels were built in Japanese shipyards (rebuilt after the war with US assistance) under an 'off-shore' procurement agreement.

The construction involved the extensive use of electric welding. At that time the technique of welding high-tensile steel had only recently been developed and had not been previously used for hull construction. The superstructure also involved a new development and was largely built of light alloy materials.

Much of the equipment and all the armament for the two destroyers was supplied to Japan under the MAP and as a result the profile of the two destroyers was similar to contemporary US destroyers. They were flush-deck vessels with a distinctive swan-neck bow line, common to Japanese Second World War-built vessels. The machinery was a mixture, *Harukaze* being fitted with Mitsubishi/Escher Weiss turbines and *Yukikaze* with Westinghouse turbines. Bunkerage for 557 tons of oil fuel is provided and the ships have a radius of action of 6000 nautical miles at 18 knots.

In January 1959 the A/S (antisubmarine) armament on the vessels was updated, one of the obsolete depth-charge racks at the stern and the depth-charge throwers (K guns) being removed, and two A/S torpedo tube launchers armed with short homing torpedoes fitted. Accommodation was improved and the crew increased to 240.

Yukikaze was further modified during 1977 for experimental use, Y 127-mm (5-in) gun and the remaining depth-charge rack being removed and the ship fitted with a passive towed sonar set.

Displacement: 1700 tons (standard), 2340 tons (full load) *Length:* 109.27 m (358 ft 6 in) oa *Beam:* 10.51 m (34 ft 6 in) *Draught:* 3.66 m (12 ft) *Machinery:* 2-shaft geared turbines, 30 000 shp=30 knots *Armament:* (As built) 3 127-mm (5-in)/38 cal (3×1); 8 40-mm (1.57-in) (2×4) AA; 2 Hedgehogs; 4 K guns; 2 depth-charge racks; (As refitted) 3 127-mm (5-in); 8 40-mm (1.57-in); 2 A/S torpedo launchers; 2 Hedgehogs; 1 DC rack *Crew:* 190

Name	builder	completed
Harukaze	Mitsubishi, Nagasaki	26/4/56
Yukikaze	Mitsubishi, Kobe	31/7/56

Haruna

Japanese destroyer class. The two vessels of the *Haruna* Class ordered under the Third (1967-71) Five Year Plan are the largest ships yet built for the postwar Japanese navy.

When provision was made for the construction of the ships there was a general movement in Western navies to develop and provide hybrid ships with the emphasis on the ASW capability by carrying a number of ASW helicopters. These generally followed similar design conceptions with a standard gun/missile armament forward and a large hangar housing the helicopters and flight deck aft (as in the hybrid Japanese battleship/carriers of the Second World War). Thus the Royal Navy converted two cruisers (*Tiger* and *Blake*), the Russians built *Moskva* and *Leningrad* and the Italians built *Vittorio Veneto*, *Andrea Doria* and *Caio Duilio*. The

Hiei, a Japanese _Haruna_ Class destroyer, makes a turn to port. Proposed sister ships in this class will have improved AA defences

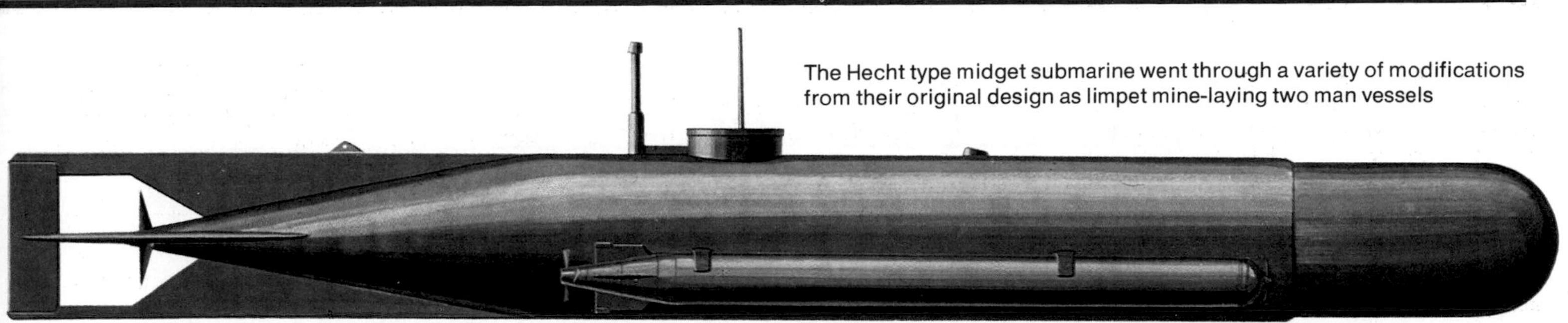
The Hecht type midget submarine went through a variety of modifications from their original design as limpet mine-laying two man vessels

Japanese initially planned to build a vessel similar to *Vittorio Veneto* capable of carrying nine ASW helicopters, but the requirement was amended and plans for two smaller ships, each with accommodation for three helicopters, were drawn up.

The basic design and layout of the vessels follows a fairly standard modern format, but there does seem to be a rather serious deficiency on the armament side. (Conforming to standard practice all the armament is supplied by the US.) The ASW capability has been concentrated to the detriment of any satisfactory self-defence system. Thus the ASW armament comprises three helicopters, an eight-tube Asroc launcher and two triple A/S torpedo tubes. The only defensive armament carried is two single 127-mm (5-in)/54-cal guns in single mounts which are of an outdated pattern no longer fitted in new US construction. These two guns have to cover both long- and short-range AA defence, as well as any antishipping requirement.

At present Japanese plans envisage the formation of four escort groups each comprising two *Haruna* type destroyers and a number of standard type destroyers and frigates. So far two *Haruna* Class are in service, having been completed in the remarkably short time of 2½-3 years, and two are on order. To bring the escort groups up to planned strength another four *Haruna* type vessels will be needed. From these plans it would seem, therefore, that the Japanese have opted for a close-knit escort group structure centred around the two *Haruna* ASW destroyers, with DDGs and frigates providing a general area defence in support of the primary ASW function of the escort group. Thus it is perhaps not so essential for the *Haruna*s to possess a high defensive capability. Nevertheless both the British and US Navies have come to realize that in modern warfare it is not advisable to have such specialized types of warship. Therefore ships are now given a good all-round capability comprising a combination of antisubmarine warfare, long- and short-range antiaircraft armament, plus antimissile and antiship capabilities.

That the lack of a suitable self-defence armament is a drawback has to some extent been realized, and the two improved *Haruna* Class vessels have been enlarged and equipped with a BPDMS Sparrow missile system and two close-range 35-mm (1.38-in) AA weapons. ASW capability will also be enhanced by fitting a variable-depth sonar system.

(*Haruna* and *Hiei*) *Displacement:* 4700 tons (standard) *Length:* 153 m (502 ft) oa *Beam:* 17.50 m (57 ft 5 in) *Draught:* 5.10 m (16 ft 8¾ in) *Machinery:* 2-shaft geared turbines, 70 000 shp=32 knots *Armament:* 2 5-in (127-mm) (2×1); 6 Mk 32 A/S torpedo tubes (2×3); 1 8-tube Asroc launcher; 3 A/S helicopters *Crew:* 364

(Improved *Haruna* as designed) *Displacement:* 5200 tons (standard) *Length:* 158.80 m (521 ft) oa *Beam:* 17.50 m (57 ft 5 in) *Draught:* 5.30 m (17 ft 4¾ in) *Machinery:* 2-shaft geared turbines 75 000 shp=32 knots *Armament:* 25-in (127-mm) (2×1); 2 35-mm (1.38-in); 1 Sea Sparrow launcher; 6 Mk 32 A/S torpedo tubes (2×3); 1 8-tube Asroc launcher; 3 A/S helicopters *Crew:* 370

Name	number	completed
Haruna	DD 141	22/2/73
Hiei	DD 142	27/11/74
—	DD 143	3/80 (planned)
—	DD 144	1981 (planned)

Hauk

Norwegian fast patrol boat class, built 1975. In 1975 orders were placed for 14 missile-armed fast patrol boats, numbered *P.986-999*, from Bergens Mekaniske Verksteder, Lakesevåg (ten boats) and Westermöen, Alta.

The new boats are similar to the preceding *Snögg* Class and were jointly developed by Sweden and Norway. The Penguin missiles and the hull design are Norwegian but the gun and fire control are Swedish.

Apart from a Bofors 40-mm (1.57-in) gun, the boats are armed with the Kongsberg Vaapenfabriek Penguin surface-to-surface missile, with a range of 27 km (17 miles). Unlike the Swedish boats they have four 53-cm (21-in) torpedo tubes, and only four Penguins.

Displacement: 120 tons (standard), 150 tons (full load) *Length:* 36.5 m (119 ft 9 in) oa *Beam:* 6.2 m (20 ft 4 in) *Draught:* 1.6 m (5 ft 3 in) *Machinery:* 2-shaft diesel, 7000 bhp=34 knots *Armament:* 1 40-mm (1.57-in); 4 Penguin SSMs (4×1); 4 53-cm (21-in) torpedo tubes (4×1) *Crew:* 22

Hayashio

Japanese submarine class. *Hayashio* and *Wakashio* were both ordered under the 1959 programme, the other two boats (*Natsushio* and *Fuyushio*) being ordered under the 1961 programme. These medium-type submarines have proved to be a most successful design with excellent manoeuvrability, and a high margin of safety for deep diving and in withstanding underwater explosions. Much of the design is based on ideas developed toward the end of the war, notably innovations produced for the *Ha 201* Class, although the *Hayashio*s are much larger than the *Ha 201*s. Unlike previous Japanese submarine designs, considerable attention has been paid to crew comfort with complete air-conditioning and a high standard of accommodation.

The two later boats are slightly larger than the first pair and are equipped with more efficient sonar. They have improved submerged manoeuvrability as well as an extra knot in speed.

In spite of the success of the class, Japan has not continued to build medium-type submarines. The limitations on seaworthiness imposed on smaller boats by the rough waters of the north Pacific have shown that the larger designs with a wider radius of action are more practicable. The relatively light torpedo armament has also restricted the operational capability of boats of this type.

No and name	completed
SS521 *Hayashio*	6/62
SS522 *Wakashio*	8/62
SS523 *Natsushio*	6/63
SS524 *Fuyushio*	9/63

Hayashio and *Natsushio* were built by Mitsubishi, Kobe; *Fuyushio* and *Wakashio* by Kawasaki, Kobe.

Displacement: 750 tons (standard); *Natsushio* and *Fuyushio* 790 tons (standard) *Length:* 59 m (193 ft 7 in) oa; *Natsushio* and *Fuyushio* 61 m (200 ft 1½ in) oa *Beam:* 6.5 m (21 ft 4 in) *Draught:* 4.1 m (13 ft 5½ in) *Machinery:* 2-shaft diesel/2 electric motors, 900 bhp/2300 hp=11/14 knots (surface/submerged); *Natsushio* and *Fuyushio* 11/15 knots *Armament:* 3 53.3-cm (21-in) torpedo tubes (bow) *Crew:* 40

Hecht

German midget submarine class. In 1943 a seven-ton midget minelaying U-Boat was planned as Type XXVIIA, codename 'Hecht' (pike). It was meant to stow a single limpet mine, and had a small electric motor to give a radius of 145 km (90 miles). Unfortunately there were many problems, principally because no small compass was available. To accommodate a standard gyro-compass the size had to be increased, and this reduced the

HMS *Hermes* (right and below) after her conversion to a Commando carrier. In the lower picture the positions for the eight Wessex or Sea King helicopters are visible on the deck. The 'chalk' positions are painted on the deck indicating where men are to form up prior to boarding the helicopter. The conversion to her commando role cost over £25 million

C & S Taylor

radius of action. Then it proved impossible to provide a suitable limpet mine, and the idea of using the craft operationally was abandoned. The programme was cut back and only 48 out of the planned 185 were completed.

Originally U-numbers were allocated: *U 2111-2200* and *U 2205-2250* were to be built by Germania, Kiel (only *U 2111-2113* completed); and *U 2251-2300* by Simmering, Graz and Pauker, Vienna (only *U 2251-2291* completed). Most of these were modified to suit them for training crews of 'Seehund' (sea dog) and other midget craft. A torpedo was slung beneath the hull, and the forward compartment, which had been designed to contain the limpet mine, was converted to provide greater battery capacity. In others the mine compartment was turned into a 'wet and dry' compartment for a frogman.

Displacement: 11¾ tons (normal) *Length:* 10.4 m (34 ft) *Beam:* 1.7 m (5 ft 6 in) *Draught:* 1.5 m (5 ft) *Machinery:* 1-shaft electric motor, 13 shp=5¾/6 knots (surfaced/submerged) *Armament:* 1 mine or 53.3-cm (21-in) torpedo *Crew:* 2

Hermes

British aircraft carrier class, built 1944-59. In 1943, the British Admiralty approved the design of a class of unarmoured medium-sized aircraft carriers which were to be capable of operating with the main fleet in all parts of the world, but which were to be economical in terms of material, size of ship's company and steaming qualities. A 'utility' class of light fleet carriers (the *Colossus* Class) had been ordered in 1942, but the 1943 carriers, later known as the *Hermes* Class, were an improvement in every respect.

The *Hermes* Class fell not far short of the standards of the armoured *Illustrious* Class, lacking only the hull and hangar armour and the heavy AA-gun armament, as well as a knot or two of speed. This was achieved by installing only two sets of machinery instead of three, omitting the 4.5-in (114-mm) guns, with their magazines and ammunition-transfer gear, and deleting all armour except for 350 tons over the crowns of the 40-mm (1.57-in) magazines and aviation-fuel tanks Standard displacement was reduced from 23 000 tons to 18 400 tons with only a slight reduction in overall size and the loss of only 372 sq m (4000 sq ft) of hangar area. Up to 45 aircraft were to be carried, compared with the 54 embarked by the armoured carriers from 1944, but the slightly increased fuel bunkerage and less powerful machinery gave the light fleet carriers an extra three days' endurance at the standard 20-knots cruising speed. The extended time on station which this allowed was an important consideration during protracted operations far from the main base.

The absence of flight-deck armour permitted the installation of lifts with double the area of the 'letter-box' lifts installed in *Illustrious*. The lifts in the *Hermes* Class were identical to those designed for the *Audacious* and *Gibraltar* Classes, and could carry aircraft of up to 13 640 kg (30 000 lb) deadweight. As originally designed, only one bow catapult was to be installed, but when the design was later recast, two were mounted with their tracks toed-in to permit side-by-side launching of aircraft.

Like the 1942 light fleet carriers, the 1943 design abandoned long-range AA-gun defence and included only close-range automatic weapons—single, twin and sextuple 40-mm Bofors. Long-range protection was provided by fighter aircraft and the 4-in (102-mm) and 4.7-in (120-mm) AA guns on other vessels of the screen. The abolition of the eight 4.5-in turrets and their fire control not only saved space and weight, but also eliminated the turret crews, ammunition-supply personnel and ordnance-maintenance staffs associated with the system, thus saving in addition on accommodation space.

Some of the eight ships of the class originally ordered had not been laid down by the end of the war, and *Hermes* herself was among the four which were then cancelled. The name was transferred to a hull building at Vickers Armstrong, Barrow, which had been laid down in June 1944, as *Elephant*. Work proceeded slowly on the other survivors, *Albion*, *Bulwark* and *Centaur* being launched between April 1947 and June 1948; completion was delayed for several years, while the designs were reworked to allow the ships to operate jet aircraft. They were completed in 1953 and 1954 to an interim standard, with a 5½° angled deck and hydraulic catapults. *Centaur* was given steam catapults and new arrester gear in 1957-58 so that she could operate the 15-ton second-generation naval jets with a 125-knot landing speed. With the recommissioning of *Centaur*, *Bulwark* was retired from fixed-wing operations and converted to carry a Royal Marine Commando Unit with 18 troop-carrying helicopters.

Work on *Hermes* began again in 1950, and she was launched on February 16, 1953. Thereafter, work proceeded extremely slowly, due mainly to changing requirements and specifications. When she was at last completed, on November 18, 1959, her external appearance was significantly different to that of the three earlier ships. Apart from the longer island and distinctive 'dustbin' radar array for the Type 984 3-D radar, the flight deck featured a port side extension to increase the off-axis angle of the landing area to 6½°. The forward centreline lift was deleted in order to give sufficient clear space for the two steam catapults, and this was replaced by a deck-edge lift forming part of the angled-deck extension.

Hermes became operational in mid-1960 and at the end of the year *Albion* was withdrawn for conversion to the commando assault role. During the next 11 years, *Hermes* operated one intercepter and two strike types—the Sea Vixen, and the Scimitar and Buccaneer. She saw service in the Atlantic, Mediterranean, Indian Ocean and East China Sea. The withdrawal of the Sea Vixen brought her fixed-wing career to a close in 1971, for she was too small to operate the F-4K Phantom which replaced the Vixen.

For a second time, *Hermes* replaced *Albion* in the front line, this time after conversion to a commando carrier which involved the removal of the catapults, arrester gear, and the sophisticated air-defence radar system. This phase of her career lasted only from 1973 until 1977, for a change of government policy resulted in her being recategorized as an antisubmarine-warfare carrier, embarking Sea King helicopters. They are due to be replaced by a squadron of Sea Harrier fixed-wing jets, and it is likely that she will still be operational on her 30th birthday. *Centaur* was withdrawn from front-line service in 1966 and was scrapped in 1971, *Albion* was paid off and sold in 1972, but *Bulwark* is scheduled to remain in service as a helicopter carrier until at least 1980.

See also *Albion*.

(As designed) *Displacement:* 18 400 tons (standard) 24 200 tons (full load) *Length:* 224.6 m (737 ft) oa, 198.1 m (650 ft) pp *Beam:* 27.4 m (90 ft) wl *Draught:* 7.6 m (25 ft) *Machinery:* 2 sets geared steam turbines, 76 000 shp=29 knots *Aircraft:* 24 fighters; 21 torpedo-bombers *Armament:* 39 40-mm (1.57-mm) AA *Crew:* 1380

(*Hermes*, 1970) *Displacement:* 23 900 (standard), 28 700 tons (full load) *Length:* 226.9 m (744 ft 4 in) oa, 198.1 m (650 ft) pp *Beam:* 48.8 m (160 ft) flight deck *Draught:* 8.8 m (29 ft) *Machinery:* 2 sets geared steam turbines, 76 000 shp=28 knots *Aircraft:* 20-22 fixed wing; 8 helicopters *Armament:* 8 Seacat AA missile launchers (2×4) *Crew:* 1950 approx

Heroj

Yugoslav submarine class. The *Heroj* Class of three submarines is only the second class to have been built in a Yugoslav shipyard, and for a country which has previously had experience of constructing only two submarines (the *Nerevta* and *Sutjeska*, commissioned in the early 1960s) and very little operational experience (four vessels of British and French construction taken over by the Italians in the Second World War, and a former Italian boat commissioned after the war) it was a bold step to embark on the construction of modern submarines. It is inconceivable that Yugoslavia can have designed these submarines without the help of technical and construction experience from outside. Although a number of Italian personnel experienced in submarine construction were probably captured at the end of the war, much of the help in building these submarines must have come from the USSR, although from the appearance and technical details available in the West it is not immediately apparent that the vessels are of Soviet design. That they are of a medium-sized conventional diesel/electric propulsion type designed for operations in the Mediterranean is undisputed.

As for the actual origins and design, details are much more obscure. From the few photos available it would appear that the boats are built on the triple-hull principle of three cylinders arranged in the form of an upright triangle. The upper cylinder would provide the accommodation, navigation and operation control centres and house the armament, while the lower two cylinders house all the machinery. In both appearance and probable design, therefore, the submarines appear to be very similar to the Dutch *Potvis* Class (also triple-hull, and completed some three to five years before the Yugoslav vessels), but rather smaller. The Yugoslav boats have a streamlined hull and conning tower, and the torpedo tubes are all mounted in the bows. The machinery is not as powerful as that in the Dutch vessels but is of an all-Yugoslav design, the shipyard responsible for construction, Uljanik of Pula, also being a

No and name	laid down	launched	completed
821 *Heroj*	1964	1967	1968
822 *Junak*	1965	1968	1969
823 *Uskok*	1966	1969	1970

specialist in diesel manufacture. Battery capacity is very restricted and, with low-powered electric motors, these vessels have a submerged speed of only 10 knots, which must greatly restrict their operational capabilities when and if pitted against a modern, well-equipped A/S escort.

Displacement: 1068 tons (submerged) *Length:* 64 m (210 ft) oa *Beam:* 7.2 m (23 ft 7 in) *Draught:* 5 m (16 ft 5 in) *Machinery:* 2-shaft diesel motors, 2400 bhp=16 knots (surfaced); 2 electric motors=10 knots (submerged) *Armament:* 6 53-cm (21-in) torpedo tubes *Crew:* 55

High Point

US hydrofoil patrol boat. In the late 1950s and early 1960s the US Navy began to try to find an effective counter to the Soviet conventional and nuclear short-range SLRM submarines. It was obvious that the nuclear attack submarine itself would provide part of this counter, but a fast, manoeuvrable surface or above-surface craft was also required. Helicopters were being developed for this role, but hydrofoils were also considered, and *High Point* (PCH-1) was designed as an experimental hydrofoil submarine chaser.

Hydrofoils offered high speed and good manoeuvrability combined with small size and an excellent weapons load for their displacement. *High Point* was particularly suitable because her new one strut forward, two struts aft system promised even better manoeuvrability and the ability to operate in relatively rough water.

High Point was designed by W C Nickum & Sons, Seattle, and built jointly by Boeing Aircraft and J M Martinac at Martinac's Tacoma shipyard. Unlike the older two struts forward, one strut aft system, *High Point*'s hydrofoil system is inherently unstable, requiring techniques developed for aircraft autopilots to ensure adequate controls. *High Point* also utilized aircraft design techniques to save weight. She was ordered in the 1959-60 fiscal year, laid down on February 27, 1961, launched on August 17, 1962 and commissioned on September 3, 1963.

She has a conventionally boat-shaped light alloy hull, with a retractable foil forward which is used to control her height above the

HMS *Hermes* with Mk 1 Westland Wessex helicopters in the foreground and Mk1 Westland Sea Kings aft. The Wessex have their chalk numbers painted on the nose

Royal Navy

sea, and main retractable foil aft, supported by two struts. Where the struts join the foil are two sets of propellers, each of which has one tractor propeller forward of the foil and one pusher propeller aft of the foil. These are driven by two Bristol Siddeley Marine Proteus gas turbines, each developing 3100 shp.

When hull-borne she is powered by one 600-bhp Packard diesel driving a retractable outboard propeller at the stern which gives a speed of 12 knots. She has a unique silhouette with a large deckhouse and an enclosed bridge forward, and two bulky engine cowlings and air intakes set well aft over the main foil struts. These struts are 4.3 m (14 ft) high when extended, and when retracted *High Point* has a draught of 1.8 m (6 ft).

When built, *High Point* carried two sonars and MAD (Magnetic Anomaly Detection) gear, and was armed with four 21-in (53-cm) A/S torpedo launchers amidships, DCTs aft and two 0.5-in (12.7-mm) machine-guns forward. After extensive trials, it became obvious that helicopters and aircraft provided a more flexible and cost-effective solution to the A/S problem. The A/S gear and armament were therefore removed and *High Point* was used as a trials boat to help to develop the new generation of hydrofoil patrol boats intended for surface-to-surface combat.

In 1968 she was fitted with a single 40-mm (1.57-in) gun forward in place of the twin machine-guns, though this was later removed, and in 1973-74 she ran trials for the lightweight Harpoon SSM launchers intended for use on the *Pegasus* Class PHM. Also in 1973, the hydrofoils were modified to improve her rough weather performance and manoeuvrability, and the forward foil was made steerable.

In 1974-75 she was evaluated by the Coast Guard to demonstrate the hydrofoil's usefulness as a fast patrol boat and for possible adoption by that service, but the later *Flagstaff* (WPGH-1) was chosen instead. *High Point* was then returned to the USN and retained for testing.

High Point has been one of the most successful of all the early hydrofoils put into service in Western navies, and she has done much to ensure the ability of later hydrofoils using the same foil system to operate a heavy armament effectively in rough seas.

Displacement: 110 tons (full load) *Length:* 35.1 m (115 ft) *Beam:* 9.5 m (31 ft) *Draught:* 5.2 m (17 ft (hull-borne, foils extended) *Machinery:* 2-shaft gas turbine, 6200 shp=48 knots (foil-borne); 1-shaft diesel, 600 bhp=12 knots (hull-borne) *Armament:* 2 0.5-in (12.7-mm) machine-guns; 4 21-in (53-cm) torpedo launchers; depth-charge throwers *Crew:* 13

The US Navy's experimental hydrofoil patrol boat PCH-1 *High Point* launches a Harpoon AGM-28A antiship missile. The Harpoon armament enables *High Point* to stand off her target and hit it from a below-the-horizon position using a low-level trajectory and active radar homing measures

Holland

Dutch destroyer class, built 1950-55. Four Type 47A destroyers were ordered in 1950 as the first instalment of the massive rebuilding programme to revitalize the Royal Netherlands Navy and allow it to make a significant contribution to NATO.

Machinery from the *Gerard Callenburgh* Class destroyers, which had been seized by the Germans in May 1940 while under construction, was to be used to save time and money in the construction of new ships. Four identical sets were available: two were from the *Philips van Almonde* and *Tjerk Hiddes*, and two were built by the Germans for sister ships which were never laid down.

Because the machinery was rather low-powered (45 000 shp rather than the 60 000 shp which the designers wanted) the Type 47A design was made a little smaller than the 47B which was to follow. Length and beam were slightly reduced to cut about 300 tons off the displacement, and only one 40-mm (1.57-in) Bofors antiaircraft gun could be mounted. In other respects the ships conformed to the Type 47 specifications.

The guns are Bofors 120-mm (4.7-in) in twin automatic gunhouses, with full remote power control (RPC) and radar fire control. The antisubmarine weapons are two Bofors 375-mm (14.76-in) quadruple rocket-launchers in B position.

The layout of these ships and their successors, the *Frieslands*, strongly resembled the contemporary British *Daring* Class, with the forefunnel rising inside the lattice foremast. Many other British features could be detected in these ships, as the Dutch constructors received considerable assistance from their British counterparts while reestablishing themselves as a design team.

Noord Brabant was damaged beyond repair on January 9, 1974, in a collision with the merchant ship *Tacoma City* off Flushing. *Gelderland* was laid up as a harbour-training ship at Den Helder in 1974. *Holland* became the Peruvian *Garcia y Garcia* in February 1978, and *Zeeland* will probably also be transferred.

Pendant No and name	launched	built
D.808 ***Holland***	11/4/1953	Rotterdam Dry Dock
D.809 ***Zeeland***	27/6/1953	Royal Schelde
D.810 ***Noord Brabant***	28/11/1953	Royal Schelde
D.811 ***Gelderland***	19/9/1953	Wilton-Fijenoord

Displacement: 2215 tons (normal), 2765 tons (full load) *Length:* 111.3 m (365 ft 2 in) *Beam:* 11.33 m (37 ft 2 in) *Draught:* 3.88 m (12 ft 9 in) mean *Machinery:* 2-shaft geared steam turbines, 45 000 shp=32 knots *Armament:* 4 120-mm (4.7-in)/50-cal (2×2); 1 40-mm (1.57-in)/60-cal *Crew:* 247

Hornet

US aircraft carrier, built 1939-41. A *Yorktown* Class carrier, *Hornet* was authorized several years after her sister ships and was the first US carrier ordered after the ending of treaty restrictions on total carrier tonnage. She was laid down in September 1939, launched on December 14, 1940, and commissioned on October 20, 1941, just seven weeks before the Japanese attack on Pearl Harbor.

Hornet worked up her air group in the Caribbean during January 1942, and on her return to Norfolk, Virginia, she embarked a pair of North American B-25 Mitchell bombers for a deck takeoff trial. The trial, which was successful, was in preparation for one of the most dramatic operations of the Second World War—a carrier-based strike against the Japanese mainland. The next two months were taken up with further training, and passage to San Francisco. Here, *Hornet* took on board 16 US Army Air Force B-25s, and left on April 2 to rendezvous to the north of Midway Island with her sister ship *Enterprise* on April 13.

President Roosevelt had been interested in the idea of an air attack on the Japanese capital since the beginning of the war in 1941. An initial report on the projected operation recommended carrier transport of B-25s to within 640 km (400 miles) of Japan. Since B-25s were too large for flight-deck landings, it was planned that they should fly on to friendly areas of China after completing their mission. After the aircraft had taken off, their carrier would head away from Japan at top speed to avoid retaliatory attacks.

Early on April 18, when they were still 1075 km (668 miles) to the east of Tokyo, *Hornet*, *Enterprise* and their escort were sighted by Japanese picket boats. Vice-Admiral William Halsey, commander of the carrier force, decided to start the mission at this point. At 0800 hours, Colonel James Doolittle led the 16 B-25s as they took off from *Hornet*'s deck for the first air raid on Tokyo. Flying at treetop height, the bombers crossed the Japanese coastline at 16 different points, and despite the sighting of the carrier force Japanese defences were caught unprepared.

Doolittle's lead aircraft dropped 910 kg (2000 lb) of incendiary bombs over downtown Tokyo. A further nine bombers hit steel plants and oil refineries in north Tokyo, and the docks to the south of the city. Factories and oil tanks in Yokohama were the targets for three of the B-25s, and another three raided the industrial town of Nagoya while en route to Kyoto. One aircraft bombed Kobe and severely damaged the Kawasaki aircraft plant. The raid was over by 1300 hours. Ninety factories had been gutted and a fuel-tank farm and six fuel tanks destroyed. Slight damage was also caused to the light carrier *Ryuho* undergoing conversion at Yokosuka dockyard. None of the B-25s was lost over Japan, and most of Doolittle's bomber crews reached safety in China, although three died in a crash-landing. One aircraft crash-landed near Vladivostok and the crew of five were detained by the Soviets, and eight airmen were taken prisoner in Japanese-held China and were eventually put on trial for alleged war crimes. Three of them were executed. *Hornet* and *Enterprise* withdrew to Pearl Harbor and arrived there a week after the raid.

Five days later, on April 30, the two carriers sailed again with two dozen Marine

The Dutch destroyer *Holland* makes a sharp turn to port during a training run in the North Sea. She was transferred to Peru in 1978

Koninklijke Marine

Corps fighters destined for delivery to Espiritu Santo. The mission was cancelled when the ships were near Fiji, and they returned to Pearl Harbor to prepare for what was to be the first clear-cut US fleet victory of the war—Midway.

On June 4, 1942, the day on which four Japanese carriers were sunk, the only aircraft from *Hornet* to sight the enemy were the 15 Douglas Devastators from the ship, together with six Grumman TBF Avengers detached to Midway Island. Torpedo Squadron 8 lost all the Devastators and five Avengers, as well as 59 of the 63 aircrew, without scoring a hit. The Douglas SBD Dauntless dive-bombers and Grumman F4F fighters failed to find the enemy. All ten F4Fs ditched after running out of fuel, as did two of the SBDs. Sixteen SBDs later attacked *Hiryu* but scored no hits. On June 6, *Hornet*'s dive-bombers made up for their earlier undistinguished performance by finishing off the damaged heavy cruiser *Mikuma* and severely damaging *Mogami*.

Hornet returned to Pearl Harbor to embark a new torpedo squadron and to carry out the further air group training which was so necessary. She thus missed the battle fought off Guadalcanal on August 24, 1942, although at the time en route for the south-west Pacific, ferrying Marine Corps fighters. Once these were unloaded at Guadalcanal, *Hornet* joined the patrols to the east of the island, covering the reinforcement convoys. On September 6, the carrier was narrowly missed by a torpedo and a submarine. Nine days later *Wasp*, in company, was sunk by a submarine. *Saratoga* had already been damaged by torpedo in the same area, on August 31, and the one remaining undamaged carrier was withdrawn to Espiritu Santo.

On October 2, *Hornet* sortied to attack the Japanese advanced base at Shortlands in the Solomon Islands. The raid, which took place on October 5, was unsuccessful due partly to poor weather, and a strike on Rekata Bay, Santa Isabel Island, found no worthwhile targets. The carrier remained at sea, covering Guadalcanal reinforcement shipping and was joined to the north of the Solomons on October 24 by the recently repaired *Enterprise*, on the eve of the fourth and last carrier battle of 1942.

The action at Santa Cruz began with the two sides locating and assessing one another's forces. On the next day, October 26, *Hornet* and *Enterprise*, with 158 aircraft between them, engaged the enemy fleet of four carriers (*Zuikaku, Shokaku, Junyo* and *Zuiho*) which had 207 aircraft. *Hornet* launched 39 out of her 50 attack aircraft, but before they reached the enemy, 27 dive- and torpedo-bombers from *Zuikaku* and *Shokaku* broke through the US fighter patrols and, in the space of 11 minutes, scored six bomb hits and two torpedo hits on *Hornet*. Two aircraft also made successful suicide attacks. *Hornet* was left dead in the water, with a 12½° list and many fires.

Ten minutes after the end of the attack on *Hornet*, her aircraft fought their way through defending Zero fighters and scored six direct hits on *Shokaku*, putting her out of action for months. Three hits were also scored on the heavy cruiser *Chikuma*, resulting in severe damage. Air Group 8 had been successful at last, but were unable to return to their own ship and had to return to *Enterprise*.

Hornet was taken in tow by a heavy cruiser at noon, after her fires were under control. The list was reduced and prospects of saving her were fair when, four hours later, a strike launched by *Junyo* scored another torpedo hit and two more bomb hits. The decision was taken to scuttle *Hornet*, but hits from torpedoes and 430 rounds of 5-in (127-mm) HE shells failed to finish her off. It was left to the Japanese destroyers *Makigumo* and *Akigumo* to provide the coup de grâce in the early hours of October 27, 1942, following an unsuccessful attempt to take the still-blazing carrier in tow.

Hornet's career had been brief and relatively unsuccessful. Although she was pre-

USS *Hornet* (CV-8) after her launch in late 1941. She lasted one year in service, but during that time launched the first carrier strike against Japan in 1942

US Navy

sent at Midway, her contribution was limited, and at Santa Cruz her aircraft had only scored hits after she had been incapacitated. But she will always be remembered as the ship which launched the 'Doolittle Raid' on Tokyo, an operation which raised American civilian morale at a time when it was most needed. Her name was revived for the eighth ship of the *Essex* Class (CV.12), which distinguished herself during the last 18 months of the Pacific War.

See also *Enterprise*.

Displacement: 20 000 tons *Length:* 232 m (761 ft) wl, 246.7 m (809 ft 6 in) oa *Beam:* 25.4 m (83 ft 3 in) *Draught:* 6.6 m (21 ft 9 in) *Machinery:* 4-shaft geared turbines, 120 000 shp=34 knots *Aircraft:* 100 *Armament:* 8 5-in (127-mm) *Crew:* 2200

Hotel

Soviet nuclear ballistic missile submarine class. The class made use of the ballistic missile launching system developed for the conventionally-powered *Zulu V* Class, and of the hull and propulsion system of the nuclear-powered *Echo* and *November* Class submarines, in order to produce some sort of counter to the US Polaris SSBN force as soon as possible.

Nine were built between 1958-62, and they were originally armed with the 480-km (300-mile) ranged SSN-4 Sark in three tubes at the aft end of the fin, but during 1963-67 these were replaced by three SSN-5 Serbs with a range of about 1125 km (700 miles). This marginally improved the survivability, but since they have to surface to launch their missiles, they are still very vulnerable to countermeasures even before they have revealed their position by firing a missile. Like all Soviet submarines of this period, the *Hotels* are extremely noisy by Western standards.

The Sark-armed boats were classified as the *Hotel I* Class, and these were redesignated *Hotel II* when they were rearmed with Serbs. One *Hotel II* was used as a test ship for the SSN-8 used in the *Delta* Class SSBN, and became the sole *Hotel III*. Their remaining armament consists of six bow 21-in (53.3-cm) and four stern 16-in (40-cm) torpedo tubes. The aft tubes are used to fire A/S torpedoes.

By 1978 the class was totally obsolete, but it is possible that they may be rearmed with a medium-ranged MIRVed tactical ballistic missile, which would enable them to be used to great effect against Western Europe or China. However, the hull and machinery is old, and such a move may not be justified.

Displacement: 4500 tons/5500 tons (surfaced/submerged) *Length:* 115.2 m (378 ft) *Beam:* 8.6 m (28 ft 2½ in) *Draught:* 7.6 m (25 ft) *Machinery:* 2-shaft nuclear steam turbines, 30 000 shp=20 knots (surfaced), 23 knots (submerged) *Armament:* 3 SSN-5 Serb; 6 21-in (53.3-cm) torpedo tubes; 4 16-in (40-cm) torpedo tubes *Crew:* 90

Howe

British battleship. The last battleship of the *King George V* Class to be completed, *Howe* was ordered from the Fairfield Shipbuilding Company under the 1937 Programme and laid down at Govan on June 1, 1937. She was originally to have been named *Beatty*, after the famous Admiral of the First World War, but was renamed *Howe* shortly before her launch on April 9, 1940. In the following month her construction was suspended while shipbuilding resources were concentrated on more urgent requirements, and work on her did not recommence for six months. Shortages of men and materials, and alterations to the ship resulting from war experience delayed her completion still further and she did not commission until June 1942. Her displacement was 39 150 tons (standard) and 44 510 tons (full load) which was about 3000 tons above the designed displacement. The increase resulted mainly from additions to the ship's structure (principally an increase in the depth of the underwater protection system), the difficulty of exercising strict control of material weights in wartime, the provision of additional AA guns, and the fitting of air-warning, sea-warning and gunnery radar equipment. Officially she was completed on August 29, 1942, her armament at this time being ten 14-in (356-mm) (2×4, 1×2), 16 5.25-in (133-mm) DP (8×2), 48 40-mm (1.57-in) AA (6×8) and 18 20-mm (0.79-in) AA (18×1); within a few months the 20-mm (0.79-in) armament was increased to 40 guns (40×1).

She joined the Home Fleet at Scapa Flow on August 27, 1942, and spent the following two months carrying out trials and working up. For the first few months of 1943 she was employed on patrol duties and covered the passage of several Russian convoys. In May she was transferred to the Mediterranean to cover Operation Husky (the invasion of Sicily) and joined Force H at Algiers on June 1. On the night of July 11/12, in company with *King George V* she bombarded airfields at the western end of Sicily. In September she was assigned to cover the landings at Salerno, and after the surrender of Italy formed part of the occupation force at Taranto. Shortly after this she escorted the surrendered Italian Battle Fleet from Malta to Alexandria prior to returning to Home Waters. Between November 1943 and May 1944 she was refitted at Devonport prior to being transferred to the Eastern Fleet. Alterations included the removal of her aircraft equipment, the addition of 16 2-pdr (2×8), 8 40-mm (1.57-in) (2×4), and 8 20-mm (0.79-in) (4×2) AA guns, and the removal of 6 20-mm (0.79-in) (6×1) AA guns.

She joined the Eastern Fleet at Trincomalee on August 8, 1944, and on September 8 covered air strikes against installations on Sumatra. On December 2, she became flagship of the newly-formed British Pacific Fleet and in February 1945 arrived in her new theatre of war. During March-May 1945 she covered the US landings at Okinawa and carried out several bombardments of islands in the Sakishima Gunto group. In

The Danish frigate *Beskytteren* (F.340), a modified version of the *Hvidbjørnen* Class built in the 1960s for patrol of fishing grounds

Danish Navy

June she was taken in hand for refit at Durban, the principal object being to increase the strength of the AA armament to counter the kamikaze threat. All her single 20-mm (0.79-in) guns were removed and 24 2-pdr (6×4) and 18 40-mm (1.57-in) (18×1) AA guns added. While she was being refitted the war ended, and when the work on her was completed in September 1945 she was attached to the East Indies station. She returned home at the end of the year and arrived at Portsmouth in January 1946 where she was refitted for service as a training ship. She served in this role at Portland until 1951 when she was placed in reserve. She was sold for scrap in 1958.

See also *King George V.*

Displacement: 39 150 tons (standard) *Length:* 227.07 m (745 ft) oa; 213.36 m (700 ft) pp *Beam:* 31.39 m (103 ft) *Draught:* 8.46 m (27 ft 9 in) *Machinery:* 4-shaft geared turbines, 110 000 shp=29 knots *Protection:* 114-380 mm (4½-15 in) main belt; 25-152 mm (1-6 in) decks; 230-406 mm (9-16 in) turrets, 406 mm (16 in) director control tower *Armament:* 10 14-in (355.6-mm) (2×4, 1×2); 16 5.25-in (133-mm) DP (8×2); 48 40-mm (1.57-in) AA (6×8); 18 20-mm (0.79-in) AA (18×1) *Aircraft:* 4 *Crew:* 1553-1558

Hvidbjørnen

Danish frigate class. In 1960 four frigates were authorized, *Hvidbjørnen* (F.348), *Vaederren* (F.349), *Ingolf* (F.350) and *Fylla* (F.351). They are diesel-driven, with a relatively light armament but have a helicopter and a comprehensive radar outfit to enable them to patrol the fishing grounds in the North Sea, Faroes and Greenland.

Unlike most frigates they have an extensive rescue capability with transportable pumps, fire-fighting gear and a fully-equipped sick bay. Their high freeboard and squat profile underlines the fact that they are designed to operate in some of the roughest seas in the world. They are strengthened for operating in icy conditions, and the margin of stability allows for 225 tons of ice on the upperworks.

The armament comprises a single 76-mm (3-in) of an elderly OTO-Melara design. The surveillance radar is a Plessey AWS-5 modified with a Selenia antenna, and includes helicopter control. The sonar is a Plessey PMS-26.

In 1974-75 a slightly modified version was built at Aalborg Vaerft, which had built *Fylla* and *Vaederren.* She is the *Beskytteren* (F.340), and she has a slightly larger hull, reduced crew and improved helicopter facilities.

Displacement: 1345 tons (standard), 1650 tons (full load) *Length:* 72.6 m (238 ft 2 in) oa *Beam:* 11.6 m (38 ft) *Draught:* 4.9 m (16 ft) *Machinery:* 1-shaft diesel, 6400 bhp=18 knots *Armament:* 1 76-mm (3-in); 1 Alouette III helicopter *Crew:* 75

Hyuga

Japanese battleship/carrier. Much of Japanese naval strategy during the Second World War was based on the fast-carrier task force concept. The vast distances over which the war was waged dictated to a large measure Japanese naval strategy. Even before the outbreak of war Japanese naval officers had realized the need for, and value of, the carrier as an integral part of the battle group, and naval doctrine and operational training had been directed to this end. Consequently the loss of four large fleet carriers at the Battle of Midway in June 1942 was a disaster of the first magnitude. Admittedly work had begun on constructing a large new class of fast fleet carriers, but they would not be ready for service for at least another two to three years. In the meantime the Japanese navy was urgently in need of carriers, or some other means of operating naval aircraft in support of the fleet far from land bases. Consequently plans were hurriedly prepared to convert a number of vessels to aircraft carriers. Among those so selected was the hull of the battleship *Shinano,* still under construction, the merchant liner *Scharnhorst* (renamed *Shinyo),* and the seaplane carriers *Chitose* and *Chiyoda.*

It was realized that even with this conversion programme these vessels would not be ready for service as carriers before the end of 1943 at the very earliest, and the Japanese decided to embark on a policy of semiconversion in an effort to provide the fleet with some sort of air support. The idea was to use the after part of some of the larger warships for a small flight deck for aircraft operations, accepting a certain loss in firepower as a consequence. The vessels selected for conversion to these 'hybrid' carriers were the battleships *Hyuga* and *Ise* and the cruiser *Mogami.* The 'hybrid' carrier was not an entirely new concept, for the British *Furious* had set the precedent in 1917 when a flying-off deck was built over the forward part of the ship, and the Swedish cruiser *Gotland* had an aircraft operating area aft.

Work on converting *Hyuga* and her sister ship *Ise* began early in 1943 and the ships re-entered service in the autumn of that year. The conversion entailed removing the two after turrets and surmounting the whole area behind the after superstructure with a large hangar (which raised the deck by two levels) topped by a small flight deck. An elevator was situated in the centre of the flight deck around which ran two sets of rails for manoeuvring the aircraft forward to the two 25-m (82-ft) catapults, sited to port and starboard on tall supports immediately forward of the flight deck. Catapults were essential for launching the aircraft, for the aft position of the small flight deck precluded any possibility of aircraft carrying out an unassisted take-off. Similarly there was insufficient space for aircraft to land on; although it was originally intended that the ship would carry 22 Judy D44 dive-bombers, it was eventually provided with 22 Paul E16A seaplanes. These were to be catapult-launched at the rate of one every two minutes, and on completion of a mission were to land on the water alongside. To lift the seaplanes back on to the deck a large crane was sited to port on the after part of the flight deck.

During the conversion the secondary casemate 140-mm (5.5-in) guns were removed and an extra eight 127-mm (5-in) AA added. The light AA was also increased and a total of 57 25-mm (1-in) AA carried.

Following the Philippine Sea battle in June 1944 the light AA was further increased to

The converted Japanese battleship/carrier *Hyuga* under attack by US Navy aircraft during the Battle of Cape Engano, October 25, 1944

US Navy

Name	conversion yard
Hyuga	Sasebo navy yard
Ise	Kure navy yard

108 25-mm (1-in) (31×3, 15×1), while in September 1944 a total of 180 127-mm (5-in) rocket launchers mounted in racks of 30 were sited at the after end of the flight deck to port and starboard. The launchers fired phosphorous rockets which trailed long wires designed to catch in the wings and propellers of attacking aircraft.

Owing to a lack of aircraft and pilots following the disastrous battles during the summer of 1944, the two battleship/carriers sailed with the decoy force for the Battle of Leyte Gulf in October 1944 without any aircraft on board. This was their one and only action in their hybrid role. Following Leyte Gulf the two ships reverted to their battleship role and the two catapults were removed to improve the arc of fire of C and D turrets. Both ships were eventually sunk in Kure harbour in July 1945 during air raids carried out by American naval aircraft of the Third Fleet.

Displacement: 35200 tons (*Ise* 35350 tons) *Length:* 219.61 m (720 ft 6 in) *Beam:* 33.83 m (111 ft) *Draught:* 8.99 m (29 ft 6 in) *Machinery:* 4-shaft geared turbines, 80825 shp=25.3 knots *Protection:* 102-305 mm (4-12 in) main belt, 32-170 mm (1.26-6.7 in) deck, 203-305 mm (8-12 in) turrets, 305 mm (12 in) barbettes, 152 mm (6 in) casemates, 152-305 mm (6-12 in) conning tower *Armament:* 8 14-in (356-mm) (4×2); 16 5-in (127-mm) AA (8×2); 57 25-mm (1-in) AA (19×3); 22 seaplanes *Crew:* 1463

I 9

Japanese submarine class, built 1938-42. Trials and operational experience with the earlier Type J designs had shown the Japanese that it was not wholly satisfactory to combine scouting, raiding and squadron-leader roles in one design. This led to the development of three different types known as 'A' (squadron leader), 'B' (scouting) and 'C' (attack). The first of the new long-range designs was the 'A', derived from the concepts underlying the *I 7* (Type J3) Class.

The *I 9* Class (Type A1) were intended as headquarters ships capable of coordinating the attacks of a group of submarines. Unlike the Wolfpack tactical system employed by German U-Boats, each group of Japanese submarines was assigned an area of operations under command from a headquarters boat, within which each boat acted independently except when concentrated for an attack on an enemy fleet. Japanese thinking, in contrast with that of other navies, regarded the submarine as an integral part of the battle fleet. Its primary role was to scout for the fleet to which it was attached and attack units of the enemy fleet. The possibilities of using submarines for mercantile warfare were almost totally ignored. This led to concentration on the construction of large, heavily armed submarines.

For their headquarters role the *I 9* Class was fitted with a wide range of sophisticated telecommunications equipment, and its complement included headquarters staff. Endurance was increased from the standard 60 to 90 days and the radius of action raised to 2000 nautical miles surfaced and by 30 nautical miles submerged. The machinery was more powerful, but with increased displacement speeds remained about the same as in the Type J submarines. The *I 9*s carried a floatplane, and the hangar (which was partially faired into the hull) and the catapult were sited forward of the conning tower. The single gun was placed aft of the conning tower where its operation would not interfere with the aircraft.

Displacement: 2919/4149 tons (surfaced/submerged) *Length:* 113.61 m (372 ft 9 in) oa *Beam:* 9.55 m (31 ft 4 in) *Draught:* 5.33 m (17 ft 6 in) *Machinery:* 2-shaft diesels/electric motors, 12400 shp/2400 hp=23.5/8 knots (surfaced/submerged) *Armament:* 6 53-cm (21-in) torpedo tubes, 18 torpedoes; 1 140-mm (5.5-in); 4 25-mm (1-in) (2×2); 1 seaplane *Crew:* 100

No	fate
I 9	lost 6/43
I 10	lost 7/44
I 11	lost 1/44
700-710	cancelled 1942

I 12

Japanese submarine, built 1942-44. *I 12* was ordered under the 1941 Additional Programme and was the only headquarters submarine of Type A2 to be built. At the time of her construction a high-priority programme for diesel-engined escort ships was just about to be implemented, and consequently *I 12* was equipped with rather inferior diesels giving her a surface speed of only 17.5 knots, compared with the 23.5 knots of the earlier Type A, B and C boats. This precluded her from operating with major units of the fleet as the Japanese high command had intended. Bunkerage, on the other hand, was increased and her radius of action was 22000 nautical miles, 6000 nautical miles more than that of the Type A1. The basic design of *I 12* was the same as that of the *I 9* Class, and like them she was fitted with a floatplane hangar and catapult.

She was laid down on November 5, 1942, launched on August 3, 1943, and completed on April 25, 1944. A second vessel was originally laid down to this design, but the plans were recast while she was still under construction and she was completed as *I 13* (Type AM). *I 12* is credited with the sinking of an Allied merchant ship of 7176 tons, and was herself lost some time after January 1945.

Displacement: 2934/4172 tons (surfaced/submerged) *Length:* 113.5 m (372 ft 4 in) oa *Beam:* 9.55 m (31 ft 4 in) *Draught:* 5.33 m (17 ft 6 in) *Machinery:* 2-shaft diesels/2 electric motors, 4700 shp/1200 hp=17.5/6.25 knots (surfaced/submerged) *Armament:* 6 53-cm (21-in) torpedo tubes, 18 torpedoes; 1 5.5-in (140-mm); 4 25-mm (1-in) (2×2); 1 floatplane (later removed) *Crew:* 100

I 13

Japanese submarine class, built 1943-45. *I 13* was originally laid down as a second unit of the *I 12* Class, but during construction the design was altered to enable an extra floatplane to be carried. The new plans, designated Type AM, called for the fitting of bulges to increase freeboard and improve stability. The hangar arrangement and conning tower and their siting were also changed, the large circular hangar with its massive watertight door being resited slightly to starboard, and the conning tower to port and extending up and over the hangar.

Orders for a further six units of this design were placed at the Kobe yard of Kawasaki, but the advanced Allied antisubmarine capabilities and ease with which US forces were sinking large Japanese submarines led to an admiralty decision to cancel these orders. Three, however, were reinstated at the express wish of Admiral Yamamoto. They were to be employed as advance scouts and pickets for the main fleet, replacing the heavy cruisers in this role.

A further aid to improving the capabilities of these submarines and extending their submerged radius was the fitting of a primitive form of snorkel in the form of two fixed curved pipes in the conning tower, details of which had been supplied by the Germans.

In spite of Admiral Yamamoto's personal order to continue construction of the submarines, work progressed at a very slow pace. Apart from *I 13*, only *I 14* had been completed by the end of the war, work on *I 1* and *I 15* ceasing in March 1945 when they were 70% and 90% complete respectively. *I 13* was lost on July 16, 1945, and *I 1*, *I 14* and *I 15* were scrapped.

Displacement: 3603/4762 tons (surfaced/submerged) *Length:* 113.61m (372 ft 9 in) oa *Beam:* 11.73 m (38 ft 6 in) *Draught:* 5.89 m (19 ft 4 in) *Machinery:* 2-shaft diesels/2 electric motors, 4400 shp/600 hp=16.75/5.5 knots (surfaced/submerged) *Armament:* 6 53-cm (21-in) torpedo tubes, 12 torpedoes; 1 140-mm (5.5-in); 7 25-mm (1-in) (2×3, 1×1); 2 floatplanes *Crew:* 108

No	laid down	launched	completed
I 1	6/43	6/44	—
I 13	2/43	11/43	12/44
I 14	5/43	3/44	3/45
I 15	4/43	4/44	—

I 15

Japanese submarine class, launched 1939-42. These submarines, designated Type B, were scouting craft designed to work in conjunction with the Type A headquarters submarines. They were developed from the Type KD6 and construction was carried out parallel with that of the Type A and Type C submarine. For scouting the *I 15* Class submarines carried a single floatplane stowed in sections in a small circular hangar extending forward of the conning tower. On the deck casing forward of the hangar there was a catapult reaching almost to the bows.

In order to simplify design and construction and to speed delivery of the boats, as many aspects of the design equipment as possible were made common to all three types. Machinery was thus identical to the Type A *I 9* Class, though bunkerage was reduced and the radius of action was thus 2000 nautical miles less. Armament was the same as in *I 9* Class, except that only 17 torpedoes were carried.

Initially only six submarines (*I 15-I 25*) were ordered to this design under the 1937 Programme, but under the 1939 Programme a further 14 vessels were ordered. The boats entered service between September 1940 and April 1943 having been built at Kure navy yard (*I 15, I 26, I 30, I 37*), Yokosuka navy yard (*I 17, I 23, I 29, I 31, I 36*), Mitsubishi-Kobe (*I 19, I 25, I 28, I 33, I 35*), Kawasaki-Kobe (*I 21*), and Sasebo navy yard (*I 27, I 32, I 34, I 38, I 39*).

During the war a number of units had a 140-mm (5.5-in) gun added in front of the conning tower to enable the boats to act as attack submarines. Towards the end of 1944 *I 36* and *I 37* were modified to carry four Kaiten suicide submarines.

Displacement: 2584/3654 tons (surfaced/submerged) *Length:* 108.66 m (356 ft 6 in) oa *Beam:* 9.30 m (30 ft 6 in) *Draught:* 5.11 m (16 ft 9 in) *Machinery:* 2-shaft diesels/2 electric motors, 12 400 shp/2000 hp=23.5/8 knots (surfaced/submerged) *Armament:* 6 21-in (53-cm) torpedo tubes, 17 torpedoes; 1 140-mm (5.5-in); 2 25-mm (1-in) (1×2); 1 floatplane *Crew:* 94

No	launched	fate
I 15	3/39	war loss 2/11/42
I 17	7/39	war loss 19/8/43
I 19	9/39	war loss 25/11/43
I 21	2/40	war loss 29/11/43
I 23	11/39	marine casualty 14/2/42
I 25	6/40	war loss 3/9/43
I 26	4/40	marine casualty 25/10/44
I 27	6/40	war loss 12/2/44
I 28	12/40	war loss 17/5/42
I 29	9/40	war loss 26/7/44
I 30	9/40	war loss 13/10/42
I 31	3/41	war loss 12/5/43
I 32	12/40	war loss 24/4/44
I 33	5/41	marine casualty 13/6/44
I 34	9/41	war loss 13/11/43
I 35	9/41	war loss 22/11/43
I 36	11/41	surrendered and scuttled
I 37	10/41	war loss 19/11/44
I 38	4/42	war loss 12/11/44
I 39	4/42	war loss 26/11/43

***I 15* during service as a supply vessel, with two 'Daihatsu' tracked landing boats loaded on her deck. Ships in this class were modified during the war to take four or six Kaiten one-man suicide torpedoes for kamikaze missions against US warships**

Shikho Fukui

I 16

Japanese submarine class, built 1938-41. This was the third type of long-range submarine (Type C) that the Japanese planned. The Type C concentrated on a comprehensive offensive weapons outfit, and the *I 16* Class was designed as an attack submarine to work in conjunction with the Type A and Type B boats. The design was developed from the Type KD6 and was similar in many ways to the *I 15* Class, with the same machinery and performance figures. A single 140-mm (5.5-in) gun was mounted, but the torpedo armament was increased with the mounting of two extra bow tubes, together with three extra torpedoes. The clear space aft of the conning tower was provided with fittings for carrying midget submarines.

Five vessels were ordered to the new design and entered service during 1940-41. Towards the end of 1942, *I 16* was converted to a transport submarine with the midget submarine fittings on the after casing adapted to enable the submarine to carry a 14-m (46-ft) landing craft while some of the reload torpedoes were removed and the space used for cargo stowage.

Displacement: 2554/3561 tons (surfaced/submerged) *Length:* 109.27 m (358 ft 6 in) oa *Beam:* 9.14 m (30 ft) *Draught:* 5.33 m (17 ft 6 in) *Machinery:* 2-shaft diesels/2 electric motors, 12 400 shp/2000 hp=23.5/8 knots (surfaced/submerged) *Armament:* 8 53-cm (21-in) torpedo tubes, 20 torpedoes; 1 140-mm (5.5-in); 2 25-mm (1-in) *Crew:* 95

No	builder	launched	fate
I 16	Mitsubishi (Kobe)	7/38	war loss 19/5/44
I 18	Sasebo navy yard	11/38	war loss 11/2/43
I 20	Mitsubishi (Kobe)	1/39	marine casualty 10/10/43
I 22	Kawasaki (Kobe)	12/38	marine casualty 1/10/42
I 24	Sasebo navy yard	11/39	war loss 11/6/43

I 40

Japanese submarine class, built 1941-43. The six scouting submarines of the *I 40* Class ordered under the 1941 War Emergency Programme were developed from the *I 15* Class. Known as the Type B2 the design was almost identical to the *I 15*. A further eight submarines planned under the 1942 Programme were subsequently cancelled.

Certain units of the *I 40* Class, like some of the *I 15* Class, were modified for use as attack submarines, their aircraft facilities being replaced by an extra 140-mm (5.5-in) gun. *I 44* was refitted towards the end of 1944 to carry six Kaiten suicide submarines, the hangar, 140-mm gun and catapult being removed.

Displacement: 2624/3700 tons (surface/submerged) *Length:* 108.66 m (356 ft 6 in) oa *Beam:* 9.30 m (30 ft 6 in) *Draught:* 5.18 m (17 ft) *Machinery:* 2-shaft diesels/2 electric motors, 11 000 shp/2000 hp=23.5/8 knots (surfaced/submerged) *Armament:* 6 53-cm (21-in) torpedo tubes, 17 torpedoes; 1 140-mm (5.5-in); 2 25-mm (1-in); 1 floatplane *Crew:* 94

No	builder	completed	war loss
I 40	Kure navy yard	7/43	11/43
I 41	Kure navy yard	9/43	11/44
I 42	Kure navy yard	11/43	3/44
I 43	Sasebo navy yard	11/43	2/44
I 44	Yokosuka navy yard	1/43	4/45
I 45	Sasebo navy yard	12/43	10/44

I 46

Japanese submarine class, built 1943-44. The six submarines comprising the class were ordered from the Sasebo navy yard under the 1941 War Programme. Only three were laid down, the others being cancelled in 1943, and a further four units planned under the 1942 Programme were also cancelled. Known as the Type C2 attack submarines, the design was identical to that of the *I 16* Class, except that they lacked fittings to carry midget submarines.

Towards the end of 1944, *I 47* and *I 48* were altered to carry four Kaiten submarines and *I 47* was later refitted to carry six.

I 46 was sunk by the US destroyer *Helm* on October 28, 1944, and *I 47* by the destroyers *Conklin, Corbesier* and *Raby* on January 23, 1945. *I 47* was surrendered at the end of the war and scuttled by the US Navy.

Displacement: 2557/3564 tons (surfaced/submerged) *Length:* 109.3 m (358 ft 6 in) oa *Beam:* 9.1 m (29 ft 9 in) *Draught:* 5.3 m (17 ft 6 in) *Machinery:* 2-shaft diesels/2 electric motors 12 400 shp/2000 hp=23.5/8 knots (surfaced/submerged) *Armament:* 8 53-cm (21-in) torpedo tubes, 20 torpedoes; 1 140-mm (5.5-in); 2 25-mm (1-in) (2×1) *Crew:* 95

No	launched	completed
I 46	1943	2/44
I 47	1943	7/44
I 48	1944	9/44

I 52

Japanese submarine class, built 1942-44. Ordered under the 1941 Additional Programme this class (Type C3) was practically identical with the previous *I 46* Class, except for its lower-powered diesels. They were, however, more powerfully armed with a second 140-mm (5.5-in) gun sited abaft the conning tower. Torpedo armament was also modified, only six tubes instead of eight being mounted.

Under the 1941 War Programme five submarines had been planned with another 15 under the 1942 Programme. Only three submarines, *I 52, I 53* and *I 55*, were completed. The orders for the remainder were cancelled in 1943.

A further class of 25 submarines to a modified design (Type C4) was planned under the 1942 Modified Programme, but this too was cancelled in 1943. The Type C4 design displaced 2756 tons, an increase of about 190 tons, and with its more powerful diesels would have reached a speed of 20.5 knots. Armament would have been the same as in the *I 46* Class.

I 53 was modified early in 1945 to carry four Kaiten suicide submarines (subsequently increased to six), and her gun armament was completely removed. *I 52* and *I 55* were sunk in action with US forces during the summer of 1944. *I 53* surrendered at the end of the war and was scuttled by American naval forces.

Displacement: 2564/3644 tons (surfaced/submerged) *Length:* 108.66 m (356 ft 6 in) oa *Beam:* 9.30 m (30 ft 6 in) *Draught:* 5.11 m (16 ft 9 in) *Machinery:* 2-shaft diesels/2 electric motors, 4700 shp/1200 hp=17.75/6.5 knots (surfaced/submerged) *Armament:* 6 53-cm (21-in) torpedo tubes, 19 torpedoes; 2 140-mm (5.5-in); 2 25-mm (1-in) *Crew:* 95

No	launched	completed
I 52	1943	12/43
I 53	1943	2/44
I 55	1943	4/44

I 54

Japanese submarine class, built 1942-44. The *I 54* Class (Type B3) was the final development of the scouting submarines to reach operational status. Like the late Types A and C, the Type B3 was almost identical to preceding types except for the lower-powered diesels and increased bunkerage. The radius of action was thus increased from the 14 000 nautical miles of the Type B2 (*I 40* Class) to 21 000 nautical miles. A floatplane hangar and catapult were fitted.

Seven vessels were originally ordered and a further 14 were planned under the 1942 Modified Programme. Only three of these boats were built, the orders and plans for the remainder being cancelled in 1943.

An improved Type B4 Class of 18 vessels was planned under the 1942 Modified Programme. Displacement would have been increased to 2800 tons with a surfaced speed of 22.5 knots from more powerful diesel engines. It was also planned to fit a total of eight 53-cm (21-in) torpedo tubes with 16 torpedoes and, for the first time since the completion of *I 22*, the boats planned would have carried eight mines. The planned Type B4 vessels were cancelled in 1943.

Towards the end of the war *I 56* and *I 58* had their 140-mm (5.5-in) gun, the seaplane hangar and the catapult removed and were adapted to carry four (subsequently six) Kaiten submarines aft of the conning tower. On July 29, 1945, *I 58* sank the US cruiser *Indianapolis* which was carrying parts of an atomic bomb to the island of Guam. *I 54* and *I 56* were both sunk by US naval forces (*I 54* on October 23, 1944, during the Battle of Leyte Gulf; *I 58* was lost off Okinawa on April 18, 1945), while *I 58* was surrendered and subsequently scuttled by the Americans.

Displacement: 2607/3688 tons (surfaced/submerged) *Length:* 108.7 m (356 ft 6 in) oa *Beam:* 9.3 m (30 ft 6 in) *Draught:* 5.2 m (17 ft) *Machinery:* 2-shaft diesels/2 electric motors, 4700 shp/1200 hp=17.75/6.5 knots (surfaced/submerged) *Armament:* 6 53-cm (21-in) torpedo tubes, 19 torpedoes; 1 140-mm (5.5-in); 2 25-mm (1-in) (1×2); 1 floatplane (deleted in some boats) *Crew:* 94

No	builder	completed
I 54	Yokosuka navy yard	3/44
I 56	Yokosuka navy yard	6/44
I 58	Yokosuka navy yard	9/44

I 76

Japanese submarine class, built 1940-43. The *I 76* Class (Type KD7) was the final development of the KD Type submarine. Ordered under the 1939 Programme, the ten vessels were laid down in 1940-41 and entered service between 1942-43.

No	fate
I 76	war loss 5/44
I 77	war loss 10/44
I 78	war loss 5/43
I 79	marine casualty 7/43
I 80	war loss 4/44
I 81	war loss 1/44
I 82	war loss 9/43
I 83	war loss 4/44
I 84	war loss 6/44
I 85	war loss 6/44

The basic design was practically identical to the *I 68* Class, but with a slight increase in tonnage and dimensions. In the original design only two twin 25-mm (1-in) AA weapons were specified. During construction, however, it was decided that a heavy deck gun was essential and so a 120-mm (4.7-in) weapon was sited forward of the conning tower, and one of the twin 25-mm (1-in) mounts was omitted.

The class was renumbered on May 20, 1942, the original numbers all being increased by 100.

I 176, *I 177* and *I 181* were converted to transport submarines early in 1943 with the removal of the deck gun and some of the reload torpedoes, to provide space for internal cargo and fittings for a 14-m (46-ft) landing craft to be carried externally.

Displacement: 1833/2602 tons (surfaced/submerged) *Length:* 105.5 m (346 ft) oa *Beam:* 8.2 m (27 ft) *Draught:* 4.6 m (15 ft) *Machinery:* 2-shaft diesels/2 electric motors, 8000 hp/1800 hp=23/8 knots (surfaced/submerged) *Armament:* 6 53-cm (21-in) torpedo tubes, 12 torpedoes; 1 120-mm (4.7-in); 2 25-mm (1-in) AA *Crew:* 86

I 201

Japanese submarine class. These Type ST submarines were designed after exhaustive tests and trials with the high underwater speed experimental submarine *No 71*. The hull was fully welded and very carefully streamlined; no gun or other deck obstruction was allowed which might impair the underwater performance. Even the 25-mm (1-in) mount retracted into a streamlined housing in the conning tower. The whole design concentrated on underwater performance, and new electric motors were installed giving the vessels an underwater speed of 19 knots. The high-capacity batteries carried sufficient energy to give the vessels an underwater radius of action of 135 nautical miles at 3 knots. The maximum submerged depth achieved by the submarines was 110 m (360 ft), the greatest depth achieved by a Japanese submarine. In many respects the vessels resembled the German Type XXI and when completed they were the first operational GUPPY type submarine in the world. Specially designed lightweight MAN diesels were used for surface propulsion, to keep displacement low. Only small bunkerage was provided, and the surfaced radius of action was only 5800 nautical miles with an endurance of 25 days.

Construction employed full mass-production techniques, with the submarines assembled in section in factories, the completed sections being welded together on the slip. The whole operation from start to finish took on average only ten months. A total of 23 units were ordered from the Kure navy yard under the 1943 Programme, construction commencing in March 1944. A further 76 units were projected under the 1944 Programme, but the progress of the war and the decision to concentrate construction on suicide units led to the cancellation of *I 209-I 223* in 1945, and the units in the 1944 Programme were never ordered at all. *I 201* entered service on February 2, 1945, followed on February 12 by *I 202* and on May 29 by *I 203*. *I 204-I 208* were laid down but never completed and all the boats were surrendered at the end of the war.

Displacement: 1291/1450 tons (surfaced/submerged) *Length:* 79 m (259 ft) oa *Beam:* 5.8 m (19 ft) *Draught:* 5.5 m (18 ft) *Machinery:* 2-shaft diesels/2 electric motors, 2750 bhp/5000 hp=15.75/19 knots (surfaced/submerged) *Armament:* 4 53-cm (21-in) torpedo tubes, 10 torpedoes; 2 25-mm (1-in) AA *Crew:* 31

I 351

Japanese submarine class, built 1943-45. The *I 351* Class (Type SH) submarines were designed as replenishment vessels for seaplanes and flying boats. The requirement laid emphasis on cargo capacity at the expense of armament, and although the design originally provided for a 140-mm (5.5-in) gun this was subsequently omitted. Speed and a high radius of action were not considered to be essential features, and at 14 knots surfaced the radius was 13 000 nautical miles. The cargo capacity was 390 tons, of which 11 tons was fresh water and 365 tons aviation fuel, while the remaining 14 tons was for aircraft armaments. These included either 60 250-kg (550-lb) bombs or 30 250-kg bombs and 15 torpedoes. Extra accommodation was provided for 13 aircrew.

Three submarines were ordered from the Kure navy yard under the 1941 Programme, with a further three in the 1942 Programme that was subsequently cancelled. The first vessel was laid down in May 1943, but by then the requirement for seaplane replenishment submarines had been superseded, and work on *I 351* and *I 352* proceeded very slowly. *I 353* was cancelled before being laid down and *I 351* and *I 352* were not launched until 1944. *I 351* was finally completed on January 28, 1945, and sunk by the US submarine *Bluefish* on July 14. The uncompleted hull of *I 352* was sunk in an air raid on June 22, 1945.

Displacement: 3512/4290 tons (surfaced/submerged) *Length:* 111 m (363 ft 9 in) oa *Beam:* 10.2 m (33 ft 6 in) *Draught:* 6.1 m (20 ft) *Machinery:* 2-shaft diesels/2 electric motors, 3700 shp/1200 hp=15.75/6.33 knots (surfaced/submerged) *Armament:* 4 53-cm (21-in) torpedo tubes (bow), 4 torpedoes; 4 3-in (76-mm) trench mortars (2×2); 7 25-mm (1-in) (2×2, 3×1) *Crew:* 77

I 361

Japanese submarine class, built 1943-44. The successful use of old submarines as transports for supplying garrisons on islands cut off by advancing US forces led the Japanese to design a special transport submarine, the Type D1. Armament and speed were of little importance but high endurance and high radius of action were essential. The radius of action was 15 000 nautical miles at 10 knots with 120 nautical miles at 3 knots submerged, and the vessels had an endurance of 60 days.

The design provided for a deck gun and two bow 53-cm (21-in) torpedo tubes. *I 361* was completed with the tubes, which were found to produce a wave. The bow tubes were therefore omitted on all subsequent units, and the bow section on these vessels was streamlined, and 2 m (6 ft 6 in) longer than the original design. The conning tower was also redesigned to a more streamlined shape. Of the 82 tons of cargo, 22 tons were stored in watertight containers between the deck casing and the pressure hull.

Eleven units were ordered under the 1942 Programme, and one slightly modified unit *(I 372)* under the 1943 Programme. A further 92 units planned under the 1943 Programme were never ordered. All surviving units were converted at the end of January 1945 to carry five Kaiten suicide submarines, the deck gun being removed and the fittings for the landing craft adapted. Thus modified the submarines carried five Kaiten.

Displacement: 1779/2215 tons (surfaced/submerged) *Length:* 75.60 m (248 ft) oa *Beam:* 8.92 m (29 ft 3 in) *Draught:* 4.72 m (15 ft 6 in) *Machinery:* 2-shaft diesels/2 electric motors, 1350 shp/1200 hp=13/6.5 knots (surfaced/submerged) *Armament:* 2 53-cm (21-in) torpedo tubes (*I 361* only); 1 140-mm (5.5-in); 2 25-mm (1-in) *Crew:* 60

No	completed	fate
I 361	5/44	war loss 30/5/5
I 362	5/44	war loss 18/1/45
I 363	7/44	war loss 20/10/45
I 364	6/44	war loss 16/9/44
I 365	8/44	war loss 28/11/44
I 366	8/44	surrendered
I 367	3/44	surrendered
I 368	8/44	war loss 27/2/45
I 369	10/44	surrendered
I 370	9/44	war loss 26/2/45
I 371	10/44	war loss 24/2/45
I 372	11/44	war loss 18/7/45

I 373

Japanese submarine class, built 1944-45. This class was a development of the *I 361* Class and was known as the Type D2. Apart from a slight increase in displacement the design was almost identical to the *I 361.* Cargo capacity was increased at the expense of the vessel's radius of action by using some of the diesel-fuel tanks for the storage of other types of fuel. Originally the craft were to have been armed with two twin 76-mm (3-in) trench mortars and seven 25-mm (1-in) guns, but they were completed with a 140-mm (5.5-in) deck gun, and two 25-mm (1-in).

The loss of many of the islands they were to have supplied led to the cancellation of many of the submarines ordered to this design. Six were originally ordered from the Yokosuka navy yard under the 1943 Programme, but *I 373-I 378* were subsequently cancelled as were 140 units planned under the 1944 Programme.

Displacement: 1926/2240 tons (surfaced/submerged) *Length:* 74 m (242 ft 9 in) oa *Beam:* 8.29 m (29 ft 3 in) *Draught:* 5.03 m (16 ft 6 in) *Machinery:* 2-shaft diesels/2 electric motors, 1750 shp/1200 hp=13/6.5 knots (surfaced/submerged) *Armament:* 1 140-mm (5.5-in); 2 25-mm (1-in) *Crew:* 60

No	fate
I 373	war loss 13/8/45
I 374	work ceased 3/45, scrapped

I 400

Japanese submarine class, built 1943-45. These submarines were the largest in the world when completed, having been built expressly at Admiral Yamamoto's request for vessels to mount a long-range bombardment mission against the Panama Canal. The design finally arrived at combined the three roles previously covered by the Type A, B and C designs. The first design, which provided for two small bomber seaplanes to be carried on a displacement of 4550 tons, was revised to provide for three seaplanes. The redesigned hangar area also enclosed the aircraft armaments of four torpedoes, three 800-kg (1760-lb) bombs and eight 250-kg (550-lb) bombs. The displacement rose to 5223 tons. To keep the draught within the required limits the hull form was redesigned, and instead of the normal vertical double-hull arrangement a double hull on its side like a pair of spectacles was adopted.

Propulsion was provided by four diesels coupled two to a shaft, one set being installed in each of the hull cylinders. The submarines were to be equipped with snorkels, and the unconventional hull design meant that two separate sets of snorkel tubes had to be provided. The engines in the starboard hull were supplied by a set in fixed curved pipes in the conning tower; the port engines were fed by a second set on a mast which retracted into a well in the deck casing.

In spite of their size and unwieldiness these submarines achieved a reasonable performance. The radius of action and endurance were the highest of any submarine of the period, with sufficient supplies for 90 days and fuel for a surfaced radius of 37 500 nautical miles at 14 knots. The maximum submerged depth was 100 m (325 ft).

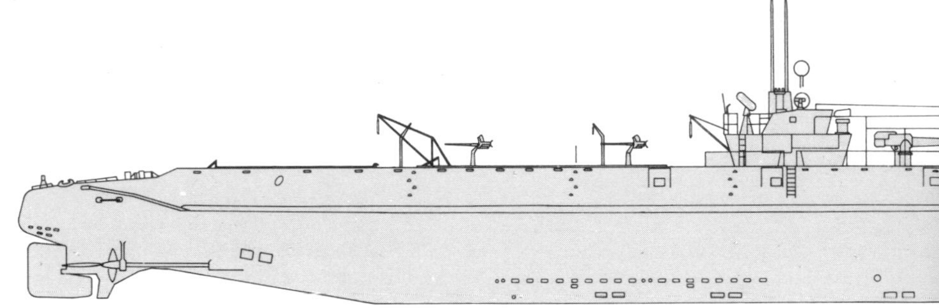

The *I 361* Class, or Type D1, submarines were designed to carry supplies to isolated Japanese garrisons in the Pacific and had a surface radius of action of 15 000 nautical miles at 10 knots

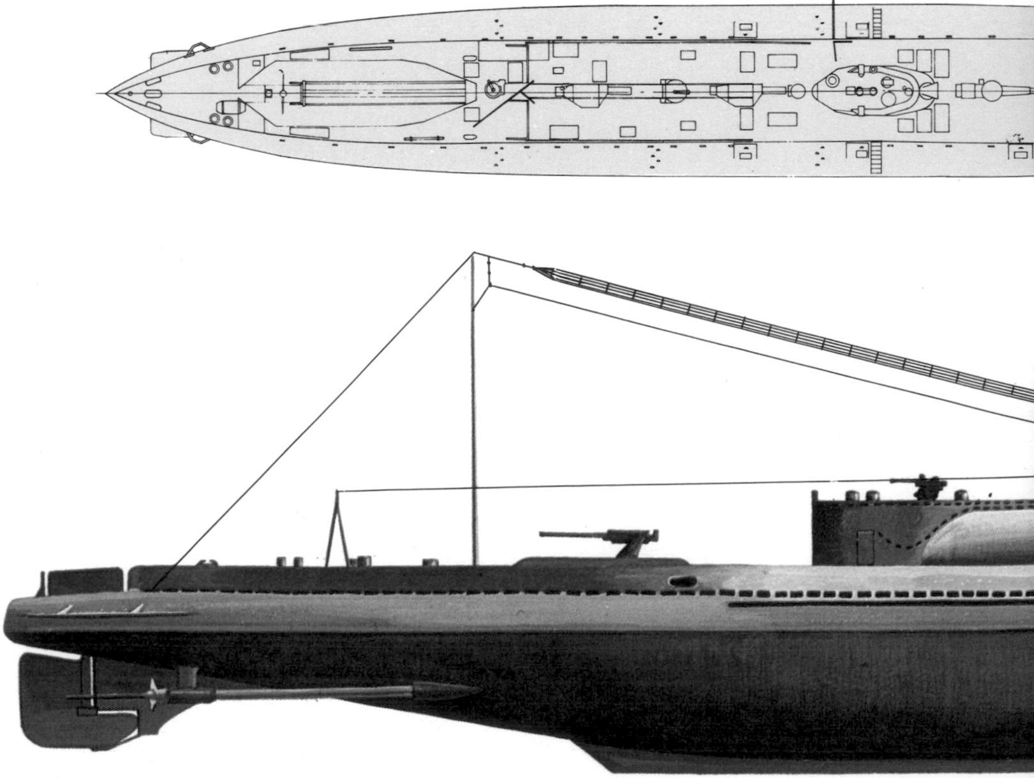

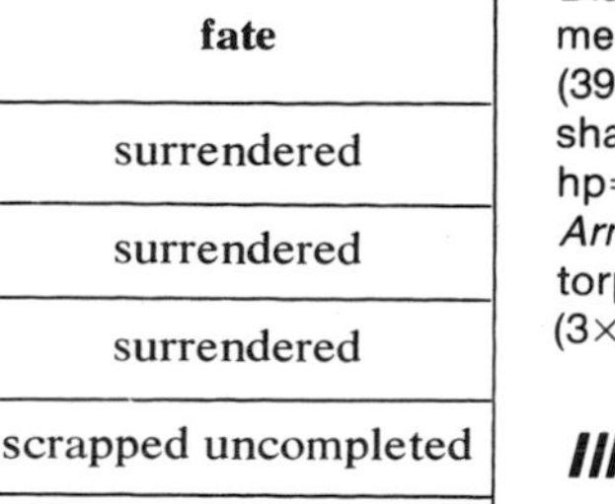

No	completed	fate
I 400	12/44	surrendered
I 401	1/45	surrendered
I 402	7/45	surrendered
I 404	—	scrapped uncompleted
I 405	—	scrapped uncompleted

With the design complete, the first vessel was ordered under the 1942 Programme, though this Programme was subsequently cancelled. But for the personal intervention of Admiral Yamamoto the order would not have been replaced, as the Japanese admiralty had lost faith in large vulnerable submarines. Yamamoto insisted that 18 units be ordered in the new 1942 Programme, and five were laid down, the rest being cancelled in March 1945. The design of *I 402* was altered during construction and she was completed as a refuelling submarine.

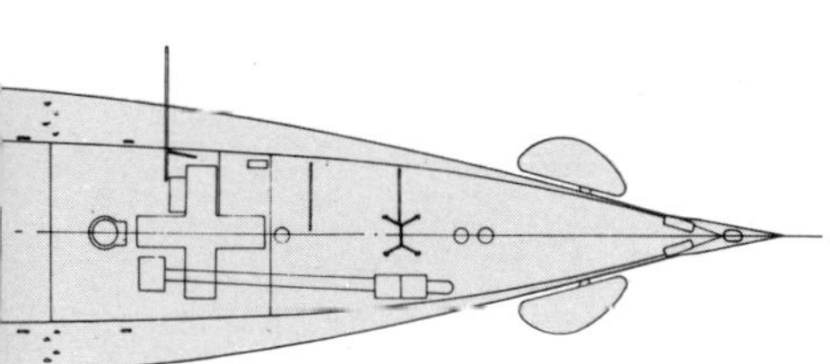

Displacement: 5223/6560 tons (surfaced/submerged) *Length:* 122 m (400 ft 3 in) *Beam:* 12 m (39 ft 4 in) *Draught:* 7 m (23 ft) *Machinery:* 2-shaft 4 diesels/electric motors, 7700 shp/2400 hp=18.75/6.5 knots (surfaced/submerged) *Armament:* 8 21-in (53-cm) torpedo tubes, 20 torpedoes; 1 140-mm (5.5-in); 10 25-mm (1-in) (3×3, 1×1); 3 seaplanes *Crew:* 144

Illustrious

British aircraft carrier class, built 1937-41. In 1935, the Admiralty took a radical step by deciding that the Royal Navy's next generation of aircraft carriers should be included in the same protection class as the big-gun units. This was to enable them not merely to stay afloat when hit but also to remain in action, by virtue of protection of their main armament, the aircraft complement.

Previous carriers had been armoured, but only on the lower hangar or main deck over machinery and magazines and in a waterline belt. The *Illustrious* Class ships were to have a hangar proof against 227 kg (500 lb) bombs or 152-mm (6-in) shells. This meant armouring the flight deck, and extending the vertical armour upwards to meet it. The flight deck between the lifts was 76 mm (3 in) thick and the hangar walls, like the belt, were 114 mm (4.5 in) thick. Both ends of the hangar could be closed off from the lift wells (elevator pits) by armoured doors. The hangar deck was proof only against splinters.

Although 5000 tons of armour was worked into the design, the displacement was limited by treaty to 23 000 tons—the same as *Ark Royal*, which had 3500 tons less armour. *Illustrious* was therefore built appreciably shorter than *Ark Royal* and, because the flight deck armour weighed 1500 tons, the second hangar deck was omitted to reduce the freeboard by 6.7 m (22 ft) and preserve stability. Designed aircraft capacity was reduced from 60 to 33, with a consequent saving in aircrew accommodation, aircraft-ordnance stowage and weight and aviation fuel, all of which contributed to keeping the displacement within the treaty limit.

Illustrious otherwise followed the general pattern established by *Ark Royal*. It featured a full-length flight deck, somewhat enlarged island and main gun armament of four pairs of 4.5-in (114-mm) dual-purpose twin turrets (unlike *Ark Royal*'s open mountings) located below flight-deck level on each side, fore and aft. Only one catapult was fitted, completely within the forward flight-deck structure, and two very narrow lifts which were unable to strike down aircraft without folding wings.

Like *Ark Royal*, the *Illustrious* Class had a three-shaft machinery installation, in order to economize on the size of the waterline beam. *Illustrious* was rather more powerful, but due to a slight increase in beam and a marked increase in draught, she was about a knot slower than *Ark Royal* on trials and two knots slower at sea.

Illustrious and *Victorious* were ordered in 1937 and *Formidabie* and *Indomitable* later in the same year. *Indomitable* was completed to a slightly different design. Shortage of armour plate contributed to fairly long building times, and *Illustrious* was not completed until May 1940, *Formidable* in November 1940, and *Victorious* in April 1941.

Illustrious was launched on April 5, 1939, and sailed from the Vickers-Armstrongs yard at Barrow just over a year later. By the time she was accepted by the Royal Navy, on May 24, she had been fitted with a warning and fighter-control radar—the first to be installed in an aircraft carrier.

After a workup in the Bermuda area, *Illustrious* was despatched to join the Mediterranean Fleet, based at Alexandria. Between September 1 and December 31, 1940, her 18 Fairey Swordfish raided numerous Italian ports and airfields around the eastern Mediterranean, as well as striking shipping at sea. Undoubtedly her most successful operation was the attack on the Italian fleet in Taranto harbour on November 11-12, for which additional Swordfish were borrowed from *Eagle*: of the 20 aircraft which attacked, only two were lost, while the Italian battleship *Cavour* was sunk and *Littorio* and *Caio Duilio* had to be beached.

Although subjected to air attack on several occasions, *Illustrious* remained undamaged until January 10, 1941, thanks largely to the efforts of her 15 Fairey Fulmar intercepters, which destroyed 25 Italian aircraft. On that day, she was attacked by Ju 87 Stukas off Malta and sustained seven direct bomb hits. Only one bomb, of 500 kg (1100 lb), penetrated the flight-deck armour, the remainder striking outside the hangar area. Still on fire, but under her own steam, *Illustrious* reached Malta, where she remained for emergency repairs until January 23. Further repairs were undertaken at Alexandria and on March 20 she left Egypt for Norfolk navy yard, Virginia.

She spent six months in dockyard hands, returning to the United Kingdom in

I 402 was a member of the *I 400* Class, the largest submarines built up to that time. They were intended to launch their aircraft in an attack on the Panama Canal, but the scheme came to nothing

December 1941. Modifications to her radar and armament were carried out after her arrival and she was not ready to begin working up until the end of February 1942. This workup was cut short by the need for carriers to take part in the occupation of the Vichy French naval harbour of Diego Suarez, at the northern end of Madagascar, and *Illustrious* sailed for the Indian Ocean on March 23, 1942. On May 5, she and *Indomitable* began three days of operations against the Vichy air and naval forces while British and Commonwealth troops landed and captured the town. *Illustrious*'s 21 Swordfish sank two submarines and an armed merchant cruiser and shared in sinking a large sloop; the 20 Grumman Martlet fighters also saw action, shooting down seven Vichy aircraft.

Illustrious remained in the Indian Ocean for the remainder of 1942, undertaking one diversionary operation, to distract Japanese attention from the south-west Pacific at the time of the Guadalcanal landings in August. In September, her aircraft covered the occupation of southern Madagascar, achieving their task without firing their guns or dropping bombs. For this operation, she had embarked 45 aircraft (18 Swordfish, 21 Martlets and six Fulmars); 41 of these could be stowed in the hangar, leaving four Martlets permanently parked on deck. Permanent deck parking had never been favoured by the Royal Navy, although it had always been a US Navy procedure, but it had to be adopted in order to embark as many aircraft as possible for operations.

Leaving the Indian Ocean in January 1943, *Illustrious* was refitted in the UK between February and June. In July, she took part in a diversionary operation off Norway, where her Martlets shot down two flying boats, and in August she sailed to join the Mediterranean Fleet. By now she had embarked 12 of the new Fairey Barracudas, 28 Martlets and ten Supermarine Seafires, the latter parked on deck. Even if there had been room for them in the hangar, they could not be struck down the narrow lifts. Between September 9-11, *Illustrious* and *Formidable* provided generally uneventful fighter patrols over a force of escort carriers which were supporting the invasion of Salerno. Thereafter, both carriers left the Mediterranean, *Formidable* to refit and *Illustrious* to prepare for another Indian Ocean deployment.

She arrived in Ceylon from Britain on January 31, 1944, with 21 Barracudas and 28 Vought F4U Corsairs embarked. Because of the lack of overhead clearance in *Illustrious*, the American-built fighters' rounded wingtips had had to be clipped to enable them to be spread and folded in the hangar. The new air group first saw action on April 19 when, in company with *Saratoga*, strikes were launched against Sabang, Sumatra. A month later, on May 17, the two carriers attacked Surabaja, Java, harbour and oil refineries, *Illustrious* having replaced her Barracudas with 18 Grumman TBF Avengers for this one operation.

Saratoga left after this operation and on June 21 *Illustrious* undertook a solo strike against the Andaman Islands. For this operation, she embarked an extra 14 Corsairs at the expense of six Barracudas: this was the greatest number of aircraft ever operated from *Illustrious* and at one time on May 21 she had 51 of the 57 airborne.

After another raid on Sabang, on July 25, in company with *Victorious*, she left for a refit at Durban and did not return to Trincomalee until November 2. In anticipation of forthcoming deployment to the Pacific, the Barracudas had given way to the faster and longer-ranged Avengers, and the number of Corsairs had been increased to 36.

The first strike was against Sumatran oil installations on December 20, but bad weather led to disappointing results. On January 24 and 29, 1945, however, *Illustrious*

HMS *Illustrious* while part of the British task force in the Far East. During strikes against Japanese installations she became the target for suicide attacks, was damaged on April 6, 1944, and withdrew from operations

IWM

was part of the carrier force which made devastating raids on the Palembang refineries, her contribution being 24 Avenger and 52 Corsair offensive sorties on the two days.

The force, designated the British Pacific Fleet, proceeded from the launching area to Sydney, which was to be the rear base for Pacific operations. *Illustrious* had been damaged by friendly AA fire on January 29 and had experienced propeller shaft vibration during the passage to Sydney and required docking for repairs and investigation of the centre shaft. The latter proved to be defective and the propeller was removed, reducing her maximum speed to 24 knots. The other three carriers of the fleet had sailed by the time *Illustrious* undocked, but she rejoined them before they left the forward base at Manus for operations in support of the American invasion of Okinawa.

Between March 26 and April 13, *Illustrious* launched 443 combat sorties on nine strike days. Targets included airfields in the Sakishima Gunto Archipelago and on Formosa. Suicide aircraft attacked on April 1 and 6. *Illustrious* was the target on the second occasion, and although her automatic AA weapons deflected the kamikaze so that it only clipped the island, the explosion of the bomb under water caused damage, the extent of which was not realized at the time. She was relieved by *Formidable* on April 14 and retired to the US forward base at Leyte, where divers examined the hull and reported that the outer plating and internal frames were cracked. Temporary repairs were effected and *Illustrious* returned to Britain via Sydney, her speed now restricted to 19 knots.

She was taken in hand for refit on return at the end of June, the work being expected to take four months. The end of the war in mid-August resulted in her completion being delayed until June 1946, the alterations being more extensive than originally planned. The forward end of the flight deck was extended and remodelled, the catapult was modified to launch heavier aircraft. The aviation-fuel capacity was increased by 30%, overcoming one of the most serious disadvantages of the class—the 229 750 litres (50 540 Imp gal) which had been barely adequate for 33 aircraft was just not sufficient for more than 50.

Between 1946 and the end of 1954, *Illustrious* was employed as the Home Fleet trials and training carrier, only once or twice embarking front-line squadrons for exercises. During this period, the initial deck-landing trials with the Royal Navy's first generation of jet aircraft were carried out aboard *Illustrious* but, unlike her sister ship *Victorious*, she was not considered for modernization. Laid up in reserve in December 1954, she was sold for scrapping on November 3, 1956.

Displacement: 23 000 tons (standard), 29 110 tons (full load) (from 1946 26 000 tons [standard], 31 630 tons [full load]) *Length:* 225.5 m (740 ft) (from 1946 229.6 m [753 ft 3 in]) *Beam:* 29.2 m (95 ft 9 in) *Draught:* 8.8 m (29 ft) *Machinery:* 3 sets geared steam turbines, 3 shafts, 113 300 shp=30.5 knots approx *Aircraft:* 33 *Armament:* 16 4.5-in (114-mm) DP (8×2); 88 2-pdr (40-mm) AA (6×8, 5×8); 3 40-mm (1.57-in) Bofors AA (3×1); 52 20-mm (0.79-in) Bofors AA (52×1) *Crew:* 1229 (from 1946, 1997)

Aldo Fraccaroli

Intrepido (above) and Impavido (below), the Italian navy's first missile-armed warships

Giorgio Arra

Impavido

Italian destroyer class. Two guided-missile destroyers were authorized under the 1956-57 and 1958-59 Programmes, the first missile-armed ships to be built for the Italian navy. *Impavido* (D.570) was launched at Riva Trigoso on May 25, 1962, and *Intrepido* (D.571) was launched at Livorno on October 21 the same year. On her sea trials *Impavido* reached 34.5 knots in light condition. In general the design follows that of the *Impetuoso* Class, though the *Impavido*s have more sheer to the forecastle, a bigger superstructure and taller funnels. The same twin 5-in (127-mm) of US Navy pattern is mounted forward, and a single-arm Tartar missile-launcher is mounted on a circular deckhouse at the after end of the superstructure. There are also four single 76-mm (3-in)/52-cal automatic guns abreast of the after funnel and triple Mk 32 torpedo tubes for antisubmarine torpedoes on either side of the bridge.

During 1974-76 both ships were modernized, and the bulky fire-control director was replaced by an Elsag (Elettronica San Giorgio) Argo NA 10 system. Two SPG-51 directors are fitted to control the Tartar missiles, together with an SPS-12 search radar and SPS-39 3-D long-range surveillance radar. They are also fitted with a hull-mounted SQS-23 sonar and a flight deck for operation of an antisubmarine helicopter, but have no hangar or maintenance facilities.

Since entering service in 1963-64 both ships have been actively employed with NATO forces in the Mediterranean and Atlantic. The Tartar missile system is to be replaced by Standard, but this will involve no outward alterations.

Displacement: 3201 tons (standard), 3851 tons (full load) *Length:* 131.3 m (430 ft 9 in) *Beam:* 13.6 m (44 ft 7½ in) *Draught:* 4.5 m (14 ft 9 in) *Machinery:* 2-shaft geared steam turbines, 70 000 shp=33 knots *Armament:* 1 RIM-24 Tartar SAM launcher; 2 5-in (127-mm)/38-cal DP (1×2); 4 78-mm (3-in)/62-cal AA (4×1); 6 32.4-cm (12.75-in) torpedo tubes (2×3) *Crew:* 335

The Italian destroyer *Impetuoso*. With her sister the *Indomito* she was among the first warships built by the Italians in the 1950s

Impetuoso

Italian destroyer class. As the first instalment of a massive rearmament programme, which was partially funded by US money, Italy began to rebuild her naval forces in 1952. The first destroyers ordered were a pair of ships broadly based on the *Gearing* Class, but with more beam to allow a greater weight of antisubmarine and antiaircraft armament.

The armament was conventional: two twin 127-mm (5-in)/38-cal guns forward and aft, and quadruple and twin 40-mm (1.57-in) Bofors AA guns disposed on the beam amidships. The fire control and the guns were supplied from the US; an Italian Menon triple-barrelled antisubmarine mortar was installed in B position; depth-charge racks were installed on the quarterdeck; and single Mk 25 53-cm (21-in) A/S torpedo tubes were installed on the beam between the funnels.

Indomito was launched on August 7, 1955, from the Ansaldo yard, Livorno, and *Impetuoso* from the Cantieri Navali dell'Tireno yard on September 16, 1956. Both ships exceeded 35 knots on trials. They have been refitted since 1966, the principal alteration being the replacement of the Mk 25 single torpedo tubes by triple Mk 32 tubes. A search radar (type SGS/6B) and SFS/6O fire-control radar are fitted, with Mk 34 radars for the Mk 51 40-mm (1.57-in) directors. The hull-mounted sonar is an SQS/11. By the late 1970s these ships had become obsolescent, lacking a good AA defence, and were due for decommissioning and replacement by more modern destroyers.

Displacement: 2755 tons (standard), 3800 tons (full load) *Length:* 127.6 m (418 ft 8 in) oa *Beam:* 13.3 m (43 ft 8 in) *Draught:* 5.3 m (17 ft 5 in) *Machinery:* 2-shaft geared steam turbines, 65 000 shp=34 knots *Armament:* 4 127-mm (5-in)/38-cal DP (2×2); 16 40-mm (1.57-in)/56-cal AA (2×4, 4×2); 1 triple Menon A/S mortar; 2 53-cm (21-in) torpedo tubes (2×1) *Crew:* 315

Implacable

British aircraft carrier class. Although *Implacable* and *Indefatigable* are usually described as the fifth and sixth units of the *Illustrious* Class, or as improved *Indomitables*, the 1938 design of fleet carrier to which they were built was quite new. Apart from standard displacement and beam, which were limited by treaty and by dock-gate dimensions, only the well-proven external layout and main armament remained unchanged.

The naval staff had demanded greater speed and an increased aircraft complement, compared with *Indomitable.* Existing machinery could not give the extra power needed for 32 knots on three shafts and so an extra set of boilers, turbines and a fourth shaft had to be squeezed into the width allowed for three in earlier fleet carriers. The extra hangar space was found by extending the lower hangar further forward than in *Indomitable.* As the hull was extended by only 7.9 m (26 ft) and the hangar was 14 m (46 ft) longer, internal accommodation was very cramped and required considerable rearrangement.

The Royal Navy had not really wanted to reduce the thickness of the hangar walls in *Indomitable,* and in the new class the thickness was increased to 51 mm (2 in) and at the same time the lower hangar deck was armoured over the machinery. The extra armour required topweight compensations and so the height of the lower hangar was reduced by 61 cm (2 ft), both hangars now having overhead clearance of 4.26 m (14 ft). The lifts were identical to those in *Indomitable,* but a new type of catapult was installed. All the flight-deck machinery was intended to handle aircraft of up to 9070 kg (20 000 lb) weight. A considerable 'stretch' was thus built into the class, since the Royal Navy's heaviest aircraft weighed barely half this figure in 1939.

The main external differences between the *Implacable* Class and their predecessors were the much enlarged funnel and longer island. The fire-control director, previously mounted above the bridge, was moved down to a position abaft the funnel and a multiple pom-pom was shifted from the flight deck abaft the island to below the port deck-edge, both changes being made to improve stability.

Implacable was ordered in 1938 and *Indefatigable* a year later. Construction was halted in 1940 by order of Churchill and even after it was resumed at the end of the year little priority was given to completion. *Implacable* took five years to build and was not commissioned until August 28, 1944, by which time her sister was fully operational and actually at sea in combat.

Indefatigable was completed by the John Brown Clydeside yard on May 3, 1944, and after trials which included the first deck landings on a British carrier by a twin-engined aircraft (the de Havilland Mosquito), she worked up at Scapa Flow. Since the low hangars prevented her from embarking Corsairs and since insufficient Hellcats were available, her fighter wing had to be equipped with Supermarine Seafires. Though Seafires were excellent intercepters, their low fuel capacity made them indifferent general-purpose fighters, and fuselage and undercarriage weaknesses made them poor carrier aircraft. As well as the 24 Seafires, *Indefatigable* embarked 21 Barracudas and the first squadron of Fairey Firefly two-seat fighters to go to sea.

The first operation, a fighter sweep off Bergen on August 3, 1944, was aborted by low cloud, but a week later the fighters covered a minelaying strike by Grumman Avengers from two escort carriers. Later in the month, all the Home Fleet's operational carriers took part in a series of strikes on the German battleship *Tirpitz* lying in her Kaafjord, Norway, anchorage. Attacks were delivered on August 22, 24 and 29, but the enemy's smoke screen resulted in only two hits being scored, one by an *Indefatigable* aircraft on August 24. On return from this operation, the carrier was modified for Pacific operations.

The Seafire wing was transferred to *Implacable*, which made her operational debut on October 19, when her Fireflys found *Tirpitz* at Tromsö. On October 26, *Implacable* began a three-day antishipping operation off Norway, in which her aircraft sank seven ships and damaged 14 others, as well as driving a U-Boat aground as a total loss.

Returning to land *Indefatigable*'s fighter wing and to work up her own, *Implacable* spent a month in the Scapa Flow area before going back to the Norwegian coast. On November 27, 11 Barracudas supported by 24 fighters attacked a convoy sinking two ships and damaging four others and two escorts, at no cost to the carrier aircraft. Soon afterwards *Implacable* sustained serious damage to her forward hull plating in a gale, and after launching one further mission on December 8 she had to return for dockyard repairs.

Indefatigable had meanwhile arrived in Ceylon to join the Eastern Fleet. Between November 19 and New Year's Day 1945, she worked up with the other armoured carriers of the fleet, all of which were now armed with Grumman Avengers in place of Barracudas. *Indefatigable* now possessed 40 Seafires out of a total air group of 73 aircraft.

Her first operation was a strike on the Pankalan Brandan oil refinery at Medan on January 4, 1945, in company with *Indomitable* and *Victorious*. This strike was a great success, as were two attacks on the Palembang refineries on January 24 and 29, while on passage to Sydney, where the redesignated British Pacific Fleet arrived on February 10.

A month later, the main body sailed for the combat area, off the Sakishima Gunto. The operation, with the British carrier force covering the Okinawa invasion against interference from the direction of Formosa, began on March 26. No enemy attacks were delivered against the fleet until April 1, when *Indefatigable* was the first British carrier to be hit by a kamikaze. This was a Mitsubishi Zero which hit the flight deck at the base of the island and broke up on the 76-mm (3-in) deck armour, causing 29 casualties. The fire on the deck was extinguished in 15 minutes and aircraft were landing within 35 minutes. An hour later, the ship was fully operational once again.

Strike missions were flown by the Avengers and Fireflys on 12 days up to April 20, while the Seafires provided the majority of the fleet's low- and medium-level fighter patrols. These intercepters suffered heavy losses through landing accidents. No fewer than 21 were written off and six damaged beyond the ship's capacity to repair them. The losses were made good during replenishments at sea and during a week spent at Leyte. In the second phase of the operation, which lasted during May 4-25, only nine Seafires were lost from all causes. Avenger and Firefly losses were light throughout and *Indefatigable* contributed over 1800 of the British Pacific Fleet's total of 5335 sorties between March 26 and May 25, 1945.

Implacable left the United Kingdom on March 10, 1945, and arrived at Sydney in mid-May, while the other carriers were off Sakishima. Before they returned, she left again for a 'training strike' on Truk, the bypassed Japanese naval base which now served as a target for units completing working up. (It was so used in a dummy run by the B-29 which was to undertake the first A-bomb raid.) *Implacable*'s 21 Avengers, 12 Fireflys and 48 Seafires flew 216 sorties against the main islands in the atoll on June 14-15, bombing, rocketing, and spotting for cruiser bombardments. The carrier proceeded to Manus, New Guinea, to await the fleet, whose next target was to be Japan itself. *Indefatigable*'s auxiliary machinery broke down shortly before the force left Sydney on June 28, and her first meeting with her sister ship, on July 7, was brief as the other ships were leaving Manus as she entered.

Implacable, Formidable and *Victorious* launched their first missions against Japan on July 17 and the honour of being the first British aircraft to fly over the Japanese home islands fell to the Fireflys of *Implacable*'s 1771 Squadron. *Indefatigable* joined in on July 24, and on that and five more days up to August 10, the four British carriers flew 2291 sorties. Airfields, the railways system, shipyards, factories, naval bases and coastal shipping were all attacked. Operations reached a climax on August 9, when 258 British strike sorties delivered over 120 tons of ordnance. *Indefatigable* and *Implacable*, with their larger air groups, were responsible for nearly two-thirds of the total, their

HMS *Implacable* at anchor in Scapa Flow during her service with the Home Fleet in 1944. She transferred to the Far East in May 1945

IWM

Seafires taking part in the offensive missions as well as providing defensive patrols.

Indefatigable remained to operate with the US 3rd Fleet when *Implacable* and the two other carriers departed for Australia after the strikes of August 10. She flew 78 sorties on August 14, in spite of bad weather, and the next day launched eight Fireflys for an offensive sweep, followed by six Avengers and eight Seafires sent to attack an airfield. The strike was intercepted by Zeros but the Seafires shot down eight of the fighters, and damaged three more, for the loss of one Seafire. This was officially the last combat of the war, for at the same time news of the Japanese surrender was received by the fleet.

Indefatigable remained with the American fleet until September 2, 1945, and was present at the surrender in Tokyo Bay. She returned to Sydney a fortnight later after a deployment which had sent her at sea for 64 days.

Both *Implacable* and *Indefatigable* remained with the British Pacific Fleet after the war, the latter making one cruise to Japan to bring back Allied prisoners of war before re-embarking her squadrons for a cruise to New Zealand. *Indefatigable* left Sydney at the end of January 1946 and reached Portsmouth on March 15. *Implacable* followed three months later, returning to the United Kingdom on June 3, 1946.

Indefatigable made one trooping voyage to the Far East during the second half of 1946 and then paid off into reserve, but *Implacable* recommissioned immediately for service as the Home Fleet's deck-landing training ship. Although an air group was allocated to her in late 1947, the two squadrons were experiencing considerable teething troubles and it was not until March 1949 that she embarked 13 de Havilland Sea Hornets and 12 Blackburn Firebrands. These were reinforced in the autumn of 1949 by the four de Havilland Sea Vampires of the Jet Fighter Evaluation Unit, which operated successfully from the carrier during a cruise to Gibraltar. In the summer of 1950 the 12 Fairey Barracudas of the Navy's only dedicated antisubmarine squadron joined for an exercise. In September 1950, she was placed in reserve, her future to be decided.

Meanwhile *Indefatigable* had been refitted as a training ship, her hangars being too low for modern aircraft but ideal for conversion to classrooms and messdecks. From 1950 she served in this role, being joined by *Implacable* from January 1952. In August 1954 both carriers paid off for the last time. *Implacable* was scrapped in late 1955 and her sister followed a year later.

Displacement: 23 450 tons (standard), 32 110 tons (full load) *Length:* 233.6 m (766 ft 6 in) *Beam:* 29.2 m (95 ft 9 in) *Draught:* 8.9 m (29 ft 4 in) *Machinery:* 4 sets geared steam turbines, 4 shafts 150 935 shp=32 knots *Aircraft:* 81 *Armament:* 16 4.5-in (114-mm) DP (8×2); 52/(*Indefatigable* 44) 2-pdr AA (3×4, 5×6/1×4, 5×8); 61/(*Indefatigable* 55) 20-mm (0.79-in) (61×1/55×1) *Crew:* 2300 approx

Independence

US aircraft carrier class, built 1942-43. In 1941 at the outbreak of the war in the Pacific, the US Navy possessed only seven fast carriers for fleet operations, and although 13 more (of the *Essex* Class) had been ordered in 1940 and 1941 only half-a-dozen of these could be expected to be operational before the end of 1943. As an emergency measure the US Navy in March 1942 ordered that nine light cruisers of the *Cleveland* Class should be completed as light carriers, capable of operating 45 aircraft. Five of the hulls had already been laid down, and three of the light carriers were commissioned by the end of March 1943. The last was laid down in November 1942 and was completed 13 months later. All were built by the New York Shipbuilding Corporation.

The original cruiser hull was completed up to the flush weather deck. Interior arrangements were altered to permit installation of bomb magazines, the ship command and control offices (which would normally have been situated in the bridge structure) and extra accommodation for personnel and stores. The hangar occupied a third of the length of the original weather deck, between two large rectangular lifts. The wooden flight deck formed the roof of the hangar, extending for 160 m (525 ft), leaving the forecastle and quarterdeck open. A diminutive island was located at the starboard deck-edge. The funnels were abaft the island in two pairs, angled outward with only short vertical portions to give a height of not more than 4.3 m (14 ft). Two parallel catapults were flush-mounted in the forward end of the flight deck.

The standard displacement of 11 000 tons was 1000 tons more than that of the *Cleveland* Class cruisers. Most of the excess was carried high up, and to restore stability shallow external bulges had to be added at and below the waterline, increasing the beam by 1.5 m (5 ft). In the first two ships, *Independence* (CVL.22) and *Princeton* (CVL.23), the cruiser's belt armour was omitted, but it was incorporated in all subsequent ships, having a thickness of 51 mm (2 in), increasing to 127 mm (5 in) outboard of the magazines. Deck armour was between 76-51 mm (3-2 in) thick, on the hangar and main decks.

The first four ships were originally armed with 22 40-mm (1.57-in) Bofors and five single 20-mm (0.79-in) Oerlikon AA guns distributed around the deck-edges and on the open forecastle, as well as a single 5-in (127-mm) 38-cal dual-purpose gun on the quarterdeck. The 5-in was removed in 1944 and replaced by a quadruple 40-mm mounting (and was fitted in the last five ships from completion) and the Oerlikons were doubled up.

The hangar was disappointingly small: only 65.5 m (215 ft) long and 17.7 m (58 ft) broad, it was smaller than those of the *Sangamon* and *Commencement Bay* Classes of escort carriers. The introduction of the large Grumman F6F Hellcat fighter and TBF Avenger torpedo-bomber resulted in the elimination of dive-bombers from the light carriers' air groups, so that the normal complement was 33 aircraft. There was a constant campaign within the Navy for the removal of the torpedo-bombers, but not until July 1945 was this implemented, too late to see action.

The name ship was laid down as the light cruiser *Amsterdam* in 1941, renamed *Independence* in March 1942 and launched on August 22 of the same year. Commissioned on January 15, 1943, she worked up in the Caribbean from the spring and arrived at San Francisco in early July. Most of August was spent at Pearl Harbor, exercising with the first two *Essex* Class carriers *Essex* and *Yorktown.*

The three carriers undertook their first strikes on September 1, 1943, when their aircraft attacked Marcus Island, 1600 km south-east of Tokyo. Five weeks later, on October 5-6, six of the new fast carriers, including three *Independence* Class ships out of the four which were then operational (*Independence, Princeton, Belleau Wood* and *Cowpens*) carried out an effective series of training strikes on Wake Island.

On November 11, *Independence* took part in a raid on Rabaul, New Guinea, with *Essex* and *Bunker Hill.* While the carriers' fighters were away escorting the strike, shore-based US Navy fighters patrolled over the task group, the Hellcats of VF-33 landing aboard *Independence* to refuel. The Japanese did attack but lost heavily without scoring any hits.

A week later, the task group began pre-invasion strikes on Tarawa, Gilbert Islands, continuing on November 19-20, the latter being the day of the landings by the Marines, who suffered the heavy losses that made Tarawa a byword. That evening, Mitsubishi Betty torpedo-bombers from the Marshall Islands attacked, and one of the six which broke through the defences scored a hit on *Independence*'s starboard quarter. In addition to the hole caused by the explosion, her bottom plates were badly damaged, a propeller shaft was bent and machinery spaces were flooded by a ruptured fire main. She was towed to Funafuti, where she was repaired sufficiently to enable her to return to Pearl Harbor and San Francisco under her own steam, arriving at the latter on January 2, 1944.

On July 4 she began her workup as a night carrier. Her fighter-direction organization and her radar outfit had been revised for this role during the refit and, in place of the 24 Hellcat day fighters and nine Avengers which were the standard load of a light carrier, she had embarked only five 'straight' F6F-3 Hellcats and 14 F6F-3N night fighters, as well as eight TBM-1D Avengers, equipped with a new lightweight high-definition radar.

Independence was in action again on September 6, 1944, when the whole of Task Force 58—eight large and eight light carriers—began preparatory strikes before the invasion of Peleliu. Lack of Japanese air opposition, by day or night, resulted in the virtual abandonment of *Independence*'s night role during the month which followed, her aircraft joining in the task force's mass daylight strikes on the Caroline Islands, the Palaus and the southern Philippines. When the carriers began their most daring operation to date, the neutralization of Okinawa and Formosa prior to the invasion of Leyte, *Independence* reverted to the night role and on October 12, her Hellcat night fighters were rewarded with five kills in four hours.

She continued to serve in a primarily defensive role during the Leyte operations later in October. On October 24, after the air-sea battle of the Sibuyan Sea, her Avengers shadowed the Japanese battle fleet which was to engage the escort carriers off Samar Island on the following day. Their warning was, however, ignored by the fleet commander,

No and name	completed	fate
CVL.22 *Independence* (ex-CL.59 *Amsterdam*)	1/43	sunk in weapons trials 30/1/51
CVL.23 *Princeton* (ex-CL.61 *Tallahassee*)	1/43	sunk by bomb 24/10/44
CVL.24 *Belleau Wood* (ex-CL.76 *New Haven*)	3/43	transferred to France as *Bois Bellau* 9/53; returned and scrapped 1962
CVL.25 *Cowpens* (ex-CL.77 *Huntington*)	5/43	scrapped 1962
CVL.76 *Monterey* (ex Cl.78 *Dayton*)	6/43	scrapped 1970
CVL.27 *Langley* (ex-CL.85 *Fargo*)	8/43	transferred to France as *Lafayette* 6/51; returned and scrapped 1964
CVL.28 *Cabot* (ex-CL.79 *Wilmington*)	7/43	transferred to Spain as *Dedalo* 8/67 (in service 1978)
CVL.29 *Bataan* (ex-CL.99 *Buffalo*)	11/43	scrapped 1959
CVL.30 *San Jacinto* (ex-CL.100 *Newark*)	12/43	stricken 1970

Admiral Halsey, who was diverted by the presence of the Japanese carriers, also being shadowed by *Independence*'s aircraft. The shadowers directed the main strike for a dawn attack but took no further part in the battle of Cape Engano, which saw the destruction of four Japanese carriers.

Thereafter *Independence* took part in operations off Luzon and accompanied Task Force 38 on its raiding cruise in the South China Sea between January 10-20, her aircraft delivering night attacks on Formosa, Hong Kong and Cam Ranh Bay, Indo-China, as well as scoring more night air-to-air kills. For this operation, *Enterprise* was also being used in the night carrier role, and when the task force withdrew she was joined by *Saratoga* which took *Independence*'s place in the 'night task group'. The light carrier left the forward area on January 30, 1945, bound for Pearl Harbor, where she was to refit and reconvert to the day role.

Independence rejoined the fast carrier force at Ulithi on March 13, 1945, and sailed on the following day to strike at Japan, prior to the opening of the Okinawa campaign. Between March 23 and June 10, her aircraft flew combat sorties on 41 days. Although carriers in company were attacked and damaged by the many kamikaze raids during this period, she escaped unharmed. A month was allowed off operations before Task Force 38 sailed again, to undertake sustained strikes against the Japanese home islands. The coming of the typhoon season and the need to remain clear of the cities of Hiroshima and Nagasaki on August 6 and 9, when the atomic bombs were dropped, reduced to 12 the number of 'strike days' between July 10 and VJ-Day, August 15, 1945. During this period, TF38's aircraft, assisted by those of the British Pacific Fleet, destroyed what little remained of the Imperial Japanese Navy and inflicted serious damage on the shipbuilding and transportation industries.

After the surrender in Tokyo Bay on September 2, *Independence* returned to San Francisco in slow time, calling en route at Guam and Pearl Harbor. Between November 15 and January 28, 1946, she was engaged on Operation Magic Carpet, returning service personnel from the Pacific islands to the US. In June 1946, she steamed to the Marshall Islands and on July 1 was moored only 800 m (0.5 miles) from ground zero during the Bikini air-burst A-bomb test. She survived this and the July 25 underwater test, although damage was very severe. On July 28 she was formally decommissioned, and some while later the radioactive hulk was towed to San Francisco for exhaustive examination and tests. By now useless for any other purpose, *Independence* was finally sunk on January 29, 1951, during US Navy weapons trials off the California coast.

Displacement: 11 000 tons (standard), 14 300 tons (*Independence* and *Princeton* 14 000 tons) (full load) *Length:* 202 m (662 ft 6 in) oa *Beam:* 21.8 m (71 ft 6 in) wl, 33.4 m (109 ft 6 in) oa *Draught:* 7.9 m (26 ft) *Machinery:* 4 sets geared steam turbines, 4 shafts 100 000 shp=31.5 knots *Aircraft:* 33 *Armament:* 26 40-mm (1.57-in) AA (2×4, 9×2), 10-12 20-mm (0.79-in) AA *Crew:* 1570

Indomitable

British aircraft carrier. Ordered as the fourth unit of the *Illustrious* Class, *Indomitable* was laid down in November 1937 at Barrow. Shortly afterwards, the Admiralty revised the design, so that the new ship would be able to operate 45 aircraft instead of 33. The extra stowage space could only be obtained by adding an extra hangar deck, above the existing hangar. It was found that by reducing the thickness of the hangar walls from 114 mm (4.5 in) to 38 mm (1.5 in) it was possible to raise the 1500-ton armoured flight deck by 4.3 m (14 ft) without reducing the stability of the ship. A full-length hangar 4.3 m (14 ft) high, was inserted into this space and only the after third of the original 4.9-m (16-ft) high hangar was retained, served by the after lift. The forward lift was widened by 50%, to 10 m (33 ft), to accommodate unfolded or non-folding aircraft. The extra volume made available by the sacrifice of the forward third of the lower hangar was used to accommodate personnel, workshops and stores, space for which had been extremely cramped in the *Illustrious* Class. Storage for 113 600 litres (25 000 Imp gal) of aviation fuel was added, at the expense of 350 tons of the ship's fuel-oil capacity, and the aircraft ordnance magazine capacity was increased by nearly 50%, to meet the requirements for the additional aircraft.

There was little external difference between *Indomitable* and *Illustrious,* apart from the increased freeboard. *Indomitable* was fractionally longer—227.1 m (745 ft) as against 225.5 m (740 ft)—but there was no difference in the layout of armament or the island and, with the same type of boilers, the funnel was identical.

Indomitable was completed on October 10, 1941, and sailed almost immediately for a workup in the West Indies. This was cut short when she ran aground off Jamaica and she was unable to sail as planned for the Far East, where she was to have joined *Prince of Wales* and *Repulse.* Her air group consisted of 24 Fairey Albacore torpedo-bombers, 12 Fairey Fulmars and nine Hawker Sea Hurricanes. The last were non-folding and could use only the forward lift and upper hangar.

Arriving in the Indian Ocean in January 1942, *Indomitable* ferried RAF Hurricanes to Java towards the end of that month and then flew off 48 more Hurricanes to Ceylon in February. Two of the latter remained on board, where they were modified and retained by 880 Squadron. During the Japanese carrier raids on Ceylon in early April *Indomitable*'s Albacores had actually sighted the enemy fleet. Following the raid, the Eastern Fleet withdrew to Mombasa, where it could provide support neither to India and Ceylon, nor to the hard-pressed Americans and Australians in the Coral Sea and southwest Pacific, and the Japanese were not even persuaded to divert any of their major naval units to guard against a foray from Mombasa. In May 1942, *Indomitable* and *Illustrious* assisted in the occupation of Diego Suarez, and in June *Indomitable* exercised with the RAF off Ceylon.

While three modern carriers were thus underemployed in the Indian Ocean, two small old carriers *Eagle* and *Argus* greatly helped in the defence of a Malta convoy. Another convoy was scheduled for August, and *Indomitable* was brought back to European waters to join the escort, arriving at Gibraltar at the beginning of the month. Prior to her departure, she had re-equipped her Fulmar squadron with Sea Hurricanes and had embarked nine Grumman Martlets to give her a total of 31 fighters; *Eagle* and *Victorious*, the other carriers with the force, had 41 Sea Hurricanes and Fulmars between them. Operation Pedestal, the most famous of all the Malta convoys, was subjected to heavy attacks by the Luftwaffe and Regia Aeronautica on August 12, 1942. *Eagle* had been sunk by a U-Boat on the previous day, but the two surviving carriers put up such a

IWM

Above: HMS *Indomitable* in 1941. A Fairey Fulmar is making a low pass, while Sea Hurricanes are parked on the deck. *Below: Indomitable* with Avengers during trials in Chesapeake Bay. With *Formidable* she made up part of the British Pacific Fleet hitting Formosa and Okinawa

IWM

strong defence that when they left the convoy that evening only one of the 14 merchant ships had been damaged. *Indomitable*'s fighters had shot down 27 enemy aircraft for the loss of only four of their own number.

Shortly after parting company with the convoy, however, the Fleet came under attack, and Ju 87 Stuka dive-bombers concentrated on *Indomitable*, scoring two hits. One 500-kg (1100-lb) bomb penetrated the flight-deck armour near the forward lift and the other struck abaft the after lift, where there was no armour. *Victorious* recovered the aircraft which were airborne, while *Indomitable* fought her fires and headed for Gibraltar. Repairs in the United States took four months, and it was not until February 1943 that she was able to begin working up again.

This commission, for which she embarked 15 Albacores and 40 non-folding Seafires (ten aircraft over her designed complement) was even shorter than the first. In late June 1943, she joined *Formidable* in the Mediterranean and from July 10 the two carriers covered the Allied invasion of Sicily, guarding against a sortie by the Italian fleet. This did not materialize, but on the night of June 15-16, a Ju 88 torpedoed *Indomitable* in the port side, causing serious damage to the port boiler room and extensive flooding. *Indomitable* returned for her third repair at Norfolk navy yard and was not ready to join the fleet until the following April.

By June 1944, *Indomitable* was with the Eastern Fleet, based on Ceylon. By this time, the *Illustrious* Class was equipped with Vought F4U Corsairs, but the lack of headroom in *Indomitable*'s upper hangar, and lack of space in the lower meant that she could not embark enough of this type of fighter, and she was supplied instead with Grumman F6F Hellcats, which had rearward, instead of upward, folding wings. At first, 24 Hellcats were embarked, with 24 Barracudas, but the number was increased to 29 in late 1944.

Indomitable and *Victorious* delivered strikes on Sumatra—on the port of Emmahaven (now Telukbajur) and cement works at Indaroeng on August 29, 1944, and on the Sigli railway yards on September 18—though neither attack was an outstanding success. On October 17 and 19 the same two carriers struck at the Nicobar Islands. Japanese aircraft attempted to close the force on this occasion, and *Indomitable*'s Hellcats scored their first victories, destroying three Nakajima Oscar fighter-bombers.

The Barracudas were disembarked after this operation and were replaced by 21 Grumman Avengers. After working up to establish new strike tactics, *Indomitable* and *Illustrious* made an unsuccessful attempt to attack the oil refinery at Medan, Sumatra, on December 20. Bad weather caused the failure of this operation, but another strike on January 4, 1945, by aircraft from *Victorious*, *Indefatigable* and *Indomitable* was entirely successful. The carrier offensive against Japanese-occupied oil refineries in Sumatra was concluded on January 24 and 29, 1945, by strikes from four ships against Pladjoe and Soengi Gerong; like that on Medan, these were completely successful.

The British Pacific Fleet (BPF) now continued to Sydney to prepare for operations in support of the invasion of Okinawa. The fleet's task was the neutralization of Japanese airfields in the Sakishima Gunto, between Okinawa and Formosa, and the carriers flew strikes on 12 days between March 26 and April 20. Only on April 1 and 6 did Japanese aircraft manage to get through the fighters to attack the fleet, but on neither occasion was *Indomitable* herself a target. After a week's replenishment at Leyte, the fleet returned to the Sakishima area on May 4. The kamikazes promptly attacked, hitting first *Formidable* and then *Indomitable*: the former was out of action for six hours, but *Indomitable*'s assailant simply slid up the armoured deck and over the side, causing no damage. When the BPF finally withdrew from the Okinawa area, on May 25, another 11 days of strikes had been provided over the islands, bringing the total to 24 in the two phases. Nearly 1000 tons of bombs and 950 rockets had been released and half a million rounds of aircraft ammunition fired: *Indomitable*'s 15 Avengers and 33 Hellcats had flown over 1100 sorties, the fighters destroying 16 enemy aircraft.

The war was now virtually over for *Indomitable*. Being in need for a short refit, she remained at Sydney when the other carriers left to strike at the Japanese Home Islands in July. She was ready for operations later in the month and left in mid-August to take part in the reoccupation of Hong Kong. On August 31 and September 1, her aircraft flew their last combat missions, against Japanese suicide boats at Hong Kong.

Indomitable returned to the United Kingdom in November 1945. Her aircraft had been thrown overboard off Sydney and the hangars were used as vast dormitories for British personnel returning from Australia. Early in 1946 she started out for the Far East again, for another trooping voyage, repeating the same voyage again later in the year.

Between 1947 and 1950, *Indomitable* was in reserve and then refitting, being equipped with modernized radar and armament and having her catapults, arrester wires and lifts strengthened to allow her to operate the last generation of piston-engined Royal Navy aircraft. During the next three years, she operated Fairey Fireflies, Hawker Sea Furies, de Havilland Sea Hornets and Blackburn Firebrands and, from 1951, the first British embarked search and rescue helicopter flight. Throughout this time she served with the Home Fleet. Her last major public appearance was the Coronation review of the fleet, held at Spithead in June 1953. Four months later, she was reduced to reserve and lay in the Clyde until October 1955, when she was finally disposed of for scrap.

Displacement: 23 000 tons (standard) 29 730 tons (full load) *Length:* 227 m (745 ft) *Beam:* 29.2 m (95 ft 9 in) *Draught:* 8.7 m (28 ft 8 in) *Machinery:* 3 sets geared turbines, 3 shafts, 113 250 shp=30.5 knots *Protection:* 114 mm (4.5 in) main belt; 114 mm (4.5 in) hangar sides; 63.5-76 mm (2.5-3 in) deck *Aircraft:* 45 *Armament:* 16 4.5-in (114-mm) dual purpose (8×2); 40 2-pdr AA (5×8); 12 40-mm (1.57-in) AA (12×1); 60 20-mm (0.79-in) (60×1) *Crew:* 2100 approx

Intrepida

Argentine fast patrol boat class. Two gun- and torpedo-armed patrol boats were ordered from Lürssenweft, Vegesack, the Netherlands, and delivered in late 1974. *Intrepida* (P.85) and *Indomita* (P.86) are armed with the Seeaal (sea eel) wire-guided torpedo aft, and the OTO-Melara 76-mm (3-in) gun forward. Four MTU diesels give a speed of 40 knots. A twin 81-mm (3.2-in) Oerlikon rocket launcher is also provided for launching flares and smoke canisters. These vessels are the first foreign fast patrol boats to have the Seeaal torpedoes, which are fired aft from two single tubes, as in the similar West German navy vessels.

Displacement: 240 tons (standard) *Length:* 50 m (164 ft) oa *Beam:* 7.3 m (24 ft) *Draught:* 2.5 m (8 ft 2½ in) *Machinery:* 4-shaft diesel, 12 000 bhp=40 knots *Armament:* 1 76-mm (3-in)/62-cal; 2 40-mm (1.57-in)/70-cal (2×1); 2 53-cm (21-in) torpedo tubes (2×1) *Crew:* 35

Invincible

British helicopter/STOL carrier class, built 1973. The cancellation in 1966 of the fleet carrier designated *CVA.01* left the Royal Navy with the dismal prospect of having to rely on shore-based air cover during the 1980s. The bitter lessons of the Second World War had shown that shore-based air support, however willing, tended to arrive too late. As an alternative to the enormous expense of fixed-wing aircraft carriers, there was a possibility that a 'mix' of antisubmarine helicopters and V/STOL aircraft could be accommodated in a much smaller hull. Once the traditional requirements of fixed-wing aircraft (arrester wires and a heavily strengthened landing deck) disappeared, it was possible to produce a utility carrier to provide local air superiority and strike.

The basis of such a design already existed in the form of a helicopter-carrying cruiser designated CCH, similar in concept to the French *Jeanne d'Arc*, with a cruiser bridge and guided weapons forward, and a flight deck aft. Despite initial political problems from a defence minister who was determined to prevent the revival of *CVA.01* in a new guise, common sense dictated that the CCH would be improved if its bridge and funnel were tidied up and put in a starboard island structure. As a precaution against political interference the clumsy designation 'through-deck cruiser' was coined. Later the design was referred to more correctly as a command cruiser, and then as an antisubmarine cruiser (CAH).

The rapid development of the Hawker Siddeley Harrier led to the design of a maritime version, the Sea Harrier, the first of which flew in 1978. The advent of this aircraft led to certain changes in the internal design of the CAH, for the workshops and magazines had to be tailored to carry spares and ordnance for the fixed-wing Sea Harriers as well as for Sea King helicopters. A slightly offset flight deck is provided to give more deck space, which was further increased with the cancellation of the Exocet surface-to-surface missiles, which were originally to be mounted alongside the twin Sea Dart launcher.

Internally the design is spacious, with accommodation for more than the planned air group of the nine Sea Kings and five Sea Harriers. It is believed that a maximum of 25 aircraft could be stowed without difficulty, and accommodation for 1000 Royal Marine

Commandos can be provided. The hydraulic lifts are of new design, which can be loaded from three sides to reduce congestion in the hangar, which is of the closed type, narrow in the middle between the two lifts.

Originally a speed of only 24 knots was envisaged as the CCH was intended for escort duty, but the CAH is intended to work with the fleet, which means a minimum of 28 knots. *Invincible* is the largest ship so far designed for gas-turbine drive, with four Olympus units coupled in pairs to each shaft. Another unusual feature is the provision of spare gas-generators, which can be replaced by the ship's own crew. The massive amounts of air needed mean that two large funnels and a long superstructure are required.

One of the most important roles for the new vessels will be as flagships for task groups, and so there is a comprehensive outfit of long-range radar (Type 1022 air-warning array), Type 992R search and two Type 909 guidance radars for the Sea Dart, as well as a big hull-mounted sonar.

The lead ship *Invincible* (CAH.1) was launched on May 3, 1977, by Vickers at Barrow-in-Furness and was due to start sea trials at the beginning of 1979. Her sister *Illustrious* (CAH.2) was laid down in 1976 by Swan Hunter at Wallsend, on the River Tyne, and *Indomitable* (CAH.3) is probably also to be laid down by Swan Hunter. The lead ship and her sisters will have the revolutionary 'ski-jump' ramp fitted to the forward end of the flight deck. This simple device, invented by Lieutenant-Commander D R Taylor of the Royal Navy, permits a Sea Harrier to take off with 454 kg (1000 lb) more payload, and also improves safety during takeoff.

Displacement: 16 000 tons (standard), 19 500 tons (full load) *Length:* 206.3 m (677 ft) oa *Beam:* 27.4 m (90 ft) wl *Draught:* 7.3 m (24 ft) approx *Machinery:* 4 gas turbines, 2 shafts 112 000 shp=28 knots *Armament:* 1 twin Sea Dart SAM launcher *Aircraft:* 9 helicopters, 5 fixed-wing aircraft *Crew:* 900+air group

Iowa

US battleship class, built 1940-44. As early as 1937 the US Navy began studies on the design of a 45 000-ton battleship, as a contingency against a failure by the Japanese to ratify the 1936 London naval treaty, which retained the 35 000-ton limit laid down in 1922. The first ideas were for a heavily armoured ship with 12 16-in (406-mm) guns and a speed of only 27 knots (the so-called 'slow' designs), but in January 1938 emphasis switched to 'fast' designs capable of 30 knots. The reason for this seems to have been that the forthcoming series of 30-knot aircraft carriers would have been able to outstrip their battleship escorts, and a new type of fast capital ship was therefore needed.

Although never regarded as battlecruisers, the *Iowa* Class were just that, as they sacrificed armour for maximum speed while having the same weight of armament as the preceding *Washington* and *South Dakota* Classes of battleships. However, the scale of the protection was adequate for a front-rank capital ship, and the *Iowas* compared well with all their contemporaries except the giant Japanese *Yamato* Class. To conceal the thinning of the armour down to 310 mm (12.2 in) it was put about for many years that the class had 460-mm (18-in) belts and massive deck armour, though the 1937 studies had shown that it would have been impossible to reconcile such heavy protection with 30 knots' speed. Although US naval intelligence suspected that the Japanese were about to adopt 18-in guns, it was hoped that US ships would never need protection against such heavy guns. It was thought that the fast carrier's aircraft would force enemy battleships to keep their distance, and that the fast battleships would prevent any cruisers from getting close.

The 16-in (406-mm)/50-cal armament selected for the new class had suffered many birth pangs. A ludicrous breakdown of communications between the Bureau of Ordnance and the Bureau of Construction and Repair meant that from April to November 1938 the two bureaux worked on different dimensions and weights for the new triple 16 in turret. Briefly, this meant that the 11.35 m (37 ft 3 in) diameter barbettes designed for the new ships were too small to accommodate the existing 16-in/50-cal Mk II, which had been built in 1916-18 for the cancelled *South Dakota* and *Lexington* classes. The solution was to fit the new lightweight Mk VII 16-in/50-cal gun. The outcome of a long process of design by the Department of Ordnance, the Mk VII was small enough to fit into the barbettes originally designed. Its construction was rushed forward, and fortunately the manufacturers were equal to the challenge, and enough guns were produced to enable the first two ships to be laid down in the summer of 1940 and completed in the first half of 1943.

Six ships were planned—*Iowa* (BB.61), *New Jersey* (BB.62), *Missouri* (BB.63), *Wisconsin* (BB.64), *Illinois* (BB.65) and *Kentucky* (BB.66). BB.61 and 63 were to be built by New York navy yard; BB.62, 64 and 65 by Philadelphia navy yard; and BB.66 by Norfolk navy yard.

Iowa was launched on August 27, 1942, and in August the following year she sailed for Newfoundland to cover convoys against *Tirpitz.* After taking President Roosevelt to North Africa she went to the Pacific for service with the 5th Fleet. She sustained minor damage from hits by a Japanese shore battery in the Marshall Islands, and at the battle of Leyte Gulf she was part of Admiral Halsey's fast carrier force. She supported the final assault on Okinawa, bombarded Hokkaido and Honshu in July 1945, and was present at the surrender in Tokyo Bay. She decommissioned in 1949 but was reactivated for the Korean war in 1952, during which she carried out a number of bombardments. She has been mothballed since 1953.

New Jersey was launched on December 7, 1942, and went straight to the Pacific in January 1944 after working up for six months. As flagship of the 3rd Fleet she fought at Leyte Gulf, and logged more than 354 000 km (220 000 miles) as an escort to the fast carrier task forces. She decommissioned in June 1948, but like her sister, was reactivated for the Korean war from 1951 to 1953. In 1967 she was selected for recommissioning to provide much-needed fire support for the Vietnam war, and after an overhaul of communications and electronics she recommissioned in April 1968 for what must surely be the last operation involving battleships. She was a notable success on the 'gun line' until 1969, when a shortage of 16-in (406-mm) barrel liners forced her retirement. It is said that a forgotten field full of gun liners was rediscovered in the US, but this came too late

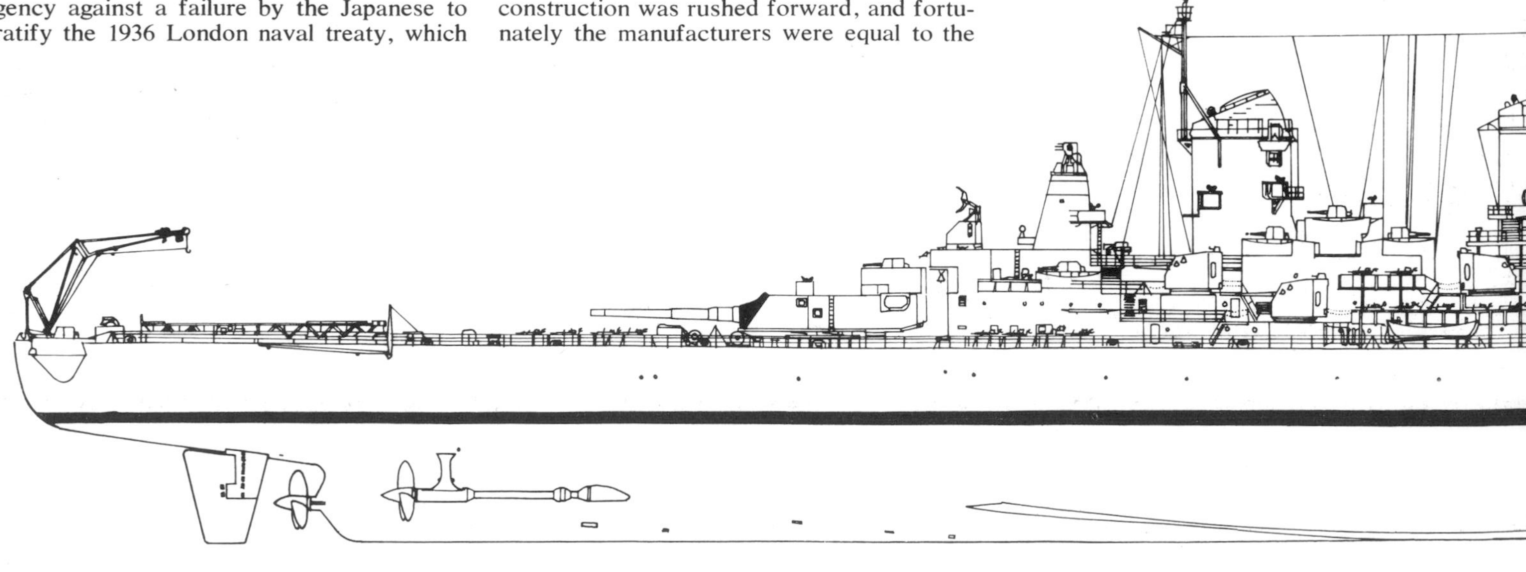

Mk II and Mk VII 16-in guns

	Mk II	Mk VII
Length oa (m/ft)	20.73/68	20.73/68
Diameter at breech (cm/in)	143.5/56.5	124.4/49
Diameter at muzzle (cm/in)	67.3/26.5	59.7/23.5
Weight of gun (kg/lb)	130 000/286 500	108 410/239 000
Weight of shell (kg/lb)	1016/2240	1225/2700
Propelling charge (kg/lb)	294/648	297/655
Muzzle velocity (m/sec/ft/sec)	808/2650	762/2500
Maximum range (m/yards)	41 240/45 100 at 46°	38 720/42 345 at 45°

The *Iowa* in 1954. After distinguished service in the Pacific she was decommissioned in 1958

Real Photographs

Below: Iowa Class battleships did not possess heavy armour protection, but their combination of speed and fire power (nine 16-in [406-mm] guns) made them formidable warships

to reprieve *New Jersey*, and she decommissioned in December 1969.

Missouri, the 'Mighty Mo', was launched on January 29, 1944, and was commissioned less than six months later. She went to the Pacific at the end of that year and saw her first action off Iwo Jima. Her fame was assured when, on September 2, 1945, in Tokyo Bay the Japanese surrender was signed on her quarterdeck. She remained in commission after her sisters, but in January 1950 she ran hard aground in Chesapeake Bay, and suffered considerable hull damage. Despite this she served in Korea for three years, and was not decommissioned until 1955. She is earmarked for preservation as a memorial, in view of her association with the Japanese surrender.

Wisconsin was launched on December 7, 1943, and commissioned in April 1944, joining the 3rd Fleet at the end of that year. She was decommissioned in 1948 and served in the Korean war from 1951 to 1953. In May 1956 she rammed and sank the US destroyer escort *Eaton*. She was repaired with the bow of her incomplete sister *Kentucky*, and was decommissioned in 1958 for the last time.

Work on *Illinois* was held up by the steel shortage of 1943, and as she was only 22% complete by August 1945 she was cancelled and eventually scrapped. She and her sister *Kentucky* differed from the others, being designed for welding throughout. It was hoped to complete *Kentucky* with an armament of guided missiles, and work continued during 1948-50, by which time she was 73% complete with main machinery on board. However the project was recognized to be operationally and financially unrealistic, and she was stricken in June 1958; her four turbines were installed in the fast replenishment ships *Sacramento* and *Camden* in 1964-66.

As built, all four ships were very similar in appearance, with massive capped funnels and a pole mast stepped against the rear side of the after funnel. Before the Korean war the two catapults and floatplanes were removed, and the pole mainmast was replaced by a big lattice tripod to carry an air-warning and surveillance radar. Subsequently twin supports were added to strengthen the structure, and boat derricks were added as the former aircraft crane aft was not heavy enough to handle the boats. All ships had the 20-mm (0.79-in) AA guns removed and the quadruple 40-mm (1.57-in) Bofors AA guns were planned to be replaced by twin 3-in (76-mm)/50-cal guns. *New Jersey* had all light guns removed in 1968 and had a massive square structure built on top of her control tower, but was otherwise unaltered.

Although not the most heavily armoured battleships of the Second World War, the *Iowas*' combination of size and speed made them magnificent ships for the Pacific. Despite their length, the twin rudders made them manoeuvrable, and with maximum fuel stowage of more than 8000 tons they had greater range than any capital ship previously built. On the basis of trial figures they could, in theory, steam 29 000 km (18 000 miles) at 12

USS *Iowa* (BB-61) on October 15, 1952 during a bombardment of Kojo on the east coast of Korea in support of amphibious operations

knots, 25 000 km (15 900 miles) at 17 knots and 8530 km (5300 miles) at 29.5 knots. During postwar NATO exercises they frequently refuelled the destroyer screen when an oiler was not available, and they had a high reputation for reliability.

See also *Montana.*

Displacement: 48 000 tons (standard), 57 000 tons (full load) *Length:* 270.43 m (887 ft 3 in) oa *Beam:* 32.97 m (108 ft 2 in) *Draught:* 11.58 m (38 ft) *Machinery:* 4-shaft geared steam turbines, 212 000 shp=33 knots *Protection:* 307 mm (12.1 in) belt, 121-38 mm (4.75-1.5 in) deck, 432-mm (17-in) turrets *Armament:* 9 16-in (406-mm)/50-cal (3×3); 20 5-in (127-mm)/38-cal DP (10×2); 60/80 40-mm (1.57-in) Bofors AA (15/20×4); 49/60 20-mm (0.79-in) Oerlikon AA (49/60×1) *Aircraft:* 3 Kingfisher floatplanes, 2 catapults *Crew:* 2788 (1626, *New Jersey* in 1968)

Iroquois

Canadian destroyer class. In December 1964 the Canadian minister of national defence announced that four helicopter-carrying destroyers (DDHs) would be built as part of a five-year programme to re-equip the Canadian forces. Although based on experience with the US *Annapolis* Class the new ships were to be much bigger, primarily in order to allow them to operate two Sea King CHSS-2 helicopters, and to have a surface-to-air missile defence. The decision to have a hangar and facilities for two Sea Kings was the most ambitious application of helicopters to small warships, which would give the new DDH-280 Class an unrivalled flexibility in anti-submarine operations. Experience in the *Annapolis* Class had shown that the big helicopter was invaluable to A/S work, and a second machine would reduce the number of occasions on which essential maintenance prevents flying.

The design grew in complexity, and rapidly outstripped the original *Annapolis* design. Gas turbines replaced the steam plant, and a special launching system for the Raytheon Mark 3 Sea Sparrow missiles had to be designed. The Italian OTO-Melara 127-mm (5-in)/54-cal gun was adopted, in a single mounting forward, with the Dutch M22 weapon-system control and radar, Canadian sonar, and US Navy torpedo tubes, Sea Sparrow missiles and gas turbines. The Sea Sparrow launching system in the forward superstructure is unique, as the missiles are swung out on extending arms, and then were reversed to face forward before firing.

Only four ships were built: *Iroquois* (DDH.280) and *Huron* (DDH.281), both by Marine Industries at Sorel, Quebec; *Athabaskan* (DDH.282) and *Algonquin* (DDH.283) by Davie Shipbuilding, Lauzon, Quebec. The names commemorate previous Canadian destroyers.

The ships are unusual in appearance, with a split, angled funnel to carry the gas-turbine exhaust away from the radar arrays on the lattice foremast. Being designed for ocean escort they have very high freeboard, with a full-width double hangar amidships to leave maximum space for the flight deck. The Canadian Beartrap hauldown device is fitted, an essential requirement for handling the big

PPL

Above and Below: **HMCS *Huron*, an *Iroquois* Class destroyer. Her split funnels are designed to vent gas turbine fumes away from the radar array on the lattice foremast**

C & S Taylor

Sea Kings on what is still a small warship. Internally they are very spacious ships, and they are specially equipped to operate in Arctic conditions. They have passive flume-stabilizers in place of the fin type.

Displacement: 3550 tons (light), 4200 tons (full load) *Length:* 129.8 m (426 ft) oa *Beam:* 15.2 m (50 ft) *Draught:* 4.4 m (14 ft 6 in) *Machinery:* 2-shaft gas turbines, 50 000 shp=29 knots *Armament:* 1 127-mm (5-in)/54-cal; 2 quadruple Sea Sparrow Mk 3 SAMs; 1 Limbo Mk 10 mortar; 6 12.75-in (32.4 cm) torpedo tubes (2×3) *Aircraft:* 2 Sea King helicopters *Crew:* 254+40 for air unit

Iwo Jima

US amphibious assault ship class, built 1960-68. *Iwo Jima*, authorized in FY 1958 was the first ship in the world to be designed and built specifically for helicopter operations. The design was prepared following the ill-fated Suez operation of 1956, during which a helicopter-borne commando assault was carried out from two small carriers lying offshore.

The amphibious capability of the *Iwo Jima* Class is based around a Marine battalion landing team and its supporting arms of guns, vehicles, equipment and supporting personnel, with sufficient helicopter capacity to provide complete mobility for the force. Being designed to carry out an amphibious assault, the ships are equipped with extensive medical facilities, including a fully equipped hospital.

The flight-deck area provides sufficient space for either seven Sea Knight or four Sea Stallion helicopters to carry out all forms of helicopter operation, while the hangar area below can house either 19 Sea Knight or 11 Sea Stallion helicopters. Being designed solely for helicopter operations there are no catapults or arrestor wires on the deck, and there is no angled deck and no landing markings for fixed-wing aircraft. Two deck-edge lifts feed the hangar, one to port amidships opposite the bridge and one to starboard aft of the island. When not in use these

No and name	completed
LPH-2 *Iwo Jima*	6/61
LPH-3 *Okinawa*	4/62
LPH-7 *Guadalcanal*	7/63
LPH-9 *Guam*	1/65
LPH-10 *Tripoli*	8/66
LPH-11 *New Orleans*	11/68
LPH-12 *Inchon*	6/70

lifts fold up against the hull, and act as hangar doors. In addition two small elevators are provided to transport cargo from the hold or hangar to the flight deck.

Between 1970-74 the ships in the class were progressively rearmed, the port quarter and flight-deck level twin 3-in (76-mm) mountings being replaced by two BPDMS Sea Sparrow launchers. Late in 1971 *Guam* was refitted to carry out tests as an interim design for the sea control ship (SCS) concept. For this she carried 12 Harrier V/STOL aircraft and a number of Sea King antisubmarine helicopters for convoy escort duties. She reverted to her amphibious role in 1974, but retained the Harriers.

Displacement: 17 000 tons (light), 17 515-18 000 tons (full load) *Length:* 180.4 m (592 ft) oa *Beam:* 25.6 m (84 ft) *Draught:* 7.9 m (26 ft) *Machinery:* 1-shaft geared turbines, 22 000 shp=23 knots *Aircraft:* 20 helicopters *Armament:* 8 3-in (76-mm) (4×2) *Crew:* 652+1724 troops

Jägaren

Swedish fast patrol boat class, built 1972-78. For many years the Swedish navy had planned to build a successor to the *Spica* Class torpedo boats, with a heavier gun armament. However, the growing threat from surface-to-surface missiles led to a change of policy. To foster interdependence with the rest of Scandinavia, and at the same time avoid the cost of developing a new missile, the decision was made to collaborate with Norway. The Norwegian *Hauk* Class was chosen as the basis, with the Kongsberg Våpenfabrikk Penguin surface-to-surface missile, while Sweden provided the electronics and the Bofors 57-mm (2.24-in) gun.

A prototype was built, the *Jägaren* (p.151), by Bätserice, Mandal and delivered in 1972. After extensive trials a further 16 boats (P.152-167) were ordered in May 1975 from Bergens Mekaniste Verksteder (11 boats) and Westermöen (five boats). The following names have been allocated: *Hügin, Kaparen, Magne, Mjolner, Mode, Munin, Mysing, Snapphann, Spejaren, Stärkodder, Syrbjornen, Tirfing, Vaktaren, Vale* and *Vider*. *Hügin* was launched in June 1977.

The boats are fitted with minelaying rails, and as they have an additional gun position amidships they can be converted to gunboats if needed.

See also *Hauk*.

Displacement: 140 tons (standard), 170 tons (full load) *Length:* 36 m (118 ft 1 in) oa *Beam:* 6.2 m (20 ft 4 in) *Draught:* 1.5 m (4 ft 11 in) *Machinery:* 2-shaft diesel, 7000 bhp=34 knots *Armament:* 1 57-mm (2.24-in)/70-cal: 6 Penguin SSMs (6×1) *Crew:* 20

Jaguar

West German fast patrol boat class, built 1957-64. A total of 40 torpedo boats was ordered for Federal Germany, 32 built in 1957-62 by Lürssenwerft, Bremen-Vegesack and eight built in 1958-64 by Krögerwerft, Rendsburg: *Iltis* (P.6058); *Jaguar* (P.6059); *Leopard* (P.6060); *Luchs* (P.6061); *Wolf* (P.6062); *Tiger* (P.6063); *Panther* (P.6064); *Löwe* (P.6065); *Fuchs* (P.6066); *Marder* (P.6067); *Seeadler** (P.6068); *Albatros** (P.6069); *Kondor** (P.6070); *Greif** (P.6071); *Falke** (P.6072); *Geier** (P.6073); *Bussard** (P.6074); *Habicht** (P.6075); *Sperber** (P.6076); *Kormoran** (P.6077); *Weihe* (P.6082); *Kranich* (P.6083); *Alk* (P.6084); *Storch* (P.6085); *Pelikan* (P.6086); *Häher* (P.6087); *Elster* (P.6088); *Reiher* (P.6089); *Pinguin* (P.6090); *Dommel* (P.6091); *Zobel*

(P.6092); *Wiesel* (P.6093); *Dachs* (P.6094); *Hermelin* (P.6095); *Nerz* (P.6096); *Puma* (P.6097); *Gepard* (P.6098); *Hyäne* (P.6099); *Frettchen* (P.6100); *Ozelot* (P.6101).

The Type 140 design, to which most of the class conform, was developed from the successful *Schnellboote* (motor torpedo boats) produced by Lürssen in the Second World War, with steel framing, diagonal mahogany planking and alloy bulkheads and superstructure. Armament comprised four single deck tubes and two single 40-mm (1.57-in) Bofors guns. Ten units marked * were Type 141, with Maybach diesels, instead of Mercedes-Benz.

The *Zobel* Group (P.6092-6101) had a different bridge, with a sloping front instead of the stepped type. They underwent modernization in 1970-72 and were then known as Type 142, or the *Zobel* Class. The conversion provided them with Dutch M20 fire control and the new Seal wire-guided torpedoes for use against surface targets. These are mounted on the stern firing aft, and the tactics are to steam away rapidly from the enemy once the torpedoes have been fired. The gun armament remained the same.

All were for disposal at the end of 1975 with the entry of the new Type 148 missile boats. Seven were sold to Greece, and seven to Turkey, with three each to cannibalize for spares.

Greek boats: P.196 *Esperos* (ex-*Seeadler*); P.197 *Kataiqis* (ex-*Falke*); P.198 *Kentauros* (ex-*Habicht*); P. 199 *Kyklon* (ex-*Greif*); P.228 *Laiaps* (ex-*Kondor*); P.229 *Scorpios* (ex-*Kormoran*); P.230 *Tyfon* (ex-*Geier*)

Turkish boats: P.330 *Firtina* (ex-*Pelikan*); P.331 *Tufan* (ex-*Storch*); P.332 *Kilic*; P.333 *Mizrak* (ex-*Löwe*); P.334 *Yildiz* (ex-*Alk*); P.335 *Kalkan* (ex-*Wolf*); P.336 *Karayel* (ex-*Tiger*)

Displacement: 160 tons (standard), 190 tons (full load) *Length:* 42.5 m (139 ft 5 in) wl *Beam:* 7.2 m (23 ft 7 in) *Draught:* 2.4 m (7 ft 10 in) *Machinery:* 4-shaft diesels, 12 000 bhp=42 knots *Armament:* 2 40-mm (1.57-in)/70-cal Bofors (2×1); (Type 140, 141) 4 53-cm (21-in) torpedo tubes (4×1), (Type 142) 2 tubes (2×1); (Type 142) 4 mines *Crew:* 39

Die Bildstelle der Marine

***Above:* Frettchen (P.6100), a German *Jaguar* Class fast patrol boat. Both *Frettchen* and *Ozelot* (below) were part of the *Zobel*, or Type 142, Group modernized in 1970-72**

PPL

Javelin

British destroyer class. Ordered in March 1937 the *Javelin* or 'J' Class destroyers were provided under the 1936 Estimates. Their design represented an attempt to combine the features of the large *Afridi* Class destroyers with those of the smaller fleet destroyers of the 'A' to 'I' Classes. The ultimate aim was to reduce the size and cost compared with the *Afridis*, but as a complex armament and fire-control system were demanded this reduction was comparatively small.

The main weight-saving feature was the adoption of two boilers in place of three which, although individually heavier and of greater power, occupied less space and allowed for a 6-m (20-ft) reduction in length and the use of one funnel instead of two. The overall machinery weight was also increased to provide for greater power and higher speed, and this weight low down in the ship improved stability and allowed the beam to be reduced by 23 cm (9 in). Thus most of the 200-ton reduction in weight over the *Afridi* design resulted from savings in the hull weight. The armament was very similar to that of the *Afridi* Class, the main difference being the omission of the fourth twin 4.7-in (120-mm) gun mounting to allow for the fitting of two quintuple torpedo-tube mountings in place of one quadruple. The close-range AA armament was the same, but was positioned differently with the pom-pom mounting abaft the funnel and the two 0.5-in (12.7-mm) mountings in the bridge wings. To improve seakeeping the new ships were given more sheer forward than in the *Afridi* Class. Unlike earlier British destroyers they were longitudinally framed for ease of construction.

Originally nine 'J' Class ships were ordered following the earlier practice of having eight destroyers and one flotilla leader. But since they were, like the *Afridi* group, large enough to allow for the leader to be one of the class instead of an enlarged vessel, the ninth ship was cancelled. *Jervis* was chosen to be fitted out as leader and was identical in appearance to the other ships of the class except for a slightly longer after superstructure which provided additional accommodation. All the vessels of the class were laid down in 1937, launched in 1938 and completed in 1939. A second flotilla of the same design, the 'K' or *Kelly* Class, were ordered in March 1937 under the 1937 Estimates and a third flotilla, the 'N' or *Napier* Class, in April 1939 under the 1939 Estimates. The 'K' Class were laid down during 1937-38, launched during 1938-39 and completed during 1939-40. The 'N' Class were laid down during 1939-40, launched during 1940-41 and completed during 1940-42. The leaders for these two flotillas were *Kelly* and *Napier.*

Wartime alterations were generally standard through the class. During 1940-41 the after bank of torpedo tubes was replaced by a 4-in (102-mm) AA gun, and two 20-mm (0.79-in) AA guns were mounted abreast the searchlight platform amidships. During 1941-42 the 0.5-in (12.7-mm) mounting in the bridge wings was replaced by two more 20-mm and air-warning, surface-warning and gunnery radar were fitted. The 'N' Class were completed incorporating many or all of these alterations. Those that survived to 1943-44 had the 4-in AA gun removed and the after torpedo tubes replaced, and the majority had their single 20-mm guns replaced by twin 20-mm mountings. Some of the 'N' Class also had two single 20-mm added on the quarterdeck. Lattice foremasts replaced the tripods in *Javelin, Jervis, Kelvin, Kimberley, Napier, Nepal* and *Norman,* and in 1945 some of the 'N' Class were fitted with 40-mm (1.57-in) AA guns.

The three flotillas saw considerable war service and much action and of the 16 ships of the 'J' and 'K' groups no less than 12 were lost. On completion the 'J' Class were formed into the 7th Destroyer Flotilla and the 'K' Class into the 5th Destroyer Flotilla, both joining the Home Fleet. The most famous ship of the class and one of the most famous destroyers of the Second World War was the leader of the 5th Flotilla, HMS *Kelly,* commanded by Captain Lord Louis Mountbatten.

One of the class's first actions occurred on December 7, 1939, when *Jersey,* patrolling off Cromer with *Juno,* was hit aft by a torpedo. This was one of a salvo fired by the German destroyers *Hans Lody* and *Erich Giese,* which were engaged in laying mines and withdrew from the scene undetected. The badly damaged *Jersey* was towed home by *Juno* and was repaired between January-September 1940. Several of the class took part in the Norwegian Campaign and on May 9, 1940, *Kelly* and *Kandahar* were carrying out a sweep for enemy minelayers in the North Sea when *Kelly* was hit by a torpedo from the E-Boat *S31.* The torpedo detonated abreast the forward boiler room and blew a hole in the port side which extended from the upper deck to the keel. Despite this extensive damage and further attacks by German E-Boats and aircraft she was towed to the Tyne, a journey which took over three days, where she was under repair until December 1940. Meanwhile another ship of the class had survived extensive damage. On the night of November 24-25, 1940, *Jackal, Javelin, Jersey, Jupiter* and *Kashmir* fought a short action with the German destroyers *Karl Galster, Hans Lody* and *Erich Steinbrinck* in the English Channel. During the action *Javelin* was torpedoed by *Hans Lody* and had both her bow and stern blown off. She was towed to Plymouth and repaired in Devonport dockyard by December 1941.

In the latter half of 1940 *Jaguar, Janus, Jervis, Juno, Kandahar, Kimberley, Kingston* and *Khartoum* were transferred to the Mediterranean to form the 14th Destroyer Flotilla. On June 23, 1940, while in the Red Sea, *Khartoum, Kandahar, Kingston* and the sloop *Shoreham* attacked and sank the Italian submarine *Torricelli* with gunfire. Later that day an air cylinder on the after torpedo tubes of *Khartoum* accidentally exploded blowing a torpedo warhead into the superstructure and starting a fire. The ship was beached off Perim Harbour where her after magazines exploded, wrecking the after part of the ship. She was subsequently stripped of useful equipment and abandoned.

In April 1940 the 5th Flotilla, now consisting of *Kelly, Kelvin, Kashmir, Kipling, Jersey* and *Jackal,* also transferred to the Mediterranean where they relieved the 14th Flotilla at Malta for antishipping patrols. On May 2, 1941, *Jersey* was mined and sunk in the entrance to Malta harbour when returning from such a patrol. Shortly after this, Malta became untenable and the 5th Flotilla left to join the 14th in the Eastern Mediterranean. Here both flotillas became involved in the battle for Crete and three more of the class were lost. On May 21, *Juno* sank when one of her magazines exploded following a bomb hit. Two days later *Kashmir* and *Kelly* were attacked by 24 Ju 87 dive-bombers. *Kashmir* was sunk in two minutes and *Kelly* was hit aft by a 454-kg (1000-lb) bomb while turning at 30 knots and capsized. She later sank leaving 279 survivors from the two ships, including Lord Mountbatten, to be picked up by *Kipling.* On December 19, 1941, *Kandahar* ran into a minefield off Tripoli and had her stern blown off. She drifted clear the following day and after the survivors had been picked up she was sunk by *Jaguar.*

On March 22, 1942, *Kipling, Kelvin, Kingston* and *Jervis* took part in the second battle of Sirte. During the action *Kingston* was damaged by a 381-mm (15-in) shell from the Italian battleship *Littorio.* The following month she was bombed while under repair in dry dock at Malta and became a constructive total loss; she was subsequently used as a blockship at Malta but was raised and broken up in 1947. A few days after Sirte, on March 26, *Jaguar* was sunk by two torpedoes from *U 652* north-east of Salūm.

On May 11, 1942, *Jackal, Jervis, Kipling* and *Lively* were attacked by aircraft north-

HMS *Jupiter* (foreground) and HMS *Kashmir, Javelin* and *Kelly* Class destroyers, during operations early in the Second World War

IWM

west of Mersa Matruh while on their way to intercept an enemy convoy. In the ensuing battle *Kipling* and *Lively* were sunk and *Jackal* badly damaged. *Jervis* took *Jackal* in tow on the following day, but an oil fire in her boiler room burned out of control and she had to be abandoned and sunk. One more ship of the class was lost in 1942, *Jupiter*, which unlike the rest did not serve in the Mediterranean. In January 1942 she joined the Eastern Fleet and on February 27 was sunk during the Battle of the Java Sea.

The last ship of the 'J' and 'K' group to be lost was *Janus* which was sunk by a glider bomb off the Anzio beachhead on January 23, 1944. Of the four survivors *Javelin, Jervis* and *Kelvin* returned home in 1944 for the Normandy invasion while *Kimberley* served in the Mediterranean until the end of the war. All four were sold for scrap in 1949.

The 'N' Class ships also joined the Home Fleet on completion but *Nepal* was the only vessel to be manned by the Royal Navy. *Napier, Nestor, Nizam* and *Norman* were manned by the Royal Australian Navy, *Nerissa* was transferred to the Polish navy and renamed *Piorun* and *Noble* and *Nonpareil* were sold to the Royal Netherlands Navy and renamed *Van Galen* and *Tjerk Hiddes* respectively. *Piorun* served for two short periods in the Mediterranean in 1941 and 1943, but otherwise served with the Home Fleet until the end of the war. She was returned to the Royal Navy in 1946 and sold for scrap in 1955.

The four Australian ships were transferred to the Mediterranean Fleet and then to the Eastern Fleet in 1941 where they were joined by the two Dutch vessels and *Nepal* in 1942. In June 1942 the Australian vessels, and *Poirun* from the Home Fleet, were temporarily transferred to the Mediterranean for the Malta convoy 'Vigorous'. During this convoy *Nestor* was badly damaged in an air attack, and after being abandoned had to be sunk by *Javelin*. In May 1945 the Eastern Fleet ships transferred to the British Pacific Fleet, where they took part in the operations against Okinawa and the final assault on Japan. Most of the class was sold for scrap during 1955-58 but *Tjerk Hiddes* was sold to Indonesia and renamed *Gadjah Mada* in 1951 and was not scrapped until 1961.

'J' Class
Jackal, Javelin—built by John Brown
Janus—built by Swan Hunter
Jaguar—built by Denny
Jervis—built by Hawthorn Leslie
Jersey—built by White
Juno—built by Fairchild
Jupiter—built by Yarrow

'K' Class
Kandahar—built by Denny
Kashmir, Kimberley—built by Thornycroft
Kelly—built by Hawthorn Leslie
Kelvin—built by Fairfield
Khartoum—built by Swan Hunter
Kingston—built by White
Kipling—built by Yarrow

'N' Class
Napier, Nestor—built by Fairfield
Nerissa, Nizam—built by John Brown
Noble, Nonpareil—built by Denny
Norman, Nepal—built by Thornycroft

Displacement: 1760 tons (standard), 2330 tons (full load) *Length:* 108.7 m (356 ft 6 in) oa *Beam:* 10.9 m (35 ft 9 in) *Draught:* 2.7 m (9 ft) *Machinery:* 2-shaft geared steam turbines, 40 000 shp=36 knots *Armament:* 6 4.7-in (120-mm) (3×2); 4 2-pdr AA (1×4); 8 0.5-in (12.7-mm) AA (2×4); 10 21-in (53-cm) torpedo tubes (2×5) *Crew:* 183

Jeanne d'Arc

French helicopter/training ship. The world's first ship to be ordered as a helicopter carrier was the French navy's *Jeanne d'Arc*. Intended to replace the 1931 vintage training cruiser of the same name, she was to be used for the seagoing instruction of junior officers in peacetime and as an antisubmarine or 'Commando' carrier in war. As the cruiser was to remain in commission until the new ship was ready to take over her duties, the latter was ordered as *La Résolue* and was known as such for a year after commissioning.

Ordered in March 1957, the carrier was not laid down, at Brest naval dockyard, until July 1960, completing for trials three years later, on July 1, 1963. By this time, two US Navy purpose-built assault helicopter carriers of the *Iwo Jima* Class were in service, the first of which had been ordered a year later than the French ship.

The layout adopted was similar to that seen 20 years before in the Japanese *Chiyoda* and *Chitose*, where the forward portion of the hull was given over to armament and command and control, and the after half-length accommodated the aviation facilities. In *La Résolue/Jeanne d'Arc*, these consisted of a hangar 'box', measuring approximately 50 m (164 ft) in length and 18 m (59 ft) in width, with a depth of two decks, located at quarterdeck level abaft the bridge structure; the roof of the hangar formed the 62×21 m (203×69 ft) flight deck. A single lift, measuring 12×6 m (39×20 ft) was situated on the centreline at the extreme after end of the 'box', opening on to the hangar and the quarterdeck. This siting, which has most of the advantages of the deck-edge lift position but none of its major disadvantages of exposure to heavy seas, was first seen in the US Navy's *Thetis Bay*, a 1945 escort carrier which completed conversion to the assault helicopter carrier role nine months before the French ship was ordered. A single crane on the port deck edge was installed to transfer helicopters from the quay-side or lighters straight to the lift.

Aircraft complement in wartime would be eight Sud 3210 Super Frelon helicopters, equipped either for submarine detection and attack or as troop carriers. In peacetime, part of the hangar is used for classrooms, the bulkheads and decks being designed for quick removal in order to clear the hangar when required. Only four aircraft can be stowed with the ship fitted for training.

Armament was intended to consist of six 100-mm (3.9-in) dual-purpose automatic guns in single turrets, but only four were installed, one on either side of the bridge and two on the quarterdeck. Also planned for installation was a quadruple 30.5-cm (12-in) antisubmarine mortar which could also fire 100-kg (220-lb) projectiles to a range of 5950 m (6500 yards) in the shore bombardment role. This was never fitted, nor was a proposed Masurca surface-to-air missile system because the plans were changed when she was under construction. Fitted with a full kit of air warning, height-finding and aircraft direction radars, she was capable of controlling fighters as well as long-range maritime patrol aircraft.

Of cruiser size (10 000 tons, 182 m [597 ft] length), *La Résolue/Jeanne d'Arc* was designed with economy of operation in mind. Her two-shaft steam turbine machinery produced 40 000 shp, giving the respectable speed of 26.5 knots and a range of 6000 nautical miles, on only 1360 tonnes of fuel. The 1924 British carrier *Hermes*, with virtually identical dimensions and power, could achieve only half the range on 50% more fuel.

After a year of trials and modifications, which included the raising of the funnel, previously set almost flush with the upper bridge level, *La Résolue* commissioned for service on June 30, 1964. On July 16, she formally relieved the old cruiser of the training task and her name. Since then, she has seen world-wide service on midshipmen's training cruises.

Displacement: 10 000 tons (standard), 12 365 tons (full load) *Length:* 182 m (597 ft) oa *Beam:* 22 m (72 ft 2 in) wl, 24 m (78 ft 9 in) max *Draught:* 7.32 m (24 ft) *Machinery:* 2 sets geared steam turbines, 2 shafts, 40 000 shp=26.5 knots *Aircraft:* 4 (as training ship) 8 (as ASW or assault

***Jeanne d'Arc*, the world's first helicopter carrier, with Super Frelon helicopters on deck**

Marius Bar

ship) *Armament:* 4 100-mm (3.9-in) DP *Crew:* 906 including cadets and midshipmen (capacity for 700 marines as assault ship)

Jeff

US assault hovercraft. Following the British success in developing the hovercraft principle the US Navy in 1965 initiated a programme of development designed to exploit the unique capabilities of the hovercraft. These are its considerable flexibility of movement, particularly the ease of transition between water and land, its ability to negotiate small obstacles, its high speed and its cost-effectiveness. Obviously a prime area for investigation was in amphibious assault roles where troops and heavy equipment have to be moved from large ocean-going ships with a deep draught and deposited on a hostile shore, possibly protected by mines and antishipping obstacles and probably under fire. The hovercraft's unique characteristics give it enormous advantages over the old-fashioned landing craft, and the US Navy began their 13-year study into the use of hovercraft in an assault role.

The programme led to the Jeff A and B assault craft designs. The contract for a Jeff A design for use by the US Marine Corps was awarded to Aerojet General Corporation in 1970. In March 1971 Bell Aerospace Textron was awarded the contract to design the Jeff B assault craft to an identical specification—a 160-ton craft capable of 50 knots with a 75-ton payload. The Jeff B was completed towards the end of 1977 and commenced trials early in 1978.

The Jeff B assault craft has a basic structure similar to that of a standard landing craft; a flat-bottomed craft with a large well deck for transporting vehicles, and high sides providing troop accommodation, etc. Six gas turbine engines provide power to four centrifugal impellers which lift the craft on a cushion of air; the gas turbines also power two large ducted fans aft on either quarter which provide horizontal thrust.

The assault craft are designed to be carried in the well decks of the American *Thomaston* and *Anchorage* LSDs (landing ship docks), *Raleigh* LPDs (amphibious transport docks) and *Tarawa* LHAs (amphibious assault ships). The LSDs can carry four Jeff assault craft and are fitted with bow and stern ramps for roll-on roll-off movement of tanks and vehicles. The assault craft can also operate alongside cargo ships for the transportation of palletized stores to troops ashore.

(Jeff A) *Weight:* 149 tons *Length:* 29.3 m (96 ft) *Beam:* 14.6 m (48 ft) *Height:* 7 m (23 ft) all dimensions on air cushion *Machinery:* 6 3750-hp gas turbines = 50 knots *Payload:* 75 tons *Crew:* 6

(Jeff B) *Weight:* 160 tons *Length:* 26.4 m (86 ft 9 in) *Beam:* 14.3 m (47 ft) *Height:* 7.2 m (23 ft 6 in) all dimensions on air cushion *Machinery:* 6 2680-hp gas turbines = 50 knots *Payload:* 75 tons *Crew:* 6

Bell Aerospace Textron

Jeff B, the US Navy's experimental assault hovercraft, comes ashore after the first overwater tests on December 16, 1977. It has a crew of six and payload of 75 tons

Jersey

British offshore patrol vessel class, built 1975-78. Faced with the need to replace the ageing 'Ton' Class minesweepers the British Ministry of Defence decided to build the cheapest possible type of ship to provide a vessel which could monitor ship movements, protect fishery rights, and release frigates from the mundane tasks of patrolling the oilfields.

The design chosen was a commercial trawler hull from the Aberdeen shipyard Hall Russell, which has long experience in this type of craft. The armament of one Mk 3 40-mm (1.57-in) Bofors of 1940 vintage caused great derision when it was announced, and the Royal Navy was harshly criticized for failing to produce a better-armed and better-equipped ship. In fact the ships have amply vindicated themselves, and the original five are to be followed by a further two. The Ministry of Defence made no attempt to improve on the commercial design, and merely drew up a series of parameters on the minimum length, beam, freeboard and other qualities needed to protect the crew against the worst effects of seasickness and tedium. A comprehensive navigation and communications outfit was provided, and the ships are highly manoeuvrable. They are fitted to

HMS *Orkney*, an 'Island' Class offshore patrol vessel, showing her bridge and stern with her controversial armament of one Bofors 40-mm (1.57-in)/60-cal AA gun

A J Watts Collection

A J Watts Collection

replenish at sea, but even without refuelling can steam 11 300 km (7000 miles) at 15 knots.

Known as the 'Island' Class, the first five are *Jersey* (P.295), *Guernsey* (P.297), *Shetland* (P.298), *Orkney* (P.299) and *Lindisfarne* (P.300). The next two are to be called *Alderney* and *Anglesey.*

Displacement: 925 tons (standard), 1250 tons (full load) *Length:* 59.54 m (195 ft 4 in) oa *Beam:* 10.92 m (35 ft 10 in) *Draught:* 4.27 m (14 ft) *Machinery:* 1-shaft diesel, 4380 bhp = 16 knots *Armament:* 1 40-mm (1.57-in)/60-cal Bofors *Crew:* 24

João Coutinho

Portuguese frigate class. The first six vessels of the *João Coutinho* Class were ordered in April 1968 for delivery in 1970. The design was prepared by Blohm und Voss and the first three vessels F475, F476 and F477 were built in the firm's Hamburg yard. F471, F484 and F485 were built by the Spanish firm Empresa Nacional Bazan. The ships were designed as antisubmarine vessels and are officially rated as corvettes, but the armament of these first six vessels can no longer be considered adequate against modern nuclear submarines.

The principal A/S equipment consists of obsolete depth charges and depth-charge throwers together with the Hedgehog A/S mortar dating from the Second World War. The armament is also outdated, consisting of a 76-mm (3-in) gun and an old-model 40-mm (1.57-in). The ships are also too slow (24.5 knots maximum) and lack modern A/S facilities such as a helicopter.

In March 1972 a further four vessels were ordered from Bazan with updated armament. A new antisubmarine torpedo-tube system replaced the obsolete depth-charge and Hedgehog equipment, and a new model French-built 100-mm (3.9-in) gun and single Bofors 40-mm (1.57-in) has replaced the outdated weapons on the earlier vessels.

The outdated armament aside, the class proved to be extremely reliable in service.

In 1977, *Baptista de Andrade, João Roby, Alfonso Cerqueira* and *Oliveira E Carmo* were sold to Colombia.

Displacement: 1203 tons (standard), 1380 tons (full load) *Length:* 84.6 m (277 ft 6 in) oa *Beam:* 10.3 m (33 ft 9 in) *Draught:* 3.6 m (11 ft 10 in) *Machinery:* 2-shaft diesels, 10 560 bhp = 24.5 knots *Armament:* (first six ships) 2 76-mm (3-in) (1×2); 2 40-mm (1.57-in) (1×2); 1 Hedgehog; 2 depth-charge throwers, (last four ships) 1 100-mm (3.9-in); 2 40-mm (1.57-in) (2×1); 2 depth-charge racks; 6 Mk 32 A/S torpedo tubes (2×3) *Crew:* 100

No and name	laid down	launched	completed
F471 ***Antonio Enes***	4/68	8/69	6/71
F475 ***João Coutinho***	9/68	5/69	3/70
F476 ***Jacinto Candido***	4/68	6/69	6/70
F477 ***General Pereira D'Eca***	10/68	7/69	10/70
F484 ***Augusto de Castilho***	8/68	7/69	11/70
F485 ***Honorio Barreto***	7/68	4/70	4/71
F486 ***Baptista de Andrade***	1972	3/73	11/74
F487 ***João Roby***	1972	6/73	3/75
F488 ***Alfonso Cerqueira***	1973	10/73	6/75
F489 ***Oliveira E Carmo***	1972	2/74	2/75

***Baptista de Andrade*, a frigate of the *João Coutinho* Class, completed in the mid-1970s**

Empresa Bazan

John C Butler

US destroyer escort class, built 1943-45. These ships resembled the *Rudderow* Class, a variant of the *Buckley* Class with lower bridgework and funnel, and two single 5-in (127-mm)/38-cal guns. Like the *Edsall* Class, they dispensed with electric drive as the shortages of turbine blades had been overcome by the time they were laid down.

The early ships of the group had a set of triple torpedo tubes, as in earlier destroyer escorts, but these were removed in 1945 to cope with the kamikaze threat. *Vandivier* and *Wagner* were launched in 1943 but not completed until 1955 as radar pickets (DER).

Built by Consolidated Steel Corporation, Orange, Texas: *John C Butler* (DE.339); *O'Flaherty* (DE.340); *Raymond* (DE.341); *Richard W Suesens* (DE.342); *Abercrombie* (DE.343); *Oberrender* (DE.344); *Robert Brazier* (DE.345); *Edwin A Howard* (DE.346); *Jesse Rutherford* (DE.347); *Key* (DE.348); *Gentry* (DE.349); *Traw* (DE.350); *Maurice J Manuel* (DE.351); *Naifeh* (DE.352); *Doyle C Barnes* (DE.353); *Kenneth M Willett* (DE.354); *Jaccard* (DE.355); *Lloyd E Acree* (DE.356); *George E Davis* (DE.357); *Mack* (DE.358); *Woodson* (DE.359); *Johnnie Hutchins* (DE.360); *Walton* (DE.361); *Rolf* (DE.362); *Pratt* (DE.363); *Rombach* (DE.364); *McGinty* (DE.365); *Alvin C Cockrell* (DE.366); *French* (DE.367); *Cecil J Doyle* (DE.368); *Thaddeus Parker* (DE.369); *John L Williamson* (DE.370); *Presley* (DE.371); *Williams* (DE.372)

Ordered from Consolidated Steel Corporation, but cancelled June 1944: *William C Lawe* (DE.373); *Lloyd Thomas* (DE.374); *Keppler* (DE.375); *Kleinsmith* (DE.376); *Henry W Tucker* (DE.377); *Weiss* (DE.378); *Francovich* (DE.379); DE.380 and 381

Built by Brown Shipbuilding, Houston, Texas: *Richard S Bull* (DE.402); *Richard M Rowell* (DE.403); *Eversole* (DE.404); *Dennis* (DE.405); *Edmonds* (DE.406); *Shelton* (DE.407); *Strauss* (DE.408); *La Prade* (DE.409); *Jack Miller* (DE.410); *Stafford* (DE.411); *Walter C Mann* (DE.412); *Samuel B Roberts* (DE.413); *Le Ray Williams* (DE.414); *Lawrence C Taylor* (DE.415); *Melvin R Nawman* (DE.416); *Oliver Mitchell* (DE.417); *Tabberer* (DE.418); *Robert F Keller* (DE.419); *Leland E Thomas* (DE.420); *Chester T O'Brien* (DE.421); *Douglas A Munro* (DE.422); *Dufilho* (DE.423); *Haas* (DE.424).

Built by Federal Shipbuilding, Kearny, NJ: *Corbesier* (DE.438); *Conklin* (DE.439);

McCoy Reynolds (DE.440); *William Sieverling* (DE.441); *Ulvert M Moore* (DE.442); *Kendall C Campbell* (DE.443); *Goss* (DE.444); *Grady* (DE.445); *Charles E Brannon* (DE.446); *Albert T Harris* (DE.447); *Cross* (DE.448); *Hanna* (DE.449); *Joseph E Connolly* (DE.450); *Gilligan* (ex-*Donaldson*) (DE.508); *Formoe* (DE.509); *Heyliger* (DE.510).

Ordered from Federal Shipbuilding, but cancelled 1943-44: *Woodrow R Thompson* (DE.451); *Steinaker* (DE.452); DE.453-507, DE.511-515.

Built by Boston navy yard: *Edward H Allen* (DE.531); *Tweedy* (DE.532); *Howard F Clark* (DE.533); *Silverstein* (DE.534); *Lewis* (DE.535); *Bivin* (DE.536); *Rizzi* (DE.537); *Osberg* (DE.538); *Wagner* (DE.539); *Vandivier* (DE.540).

Ordered from Boston navy yard, but cancelled 1943-46: DE.425-437; *Sheehan* (DE.541); *Oswald A Powers* (DE.542); *Groves* (DE.543); *Alfred Wolf* (DE.544); *Harold J Ellison* (DE.545); *Myles C Fox* (DE.546); *Charles R Ware* (DE.547); *Carpellotti* (DE.548); *Eugene A Greene* (DE.549); *Gyatt* (DE.550); *Benner* (DE.551); *Kenneth D Bailey* (DE.552); *Dennis J Buckley* (DE.553); *Everett J Larson* (DE.554); DE.555-562; DE.801-832.

DE.833-840 were ordered from Mare Island navy yard, Vallejo, but were cancelled in 1943; DE.841-872 were ordered from Brown Shipbuilding, Houston, but were cancelled in 1943; DE.873-886 were ordered from the Dravo Corporation, Wilmington, but were cancelled in 1943; DE.887-898 were ordered from Western Pipe, San Pedro, but were cancelled in 1943; DE.889-904 were ordered from Federal Shipbuilding, Newark, but were cancelled in 1943.

As the last class of DEs authorized, they suffered the most drastic cutbacks in 1943-44, when the shortage of escorts in the Atlantic eased.

Oberrender was a constructive total loss after a kamikaze attack off Okinawa on May 9, 1945. *Shelton* was torpedoed by the Japanese submarine *RO.41* off Morotai, North Moluccas, on October 3, 1944, and on October 28, *I.45* sank *Eversole* off Leyte. *Samuel B Roberts* was sunk by gunfire from Japanese cruisers off Samar, East Philippines, on October 25, 1944. After the war the class saw considerable service.

In 1957 *McCoy Reynolds* and *Formoe* were transferred to Portugal as *Corte Real* and *Diego Cao*. Being too slow and too small to warrant modernization the class was disposed of between 1966 and 1972.

Displacement: 1350 tons (standard), 1660 tons (full load) *Length:* 93.3 m (306 ft) oa *Beam:* 11.2 m (36 ft 9 in) *Draught:* 4 m (13 ft 3 in) max *Machinery:* 2-shaft geared steam turbines, 12000 shp= 24 knots *Armament:* 2 5-in (127-mm)/38-cal (2×1); 4/10 40-mm (1.57-in) AA (2×2; or 1×4, 3×2); 10/16 20-mm (0.79-in) AA (10×1, 3× 2); 3 21-in (53-cm) torpedo tubes (1×3) (early ships only); Hedgehog depth-charge mortar *Crew:* 200

Juliet

Soviet submarine class, built 1961-67. The *Juliet* submarines were diesel-electric boats designed to launch SS-N-3 surface-to-surface missiles in the same manner as their contem-

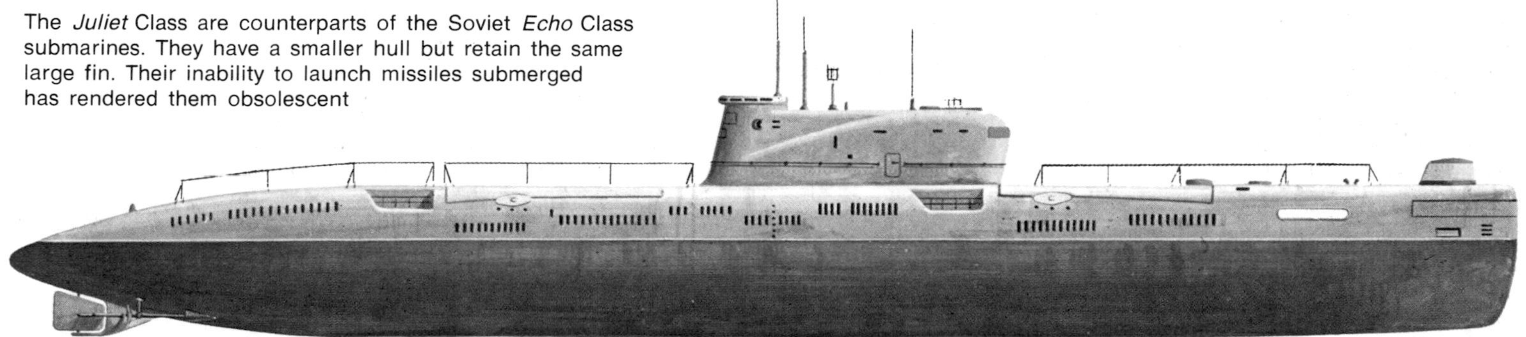

The *Juliet* Class are counterparts of the Soviet *Echo* Class submarines. They have a smaller hull but retain the same large fin. Their inability to launch missiles submerged has rendered them obsolescent

A Soviet *Juliet* Class missile submarine pictured in 1973. The black shadows in the casing indicate the blast deflectors for the SS-N-3 missiles

US Navy

porary nuclear counterparts the *Echo* Class. The *Juliet* boats had a smaller hull, however, and could accommodate only four missile launchers in the casing. It is reported that 72 boats were planned, but the number was reduced to 16 in 1962, when production problems were encountered with the launchers. In any case the *Juliet* submarines have now been overtaken by later developments, and would stand little chance of firing their SS-N-3s on the surface.

The *Juliets* have a very unusual appearance, with high freeboard and a very long fin. As in the *Echo* boats the missile tubes are elevated to 20-30° for firing, and when stowed are concealed under hatches. Behind each tube the casing is indented to form a blast deflector.

See also *Echo*.

Displacement: 2200/3550 tons (surfaced/submerged) *Length:* 87 m (285 ft 5 in) oa *Beam:* 9.4 m (30 ft 10 in) *Draught:* 6 m (19 ft 8 in) *Machinery:* 1-shaft diesel/electric, 6000 bhp =19/10 knots (surfaced/submerged) *Armament:* 4 SS-N-3A SSM launchers (4×1); 6 53-cm (21-in) torpedo tubes (bow); 4 40-cm (15.7-in) A/S torpedo tubes (stern); 36 mines (in place of torpedoes) *Crew:* 79

K.1

Soviet submarine class, built 1936-44, also known as the *Katyusha* Class. A class of large ocean-going submarines, known as project KE-9 or Series XIV *bis*, was designed in the mid-1930s. The K designation is an abbreviation of *kreiser* (cruiser), and it is believed that the original intention was to embark a small SPL floatplane in a hangar, as in contemporary Japanese submarines. Two prototypes of the aircraft were flown in 1933-35, but the submarines were never fitted to operate them.

The class proved only a qualified success, and as they were large and complex, production was cut back during the Second World War. Only 13 boats were apparently completed: *K.1-3* and *K.51-56* by the Marti yard, Leningrad and *K.21-23* by the Ordzhonikidze yard. The others were apparently not built, and postwar reports of submarines numbered *K.57-60* and *K.77-78* probably refer to some of the original boats being renumbered after assignments to different fleets, or merely an attempt to confuse Western intelligence.

The first to complete were *K.2* and *K.3* in 1939, while *K.54* and *K.55* joined the fleet in 1945. On June 22, 1941, when the Germans launched Operation Barbarossa (the attack on the Soviet Union), *K.1* and *K.2* were with the Northern fleet and *K.3* and *K.21-23* were in the Baltic. In August 1941 the four Baltic fleet boats were transferred to the Arctic via the White Sea or the Stalin Canal. *K.1* was lost about September 30, 1943, in the Kara Sea, probably to a German mine; *K.2* failed to return from a patrol off the Norwegian coast in August-September 1943; and *K.3* was sunk by German ships off Batsfjord on March 21, 1943.

K.21 was given credit by both the Soviets and their Western allies for scoring a torpedo-hit on the battleship *Tirpitz*, but as German records show no record of any damage from a torpedo, this claim is almost certainly false. However, Soviet histories still maintain the claim. The submarine was decommissioned in 1959 for use as a permanent training unit and was preserved as a memorial at Polyarnoe, near Murmansk.

K.22 was lost early in February 1943, probably to a mine. *K.23* was sunk on May 12, 1942, by German warships off Oksafjord. In August 1948 *K.52-56* were transferred from the Baltic to the Arctic via the Great Belts. All the survivors were out of service by the early 1960s.

Displacement: 1480/2095 tons (surfaced/submerged) *Length:* 97.65 m (320 ft 4 in) oa *Beam:* 7.4 m (24 ft 3 in) *Draught:* 4.51 m (14 ft 9 in) *Machinery:* 2-shaft diesel/electric, 4200 bhp/1200 shp=22.5/10 knots (surfaced/submerged) *Armament:* 2 100-mm (3.9-in) (2×1); 2 45-mm (1.77-in) AA (2×1); 10 53-cm (21-in) torpedo tubes (4 bow, 4 stern, 2 above water in casing); 20 mines *Crew:* 60

K.1

US submarine class, built 1949–52. Three small hunter-killer submarines were built under the Fiscal Year 1948 Programme for high-speed antisubmarine work. The displacement was kept as small as possible to break away from what was felt to be the excessive size of the *Tang* Class attack submarines and the fleet types modified under the GUPPY (greater underwater propulsive power) programme. They were given numbers *K.1-3* to underline this, and it was hoped to mass produce them to counter the big Soviet fleet. They were unique in having a massive square bow housing the big BQR-4 passive sonar, although this was later removed.

In December 1955 they were named *Barracuda* (SSK.1), *Bass* (SSK.2) and *Bonita* (SSK.3). By 1959 they were considered to be outclassed as they lacked the speed, range and weaponry for modern A/S warfare. In that year *Bass* and *Bonita* were reclassified as SS.551 and SS.552 but *Barracuda* became a training submarine (SST.1). The first two were stricken from the navy list in April 1965 but *Barracuda* was not finally retired until October 1973.

Above: The Soviet prewar 'K' Class or *kreiser* (cruiser) large ocean-going submarines were also known as *Katyushas* by their crews

Displacement: 765/1160 tons (surfaced/submerged) *Length:* 59.7 m (196 ft) oa *Beam:* 7.5 m (24 ft 9 in) *Draught:* 4.9 m (16 ft) *Machinery:* 2-shaft diesel/electric, 1050 bhp=10/8 knots (surfaced/submerged) *Armament:* 4 21-in (53-cm) torpedo tubes (2 forward, 2 aft) *Crew:* 50

Kagero

Japanese destroyer class. Known as the Type A destroyers, the 15 vessels of the class were ordered under the 1937 and 1939 Programmes, and laid down between August 1937 and April 1940. The design was practically identical with the preceding *Asashio* Class but improved boilers and other minor alterations increased the displacement by 72 tons. The three improved Kanpon boilers developed a steam pressure of 30 kg/sq cm (427 lb/sq in) at 350°C, resulting in a maximum output from the turbines of 52020 shp, and a trials speed of 35 knots. (Compared with 22 kg/sq cm [284 lb/sq in] at 300°C, 50 100 shp and 35 knots in the *Asashios*.) The bunkerage of 400 tons of oil fuel, and the radius of action of 5000 nautical miles at 18 knots both remained the same.

The problems of instability caused by excessive topweight, encountered in the previous Special-type destroyers, were largely overcome. The bridge was much smaller than in earlier designs, as were the engine-room vents, which were sited lower down the

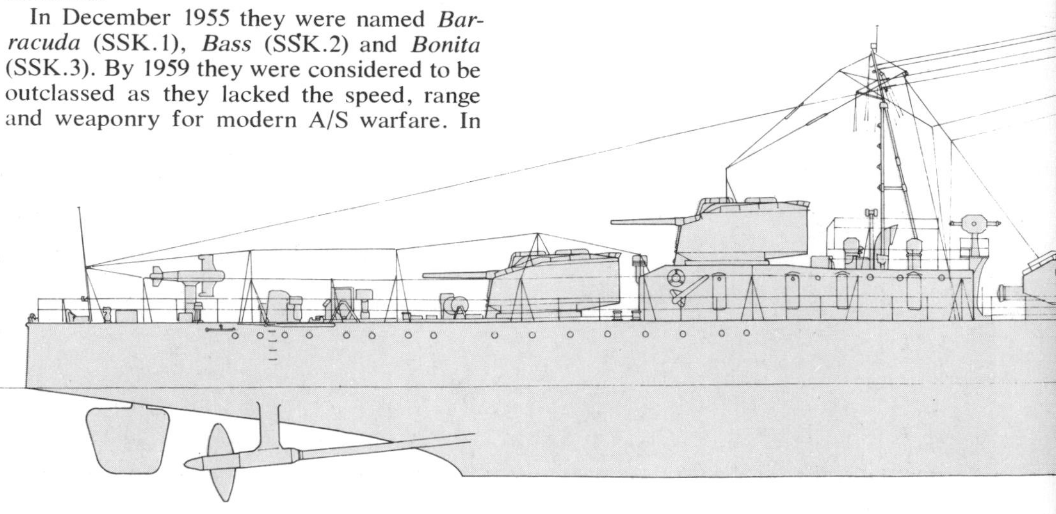

funnel. The forward torpedo reloads were sited two on each side of the forefunnel, rather than in the single bank of four mounted to one side found in earlier designs.

The final design conformed well to the specifications and requirements laid down by the Japanese naval staff. The *Kagero* Class were far superior to British and US destroyers, the heavy torpedo armament being mounted in splinterproof turrets with a full set of spare torpedoes which could be reloaded in 15 minutes. The gun armament was also superior, the heavy calibre dual-purpose weapons being mounted in enclosed turrets.

Amatsukaze was used as a testbed for developing a new superheated high-pressure boiler. These small boilers occupied much less space than previous models and delivered steam at 40 kg/sq cm (569 lb/sq in) at 400°C. On trials, the turbines in *Amatsukaze* developed a maximum of 52 150 shp to give a speed of 34.55 knots on a displacement of 2553 tons.

The destroyers entered service between November 1939-July 1941 and were extensively used throughout the Pacific during the war. Five yards were engaged in the construction of the *Kagero* Class.

Amatsukaze, Arashi, Kagero, Nowaki and *Oyashio*—built Maizure navy yard
Hagikaze Hamakaze, Hayashio, Shiranui and *Tokitsukaze*—built Uraga
Hatsukaze—built Kawasaki
Isokaze and *Yukikaze*—built Sasebo navy yard
Kuroshio, Maikaze, Natsushio, Tanikaze and *Urakaze*—built Fujinagata

Name	launched	fate
Amatsukaze	10/39	sunk USAAF 6/4/45
Arashi	4/40	sunk USN destroyers *Dunlap, Craven, Maurey* 7/8/43
Hagikaze	6/40	sunk with *Arashi*
Hamakaze	11/40	sunk US aircraft of *Hornet, Cabot* 7/4/45
Hatsukaze	1/39	sunk US destroyers *Spence, Ausburne, Dyson, Claxton, Stanley* 2/11/43
Hayashio	4/39	sunk USAAF 24/11/42
Isokaze	6/39	war loss 7/4/45
Kagero	9/38	mined and bombed 8/5/43
Kuroshio	10/38	sunk with *Kagero*
Maikaze	3/41	war loss 17/2/44
Natsushio	2/39	torpedoed US submarine 8/2/42
Nowaki	9/40	sunk US destroyers *Owen, Miller* 26/10/44
Oyashio	11/38	sunk with *Kagero*
Shiranui	6/38	war loss 27/10/44
Tanikaze	11/40	torpedoed US submarine *Harder* 9/6/44
Tokitsukaze	11/39	sunk USAAF 3/3/43
Urakaze	4/40	torpedoed US submarine *Sealion* 21/11/44
Yukikaze	3/39	surrendered. Chinese *Tan Yang* 1947; scrapped 1971

With the increasing dominance of US aircraft in the Pacific many of the class had X turret removed in 1943-44 and replaced by two triple 25-mm (1-in) AA. In addition the minelaying equipment was replaced by depth-charge equipment. Following the disastrous Marianas battle in June 1944, when US aircraft swept the remnants of Japanese naval aircraft out of the sky, all surviving units had their AA substantially increased, mounting between 18-28 25-mm (1-in) AA.

Displacement: 2490 tons (normal), 2033 tons (full load) *Length:* 118.4 m (388 ft 6 in) *Beam:* 10.8 m (35 ft 5 in) *Draught:* 3.8 m (12 ft 5 in) *Machinery:* 2-shaft geared turbines, 52 000 shp=35 knots *Armament:* 6 5-in (127-mm) (3×2); 4 25-mm (1-in) (2×2); 8 24-in (61-cm) torpedo tubes (2×4) *Crew:* 240

Kairyu

Japanese midget submarine class. Following the construction in 1943 and 1944 of two small experimental midget submarines with fixed side-hydroplanes, a preproduction model, known as Kairyu, was ordered. The design was developed from the Type A midget submarine, and retained the torpedo-

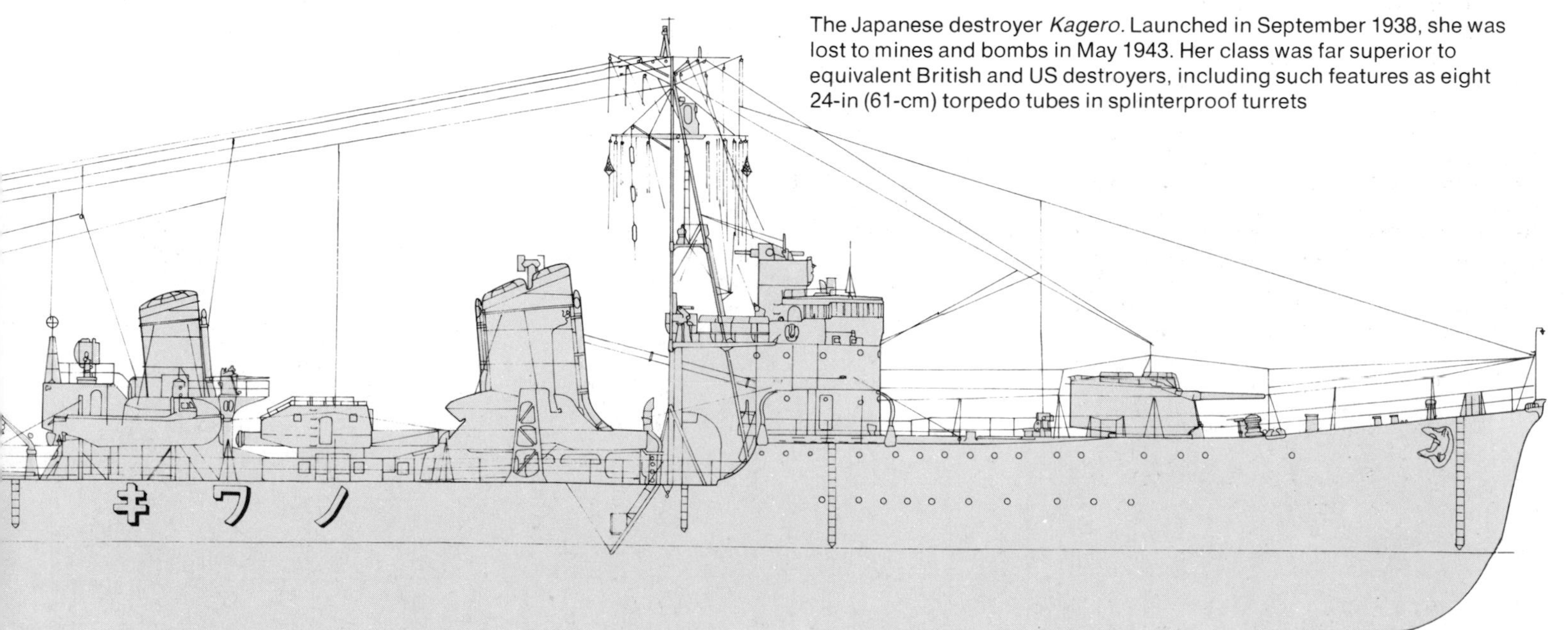

The Japanese destroyer *Kagero*. Launched in September 1938, she was lost to mines and bombs in May 1943. Her class was far superior to equivalent British and US destroyers, including such features as eight 24-in (61-cm) torpedo tubes in splinterproof turrets

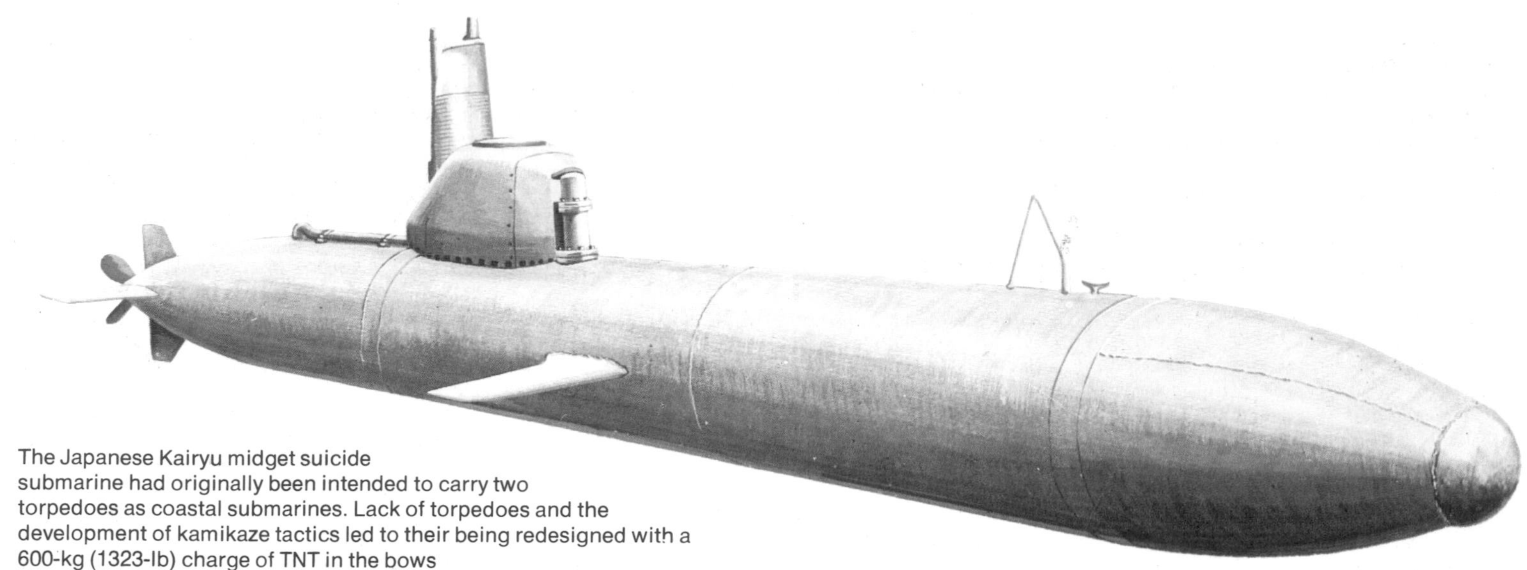
The Japanese Kairyu midget suicide submarine had originally been intended to carry two torpedoes as coastal submarines. Lack of torpedoes and the development of kamikaze tactics led to their being redesigned with a 600-kg (1323-lb) charge of TNT in the bows

shaped hull of the two experimental models. Production Kairyu differed from the experimental models in having a conning tower housing the periscope standard. The normal torpedo-type hydroplane and rudder were sited aft while fixed hydroplanes were fitted abreast the conning tower on either side of the main pressure hull.

Kairyu were originally designed for a defence role, operating with Koryu craft around the coastline of Japan, and they were intended to carry two 46-cm (18-in) torpedoes slung beneath the hull to port and starboard. A shortage of torpedoes, however, meant that they were usually armed with a heavy explosive charge in the bows, and used as suicide craft. For such small craft they were very strongly constructed, and the maximum submerged depth when armed was 100 m (330 ft).

Full production of the Kairyu commenced in 1944, ten yards being responsible for the final assembly. Shortages of materials led to many minor differences between individual craft, this being particularly true of the propulsion units. The Kairyu craft were mass produced in three sections and welded together in a machine shop ashore, construction time being about 30 days. A production run of 760 Kairyu was projected for completion by September 1945, but by the end of the war in August only 215 craft had been completed, while a further 207 were still under construction.

Displacement: 19.25 tons (submerged) *Length:* 17.3 m (56 ft 9 in) *Beam:* 1.4 m (4 ft 7 in) *Draught:* 1.4 m (4 ft 7 in) *Machinery:* 1-shaft Isuzu gasoline motor/1 electric motor, 85 hp/80 hp=7.5/10 knots (surfaced/submerged) *Armament:* 2 46-cm (18-in) torpedoes or 600 kg (1325 lb) TNT *Crew:* 2

Kaiten

Japanese suicide submarines. During the Solomons campaign of 1943 the Japanese were increasingly forced on the defensive, incurring heavy naval losses. This led a number of Japanese naval officers to study alternative means of attacking the heavily defended US warships which somehow always managed to evade Japanese naval forces. One of the new forms of attack suggested was the possibility

A store of Kaiten warheads captured by the Americans at Maizuru Naval Base, Japan

US Army

Japanese sailors ready a Kaiten 1 aboard a submarine. Early Kaitens allowed the pilot to escape once the craft was on course for a target, but later models sealed him inside

Fujifotos

of using manned torpedoes. These could be easily hidden among the numerous islands of the Pacific or transported to the area of operations aboard submarines and then launched to search for suitable targets. The theory behind the concept was that the enemy vessel, although able to take evading action, would be unable to escape, for the pilot aboard the torpedo would be able to counter any evasive manoeuvre and steer the torpedo directly onto its target.

The design of the new weapons was based around the body of the Type 93 torpedo and initial trials of the Kaiten, as the new weapon was called, were held in the spring of 1944. The initial Kaiten were completed with a watertight hatch which could be released from inside the craft, so that the pilot could abandon the craft after aiming it at the target. The system proved difficult to operate and it was soon realized that the enemy ships could still evade the weapon. Many of the volunteers who came forward to operate the Kaiten indicated that they were more than willing to die for their country. Consequently the craft was modified and the watertight hatch was omitted. Instead an entry hatch was fitted underneath the craft so that the pilot could enter through a watertight tunnel in the parent submarine. Once the Kaiten pilot was seated at the controls the entrance was sealed off from the outside. The training of pilots for the suicide Kaiten involved a rigid psychological preparation and ritual on the final operation.

Once a pilot had set out on his one-way journey to the intended target he remained in radio contact with the commander of the submarine who passed him bearings and ranges of the target. When the pilot had sighted the target through his small periscope at about 180-m (600-ft) range he fully submerged his craft and locked the controls to set the torpedo on its target.

The first Kaiten operation was carried out in November 1944, and by the end of the war over 50 Kaiten attacks had been carried out. In spite of the dedication of the pilots only a few minor successes were achieved.

Many craft were never completed owing to a lack of torpedoes and the partially constructed craft, lacking a propulsion unit, were adapted for use as fuel tanks on transports.

Apart from the Kaiten 1, three other models were built during the war. The propulsion plant in the Kaiten 2 and 3 was powered by a hydrogen-peroxide system, basic details of which had been supplied by the Germans. Production problems with the engine and its novel fuel system seriously curtailed production of the Kaiten 2 and 3. Only one version of the Kaiten 3 was built and this was used as a testbed. Owing to the problems encountered with the hydrogen-peroxide propelled units many were completed with a standard torpedo propulsion unit, but with a much more powerful explosive charge. These craft were known as Kaiten 4. Continuing problems with the supply of torpedo units, however, resulted in many craft being found uncompleted at the end of the war.

(Kaiten 1) *Displacement:* 8.3 tons (submerged) *Length:* 14.8 m (48 ft 7 in) *Beam:* 1 m (3 ft 3 in) *Machinery:* 2 Type 93 torpedo engines, 550 hp=30 knots *Armament:* 1550 kg (3400 lb) TNT *Crew:* 1

(Kaiten 2) *Displacement:* 13.3 tons (submerged) *Length:* 16.5 m (54 ft 2 in) *Beam:* 1.3 m (4 ft 3 in) *Machinery:* 1-shaft hydro-hydrazine engine, 1500 hp=40 knots *Armament:* 1550 kg (3400 lb) TNT *Crew:* 2

(Kaiten 3) *Displacement:* 13.3 tons (submerged) *Length:* 16.5 m (54 ft 2 in) *Beam:* 1.3 m (4 ft 3 in) *Machinery:* 1-shaft peroxide-hydrazine engine, 1800 hp=30 knots *Armament:* 1500 kg (3300 lb) TNT *Crew:* 2

(Kaiten 4) *Displacement:* 18 tons (submerged) *Length:* 16.5 m (54 ft 2 in) *Beam:* 1.3 m (4 ft 3 in) *Machinery:* 1 torpedo engine, 1500 hp=40 knots *Armament:* 1800 kg (4000 lb) TNT *Crew:* 2

Kaiyo

Japanese escort carrier. Although the Japanese had more practical experience in the conversion of merchant ships to aircraft carriers, and commissioned their first auxiliary (escort) carrier as early as September 1941, the Imperial Japanese Navy devoted little effort to building up a force of such ships, in spite of heavy merchant shipping losses at the hands of US submarines. Only two new escort carriers were commissioned in 1942 but in that year, two 12 750-grt, 21-knot merchant vessels, built in 1938-39 and requisitioned as naval transports at the outbreak of war, were earmarked for conversion. *Brazil Maru* was sunk near Truk by a submarine in August 1942, but her sister *Argentina Maru*, built for OSK lines by Mitsubishi, Nagasaki, arrived at Kure in December 1942 to begin conversion and was renamed *Kaiyo*.

Unlike the US and British carrier conversions, which retained the original merchant design's main machinery, *Kaiyo* was equipped with destroyer-type steam turbines in place of the original diesel motors. A speed of 24 knots was demanded by the Japanese navy, while the Allied navies were satisfied with 17-19 knots. Gun armament was also more elaborate, for *Kaiyo* was armed with four twin 127-mm (5-in) dual-purpose guns and, initially, six triple 25-mm (1-in) AA mountings.

The passenger liner's superstructure was cut down to the forecastle-deck level. The navigating bridge was moved to a position at the forward end of a 113-m (370-ft) hangar erected on the forecastle deck, and the boiler uptakes were led to the starboard side, where the smoke was exhausted outboard and downward in the usual Japanese fashion. The hangar extended between two aircraft lifts and was intended to accommodate 24 aircraft.

The steel-plate flight deck was supported by the hangar walls and, fore and aft of the hangar, by pillars, thus leaving the forecastle and quarterdeck open to the weather. As was common in Japanese carriers, the deck tapered fore and aft, conforming approximately with the planform of the hull. Though this 'ship-shaped' flight deck was 166.6 m (546 ft 6 in) long, some 26.5 m (87 ft) longer than in the US Navy's *Casablanca* Class, the US ships' decks were slightly wider and were rectangular, giving a greater usable aircraft parking area. *Kaiyo* had no island, and aircraft control and gunnery fire-control was exercised from open positions at the deck-edges. Eight arrester wires were installed, as well as a safety barrier, but there was no catapult.

Kaiyo commissioned as an escort carrier on November 23, 1943, and after trials was allocated to the newly formed General Escort Command, organized in a belated effort to reduce US submarine successes. In spite of the urgent need for close air escort for convoys, *Kaiyo* was frequently diverted to aircraft transport duties, ferrying short-range aircraft to China, Formosa and more distant destinations around the South China Sea. She also carried out the training of replacement carrier pilots.

After the Allied invasion of Luzon in January 1945, all Japanese carriers remained in their home waters, venturing only as far as the Chinese ports in the Yellow Sea. On March 19, *Kaiyo* was one of the carriers which sustained slight damage during US carrier strikes on Kure. A month later she was paid off as a carrier, although her gun crews and a steaming crew were retained. On July 18, she was proceeding to a port on Kyushu when she sustained minor damage from a magnetic mine. She put into Beppu Bay, Kyushu, to effect repairs but she was found there and attacked by British carrier aircraft. On this occasion, she was severely damaged. Her hull was holed and her back broken, and she had to be beached and abandoned. The derelict *Kaiyo* was still in Beppu Bay at the end of the war and it was not until 1948 that a local firm completed the task of scrapping her.

See also *Hiyo, Taiyo*.

Displacement: 13 600 tons (standard) 18 000 tons (full load) *Length:* 166.6 m (546 ft 6 in) oa *Beam:* 21.9 m (72 ft) wl *Draught:* 8.2 m (27 ft) *Machinery:* 2 sets geared steam turbines, 2 shafts, 52 100 shp=23.8 knots (trials) *Aircraft:* 24 *Armament:* (1943) 8 127-mm (5-in) DP (4×2); 24 25-mm (1-in) AA (8×3); (From 1944) 8 127-mm (5-in) DP (4×2); 44 25-mm (1-in) AA; 168 12-cm (4.7-in) AA rocket launchers (6×28) *Crew:* 829

'Kanin'

Soviet SAM destroyer class. The vessels of the class were originally members of the 'Krupny' Class, which underwent a series of major conversions from 1967-68 into the early 1970s. At least six of the eight 'Krupny' Class vessels have been converted to 'Kanins', and are named *Boiky, Derzhky Gnevny, Gremyashchy, Zhguchy* and *Zorky*. It is probable that Baltic yards have been responsible for the conversion work and rebuilding of the superstructure.

The radical modernization involved the replacement of the two SS-N-1 Scrubber launchers and their magazines by a single SA-N-1 Goa launcher for surface-to-air missiles in an installation which resembles that of the 'Kotlin SAM' modification. The launcher was placed on top of its magazine. The 'Krupnys' lattice mast amidships was replaced by a short pyramidal tower carrying the Peel Group guidance radar. The after 57-mm (2.24-in) mounting was shifted forward in a return to the 'Kildin'-type layout, while the two mountings amidships were replaced by 12-barrelled A/S mortars. A third mortar was placed on the forecastle, while the triple torpedo tubes were replaced by quintuple mountings. A bow sonar was fitted to complement this increase in antisubmarine capability, the shape of the bow being changed accordingly. The helicopter deck was enlarged and moved further forward, becoming an extension of the shelter deck aft. Some ships have subsequently been fitted with four twin 30-mm (1.18-in) guns with accompanying Drum Tilt directors on platforms projecting from the radar tower—a feature also of some ships of the 'Kotlin SAM' Class.

With the advantage of the larger 'Krupny'-type hull, the 'Kanin' conversion is undoubtedly more successful than the 'Kotlin SAM' modification. In 1978, ships of the 'Kanin' Class were distributed evenly between the Northern, Baltic and Pacific fleets, and carried pennant numbers in the 200, 500 and 900 ranges.

Displacement: 3650 tons (standard), 4500 tons (full load) *Length:* 139.5 m (457 ft 8 in) oa *Beam:* 14.6 m (47 ft 11 in) *Draught:* 5 m (16 ft 5 in) *Machinery:* 2-shaft steam turbines, 80 000 shp=34 knots *Armament:* 2 SA-N-1 launchers (1×2); 8 57-mm (2.24-in) AA (2×4); 8 30-mm (1.18-in) AA (4× 2) (some ships only); 10 53-cm (21-in) torpedo tubes (2×5); 36 MBU 2500A A/S mortars (3×12) *Crew:* 350

'Kara'

Soviet missile cruiser class. *Nikolayev*, the first ship of the class, was laid down in 1969 and completed in 1973; *Ochakov, Kerch, Azov* and *Petropavlovsk* followed at yearly intervals. (*Azov* is reported to be a modified version.)

Developed from the 'Kresta-II' design, the 'Kara' Class is apparently intended to accompany the new aircraft carriers, for which they provide added defence against aircraft and submarines. The hull has been lengthened by 16 m (52 ft 6 in), the increase being accounted for by an extra section inserted between the forward Head Light radar and the main radar tower. The change of layout appears to have been dictated by the change to gas-turbine propulsion, evidenced by the massive square funnel. Since the back-to-back search radar could no longer be accommodated above the uptakes because of the hot exhaust gases, it has had to be moved forward to the after end of an enlarged bridge structure on a lattice mast modelled on that of the 'Krivaks'.

While the main armament of SA-N-3 Goblet surface-to-air missiles and SS-N-14 antisubmarine missiles has remained identical in layout to that of the 'Kresta-II', advantage has been taken of the added section amidships to ship two twin 76-mm (3-in) mountings, the twin 57-mm (2.24-in) of the 'Krestas' being omitted. This in turn has freed space abreast and aft of the funnel which, with the increase in beam, has been used to resite the four Gatling close-range mountings and to add two SA-N-4 'pop-up' launchers for short-range surface-to-air missiles together with their Pop Group directors. As there has been no change in the main armament of the ships, the main sensor outfit is identical to that of the 'Krestas', the only significant addition being the variable-depth sonar beneath the flight deck on the stern. The complex helicopter-handling arrangements of the earlier design have been retained, presumably to avoid having to increase the height of the hangar with attendant effects on the siting of the after SA-N-3 Goblet launcher and its guidance radar. Similarly, no attempt has been made to rationalize the rambling system of shelter decks of the 'Krestas', which distinguishes them from modern Western warships. The 'Kara' Class are almost certainly slower than earlier missile cruisers, partly because there is less need for high speed in ships such as these and the new carriers built for an ocean-going role, but presumably also because of the problems in getting the necessary power from a maximum of four gas turbines. Given the present state of the art, these are probably rated at about 25 000 hp each, with two on each shaft. The 'Kara' Class were the largest ships in the world to be powered exclusively by gas turbines, a distinction which remained with them until after the completion of *Invincible* for the Royal Navy.

Displacement: 8200 tons (standard), 9500 tons (full load) *Length:* 174 m (570 ft 10 in) oa *Beam:* 18 m (59 ft) *Draught:* 6 m (19 ft 8 in) *Machinery:* 4 gas turbines, 2 shafts, 100 000 shp=30+ knots *Armament:* 4 SA-N-3 launchers (2×2); 8 SS-N-14 launchers (2×4); 4 SA-N-4 launchers (2×2); 4 76-mm (3-in) AA (2×2); 4 Gatling-type guns; 10 53-cm (21-in) torpedo tubes (2×5); 24 MBU 2500A A/S mortars (2×12); 12 MBU 4500A A/S mortars (2×6); Hormone A ASW helicopter *Crew:* 500

'Kashin'

Soviet destroyer class, built between 1960-69. The first ship of the class was completed in 1963. Names are *Bezuprechny, Komsomolets Ukrainy, Krasny-Kavkaz, Krasny-Krim, Odarenny, Obraztsovy, Ognevoi, Provorny, Otvazhny, Otlichny, Sderzhanny, Skory, Slavny, Smely, Smetlivy, Smyslenny, Soobrazitelny, Sposobny, Steregushchy, Strogy Stroyny*. The Zhdanov yard at Leningrad built about six of the total of 19 while the rest

A Soviet 'Kanin' Class guided missile destroyer shadows the Commando Carrier HMS *Hermes* during a NATO exercise in October 1973

MOD

MOD

A 'Kara' Class guided missile destroyer belonging to the Soviet navy photographed by an RAF Nimrod during an exercise in the Mediterranean

of them were built in the Nosenko yard at Nikolayev.

The 'Kashin' Class was designed to succeed the 'Kotlin' Class as a fleet escort type. More specifically, it was envisaged that they would operate in pairs in support of the new missile cruisers of the 'Kynda' and 'Kresta' Classes, for which they would provide additional defence against aircraft and submarines. They therefore carried no major offensive weapon, having instead an SA-N-1 'Goa' launcher for surface-to-air missiles fore and aft, each mounted on a deckhouse which serves as magazine. Below each launcher at upper-deck level was a twin 76-mm (3-in) mounting which provided a more conventional defence against aircraft. The antisubmarine armament comprised two 12-barrelled mortars carried forward, two new six-barrelled long-range mortars abreast the after radar tower, and a quintuple bank of 53-cm (21-in) torpedo tubes on the centreline amidships. The symmetry of the armament layout was matched by that of the main sensors, with two central lattice masts carrying identical search antennae flanked by two shorter towers for the 'Peel Group' guidance radars.

The hull form, unlike that of the 'Kyndas', was the development of the 'Kotlin'/'Kildin'/'Krupny' shape, with a flush deck rising steeply towards the bow to enable the ships to maintain a high speed in rough seas. The bow, however, was given more overhang than the straight stems of the earlier classes in order to accommodate a small sonar.

When completed, they were the largest vessels in the world to be propelled exclusively by gas turbines, and were to remain so until the early seventies. The USSR had for some time experimented with the concept of the high-speed destroyer, but with little success until the advent of marine gas turbines. The importance of high speed to the 'Kashin' design can be seen in the complete domination of the centre part of the ship by engine rooms. Consequently the main weapons have been pushed to both ends of the ship—also a feature of the high-speed 'Tallin' Class which they otherwise little resemble. The superstructure of the 'Kashins' is likewise dominated by the four large box-shaped uptakes for the turbines, arranged in two pairs and canted outwards to form V-shapes in order to avoid 'cooking' the centreline sensors. The size and layout of the uptakes and the wide spacing between the forward and after pair suggested a propulsion system consisting of eight gas turbines, but it is now known that four 23 500-hp turbines are installed, giving a total of over 90 000 hp for a top speed estimated at 36-39 knots. Early ships had very low funnels which were subsequently lengthened to take the hot gases clear of the decks, and to lessen the ingress of seaspray. The forefunnels were raised by about 3 m (10 ft) and the after funnels by 1 m (3 ft). Later ships can be distinguished by the 'Big Net' air-search scanner on the mainmast, the search antenna on the foremast being replaced by a back-to-back version of the same radar. These include *Krazny Kavkaz, Krasny Krim, Sderzhanny, Steregushchy, Slavny, Sposobny*, and *Strogy*.

From 1971 onwards, significant modifications were made to *Ognevoi, Bezuprechny, Sderzhanny, Slavny, Smely, Smyslenny* and possibly *Otvazhny* (which was lost in the Black Sea in 1974 following an internal explosion and fire). Four single horizon-range SS-N-11 surface-to-surface missile launchers were added abreast the second pair of uptakes, the six-barrelled A/S mortars were replaced by a structure on which four Gatling-type AA guns were mounted as a defence against missiles, complete with 'Bass Tilt' radar directors. Variable-depth sonar was added to the stern (which was lengthened to accommodate it) and a helicopter deck was built on stanchions above it. It remains to be seen whether this modification will prove to be successful in view of the considerable increase in topweight.

'Kashin' Class destroyers serve in all four major Soviet fleets, although most are in the Black Sea and the Pacific. A variety of pendant numbers have been carried, the most recent being in the 100, 200, 400 and 500 ranges.

Displacement: 3750 tons (standard), 4600 tons (full load) *Length:* 143 m (469 ft 2 in) (modified ships, 146 m [479 ft]) oa *Beam:* 15.8 m (51 ft 10 in) *Draught:* 6.5 m (21 ft 4 in) *Machinery:* 8 gas turbines, 2 shafts, 96 000 hp=38 knots *Armament:* 4 SA-N-1 launchers (2×2); 4 76-mm (3-in) AA (2×2); 5 53-cm (21-in) torpedo tubes (1×5); 2 MBU 2500A 12-barrelled A/S mortars; 2 MBU 4500A 6-barrelled A/S mortars (unmodified ships only); 4 SS-N-11 launchers (modified ships only); 4 Gatling-type AA guns (modified ships only) *Crew:* 400

Katori

Japanese cruiser class. The four cruisers of this class, ordered under the 1937-39 Programmes, were built by Mitsubishi, Yokohama, as training ships exclusively for the instruction of cadets and junior officers in ship handling and control. They shipped every item of equipment that was to be found in the larger warships of the Japanese navy (except the heavy guns) including a seaplane and catapult which were considered an important feature of the class. The seaplane performed a vital function, especially on cruisers, for the Japanese laid great emphasis on the scouting role of such aircraft in support of the main battle fleet. *Katori* was completed in April 1940, *Kashima* in May 1940, and *Kashii* in July 1941.

The ships were fully equipped with an advanced gunnery-control system such as could be found on all the battleships and cruisers, as well as a complete torpedo-control system and torpedo tubes. The bridge was an extensive structure for a small vessel, and housed a fully equipped command centre and navigating complex. Training for engineer officers was provided by a dual propulsion plant of diesels and turbines.

As soon as *Kashima* and *Katori* were completed they embarked on an extensive training cruise, the only such operation undertaken by these ships. Soon after they returned from the cruise, war broke out and together with *Kashii* the three ships were assigned as flagships to various squadrons in the Combined Fleet. They proved ideal as flagships for squadrons of smaller warships, with their extensive equipment.

A fourth unit, *Kashiwara*, was under construction at the outbreak of war in December 1941. She had been ordered under the 1940 Programme, but with war imminent all work on the vessel ceased in November 1941 to enable more urgent construction to be completed. The Japanese decided that as these ships were weakly armed and slow, and as there would be no further use for training ships as such, *Kashiwara* would be surplus to requirements and so the order was cancelled and the material broken up on the slip. A further four modified training cruisers planned under the 1942 Programme were also cancelled. These ships would have been armed with four twin turrets mounting the new 100-mm (3.9-in) gun fitted to the *Terutsuki* Class destroyers.

Soon after the outbreak of war the torpedo tubes (which were sited abreast the funnel) were removed and replaced by twin 127-mm (5-in) dual-purpose mountings. Subsequently a further 16 25-mm (1-in) AA weapons were also mounted.

During the summer of 1944 *Kashima* and *Kashii* were refitted as A/S escorts, the catapult and seaplane being removed. The light AA armament was increased to 30 25-mm (25 in *Kashii)* and eight 13-mm (0.51-in). Stowage was provided for a large number of depth charges (100 in *Kashima* and 300 in *Kashii).*

Kashima survived the war and was eventually scrapped in 1947. *Kashii* was sunk by US naval aircraft on January 12, 1945, while *Katori* was sunk by gunfire from the US cruisers *Minneapolis* and *New Orleans* and the destroyers *Radford* and *Burns* on February 17, 1945.

Displacement: 5890 tons (standard) *Length:* 133.5 m (438 ft) oa *Beam:* 16 m (52 ft 6 in) *Draught:* 5.7 m (18 ft 8 in) *Machinery:* 2-shaft geared turbines and diesels, 8000 shp=18 knots *Protection:* 50 mm (2 in) deck *Armament:* 4 140-mm (5.5-in) (2×2); 2 127-mm (5-in) (1×2) AA; 4 25-mm (1-in) AA; 4 53-cm (21-in) torpedo tubes (2×2); 1 seaplane *Crew:* 340

Katori

Japanese training ship, built 1967-69. *Katori* is basically a large frigate specially equipped to accommodate and train cadets, but equally useful as an escort in wartime.

The armament of two twin 3-in (76-mm)/50-cal AA mountings is forward, with a Bofors 375-mm (14.76-in) quadruple A/S rocket launcher set back at 02 deck level. Triple Mk 32 A/S torpedo tubes are positioned on either side of the funnel at 01 level. (Decks are numbered from upper to lower in numerical order.) A big helicopter flight deck is provided aft, but what appears to be a hangar is actually a big lecture room for cadets, with their accommodation below. A full outfit of sonar and radar is provided.

Katori has carried out several foreign cruises. She was built by Ishikawajima Heavy Industries.

Displacement: 3350 tons (standard), 4000 tons (full load) *Length:* 128.7 m (422 ft 3 in) oa *Beam:* 15 m (49 ft 3 in) *Draught:* 4.4 m (14 ft 5 in) *Machinery:* 2-shaft geared steam turbines, 20 000 shp=25 knots *Armament:* 4 76-mm (3-in)/50-cal AA (2×2); 1 quadruple 375-mm (14.76-in) A/S rocket launcher; 6 32.4-cm (12.75-in) A/S torpedo tubes (2×3) *Crew:* 460

Kiev

Soviet aircraft carrier class, formerly designated the 'Kuril' Class. *Kiev*, the first ship, was laid down in 1970, launched in 1972, and

The Soviet carrier *Kiev* photographed by the Royal Navy frigate HMS *Torquay* during a cruise and A/S exercise in the summer of 1976

MOD

ran sea trials in the Black Sea during 1975 and 1976. The second ship, *Minsk*, is thought to have been laid down in 1972, launched in 1975, and completed in 1977. A third ship, *Kharkov*, was laid down in 1975 and launched in 1977, and two further ships of the class may well follow.

When *Kiev* emerged from the Bosphorus into the Mediterranean on July 25, 1976, she was hailed by the Western press as the 'first Russian aircraft carrier'. *Kiev* is, however, not a conventional 'attack carrier' on the US model, designed to project airpower to wherever it may be needed, but a 'cruiser/carrier' designed to engage in long-range antisubmarine operations. In this sense *Kiev* is a development of the *Moskva* Class, but with two significant capabilities that the earlier ships lacked. She can engage surface ships or land targets at long range with SS-N-12 missiles, and attack aircraft at significantly greater distances by means of the Forger VTOL fighter-bombers she carries. The Forgers can also carry out attacks on shipping and provide ground support. These two new weapons have influenced the design of *Kiev*, which is quite unlike any Western carrier built or projected.

The division between cruiser and carrier functions in the layout of the ship is visually striking. The bow, despite its exaggerated dimensions, resembles that of the later missile cruisers, with its considerable sheer and a severe overhang testifying to the presence of a very large bow sonar. The entire forecastle section is given over to cruiser functions, with two 12-barrelled A/S mortars right forward on the centreline, then a twin-arm antisubmarine missile launcher, and two deckhouses carrying a twin 76-mm (3-in) mounting and a twin-arm SA-N-3 Goblet surface-to-air missile launcher respectively. On either side of these two weapons are four pairs of launchers for the massive SS-N-12 surface-to-surface missiles, reloads for which are carried in magazines served by a centreline lift sited between the deckhouses. An SA-N-4 'pop-up' launcher for short-range surface-to-air missiles is just aft and to port of the second group of launchers.

Aft of the forecastle the ship takes on a more conventional carrier shape, with a flight deck some 185-m (607-ft) long, angled at 5°, and a large island to starboard with a deck park aft of it. The sheer ends abruptly at this point, and the tapered bow section widens to a much fuller hull form which can be distinguished from Western carriers only be its very low freeboard—4 m (13 ft 2 in) to the hangar deck compared with 8.5 m (27 ft 11 in) for the US *Essex* Class. The hull shape together with the active stabilizers give the *Kiev* Class ships the stability necessary for successful V/STOL operations.

The flight deck itself is marked out with seven helicopter circles plus a larger circle aft which may be intended for V/STOL operations. The deck is covered with brown heat-resistant tiles, each about 0.5 sq m (5.4 sq ft), and is served by two aircraft lifts; one between the island and the angled deck and the other of identical length but half the width, aft of the island. The Forger is a close fit in the smaller lift. There is also a stores lift at the forward end of the flight deck, and several very small munitions lifts aft of the island. These are served by a 'railway track' that runs along the starboard deck-edge to the forecastle, where it encircles the forward missile launchers to end just above the port-side Gatling-type armament. This track operates in conjunction with the two large starboard-side cranes to move stores and munitions around the ship during replenishment.

Estimates of the full complement of aircraft vary, but it appears that between 20 and 25 Hormone ASW helicopters and about 12 Forger VTOL aircraft are carried.

The island is much larger than is normal in Western practice, since it incorporates many of the ship's cruiser functions. In addition to a further SA-N-3 Goblet launcher and a second twin 76-mm (3-in) mounting (sited at the after end in order to complete all-round coverage for these weapons) the island carries all the main search and guidance radars, which are surmounted by a large spherical radar for tactical air navigation. The massive funnel, thought at first to indicate gas-turbine propulsion, is now believed to contain uptakes for a doubled-up cruiser-size powerplant, giving a top speed of just over 30 knots. Outboard of the superstructure, at the deck-edge, is a second SA-N-4 launcher.

Below flight-deck level *Kiev* has three pairs

The Royal Navy frigate HMS *Danae* shadows the *Kiev* as the Soviet carrier heads for the Shetland/Faroes gap in the August of 1976

MOD

Inset and below: Kiev and her sister *Minsk* are intended for an advanced A/S role in wartime while in peace they can be deployed as intervention warships. However, unlike US carriers, they do not have a large number of aircraft, being limited to the Forger VTOL and some Hormone A helicopters. They have a considerable SSM capability, A/S weapons and gun armament with point-defence systems, sonar and radar, which reflects the Soviet plan for multipurpose ships. The deck has two lifts—a large one abaft the island for V/STOL and a smaller one amidships abreast the bridge. Six spots are provided with a seventh forward on the tip of the flight deck. The central larger spot is apparently for the Forger aircraft

of Gatling-type close-range AA guns, one on either side of the stern and one on a sponson below the lead edge of the angled deck forward. A fourth pair is sited on the forward end of the island. She also carries quintuple banks of torpedo tubes in hull embrasures close to the waterline.

Before commissioning *Kiev* carried the pendant number 852, but this was subsequently changed to 860. Since she emerged into the Mediterranean, she has had a lengthy spell with the Northern Fleet, with which she has engaged in exercises. In 1978, however, she returned to the Black Sea, possibly for modifications.

The *Kiev* Class are by far the largest ships ever completed by the Soviet Union, and in view of the novelty of the type it would be surprising if the design of later ships of the class did not show some changes, as a result of experience with the *Kiev* and her sister *Minsk*.

Displacement: 32 000 tons (standard), 37 000 tons (full load) *Length:* 273 m (895 ft 8 in) oa *Beam:* 48 m (157 ft 6 in) *Draught:* 9 m (29 ft 6 in) *Machinery:* 4-shaft steam turbines, 180 000 shp=30+ knots *Aircraft:* 12 VTOL Yak-36 Forgers; 25 Ka-25 Hormone helicopters *Armament:* 8 SS-N-12 missile launchers (4×2); 4 SA-N-3 missile launchers (2×2); 4 SA-N-4 missile launchers (2×2); 2 SUW-N-1 A/S missile launchers (1×2); 24 MBU 2500A A/S mortars (2×12); 4 76-mm (3-in) AA (2×2); 8 Gatling-type AA; 10 53-cm (21-in) torpedo tubes (2×10) *Crew:* 1900

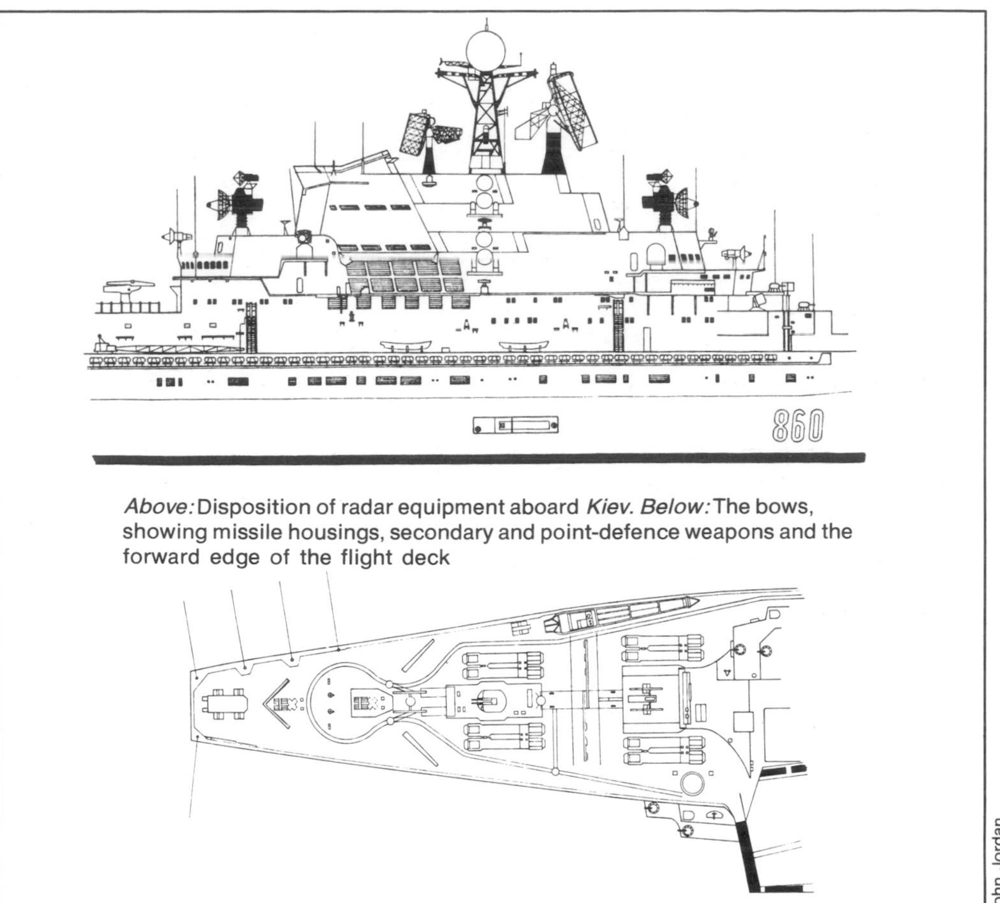

Above: Disposition of radar equipment aboard *Kiev*. *Below:* The bows, showing missile housings, secondary and point-defence weapons and the forward edge of the flight deck

John Jordan

Kiev showing her forward 47-mm guns with the four twin SS-N-12 SSM launchers. She also mounts AA and A/S missiles and AA guns

MOD

'Kildin'

Soviet missile destroyer class. The ships comprising the class were laid down in 1957-58 at the Zhdanov yard, Leningrad, and the Nosenko yard, in the Black Sea. Completion of the first ship was in 1960. The 'Kildin' Class—*Bedovy, Neulovimy, Prozorlivy* and *Neuderzhimy*—have the distinction of being the world's first guided-missile destroyers. For the Soviets, however, they were an intermediate design which preceded the first generation proper of Soviet missile-ships. Four 'Kotlin' Class hulls were taken over on the stocks and the upperworks considerably modified. A bulky SS-N-1 'Scrubber' surface-to-surface missile launcher was mounted aft, with a large magazine forward of it. Opinion varies as to the number of missiles carried, but it is probably between four and six. Two of the new quadruple 57-mm (2.24-in) mountings were sited amidships, and a further two forward. No guns larger than this are carried. A large lattice foremast, designed to extend the range of the missiles by mounting the search and guidance radars at a higher level, meant that the forefunnel was further aft than in the 'Kotlins'. Antisubmarine weapons comprised two twin torpedo mountings amidships and two 16-barrelled A/S mortars forward. *Bedovy*, which was in a more advanced state of completion when the hull was taken over, can be distinguished from the others by her funnels, which are similar to those of the 'Kotlin' Class, and (as completed) by the spherical Wasp Head director above the bridge. She also carries the earlier model 45-mm (1.77-in) AA guns.

When the SS-N-1 missile became obsolescent in the late 1960s it was decided to give these ships a radical modernization. The launcher and hangar were removed and replaced by a new deckhouse on either side of which four single launchers for the new SS-N-2 surface-to-surface missile were mounted on angled ramps. Two twin 76-mm (3-in) AA guns were mounted aft, and corresponding changes were made in the ships' sensors. The lattice mast was reduced in height, possibly to compensate for an increase in topweight, and a new back-to-back search antenna fitted. Surprisingly, the ancient 16-barrelled A/S mortars have not been replaced by one of the more recent models available.

Bedovy and *Neulovimy*, the only two which had undergone conversion by the end of 1978, serve in the Black Sea fleet, the other pair having been moved from the Pacific to the Baltic about 1975.

Displacement: 3000 tons (standard), 4000 tons (full load) *Length:* 128 m (420 ft) oa *Beam:* 13 m (42 ft 8 in) *Draught:* 5 m (16 ft 5 in) *Machinery:* 2-shaft steam turbines, 72 000 shp=36 knots *Armament:* 1 SS-N-1 missile launcher (later deleted); 4 SS-N-2 missile launchers (4×1); 32 MBU A/S mortars (2×16); 4 76-mm (3-in) AA (2×2); 16 57-mm (2.24-in) AA *(Bedovy*, 45-mm [1.77-in]) (4×4); 4 53-cm (21-in) torpedo tubes (2×2) *Crew:* 350

King George V

British battleship class, built 1937-42. The class represented the capital ships of the rearmament programme begun in 1936. They were also the first of the 'second generation' battleships built under the restrictions of the international disarmament treaties. Because they were overshadowed by later and much larger ships, they have always been underrated and criticized for alleged weaknesses. Yet, with the exception of the Japanese giants they had the thickest armour of any battleships built in the Second World War and were technically equal to most of their contemporaries. Furthermore, three of the class succeeded in helping to destroy two German capital ships.

As early as 1934 the British government realized that the country was likely to be at war with either Germany or Japan by 1941, and possibly both, with Italy conceivably intervening. What disturbed the Admiralty was the fact that the Royal Navy was considerably understrength for such a struggle. Although nominally still the largest in the world the Royal Navy had a large proportion of elderly capital ships, the majority of which would be unfit to fight their opposite numbers.

The leading naval powers were anxious to continue the limitations enshrined in the treaties but not at the cost of their fighting efficiency. The London Naval Treaty was due to expire in December 1936, and a new conference was on the verge of being convened to discuss how the limitations on the world's fleets might be continued. Concerned with rectifying what it saw as a serious weakness in the Royal Navy's strength the Admiralty advised the Cabinet in May 1934 that the new Naval Treaty must allow Great Britain to build new battleships. The Admiralty was particularly anxious that they must

HMS *King George V*, launched in 1939, with her 14-in (356-mm) guns trained to port. The ship was lost in action at Honshu in July 1945

IWM

be laid down as soon as the existing Treaty expired, even if its successor produced lower limits on size and guns.

Design studies for new capital ships had begun in the spring of 1933 to allow the British delegates to have clear objectives at the 1935 conference, just as they had had at Washington. Armour protection was given top priority, since it was recognized that even if the conference agreed to reduce gun calibre the new ships would have to face opponents with 15-in (381-mm) and 16-in (406-mm) guns for some years. Air attack with bombs of up to 910-kg (2000-lb) weight was to be taken into account. Speed was to be no more than 23 knots, the same as foreign battleships and the *Nelson* Class. The decisive battle range was held to be 11 000-14 600 m (12 000-16 000 yards); it was felt that although a higher speed of 30 knots would permit action at greater ranges, experience showed that destruction of an enemy battleship would only take place at the lower ranges.

The question of speed vexed the designers of what had now been labelled the '1937 Capital Ships'. The 1935 conference led to the Three-Power Treaty between Great Britain, the US and France, but the French, with a nervous eye on Italy, would not renounce their right to build 35 000-ton ships with 15-in (381-mm) guns. The battlecruisers *Dunkerque* and *Strasbourg* were also fast, as were the German replies to them, *Scharnhorst* and *Gneisenau.* Gun calibre was also the subject of violent changes of policy. At the conference in 1935 the British were still pressing for a reduction to 12-in (305-mm) guns for battleships, although the US wanted to retain the 16-in (406-mm), while the French and Italians had secretly already committed themselves to 15-in guns for their new ships. But the British remained optimistic about a reduction to 14-in (356-mm) calibre, and won the United States round. Since naval guns and their massive mountings take a long time to design and even longer to build, the weapons had to be ordered before the end of 1935 if the first two battleships were to be ready in 1940.

The result was that in October 1935, two months before the convening of the London Naval Conference, the Board of Admiralty recommended that the new capital ships should be 35 000-ton, 28-knot ships armed with 12 14-in (356-mm) guns. The United States insisted on a clause to allow 16-in (406-mm) guns to be reinstated if the Japanese refused to accept the Treaty terms by April 1937. In the event this happened, and so Great Britain ended up as the only country to build 14-in gunned battleships. This was at the core of most of the criticism levelled at these ships, although Second World War experience was to show that the theoretically greater range and hitting power of 15-in (381-mm) and 16-in shells made little difference in action. But in 1935 the British designers felt that to compensate for the lighter shell they should increase the number of guns from eight or nine to 12, in three quadruple mountings, a solution adopted by the Americans as well in their 14-in design, despite their 16-in.

As work on the new ships progressed several radically novel features were incorporated. A new 5.25-in (133-mm) surface/antiaircraft gun mounting was adopted for the battleships in place of the planned 4.5-in (114-mm) gun—the first example of a dual-purpose armament. The thick horizontal armour against plunging shells and bombs was raised from the middle deck to the main deck to improve stability of the ship in a damaged condition and to reduce the volume of structure vulnerable to semiarmour piercing (SAP) bombs. The original requirement for six aircraft had been altered, but now provision was to be made for two aircraft hangars in the superstructure, the first time this had been done in any battleships. The underwater protection system which had proved such an important feature of the *Nelson* Class was retained but in a much improved form.

King George V/Prince of Wales Construction programme	**provisional date**	**actual date**
Order for the gun mountings	4/36	4/36
Order for 2 ships	9/36	7/36
Laying down of ships	2/37	1/37
Launch	1/39	2/39, 5/39
1st turret installed	3/39	2/40
2nd turret installed	5/39	4/40
3rd turret installed	12/39	5/40
Completion of ships	7/40	12/40, 3/41

In February 1936 a provisional programme was drawn up for the two ships which gives some idea of the time-scale for building battleships, and the actual completion dates are given for comparison (see table above).

It can be seen clearly that the main source of delay was the armament. The guns themselves presented no problems, unlike the turrets. Three quadruple turrets had been stipulated to achieve the maximum weight of broadside, although for a time the designers toyed with the idea of nine 14-in (356-mm) guns in three triple mountings. Finally it was decided to alter the number of guns to ten by substituting a twin mounting for one of the quads to save weight. As time was so short this sudden change can only be described as capricious. With hindsight it is clear that nine 14-in would have been nearly as good as 12, for the simple reason that a triple turret was roomier and easier to work than a quadruple one. But either arrangement was preferable to incurring further delay while a new twin 14-in turret was designed. In any case the design of the new turrets proved more complex than the Director of Naval Construction had envisaged, and the quadruple turrets were 11 months late because of a shortage of draughtsmen.

The first two ships were *King George V*, ordered from Vickers-Armstrongs, Barrow, and *Prince of Wales* from Cammell Laird, Birkenhead. The Board of Admiralty wanted to go to a 16-in (406-mm) gunned design to match the ships which it believed the Japanese were building, but to save further delay the next three battleships authorized under the 1937 Programme were repeats of *King George V*. Despite all the delays it was still hoped to have the first ship at sea in September 1940 and the others in 1941, and *King George V* began her trials in October 1940. During the crisis at the time of Dunkerque, work on the last two, *Anson* and *Howe*, was stopped, but only for a few months, and they joined the fleet in 1942.

Although *King George V* joined the Home Fleet in December 1940 she was soon withdrawn for 'diplomatic' service, ferrying Lord Halifax to the US. This apparent waste of a powerful warship was, of course, to bolster British prestige by making it clear that the situation in the Atlantic was sufficiently under control to allow a new battleship to be spared. In March 1941 her sister ship, *Prince of Wales*, finished her builders' trials and a month later *King George V* became the flagship of Admiral Sir John Tovey, Commander-in-Chief of the Home Fleet.

On May 27, 1941, she and *Rodney* brought *Bismarck* to action. No detailed re-

Name	**launched**	**builder**
King George V	2/39	Vickers-Armstrongs, Barrow
Prince of Wales	5/39	Cammell Laird, Birkenhead
Duke of York (ex-*Anson*)	2/40	John Brown, Clydebank
Anson (ex-*Jellicoe*)	2/40	Swan Hunter, Wallsend
Howe (ex-*Beatty*)	4/40	Fairfield, Govan

port of the *King George V*'s gunnery has been found, but eye witnesses report that she stood off at a range of about 12 800 m (14 000 yards) firing plunging salvoes, while *Rodney* fired at a much shorter range. Although *Bismarck* took nearly two hours to sink she was completely silenced after only half an hour.

The lessons learned from the sinking of the *Prince of Wales* were incorporated in the *Anson* and *Howe*, and improvements were made to the two sister ships already in service. By this time the importance of shockpoof mountings was recognized, as was the need to provide generators and pumps relying on more than one source of power. But above all, the loss of *Prince of Wales* put an end to any dreams of the battleship holding her own against air attack. Thereafter battleships could not operate without a properly coordinated air defence, however useful they might be as antiaircraft ships.

In October 1944, *King George V* left England to join the new British Pacific Fleet, followed by *Duke of York*, *Anson* and *Howe*. She saw strenuous if unexciting work, escorting aircraft carrier task groups and bombarding shore targets. In July 1945 *King George V* bombarded targets in the Japanese home island of Honshu, the last occasion on which a British battleship fired her guns in anger.

In 1957, the order was given to sell all four for scrap, and so, after less than a decade of active service the *King George V* Class disappeared. Part of their relative obscurity may stem from the fact that they disappeared from public view so quickly and possibly because their achievements were overshadowed by other events. Yet they were in their day the best-protected and best-designed British capital ships yet built. Despite the international restrictions under which they had been designed they proved more than adequate for their wartime tasks. On the two occasions that they saw action against enemy battleships they proved well able to look after themselves, and the single casualty was sunk under an attack which would have sunk any battleship.

See also *Anson*, *Duke of York*, *Howe*.

Displacement: 35 990 tons (standard), 40 990 tons (full load) *Length:* 227 m (745 ft) oa *Beam:* 31.4 m (103 ft) *Draught:* 8.5 m (28 ft) mean, 9.6 m (31 ft 6 in) max *Machinery:* 4-shaft steam turbines, 110 000 shp=27.5 knots (28 knots maximum) *Protection:* 381-356 mm (15-14 in) belt, 152-127 mm (6-5 in) deck *Armament:* 10 14-in (356-mm) Mk II (2×4, 1×2); 16 5.25-in (133-mm) Mk I (8×2); 34 2-pdr (40-mm, 1.57-in) Mk Vi pom-poms (4×8); (Light AA, from 1945) 48 2-pdr pom-poms (6×8); 10 40-mm (1.57-in) Bofors (2×4, 2×1); 36 20-mm (0.79-in) Oerlikon (6×2, 24×1) *Crew:* 1500-1600 (approx)

Kirov

Soviet heavy cruiser class, built 1935-41. As part of the expansion of the Soviet navy authorized by Stalin in the early 1930s plans were drawn up for a new class of big cruisers to be armed with the 180-mm (7.1-in) gun first tried in the reconstructed *Krasni Kavkaz*. With technical assistance from the Italian Ansaldo firm a design known as Project 26 was drawn up, with nine guns in triple mountings on a displacement of 8800 tons.

Six ships were authorized under the Second Five-Year Plan (1933-38); two were laid down in 1935, two more in 1936 and the last pair in 1939 for the Pacific Fleet. *Kirov* was launched in 1935 at the Ordzhonikidze yard, Leningrad, which launched her sister *Maksim Gorky* in 1938. *Molotov* and *Voroshilov* were launched in 1939 by the Marti South yard, Nikolaiev, and *Kalinin* and *Kaganovich* were launched by the Amur yard, Komsomolsk, in 1943.

Kirov was completed in the autumn of 1938 and *Maksim Gorky* joined her in the Baltic Fleet in November 1940. *Voroshilov* joined the Black Sea Fleet in June 1940, but the *Molotov* was not ready until just before the German invasion in June 1941. The Far East ships did not appear until 1943-44 as there were difficulties in supplying materials from Central Russia. There were some problems with these ships, and they were a disappointment in service, although it is claimed by officers who served in them that the 180-mm gun was accurate and reliable.

As completed the ships had triple 53-cm (21-in) torpedo tubes and an aircraft catapult between the funnels, but after 1941 the catapult was removed to allow additional AA guns to be mounted. *Kirov* and *Voroshilov* had a tetrapod (four-legged) foremast surmounted by a rangefinder and fire control, but the later ships were built to the modified 26b design, with a typically Italian control tower at the forward end of the bridge and a much lighter tripod abaft it.

Kirov bombarded Finnish shore positions during the Winter War in 1939. She was damaged by German bombers in 1941. In April 1942 bomb hits caused more damage, but she was repaired and put back in service by early 1943. She has only recently been paid off after serving as a training ship. *Maksim Gorky* was mined and lost her bow on June 23, 1941. In April she was damaged by bombs and hits from German land artillery, but was not out of action for long. She was scrapped in 1958-59.

Voroshilov was hit aft by two bombs at Novorossiisk in October 1941, and had to be towed to Poti by *Krasni Kavkaz* for repairs. In November 1942 she was badly damaged by two mines off Kmeiny Island in the western Black Sea, but limped to Batum. She was scrapped in the 1960s. Her sister *Molotov* was badly damaged by a torpedo from an Italian MTB off the Crimean coast in August 1942, but was repaired with the stern section of the incomplete *Frunze*. She was renamed *Slava* in 1958, and until recently served as a training ship.

Kaganovich was reported to have been handed over to Communist China in about 1952, but there has never been any confirmation of this. Her sister *Kalinin* was renamed *Petropavlosk* in 1957, and was scrapped in the 1960s.

Displacement: 8800 tons (normal), 11 500 tons (full load) *Length:* 191 m (626 ft 8 in) pp *Beam:* 18 m (59 ft) *Draught:* 6.1 m (20 ft) *Machinery:* 2-shaft geared steam turbines, 113 000-129 000 shp=35 knots (in light condition) *Protection:* 75 mm (3 in) belt, 50 mm (2 in) deck, 100 mm (3.9 in) turrets *Armament:* 9 180-mm (7.1-in)/57-cal (3×3); 6 100-mm AA (6×1); 6 45-mm (1.77-in) AA (6×1) or 10 37-mm (1.46-in) AA (10×1); 4 12.7-mm (0.5-in) AA machine-guns; 6 53-cm (21-in) torpedo tubes (2×3); 2 floatplanes, 1 catapult *Crew:* 734-953

Kitty Hawk

US aircraft carrier class, built 1956-68. The design of *Kitty Hawk* was a considerable improvement on that of the *Forrestal* upon which it was based. Both classes are equipped with four deck-edge lifts, three to starboard and one to port. However, operating experience with the *Forrestal* Class had shown that the arrangement of deck-edge aircraft lifts was unsatisfactory because it tended to impair flight deck operations. The port-side elevator in the *Forrestal* at the forward end of the angled deck was largely unusable in heavy seas. If the elevator failed it rendered the angled deck dangerous for landing operations, thus severely reducing the carrier's capability. In addition the use of this elevator was restricted when flying operations were in progress. In the *Kitty Hawk* Class it was moved aft of the angled deck.

The position of the starboard elevators was also altered in the *Kitty Hawk*s, when the island was moved aft by 30.5 m (100 ft) and two elevators sited forward of it and a third one aft. The height of the island was raised by one level to compensate for the restricted view of the bow catapult area caused by the resiting. The island is also much smaller in the *Kitty Hawk*s and designed and treated to reduce noise interference within the command area during flying operations.

As built all four ships were rated as attack carriers (CVAs), but in 1973-74 *Kitty Hawk* and *Constellation* became multimission carriers, with antisubmarine command centres and facilities for operating Viking S-3 aircraft and Sea King SH-3 helicopters. *America* and *John F Kennedy* were also rerated from CVA to CV in June 1975.

With *America*, *Constellation* (which had been gutted by fire while completing in New York navy yard in December 1960) introduced the concept of guided missiles for carrier self-defence, and was armed with the Terrier. *John F Kennedy* has the BPDMS (basic point–defence missile system) NATO Sea Sparrow.

See also *Enterprise*, *Forrestal*.

No and name	launched	builder
CV.63 *Kitty Hawk*	5/1960	New York, Camden
CV.64 *Constellation*	10/1960	New York navy yard
CV.66 *America*	2/1964	Newport News
CV.67 *John F Kennedy*	5/1967	Newport News

Displacement: 60 100 tons (standard), 80 800 tons (full load) *Length:* 301.75 m (990 ft) wl *Beam:* 39.62 m (130 ft) *Draught:* 10.95-11.28 m (35 ft 11 in-37 ft) *Machinery:* 4-shaft geared turbines, 28 000 shp=30+ knots *Aircraft:* 85 *Armament:* 4 Terrier surface-to-air missile launchers (2×2) *Crew:* 4950 (2800+2150 air wing)

Knox

US destroyer escort (or frigate) class, built 1965-74. A total of 56 utility destroyer escorts (DE.1052-1107) was authorized by Congress in the mid-1960s to replace ageing destroyers. They were authorized in five groups assigned to consecutive Fiscal Years: ten ships in 1964, 16 in 1965, ten in 1966, ten in 1967, and ten in 1968. In early 1969, however, all of the Fiscal Year 1968 ships were cancelled by Congress to finance cost overruns on the nuclear submarine programme and to reduce defence expenditure. Even so, the 46 ships built represent the largest single group of major warships added to any Western navy since 1945.

The design is based on the *Brooke* and *Garcia* Classes, but without pressure-fired boilers in order to reduce cost and complexity. The single shaft has been heavily criticized by US Navy officers, who fear that a machinery breakdown would cause total immobilization. The cancelled DE.1101 was to have had General Electric LM 2500 gas turbines and was to be a prototype for the *Spruance* Class.

Knox (DE.1052); *Roark* (DE.1053); *Gray* (DE.1054); *Whipple* (DE.1062); *Lockwood* (DE.1064); *Marvin Shields* (DE.1066); *Downes* (DE.1070); *Badger* (DE.1071)—built by Todd shipyards, Seattle.

Hepburn (DE.1055); *Meyerkord* (DE.1058); *Lang* (DE.1060); *Francis Hammond* (DE.1067); *Harold E Holt* (DE.1074); *Fanning* (DE.1076)—built by Todd shipyards, San Pedro.

Rathburne (DE.1057); *Reasoner* (DE.1063); *Stein* (DE.1065); *Bagley* (DE.1069); *Robert E Peary* (ex-*Connolly*) (DE.1073)—built by Lockheed Shipbuilding and Construction company.

Connole (DE.1056); *W S Sims* (DE.1059); *Patterson* (DE.1061); *Vreeland* (DE. 1068); *Blakely* (DE. 1072); *Trippe* (DE.1075); *Ouellet* (DE.1077); *Joseph Hewes* (DE.1078); *Bowen* (DE.1079); *Paul* (DE.1080); *Aylwin* (DE.1081); *Elmer Montgomery* (DE.1082); *Cook* (DE.1083); *McCandless* (DE.1084); *Donald B Beary* (DE.1085); *Brewton* (DE.1068); *Kirk* (DE.1087); *Barbey* (DE.1088); *Jesse L Brown* (DE.1089); *Ainsworth* (DE.1090); *Miller* (DE.1091); *Thomas C Hart* (DE.1092); *Capodanno* (DE.1093); *Pharris* (DE.1094); *Truett* (DE.1095); *Valdez* (DE.1096); *Moinester* (DE.1097)—built by Avondale shipyards, Westwego, Louisiana.

The Avondale ships were built by a new method of mass production, with the keel uppermost to facilitate 'downhead' welding. Prefabricated inverted modules were assembled on a permanent platen, then lifted by hydraulic crane and moved sideways into a giant turning ring, which rotated the hull into the upright position. The ships were launched broadside on.

The original armament did not include a missile defence against air attack but provision was made for eventual fitting of the Sea Sparrow basic point defence missile system (BPDMS) aft. A hangar for the DASH (drone antisubmarine helicopter) was provided, but the failure of that system left them without a helicopter. The landing deck was later strengthened to take the Kaman Seasprite, which is the interim LAMPS (light airborne multipurpose system) machine. So far two of the class have been fitted with Harpoon surface-to-surface missiles in two quadruple launchers, and others will follow. Two of the eight Asroc missile-launchers have been modified to fire standard SM-1 surface-to-air missiles. Unlike most US ships they do not carry Mk 32 A/S torpedo tubes on deck; instead there are two fixed tubes in the transom stern for firing wire-guided Mk 37 torpedoes and fixed Mk 25 tubes in the superstructure.

In June 1975 the class designation was changed to frigates, and so they are now numbered *FF. 1052-1097.*

The *Kitty Hawk* Class aircraft carrier USS *John F Kennedy* (CV-67) prepares to launch three F-14 Tomcats during operations in the Ionian Sea on October 22, 1975

US Navy

C & S Taylor

USS *Valdez*, a *Knox* Class destroyer escort (or frigate) with a Kaman Seasprite on the helicopter deck on the stern originally designed for the DASH

The cost of the class rose considerably during construction. The 14 ships ordered from Todd shipyards were contracted for at a cost of $151 000 000 in 1964; by January 1970 the cost had risen by $96 000 000. The final cost for the whole class was an average of $30 959 000 per ship, excluding the LAMPS helicopter, standard missile, variable-depth sonar or Sea Sparrow modifications, which accounted for another $2 150 000 per ship.

In March 1966 the US Government gave permission for the Spanish navy to build five modified *Knox* Class (DEG.7-11). The Spaniards preferred to have a Standard SM-1 area-defence missile in place of the helicopter facility and the Sea Sparrow BPDMS, and so the firm of Gibbs & Cox modified the design. The *Baleares* (F.71), *Andalucia* (F.72), *Cataluña* (F.73), *Asturias* (F.74) and *Extremadura* (F.75) were built in 1968-76 by Empresa Bazán at El Ferrol, with the steam turbines and boilers also built in Spain.

The armament of the Spanish ships includes a Mk 22 single-arm launcher for the 16 Standard missiles carried and an Asroc launcher forward, and there is also provision for the Spanish Meroka 20-mm (0.79-in) Close-In Weapon System (CIWS), as a defence against missiles.

A *Knox* Class destroyer escort in line astern with a NATO task force during an exercise. The class has also been built under licence by Spain

Ambrose Greenway

Displacement: 3011 tons (standard), 3900 tons (average standard) *Length:* 113.5 m (438 ft) oa *Beam:* 14.2 m (46 ft 9 in) *Draught:* 7.5 m (24 ft 9 in) *Machinery:* 1-shaft geared steam turbine, 35 000 shp=27 knots *Armament:* (US ships) 1 5-in (127-mm)/54-cal DP Mk 42; 1 Sea Sparrow RIM-7H SAM launcher; 1 Asroc A/S missile launcher (with 2 standard RIM-66A SAMs); 8 Harpoon SSMs (to be fitted); 4 12.8-in (32.5-cm) Mk 32 A/S torpedo tubes (4×1); 2 19-in (48.3-cm) A/S torpedo tubes (2×1); (Spanish ships) 1 5-in (127-mm)/54-cal; 1 Standard RIM-66A SAM launcher; 1 Asroc RUR-5A A/S missile launcher (1×8); 4 12.8-in (32.5-cm) torpedo tubes (4×1); 2 19-in (48.3-cm) A/S torpedo tubes (2×1); 1 Seasprite helicopter (US ships only) *Crew:* 245-283

'Kola'

Soviet frigate class. Ten ships of the class are thought to have been built at Kaliningrad and on the Black Sea, with the first one being laid down in 1950 and completed in 1954. Names are doubtful, but the five remaining ships have been identified as *Krechet, Sokol, Sovetski Azerbaidzhan, Sovetski Dagestan* and *Sovetski Turkmenistan.*

This class succeeded the much smaller *Yastreb* Class of torpedo boats completed just after the Second World War. The increase in size, combined with the adoption of a flush deck, led some commentators to suggest that they were influenced by the German Type 1939 fleet torpedo boats.

The 'Kola' Class carry a heavy armament for their size, with two single 100-mm (3.9-in) guns mounted forward, a further pair aft, and a triple bank of torpedo tubes amidships. Light AA guns are few, however, with only two twin 37-mm (1.46-in) supplemented by two twin 25-mm (1-in) in some ships. In addition to the original depth-charge racks, some ships were fitted with racks for launching antisubmarine rockets, later replaced by quintuple hand-loaded A/S mortars.

Too much loading seems to have been attempted on the displacement and the poor seagoing qualities of the ships are reflected in their present relegation to the calm waters of the Caspian Sea.

Displacement: 1500 tons (standard), 1900 tons (full load) *Length:* 96 m (315 ft) *Beam:* 10 m (32 ft 10 in) *Draught:* 3.5 m (11 ft 6 in) *Machinery:* 2-shaft steam turbines, 30 000 shp=30 knots *Armament:* 4 100-mm (3.9-in) (4×1); 2 37-mm (1.46-in) (2×2); 2 25-mm (1-in) (2×2) (some ships); 2 groups MBU 900 A/S rocket-launchers or 5 MBU 1800 A/S mortar (1×5); 3 53-cm (21-in) torpedo tubes (1×3) *Crew:* 190

Köln

German frigate class, built 1958-64. In March 1957 the new Federal German navy or Bundesmarine ordered its first major warships, six antisubmarine escorts *(gleitboote).* All were built by H C Stulcken Sohn, of Hamburg and comprised *Köln* (F.220), *Emden* (F.221), *Augsburg* (F.222), *Karlsruhe* (F.223), *Lübeck* (F. 224) and *Braunschweig* (F.225).

The Type 120 design, the basis of the class, was broadly influenced by torpedo boats on the drawing board at the end of the Second World War. There were, however, important improvements. Instead of steam turbines or diesels, a twin-shaft CODAG (combined diesel and gas) plant was chosen, with two MAN diesels and a Brown-Boveri gas turbine coupled to each shaft. A heavy armament of two Creusot-Loire 100-mm (3.9-in) dual-purpose guns and six Breda 40-mm (1.57-in) Bofors was adopted, since the ships would be operating in waters dominated by shore-based aircraft. The antisubmarine armament was supplied from Sweden and consisted of FFV homing torpedoes and quadruple 375-mm (14.76-in) Bofors rocket launchers.

The class is not an unqualified success. The CODAG machinery is large and complex, the ships are cramped and suffer from low freeboard and excess topweight. After a few years in service, the foremost M45 fire-control director was removed to save weight. They will not be modernized, and are due for replacement by the *F-122* frigates in the next five years.

The appearance of the ships is distinctive, with a huge trunked funnel surmounted by a wedge-shaped fin.

Displacement: 2100 tons (standard), 2550 tons (full load) *Length:* 110 m (360 ft 11 in) oa *Beam:* 11 m (36 ft 1 in) *Draught:* 3.4 m (11 ft 2 in) *Machinery:* 2-shaft diesel/gas turbine, 12 000 bhp/24 000 shp=32 knots *Armament:* 2 100-mm (3.9-in)/55-cal (2×1); 6 40-mm (1.57-in)/70-cal (3×2, 2×1); 8 375-mm (14.76-in) A/S rocket-launchers (2×4); 4 53-cm (21-in) A/S torpedo tubes (4×1) *Crew:* 212

'Komar'

Soviet missile patrol boat class, built 1959-61. They were, like the 'Kildin' Class destroyers, an intermediate design based on a conventionally armed type already in production, with the object of taking the new SS-N-2 surface-to-surface missile to sea as soon as possible, and before the first purpose-built missile patrol boats of the 'Osa' Class could be completed. When the 'Osas' were ready, production of the 'Komars' ceased. They nevertheless hold the distinction of being the world's first missile patrol boats.

Since standard P-6 hulls were used for the conversion, platforms braced by struts had to be built out from the sides in order to accommodate the two SS-N-2 launchers alongside the bridge, which was moved aft to provide a better balance. The launchers themselves, angled slightly outboard, were diamond-shaped in cross section, and were not capped at the ends. This meant that the missiles were exposed to corrosion by spray, a defect remedied on later missile boats. The only other armament was a twin 25-mm (1-in) AA mounting just forward of the bridge.

The class were of little use outside coastal waters because of their small size, and by 1977 only two were estimated to remain in service with the Soviet navy out of the original hundred or so built. In the early and mid-sixties, however, many of these had been transferred to other countries: seven or eight to the People's Republic of China, ten to North Korea, three to North Vietnam, 12 to Indonesia, seven to Egypt, 18 to Cuba, nine to Syria, with three boats going to Iraq as late as 1972. China and Egypt also built craft of their own modelled on the 'Komars'.

The boats transferred to Egypt and Syria took an active part in the Middle East wars of 1967 and 1973. In the 1967 war an Egyptian 'Komar' was responsible for the sinking of the Israeli destroyer *Eilath.* By 1973, however, the Israelis had far more sophisticated missile boats and claimed the sinking of three Syrian and two Egyptian 'Komars'.

Displacement: 75 tons (standard), 80 tons (full load) *Length:* 26.8 m (87 ft 11 in) oa *Beam:* 6.4 m (21 ft) *Draught:* 1.8 m (5 ft 11 in) *Machinery:* 4 shafts, 4 diesels, 4800 hp=40 knots *Armament:* 2 SS-N-2 missile launchers; 2 25-mm (1-in) AA (1×2) *Crew:* 11

Kormoran

German auxiliary cruiser of Second World War. Formerly the HAPAG Line's *Steiermark,* she was a 8736-grt cargo liner built at Kiel in 1938. She was converted at Hamburg as *Hilfskreuzer 8* or *Kormoran,* but was also known as *Schiff 41.* To the British she was 'Raider G'.

Under Captain Theodor Detmers, *Kormoran* became the most skilful of the disguised merchant raiders. She sailed from Gdynia on

The *Köln* Class frigate *Karlsruhe* (F.223), one of the first major warships to be ordered by the Bundesmarine in March 1957. They are due to be replaced in the late 1970s

Bildstelle der Marine Marineamt

Foto Droppel

The converted cargo liner *Kormoran* had an active career during 1941, and achieved the distinction of being the only auxiliary cruiser to sink a regular cruiser

December 3, 1940, masquerading as a *Sperrbrecher* or minesweeper, but soon adopted a Soviet disguise, and slipped through the British blockade. Between January and September 1941 she sank or captured 11 ships totalling 68264 grt. On November 19, 1941, she fell in with the Australian cruiser HMAS *Sydney* off Sharks Bay, Western Australia, and it seemed that the raider would be forced to surrender or scuttle herself.

Captain Detmers lulled the Australians into a false sense of security by pretending to be an agitated neutral, and sending out the standard 'raider sighted' signal to the Admiralty. The cruiser apparently stood down her guns' crews and approached to within half a mile. Suddenly *Kormoran*'s concealed 15-cm (5.9-in) guns opened fire, and although the cruiser was soon able to pour in a withering fire from her own guns she was still near enough to be hit by one of *Kormoran*'s concealed torpedoes. The two ships were badly mauled and drifted apart, blazing furiously. Eventually the *Kormoran*'s mines blew up, but nothing was ever seen or heard of *Sydney* again. A few *Kormoran* survivors later said that they had seen a sheet of flame on the horizon at about midnight, presumably the cruiser blowing up.

Kormoran was the only armed merchant cruiser ever to sink a regular cruiser.

Tonnage: 8736 grt *Length:* 164 m (538 ft 1 in) oa *Beam:* 20.2 m (66 ft 3 in) *Draught:* 8.5 m (27 ft 11 in) *Machinery:* 2-shaft diesel, 16000 bhp=18 knots *Armament:* 6 15-cm (5.9-in)/45-cal (6×1); 1 75-mm (2.95-in)/35-cal (removed before December 1940); 2 37-mm (1.46-in) (2×1); 2 37-mm AA (2×1); 6 53-cm (21-in) torpedo tubes (2×2 in revolving deck-mountings, 2×1 submerged); 360 EMC mines; 2 Arado 196 A1 floatplanes *Crew:* 400

Kortenaer

Dutch frigate class. In the early 1970s the Royal Netherlands Navy began to design a new frigate to replace its ageing *Holland* and *Friesland* Class destroyers. At the same time NATO initiated studies for what became known as the 'NATO frigate', an attempt to produce a standard design for all the European navies that are members of NATO.

The Dutch went on to work out their own ideas, but tailored to make them attractive to NATO, and the result was the *Standaard* or Standard frigate.

In December 1973 the Dutch government approved the design, and in August 1974 the first four ships were ordered, followed by another four three months later, and a third series of four in December 1976.

Ten ships are to be built at the Royal de Schelde yard, Flushing: *Kortenaer* (F.807); *Callenburgh* (F.808); *Van Kinsbergen* (F.809); *Banckert* (F.810); *Piet Hein* (F.811); *Pieter Florisz* (F.812); *Witte de With* (F.813); *Abraham Crijnssen* (F.816); *Jan van Brakel* (F.825); *Willem van der Zaan* (F.826).

Philips van Almonde and *Blois van Treslong* are to be built by Wilton-Fijenoord, and a thirteenth order, for a modified version with an antiaircraft armament, has been delayed.

The Standard design is intended for ocean escort, and so it has good seakeeping and endurance. The propulsion is the same as in the *Tromp* Class DDGs and contemporary British ships, a COGOG arrangement of Rolls-Royce Olympus and Tyne gas turbines. Two WG13 Lynx helicopters are carried for antisubmarine work, Harpoon surface-to-surface missiles, and OTO-Melara 76-mm (3-in) guns and NATO Sea Sparrow missiles for air defence. The air-defence version will probably be armed with Standard SM-1 missiles. The question of which very short-range air-defence system (VSRADS) to adopt is unsettled, and for the moment a second OTO-Melara gun is shipped aft, but it will be replaced in due course. It is believed that the

The Dutch frigate *Kortenaer* (F.807). She is the basis for the Federal German *F-122* Class and nine other ships ordered for the Dutch

Royal Netherlands Navy

choice will be the SEM-30 'Goalkeeper', a four-barrelled mounting with 35-mm (1.38-in) Oerlikon guns; with its integrated search- and fire-control radar and a rate of fire of 3200 rds/min.

Kortenaer started her trials in April 1978, to commission at the end of that year; the twelfth ship is to commission in mid-1984. The design has been adopted by the West German navy as the basis for its *F-122* design, and early in 1978 the Imperial Iranian Navy announced that it would order 12 *Kortenaer* Class, eight of which would be built by Dutch shipyards and the remaining four from German yards.

Displacement: 3500 tons (standard), 3785 tons (full load) *Length:* 130 m (426 ft 6 in) oa *Beam:* 14.6 m (47 ft 11 in) *Draught:* 6 m (19 ft 8 in) *Machinery:* 2-shaft gas turbines, 56800 shp+10800 shp cruising turbines=30 knots *Armament:* 2 76-mm (3-in)/62-cal (2×1); 1 SEM-30 quadruple mounting (to be mounted in place of one 76-mm gun); 8 Harpoon RGM-84A SSM-launchers (2×4); 8 NATO Sea Sparrow AIM-7E SAM-launchers (1×8); 4 Mk 32 A/S torpedo tubes (4×1); 2 WG13 Lynx helicopters *Crew:* 200

'Kotlin'

Soviet destroyer class, built between 1954 and 1958 in yards at Leningrad, Nikolayev and Komsomolsk. The ships are: *Bessledny, Blagorodny, Blestyashchy, Burlivy, Byvaly, Dalnevostochny Komsomolets, Moskovsky Komsomolets, Naporisty, Plamenny, Smeshny, Spechny, Spokoiny, Svedushchy, Svetly, Vliyatelny, Vozmushchenny, Vyderzhanny, Vesky, Vysyvayushchy, Bravy, Nakhodchivy, Nastoychivy, Nesokrushimy, Skromny, Skrytny, Soznatelny, Vozbuzhdenny* and *Warszawa.* The last nine ships (*Bravy-Warszawa*) are known as the 'Kotlin SAM' Class. *Warszawa* was transferred to Poland in 1970.

It was apparently intended that the class should comprise 36 units, but only 32 ships were laid down, and four of these were converted during construction to become the 'Kildin' Class.

Although displaying many of the features of the 'one-off' 'Tallin' Class laid down in 1952, the 'Kotlins' exemplify a return to a more conventional machinery layout, with the second funnel sited further forward between the two banks of torpedo tubes. A reduction in engine power compared with *Neustrashimy* brought with it a hull of smaller dimensions and of a very different shape, with the reduced freeboard compensated for by a sharply angled bow. This enabled high speeds to be maintained in rough seas and resulted in a more successful and stable ship than *Neustrashimy.*

The main armament of the ships comprised two of the new stabilized twin 130-mm (5.1-in) dual-purpose turrets, mounted at upper deck level fore and aft. Because of the change in superstructure layout, two quadruple 45-mm (1.77-in) mountings could be accommodated amidships, and the remaining two superimposed above the main turrets. This enabled three mountings to fire on the broadside compared with only two on *Neustrashimy.*

Beginning in 1962, 11 of the class underwent a minor modification when one of the quintuple banks of torpedo tubes was removed and two 16-barrelled A/S mortars fitted beneath the bridge. Some ships were fitted with six-barrelled A/S mortars aft, while others had a platform built out from the second funnel to the ship's sides. On this four twin 25-mm (1-in) AA were mounted. Later modifications gave some unmodified ships two 12-barrelled A/S mortars forward.

A much more radical modification of the class emerged in 1962, to be known as the 'Kotlin SAM' Class. The after two gun mountings had been replaced by a large magazine for SA-N-1 Goa missiles with the launcher on top of it, and the lattice mainmast by a short pyramidal tower for the Peel Group guidance radar. The funnel was redesigned and moved aft to serve as a blast deflector for the missiles. At first, the centre pair of 45-mm mountings and the forward bank of torpedo tubes were removed, but these were replaced in 1964.

Although *Bravy* was clearly a prototype conversion, no further ships modified in this way appeared until 1968. The eight ships of the 'Kotlin SAM-II' Class retained the forward bank of torpedo tubes but dispensed with the 45-mm mountings amidships. The latter were replaced in the mid-1970s on some ships by four twin 30-mm (1.18-in) mounts, with their Drum Tilt directors carried on platforms projecting from the radar tower. They were also fitted with 12- or 16-barrelled mortars. The original funnel has been retained, and a separate blast deflector fitted to the end of the magazine. This indicates that the modified funnel in *Bravy* was not entirely successful.

Displacement: 2850 tons (standard), 3885 tons (full load) *Length:* 128 m (419 ft 11 in) oa *Beam:* 13 m (42 ft 8 in) *Draught:* 5 m (16 ft 5 in) *Machinery:* 2-shaft steam turbines, 72000 shp=36 knots *Armament:* ('Kotlin') 4 130-mm (5.1-in) DP (2×2); 16 45-mm (1.77-in) AA (4×4); 8 or 4 25-mm (1-in) AA (4×2 or 2×2), some ships; 32 MBU 2500 A/S mortars (2×16); or 24 MBU 2500A A/S mortars (2×12); 5 or 10 53-cm (21-in) torpedo tubes (1×5 or 2×5); ('Kotlin SAM') 2 SA-N-1 missile-launchers (1×2); 2 130-mm (5.1-in) DP (1×2); 4 (*Bravy* 12) 45-mm (1.77-in) AA (1×4; *Bravy* 3×4); 8 30-mm (1.18-in) AA (2×4), some ships; 24 MBU 2500A A/S mortars (2×12); 5 53-cm (21-in) torpedo tubes (1×5) *Crew:* 326 ('Kotlin'); 285 ('Kotlin SAM')

A Soviet 'Kotlin' Class destroyer. Nine of these ships are in service with the Polish navy

C & S Taylor

'Kresta'

Soviet missile cruiser class, built 1963-78. The class is remarkable because the first four ships were the last of the 'first generation' of missile cruisers, while the ten ships completed from 1970 onwards belong, in terms of their armament and designed role, to the 'second generation'. The 'Kresta-I' variation consists of four ships: *Vize-Admiral Drozd, Admiral Zozulya, Sevastopol* and *Vladivostok.* All were built at the Zhdanov yard, Leningrad. The first ship was completed in 1966, the others following at yearly intervals.

The design was a development of the 'Kynda' Class 'rocket-cruisers', with a hull of slightly increased dimensions and with the freeboard aft increased by the extension of the forecastle deck towards the stern. Topweight, which seems to have been a serious problem with the 'Kyndas', was significantly reduced by retaining only one of the radar towers, and by trunking the boiler room uptakes together into a single wide funnel or 'mack'. This is divided into two halves so that a Big Net air search radar could be accommodated above it. Such an arrangement was the result of a significant change of emphasis in the ship's armament: a halving of the battery of surface-to-surface missiles. Besides dispensing with the big quadruple launchers this change eliminated one of the bulky guidance radars—therefore the need for a second tower—and allowed the surface-to-air missile systems to be increased from one to two. These modifications were a firm indication that the ships were to operate in more open waters than their predecessors. The two SAM launchers now occupied prominent positions fore and aft, mounted on deckhouses which form their magazines. Their Peel Group radars are mounted on small towers on either side of the large central mack. The SS-N-3 SSMs, on the other hand, were now relegated to a secondary position, with one pair of launching tubes on each side of the bridge. The launchers can be raised to about 20°, and can probably be reloaded from the large forward deckhouse. At least one reload is carried for each launcher. An undoubted improvement in the operational effectiveness of this weapon against other ships was the provision—for the first time on a Soviet warship—of a helicopter for missile guidance. This was accommodated in a hangar which opened onto the low stern.

The 'Kresta-II' variation consists of ten ships. The first was laid down in 1967, and was completed in 1970. These ships are: *Admiral Nakhimov, Admiral Makarov, Admiral Isakov, Admiral Oktyabrsky, Admiral Isachenkov, Vasily Chapaev, Kronstadt, Marshal Voroshilov, Marshal Timoshenko* and *Admiral Yumashev*.

'Kresta-II' modifications were the result of a change in operational priorities towards antisubmarine warfare. The bow, like that of the 'Kashin' Class, was given considerable overhang, suggesting the presence of a large bow sonar set. The SA-N-1 Goa launchers were replaced by the new SA-N-3 Goblet, introduced on the 'Moskva' Class, and the Peel Group guidance radars by the aptly named Head Lights. Installation of the new SAM outfit also entailed a reduction in size of the massive pyramidal tower of the 'Kresta-I', so that the large Top Sail 3-D radar could be accommodated without harming the stability of the design. The most significant change, however, was the replacement of the twin SSM launchers by two quadruple launchers for the SS-N-14 antisubmarine missile. This enabled the Hormone B missile guidance helicopter to be exchanged for the antisubmarine 'A' version. These two measures significantly improved ASW capabilities at the expense of antiship capabilities. However, there is evidence to suggest that the SA-N-3 may be a dual-purpose weapon. The helicopter deck itself was raised to the level of the forecastle deck, but the hangar remained at the same level. The advantage thus gained in operating the helicopter from a higher level is therefore set against a complex method of stowage which involves the raising of the hangar roof and the use of the hangar floor as a lift.

Conventional weapons are basically the same for both versions of the class: two twin automatic 57-mm (2.24-in) AA, two quintuple banks of torpedo tubes, and the same 12- and six-barrelled A/S mortars as in the 'Kashin' Class. In addition, the 'Kresta-II' Class carry four Gatling-type guns for defence against missiles, and the *Vize-Admiral Drozd* of the earlier group has emerged from a recent refit similarly equipped.

The Soviets clearly regard the 'Kresta' Class as a successful design, because they have continued in production despite the advent of the 'Kara' Class. The 'Krestas' are deployed in all four fleets, and in particular form the backbone of the powerful Northern fleet. Pennant numbers in the 200, 500 and 800 ranges are carried.

('Kresta-I') *Displacement:* 5140 tons (standard), 6500 tons (full load) *Length:* 155 m (508 ft 6 in) oa *Beam:* 17 m (55 ft 9 in) *Draught:* 5.5 m (18 ft) *Machinery:* 2-shaft steam turbines, 100 000 shp=35 knots *Armament:* 4 SA-N-1 missile-launchers (2×2); 4 SS-N-3 missile-launchers (2×2); 4 57-mm (2.24-in) AA (2×2); 24 MBU 2500A A/S mortars (2×12); 12 MBU 4500A A/S mortars (2×6); 10 53-cm (21-in) torpedo tubes (2×5); Hormone B missile-guidance helicopter *Crew:* 400

('Kresta-II') *Displacement:* 6000 tons (standard), 7500 tons (full load) *Length:* 158 m (518 ft 4 in) *Beam:* 17 m (55 ft 9 in) *Draught:* 5.5 m (18 ft) *Machinery:* 2-shaft steam turbines, 100 000 shp=34 knots *Armament:* SA-N-3 missile-launchers (2×2); SS-N-14 missile-launchers (2×4); 24 MBU 2500A A/S mortars (2×12); 12 MBU 4500A A/S mortars (2×6); 4 Gatling-type guns; 10 53-cm (21-in) torpedoes (2×5); Hormone A A/S helicopter *Crew:* 500

'Krivak'

Soviet missile cruiser class. The lead ship was laid down in 1968 and completed in 1971, and the class remained in production towards the end of the 1970s, with new vessels being built at the rate of two units a year. The ships are: *Bditelny, Bodry, Dejatelny, Doblestny, Dostoiny, Druzhny, Razumny, Silny,*

MOD

Above: A 'Kresta I' Soviet missile cruiser in March 1975. _Below:_ A 'Kresta II' photographed by a helicopter from HMS _Ark Royal_ during a NATO exercise in the Atlantic in November 1975

MOD

Storozhevoy, Retivy, Razyashchy, Zharky, Rezvy, Rezky and *Razitelny*. The last three were built to a modified design.

Although chronologically they followed the 'Kashin' Class, the 'Krivaks' are a reversion to a smaller, general-purpose destroyer type, and in this sense can be more accurately described as the true successors to the 'Kotlins'. A major factor in the reduction of size was the desire to place the orders in smaller yards, leaving the traditional yards to concentrate on the new generation of missile cruisers and carriers. The two yards chosen at Kaliningrad and Kerch previously built ships little bigger than corvettes.

The 'Krivaks' have a comprehensive range of weapon systems. For the antisubmarine role—their main function—they carry a large quadruple launcher mounted forward for SS-N-14 missiles which were first seen on the 'Kresta' Class cruisers. Directly beneath the bridge there are two 12-barrelled A/S mortars, and two quadruple banks of torpedo tubes mounted amidships. For close-range defence against aircraft the ships carry an SA-N-4 'pop-up' launcher fore and aft, and two twin 76-mm (3-in) mountings on the stern. The sensor array is equivalent to that on other modern Soviet warships. The antisubmarine orientation of the armament is reflected in the provision of a bow sonar and a variable depth sonar. Unlike Western antisubmarine vessels the 'Krivaks' do not carry a helicopter. This is a result partly of the Soviet practice of using both ends of the ship to accommodate the maximum number of weapon systems, but also of their failure to produce an ASW helicopter suitable for smaller warships.

As in the contemporary 'Kara' Class, propulsion is by gas turbine. A large square funnel is sited well aft to keep the hot exhaust gases clear of the sensors. Claims have been made for very high speeds, but the presence of a single funnel makes this unlikely. The reduced emphasis on high speed in recent Soviet warships suggests that they can probably make just over 30 knots, which for a ship of this size would only require two main turbines similar to those of the 'Kara' Class (about 25 000 hp each), possibly combined with smaller cruise turbines in a COGOG (combined gas or gas) arrangement.

In appearance the 'Krivaks' resemble modern Western warships more than any other Soviet warships. The hull is well-designed for seakeeping without having the angular appearance of earlier generations, and the superstructure is laid out neatly in blocks, giving the ships a compact and handsome look.

In 1976 a variant of the class, now known as the 'Krivak-II', appeared. In these the twin 76-mm (3-in) mountings aft have been replaced by new model single 100-mm (3.9-in) guns, which presumably have a better dual-purpose capability, and a larger variable depth sonar has been fitted, necessitating a slight lengthening of the stern. The original version is, however, continuing in parallel production.

Ships of the 'Krivak' Class serve mainly in the Baltic and the Mediterranean, and they carry pennant numbers in the 200 and 500 ranges.

Displacement: 3200 tons (standard), 3900 tons (full load) *Length:* 122 m (400 ft 3 in) oa, ('Krivak-II') 125.5 m (411 ft 9 in) *Beam:* 14 m (45 ft 11 in) *Draught:* 5 m (16 ft 5 in) *Machinery:* 2-shaft gas turbines, 50-60 000 hp=31 knots *Armament:* 1 quadruple SS-N-14 missile-launcher; 2 twin SA-N-4 missile-launchers; 4 76-mm (3-in) AA (2×2) ('Krivak-II', 2 100-mm [3.9-in] DP); 24 MBU 2500A A/S mortars (2×12); 8 53-cm (21-in) torpedo tubes (2×4) *Crew:* 210

Kromantse

Ghanaian corvette class, built 1963-65. The design and construction of *Kromantse* was shared by Vosper Thornycroft, Portsmouth, and Vickers-Armstrongs, Barrow. It is an unsophisticated concept prepared for Third World countries and emerging naval powers with only limited funds and expertise available. *Kromantse* was the first of a series of similar basic corvette designs to be evolved for this market.

The standard of equipment fitted in *Kromantse* and her sister ship *Keta* has been dictated by the need for simplicity and cost-effective design for a small patrol craft capable of antisubmarine duties. The machinery consists of two high-speed diesels which are remote-controlled and this reduces the number of highly trained, experienced engine-room personnel required. Further, the system ensures that at the press of a button the craft is always ready for steaming.

The hull is constructed of prefabricated steel with all superstructures and internal partitioning of aluminium. Armament by modern standards would be considered obsolete, but its operation and maintenance is well within the capabilities of the young Ghanaian navy. The ships are fitted with two Vosper-designed, non-retractable, roll-damping fins. These greatly reduce the rolling motion and provide a very stable weapons platform and give as an additional bonus much greater crew comfort in the heavy swells experienced in the Atlantic. Both *Kromantse* and *Keta* underwent a comprehensive refit carried out by Vosper Thornycroft in 1974-75.

Displacement: 440 tons (standard), 500 tons (full load) *Length:* 54 m (177 ft) oa *Beam:* 8.7 m (28 ft 6 in) *Draught:* 4 m (13 ft) *Machinery:* 2-shaft diesels, 7100 bhp=20 knots *Armament:* 1 4-in

A Soviet 'Krivak' Class guided missile destroyer photographed by a Sea King from HMS *Blake* as the destroyer passes through English Channel

MOD

The Ghanaian corvette *Kromantse*, on trials after her 1974-75 refit by Vosper Thornycroft. With her sister *Keta* she can be used for patrol work and antisubmarine duties using Squid A/S mortars

Vosper Thornycroft

Name	builder	launched	completed
Kromantse	Vosper Thornycroft, Portsmouth	9/63	7/64
Keta	Vickers, Barrow	1/65	5/65

(102-mm); 1 40-mm (1.57-in) (originally designed to carry a twin mount); 3 Squid A/S mortars (1×3) *Crew:* 54

'Krupny'

Soviet missile destroyer class, laid down 1958-59. The ships comprising the class were built at the Zhdanov yard, Leningrad, the Nosenko yard, Nikolayev, and possibly at Komsomolsk in the Pacific. The first unit was completed in 1961. The ships are: *Boiky, Derzhky, Gordy, Gnevny, Gremyashchy, Uporny, Zhguchy,* and *Zorky.*

The class was basically an enlargement of the 'Kildin' Class, for which they could be easily mistaken were it not for the second bulky SS-N-1 launcher mounted forward, and the helicopter deck on the stern. This arrangement entailed a resiting of the two quadruple 57-mm (2.24-in) AA mountings carried forward on the 'Kildins'. The mounting directly below the bridge was now placed on top of the forward magazine, while the other mounting was moved aft to a position between the second funnel and magazine. The A/S mortars were carried a deck higher abreast the magazine, and the twin torpedo tubes increased to triples. Each of the two magazines were roughly the same size as the single magazine on the 'Kildins'. This suggests that they carry twice the number of missiles.

The hull was essentially a lengthened version of the 'Kotlin' hull, with an increase in propulsive power to match. While the massive lattice foremast of the 'Kildins' was retained, the funnels were even smaller than those of their predecessors, giving the ships an awkward, ungainly appearance. When the decision to phase out the obsolescent SS-N-1 was taken in the mid-1960s, it was decided to convert the 'Krupny' Class in a similar way to the 'Kotlin SAMs'. Conversions began in 1967-68 and continued throughout the early seventies.

See also 'Kanin' Class.

Displacement: 3650 tons (standard), 4500 tons (full load) *Length:* 138 m (452 ft 9 in) oa *Beam:* 14.6 m (47 ft 11 in) *Draught:* 5 m (16 ft 5 in) *Machinery:* 2-shaft steam turbines, 80000 shp=34 knots *Armament:* 2 SS-N-1 missile-launchers; 16 57-mm (2.24-in) AA (4×4); 32 MBU 2500 A/S mortars (2×16); 6 53-cm (21-in) torpedo tubes (2×3) *Crew:* 360

'Kynda'

Soviet missile cruiser class, built 1957-65. The ships comprising the class were laid down at the Zhdanov yard, Leningrad, between 1957 and 1961, probably at yearly intervals, and completed between 1961 and 1965. The ships are: *Admiral Golovko, Admiral Fokin, Grozny* and *Varyag.* Various pennant numbers have been carried by all the ships, but since 1970 these have all been in the 800 range.

These were the first modern warships built by the Soviet Union, and introduced a wide range of weapons and sensors not seen previously on their vessels. Armament included the large SS-N-3 long-range surface-to-surface missiles, the SA-N-1 Goa surface-to-air missile, a twin 76-mm (3-in) AA turret, and a new 12-barrelled version of the A/S mortars first seen on the 'Kotlin' Class destroyers.

The hull-form was a departure from that of the 'Kotlin', 'Kildin' and 'Krupny' Classes, with a long forecastle deck rising only slightly towards the bow, and breaking aft of the second funnel, to give the ships a much squarer, less rakish appearance than their predecessors.

The novelty of the 'rocket-cruiser' concept, however, seems to have presented the designers with new problems, and too much was attempted on the displacement. In addition to the two giant quadruple launchers for the Shaddock SSMs, eight reloads were carried in the superstructure above upper deck level. Moreover, the bulky Scoop Pair guidance radars for the missiles had to be carried high on two pyramidal towers. On these were also mounted twin search radars and several tiers of electronic countermeasures (ECM) equipment. The Peel Group guidance radar for Goa, no less bulky, was carried above the bridge. The low freeboard aft and the use of stabilizers proved inadequate compensation for this considerable topweight and the four ships have been relegated to the two 'calm-water' fleets. *Grozny* and *Admiral Golovko* went in the Black Sea and the other two to the Pacific Fleet.

The 'Kyndas' were designed at a time when the Soviet Union saw the US attack-carrier force as the main threat to their security. This is reflected in the predominance of antiship weapons in the 'Kyndas' armament. The 400-km (250-mile) range with which the SS-N-3 missiles are credited is, however, negated to a certain extent by the lack of any on-board provision for mid-course guidance, such as the Hormone B helicopter carried by the later 'Kresta-I' Class. This means that in open waters the possibility of engaging hostile ships is limited by the horizon. It may well be, therefore, that an important role envisaged for them was shore bombardment in support of the army, a role which would enable them to use their Shaddock missiles to the limits of their range.

Propulsion, unlike that of the 'Kashin' Class destroyers designed round about the same time, was conventional. It was to be a further ten years before the Soviet Union attempted to propel a cruiser-sized ship by gas turbines. The funnels on the 'Kyndas' are wide, box-like structures which appear narrow in profile. *Varyag* does not have a sloping cowl on her funnels, and this distinguishes her from the rest of the class.

US Navy

The USS *Daniel Boone* (SSBN.629), a *Lafayette* Class fleet ballistic missile submarine, in 1964

Displacement: 4500 tons (standard), 5700 tons (full load) *Length:* 142 m (465 ft 11 in) oa *Beam:* 15.4 m (50 ft 6 in) *Draught:* 5 m (16 ft 5 in) *Machinery:* 2-shaft steam turbines, 85 000 shp=35 knots *Armament:* 8 SS-N-3 missile launchers (2×4); 2 SA-N-1 missile launchers (1×2); 4 76-mm (3-in) AA (2×2); 6 53-cm (21-in) torpedo tubes (2×3); 24 MBU 2500A A/S mortars (2×12) *Crew:* 390

Lafayette

US ballistic missile submarine class, built 1961-64. Four improved *Ethan Allen* Class Polaris submarines (SSBN.616-17, 619-20) were authorized under Fiscal Year 1961, followed by SSBN.622-626 under a supplementary programme in the same year and SSBN.627-636 in Fiscal Year 1962.

The first eight boats were armed with A-2 Polaris missiles, but the later series had the A-3 Polaris. During the routine renewal of nuclear reactor cores in 1968-70 SSBN.620 and 622-625 were rearmed with the A-3, and subsequently the whole class received the C-3 Poseidon. In October 1963 *Andrew Jackson* became the first submarine to fire the A-3. *James Madison* was the first to launch the C-3, in August 1970, having undergone the conversion in 1969-70. Certain boats of this class are scheduled to receive the Trident ballistic missile, with the first being refitted in 1979.

See also *Benjamin Franklin.*

Lafayette (SSBN.616), *Alexander Hamilton* (SSBN.617), *Nathan Hale* (SSBN.623), *Daniel Webster* (SSBN.626), *Tecumseh* (SSBN.628), *Ulysses S Grant* (SSBN.631) and *Casimir Pulaski* (SSBN.633)—built by General Dynamics Electric Boat Division
Andrew Jackson (SSBN.619), *Woodrow Wilson* (SSBN.624), *Daniel Boone* (SSBN.629) and *Stonewall Jackson* (SSBN.634)—built by Mare Island navy yard
John Adams (SSBN.620) and *Nathanael Greene* (SSBN.636) were built by Portsmouth naval shipyard
James Monroe (SSBN.622), *Henry Clay* (SSBN.625), *James Madison* (SSBN.627), *John C Calhoun* (SSBN.630), *Von Steuben* (SSBN.632) and *Sam Rayburn* (SSBN.635)—built by Newport News Shipbuilding and Dry Dock company

Displacement: 7250/8250 tons (surfaced/submerged) *Length:* 129.5 m (425 ft) oa *Beam:* 10.1 m (33 ft) *Draught:* 9.6 m (31 ft 6 in) *Machinery:* 1-shaft nuclear, geared steam turbines, 15 000 shp=20/30 knots (surfaced/submerged) *Armament:* 16 Poseidon C-3 SLBMs (16×1); 4 21-in (53-cm) torpedo tubes (bow, 12 torpedoes carried) *Crew:* 168

Laforey

British destroyer class, built 1938-42. The *Laforey* or 'L' Class destroyers, constructed under the Naval Estimates for 1937, were designed to carry a new design of twin 4.7-in (120-mm) gun mounting. Some thought was also given to providing them with high-speed machinery to give a maximum of up to 42 knots. The intention was to increase their margin of speed over that of the latest battleship design, the *King George V* Class, of 27 knots. However, the increased size and cost of the vessels was considered unacceptable and the finally approved design was little different from the previous *Javelin* Class, which had a similar speed and armament. The new 4.7-in mounting, the Mk XX, differed from earlier types in having a fully enclosed weatherproof gunshield into which ammunition was supplied direct, and in providing 50° elevation for the guns instead of the maximum 40° of earlier mountings. The high elevation was intended for use against aircraft although 50° was hardly sufficient for a proper dual-purpose mounting. The guns were also of new type, being 50-calibre Mk XI firing a heavy 28-kg (62-lb) shell. The extra topweight involved by the adoption of the mountings meant a return to quadruple torpedo tubes and an increase in beam to maintain stability. In turn this required an increase in length and engine power to maintain the 36 knots of the 'J' Class. Nevertheless, the rise in design weight was only 160 tons.

The eight ships of the class were laid down during 1938-39, launched during 1939-41 and completed during 1940-42. *Larne* was renamed *Gurkha* in 1940 following the loss of the *Tribal* Class vessel of that name. Delays in the production of the 4.7-in armament resulted in four vessels of the class, *Lance, Gurkha, Lively* and *Legion*, being fitted with twin 4-in (102-mm) HA/LA mountings to secure their early completion. Although these weapons were smaller they had the advantage of 80° elevation, while the addition of a fourth mounting on the after superstructure increased the number of guns to eight. The remaining four vessels, not having the advantage of a full AA armament, were completed with a 4-in AA gun in place of the after bank of torpedo tubes although these were subsequently reinstated in some of the ships. During 1941-42 two 20-mm (0.79-in) AA guns were added abreast the searchlight platform amidships while some ships had two more added aft and gunnery and air warning radar were added. Later the 0.5-in (12.7-mm) guns in the bridge wings were also replaced by 20-mm AA guns.

The first units to complete joined the Home Fleet, but all were to serve the majority of their very active wartime careers in the Mediterranean where all but one of the class was either sunk or written off. The first to be lost was *Gurkha*, torpedoed by *U 133* north of Sidi Barrani on January 17, 1942. She was followed by *Legion* which was damaged by a bomb which just missed her, and was beached at Malta on March 23, 1942. On March 25 she was towed into Grand Harbour for repairs, but on the following day she was hit by two bombs during an air raid, one of which detonated her forward magazines. Her wreck was broken up where it lay between 1943 and 1946. *Lance* suffered a similar fate after being bombed twice, on April 5 and April 9, 1942, while in dock at Malta. She was written off as a total loss and was eventually

The second HMS *Laforey* was sunk in $3\frac{1}{2}$ minutes by torpedoes from *U223* on March 3, 1944

IWM

No and name	completed	built
CG 16 ***Leahy*** (ex-DLG 16)	8/62	Bath Iron Works, Maine
CG 17 ***Harry E Yarnell*** (ex-DLG 17)	5/60	Bath Iron Works, Maine
CG 18 ***Worden*** (ex-DLG 18)	8/63	Bath Iron Works, Maine
CG 19 ***Dale*** (ex-DLG 19)	11/63	New York SB corp
CG 20 ***Richmond K*** (ex-DLG 20) ***Turner***	6/64	New York SB corp
CG 21 ***Gridley*** (ex-DLG 21)	5/63	Puget Sound
CG 22 ***England*** (ex-DLG 22)	12/63	Todd Shipyards
CG 23 ***Halsey*** (ex-DLG 23)	7/63	San Francisco naval yard
CG 24 ***Reeves*** (ex-DLG 24)	5/63	Puget Sound

broken up in 1944. On May 11, 1942, *Lively* was bombed and sunk by aircraft off Sollum and on March 12, 1943, *Lightning* was torpedoed and sunk by an E-Boat north of Algeria. On March 3, 1944, *Laforey* was hit by three torpedoes fired by *U 223*, the submarine she was hunting in company with other destroyers. She sank in 3½ minutes taking with her most of her crew. The submarine was sunk by her consorts. The last casualty of the class was *Loyal*, which was mined off the north-east coast of Italy on October 12, 1944, and, after partial repairs, declared a constructive total loss. She was eventually sold for scrapping in 1948, along with *Lookout*, the only member of the class to survive the war.

Laforey, Lance—built by Yarrow
Larne, Lively—built by Cammell Laird
Legion, Lightning—built by Hawthorn Leslie
Lookout, Loyal—built by Scotts

Displacement: 1920 tons (standard), 2660 tons (deep) *Length:* 110.4 m (362 ft 3 in) oa *Beam:* 11.3 m (37 ft) *Draught:* 3 m (10 ft) *Machinery:* 2-shaft geared steam turbines, 48 000 shp=36 knots *Armament:* (*Lightning, Laforey, Lookout, Loyal*) 6 4.7-in (120-mm) (3×2); 1 4-in (102-mm) AA; 4 2-pdr AA (1×4); 2 20-mm (0.79-in) (2×1); 8 0.5-in (12.7-mm) (2×4); 4 21-in (53-cm) torpedo tubes (1×4); (Remainder) 8 4-in (102-mm) (4×2); 4 2-pdr AA (1×4); 2 20-mm (0.79-in) AA (2×1); 8 0.5-in (12.7-mm) AA (2×4); 8 21-in (53-cm) torpedo tubes (2×4) *Crew:* 190 (4.7-in gun ships), 224 (4-in gun ships)

Lazaga

Spanish fast patrol boat class, built 1972-77. Six patrol craft intended primarily for fishery protection, but capable of carrying guns and missiles, were ordered in 1972. The hull design is based on the Israeli *Reshef* Class, but fitted with only two MTU diesels built under licence by Bazán.

The first of the class, *Lazaga* (P.01) was built in W Germany by Lürssen at Vegesack but *Alsedo* (P.02), *Cadarso* (P.03), *Villamil* (P.04), *Bonifaz* (P.05) and *Recalde* (P.06) were all built by Empresa Bazán at La Carraca.

The basic armament is one OTO-Melara 76-mm (3-in)/62-cal dual-purpose gun forward, a single Breda 40-mm (1.57-in) Bofors gun aft and two single 20-mm (0.79-in) Oerlikons in the bridge wings. Drawings of an antisubmarine version show that depth-charge racks and triple Mk 32 torpedo tubes would be fitted aft, while the missile version shows four Exocet MM38 SSMs aft (though the Exocets would probably give way to Harpoons, as mounted by the *Descubierta* Class frigates). A Hollandse Signaalapparaten M20 radome is mounted on a short lattice foremast, with a CSEE HSM Mk 22 optical director abaft the bridge.

Displacement: 275 tons (standard), 400 tons (full load) *Length:* 58 m (190 ft 3 in) wl *Beam:* 7.6 m (24 ft 11 in) *Draught:* 2.6 m (8 ft 6 in) *Machinery:* 2-shaft diesel, 8000 bhp=28 knots *Armament:* 1 76-mm (3-in)/62-cal DP; 1 40-mm (1.57-in)/70-cal AA; 2 20-mm (0.79-in) AA (2×1) *Crew:* 30

Leahy

US missile frigate class. The nine vessels of the *Leahy* Class were ordered under the 1958 Fiscal Year (DLG 16-18) and 1959 Fiscal Year Programmes (DLG 19-24). They were designed as escorts for fast carrier task groups to be formed around the *Kitty Hawk* Class carriers, two of which were then under construction. The vessels followed on from the *Farragut* Class and were completed with 'macks' (combined mast and funnel) instead of the separate arrangement as in the *Farragut.*

Referred to as 'double-enders', the ships were designed to provide long-range AA defence and were armed with two twin Mk 5 Terrier surface-to-air missile launchers; one fore and one aft. Each launcher was provided with an associated magazine which was reported to hold 80 missiles. Apart from the Terrier launchers there was limited close range AA and surface gunfire provided by two twin 3-in (76-mm) mountings amidships. A/S defence was provided by an eight-tube Asroc launcher sited just aft of the forward Terrier launcher on the main deck. The Asroc was linked to the bow mounted SQS 23 sonar set, possibly to be replaced by the more modern SQS 26. A separate launcher for Asroc had to be fitted for the Mod 5 Terrier launcher was unable to handle the Asroc missile. Further A/S defence was provided by two Mk 32 triple A/S torpedo tubes sited to port and starboard at main deck level at the after end of the bridge structure. The surface-to-air missiles were controlled by four Mk 76 Mod 5 systems linked to four SPG 55 radars, while the 3-in (76-mm) guns were linked to two SPG 50 radars directed by two Mk 63 Mod 28 fire-control systems. The ships originally mounted either the SPS39 or 52 search radar on the forward mack, but this was replaced by the SPS 48 3D search radar. The SPS 10 and SPS 37 search radars were mounted on the after mack.

A general lack of adequate surface-to-surface armament on board US ships was highlighted by the Vietnam war and the following cut-back in the carrier force. This reduced the antiship air strike capability of the US Navy and led to a reappraisal of the surface-to-surface capability of the *Leahy* and other classes. As a result the *Leahy* Class were being continually updated. Between 1967-72 the class was extensively modernized, and the superstructure amidships was plated in to provide extra space for the electronics associated with the new NTDS (naval tactical data system—a fully computerized weapons-control system) which was fitted. In addition improved guidance systems for the surface-to-air missiles was provided and larger turbogenerators for the increased electrical power needed to work the extra electronic equipment.

The surface-to-surface capability of the class has been slightly enhanced by the replacement of the Terrier missiles with the Standard missile. This weapon has a limited surface-to-surface capability, but because of its parabolic trajectory it is susceptible to ECM jamming and antimissile missiles. It is highly probable that the ships will be equipped with the surface-to-surface Harpoon missile which can be fired from the Asroc launcher. Lack of adequate close-in AA defence has also been noted and the ships will be fitted with the Vulcan Phalanx 20-mm (0.79-in) gun system, two such systems being mounted. A RBOC Mk 36 Chaff dispenser for ECM is also to be fitted.

Because of the twin missile launcher aft, there was insufficient space available to provide a helicopter and full handling facilities. There was a landing pad with limited helicopter facilities aft on the quarterdeck, but no aircraft was permanently carried.

The ships were reclassified as guided missile cruisers (CG) in June 1975, and retained their original numbers.

Displacement: 5670 tons (standard), 7800 tons (full load) *Length:* 162.5 m (533 ft) oa *Beam:* 16.8

m (55 ft) *Draught:* 7.5 m (24 ft 6 in) *Machinery:* 2-shaft geared turbines, 85 000 shp=34 knots *Armament:* 4 Terrier/Standard surface-to-air launchers (2×2); 4 3-in (76-mm) (2×2); 1 8-tube Asroc launcher; 6 Mk 32 A/S torpedo tubes (2×3) *Crew:* 396

Leander

British frigate class, built 1959-73. The first group was laid down 1959-63 and completed 1963-66 and consisted of *Leander* (F109), *Dido* (F104), *Ajax* (F114), *Penelope* (F127), *Aurora* (F10), *Galatea* (F18), *Euryalus* (F15), *Naiad* (F39), *Arethusa* (F38), and *Cleopatra* (F28). The second group was laid down 1963-64 and completed 1966-67 and comprised *Phoebe* (F42), *Minerva* (F45), *Sirius* (F40), *Juno* (F52), *Argonaut* (F56) and *Danae* (F47). The final group was laid down 1966-69 and completed 1968-73 and consisted of *Andromeda* (F57), *Charybdis* (F75), *Hermione* (F58), *Jupiter* (F60), *Bacchante* (F69), *Scylla*, (F71), *Achilles* (F12), *Diomede* (F16), *Apollo* (F70) and *Ariadne* (F72). Orders for the first two groups were distributed among all the British shipbuilders capable of building vessels of this size, but in the mid-1960s it was decided that in future frigates would be built in one or two specialist yards. Consequently five ships of the final group were ordered from Yarrow, and a further unit, *Hermione*, was transferred there from Alexander Stephen following her launch.

The *Leander* Class was a product of two separate lines of development. Broadly speaking, the hull of the Type 12 antisubmarine frigates, with its proven seakeeping qualities, was combined with the concept of the general-purpose frigate embodied in the 'Tribal' Class.

The first three ships were in fact laid down as units of the *Rothesay* Class—the fourth, *Penelope*, was to have been the fifth ship of the *Salisbury* Class—and the hull of the first two groups of *Leanders* would have had identical dimensions to that of their predecessors had not the forecastle deck been continued aft to the stern to provide a helicopter deck aft. The well-tried steam propulsion plant of the *Whitby* and *Rothesay* Classes was also retained, and no attempt was made to incorporate the innovatory gas turbines introduced by the 'Tribals'.

The Type 965 air-search 'bedstead' of the 'Tribals' was moved to the mainmast. This freed the foremast for the Type 993 search radar and 978 navigation radar, thus avoiding the clumsy arrangement of the earlier ships. The twin 4.5-in (114-mm) Mk 6 mounting of the *Rothesays* was adopted in preference to the single mountings used in the 'Tribals', and an MRS 3 director was provided. The first seven ships were completed too early to carry the Seacat short-range surface-to-air missile and instead carried two single 40-mm (1.57-in) Bofors on the hangar roof. Later ships, starting with *Naiad*, had a quadruple Seacat launcher on the after end of the hangar to port and a modified MRS 3 director (known as the GWS 22) on the starboard side, but further forward to improve the arcs of the launcher. To provide close-range surface coverage two single 20-mm (0.79-in) Oerlikons were placed abreast the mainmast in these ships. The armament was completed by a Limbo Mk 10 A/S mortar, located in a well just aft of the flight deck, and a Wasp helicopter for antisubmarine operations. Because of the provision of a separate flight deck and hangar, the helicopter was no longer subject to the same constraints as in the 'Tribal' Class, which had an economical but cramped hangar/lift arrangement, with the flight deck above the hangar.

In additon to the customary Type 184 hull sonar, most of the first group were fitted with variable-depth sonar, the lowering mechanism being located in a large well in the centre of the stern. The only distinguishing features among the first ten ships of the class was that *Leander, Dido, Ajax* and *Penelope* had the HF/DF mast of the *Rothesays*, while the other six had a version similar to that of the early *Devonshire*, or 'County', Class destroyers.

The next six ships completed had a slightly different machinery arrangement, and none seem to have been fitted with VDS, but they were otherwise similar to the later ships of the first group. The New Zealand *Waikato* (F55), laid down in 1964 by Harland and Wolff and completed in 1966, can also be said to belong to this group.

The last ten ships completed for the Royal Navy not only had a further modification to their machinery but also had their beam increased by 60 cm (24 in) and are known as the 'broad beam' type. In external appearance these ships differed from the first two groups in having the navigation radar angled out to port so that it could be used to assist helicopter operations. They also mounted Corvus chaff dispensers (for electronic countermeasures) just forward of the mainmast. Both these modifications were extended to the second group as they refitted in the early 1970s but not to the first group. In addition the last two ships, *Apollo* and *Ariadne*, had a new type of topmast forward, surmounted by a distinctive cone. Several of the the earlier ships carried VDS, but *Apollo* and *Ariadne* had the stern well plated in, and this modifi-

HMS *Leander*, a postwar frigate launched on June 28, 1961, and the first of 26 frigates of the *Leander* Class commissioned between 1963 and 1973

C & S Taylor

MOD

The *Leander* Class destroyer HMS *Aurora* after refitting with Ikara A/S missiles in 1972-76

cation was extended to all ships of the second group, *Andromeda, Scylla, Achilles* and *Diomede* of the third group, and *Dido* of the first group.

At about the same time that the early 'broad beam' ships were being laid down for the Royal Navy, the first Indian *Leander* was laid down at Mazagon shipyard, Bombay. Named *Nilgiri* (F33), she and her sister *Himgiri* (F34) were to the standard 'broad beam' design, although modified to suit Indian conditions, and were constructed with British assistance. They were the first major warships to be built in India, and the first two took six years or more to complete. The second pair, *Udaygiri* (F35) and *Dunagiri* (F36), were laid down in 1970 and 1973 respectively and completed in 1976 and 1977, and have a markedly different appearance owing to the adoption of Dutch search radars and fire-control equipment. In particular, the adoption of the Hollandse Signaal Apparaten Mk 44 fire-control radar for the Seacat missiles has meant that two quadruple launchers can be accommodated on the hangar roof, as in the Dutch *Van Speijk* Class. Two further ships of an expanded *Leander* design reported to carry a big Sea King A/S helicopter are also under construction, the first being named *Taragiri.*

In addition to building most of the later Royal Navy ships, Yarrow also built a further ship, *Canterbury* (F421), for New Zealand. She was laid down in 1969 and completed in 1971. She differed from other 'broad beam' ships in carrying a triple Mk 32 A/S torpedo mounting on either side of the mainmast, and in having a modified funnel cap.

A further development of this particular design was that of two ships for Chile, *Almirante Condell* (06) and *Almirante Lynch* (07), also built by Yarrow. Both were laid down in 1971, being completed in 1973 and 1974 respectively. In addition to the A/S tubes carried by *Canterbury*, they have four ramps for Exocet antiship missiles on the stern, and can otherwise be distinguished by a taller foremast surmounted by the bar-shaped Type 992Q search radar (in place of Type 993), with the more modern Type 1006 navigation radar replacing Type 978.

From 1970 onwards many of the earlier Royal Navy *Leanders* began a major conversion. Seven of the first group had their twin 4.5-in (114-mm) mounting replaced by a large housing which extended forward from the bridge structure and in which a launcher for Ikara A/S missiles was located. The MRS 3 director was replaced by a small domed radar for tracking and guiding the missile. Other modifications included an additional Seacat launcher on the starboard side of the hangar, the GWS 22 director being moved to a centreline position beneath the mainmast; the removal of the air-search radar and its replacement by a small IFF antenna; the addition of two single 40-mm (1.57-in) Bofors abreast the foremast, which besides carrying yet another variety of topmast also had two platforms for Satellite Communication Terminals (SCOTs); the addition of two Corvus chaff dispensers in the same position as the 'broad beam' ships; and the replacement of Type 978 navigation radar by Type 1006. The ships converted to this pattern were *Leander* (1970-73), *Ajax* (1971-74), *Galatea* (1971-74), *Naiad* (1972-75), *Aurora* (1972-76), *Euryalus* (1972-76) and *Arethusa* (1973-77). Except for *Aurora* (Chatham dockyard) and *Arethusa* (Portsmouth dockyard) these conversions took place at Devonport dockyard. All ships of this group now carry VDS (variable depth sonar).

The '*Leander* Ikara' conversions put these ships firmly in the antisubmarine category. In the next set of conversions, however, the general-purpose conception of the class was maintained. The twin 4.5-in (114-mm) mounting was in this case replaced by four launchers for Exocet missiles. In addition to the two Seacat launchers on the hangar roof they mounted a third launcher on the forecastle forward of the Exocet launchers, with an extra GWS 22 director replacing the MRS 3 above the bridge. The hangar itself was considerably lengthened to accommodate the new Lynx A/S helicopter, and this involved the removal of the Limbo A/S mortar to enable the flight deck to be extended aft. The role of the mortar was taken over by triple A/S torpedo mountings on either side of the hangar. As in the Ikara conversions, two single 40-mm Bofors were fitted abreast the foremast, the shape of which was considerably altered in the first two ships, *Cleopatra* (1973-75) and *Phoebe* (1974-77), which have a topmast similar to *Apollo* and *Ariadne.* The third ship, *Sirius* (1975-78), retains her original foremast, although Type 978 navigation radar has been replaced by Type 1006 as in the first two. Other ships which commenced conversion to this design are: *Dido* (1975), *Minerva* (1975), *Argonaut* (1976), *Danae* (1977) and *Penelope* (1978). *Minerva* is being converted by Chatham dockyard, the others by Devonport dockyard. VDS will not be fitted in this conversion.

The reason for the late conversion of *Penelope* was her disarmament and use as a trials ship, first for the triple A/S torpedo tubes carried by the Exocet conversions, then for the short-range Seawolf antiaircraft and antimissile missile. The 4.5-in (114-mm) mounting was first cocooned and then removed altogether, along with its director. The Seawolf trials involved major rebuilding above the upper deck aft of the mainmast, which was heightened to carry the Type 967/8 surveillance radars associated with the system. Two deckhouses were constructed on the former helicopter deck and the Type 910 tracker radar mounted on the after one, with the sextuple Seawolf launcher below it at upper deck level.

Conversion has undoubtedly spoilt the clean, uncluttered lines of the early ships, but it has also testified to the capacity of the original design to accept major updating of weapons and electronics which is the key to warding off obsolescence in modern warships.

(Royal Navy Ships) *Displacement:* 2450-2500 tons (standard), 2800-2962 tons (full load) *Length:* 113.4 m (372 ft) oa *Beam:* 12.5 m (41 ft), (broad beam 13.1 m [43 ft]) *Draught:* 5.5 m (18 ft) *Machinery:* 2-shaft geared steam turbines, 30 000 shp=30 knots *Armament:* 2 4.5-in (114-mm) Mk 6 DP (1×2); 4 Seacat SAM launchers (1×4); 2 40-mm (1.57-in) (2×1) (in early ships); 2 20-mm (0.79-in) (2×1) (not in early ships); 1 Limbo Mk 10 A/S mortar; Wasp A/S helicopter. (Ikara conversions) 1 Ikara A/S missile launcher; 8 Seacat SAM launchers (2×4); 2 40-mm (1.57-in) (2×1); 1 Limbo Mk 10 A/S mortar; Wasp A/S helicopter; (Exocet conversions) 4 Exocet SSMs; 12 Seacat SAM launchers (3×4); 2 40-mm (1.57-in) (2×1); Lynx A/S helicopter *Crew:* not known

Leopard

British frigate class. Known as the Type 41 frigates, the four ships of the *Leopard* Class were ordered in 1951. They were designed as AA vessels to operate in conjunction with the Type 61 aircraft-direction *Salisbury* Class, and Type 12, antisubmarine *Whitby* Class, to form convoy escort groups. One further ship of the class, *Panther,* was subsequently transferred to the Indian navy as *Brahmaputra,* and was joined by two other sisters specially built for India. Another *Panther,* ordered as a replacement under the 1956-57 Estimates, was eventually cancelled under the 1957 defence cuts.

The fully welded stabilizer-equipped hull of the Type 41 is slightly shorter than the *Whitby* Class. The construction of the *Leopard* Class enabled the Admiralty to study the problems associated with the rapid production of warships in an emergency. Propulsion for the *Leopard* Class was to have been provided by geared turbines of 16 000 shp. This machinery, however, was not available in time and the ships were completed with a lightweight Admiralty diesel engine, rated at 17 lb/shp, then under development. Four of these new diesels were coupled to each of the shafts through hydraulic units and reduction gearing. The diesel system was an improvement over the steam turbines, and with the bunkerage provided easily gave the extended radius of action specified for the new frigates. With 220 tons of oil fuel the radius of action was 7500 nautical miles at a speed of 16 knots. The fuel tanks were equipped with a compensating system in which sea water replaced the oil fuel as it was used, thus maintaining the stability of the vessel. *Jaguar,* the last of the class to be completed, was the first vessel in the Royal Navy to be fitted with controllable-pitch propellers.

The original design specification called for a standard displacement of 1800 tons, but the modifications and additions incorporated during construction resulted in this increasing to 1950 tons displacement light loaded.

The main armament of two twin 4.5-in (114-mm) Mk 6 turrets is similar to that mounted in the *Daring* Class. The turrets are fully automatic, and are controlled by the combined HA/LA director on the bridge. Close-range AA defence is provided by a single 40-mm (1.57-in) gun and associated director sited on the superstructure behind the mainmast. The 40-mm weapon was to have been replaced by a quadruple Seacat mounting, but since the *Leopard* Class was considered to be obsolescent, none of the ships have ever been fitted with the missile system. Their limited A/S capability is provided by a single Squid mounting aft.

Between 1963-66 the ships were extensively modernized. The mainmast was plated to form a combined mast and stack (or mack), with sufficient strength to support the new antenna of their Type 965 radar. During the 'cod war' of 1976 *Jaguar* was fitted with wooden sheathing round the bows as a defence against the ramming tactics of Icelandic patrol vessels. The class is now considered obsolete, although *Jaguar* and *Lynx* remained in reserve in the late 1970s.

Name	builder	completed
Jaguar	Denny Bros	12/59
Leopard	Portsmouth dockyard	9/58
Lynx	J Brown, Clydebank	3/57
Puma	Scotts	4/57
INDIAN SHIPS		
Beas	Vickers, Tyne	5/60
Betwa	Vickers, Tyne	12/60
Brahmaputra (ex-*Panther*)	J Brown, Clydebank	3/58

Below: **The *Leopard* Class frigate HMS *Puma* anchored in Table Bay, South Africa. *Bottom:* HMS *Lynx* photographed in 1977, when, along with *Jaguar*, she had been placed in reserve**

R M Scott

C & S Taylor

Displacement: 2300 tons (standard), 2520 tons (full load) *Length:* 103.5 m (339 ft 9 in) oa *Beam:* 12.2 m (40 ft) *Draught:* 4.9 m (16 ft) *Machinery:* 8 diesels, 2 shafts, 14 400 bhp=24 knots *Armament:* 4 4.5-in (114-mm) (2×2); 1 (Indian ships, 2) 40-mm (1.57-in); 1 Squid *Crew:* 235

Littorio

Italian battleship class. The design for the four *Littorio* Class battleships was developed following the failure of France to ratify a new London Naval Agreement. The French had already begun construction work on the *Richelieu* Class and, faced with a worsening situation in Europe, the Italians decided to begin building up their fleet. Plans for a battleship drawn up in 1928-29 were reexamined, and specifications were drawn up for a 35 000-ton ship armed with six 406-mm (16-in) guns in twin turrets and a speed of 30 knots, a design which would, on paper at least, have conformed to the Washington Treaty limitations. Although the calibre of the guns matched that of the British *Nelson* and US *Maryland* Classes, the ships were considered to be undergunned. The British and US vessels all disposed a nine-gun broadside compared with the six-gun Italian design. It was decided, therefore, to accept the disadvantage of smaller-calibre main armament in order to mount triple turrets disposing a nine-gun broadside.

The design paid great attention to underwater protection against mine and torpedo damage. An ingenious new form of internal bulge protection was devised and developed by the engineer Umberto Pugliese, who gave his name to the system. It consisted of a heavy armoured belt inclined at 14° resting on top of a lower, bulge-shaped hull section. Behind the armoured belt ran an armoured bulkhead, also inclined at 14°. An armoured deck lay on top of this assembly and another longitudinal armoured bulkhead 38 mm (1.5 in) thick was sited inboard of the inclined armoured bulkhead. Below the armoured belt ran a semicircular torpedo bulkhead extending obliquely downwards and outwards to the double bottom. The semicircular bulkhead was retained as an empty cylinder (or internal bulge) designed to act as a shock absorber against underwater explosions. The new protection scheme proved itself on a number of occasions, since both *Littorio* and *Vittorio Veneto* were able to continue steaming after being struck by torpedoes.

Apart from the excellent armour scheme the ships were lightly constructed, and this proved a distinct disadvantage when they had to face rough weather in the Mediterranean. They were considered to be the finest-looking ships ever built and the design is generally considered to have been a success, although their handling left something to be desired.

The original design provided for a tripod mainmast, but the ships were completed with a pole structure. Catapults were to have been installed amidships to port and starboard, with a hangar forward, and this would have required the second funnel to have been omitted with all exhaust gases vented through the forward funnel. Instead, a catapult was sited aft on the quarterdeck; while *Littorio* was undergoing repair for torpedo damage in 1942 she was fitted with a new catapult designed for launching the shore-based Reggiane Re 2000 Falco fighter.

Both *Vittorio Veneto* and *Littorio* were involved in a number of actions during the Second World War. *Littorio* was seriously damaged during the air raid on Taranto on November 12, 1940, and was under repair until August 1941. *Vittorio Veneto* had suffered slight damage from a torpedo during the Cape Matapan action on March 28, 1941, and was also under repair until August. She was again torpedoed on December 14, 1941, by the British 'U' Class submarine *Urge* and was under repair until the spring of 1942. She saw no action after June and was transferred to Malta following the surrender of Italy in 1943. She was interned in the Suez Canal until after the war.

Following repairs to the damage received at Taranto, *Littorio* returned to service and was again torpedoed on June 14, 1942, and was under repair until February 1943. She was renamed *Italia* on June 30, 1943, and following Italy's surrender she was transferred to Malta. During the voyage she was damaged by a German Type SD 1400 X glider bomb. The damage was not repaired and she joined *Vittorio Veneto* in internment in the Suez Canal. *Roma* saw no active service during the war and was sunk by a Type SD 1400 X glider bomb while being transferred to Malta after the Italian surrender.

Impero was transferred to Brindisi in June 1940 for completion, but work ceased owing to the shortage of steel. She transferred uncompleted to Trieste in 1942 and was

Name	builder	laid down	launched	completed	fate
Impero	Ansaldo, Genoa	5/38	11/39	—	lost 2/45
Littorio	Ansaldo, Genoa	10/34	8/37	5/40	scrapped 1948
Roma	CRA Trieste	9/38	9/40	6/42	lost 9/43
Vittorio Veneto	CRA Trieste	10/34	7/37	4/40	scrapped 1948

Aldo Fraccaroli

The Italian battleship *Littorio*, with her elaborate dazzle camouflage, during the Second World War. A seaplane is visible on its catapult on the stern. After 1942 she had a Re 2000 fighter

seized by the Germans there when Italy surrendered. She was used as a target ship and was sunk in Trieste harbour during an American air raid.

Displacement: 41 650 tons (standard), 46 215 tons (full load) *Length:* 237.8 m (780 ft); *(Impero* and *Littorio,* 240.7 m [789 ft 8 in]) oa *Beam:* 32.9 m (108 ft) *Draught:* 10.5 m (34 ft 5 in) *Machinery:* 4-shaft geared steam turbines, 128 206 shp=30 knots *Protection:* 345-60 mm (13.6-2.4 in) main belt, 162 mm (6.4 in) deck, 350-200 mm (13.8-7.9 in) turrets, 280 mm (11 in) barbettes, 260 mm (10.24 in) conning tower *Armament:* 9 381-mm (15-in)/55-cal (3×3); 12 152-mm (6-in)/55-cal (4×3); 12 90-mm (3.54-in); 20 37-mm (1.46-in) (10×2); 16 20-mm (0.79-in) (8×2); 3 seaplanes *Crew:* 1872

Liuzzi

Italian submarine class. The four submarines of this class, completed between November 1939 and March 1940 by Tosi, Taranto, were similar to the preceding *Marconi* Class. They were designed as long-range vessels, with a radius of action of 13 000 nautical miles at 8 knots surfaced, and 108 nautical miles at 4 knots submerged, for patrols in the Indian Ocean. They were heavily armed boats ideally suited for long-range ocean patrols, but experienced difficulty in weathering the waves in heavy following seas. In other respects they proved satisfactory with a reasonable performance. Because they were designed as ocean-going boats, they encountered severe problems in Mediterranean conditions, being easily visible even when submerged in the clear Mediterranean water.

They nevertheless operated in the Mediterranean for the first few months of the war. On June 12, 1940, *Bagnolini* sank the British cruiser *Calypso*, but on June 27 *Liuzzi* was sunk south of Crete by the British destroyers *Dainty*, *Defender* and *Ilex*. After this, the three remaining boats were transferred to the German-controlled Atlantic port of Bordeaux. *Tarantini* was sunk on December 15, 1940, while returning from her first patrol in the Atlantic by the British submarine *Thunderbolt*. *Giuliani* was transferred to the Baltic port of Gdynia in March 1941, and from then until May 1942 she was used to train Italian officers in convoy-attack techniques. During 1943 *Bagnolini* and *Giuliani* were converted to transport submarines for carrying valuable cargoes to and from the Far East. In the summer of 1943 *Giuliani* sailed for the Far East with a secret cargo consisting possibly of German radar parts and information, and details of the Walther hydrogen peroxide engine. The cargo had been handed over to the Japanese, and the submarine was refitting at Singapore prior to returning to Europe when Italy surrendered. The boat was seized by the Japanese, handed over to German authorities in the Far East and renumbered *UIT23*. She sailed for Europe but was sunk in the Malacca Straits by the British submarine *Tally Ho* on February 14, 1944.

Bagnolini was still lying at Bordeaux when

the Italians surrendered. She was taken over by the Germans and renumbered *UIT22* but was eventually sunk off the Cape of Good Hope by two South African Catalina aircraft on March 11, 1944, while carrying a secret cargo to the Far East.

Displacement: 1166/1484 tons (surfaced/submerged) *Length:* 76.1 m (249 ft 8 in) oa *Beam:* 7 m (23 ft) *Draught:* 4.5 m (14 ft 9 in) *Machinery:* 2-shaft diesels/2 electric motors, 3500 bhp/1500 hp=18/8 knots (surfaced/submerged) *Armament:* 1 100-mm (3.9-in); 4 13.2-mm (0.52-in); 8 53-cm (21-in) torpedo tubes (4 bow, 4 stern), 12 torpedoes *Crew:* 58

Livermore

US destroyer class, built 1939-41. This was a general-purpose destroyer design developed from experience gained with the previous *Gridley*, *Benham* and *Sims* Classes. The machinery was installed in a 'unit' arrangement with alternate boiler and engine rooms which gave a two-funnelled silhouette. By adopting a system whereby a boiler and associated turbine were in separate compartments there was less chance of a single torpedo or shell hit completely crippling the destroyer.

The extended machinery casing resulting from the new machinery arrangement became a permanent feature in US destroyers. The casing stretched aft almost to the shelter deck with only a short break before that structure.

The two torpedo mounts were sited on top of the engine-room casing fore and aft of the second funnel. The 5-in (127-mm) guns were mounted in turrets in A, B and Y positions, with Q and X guns sited on the after shelter deck in open mounts. Scant attention was paid to the light AA armament, for it was felt that this was more than covered by the 5-in dual-purpose guns. On completion, however, the heavy torpedo and gun armament, sited high up on the superstructure, was found to have made the ships top heavy, leading to stability problems. Early in the war the after torpedo mount and Q gun were therefore removed. The need for light AA had by then been proven and six or seven 20-mm (0.79-in) in single mounts were added, two of them on the after shelter deck where Q gun had been sited. X gun was remounted in a turret. Later in the war the two 20-mm weapons on the shelter deck were removed and sponsons added on either side for mounting two twin 40-mm (1.57-in) mounts.

Three ships of the class were lost in action during the war, all in the area of the Solomon Islands. *Meredith* was sunk by naval aircraft from the carrier *Ziukaku* south of Guadalcanal on October 15, 1942. *Monssen* was sunk a month later on November 13 in the same area by gunfire from Japanese battleships. *Gwin* was torpedoed by Japanese destroyers during the battle of Kolombangara on July 13, 1943. *Ingraham* sank in fog off Nova Scotia on August 22, 1942, after colliding with the oiler *Chemung*.

The remainder of the class survived the war and in 1951 *Eberle* and *Ludlow* were transferred to Greece and renamed *Niki* and *Doxa* respectively. They were both discarded in 1972. *Nicholson* was transferred in 1951 to Italy where she was renamed *Aviere*;

No and name	laid down	launched	completed	builder
DD.429 *Livermore* (ex-*Grayson*)	3/39	8/40	10/40	Bath Iron Works
DD.430 *Eberle*	4/39	9/40	12/40	Bath Iron Works
DD.431 *Plunkett*	3/39	3/40	7/40	Federal SB, Kearny
DD.432 *Kearny*	3/39	3/40	9/40	Federal SB, Kearny
DD.433 *Gwin*	—	5/40	—	Boston navy yard
DD.434 *Meredith*	—	4/40	—	Boston navy yard
DD.435 *Grayson* (ex-*Livermore*)	7/39	8/40	4/41	Charleston navy yard
DD.436 *Monssen*	—	5/40	—	Puget Sound navy yard
DD.437 *Woolsey*	10/39	2/41	5/41	Bath Iron Works
DD.438 *Ludlow*	12/39	11/40	3/41	Bath Iron Works
DD.439 *Edison*	3/40	11/40	1/41	Federal SB, Kearny
DD.440 *Ericsson*	3/40	11/40	3/41	Federal SB, Kearny
DD.441 *Wilkes*	11/39	5/40	6/41	Boston navy yard
DD.442 *Nicholson*	11/39	5/40	1941	Boston navy yard
DD.443 *Swanson*	11/39	11/40	7/41	Charleston navy yard
DD.444 *Ingraham*	—	2/41	—	Charleston navy yard

she was classified as an experimental ship in 1971, but discarded in 1974. *Plunkett* was transferred to China (Formosa) in 1959 and renamed *Nan Ying*; she was stricken in 1975. *Livermore* was cannibalized for spares and finally sold for breaking in March 1961. *Edison* was sold for scrap in November 1966. *Ericsson* was stricken in June 1970; *Wilkes* and *Swanson* in March 1971; *Kearny* and *Grayson* in June 1971, and *Woolsey* in July 1971.

Displacement: 1620 tons (DD.437-444, 1630 tons) (standard), 2525 tons (full load) *Length:* 106 m (348 ft) oa *Beam:* 11 m (36 ft) *Draught:* 5.4 m (17 ft 9 in) max *Machinery:* 2-shaft geared turbines, 50 000 shp=37.5 knots *Armament:* 5 5-in (127-mm)/38-cal DP (5×1); 6 (DD.431-436, 12) 0.5-in (12.7-mm) AA machine-guns (6/12×1); 10 21-in (53-cm) torpedo tubes (2×5) *Crew:* 208 (peacetime); 276 (wartime)

'Loch'

British frigate class. Ordered in 1943 the 'Loch' Class were essentially versions of the 'River' Class frigates modified for prefabricated construction. The main variation from the earlier class was in the hull form, which was made as square as possible to simplify the construction and assembly of the prefabricated sections. These were comparatively small and were restricted to a maximum 2.5 tons by the capacity of existing shipyard crane. In addition the beam was increased by 0.6 m (2 ft) to improve stability, and the length by 1 m (3 ft) to reduce the draught. In the end, the displacement was only 60 tons greater than the 'Rivers'. The A/S armament was substantially improved by the fitting of two three-barrel Squid ASW in B position, while the AA armament was improved by substituting a four-barrel 2-pdr pom-pom for the after 4-in (102-mm) gun mounting. The triple-expansion machinery was identical to that in the 'River' Class. The exceptions were *Loch Arkaig* and *Loch Tralaig* which were fitted with steam turbines. The fuel stowage in the 'Lochs' was, however, increased from 650 to 750 tons, giving them an endurance of 16 100 km (10 000 miles) at 10 knots.

Originally 113 'Loch' Class vessels were ordered, but 26 of these were subsequently modified to AA escorts, becoming the 'Bay' Class, while a further 57 were cancelled at the end of the Second World War. Of the remainder, 25 were completed for service in the Royal Navy; three, *Loch Ard*, *Loch Boisdale* and *Loch Cree*, were transferred to the South African Navy prior to completion and renamed *Transvaal*, *Good Hope* and *Natal* respectively; two were converted while under construction to coastal forces depot ships *Derby Haven* (ex-*Loch Assynt*) and *Woodbridge Haven* (ex-*Loch Torridan*), and later had their superstructures enlarged and the armament altered to 2 4-in (102-mm) (1×2) and 6 20-mm (0.79-in) (6×1). They were somewhat heavier than their sisters at 1650 tons standard.

The 30 ships of the class were laid down during 1943-44 and completed during 1944-45. During 1944-45 the majority were employed on escort duty in the Atlantic, Arctic, North Sea and the English Channel and although their war service was comparatively short they saw a considerable amount of action and between them sank or helped to sink 13 German submarines. In the North Atlantic *Loch Insh* and *Starling* sank *U 333* on July 31, 1944, and *Loch Eck* and *Loch Dunvegan* helped to sink *U 1278* on February 17, 1945. In the Arctic *Loch Dunvegan* assisted in the sinking of *U 344* on August 24, 1944, and during the last convoy battle of the war on April 29, 1945, *Loch Insh* first sank *U 307* and then, with the assistance of *Loch Shin* and two other vessels, sank *U 286*. In the English Channel *Loch Craggie* sank *U 482* on January 16, 1945. *Loch Fada* sank *U 1010* and then, with assistance, *U 327* on February 27, 1945. *Loch Ruthven* and *Wild Goose* sank *U 683* on March 12, 1945, and *Loch Killin* sank *U 1063* on April 16, 1945. Off Scapa Flow on December 6, 1944, *Loch Insh* and *Goodall* sank *U 297*. Off the Minches on February 4, 1945, *Loch Scavaig* and *Loch Shin* assisted in the sinking of *U 1014*, and in the Firth of Forth on March 14, 1945, *Natal* sank *U 714*.

IWM

HMS *Loch Glendhu* in 1945. 'Loch' Class frigates were also crewed by the South African Navy

In 1948 *Loch Morlich, Loch Shin, Loch Katrine, Loch Achanalt, Loch Achray* and *Loch Eck* were transferred to the Royal New Zealand Navy and renamed *Tutira, Taupo, Rotoiti, Pukaki, Kaniere* and *Hawea* respectively. While in New Zealand hands they were changed little and were eventually sold for scrapping during 1961-69. In 1949 *Derby Haven* was sold to Persia, after reconversion to a frigate, and renamed *Babr*. She was scrapped in the late 1960s. In the late 1950s *Loch Ruthven, Loch Fyne, Loch Lomond, Loch Killisport, Loch Tralaig, Loch Fada, Loch Insh, Loch Alvie* and the South African ships had their single 4-in (102-mm) gun replaced by a twin 4-in mounting, the pompom mounting replaced by a twin 40-mm (1.57-in), and the 20-mm (0.79-in) guns replaced by single 40-mm guns (4×1). The remaining ships of the class were sold into merchant service in 1961. *Woodbridge Haven* served as a submarine target ship during 1946-54 after which she was generally employed as a minesweeper support ship (she was officially classified as such in 1960) until sold for scrap in 1965. In 1964 *Loch Insh* was sold to Malaysia and renamed *Hang Tuah*. The surviving Royal Navy vessels were sold for scrapping during 1965-75.

Natal was sunk as a target in 1972 but all the other South African vessels were still in service in 1978.

Loch Achanalt, Loch Insh, Loch Katrine—built by H Robb
Loch Tarbert, Loch Veyatie—built by Ailsa Craig
Loch Achray, Loch Eck—built by Smiths Dock
Loch Alvie—built by Barclay Curle
Loch Arkaig, Loch Lomond, Loch More, Loch Tralaig—built by Caledon
Natal, Derby Haven, Woodbridge Haven, Loch Morlich, Loch Shin—built by Swan Hunter
Transvaal, Good Hope, Loch Killisport—built by Harland & Wolff
Loch Craggie, Loch Gorm—built by Harland & Wolff, completed by John Brown
Loch Dunvegan, Loch Ruthven, Loch Scavaig—built by C Hill
Loch Fada—built by John Brown
Loch Fyne, Loch Glendhu, Loch Killin—built by Burntisland
Loch Quoich—built by Blyth

See also *Bigbury Bay*.

Displacement: 1430 tons (standard), 2260 tons (full load) *Length:* 93.57 m (307 ft) *Beam:* 11.73

The frigate *Loch Veyatie* after the Second World War, during which members of the class sank or helped to sink 13 German submarines

PPL

m (38 ft 6 in) *Draught:* 4.47 m (14 ft 8 in) *Machinery:* 2-shaft 4-cylinder triple-expansion engines, 5500 ihp=20 knots *Armament:* 1 4-in (102-mm); 4 2-pdr AA (1×4); 6 20-mm (0.79-in) AA (2×2, 2×1); 2 Squid ASW; 15 depth charges *Crew:* 130

Long Beach

US guided missile cruiser, built 1957-61. USS *Long Beach,* ordered in October 1956 from Bethlehem Steel, Quincy, was the world's first nuclear-powered surface warship and the first to be armed solely with guided missiles. The ship was originally designed as a 7800-ton nuclear-powered destroyer to be named *Brooklyn,* to test the feasibility of using nuclear propulsion for surface warships. However, early in 1956 it was decided to capitalize on the advantages of nuclear propulsion and the displacement was increased to 11 000 tons. Many design changes were effected during the planning stage since the final role of the vessel was uncertain. It was finally decided to build the ship as a general-purpose cruiser capable of carrying out antishipping, antiaircraft and antisubmarine roles. The resulting increase in the armament outfit—a second Terrier missile launcher and Talos equipment aft was added—further increased the design displacement to 14 000 tons. Renamed *Long Beach,* the vessel was laid down in December 1957 and launched in July 1959.

As completed in July 1961, the final armament outfit provided for the twin Terrier launchers to be sited in A and B positions with their associated acquisition and guidance radars aft of B mounting and on top of the bridge structure. Aft, in Y position, a twin Talos missile launcher is sited for air defence against both aircraft and missiles, and can be used in shore-bombardment and antishipping roles. The Talos incorporates exceedingly complicated control and handling equipment weighing over 300 tons, which automatically selects and loads the launcher with the correct type of missile (either HE or nuclear warhead) chosen by the missile control officer. Talos missiles are believed to have recorded the first combat surface-to-air kill by ship-launched missile when they downed a North Vietnamese MiG fighter in the Tonkin Gulf on May 23, 1968.

Amidships *Long Beach* was to have been armed with the Regulus II strategic missile system. When the Regulus programme was cancelled, before *Long Beach* was completed, it was proposed to site eight vertical Polaris missile launchers in the space provided for the Regulus. Escalating costs in the Polaris programme led to the abandonment of this idea early in 1961. The midships space was finally used for an eight-tube Asroc launcher, which is linked to the bow mounted SQS-23 sonar set. Further antisubmarine defence is provided by two triple Mk 32 antisubmarine torpedo tubes. The lack of a suitable close-range defence armament for use against small, high-speed targets and low-flying aircraft was soon realized, and during 1962-63 two 5-in (127-mm)/38-cal dual-purpose single turrets were sited amidships. These, however, suffered from a limited arc of fire.

Long Beach is distinguished by the lack of any funnel and the large, square bridge structure. This is further accentuated by the flat 'billboard' SPS-32 and SPS-33 radar aerials sited around the bridge. These fixed aerials provide range, bearing and tracking information. A conventional mast is sited on top of the bridge, carrying the usual search and navigational radars, TACAN and ECM arrays. On the quarterdeck aft of the Talos launcher is a helicopter landing pad, for a small utility-type helicopter.

Long Beach underwent her first major refit in 1965 when her reactor rods were renewed. During the first commission she had steamed a total of 269 000 km (167 000 miles), and the reactor core is recorded as having been capable of providing the ship with a radius of action of 579 000 km (360 000 miles) at 20 knots. During the refit, which lasted from August 1965 to February 1966, improved fuel rods were inserted into the reactor, substantially improving the radius of action. *Long Beach* is due to undergo a half-life refit in the early 1980s when the Harpoon missile system will be installed. It had been planned to equip her with the Aegis anti-aircraft system, but for cost reasons this idea has now been abandoned and the cruiser will instead be updated with more modern radar and electronic missile-control systems.

Displacement: 14 200 tons (standard), 17 350 tons (full load) *Length:* 219.8 m (721 ft 2 in) oa *Beam:* 22.3 m (73 ft 2 in) *Draught:* 9.5 m (31 ft) *Machinery:* 2 pressurized water-cooled Westinghouse nuclear reactors, 2-shaft geared General Electric steam turbines, 80 000 shp=35+ knots *Armament:* 2 twin Terrier missile launchers, 120 missiles; 1 twin Talos missile launcher, 46 missiles; 2 5-in (127-mm) (2×1); 1 8-tube Asroc launcher; 6 torpedo tubes Mk 32 (2×3) *Crew:* 1000

The USS *Philadelphia*, a *Los Angeles* Class nuclear submarine, during her initial sea trials

General Dynamics

Los Angeles

US nuclear submarine class. In Fiscal Year 1970 the US Congress authorized three nuclear attack submarines of a new type, SSN.688-690. These were followed by four in FY 1971, five in FY 1972, six in FY 1973, five in FY 1974, three in FY 1975, two in FY 1976, and three in FY 1978. A further six are projected for FYs 1979-82. By mid-1978 the following contracts had been awarded: *Los Angeles* (SSN.688), *Baton Rouge* (SSN.689), *Memphis* (SSN.690), *Cincinnati* (SSN.693), *Birmingham* (SSN.695), and *SSN.711-715*—to Newport News Shipbuilding and Dry Dock; *Philadelphia* (SSN.690), *Omaha* (SSN.692), *Groton* (SSN.694), *New York City* (SSN.696), *Indianapolis* (SSN.697), *Bremerton* (SSN.698), *Jacksonville* (SSN.699), *Dallas* (SSN.700), *La Jolla* (SSN.701), *Phoenix* (SSN.702), *Boston* (SSN.703), *Baltimore* (SSN.704), and *SSN.705-710*—to General Dynamics (Electric Boat Division).

Like other modern US nuclear submarines the *Los Angeles* Class boats have only four torpedo tubes, positioned amidships. These fire Mk 48 wire-guided torpedoes and Subroc missiles. In FY 1978 funds were voted to arm them with the Sub-Harpoon surface missile as well. They are considerably bigger than the preceding *Sturgeon* Class, and are driven by a General Electric S6G reactor, similar to the D2G type in the surface ships *Bainbridge* and *Truxtun.*

The construction of the class has been marked by rapid inflation of costs from the 1976 estimate of $221.25 million to $330 million a year later. Great delays have been caused by the Navy Department's alterations

US Navy

The launch of the USS *Los Angeles* at Newport News on April 6, 1974. She commissioned in 1976

to the design. *Los Angeles* took five years to build, and in March 1978 General Dynamics suspended work on their boats in protest at the delays and arguments over contractual details. *Los Angeles* commissioned at the end of 1976. Five more boats commissioned in 1977, and five more were expected to have commissioned by the end of 1978. It was hoped to complete a further two or three each year during 1979-85.

Displacement: 6000/6900 tons (surfaced/submerged) *Length:* 109.7 m (360 ft) oa *Beam:* 10.1 m (33 ft) *Draught:* 9.85 m (32 ft 4 in) *Machinery:* 1 nuclear reactor, 1-shaft geared steam turbines, 30 000 shp approx=30 knots (surfaced/submerged)' *Armament:* 4 21-in (53-cm) torpedo tubes, Mk 48 torpedoes; Subroc, Sub-Harpoon missiles *Crew:* 127

Luigi Rizzo

Italian frigate class, built 1957-62. Originally classified as fast corvettes, the *Luigi Rizzo* Class were designed specifically for convoy escort in the Mediterranean. The original plans, of which the last showed a conventional armament of two quick-firing 76-mm (3-in)/62-cal guns and a Menon A/S mortar forward and a further single 76-mm gun and A/S mortar aft of the funnel, were finally changed to include an A/S helicopter. This was the tiny Agusta-Bell 47J, a US machine built under licence. A flight deck replaced the after A/S mortar and a more compact mast/funnel arrangement compared with the original designs enabled a telescopic hangar to be squeezed in amidships. Two triple mountings for A/S torpedoes were fitted beneath the flight deck.

The Italian frigate *Carlo Margottini*, one of the *Luigi Rizzo* Class built for fast escort work

Italian Defence and Naval Attaché

No and name	completed
F593 *Carlo Bergamini*	6/62
F594 *Virginio Fasan*	10/62
F595 *Carlo Margottini*	5/62
F596 *Luigi Rizzo*	12/61

When in the late 1960s the larger and more capable Agusta-Bell 204B helicopter became available, it was decided to modify the ships accordingly. The after 76-mm gun was removed so that the flight deck could be extended aft, and its director (aft of the funnel) was also suppressed. These modifications took place between 1968-71, making them the smallest warships in the world to carry their own helicopter. This was made possible by the fitting of fin stabilizers which reduce a 20° roll to 5°.

Two Fiat or Tosi diesel engines, driving on two shafts, give the *Luigi Rizzos* a speed of 24 knots, which is more than adequate for their designed role. In spite of their small size, they were apparently regarded as successful ships, and they greatly influenced the design of the two-helicopter *Alpino* Class laid down shortly after their completion.

Displacement: 1410 tons (standard), 2100 tons (full load) *Length:* 93.95 m (308 ft 3 in) oa *Beam:* 11.35 m (37 ft 3 in) *Draught:* 3.1 m (10 ft 2 in) *Machinery:* 2-shaft diesels, 16 000 hp=25 knots *Armament:* 3 (later 2) 76-mm (3-in)/62-cal AA (3×1 or 2×1); 1 Menon A/S mortar (1×1); 6 A/S torpedo-tube mountings (2×3); 1 Agusta-Bell 47J helicopter (later 204B) *Crew:* 155

Lupo

Italian frigate class. Four frigates were

ordered to an improved *Alpino* design from the modernized Riva Trigoso yard of Cantieri Navali Riuniti, to be armed with Otomat surface-to-surface missiles. The name ship was laid down in 1974 and launched two years later.

There are many novel features about the new class. They are propelled by General Electric LM 2500 gas turbines, built under licence by FIAT Aviazione, and Grandi Motori Trieste diesels, in a novel CODOG arrangement. They are the first large ships to have the Otomat missile and the Breda twin 40-mm (1.57-in) L70 Compact gun for close-in defence against sea-skimming missiles. The design also caters for modular construction, and the Riva Trigoso yard has been specially equipped to handle prefabricated sections of anything up to 175 tons in weight.

As the *Lupos* are cheap, general-purpose escorts with a powerful armament and as Cantieri Navali Riuniti can guarantee rapid delivery, with two ship-construction lines permitting simultaneous assembly, the design has suddenly become the most popular on the market. In addition to the four ordered for the Italian navy, *Lupo, Sagittario, Perseo* and *Orsa*, the Peruvian navy has ordered four and the Venezuelan navy six. *Lupo* was launched in July 1976, followed by the Peruvian *Carvajal* in November of the same year. *Sagittario* was launched in June and the Peruvian *Villavicencio* in November 1977. The remaining two Peruvian *Lupo* Class will be built at the state-owned SIMA shipyard at Callao with technical assistance from Italy. The Venezuelan *Mariscal Sucre* was laid down in November 1976.

The ships have an unusual appearance, with a square funnel and a distinctive exhaust fin to reduce infrared emissions. The Otomat missiles are mounted singly alongside the superstructure, with an eight-cell NATO Sea Sparrow SAM launcher above the helicopter hangar. The Peruvian ships differ slightly in that they have the Breda 40-mm guns mounted a deck higher, abreast of the helicopter hangar. The pendant numbers for the class are as follows: F.564-567—*Lupo, Saggittario, Perseo* and *Orsa*; 51-54— *Carvajal, Villavicencio* and Peruvian ships Nos 3 and 4. Numbers of the Venezuelan ships not yet announced.

Displacement: 2304 tonnes (normal), 2900 tonnes (full load) *Length:* 112 m (367 ft 5 in) oa *Beam:* 11.3m (37 ft 2 in) *Draught:* 3.66 m (12 ft) *Machinery:* 2-shaft gas turbine/diesel, 50 000 bhp/14 600 bhp=34 knots *Armament:* 1 127-mm (5-in)/54-cal DP; 4 40-mm (1.57-in)/70-cal Breda Compact AA (2×2); 8 Otomat Teseo Mk 2 SSM launchers (8×1); 8 NATO Sea Sparrow SAM launchers (1×8); 6 32.4-cm (12.75-in) Mk 32 A/S torpedo tubes (2×3) *Crew:* 185

Mackenzie

Canadian destroyer class, built 1958-63. The four vessels of the *Mackenzie* Class followed on from the seven *Restigouche* Class ships, which they closely resemble. Like the *Restigouches* they have a higher bridge than the *St Laurent* design on which they are based, and their twin 3-in (76-mm) guns are in enclosed turrets. Three of the class had a British-model 3-in/70-cal mounting forward and a US model 3-in/50-cal mounting aft, while *Qu'Appelle* has the 50-cal mounting fore and aft. Two Limbo Mk 10 A/S mortars are carried in a large well aft of the second gun mounting. In accordance with Canadian practice the well is protected by a weatherproof cover when not in use. The sensor outfit is the same as that of the *Restigouche* Class, as is the propulsion machinery, which gives a moderate top speed of 28 knots. Significant improvements were made in the air-conditioning system, and the pre-wetting system was extended to counter nuclear fallout.

Considerable use is made of aluminium for the superstructure and this, combined with the rather light armament, gives the *Mackenzies* the stability necessary for the difficult weather conditions in which they are intended to operate.

Displacement: 2380 tons (standard) 2890 tons (full load) *Length:* 111.5 m (365 ft 10 in) oa *Beam:* 12.8 m (42 ft) *Draught:* 4.1 m (13 ft 5 in) *Machinery:* 2-shaft steam turbines, 30 000 shp=28 knots *Armament:* 4 3-in (76-mm) (2×2); 2 Limbo A/S mortars; 2 A/S torpedo tubes (2×1) *Crew:* 245

Mackerel

US submarine class, built 1940-41. *Mackerel* and *Marlin* were built as experimental units for use in the Atlantic, though the concept was not pursued as it was felt that the larger submarines designed for the Pacific would prove equally satisfactory. Neither did the US wish to design and build separate classes of submarines just for use in the Mediterranean, where the British were well used to operating.

No and name	builder	launched
SS204 *Mackerel*	Electric Boat company, Groton	9/40
SS205 *Marlin*	Portsmouth navy yard	1/41

The two boats were used for training throughout the war. *Mackerel* was sold for scrap in 1947 and *Marlin* in 1946. The two ships differed slightly, the diesels in *Mackerel* being directly coupled to the shafts while those in *Marlin* operated through reduction gearing. During the war *Marlin* was fitted with single 20-mm (0.79-in) antiaircraft mounts fore and aft of the conning tower in place of the 0.30-in (7.62-mm) machine-guns originally fitted.

Displacement: 825/1179 tons (surfaced/submerged) *Length:* 72.8 m (239 ft) oa *Beam:* 6.6 m (21 ft 9 in) *Draught:* 3.7 m (12 ft) *Machinery:* 2-shaft diesels/2 electric motors, 3360 (*Marlin* 3400) bhp/1500 hp=16/9 knots (surfaced/submerged) *Armament:* 1 3-in (76-mm); 2 0.5-in (12.7-mm) machine-guns; 2 0.30-in (7.62-mm) machine-guns; 6 21-in (53-cm) torpedo tubes (4 bow, 2 stern), 12 torpedoes *Crew:* 38

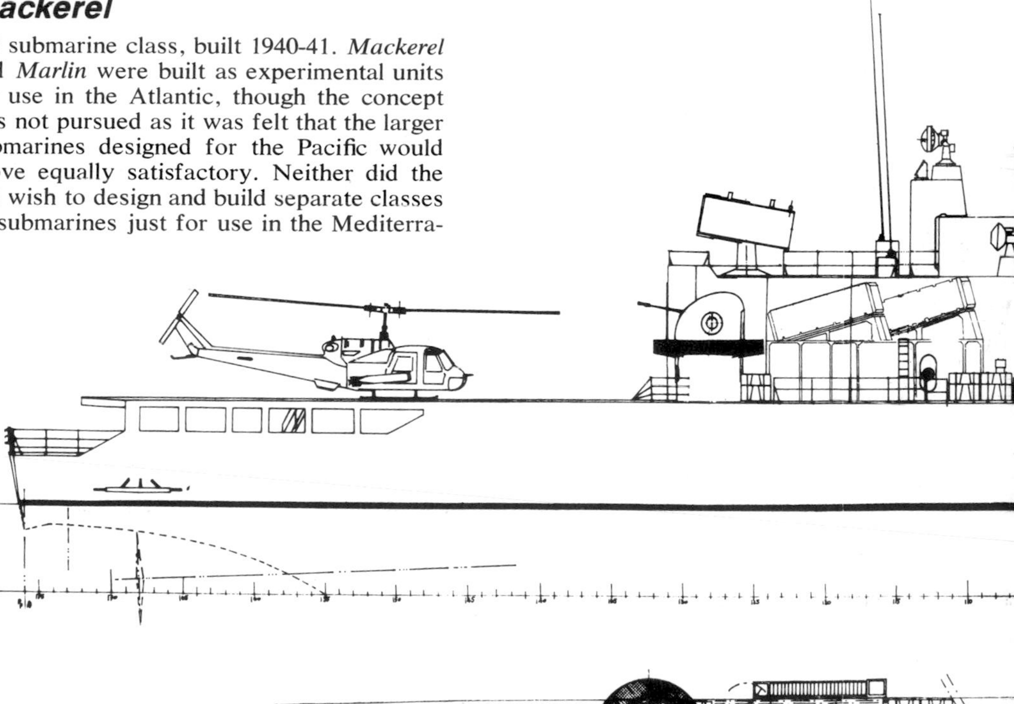

No and name	built	completed
DDE 261 *Mackenzie*	Canadian Vickers	10/62
DDE 262 *Saskatchewan*	Victoria Machinery (completed Yarrow)	16/63
DDE 263 *Yukon*	Burrard	5/63
DDE 264 *Qu'Appelle*	Davie	9/63

Mackerel

US submarine class, built 1952-53. Ordered under the 1951-52 Programmes from the Electric Boat company, Groton, these two submarines were the smallest built for the US Navy since the Holland-type 'C' Class of 1906. They were completed in November and October 1953 as the *T-1* and *T-2* respectively, but in 1956 were renamed *Mackerel* (SST.1) (July 15) and *Marlin* (SST.2) (May 15). The basic design followed the GUPPY configuration of the earlier *Barracuda*, the boats being designed specifically for use as targets for antisubmarine training. Although they were slow vessels, their small size and consequent poor response to A/S search equipment made them realistic targets. Both vessels were based at the A/S base at Key West, Florida. They required only a small radius of action (2000 nautical miles at full speed) and therefore carried only 18 tons of diesel fuel.

The advent of the nuclear-powered submarine with its high underwater speed made these boats completely inadequate for A/S training and they were stricken on January 31, 1973. Between May-June 1966 *Mackerel* was refitted to evaluate new equipment for the nuclear-powered research submarine *NR-1*. For the trials, carried out during 1966-67, *Mackerel* was equipped with an experimental sonar, external TV cameras and a manipulator arm. In addition a series of wheels were built into the keel to enable the submarine to propel itself along the ocean floor using a thruster unit which was also fitted. The trials lasted for nine months during which *Mackerel* carried out about 225 separate operations along the seabed.

Displacement: 303/347 tons (surfaced/submerged) *Length:* 40 m (131 ft 3 in) oa *Beam:* 4.1 m (13 ft 6 in) *Draught:* 3.7 m (12 ft 3 in) *Machinery:* 1 shaft, 2 General Motors diesels/2 Elliott electric motors, 380 bhp=8/9.5 knots (surfaced/submerged) *Armament:* 1 21-in (53-cm) torpedo tube (bow) *Crew:* 18

Majestic

British aircraft carrier class. Also known as modified light fleet carriers, six ships of the *Majestic* Class were planned for the Royal Navy. The hull and machinery were practically identical with those of the earlier *Colossus* Class carriers, the main differences being the *Majestic*'s different armament and strengthened flight deck and aircraft-handling machinery which added over 2500 tons to the standard displacement and 0.7 m (1 ft 6 in) to the draught.

All the *Majestic*s were launched during 1944-45 but none saw service with the Royal Navy, five were completed for Commonwealth navies, while the last, *Leviathan*, was never completed. Such was the 'stretch' built into the basic design that these ships were able to operate 13 600-kg (30 000-lb) antisubmarine aircraft and 11 000-kg (24 000-lb) strike fighters with hook-on speeds of up to 100 knots, thanks to modern introductions

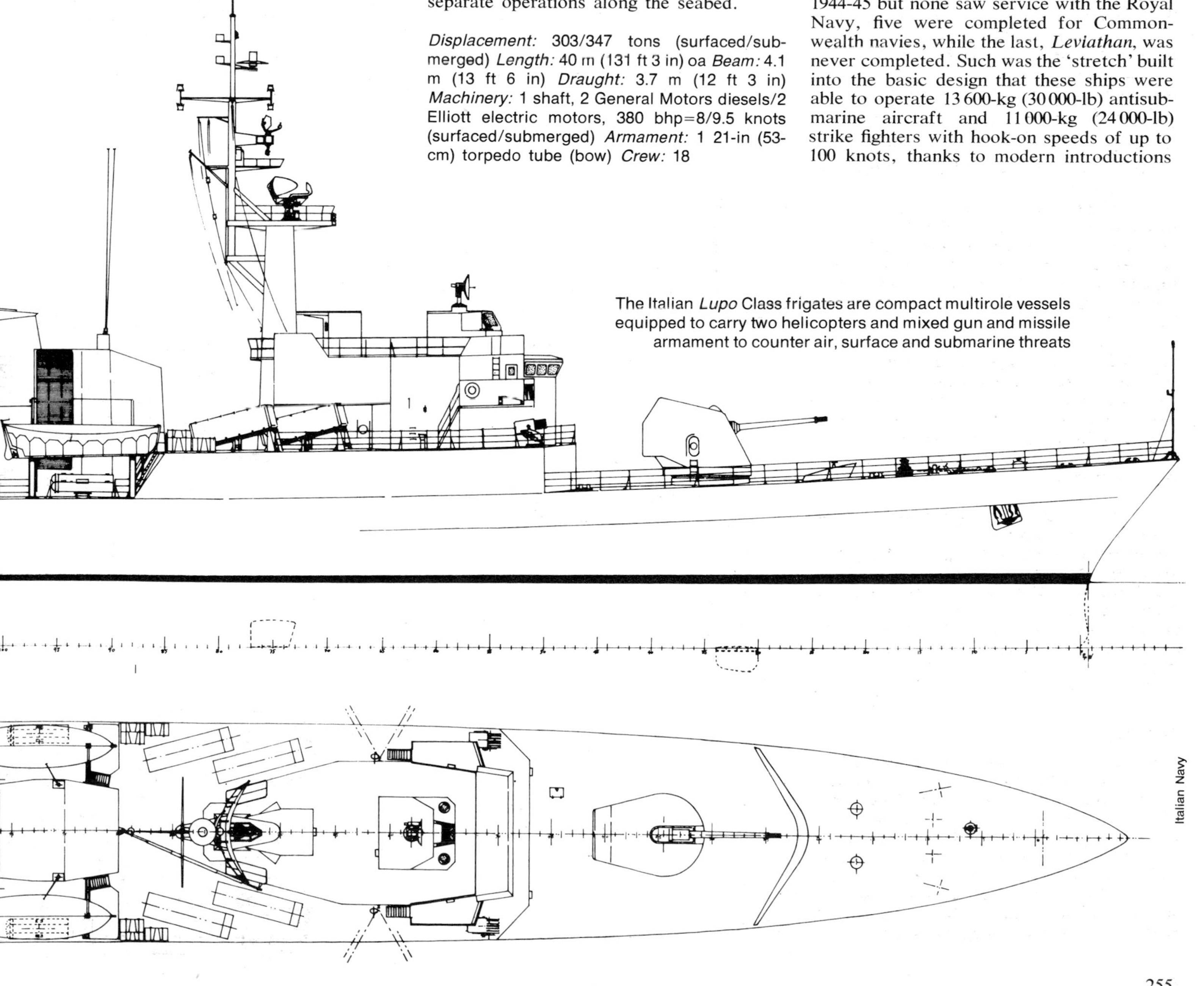
The Italian *Lupo* Class frigates are compact multirole vessels equipped to carry two helicopters and mixed gun and missile armament to counter air, surface and submarine threats

Italian Navy

Rawlston

The Thai frigate *Makut Rajakumarn* was designed and built by Yarrow using their experience with the Malaysian frigate *Rahmat*

Name	built	completed	fate
Hercules	Vickers-Armstrongs (Tyne)	3/61	Indian navy as *Vikrant*
Leviathan	Swan Hunter (Wallsend)	—	scrapped 1969
Magnificent	Harland and Wolff	5/48	Royal Canadian Navy, 1948-57; scrapped 1962
Majestic	Vickers-Armstrongs (Barrow)	10/55	Royal Australian Navy as *Melbourne*
Powerful	Harland and Wolff	1/57	Royal Canadian Navy as *Bonaventure*; scrapped 1971
Terrible	Devonport dockyard	10/49	Royal Australian Navy as *Sydney*; fast transport from 1962

such as the steam catapult and angled deck.

Displacement: 15 770 tons (standard), 19 550 tons (full load) *Length:* 211.5-212.8 m (694-698 ft) oa *Beam:* 24.4 m (80 ft) wl, 34.3 m (112 ft 6 in) max *Draught:* 7.6 m (25 ft) *Machinery:* 2-shaft geared steam turbines, 40 000 shp=23.5 knots *Aircraft:* 34 *Armament:* 30 40-mm (1.57-in)/60-cal AA *Crew:* 1350

Makut Rajakumarn

Thai frigate. *Makut Rajakumarn* was designed and built by Yarrow, and is a development of the Yarrow-built Malaysian frigate *Rahmat*. The requirement was for a relatively inexpensive, long-range patrol vessel with the firepower of a much larger frigate but needing only a small crew. *Makut Rajakumarn* was ordered in late 1969 and laid down at the Scotstoun yard in January 1970. She was launched in November 1971 and was handed over to the Royal Thai Navy in May 1973, well before the contract date. She is slightly larger than *Rahmat* with more powerful machinery of the CODOG configuration and was designed as a multipurpose ship and flagship of the Royal Thai Navy. She is equipped with accommodation for an admiral and three staff officers, and an admiral's bridge is superimposed on the main bridge.

Makut Rajakumarn is of all-welded construction with aluminium superstructure, mast and funnel. Being designed for service in the rough waters of the Pacific she has a generous freeboard and well-designed flare at the bows which ensure a dry ship. Her stability as a stable weapons platform is further enhanced by a pair of stabilizers.

For her size she is a well-armed ship carrying a variety of weapons systems to fulfil her role as a general-purpose escort. Two single Vickers Mk 8 4.5-in (114-mm) guns are sited fore and aft and two single 40-mm (1.57-in) Bofors on wings abreast the funnel. Antiaircraft defence is provided by a quadruple Seacat missile launcher sited at the after end of the superstructure. The weapons are controlled by two Hollandse Signaal-appareten fire-control systems: an M 20 in a radome for the 4.5-in and an M 44 for the Seacat. Long-range surveillance is provided by a Hollandse LW 04 radar sited on a short mast in front of the funnel. For antisubmarine duties the ship is armed with a triple-barrelled Limbo mortar linked to two sonars; in addition there are two depth-charge throwers and a depth-charge rack which can be fired from the bridge.

Displacement: 1650 tons (standard), 1900 tons (full load) *Length:* 97.5 m (320 ft) *Beam:* 11 m (36 ft) *Draught:* 5.5 m (18 ft 2 in) *Machinery:* 2 shafts, 2 Rolls-Royce Olympus gas turbines, 23 125 shp=26 knots, 2 Crossley-Pielstick diesels, 6000 bhp=18 knots *Armament:* 2 4.5-in (114-mm) (2×1); 2 40-mm (1.57-in) (2×1); 4 Seacat missile launchers (1×4); 1 Limbo A/S mortar; 2 depth-charge throwers; 1 depth-charge rack *Crew:* 140

Marconi

Italian submarine class. The six ocean-going submarines of the *Marconi* Class, completed April-July 1940, are considered to have been the finest and most successful Italian submarine class. The single-hull design with blisters was developed from the preceding *Marcello* Class. In order to accommodate greatly increased fuel bunkerage without a corresponding increase in displacement they sacrificed some offensive capability: the second deck gun aft of the conning tower was omitted and only four reload torpedoes were carried instead of the eight of the *Marcello* Class.

The *Marconi* Class were equipped with more powerful machinery, but because of the increased displacement this resulted in only a half-knot increase in surface speed, while the submerged speed remained the same.

During 1942 the conning tower was reduced in size and the periscope standards lowered. *Da Vinci* was temporarily modified to carry a Type CA midget submarine during the summer of 1942, and this involved the replacement of the 100-mm (3.9-in) gun by chocks and clamps to secure the midget. The clamps were so designed that the midget could be released while the submarine was still submerged and retrieved with the deck casing just awash. When trials showed that the CA midgets required more design modifications before they could become operational the idea was abandoned and *Da Vinci* reshipped her gun and returned to operational patrols in the Atlantic.

The class spent the majority of their war patrols in the Atlantic, where they accounted for 38 ships totalling 216 227 grt sunk and seven (24 465 grt) damaged. *Da Vinci* was the most successful, sinking 16 ships (116 686 grt), six of them (58 973 grt) in one patrol. Her score also included the largest sinking by an Italian submarine, *Empress of Canada* (21 517 grt).

Only *Luigi Torelli* survived the war, the rest of the class being sunk in the North Atlantic while operating out of Bordeaux. *Baracca* was sunk by the escort *Crome*; *Bianchi* by the submarine *Severn*; *Da Vinci* by the escorts *Active* and *Ness*; *Malaspina* by the destroyer *Vimy*; and *Marconi* probably by the German submarine *U 67* in error on November 5, 1941. *Luigi Torelli* was converted to a transport submarine early in 1943 and was in Singapore with a cargo of precious raw materials preparing to return to Europe when Italy surrendered. She was ceded by the Japanese to the Germans as *UIT 25*, but in May 1945 was taken over again by the Japanese as *I 504*. She was captured at Kobe at the end of the war and scrapped soon after.

Maggiore Baracca, Michele Bianchi, Alessandro Malaspina, Luigi Torelli—built by OTO, Muggiano
Leonardo da Vinci, Guglielmo Marconi—built by CRDA, Monfalcone

Displacement: 1195/1489 tons (surfaced/submerged) *Length:* 76.5 m (251 ft) oa *Beam:* 6.8 m (22 ft 4 in) *Draught:* 4.7 m (15 ft 5 in) *Machinery:* 2-shaft diesels/2 electric motors, 3600 bhp/1500 hp=18/8 knots (surfaced/submerged) *Armament:* 1 100-mm (3.9-in); 4 13.2-mm (0.52-in) machine-guns; 8 53-cm (21-in) (4 bow, 4 stern) torpedo tubes, 12 torpedoes *Crew:* 57

Marder

German midget submarine. Following the Neger, a similar type of one-man midget was developed to run submerged. The propulsive section, which contained the pilot, was a T3b electric torpedo; it weighed 1350 kg (2970 lb) and normally ran for 4000 m (4400 yards) at 18.5 knots. Below this was a standard G7e torpedo.

The main difference between the original Neger and the Marder (marten), was the provision of a small diving tank, which enabled the midget to submerge to a maximum depth of 30 m (98 ft). About 300 were completed, and they were credited with the following successes during the second half of 1944: extensive damage to Polish cruiser *Conrad* off Normandy on July 8; sinking of minesweepers *Magic*, *Cato* and *Pylades*, July 6-8; trawler *Colsay* sunk off Ostend on November 2; and three landing craft sunk.

A Marder without its protective dome for the crewman. Marders attacked shipping massed around the D-Day beach heads and sank three minesweepers and damaged a Polish cruiser

Displacement: 5.5 tons *Length:* 8.3 m (27 ft 3 in) oa *Beam:* 0.53 m (1 ft 9 in) *Draught:* 0.53 m (1 ft 9 in) *Machinery:* 1-shaft electric, 12 shp=4.2/3.2 knots (surfaced/submerged) *Armament:* 1 53-cm (21-in) torpedo *Crew:* 1

Marksman

British destroyer class. The *Marksman* or 'M' Class destroyers ordered in July 1939 under the 1939-40 Programme were repeats of the *Laforey* Class of the 1937-38 Programme. They were laid down during 1939-40, launched during 1940-42 and (except *Marksman*) completed during 1941-42. The original hull of *Marksman* was wrecked during an air raid on Scotts shipyard at Greenock in May 1941; a new hull was laid down in 1941 and launched in 1942 as *Marksman*, but was renamed *Mahratta* prior to completion in August 1943. The second 'M' Class ship ordered from Scotts, the class leader *Milne*, had to be transferred to John Brown for completion owing to the damage caused to the shipyard during the air raid. Prior to completion *Myrmidon* was transferred to Poland and renamed *Orkan*.

The class was completed with modifications already approved for the *Laforey* Class. The after bank of torpedo tubes was omitted in favour of a 4-in (102-mm) AA gun; two 20-mm (0.79-in) AA (2×1) were mounted abreast the searchlight platform amidships; four 0.5-in (12.7-mm) AA (2×2) were fitted on the quarterdeck; and air-warning and gunnery radar sets were fitted. Later the quadruple 0.5-in mountings in the bridge wings and the twin 0.5-in mountings aft were replaced by four 20-mm (4×1). During 1943-44 (excepting *Martin* and *Orkan* which had been lost) the after torpedo tubes were replaced and the 4-in gun removed. During the same period the 20-mm singles in the bridge wings were replaced by twin 20-mm (except in *Meteor*), while *Marne, Matchless* and *Musketeer* also had those amidships replaced by twins. In addition the tripod foremast was replaced by a lattice mast to carry the surface- and air-warning radars, except in *Musketeer* which carried her surface-warning radar on the searchlight platform amidships. *Matchless* was also fitted with an HF/DF mast on the after superstructure and all had their searchlights removed in order to reduce topweight.

On completion all eight joined the Home Fleet and were employed extensively as escorts for Russian convoys until the end of 1944. There were, however, occasional excursions to other areas. In June 1942 *Marne* and *Matchless* transferred to the Mediterranean to cover a Malta convoy (Harpoon). *Matchless* was damaged by a mine off Malta and was out of action until November. In October 1942 *Martin, Meteor* and *Milne* were detached to take part in the North African landings, and *Martin* was torpedoed and sunk north of Algiers by the German submarine *U 431* while escorting one of the invasion convoys. Ships were also detached occasionally for service as North Atlantic

A Marder midget submarine is lowered into the sea during a training exercise in 1944

Foto Drüppel

convoy escorts and this also led to losses. On November 11, 1942, *Marne* had her stern blown off by a torpedo from the German submarine *U 515* while escorting a convoy west of Gibraltar. She survived, but was under repair for nearly two years. *Orkan* suffered a similar fate but did not survive: on October 7, 1943, while operating in the North Atlantic with the 10th Escort Group she was hit in the stern by an acoustic torpedo fired from the *U 758*. The following day she was hit by a second acoustic torpedo, this time fired from *U 378*, and sank leaving only 44 survivors. The third and last member of the class to be lost was *Mahratta*, which was torpedoed and sunk by *U 956* in the Barents Sea on February 25, 1944. *Matchless* and *Musketeer* took part in the battle of North Cape, in which the German battlecruiser *Scharnhorst* was sunk, the latter vessel being responsible for two of the torpedo hits on the enemy ship. The class also had two U-Boat successes in the Arctic. On January 30, 1944, *Meteor* and *Whitehall* sank *U 314* and on May 30, 1944, *Milne* sank *U 289*.

The five surviving ships transferred to the Mediterranean at the end of 1944 where they operated mainly in the Aegean. They returned home in 1946 and were paid off into reserve. *Musketeer* was sold for scrapping in 1955 but the other four were transferred to Turkey following an agreement signed at Ankara in 1957. Prior to transfer they were refitted, the pom-pom mounting being replaced by a twin 40-mm (1.57-in) AA and the 20-mm by four single 40-mm AA (two in the bridge wings, two amidships). They also had the after torpedo tubes replaced by a deckhouse carrying a three-barrelled Squid A/S mortar. The ships were officially transferred in 1959 being renamed *Alp Arslan (Milne), Kilic Ali Pasha (Matchless), Maresal Fevzi Cakmak (Marne)* and *Piyale Pasa (Meteor)*. They served with the Turkish navy until the 1970s, when all were discarded.

Milne, Mahratta—built by Scotts
Marne, Martin—built by Vickers-Armstrongs
Matchless, Meteor—built by Stephen
Musketeer, Orkan—built by Fairfield

Displacement: 1920 tons (standard), 2725 tons (full load) *Length:* 110.4 m (362 ft 3 in) oa *Beam:* 11.3 m (37 ft) *Draught:* 3 m (10 ft) *Machinery:* 2-shaft geared steam turbines, 48 000 shp=36 knots *Armament:* 6 4.7-in (120-mm) (3×2); 1 4-in (102-mm) AA; 4 2-pdr (1×4); 12 0.5-in (12.7-mm) (2×4, 2×2); 2 20-mm (0.79-in) (2×1); 4 21-in (53-cm) torpedo tubes (1×4) *Crew:* 190

Matsu

Japanese destroyer class. By 1943 the Japanese navy had begun to suffer from an acute shortage of destroyers, and the merchant marine was being decimated by US submarine activity. The war had left Japan with little time in which to make good the losses and a requirement was drawn up for a new escort, similar in concept to those being mass produced by the Allies, and lacking the sophistication of the Special Type destroyers of the *Kagero* and *Terustuki* Classes. There would in any case be no time in which to train crews in the use of complex equipment. The design, drawn up in 1943, was spartan in the extreme, dispensing with all non-essential equipment and sophisticated items. The requirement called for a vessel capable of carrying out both fleet and mercantile escort duties and the *Matsu* Class therefore differed from destroyer escorts built for the Allies which were designed principally for A/S duties in support of convoy operations.

The ships were 15-20 m (50-70 ft) longer than corresponding Allied vessels, but the heavy cut-back in equipment left their displacement almost the same. For their size the *Matsu* Class were very heavily armed, mounting three 127-mm (5-in) guns either in open mountings or behind plain splinter shields. In addition they carried a very heavy AA armament of about 24 light guns. Being designed for fleet duties they also mounted a bank of torpedo tubes, originally specified as 53-cm (21-in) but completed with 61-cm (24-in), and they were powered by turbines to give them the speed which such duties required. They nevertheless fell short of the 35-knot requirement, for their maximum speed was at best only 28 knots.

The *Matsu* Class were designed for mass production using arc welding, and were of rugged construction and capable of withstanding severe damage. Damage control was further improved by rearranging the machinery layout so that a single hit did not completely cripple the ships, since in the event of either boiler or engine room being put out of action the remaining units could be coupled together.

Twenty-eight ships were ordered under the 1943-44 Programme, but 11 units were cancelled in the summer of 1944 and reordered as 13 units of a slightly modified design. Subsequently another 20 ships of the modified design were ordered, but ten ships of this later order were never laid down and were cancelled in March 1945.

The ships were laid down between August 1943 and March 1945. A further 80 vessels planned under the 1944-45 War Programme were also cancelled before any orders were placed.

Azusa, Hagi, Hatsuzakura, Hinoki, Kaede, Kaki, Keyaki, Kiri, Kusunoki, Kuzu*, Momi, Sakaki*, Sakura, Sumire, Tachibana, Take, Tsuta, Yadake*, Yaezakura**—built by Yokosuka navy yard.
Enoki, Hatsuyume, Hishi, Kaya, Maki, Matsu, Momo, Nire, Odake, Shii, Tochi* Tsubaki*—built by Maizuru navy yard.
Kaba, Kashi, Katsura, Kuwa, Nara, Sugi, Ume, Wakazakura*, Yanagi*—built by Fujinagata, Osaka.
(*not completed)

The following units surrendered at the end of the war and scrapped in 1947: *Hagi, Kaba, Kaki, Kashi, Kusunoki, Maki, Nara, Nire, Odake, Tsubaki* and *Yanagi*. *Keyaki* and *Sumire* were expended as targets in 1947.

The Australian aircraft carrier *Melbourne* was laid down as HMS *Majestic*. Work was suspended in 1945 until her transfer in 1949

C & S Taylor

The following were transferred and subsequently scrapped in the late 1950s: *Hatsuyume* (to China, as *Hsin Yang*), *Hatsuzakura* (to USSR), *Kaede* (to China, as *Hen Yang*), *Kaya* (to USSR), *Kiri* (to USSR), *Shii* (to USSR), *Sugi* (to China, as *Hwei Yang*), *Tsuta* (to China, as *Hua Yang*).

The following were sunk in action: *Enoki* (mined 26/6/45), *Hinoki* (sunk by US destroyers 7/1/45), *Kuwa* (sunk by US destroyers 3/12/44), *Matsu* (sunk by US destroyers 4/8/44), *Momi* (sunk by aircraft 5/1/45), *Momo* (sunk by US submarine *Hawkbill* 15/12/45), *Sakura* (mined 11/7/45), *Tachibana* (sunk by US aircraft 14/7/45) and *Ume* (sunk by US aircraft 31/1/45). *Nashi* (sunk by US aircraft 28/7/45) was subsequently refloated and commissioned into the Japanese Self Defence Force as the *Wakaba* in 1955 and scrapped in 1972-73.

Displacement: 1262 tons (standard) *Length:* 100 m (328 ft) oa *Beam:* 9.3 m (30 ft 6 in) *Draught:* 3.3 m (10 ft 10 in) *Machinery:* 2-shaft geared turbines, 19 000=28 knots *Armament:* 3 127-mm (5-in) (1×2, 1×1); 24 25-mm (1-in) AA (4×3, 12×1); 4 61-cm (24-in) torpedo tubes, 4 torpedoes; 4 depth-charge throwers, 36-60 depth-charges *Crew:* 210

Melbourne

Australian light fleet carrier. *Melbourne* was laid down as the name-ship of the British *Majestic* Class, and launched at Vickers, Barrow, on February 28, 1945. She was incomplete when the war ended in August 1945. Work was suspended until 1949, when it was decided to complete her for transfer to the Royal Australian Navy. Work progressed slowly so that from 1952 the latest innovations, such as the angled flight deck, steam catapult and mirror landing aid could be incorporated.

When the carrier was commissioned with her new name on October 28, 1955, she was one of the best equipped in the world, in spite of her small size, being only the second British-built operational carrier to be fitted with the steam catapult. She operated eight de Havilland Sea Venom all-weather fighters and 12-16 Fairey Gannet ASW aircraft until the early 1960s, when the latter were replaced by Westland Wessex helicopters and, later, Grumman S-2E Trackers. In 1967-69, *Melbourne* underwent an extended refit which included modernization of her radar fit, strengthening of the lifts and deck and alteration necessary to permit operation of McDonnell Douglas A-4G Skyhawk fighter-bombers. In 1975, she was operating 14 fixed-wing aircraft and ten A/S helicopters—the complement which will probably remain until her retirement in the early 1980s.

Displacement: 16 200 tons (standard), 19 990 tons (full load) *Length:* 213.8 m (701 ft 6 in) oa *Beam:* 24.5 m (80 ft 3 in) wl, 38.4 m (126 ft) max *Draught:* 7.8 m (25 ft 6 in) *Machinery:* 2 shafts, 2 sets geared steam turbines, 40 000 shp=23 knots *Armament;* 10 40-mm (1.57-in) AA *Aircraft:* 24 *Crew:* 1335

RAN

HMAS *Melbourne* after her refit in 1967-69 to enable her to operate more modern aircraft

Midway

US aircraft carrier class. Following the development of the deck-edge lift and experience gained in the battles of the Coral Sea and Midway in 1942, US policy regarding carrier design was radically altered to include provision for a greatly increased aircraft complement and an armoured flight deck to protect the hangars against dive-bombing. These changes necessitated the removal of previous limitations on size and displacement.

The new carrier, *Midway*, ordered in October 1942, had a standard displacement of 45 000 tons, more than half as much again as that of the previous *Essex* Class. The extra topweight of the armoured flight deck and aircraft was compensated by a huge increase in beam at the waterline, matched by a wider hangar. A longer hull preserved a length: beam ratio which would permit high speeds without extravagant power being necessary.

The gain in aircraft complement was not commensurate with the increased displacement, a maximum of 137 aircraft being accommodated in *Midway* compared with up to 100 in *Essex*. The allowance for fuel, ordnance and stores for the aircraft was more generous, however, allowing the ship to stay in action longer between replenishments. The ship carried 10 600 tons of fuel oil for her own boilers, giving a range of over 20 000 miles.

The disposition of the main gun armament was better than in the *Essex* Class, being mounted in single enclosed turrets located on either side of the hull well below the level of the flight deck, where they enjoyed a good field of fire without exposing aircraft on deck to the muzzle blast.

Midway was laid down on October 27, 1943, as CV.41. Three more ships were ordered in 1943, but of these only CV.42 and CV.43 were laid down, the former (*Coral Sea*) on December 1, 1943, and the latter (still unnamed) on July 10, 1944. *Midway* was launched on March 20, 1945. The second ship was due to be launched as the *Coral Sea* but was renamed *Franklin D Roosevelt* upon the death of the President, and launched on April 29, 1945. The third carrier became the *Coral Sea* and was launched on April 2, 1946.

Midway commissioned on September 10, 1945. Trials and training continued until the end of October 1947, when she sailed for the first of her operational deployments in the Mediterranean with the US 6th Fleet. She had been preceded in the 6th Fleet by *Franklin D Roosevelt*, which had commissioned on October 27, 1945, and had arrived in the Mediterranean in August 1946 for her first tour of duty. Both carriers were modernized in the summer of 1947, the most obvious external change being the replacement of the quadruple 40-mm (1.57-in) AA guns by twin 3-in (76-mm)/50-cal guns. *Coral Sea* was already fitted with the 3-in guns and her main battery had been reduced from 18 to 14 5-in (130-mm) guns. When she commissioned, on October 1, 1947, she too was allocated to the Atlantic Fleet and began her first Mediterranean deployment in June 1948.

The three ships of the class continued this pattern of activity (work-up, Atlantic training, Mediterranean deployment, overhaul) until the beginning of 1954, supporting those *Essex* Class carriers not serving off Korea. In January 1954, *Franklin D Roosevelt* left Norfolk, Virginia, and sailed around Cape Horn to the Puget Sound navy yard, Washington, where, during the next two years, she was virtually reconstructed. This was in order to accommodate a new generation of heavy attack aircraft then being developed to replace the jet fighters embarked since 1949. She was given a new angled deck and three steam catapults, the third track being installed in the waist position on the port edge of the angled deck. The centre-line aircraft lift aft was eliminated and a new deck-edge lift was fitted just abaft the island on the starboard side; the area of the port deck-edge lift was increased and, like the forward centre-line lift, the platform and machinery were strengthened to move 75 000 lb (34 000 kg) aircraft. The British-designed mirror landing aid was also installed, but the 'batsman' was retained to control the final stages of landing by the piston-engined Douglas AD (A-1) Skyraider attack aircraft which were to continue to operate from these ships until the late 1960s.

Franklin D Roosevelt recommissioned in April 1956 and returned to the Atlantic. Meanwhile, *Midway* was shifted to the Pacific early in 1955, to join *Franklin D Roosevelt* at Puget Sound in the autumn of the year. Her conversion was not completed until September 1957 and thereafter she was permanently allocated to the Pacific Fleet, deploying at regular intervals to the South China Sea area in support of the South-East Asia Treaty Organization.

Coral Sea continued unmodified until May 1957, operating her jets from the axial deck long after most other Attack Carriers—a designation introduced in October 1952 to denote those ships with an offensive mission. Like her sisters, *Coral Sea* was reconstructed at Puget Sound and her general arrangements were virtually the same, but the forward lift was moved to the starboard deck-edge, just forward of the island, leaving her with no inboard lifts. She recommissioned in January 1960 and by the following September she was operational with the Pacific Fleet.

By 1965, the *Midway* Class carriers were operating Vought F-8E Crusader and McDonnell F-4B Phantom intercepters, Douglas A-4C Skyhawk light attack aircraft, Douglas KA-3B tankers and a variety of A-1 Skyraider attack and electronic warfare aircraft. Airborne early warning was provided by a flight of Grumman E-1B Tracers.

US Navy

The USS *Midway* in the Gulf of Tonkin during operations off North Vietnam in June 1971

On February 7, 1965, *Coral Sea*'s aircraft went into action against military targets in North Vietnam, in retaliation for a Viet Cong attack on American forces in South Vietnam. Four days later, Chanh Hoa was attacked by 99 aircraft from *Coral Sea* and *Hancock*, an *Essex* Class carrier. These retaliatory strikes had no apparent deterrent effect on the Communists and on March 18 the carriers in the Gulf of Tonkin and US Air Force and Marine forces in South Vietnam and Thailand began the campaign of air strikes codenamed Rolling Thunder, attacking transportation systems and military installations in North Vietnam.

Coral Sea was relieved by *Midway* in April and three months later, on June 17, a pair of Phantoms from the latter scored the first US air combat victory of the war, destroying two MiG-17 fighters south of Hanoi. *Midway* remained in the area, flying strike missions against the North and against enemy-held targets in the South, until the autumn of 1965, when she left for an extended refit at San Francisco. This refit was a further reconstruction, locating the port deck-edge lift further aft, as in *Coral Sea*, moving the forward lift to the starboard deck-edge, remodelling the angled deck extension and strengthening the deck and machinery to cope with 100 000-lb (45 500-kg) aircraft. Originally intended to cost $88 million for 24 months' work, the refit stretched out over 52 months and the cost soared to $202 million. *Franklin D Roosevelt*, which had been with the Atlantic Fleet since 1957, underwent a simpler 'austerity overhaul' in 1969 to enable her to operate Grumman A-6 Intruders and LTV A-7 Corsair IIs.

Coral Sea had returned to the Gulf of Tonkin in early 1966 and saw out three more combat tours until the bombing halt in November 1968, her aircraft striking in both the North and the South. When bombing started again in May 1972, following the North Vietnamese invasion of the South, *Midway* took part in the Linebacker operations which contributed to the Communists' military defeat, early in 1973.

The Congressional decision to reduce the active strength in carriers to 12, following the end of the war in Vietnam, led to the decommissioning of *Franklin D Roosevelt* as soon as the second nuclear carrier, *Nimitz*, became operational at the end of 1977. *Midway* was planned to be the only survivor when *Eisenhower* became operational in early 1979.

(*Midway*, 1945) *Displacement:* 45 000 tons (standard), 60 000 tons (full load) *Length:* 295 m (968 ft) oa; 274.3 m (900 ft) wl *Beam:* 34.4 m (113 ft) wl; 41.5 m (136 ft) flight deck *Draught:* 10 m (33 ft) mean *Machinery:* 4-shaft geared steam turbines, 212 000 shp=33 knots (designed) *Armament:* 18 5-in (127 mm)/54-cal DP (18×1); 84 40-mm (1.57-in) QF (21×4), replaced by 40 3-in (76-mm)/50-cal (20×2); 56 20-mm (0.79-in) AA (28×2) *Aircraft:* Approx 75 (137 max) *Crew:* 4100 approx

(*Coral Sea*, 1965) *Displacement:* 52 000 tons (standard), 64 000 tons (full load) *Length:* 298.4 m (979 ft) oa; 274.3 m (900 ft) wl *Beam:* 36.9 m (121 ft) wl; 72.5 m (238 ft) flight deck *Draught:* 10.8 m (35 ft 4 in) mean *Machinery:* 4-shaft geared steam turbines, 212 000 shp=33 knots (designed) *Armament:* 3 5-in (127-mm)/54-cal DP (3×1) *Aircraft:* Approx 75 (137 max) *Crew:* 4500 approx

Mikura

Japanese escort class. The eight *Mikura* Class escorts, ordered under the 1941 War Programme, were laid down under the 1942-43 Estimates between October 1942 and November 1943. Known as the Type B, the design dispensed with the minesweeping equipment carried by the previous escorts and concentrated on the vessels' A/S role. With reduced bunkerage (the radius of action dropped from 8000 nautical miles to 5000

Name	builder	launched
Awaji	Hitachi, Sakurajima	10/43
Chiburi	Tsurumi, Asano	11/43
Kurahashi	Tsurumi, Asano	10/43
Kusagaki	Tsurumi, Asano	1/44
Mikura	Tsurumi, Asano	7/43
Miyake	Tsurumi, Asano	8/43
Nomi	Hitachi, Sakurajima	12/43
Yashiro	Hitachi, Sakurajima	2/44

nautical miles) sufficient space was provided for the storage of extra depth charges (120 were carried compared to the six in the Type A). In addition asdic and hydrophones were fitted. Apart from this, however, the basic design remained the same as the Type A *Shumushu* and *Etorofu* Classes, with a marginal increase in displacement. Newer 120-mm (4.7-in) guns with a much higher elevation capable of engaging aircraft were mounted in splinter shields, one forward in A position and a twin mount aft.

During the war the light AA was considerably augmented with three triple 25-mm (1-in) AA and a single mount. *Miyake* was given 12 single 25-mm in lieu of the triple mounts owing to a shortage of triple mounts. A number of vessels subsequently had four extra single 25-mm mounts added.

Three of the class were surrendered at the end of the war, *Kurahashi, Miyake* and *Yashiro. Kurahashi* and *Yashiro* were used to sweep mines around the Japanese coast before being handed over to Britain *(Kurahashi)* and China *(Yashiro). Kurahashi* was scrapped in 1948 while the *Yashiro* was renamed *Cheng An* and served in the Taiwanese navy until 1963 when she was discarded. *Miyake* had been severely damaged by a mine in August 1945, and although earmarked for repatriation duties, for which purpose she was repaired at the Kure navy yard, she was eventually scrapped in 1948 without being used. The remainder of the class were all sunk during the war. *Awaji* and *Kusagaki* were both sunk by the US submarine *Guitarro* on June 2 and August 7, 1944, respectively. US submarines also sank two other vessels in the class: *Threadfin* sank *Mikura* on March 28, 1945, and *Tirante* sank *Nomi* on April 14, 1945. *Chiburi* was sunk by US naval aircraft on January 12, 1945.

Displacement; 940 tons (standard), 1020 tons (full load) *Length:* 78.1 m (256 ft 3 in) oa *Beam:* 9 m (29 ft 6 in) *Draught:* 3 m (9 ft 10 in) *Machinery:* 2-shaft diesels, 4200 bhp=19.5 knots *Armament:* 3 120-mm (4.7-in) (1×2, 1×1); 4 25-mm (1-in) (2×2) AA; 1 76-mm (3-in) A/S mortar; 120 depth charges *Crew:* 150

Minas Gerais

Brazilian light fleet carrier, built 1942-45. Laid down and launched as HMS *Vengeance* at the Swan Hunter yard at Wallsend-on-Tyne, the Brazilian navy's first aircraft carrier saw service on loan to the Royal Australian Navy before she was purchased from the British government in December 1956. Tenders for modernization had already been received from various shipyards and that submitted by the Dutch Verolme Dock, Rotterdam, was accepted, and work commenced during the summer of 1957. The reconstruction was more extensive than those attempted in other light fleet carriers. The port-side extension for the angled deck was larger than those given to *Karel Doorman* (rebuilt in Holland) or *Bonaventure, Melbourne* and *Vikrant* (all converted in Britain). The island was completely rebuilt as a rectangular box of considerably greater height, new lifts were installed and the numerous deck-edge gun sponsons were removed, with the exception of a position for a twin 40-mm (1.57-in) Bofors on the port side, aft. The only other gun armament comprised a quadruple 40-mm mounting above the navigating bridge and another at the same level at the after end of the island.

Between decks, the DC electrical system was replaced by an alternating-current system, compatible with the US Navy-pattern radar and ESM fit. The boilers were retubed and given more steam-producing capacity than was needed for her 40 000-shp turbines, to provide sufficient motive power for continuous operation of her steam catapult. When completed in December 1960 she was regarded by Royal Navy aircrew as being one of the best-equipped carriers in the world, in spite of her small size. *Minas Gerais*, as she was then renamed, had cost £3.2m to purchase from Britain and £9.65m to modernize.

It was a pity, therefore, that although Brazil had already bought aircraft for her, a protracted squabble between the air force, which operated the fixed-wing Grumman S-2A Trackers, and the navy, which was responsible for the Sikorsky SH-34J and SH-3D Sea King helicopters, was not resolved until the late 1960s, so that for the first years of her career she carried only helicopters as an ASW ship. Once the matter had been resolved, *Minas Gerais* soon became an extremely useful addition to the forces available to NATO in the Central Atlantic area.

Displacement: 15 890 tons (standard), 19 890 tons (full load) *Length:* 211.8 m (695 ft) oa *Beam:* 24.4 m (80 ft) wl, 36.9 m (121 ft) flight deck *Draught:* 7.8 m (25 ft 6 in) *Machinery:* 2-shaft geared steam turbines, 40 000 shp=25.3 knots (1960 trials) *Armament:* 10 40-mm (1.57-in) AA *Aircraft:* 20 maximum (antisubmarine types) *Crew:* 1300

Minotaur

British cruiser class, built 1943-45. Seven ships of the *Minotaur* Class were ordered under the 1941 Programme but only three, *Minotaur* (built by Harland and Wolff), *Swiftsure* (built by Vickers-Armstrong) and *Superb* (built by Swan Hunter) were completed to the original design. The remaining four, *Bellerophon, Defence, Blake* and *Tiger*, were suspended at the end of the war. The last named vessel was cancelled in 1946 but the remaining three were eventually completed to a substantially different design during 1959-61, the first pair having been renamed *Tiger* and *Lion*, respectively. Only *Swiftsure*, launched in 1943 and completed in 1944, was constructed in time to see any extensive war service. *Minotaur* and *Superb* were also launched in 1943 but due to labour shortages and other more urgent shipbuilding requirements they did not complete until 1945. It was intended that both these latter ships should be manned by the Royal Canadian Navy but in the event only *Minotaur* was transferred, and was renamed *Ontario.*

Basically they were the same as the *Fiji* Class cruisers but modified to incorporate war experience as applied in the earlier class. This involved increasing the beam by 0.3 m (1 ft) to improve stability and omitting *Fiji*'s X turret, the aircraft equipment and hangars to reduce topweight in order to allow for additional AA weapons, fire-control gear and electronic equipment. These alterations were partly made in the original design and partly while the ships were under construction. In all except *Minotaur* and *Swiftsure*, which were too far advanced, the beam was subsequently increased another foot to further improve stability.

In place of X turret they carried a fifth twin 4-in (102-mm) DP mounting while the 2-pdr armament was increased to four quadruple mountings, two abreast the bridge and two on the after superstructure. *Swiftsure* also carried 22 20-mm (0.79-in) AA (8×2, 6×1) on completion but in 1945 these were removed and replaced by 13 single 40-mm (1.57-in). In the 1950s her quadruple 2-pdr mountings were replaced by twin 40-mm mountings which gave her a uniform close-range armament. *Ontario* completed with a close-range AA armament of six single 40-mm and six single 20-mm, and *Superb* with six single 40-mm, two single 2-pdr and two single 20-mm in addition to their quadruple 2-pdr mountings. They also carried a very complete outfit of the latest gunnery and radar equipment which included three AA directors. *Swiftsure* carried the Mk IV AA director, while *Ontario* and *Superb* carried the later and more sophisticated Mk VI AA director.

Other improvements over the *Fiji* design included increasing the fuel stowage from 1700 to 1850 tons which gave higher endurance at economic speeds (12 900 km [8000 miles] compared with 9500 km [5900 miles] at ten knots) and improvements in damage-control and water-tight integrity.

Swiftsure served in the Home and Eastern Fleets before joining the British Pacific Fleet in 1945. She took part in the assault on

Okinawa, in March-May 1945, bombarded the island of Moen during a carrier assault on Truk in June 1945 and was part of the Hong Kong occupation force in August 1945. Shortly before the end of the war, *Ontario* also joined the Pacific Fleet but *Superb* was commissioned too late to see any war service. *Ontario* and *Superb* were sold for scrapping in 1960. *Swiftsure* was modernized, but when the work was nearly complete, the job was cancelled and she followed her sisters in 1962.

See also *Tiger*.

Displacement: 8800 tons (*Superb* 8885 tons) (standard), 11 480 tons (*Superb* 11 560 tons) (full load) *Length:* 169.3 m (555 ft 6 in) oa *Beam:* 19.2 m (63 ft) (*Superb* 19.5 m [64 ft]) *Draught:* 5.3 m (17 ft 3 in) *Machinery:* 4-shaft geared steam turbines, 72 500 shp=32.5 knots *Protection:* 89 mm (3.5 in) sides, 51-38 mm (2-1.5 in) decks, 51-25 mm (2-1 in) turrets. *Armament:* 9 6-in (152-mm) (3×3); 10 4-in (102-mm) (5×2); 16 2-pdr AA (4×4); 6 21-in (53-cm) torpedo tubes (2×3) *Crew:* 860

Mitscher

US destroyer leader class, built 1949-54. Intended as flagships for the destroyer squadrons, the *Mitscher* Class was designed to provide antiaircraft and antisubmarine protection to fast task forces, and incorporated the latest technology. The propulsion system used new turbines with a high power-to-weight ratio, giving them a top speed of 35 knots. They had a single 5-in (127-mm) of a new automatic model at either end with twin 3-in (76-mm)/50-cal AA guns (replaced by a 70-cal model in 1957-58) superimposed above them. Antisubmarine armament comprised a Weapon Alpha A/S mortar, which fired over the forward gun mountings, and four fixed torpedo tubes. The ships carried the most modern search radars and sonars.

Beginning in 1960 the class underwent a modification involving the removal of the after AA guns and the construction in their place of a small flight deck and hangar to enable them to operate two drone A/S helicopters (DASH).

Willis A Lee and *Wilkinson* were further modified to accommodate big prototype bow-mounted SQS 26 sonars. These, however, were not integrated with the ASW fire-control system, and in 1969 (by which time they had also lost their forward 76-mm [3-in] mounting and A/S mortar) it was decided that they lacked the advanced A/S weapons which would have justified their retention. They were therefore placed in reserve.

In 1966-69, however, *Mitscher* and *John S McCain* had undergone a major conversion which changed their status to guided-missile destroyers (DDG). The helicopter hangar and flight deck were replaced by a Mk 13 launcher for Tartar surface-to-air missiles mounted above a cylindrical magazine. The forward 76-mm mounting and the A/S mortar were replaced by an Asroc A/S missile launcher. Heavy lattice masts placed above funnels carried a new sensor array dominated by the big SPS-48 three-dimensional radar on the mainmast. Finally, the old fixed A/S torpedo tubes were replaced by the more modern Mk 32 triple tubes, shipped abreast the second funnel. Although the two DDGs remained active in the late 1970s their conversion is not regarded as particularly successful because of the increase in topweight which resulted.

Displacement: 3675 tons (standard), 4730 tons (full load) (1969, 5155 tons [full load]) *Length:* 150.3 m (493 ft) *Beam:* 15.2 m (50 ft) *Draught:* 6.4 m (21 ft) *Machinery:* 2-shaft steam turbines, 75 000 shp=35 knots *Armament:* 2 127-mm (5-in) Mk 42 (2×1); 4 76-mm (3-in)/50-cal (2×2) (70-cal from 1957-58); 4 20-mm (0.79-in) AA; 1 Weapon Alpha A/S mortar; 4 A/S torpedo tubes (fixed) *Crew:* 378

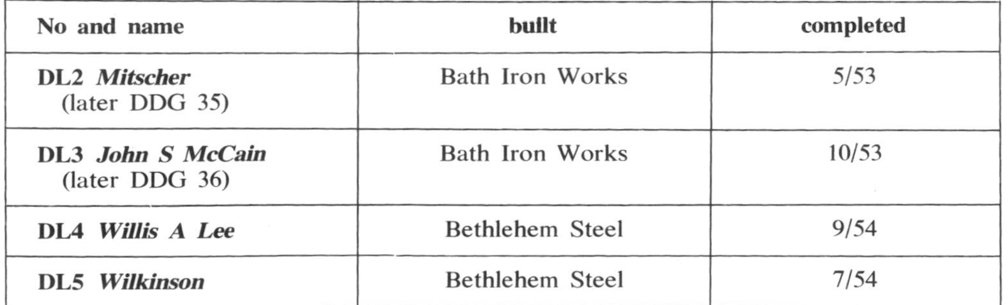

No and name	built	completed
DL2 *Mitscher* (later DDG 35)	Bath Iron Works	5/53
DL3 *John S McCain* (later DDG 36)	Bath Iron Works	10/53
DL4 *Willis A Lee*	Bethlehem Steel	9/54
DL5 *Wilkinson*	Bethlehem Steel	7/54

Mjölner

Swedish coastal-destroyer class, built 1941-42. As an emergency measure in 1941 four small destroyers were built to a design based on the Italian-built *Romulus* Class bought the year before. They were simple and easy to build, and did not represent a logical evolution of Swedish destroyer design. *Mode* (73) and *Magne* (74) were built by Gotaverken, *Munin* (75) was built by Öresundsvarvet and *Mjölner* (76) was built by Eriksberg. In the mid-1950s they were rerated from *kustjagare* to *fregatter*, with torpedo tubes removed and depth-charge throwers and a sonar added. They were stricken from 1967.

Displacement: 700 tons (standard), 900 tons (full load) *Length:* 78 m (256 ft) oa *Beam:* 8 m (26 ft 3 in) *Draught:* 2.3 m (7 ft 7 in) *Machinery:* 2-shaft geared steam turbines, 16 000 shp=30 knots *Armament:* 3 (*Munin* 2) 10.5-cm (4.1-in) Bofors (3×1); 2 40-mm (1.57-in)/60-cal Bofors AA (2×1); 2 20-mm (0.79-in) Bofors AA (2×1); 3 53-cm (21-in) torpedo tubes (1×3) (removed 1954-55) *Crew:* 100

Molch

German midget submarine. The Molch (salamander) was built during the Second World War by Lübecker Flenderwerft, and was one of the earlier types of midget. It was a one-man type, intended to operate fully submerged. It had a long cylindrical body with the conning position set right aft. Two G7e torpedoes were slung underneath. Submerged endurance was about 65 km (40 miles) at 5 knots.

In all 390 were built. They were not apparently used off the Normandy invasion beaches, but large numbers were captured in Denmark and Norway.

Displacement: 11 tonnes *Length:* 10.8 m (35 ft 6 in) *Beam:* 1.8 m (6 ft) *Draught:* 1.8 m (6 ft) *Machinery:* 1-shaft electric motor, 13 shp=5 knots *Armament:* 2 53-cm (21-in) torpedoes *Crew:* 1

Montana

US battleship class. Authorized in 1940 but cancelled in 1943, the *Montana* Class was the last battleship class to be planned. They were the most powerful US capital ships ever projected, and would have been the world's second largest battleships after the Japanese *Yamoto* Class. Following the fast but

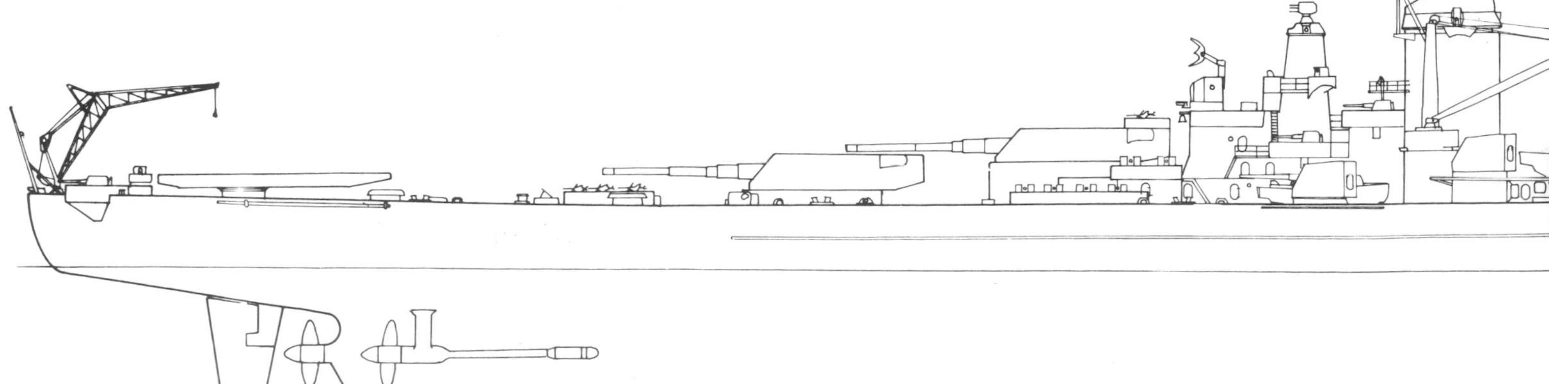

lightly protected *Iowa* Class, there was a reversion to heavy armour and modest speed, to provide main battle units rather than fast carrier escorts. The general lines of *Iowa* were followed in the *Montana* design, but an extra triple 16-in (406-mm) turret was to be mounted aft, and *North Carolina's* armour distribution was to be followed. It was calculated that the 409-259-mm (16.1-10.2-in) tapered belt and the 152-mm (6-in) deck would provide an immunity zone between 16 500-28 300 m (18 000-31 000 yards) against 16-in gunfire. An underwater bulge was provided, with a triple bottom against mines and explosions beneath the keel.

Five ships were projected, *Montana* (BB.67) and *Ohio* (BB.68) to be built by Philadelphia navy yard, *Maine* (BB.69) and *New Hampshire* (BB.71) by New York navy yard and *Louisiana* (BB.70) by Norfolk navy yard. Although orders were placed in May 1940, the colossal size and the thickness of armour plates posed severe technical problems. The US war economy was hit by a severe steel shortage in 1943, and as they had still not been started they were officially cancelled in July of that year.

Displacement: 60 500 tons (standard), 70 500 tons (full load) *Length:* 282 m (925 ft) *Beam:* 36.93 m (121 ft 2 in) *Draught:* 11.23 m (36 ft 10 in) max *Machinery:* 4-shaft geared steam turbines, 172 000 shp=28 knots *Protection:* 409-259 mm (16 1-10.2 in) belt, 155-147 mm (6.1-5.8 in) decks, 457 mm (18 in) turrets *Armament:* 12 16-in (406-mm)/50-cal Mk 7 (4×3); 20 5-in (127-mm)/54-cal Mk 16 (10×2); 32 40-mm (1.57-in)/56-cal Bofors AA (8×4); 20 20-mm (0.79-in)/70-cal Oerlikon (20×1) *Crew:* 2247

Murasame

Japanese destroyer class, built 1958-59. The three destroyers of this class (known as the 'Rain' Class) were ordered to a Japanese design for the Maritime Self Defence Force (MSDF) in the mid-1950s. *Murasame* (shower) and *Yudachi* (evening shower) were ordered under the 1956 Programme and the *Harusame* (spring rain) under the 1957 Programme. Except for the armament and radar the main components were all built in Japan. *Murasame* was fitted with Mitsubishi-Escher-Weiss turbines and Mitsubishi boilers; *Yudachi* and *Harusame* with Kaupon-Ishikawajima-type turbines and boilers.

No and name	laid down	launched	completed	builder
DD107 *Murasame*	12/1957	7/1958	2/1959	Mitsubishi, Nagasaki
DD108 *Yudachi*	12/1957	7/1958	3/1959	Ishikawajima, Tokyo
DD109 *Harusame*	6/1958	6/1959	12/1959	Uraga

The destroyers were designed as general-purpose vessels with an adequate surface and antisubmarine armament. This has become obsolete since the vessels were first completed and they have been updated with more modern AA and A/S equipment and fire-control systems. The forward twin 3-in (76-mm) AA mount in B position has been mounted in a turret, and in September 1975 *Murasame* had her obsolete depth-charge equipment removed and the two Mk 32 torpedo tubes replaced by two triple tubes. Two sonar sets are carried; a hull-mounted SQS29, and a variable-depth OQA-1 added in 1968 and operated from a well in the stern.

The gunnery system is of pure US design and consists of three 5-in (127-mm)/54-cal guns in single mounts in A, X and Y positions. Fire control is exercised through a US Mk 57 and 63 system directed by a Mk 34 radar. Air-warning radar consists of an OPS-1 set, and surface warning an OPS-15 set.

Displacement: 1800 tons (standard), 2500 tons (full load) *Length:* 108 m (354 ft 4 in) oa *Beam:* 11 m (36 ft) *Draught:* 3.7 m (12 ft 2 in) *Machinery:* 2-shaft geared turbines, 30 000 shp=30 knots *Armament:* 3 5-in (127-mm); 4 3-in (76-mm) (2×2); 2 Mk 32 torpedo tubes (6 in *Murasame* [2×3]); 1 Hedgehog (not in *Murasame*); 1 depth-charge rack (not in *Murasame*) *Crew:* 250

Näcken

Swedish submarine class. In the early 1960s the Swedish naval staff initiated studies for a new type of boat to replace the ageing *Hajen* Class. In the resulting A.14 type the crew was reduced by almost half, from the 44 men required in the *Hajen*. This was achieved through a high degree of automation, using a digital computer not only to coordinate weapon control but also for monitoring the batteries, and for engine control and weight compensation. The automatic control system was devised by Saab-Scania.

All three boats of the *Näcken* Class were ordered from Kockums at Malmö, and *Näcken* made history on April 17, 1978, by being the first Swedish submarine to be lowered into the water by crane. *Najad* and *Neptun* were planned to be launched in 1979. The boats will carry the recognition letters NÄC, NAJ, and NEP.

The armament comprises eight 53-cm (21-in) TP61 wire-guided torpedoes, using data supplied by a large passive sonar mounted in the bow. The TP61 torpedo is unusual in using high-test peroxide (HTP) for higher thermal efficiency to give greater range and speed. The TP61 may eventually be replaced by the Mk 42 free-running homing torpedo.

The general configuration of the *Sjöormen* Class has been followed, with its unusual X-form rudders and diving planes aft. It is claimed that this arrangement gives better results than the normal cruciform arrangement found in other navies' submarines. The *Näcken* Class are propelled by Stirling closed-cycle engines, which may also be used for the projected A-17 version.

Displacement: 1078/1303 tons (surfaced/submerged) *Length:* 49.5 m (162 ft 5 in) oa *Beam:* 5.7 m (18 ft 8 in) *Draught:* 5.5 m (18 ft 1 in)

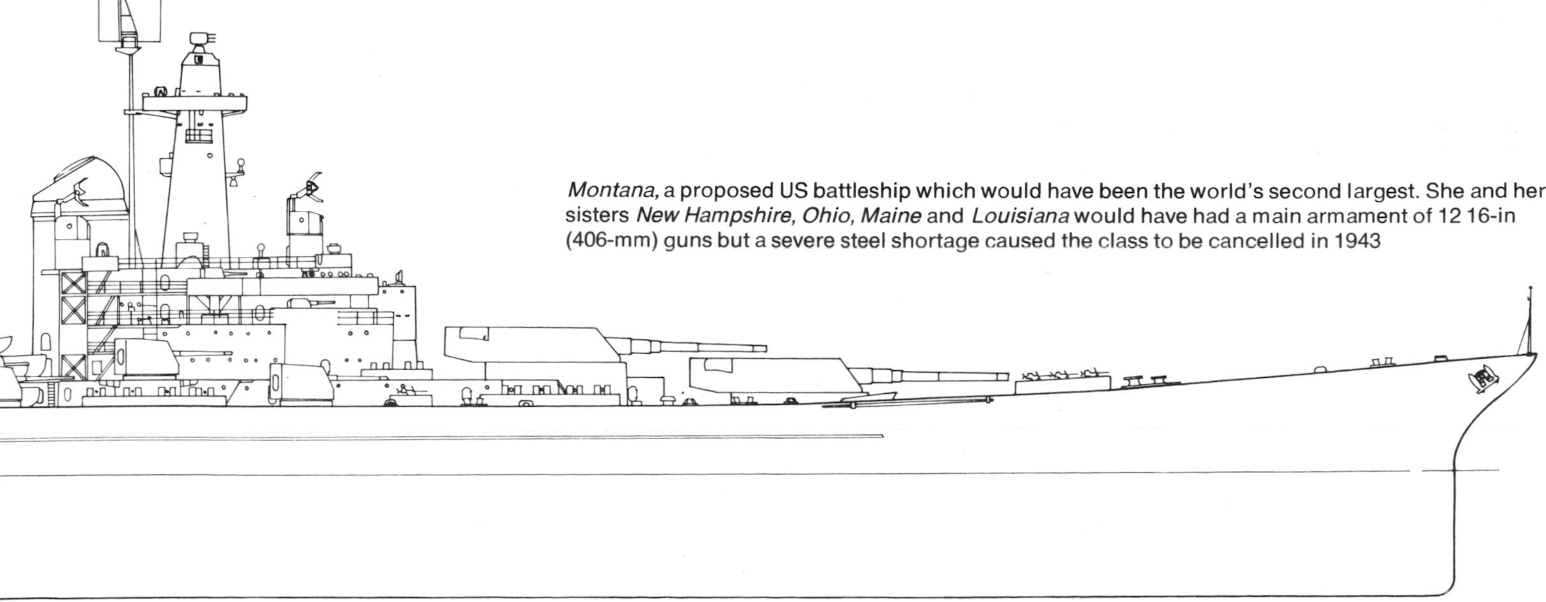

Montana, a proposed US battleship which would have been the world's second largest. She and her sisters *New Hampshire, Ohio, Maine* and *Louisiana* would have had a main armament of 12 16-in (406-mm) guns but a severe steel shortage caused the class to be cancelled in 1943

Kockums

The launch of the Swedish submarine *Näcken*. She uses a digital computer for crew tasks

Machinery: 1-shaft diesel/electric (bhp not known)=20/20 knots (surfaced/submerged) *Armament:* 8 53-cm (21-in) torpedo tubes (bow) *Crew:* 19

Narval

French submarine class, built 1951-60. As soon as French shipyards had been rebuilt after the devastation of the Second World War, a new class of modern hunter-killer submarines was ordered, based on the German Type XXI and on Allied wartime experience. Two boats were ordered under the 1949 budget, with a further two under the following year's budget. These boats were built in seven prefabricated 10-m (33-ft) sections, but the last two boats, ordered under the 1954 budget, were built at different yards by conventional methods.

The original diesel-electric propulsion system of two Schneider 4000-hp 7-cylinder 2-stroke diesels was replaced in a reconstruction programme phased over the years 1965-70, carried out at Lorient arsenal. The new propulsion system uses three SEMT-Pielstick 12-cylinder diesels driving two electric motors developing 1500 hp each, and two 40-hp cruising motors. During the reconstruction the submarines were equipped with a new streamlined sail housing the periscope standards. A new weapons system and modern sensors were fitted, and the two stern tubes were removed. The boats are fitted with Thomson-CSF DUUA-1 sonar. The *Narval* Class are spacious boats, and have proved popular and successful in the Marine Nationale.

Displacement: 1640/1910 tons (surfaced/submerged) *Length:* 78 m (256 ft) oa *Beam:* 7.2 m (23 ft 7 in) *Draught:* 5.5 m (18 ft) *Machinery:* 2-shaft diesels/2 electric motors, 4000 bhp/5000 hp=16/18 knots (surfaced/submerged) *Armament:* 8 55-cm (21.7-in) torpedo tubes (6 bow, 2 stern), 22 torpedoes *Crew:* 68

No and name	builder	launched	completed
S.631 ***Narval***	Cherbourg arsenal	12/54	12/57
S.632 ***Marsouin***	Cherbourg arsenal	5/55	10/57
S.633 ***Dauphin***	Cherbourg arsenal	9/55	8/58
S.634 ***Requin***	Cherbourg arsenal	12/55	8/58
S.637 ***Espadon***	Normand, Le Havre	9/58	4/60
S.638 ***Morse***	Seine Maritime	12/58	5/60

Narwhal

US submarine. The nuclear attack submarine *Narwhal*, authorized under the 1964 Programme, was laid down in January 1966 by the Electric Boat division of General Dynamics. She was launched in September 1967 and completed in July 1969. She is powered by a single prototype S5G General Electric nuclear reactor which uses circulation cooling plant, instead of the noisy pumped system. The hull design is generally similar to the *Sturgeon* Class.

Narwhal is fitted with a fully comprehensive electronic weapons-control system, including a BQS-8 upward-looking sonar set for missions under the Polar ice cap, as well as active BQS-6 and passive BQR-7 sonars. The torpedo control system consists of a Mk 113 Mod 6 fire-control system (due to be replaced by the Mk 117 system). Anti-submarine weapons carried include A/S torpedoes and Subroc, and the boat is to be fitted with the Harpoon missile system.

Displacement: 4450/5350 tons (surfaced/submerged) *Length:* 95.9 m (314 ft 6 in) oa *Beam:* 13.1 m (43 ft) *Draught:* 8.2 m (27 ft) *Machinery:* 1 shaft, 1 pressurized water-cooled nuclear reactor, 2 steam turbines, 17 000 shp=20+/30+ knots (surfaced/submerged) *Armament:* 4 21-in (53-cm) torpedo tubes, A/S torpedoes, Subroc *Crew:* 107

Nasty

Norwegian motor torpedo boat class, built 1957-66. As a private venture the Norwegian company Boat Services AS built a prototype MTB, armed with four 21-in (53-cm) torpedo tubes and capable of 45 knots. The hull was built of two layers of mahogany, with a layer of fibreglass between, and the keel and decks were made of ash, while the twin turbo-charged Napier Deltic diesel engines were imported from Britain. The trials of *Nasty* attracted great attention, and it was not long before the Royal Norwegian Navy placed orders for 12 boats followed by eight more, and known as the *Tjeld* Class.

The prototype was sent to the United States for demonstrations, and as the US Navy was going through one of its many short-lived flirtations with high-speed attack craft, 14 more were ordered. A further eight ships were ordered, two by Turkey and six by Greece.

Norwegian boats: *Tjeld* (P.343), *Skarv* (P.344), *Teist* (P.345), *Jo* (P.346), *Lom* (P.347), *Stegg* (P.348), *Hauk* (P.349), *Falk* (P.350), *Ravn* (P.357), *Skrei* (P.380), *Hai* (P.381), *Sel* (P.382), *Hval* (P.383), *Laks* (P.384), *Knurr* (P.385), *Delfin* (P.386), *Lyr* (P.387), *Grib* (P.388), *Geir* (P.389), *Erle* (P.390)
US boats: *PTF.3* (ex-*PT.812*), *PTF.4* (ex-*PT.813*), *PTF.5-16*
Turkish boats: *Dogan* (ex-Norwegian *Hugin*), *Marti* (ex-Norwegian *Munin*)
Greek boats: *Andromeda*, *Inionos*, *Kastor*, *Kykonos*, *Pigassos*, *Toxotis*

The US Navy used its motor torpedo boats in Vietnam. *PTF.4* was sunk on November 4, 1965, *PTF.9* on March 7, 1961, *PTF.14* and *PTF.15* on April 22, *PTF.8* on June 16 and *PTF.16* on August 19. *PTF.13* was stricken in 1972, as was the Greek *Inionos*. The two Turkish boats were stricken a year later, and by 1977 the last of the USN boats had been stricken or transferred to reserve units. The Norwegian and Greek boats were not expected to last long after 1978 as they were near the age limit for light wooden hulls.

Displacement: 70 tons (standard), 82 tons (full load) *Length:* 24.5 m (80 ft 4 in) oa *Beam:* 7.5 m (24 ft 6 in) *Draught:* 2.1 m (6 ft 10 in) *Machinery:* 2-shaft diesel, 6200 bhp=45 knots *Armament:* 4 21-in (53-cm) torpedo tubes (4×1); 1 40-mm (1.57-in); 1 20-mm (0.79-in) *Crew:* 18

Nautilus

US nuclear submarine, built 1952-54. Funds for the construction of the world's first nuclear-powered submarine were approved by Congress in Fiscal Year 1952. Work had started in 1948 on a submarine thermal reactor (STR), and *Nautilus* (SSN. 571) was finally given an STR Mk II reactor built by Westinghouse, later designated S2W.

Although commissioned on September 30, 1954, she put to sea for the first time on January 17, 1955, and flashed the historic message 'Under way on nuclear power.' She proceeded to shatter long-standing records while exploring the possibilities opened up by nuclear propulsion. On her shakedown cruise she ran 2090 km (1300 miles) submerged from New London to Puerto Rico, averaging 16 knots. On August 3, 1958, she made the first submerged passage under the North Pole in the course of another record run from Pearl Harbor, Hawaii, to Portland, England, by the polar route.

The design of *Nautilus* was relatively unsophisticated by later standards, being merely an enlargement of the conventional *Tang* Class to permit the installation of the bulky reactor, heat-exchanger and two-shaft steam turbines. Six torpedo tubes were fitted, with a big BQS-4 passive sonar in the bow. Nuclear power freed the submarine from the need to recharge batteries, either by the dangerous means of surfacing at night or the uncomfortable process of snorkelling, and its cruise was limited only by the endurance of the crew and the supply of fresh water and provisions. In April 1957 *Nautilus* decommissioned to allow the reactor to receive a new core, after she had logged 100684 km (62562 miles); the second core lasted for 146971 km (91324 miles) and the third installed in 1964, lasted for approximately 241000 km (150000 miles). Her biggest problem was noise, and it was reported that her cooling pumps could be heard 16 km (10 miles) away.

In her day *Nautilus* was credited with staggering speeds, up to 30 knots underwater. She was, in fact, never good for more than 20 knots, though this was still more than any submarine had ever achieved before, and could be maintained for long periods. Unfortunately it set a precedent, and ever-higher fictitious speeds for nuclear submarines have been quoted since.

After nearly 25 years of hard work *Nautilus* was beginning to show signs of age, and was expected to decommission in 1979. She was overhauled in 1972-74 at the Electric Boat company yard at Groton, Connecticut and has since been engaged in experiments in submarine communications. It is highly likely that this historic ship will be preserved as a memorial to the birth of nuclear power at sea and to her patron, Admiral Hyman G Rickover.

Displacement: 3764/4040 tons (surfaced/submerged) *Length:* 98.7 m (323 ft 9 in) oa *Beam:* 8.4 m (27 ft 8 in) *Draught:* 6.7 m (22 ft) mean *Machinery:* nuclear reactor, 2-shaft steam turbines, 15000 shp=20/18 knots (surfaced/submerged) *Armament:* 6 21-in (53-cm) torpedo tubes (bow), at least 18 torpedoes *Crew:* 105

Neger

German midget submarine. As part of plans to defeat an Allied amphibious landing several designs for one-man midgets were drawn up during the Second World War. The Neger (negro) was basically a torpedo carrier. The upper body was made of the propulsive section and a cockpit for the operator, while a torpedo was slung underneath. The motor and batteries were from a T3a electric torpedo (designated T3b), and the torpedo was the standard G7e.

About 200 Negers were made, and they were used at Anzio and Normandy. Originally the cockpit was open, as the craft could not submerge, but it was later fitted with a Plexiglas dome. No breathing apparatus was used.

The only reported success of the Negers was the sinking of the destroyer HMS *Isis* off Normandy on July 20, 1944.

Displacement: 5 tons *Length:* 7.65 m (25 ft 1 in) oa *Beam:* 0.53 m (1 ft 9 in) *Draught:* 0.5 m (1 ft 8 in) *Machinery:* 1-shaft electric, 12 shp=4.2/3.2 knots (surfaced/submerged) *Armament:* 1 53-cm (21-in) torpedo *Crew:* 1

Nimitz

US nuclear-powered aircraft carrier class. As a result of the expense involved in building the world's first nuclear-powered aircraft carrier, USS *Enterprise*, launched in 1960, the US Navy reverted to oil-fired boilers for its next two carriers, *America* and *John F Kennedy*. In 1965 a design contract was awarded to Newport News, the only US shipyard capable of building such vessels, for the design of a new nuclear-propelled carrier, powered by only two Westinghouse A4W pressurized-water-cooled nuclear reactors.

The new carrier, to be named *Nimitz* (CVN.68) was ordered in Fiscal Year 1967 and laid down at Newport News on June 22, 1968. Problems with the nuclear reactors delayed her completion by almost two years, and she was finally launched on May 13, 1972 and commissioned three years later on May 3 1975. A second ship, *Dwight D Eisenhower*, (CVN.69), was authorized in FY-1970 and laid down on August 14, 1970. Her completion was also delayed by reactor problems, and she was not launched until October 11, 1975, and was commissioned on October 10, 1977. The third member of the class, *Carl*

The nuclear-powered carrier USS *Nimitz* launches a Grumman Intruder as she cruises in formation with the USS *California* in the Mediterranean

US Navy

Vinson (CVN.70), was laid down on October 11, 1975. Originally due to be launched in March 1979 and commissioned in 1981, her completion has been delayed by contractual problems between the builders and the navy.

The design of the *Nimitz* Class was closely based on that of the *America*, with three starboard deck-edge lifts, two forward and one aft of the superstructure, and another aft on the port side, though the absence of necessity for exhaust uptakes permits a smaller island. Four steam catapults are provided for the two flight decks. No sonar is fitted, though they are equipped with the Naval Tactical Data System and SPS-10 surface search and SPS-43A two-dimensional and SPS-48 three-dimensional air search radars. Normal aircraft complement of up to 100 includes two fighter squadrons of F-4 Phantoms or F-14 Tomcats, two attack squadrons of A-7 Corsairs and one medium attack squadron of A-16 Intruders plus S-3 Viking antisubmarine aircraft, SH-3 Sea King A/S helicopters (to be replaced by the new Lamps helicopter), and RA-5C Vigilante reconnaissance, EA-6B Prowler and E-2 Hawkeye AEW and KA-6 tanker aircraft. Armament comprises three Basic Point Defence Missile System launchers with Sea Sparrow missiles. With their nuclear cores estimated to need replacement only once every 13 years, these vessels have a theoretical maximum range of up to one million miles at full speed.

Since entering service the *Nimitz* has been assigned to the US 6th Fleet in the Atlantic, her first deployment being in a naval exercise in July 1976. Since then she has participated in a number of US Navy and NATO exercises. *Dwight D Eisenhower* had not been assigned by the end of 1978.

The *Nimitz* Class, the largest warships in the world, are intended to serve well into the twenty-first century, with a projected life of 45 years. They were planned to be augmented by further members, with authorization planned for a fourth member in FY-1979 and a fifth two years later, in order to maintain a minimum force of 12 aircraft carriers (the navy had planned for 14 or 15), but the US government's desire to reduce defence expenditure has led to alternative designs being prepared for smaller carriers under the project title CVNX. These would carry about two-thirds the number of aircraft maintained by the *Nimitz*, and would presumably carry the new McDonnell Douglas F-18 Hornet rather than the more powerful but prohibitively expensive F-14 Tomcat. There would also be little room for antisubmarine helicopters or even fixed-wing A/S aircraft. However, the work involved in preparing a new design would result in the cost of these smaller and less capable carriers being not much less than that of the *Nimitz* Class ships—approximately $2000 million each.

Displacement: 81 600 tons (standard), 91 400 tons (full load) *Length:* 333 m (1092 ft) oa *Beam:* 40.84 m (134 ft) *Draught:* 11.27 m (37 ft) *Reactors:* 2 Westinghouse A4W pressurized-water cooled *Machinery:* 4-shaft geared steam turbines, 280 000 shp=30+ knots *Armament:* 3 BPDMS Sea Sparrow Missile launchers *Crew:* 3300 plus 3000 Air Group Personnel

Niteroi

Brazilian destroyer class, built 1972-78. The general layout of the six Brazilian destroyers closely resembles that of the British *Sheffield* Class (Type 42) guided-missile destroyers. The major difference between these two classes lies in the system of propulsion. In *Sheffield* and the other new Royal Navy designs (*Amazon* and *Broadsword* Class frigates) the Admiralty has settled on the COGOG (combined gas-turbine or gas-turbine) system whereas the Brazilians have opted for the CODOG (combined diesel or gas-turbine) arrangement. The Brazilian destroyers' machinery is controlled by an automated system which results in a considerable saving of manpower. The commands 'start', 'stop' and 'astern' and the mode of propulsion (gas-turbine, diesel, or a combination of both) are selected by push button, while a

No and name	completed
F40 *Niteroi*	11/76
F41 *Defensora*	3/77
F42 *Independencia*	3/78
F43 *União*	10/78
F44 *Constituicão*	2/78
F45 *Liberal*	8/78

PPL

Left: The Brazilian destroyer *Niteroi*. Built by Vosper Thornycroft as an A/S vessel, she has an Ikara A/S system, A/S torpedoes and a Bofors rocket launcher. *Below:* The *Niteroi* Class destroyer *Constituicão* during trials in 1978

Vosper Thornycroft

single control column regulates the power required. The diesel and gas-turbine units are controlled by a computer which responds to commands from the push buttons and control column.

The class is divided into two distinct groups. *Niteroi, Defensora, Constituicão* and *Liberal* were built by Vosper Thornycroft and were completed as A/S vessels; *Independencia* and *União* were built by the Arsenal de Marinho, Rio de Janeiro as general-purpose destroyers. The A/S units are armed with the Ikara weapon system on the quarter-deck with the missile magazine, holding about 12 missiles, sited immediately forward of the launcher under the helicopter flight deck. These ships also have two sets of triple Mk 32 A/S torpedo tubes abreast the helicopter hangar, and a Bofors rocket launcher in front of the bridge. Surface armament consists of a single 4.5-in (114-mm) gun in A position. The general-purpose ships are armed with a second 4.5-in gun in place of the Ikara, and carry two single 40-mm (1.57-in) Bofors abreast the bridge. All the ships are armed with the close-range Seacat missile system, while *Constituicão* and *Liberal* also carry four Exocet missile launchers.

Displacement: 3200 tons (standard), 3800 tons (full load) *Length:* 129.2 m (424 ft) oa *Beam:* 13.5 m (44 ft 3 in) *Draught:* 5.6 m (18 ft 3 in) *Machinery:* 2-shaft CODOG, 2 Rolls-Royce Olympus gas turbines, 56 000 bhp=30 knots, 4 MTU diesels, 18 000 shp=22 knots *Armament:* (A/S units) 1 Ikara launcher; 2 36-cm (14-in) Bofors A/S rocket launchers (1×2); 6 torpedo tubes Mk 32 (2×3); 6 Seacat launchers (2×3); 1 4.5-in (114-mm); 1 Lynx A/S helicopter; (GP units) 2 4.5-in (114-mm); 4 Exocet launchers; 2 40-mm (1.57-in) Bofors; 6 Seacat launchers (2×3); 2 torpedo tubes Mk 32; 1 Lynx A/S helicopter *Crew:* 200

Northampton

US command cruiser, completed 1953. Laid down in August 1944 as one of the *Oregon City* Class of 8-in (203-mm) gun cruisers, *Northampton* was 57% complete when she was cancelled 12 months later. Construction was resumed in mid-1948 when she was redesigned to serve as a flagship for fast-carrier task forces or for amphibious assault groups. The hull was raised by one deck to provide additional office space, and the superstructure reduced to two blocks with the single funnel between. All living and working spaces were fully air-conditioned, and the ship could be closed down in the event of nuclear attack.

CLC.1 *Northampton* was commissioned in March 1953. Her external appearance was dominated by the most extensive and comprehensive electronics and communications equipment carried by a warship of that period. A massive diamond-shaped SPS-2 air-search scanner—the largest seaborne radar in the world—was carried on the forward radar tower, with a smaller search aerial (later replaced by an SPS-37) on the main-mast and an SPS-8 height-finding radar below it on the after superstructure. A variety of pole masts carried communications antennae, including one of 38 m (125 ft)—the tallest unsupported mast on any ship. Information from these antennae was coordinated for command purposes in an elaborate combat information centre.

US Navy

USS *Northampton* (CLC.1) showing her diamond-shaped SPS-2 air-search radar scanner

Armament was restricted to a few AA weapons. Four of the new single 5-in (127-mm)/54-cal Mk 42 guns were carried, two forward and two aft. On either side of the funnel were two twin 3-in (76-mm)/50-cal mountings, but these were soon replaced by a new enclosed 70-cal mounting.

During the 1950s *Northampton* served as flagship of the 6th Fleet (1954-55) and the 2nd Fleet (1955-61). In 1961 she was made available for use by the National Authorities and was reclassified as a tactical command cruiser (CC.1). In 1962 the 3-in mountings were removed because of maintenance problems and to provide additional space for berthing and electronics. The SPS-2 scanner was removed the following year, and was later replaced by a large dish-shaped aerial, which *Northampton* carried until she decommissioned in August 1970. The 1960s also saw the removal of the remainder of the armament except for a single mounting in X position. A helicopter deck was marked out aft, but although two helicopters could be operated no hangar space or maintenance facilities were provided.

Displacement: 14 700 tons (standard), 17 200 tons (full load) *Length:* 206 m (675 ft 10 in) oa *Beam:* 21 m (68 ft 11 in) *Draught:* 8.8 m (28 ft 10 in) *Machinery:* 4-shaft steam turbines, 120 000 shp=32 knots *Protection:* 152 mm (6 in) side, 76-51 mm (3-2 in) decks *Armament:* 4 5-in (127-mm) DP (4×1); 8 3-in (76-mm) AA (4×2) *Crew:* 1675

Oberon

British submarine class, built 1957-78. The original 13 boats were laid down in 1957-62, launched between 1959-64, and completed between 1961-64. The orders were placed with yards with a tradition of submarine construction.

S.09 *Oberon*, S.14 *Onslaught*, S.17 *Ocelot*, S.21 *Onyx*—built by Chatham dockyard
S.10 *Odin*, S.16 *Oracle*, S.19 *Opossum*—built by Cammell Laird, Birkenhead
S.11 *Orpheus*, S.12 *Olympus*, S.13 *Osiris*—built by Vickers-Armstrongs, Barrow
S.15 *Otter*, S.18 *Otus*, S.20 *Opportune*—built by Scotts, Greenock

The basic design is identical to that of their predecessors, the *Porpoise* Class, from which they can scarcely be distinguished. They can undertake continuous submerged patrols in any part of the world. High underwater speed, great diving depth and long endurance are their outstanding features. They have a prominent bow-mounted sonar dome in addition to a surveillance radar,

The *Oberon* Class submarine HMS *Osiris* leaving Portsmouth harbour in 1975

MOD

which can detect surface ships and aircraft while the submarine is at periscope depth. Eight torpedo tubes for 21-in (53-cm) homing torpedoes are mounted, six in the bow and two in the stern. Propulsion is by Admiralty Standard Range Diesels when snorting or surfaced, and by English Electric motors while submerged. The class has earned high praise for its quiet operation.

Apart from a slight reduction in crew, the most significant advance over their predecessors was the use of glass-fibre laminate in the construction of the fin (that of *Orpheus* is of light aluminium alloy). The design had many attractive features for other countries with deep waters to patrol, and in 1962 the Royal Canadian Navy placed an order for three boats with Chatham dockyard. The first of these was obtained from the Royal Navy construction programme, *Onyx* being launched as HMCS *Ojibwa* (72) in February 1964, and commissioned in 1965. A replacement *Onyx* was ordered from Cammell Laird, commissioning in 1967. *Ojibwa* was followed by *Onondaga* (73) and *Okanagan* (74), laid down during 1964-65 and completed during 1967-68. Special RCN requirements included an enlargement of de-icing and air-conditioning systems to cope with the extremes of climate within Canadian operating areas.

Four boats were ordered in 1963 for the Royal Australian Navy. Named *Oxley* (S.57), *Otway* (S.59), *Ovens* (S.70) and *Onslow* (S.50), they were laid down at Scotts between 1964-67, launched between 1965-68, and commissioned during 1967-69. A follow-up order for two further boats, *Orion* and *Otama*—also from Scotts—was announced in 1970. Laid down in 1972-73, they were launched in 1974-75 and completed 1977-78.

An order for two boats for Brazil, *Humaita* (S.20) and *Tonelero* (S.21), was placed with Vickers in 1969. They were laid down in 1970-71, but whereas *Humaita* commissioned in 1973, *Tonelero* was badly damaged by fire and was not completed until 1976. Meanwhile a third boat, *Riachuelo* (S.22), had been laid down at Vickers in 1973 and was commissioned in 1977. At about the same time as the first Brazilian order, two submarines were ordered by Chile from Scotts. *O'Brien* (SS.22) and *Hyatt* (SS.23) were laid down in 1971-72, launched in 1973-74 and completed in 1976.

Displacement: 1610 tons (standard), 2030/2410 tons (surfaced/submerged) *Length:* 90 m (295 ft 3 in) oa *Beam:* 8 m (26 ft 3 in) *Draught:* 5.5 m (18 ft) *Machinery:* 2 shafts, 2 ASR diesels/electric motors, 3680 bhp/6000 shp=12/17 knots (surfaced/submerged) *Armament:* 8 21-in (53-cm) torpedo tubes (6 bow, 2 stern) *Crew:* 68

Ognevoi

Soviet destroyer class. Design work on the class began in 1937, and out of some 30 projected vessels, 17 are known to have been laid down between 1939-41. *Otlichny*, *Otvazhny*, *Odarenny* and four unnamed ships were laid down at Nikolayev, Leningrad; *Ognevoi*, *Ozornoi*, *Opasny* and *Otverzhdenny* were laid down on the Black Sea; *Osmotritelny* and *Okhotlivy* were laid down at Molotovsk; and *Vlastny*, *Vnushitelny* and *Vynoslivy* were laid down at Komsomolsk on the Amur river.

Higher freeboard and the concentration of the four 130-mm (5.1-in) guns into twin turrets fore and aft resulted in a significant improvement in seaworthiness over their Italian-designed predecessors. As in the experimental *Opitny* the torpedo armament was increased to two banks of four tubes. A twin 85-mm (3.3-in) enclosed mounting was superimposed above the after 130-mm turret, and the AA armament was completed by six single 37-mm (1.46-in), with two mountings abreast the bridge and four around the second funnel. Eighty mines could be carried.

Opasny was destroyed on the stocks at Nikolayev by the Germans in 1941, and three further ships building at Leningrad were never completed. Of the remaining vessels, between eight and 11 were completed after the war, while the remainder were cancelled. Search radars were added to the foremast, and tripod legs added but the appearance of the class remained otherwise unaltered. By the mid 1960s the few ships left in commission were used only for training.

Displacement: 1800 tons (standard), 2650 tons (full load) *Length:* 117 m (383 ft 10 in) oa *Beam:* 11.6 m (38 ft 1 in) *Draught:* 4.2 m (13 ft 9 in) *Machinery:* 2-shaft steam turbines, 60 000 shp=36 knots *Armament:* 4 130-mm (5.1-in)

The British *Oberon* Class were the last conventional vessels to enter service with the Royal Navy. They owed some of their design features to the successful German Type XXI Class and have the reputation of being the quietest submarines in service

The *Oberon* Class submarine HMS *Opportune* at anchor in June 1977 during the Jubilee Naval Review

(4×1); 1 85-mm (3.3-in) AA (1×2); 6 37-mm (1.46-in) AA (6×1); 8 53-cm (21-in) torpedo tubes (2×4); 80 mines *Crew:* 250

Ooshio

Japanese submarine class. In May 1959 Japan notified her intention of designing and building her third class of postwar submarines, comprising two boats. At the same time the director of the Japanese Defence Agency stated that Japan was studying the possibility of building a nuclear-powered submarine, though there has been no subsequent sign of that scheme becoming a reality.

The name-ship of this class, *Ooshio*, was finally ordered under the 1961 Programme. She was much larger than the previous two postwar submarine types and, with the increased dimensions and displacement, torpedo armament was doubled and comprehensive sonar and electronic control systems were installed. The vessels are much more seaworthy than the earlier boats and are capable of deep diving. With the double-hulled GUPPY-type design and powerful electric motors these vessels are capable of high underwater speed.

The boats were refitted and modernized during the mid 1970s, the two stern 21-in (53-cm) torpedo tubes being removed and the boats fitted with two 12.7-in (32-cm) A/S torpedoes in swim-out tubes.

Displacement: 1650 tons (*Ooshio*, 1600 tons) (standard) *Length:* 88 m (288 ft 9 in) *Beam:* 8.2 m (27 ft) *Draught:* 4.7 m (15 ft 5 in) *Machinery:* 2-shaft Kawasaki-MAN diesels/2 electric motors, 2300 bhp/6300 hp=14/18 knots (surfaced/submerged) *Armament:* 8 21-in (53-cm) torpedo tubes (6 bow, 2 stern) *Crew:* 80

No and name	completed
SS 561 *Ooshio*	4/65
SS 562 *Asashio*	10/66
SS 563 *Harushio*	12/67
SS 564 *Michishio*	9/68
SS 565 *Arashio*	7/69

Opitny

Soviet destroyer, built 1936-41. *Opitny* was constructed as an experimental vessel with a view to producing an indigenous class of high-speed destroyers. Vessels of this type were a constant Soviet obsession because of the enclosed waters in which their two major fleets were expected to operate. She was the first Soviet destroyer designed and built without foreign assistance. Laid down at Zholanov, Leningrad, in 1936, she was launched in 1938 and commissioned in 1941. She carried only three single 130-mm (5.1-in) guns, compared with four on the contemporary Italian-designed *Gnevny* Class, B mounting being suppressed for better seakeeping at the high speeds envisaged. The torpedo armament was increased from six to eight, in two banks of four, underlining the hit-and-run role for which *Opitny* was designed. The AA armament consisted of four single 45-mm (1.77-in) and three single 37-mm (1.46-in). Rails for a maximum of 60 mines ran on either side of the ship from abreast the forward bank of torpedo tubes to the stern.

Opitny's turbines produced 70 000 shp (compared with 48 000 shp for *Gnevny*), and unlike the latter she had the unit arrangement of machinery adopted by the *Silny* Class. The forefunnel was thinner than the second funnel, indicating one boiler room forward and two aft. *Opitny* reportedly exceeded her designed speed, attaining 41.6 knots on trials. The lightly built hull was not, however, equal to the vibration which occurred at high speeds, nor to the stresses of salvoes fired from her own guns. Her war service was restricted to use as a floating battery in defence of Leningrad, and she was scrapped soon after the end of the Second World War.

Displacement: 1670 tons (standard), 1870 tons (full load) *Length:* 118 m (387 ft 2 in) oa *Beam:*

The Soviet destroyer *Opitny* on the Neva during the siege of Leningrad in the winter of 1942

11.6 m (38 ft 1 in) *Draught:* 4.2 m (13 ft 9 in) *Machinery:* 2-shaft steam turbines, 70 000 shp=42 knots *Armament:* 3 130-mm (5.1-in) (3×1); 4 45-mm (1.77-in) AA (4×1); 3 37-mm (1.46-in) AA (3×1); 8 53-cm (21-in) torpedo tubes (2×4); 60 mines *Crew:* 197-212

Oregon City

US heavy cruiser class. Designed during the Second World War as successors to the *Baltimore* Class, eight ships were ordered from Bethlehem, Quincy. By the end of the war only three had been launched: *Oregon City* (CA.122) on April 9, 1945, *Albany* (CA.123) on June 30, and *Rochester* (CA.124) on August 28. All three were completed during the following year. *Cambridge, Bridgeport, Kansas City* and *Tulsa* were all cancelled, and work on *Northampton* was suspended until 1948 when she was earmarked to undergo conversion to a command cruiser.

The hull was that of the *Baltimore* Class, but the superstructure was significantly modified, the slim twin funnels of the earlier ships being replaced by a large single funnel. This had the effect of compressing the superstructure, with a consequent improvement in the AA arcs. The bridge was further aft, enabling the forward high-angle gunnery director to be mounted before it at a lower level, instead of above it as in the *Baltimore* Class. Layout of the three triple 8-in (203-mm) turrets and the six twin 5-in (127-mm) mountings was unchanged, and the light AA guns were similarly disposed. Three quadruple 40-mm (1.57-in) mountings were located in tubs on either side of the funnel, with two mountings abreast B turret and two abreast the after 5-in mounting, a further mounting forward of A turret and one above the stern to starboard of the aircraft crane. Between 20 and 24 20-mm (0.79-in) guns were also carried.

The armament of *Oregon City* remained unchanged until she decommissioned during the 1950s, as did that of *Albany* until her conversion to a missile cruiser (CG) in 1959. *Rochester* had all but the two centre 40-mm mountings replaced by twin 3-in (76-mm)/50-cal weapons, and had her 20-mm AA removed. The four aircraft originally carried were replaced by a helicopter, and she had her electronics updated in the 1950s. Following the abandonment of plans to convert *Rochester* to a CG she was decommissioned in 1961.

See also *Baltimore, Northampton*

Displacement: 13 260 tons (standard), 17 070 tons (full load) *Length:* 205 m (672 ft 6 in) oa *Beam:* 21 m (69 ft) *Draught:* 7.5 m (24 ft 6 in) *Machinery:* 4-shaft steam turbines, 120 000 shp=32 knots *Protection:* 152 mm (6 in) side, 76-51 mm (3-2 in) decks *Armament:* 9 8-in (203-mm) (3×3); 12 5-in (127-mm) DP (5×2); 48-52 40-mm (1.57-in) AA (12-13×4); 20-24 20-mm (0.79-in); 4 aircraft *Crew:* 1142 (1969 wartime)

Oribi

British destroyer class. In 1938 the Admiralty began formulating the requirements for an 'intermediate type' destroyer intended for general Fleet work and to replace the older Royal Navy destroyers, which were nearing the end of their useful lives. The intention was to produce vessels which were smaller, cheaper and less sophisticated than the large Fleet destroyers which had been under construction since the advent of the *Tribal* Class, but larger and more battleworthy than the *Hunt* Class escort destroyers recently laid down: hence the term 'intermediate type'. It was decided that the general lines of the earlier 'A' to 'I' Class destroyers would meet these requirements, and the design finally approved in May 1939 was similar to these vessels. The new vessels were to have the same armament, a slightly larger hull, and improved machinery with two boilers instead of three. They had a more modern appearance, with a single funnel instead of two, a raked stem and a streamlined bridge.

The first destroyers to this design, the *Oribi* or 'O' Class, were ordered on the outbreak of war on September 3, 1939. A second class, the *Paladin* or 'P' Class, were ordered a few weeks later on October 20. The 16 vessels of these two groups were laid down in 1940, and were subsequently launched and completed during 1941-42.

The ships were subject to several alterations of armament prior to completion. Early in 1940 it was decided to rearm six of the 'P' Class and two of the 'O' Class as AA destroyers, their 4.7-in (120-mm) guns being replaced by 4-in (102-mm) AA guns. Later the two 'O' Class ships exchanged names with the two 4.7-in gunned P's to provide a uniform class of AA vessels. In mid 1940 it was decided to replace the after bank of torpedo tubes with a 4-in AA gun in all 16 vessels, but the tubes were reinstated prior to completion in *Petard, Pathfinder* and *Onslow* and the four 'O' Class minelayers. These latter, *Opportune, Orwell, Obdurate* and *Obedient*, were fitted for rapid conversion to minelayers and like the 'P' Class had 4-in guns instead of the 4.7-in. When fitted for minelaying, they landed their torpedo tubes and Y 4-in gun mounting to compensate for the added weight of 50-60 mines.

The close-range AA armament was also subject to several changes, and while all completed with the four-barrel pom-pom mounting only a few mounted an 0.5-in (12.7-mm) AA gun armament. Most completed with four 20-mm (0.79-in) AA (4×1), the earlier units being brought up to this standard when their 0.5-in were removed, and during 1943-44 the surviving units had two of these replaced by twin 20-mm mountings. *Petard* was given a major refit at Portsmouth in 1944 and was completely rearmed with four 4-in HA/LA (2×2), and eight 20-mm AA (4×1, 2×2).

The 'O' Class served with the Home Fleet throughout the war, and were employed extensively in Arctic waters particularly on the Soviet convoys. The most famous ship of the class was *Onslow* which, together with *Obedient, Orwell, Obdurate* and *Oribi* took part in the Battle of the Barents Sea in December 1942. This action took place when the German cruiser *Hipper* and armoured ship *Lützow*, together with six destroyers, attempted to attack a Soviet convoy and were held off by the escort vessels under the command of Captain Sherbrooke in *Onslow*. The German force was eventually driven off by the British covering force after causing comparatively minor damage to the escort. Captain Sherbrooke, who was wounded, was awarded the VC for his part in the Battle.

The 'P' Class went to the Mediterranean, where AA vessels were badly needed. Like their sister class they were very active, and were employed extensively on convoy escort work. However the Mediterranean proved a much more dangerous area and four of the 'P' Class were lost or damaged beyond repair while the 'O' Class had no war losses. The first to go was *Porcupine*, which was torpedoed on December 9, 1942, by the German submarine *U 602* while on passage to Oran. She finished her journey under tow and was later cut in two and towed home for repair, but was subsequently declared a total loss. The two parts were christened *Pork* and *Pine* and employed as harbour hulks until 1947 when they were sold for scrapping. A few days later, on December 18, *Partridge* was torpedoed and sunk off Oran by *U 565*. On April 16, 1943, *Paladin* and *Pakenham* fought a short engagement with the Italian torpedo boats *Cigno* and *Cassiopea*. *Pakenham* sank

Cigno but was herself so badly damaged that she had to be taken in tow by *Paladin*. On the following day they were still within easy reach of enemy airfields so *Paladin* took off the crew of her sister ship and sank her with a torpedo. The last loss in the Mediterranean was *Panther* which was bombed and sunk by German aircraft in the Scarpanto Strait on October 9, 1943.

The four surviving ships transferred to the Eastern Fleet in 1944, where one more of the class was to become a total loss. On February 11, 1945, *Pathfinder* was bombed and heavily damaged by Japanese aircraft. She was later towed home and used as a target for aircraft until sold for scrapping in 1948.

In 1946 *Oribi* was sold to Turkey and renamed *Gayret*, and in 1949 *Onslow, Offa* and *Onslaught* were transferred to Pakistan and renamed *Tippa Sultan, Tariq* and *Tughril* respectively. *Penn* was sold for scrapping in 1950 and *Opportune* in 1955.

During 1952-56 *Orwell, Petard* and *Paladin* were converted to Type 16 (limited conversion) fast A/S frigates. This involved the removal of the original gun armament and the fitting of a twin 4-in HA/LA gun in B position, two Squid A/S mortars in X position and a twin 40-mm AA mounting amidships. The after bank of torpedo tubes was retained, but that forward was replaced by a deckhouse. In 1957 *Paladin* was fitted for minelaying and had the remaining torpedo mounting removed. During 1957-59 *Tippu Sultan* and *Tughril* were also given the Type 16 conversion, but differed from the earlier vessels in carrying three extra single 40-mm. The third Pakistani vessel, *Tariq*, was returned to Britain in 1959 and sold for scrap. She was followed by most of the remainder of the class, including the Type 16 conversions and the Turkish *Gayret*, during 1962-65 but *Tippu Sultan* and *Tughril* remained in service in the late 1970s in subsidiary roles.

Obdurate, Obedient—built by Denny
Offa, Onslaught, Oribi—built by Fairfield
Onslow—built by John Brown
Opportune, Orwell—built by Thornycroft

Pakenham, Pathfinder—built by Hawthorn Leslie
Paladin—built by John Brown
Panther, Partridge—built by Fairfield
Penn, Petard, Porcupine—built by Vickers-Armstrongs

Displacement: 1610 tons (standard), 2220 tons (full load) *Length:* 105.2 (345 ft) oa *Beam:* 10.7 m (35 ft) *Draught:* 2.7 m (9 ft) *Machinery:* 2-shaft geared steam turbines, 40 000 shp=36 knots *Armament:* 4 4.7-in (120-mm) (4×1); 4 2-pdr AA (1×4); 8 0.5-in (12.7-mm) AA (2×4); 8 21-in (53-cm) torpedo tubes (2×4) *Crew:* 176

Oyodo

Japanese cruiser. The design of the cruiser *Oyodo* was developed from the previous *Agano* Class light cruisers, though she was intended for a completely different tactical role. *Oyodo* was designed for the role of flagship to a hunting group of submarines. She was to be equipped with a new type of reconnaissance floatplane, and was intended to roam ahead of the submarines and use her floatplanes to locate worthwhile targets. Reconnaissance information would be collated on board in order to coordinate the submarines' attack. For this *Oyodo* was to be equipped with extensive communications facilities and the most up-to-date radar available to the Japanese.

The general appearance of the cruiser was similar to that of the *Agano* Class, but she was much larger and more heavily armed, displacement being increased by 1500 tons and length by 18 m (59 ft). Unlike *Agano*, her armament was concentrated forward and was composed of two triple 6.1-in (155-mm) turrets sited in A and B positions. These had been removed from the *Mogami* Class cruisers when they were rearmed with 8-in (203-mm) guns. Antiaircraft armament was provided by four twin 3.9-in (100-mm) guns of the new pattern fitted to the *Terutsuki* Class destroyers, mounted amidships. Light AA comprised 12 25-mm (1-in) guns, but was increased in 1944-45 to 54 25-mm (12×3, 18×1). The aircraft facilities were sited aft, where the usual after shelter deck was replaced by an enormous hangar designed to house the six floatplanes which *Oyodo* was to carry. On the quarterdeck was a very large catapult 45 m (147 ft 6 in) long specially designed for launching the floatplanes in rapid succession. Two large cranes for handling the aircraft were sited at the corners of the hangar. The floatplanes were to be much larger than previous types, with a high speed and wide radius of action.

For her scouting/command role *Oyodo* was provided with extensive bunkerage giving her a radius of action of 16 000 km (10 000 miles) at 18 knots. She was equipped with the same machinery as the *Aganos*, and protection was sacrificed in order to retain high speed; and she was given a minimum of armour amidships and around the magazines and turrets.

Oyodo was laid down at the Kure navy yard on February 14, 1941, launched on April

MOD

Above: The destroyer HMS *Oribi*, which survived the war and was sold to Turkey and renamed *Gayret*. **Below:** HMS *Opportune*, which was fitted for minelaying and could carry 50-60 mines

MOD

Name	laid down	launched	completed
Cachalot	8/55	12/57	9/59
Finwhale	9/56	7/59	8/60
Grampus	4/55	5/57	12/58
Narwhal	3/56	10/57	5/59
Porpoise	6/56	4/56	4/58
Rorqual	1/55	12/56	10/58
Sealion	6/58	12/59	7/61
Walrus	2/58	9/59	2/61

2, 1942, and completed on February 28, 1943. Her aircraft were never built, and by the time *Oyodo* was launched many Japanese submarines were being employed on transport duties, and the navy was turning more and more towards a defensive role. *Oyodo* therefore never operated in her designed role. She entered service with two standard-type scoutplanes, and when it was realized that the specially designed floatplanes would not be built the large catapult was replaced by a smaller model and the hangar was used for crew's quarters.

Oyodo was severely damaged in an air raid on March 19, 1945, and temporary repairs were effected. She was again bombed on July 28, 1945, and capsized. A sister ship was ordered under the 1939 Programme, but was cancelled before work had started on her construction.

Displacement: 8164 tons (standard), 11 433 tons (full load) *Length:* 192 m (630 ft) oa *Beam:* 16.6 m (54 ft 6 in) *Draught:* 6 m (19 ft 6 in) *Machinery:* 4-shaft geared turbines, 110 000 shp=35 knots *Protection:* 50 mm (2 in) belt, deck and magazines, 63 mm (2.5 in) turrets *Armament:* 6 6.1-in (155-mm); 8 3.9-in (100-mm); 12 25-mm (1-in); 2 floatplanes *Crew:* not known

HM Submarine *Finwhale*, a *Porpoise* Class vessel built by Cammell Laird at Birkenhead in 1959, entering the harbour at Douglas, Isle of Man, during a courtesy visit in February 1977

P.551-556

British submarine class. Six single-hulled Holland-type boats of the US *S.18* Class were transferred to Britain during 1941-42 under the Lend-Lease agreement. They were slower and smaller than the contemporary British 'L' Class, but were more powerfully armed, carrying two spare torpedoes for each tube. They were capable of diving to a depth of 60 m (200 ft). Bunkerage was provided for 92 tons of oil fuel and the boats had a surfaced radius of action of 8000 km (5000 miles) at 10.5 knots.

At first some were occasionally used as convoy escorts, but this idea was soon dropped and they were used mainly for training. Of the vessels handed over to the Royal Navy the *P.551* (ex-*S.25*) was further passed on to the Polish navy-in-exile in 1941 and renamed *Jastrzab*. She was sunk in error on May 2, 1942, by the Norwegian destroyer *St Albans* and the minesweeper *Seagull* when she strayed from a covering position while escorting Convoy PQ 15 to North USSR. The remaining submarines were returned to the US in 1944, and were eventually scrapped or used as targets at the end of the war.

Displacement: 854/1062 tons (surfaced/submerged) *Length:* 66.8 m (219 ft 3 in) *Beam:* 6.3 m (20 ft 9 in) *Draught:* 4.9 m (16 ft) *Machinery:* 2-shaft NLSE diesel engines/2 Ridgway (*P.552* Electric Dynamics) electric motors, 1200 bhp/1500 shp=14.5/11 knots (surfaced/submerged) *Armament:* 1 4-in (102-mm); 4 21-in (53-cm) torpedo tubes (bow), 12 torpedoes *Crew:* 42

P.611

British submarine class. Four submarines were under construction for Turkey at Vickers-Armstrongs, Barrow, in 1939. On the outbreak of war they were impounded and handed over to the Royal Navy, but eventually only two of the boats (*P.611* and *P.612*) were retained. The other two were delivered to the Turkish navy on completion, though they were temporarily commissioned into the Royal Navy for the passage to Turkey.

The design was similar to the British 'S' Class. Much of the equipment was of standard British design but the arrangement of the torpedo armament was altered. Only four tubes were mounted in the bow instead of the six of the 'S' Class but a single tube was fitted aft (as fitted only on later 'S' Class boats). They carried 38 tons of oil fuel and achieved a radius of action of 4000 km (2500 miles) at 10 knots on the surface. The maximum diving depth was 98 m (320 feet).

P.615 was torpedoed by the German *U 123* on April 18, 1943, while on patrol 320 km (200 miles) south of Freetown, West Africa. *P.614* was returned to the Turkish navy in 1945, and together with her two sisters continued in service until 1957 when they were finally discarded and scrapped.

Displacement: 687/861 tons (surfaced/submerged) *Length:* 61.4 m (201 ft 6 in) oa *Beam:* 6.8 m (22 ft 3 in) *Draught:* 3.2 m (10 ft 6 in) *Machinery:* 2-shaft Vickers diesels/2 electric motors, 1550 bhp/1300 shp=13.75/10 knots (surfaced/submerged) *Armament:* 1 3-in (76-

Number	launched	fate
P.611	7/40	to Turkey, *Oruc Reis* 1942; scrapped 1957
P.612	2/40	to Turkey, *Murat Reis* 1942; scrapped 1957
P.614	10/40	to Turkey, *Burak Reis* 1945; scrapped 1957
P.615	11/40	lost 18/4/43

Royal Navy

Foto Drüppel

The slim lines of *Prinz Eugen* probably before the war. She was used as a test vessel by the United States for the atomic-bomb explosion at Bikini Atoll on June 17, 1947

mm) AA; 1 20-mm (0.79-in); 5 21-in (53-cm) torpedo tubes, 9 torpedoes *Crew:* 40

Porpoise

British submarine class, built 1955-61. This was the first British submarine class to be designed after the end of the Second World War. It incorporated all the experience gained from operations with the 'T' Class as well as immediate postwar trials with the German Type XXI, and later with the modified 'T' Class and 'A' Class submarines.

The design represents a high level of refinement of the diesel-powered submarine, the boats being capable of remaining submerged for extended patrols, normally surfacing only when entering or leaving harbour. Diesel-electric propulsion is used when snorting or running surfaced, and the boats are notably quiet in operation. The batteries may be grouped in series to provide power for high-speed bursts. The conning tower is the now-standard sail structure, and houses the periscope standards, radar, W/T aerials and snorkels. The boats of this class also feature much better crew accommodation than previous designs and improved habitability.

Four vessels remained in Royal Navy service in 1978, *Cachalot* having been sold to Egypt late in 1977. *Grampus* was being used as an immobile tender and *Narwhal* was in reserve. *Rorqual* was scrapped in 1976.

Displacement: 1605/2405 tons (surfaced/submerged) *Length:* 90 m (295 ft 3 in) oa *Beam:* 8.1 m (26 ft 6 in) *Draught:* 5.5 m (18 ft) *Machinery:* 2-shaft diesel-electric/2 electric motors, 3680 bhp/6000 shp=15/19 knots (surfaced/submerged) *Armament:* 8 21-in (53-cm) torpedo tubes (6 bow, 2 stern), 26 torpedoes *Crew:* 70

Prinz Eugen

German heavy cruiser class, built 1936-40. A modified *Admiral Hipper* Class cruiser, ordered under the 1935 Programme from Krupp's Germania yard, was launched on August 22, 1938, as *Prinz Eugen*. Two sisters were ordered from AG Weser at Bremen under the 1936 Programme; *Seydlitz* was launched in January 1939, and *Lützow* followed six months later. The design was basically that of the *Hipper* Class, but with an 'Atlantic' clipper bow and a prominent cap to the funnel. The aircraft arrangements were improved, with the catapult resited over the hangar and the crane moved forward. Another innovation was to provide temporary accommodation for up to 900 troops in collapsible three-tier bunks.

Prinz Eugen had one of the most active careers of any unit of the Kriegsmarine. After being damaged by a magnetic mine in April 1941 she was repaired in time to accompany *Bismarck* on her sortie into the Atlantic. On May 24 she joined in the action against the British battlecruiser *Hood* in the Denmark Strait. She scored hits on the British ship, and it was probably her 8-in (203-mm) shells, rather than 15-in (381-mm) shells from *Bismarck* which caused the fatal fire and explosion. As she was running low on fuel *Prinz Eugen* was ordered to break away to Brest and so she escaped the fate of *Bismarck* three days later.

In February *Prinz Eugen* accompanied *Scharnhorst* and *Gneisenau* in Operation Cerebus, the daylight dash through the Channel from Brest to the North Sea, but in 1943 she was relegated to training duties in the Baltic. On October 15, 1944, while helping to evacuate German troops from the eastern Baltic she rammed the cruiser *Leipzig* amidships, badly damaging her. *Prinz Eugen* was surrendered at Copenhagen in May 1945 and handed over to the US as a prize. She was subjected to the Bikini atomic-bomb tests in 1946 and was sunk as a target on November 15, 1947, off Kwajalein Island in the western Pacific.

Work on *Seydlitz* stopped in 1942, when she was taken to Königsberg to begin conversion into an aircraft carrier. Little information survives about what sort of a ship she would have become as she was scuttled incomplete on April 10, 1945, when the Red Army was close to capturing the port. After the war she was raised by the USSR and towed to Leningrad. She is reported to have been renamed *Poltava* but when it was discovered that the damage was beyond repair she was scrapped.

The incomplete hull of *Lützow* was sold to the USSR in 1940 and towed to Leningrad where it was renamed *Petropavlovsk*; she was again renamed *Tallinn* in 1942. With only three 203-mm (8-in) and some AA guns installed she was used as a floating battery in defence of Leningrad, and although damaged by German air attacks she survived the war. Work on her restarted after the war but was abandoned in 1950. She may have survived as an accommodation hulk in the Neva River until 1957.

Displacement: 14 800 tons (standard), 19 800 tons (full load) *Length:* 210 m (689 ft) oa *Beam:* 21.8 m (71 ft 6 in) *Draught:* 7.9 m (26 ft) max *Machinery:* 3-shaft geared steam turbines, 132 000 shp=32 knots *Protection:* 83 mm (3.25 in) belt, 64-32 mm (2.5-1.25 in) decks, 165 mm (6.5 in) turrets *Armament:* 8 20.3-cm (8-in)/60-cal (4×2); 12 10.5-cm (4.1-in)/65-cal (6×2); 12 37-mm (1.46-in) AA (6×2); 8 20-mm (0.79-in) AA (8×1); 12 53-cm (21-in) torpedo tubes (4×3); 3 Ar 196 floatplanes, 1 catapult *Crew:* 1599

Quilliam

British destroyer class. The *Quilliam* and *Rotherham* Class destroyers (also known as the 'Q' and 'R' Classes) were provided under the 1940 Programme to form the 3rd and 4th Emergency Flotillas, each consisting of eight ships. In general principles of simple production they followed the *Oribi* and *Paladin* ('O' and 'P') Classes which made up the first two flotillas, but differed in adopting the hull-form of the prewar *Javelin* ('J') Class. Like the 'O' and 'P' Classes they used the *Javelin*-type machinery, and except for their simple armament they were thus virtually repeats of the 'J' Class. Drawings and building moulds for the *Javelin* hull were already available, and it was expected that this would speed up production. The *Javelin* hull was larger than the *Oribi* type, providing space for the additions likely to result from war experience. The new vessels carried only two single 4.7-in (120-mm) guns (instead of the twin mountings of the 'J' Class) and so required only half the magazine space of the original design. The space formerly occupied by B magazine was used for extra fuel tanks, and the total bunkerage was increased to 615 tons and endurance to 7530 km (4680 miles) at 20 knots. Orders for all 16 vessels were placed in April 1940, but work was suspended the next month as design and construction facilities became overloaded, particularly with repairs from the Dunkerque evacuation and the Norwegian campaign. Work was resumed in September, and the ships were eventually laid down during late 1940 and early 1941. They were launched during 1941-42 and completed during 1942-43.

'Q' Class
Quadrant, Quail, Quilliam—built by Hawthorn Leslie
Quality, Queensborough—built by Swan Hunter
Quentin, Quiberon, Quickmatch—built by White

'R' Class
Racehorse, Redoubt, Relentless, Rotherham—built by John Brown
Raider, Rapid—built by Cammell Laird
Rocket, Roebuck—built by Scotts

The class was designed to carry a close-range AA armament of one four-barrel pom-pom and two four-barrel 0.5-in (12.7-mm) machine-guns, but six single 20-mm (0.79-in) were substituted for the latter prior to completion, two being mounted in the bridge wings and four amidships. *Roebuck* and *Rocket* completed with twin 20-mm in the bridge wings in place of the singles, and during 1943-44 this modification was also carried out in the other ships of the 'Q' and 'R' Classes (with the exception of *Quentin* which had already been lost). In 1945 *Raider* was fitted with a lattice foremast, and four 40-mm (1.57-in) (4×1) Bofors AA, in place of her single 20-mm.

On completion the 'Q' and 'R' Classes went to the Mediterranean where they formed the 4th and 24th Destroyer Flotillas respectively. Here the only two ships of the group to be sunk were lost. *Quentin* was torpedoed by an aircraft off North Africa on December 2, 1942; *Quail* was mined in a field laid by *U 453* off Bari and sank three days later, on June 18, 1944, while in tow to Taranto. The remaining ships were transferred to the Eastern Fleet during 1943-44 and in 1945 the 'Q' Class, which had by then become the 11th Destroyer Flotilla, joined the British Pacific Fleet for the final assault on Japan.

Quiberon, Quality and *Quickmatch* had been transferred on completion to the Royal Australian Navy, and they were joined in 1945 by *Queensborough* and *Quadrant. Quilliam*, the remaining ship of the 'Q' flotilla, was sold to the Netherlands in 1945 and renamed *Banckert*; she was sold for scrap in 1957. In 1949 *Rotherham, Raider* and *Redoubt* completed a two-year refit in which a lattice mast was fitted and the 20-mm guns were replaced by four single 40-mm AA; they were immediately sold to the Indian Navy, renamed *Rajput, Rana* and *Ranjit* respectively, and survived into the 1970s with virtually no further modification apart from the removal of their torpedo tubes in the early 1960s.

In 1949 *Racehorse* was sold for scrap but the remaining ships of the 'R' Class were taken in hand during the early 1950s to undergo conversion to become the first Type 15 fast antisubmarine frigates. This conversion was produced in response to a need for cheap vessels which were faster than existing escort types, required to counter the greater underwater speeds of postwar submarines. The modifications involved the removal of the existing armament and superstructure, extending the forecastle deck almost to the stern and providing a new full-width deck forward with an enclosed bridge across its forward edge. New radar, fire-control, sonar and communication equipment, together with lattice foremasts and mainmasts, were also fitted while the armament was altered to a twin 4-in (102-mm) aft, a twin 40-mm between the bridge and foremast and two three-barrel Limbo (Squid in *Rapid* and *Roebuck*) A/S mortars on the quarterdeck. For a short time they also carried a pair of A/S torpedo tubes on each side amidships.

All the Australian vessels (except *Quality* which was sold for scrap in 1958) were also converted to Type 15s in the mid-1950s but differed from the 'R' conversions in having the bridge positioned further aft, with the twin 40-mm mounting forward of it. *Quadrant* had Squid launchers in place of the Limbos. The 'Q' and 'R' Type 15s were sold for scrap during the late 1960s and early 1970s.

Displacement: 1690 tons (standard), 2400 tons (deep) *Length:* 109.2 m (358 ft 3 in) oa *Beam:* 10.9 m (35 ft 8 in) *Draught:* 2.9 m (9 ft 6 in) *Machinery:* 2-shaft geared steam turbines,

40 000 shp=36 knots *Armament:* 4 4.7-in (120-mm) (4×1); 4 2-pdr AA (1×4); 6 20-mm (0.79-in) AA (6×1); 8 21-in (53-cm) torpedo tubes (2×4) *Crew:* 176

Rahmat

Malaysian frigate. *Rahmat* was the first of two general-purpose frigates built by Yarrow to their own design during the late 1960s, the other being the Thai *Makut Rajakumarn*. The Yarrow frigate design aimed to take advantage of the latest developments in propulsion and miniaturized electronics to provide smaller navies with a well-armed and fully automated ship which would be economical from the point of view both of manpower and initial cost. A key element in the design is the use of an Olympus gas turbine for boost to give a top speed of 26 knots. This is linked in a CODOG arrangement to a single Crossley-Pielstick diesel which gives the ship a cruising speed of 16 knots. The Olympus engine room is forward of the diesel engine room, and is fed from the prominent air intakes at the after end of the bridge structure. The twin shafts with controllable-pitch propellers are driven through a gearbox sited between the two engine rooms.

Rahmat was ordered in February 1966, launched in December 1967 and completed in March 1971. Originally she was to have been named *Hang Jebat*, but this was changed on completion. The weapon fit chosen by the Malaysian navy comprises a single 4.5-in (114-mm) Mk 5 forward, a quadruple Seacat surface-to-air missile launcher on the after end of the superstructure, two single 40-mm (1.57-in) Bofors just forward of the funnel, and Limbo Mk 10 A/S mortar. The Limbo is sited in a well which can be covered over to provide a helicopter landing pad. The weapons themselves are all in service with the Royal Navy, while main above-water sensors are of Dutch origin. The big LW 03 aerial provides long-range air-search capabilities while a WM 22 radome on the foremast controls the 4.5-in in aerial or surface engagements. The director for the Seacat missiles is the lightweight WM 44, which is used for the same purpose in the Dutch *Van Speijk* Class frigates. Data provided by these sensors are coordinated in a modern operations room.

Displacement: 1250 tons (standard), 1600 tons (full load) *Length:* 94 m (308 ft 6 in) oa *Beam:* 10.4 m (34 ft) *Draught:* 4.5 m (14 ft 9 in) *Machinery:* 1 Olympus gas turbine, 19 500 hp=26 knots; 1 Crossley-Pielstick diesel, 3850 bhp=16 knots *Armament:* 1 4.5-in (114-mm) Mk 5 DP; 2 40-mm (1.57-in)/70-cal Bofors AA (2×1); 1 quadruple Seacat launcher; 1 Limbo Mk 10 A/S mortar *Crew:* 140

Rapid

British frigate class. At the end of the Second World War, Germany had under development a number of new and revolutionary submarines capable of higher submerged speeds than any others in existence. Examples of these vessels and the details of their designs fell into the hands of the Allies and in the immediate postwar years the work begun

The Malaysian frigate *Rahmat* which was built by Yarrow using electronics and automation to save manning costs and provide a small versatile ship for the world's newer navies

Yarrow Shipbuilders

TYPE 15 CONVERSIONS

Name	navy	converted by	conversion completed
Algonquin	RCN	Esquimalt dockyard	1954
Grenville	RN	not known	1954
Crescent	RCN	Esquimalt dockyard	1956
Quadrant	RAN	Cockatoo dockyard	1953
Queensborough	RAN	Cockatoo dockyard	1953
Quiberon	RAN	Williamstown dockyard	1957
Quickmatch	RAN	Williamstown dockyard	1955
Rapid	RN	Stephen	1953
Relentless	RN	Portsmouth dockyard	1951
Rocket	RN	Devonport dockyard	1951
Roebuck	RN	Devonport dockyard	1953
Troubridge	RN	Portsmouth dockyard/ J S White, Cowes	1957
Ulster	RN	Chatham dockyard	1953
Ulysses	RN	Devonport dockyard	1953
Undaunted	RN	White, Cowes	1953
Undine	RN	not known	1954
Urania	RN	Harland & Wolff, Liverpool	1954
Urchin	RN	Barclay Curle	1953
Ursa	RN	Palmer, Hebburn	1954
Venus	RN	not known	1952
Verulam	RN	Portsmouth dockyard	1952
Vigilant	RN	Thornycroft	1952
Virago	RN	not known	1952
Volage	RN	White, Cowes	1952
Wakeful	RN	Scotts	1953
Whirlwind	RN	Palmer, Hebburn	1953
Wizard	RN	Devonport dockyard	1954
ex-*Wrangler* (*Vrystaat*)	SAN	Harland & Wolff, Belfast	1952
Zest	RN	Chatham dockyard	1956

MOD

HMS *Undaunted*, a *Rapid* Class frigate converted in 1953 for A/S work, at the end of her career on the way to becoming a target ship

in Germany was continued in both East and West. The resultant advances posed a serious problem, as none of the vast fleet of A/S vessels constructed during the war possessed the speed necessary to counter these new high-performance submarines. The problem was further aggravated by the promised future development of nuclear-powered submarines with even greater potential, and the fact that the Admiralty was faced with the usual postwar retrenchment in which government sanction for the construction of a large number of new A/S escorts was unlikely. Britain did, however, possess a large number of destroyers constructed under the Emergency War Programme, most of which were in reserve and would soon become surplus to requirements unless given a major refit. Being 31-knot vessels they already possessed the necessary speed and only needed limited reconstruction to fit them for A/S duty. They could also be converted comparatively cheaply and quickly and would serve to fill the gap until new construction became available in later years. Accordingly in 1949 *Relentless* and *Rocket*, two destroyers of the *Rotherham* Class, were taken in hand for prototype conversion into Type 15 fast A/S frigates. All the existing armament and superstructure was removed and the forecastle deck lengthened from 38.1 m (125 ft) to 85.3 m (280 ft) from the stem. A new superstructure block, extending to the full width of the ship, was added forward of amidships containing a fully enclosed, slightly raised, bridge at its forward end, an operations room, sonar-control room and radar and communication offices. The new armament consisted of a twin 4-in (102-mm) mounting at the after end of the forecastle deck, a twin 40-mm (1.57-in) Bofors mounting abaft the bridge, two three-barrel Limbo A/S mortars on the quarterdeck and two fixed A/S homing torpedo tubes on each side of the forecastle deck amidships. An AA director to control the guns was added on a small deckhouse forward of the 4-in mounting and new lattice masts were stepped on the forward superstructure and abaft the funnel. The new structure was mainly aluminium alloy to avoid an excessive increase in topweight, and was designed to improve seakeeping qualities and hull strength so the ships could maintain higher speeds in heavy weather. The two ships were tried during 1951-52 and proved highly successful.

Between 1951-55 a further 27 destroyers were taken in hand for full conversion including two Canadian, one South African and four Australian vessels. In general these conversions followed closely those of the

Relentless and *Rocket* but inevitably there were a number of minor variations. *Rapid* and *Roebuck* and all the *Venus* and *Wakeful* Class ships were fitted with Squid mortars instead of Limbos. The eight A/S torpedo tubes provided were removed from the majority of the Type 15s before 1960. The last of the conversions, *Troubridge*, *Zest* and *Ulster* had their 40-mm twin mountings fitted on the forward edge of the superstructure and a modern enclosed bridge, of the type being fitted in new-construction frigates, fitted on the superstructure further aft. The RAN ships had a similar arrangement except that the 40-mm mounting was slightly further aft and the bridge was of more simple design. The RCN ships showed the greatest variations, having a larger forward superstructure, funnel caps and an armament of different type. *Crescent* had a twin 3-in (76-mm) AA mounting aft while the 4-in mount was moved forward to the forecastle and two single 40-mm AA mounted abreast the foremast. *Algonquin* was similarly armed but had the positions of the 4-in and 3-in mountings transposed. During the early 1960s *Crescent* was fitted with a variable-depth sonar on the quarterdeck, which necessitated the removal of one of her Limbo mountings, a shield on her 3-in mounting and three A/S torpedo tubes. *Grenville* and *Undaunted* were fitted with helicopter platforms over their quarterdecks, and in 1962 the latter vessel became the first RN ship to carry an A/S helicopter; the platforms were later removed.

The Type 15 conversion greatly extended the lives of ships which would have otherwise become obsolete, but by the 1960s they were rapidly being replaced by new-construction frigates. They continued to be employed in subsidiary roles for several years and were used extensively for A/S training and for trials and tests. They were gradually removed from the effective list between 1961 and the mid-1970s.

Displacement: 2200-2300 tons (standard) *Length:* 110.6 m (362 ft 9 in) (ex-*Quilliam* and *Rotherham* Class vessels 109.2 m [358 ft 3 in]) *Beam:* 10.9 m (35 ft 9 in) *Draught:* 4.4 m (14 ft 6 in) *Machinery:* 2-shaft geared steam turbines, 40 000 shp=36 knots *Armament:* 2 4-in (102-mm) (1×2); 2 40-mm (1.57-in) (1×2); 2 A/S mortars *Crew:* 195

le Redoutable

French nuclear-powered ballistic missile submarine class. At about the time of the British decision to send the nuclear deterrent to sea the French decided to do likewise, and the *Force de Disuasion* was born. *Le Redoutable*, the first of the class, was ordered in 1963, and four further hulls were laid down at two- to three-year intervals. All five were built at Cherbourg dockyard. The name-ship commissioned in 1971 but the fifth ship is not due to complete until 1980. The lengthy period taken to construct these vessels—by the time *le Redoutable* was accepted in 1971 all four Royal Navy boats had been in commission for two years or more—is a reflection of the complex problems the French had to solve in order to create their own independent ballistic-missile submarine force. The Polaris technology for the *Resolution* Class was handed over to Britain by the US, and

ECP Armées

The launch of the French nuclear-powered ballistic missile submarine *le Foudroyant* (S.610) at Cherbourg naval dockyard in December 1971. She was completed in July 1974

ECP Armées

The French submarine *le Terrible* (S.612), one of the *le Redoutable* Class of nuclear vessels built as part of the *Force de Disuasion* during her running trials in the spring of 1973

ECP Armées

The helmsman's position in *le Redoutable*, the first French nuclear-powered ballistic submarine which was designed and built without American experience or technical assistance

MOD

HMS *Resolution*, a British nuclear-powered Polaris submarine, leaves Gare Loch at the beginning of a patrol in February 1977

the Royal Navy already had the nuclear-powered *Dreadnought* in commission before the *Resolution* Class were laid down. The French, on the other hand, were building from scratch, and had to develop their own missile and propulsion technology in parallel with their construction programme. The submarine *Gymnote* was rebuilt as a trials ship for testing the ballistic missiles.

Since the completion of *le Redoutable* two uprated versions of the original missile, the 2500-km (1550-mile) M-1, have appeared. The first three ships are now fitted with the M-2 missile, which has a range of 3000 km (1860 miles), still inferior to that of the Polaris A-3. *L'Indomptable,* the fourth boat, has the later M-20 missile, which will probably be retrofitted to the earlier ships. Eventually, it is planned to refit the earlier boats with the larger M-4 missile. Sixteen missiles are carried, as in the British and US boats.

The class follows US practice in having the diving planes fitted to the fin, but they can be easily distinguished from equivalent US and British ships by the contrast between the low bow section and the prominent casing which houses the missile-launching tubes aft of the fin. Four bow 55-cm (21.7-in) torpedo tubes are fitted. The steel hull allows diving to depths of more than 200 m (660 ft). A pressurized gas-cooled reactor produces the steam to power two turbines and two turbo-alternators; an auxiliary diesel and electric motor can substitute for the main engines in an emergency. The vessels can cruise submerged for about three months. Two crews alternate to keep them on continuous patrol.

In 1974 a sixth boat was ordered to be laid down in 1982. Named *l'Inflexible*, she will be the lead ship of an improved class, with a modified reactor, deeper diving depth and the new M-4 missile.

No and name	laid down	launched	completed	builder
S.22 ***Resolution***	2/64	9/66	10/67	Vickers-Armstrongs
S.23 ***Repulse***	3/65	11/67	10/68	Vickers-Armstrongs
S.26 ***Renown***	6/64	2/67	2/69	Cammell Laird
S.27 ***Revenge***	5/65	3/68	12/69	Cammell Laird

No and name	laid down	launched	completed
S.611 ***le Redoutable***	3/64	3/67	12/71
S.612 ***le Terrible***	6/67	12/69	1/73
S.610 ***le Foudroyant***	12/69	12/71	7/74
S.613 ***l'Indomptable***	12/71	8/74	12/76
S.614 ***le Tonnant***	10/74	9/77	—

Displacement: 7500/9000 tons (surfaced/submerged) *Length:* 128 m (419 ft 11 in) oa *Beam:* 10.6 m (34 ft 9 in) *Draught:* 10 m (32 ft 10 in) *Machinery:* 1 gas-cooled nuclear reactor, 2 turbines=20/25 knots (surfaced/submerged) *Armament:* 16 M-2 *(l'Indomptable* M-20) ballistic missiles; 4 55-cm (21.7-in) torpedo tubes (bow), 18 torpedoes *Crew:* 135

Reshef

Israeli guided-missile patrol boat class. *Reshef* was laid down in 1971 by Israeli Shipyards, followed by *Keshet, Romach,*

HMS *Resolution,* ordered in 1964, was the first British FBM (fleet ballistic missile) submarine. She was commissioned in 1967 as the most powerful vessel ever to fly the White Ensign. Her 16 Polaris missiles have a range of 4630 km (2880 miles) and nuclear warheads. Unlike USN vessels armed with nuclear missiles she also carries 21-in torpedoes in six bow tubes

Kidon, Tarshish and *Yaffo.* The first two were launched in 1973 and completed the same year. The second pair were launched and completed in 1974 and the other two in 1975. An order for a further six boats soon followed from South Africa, with three due to complete in Israel during 1978 and the other three built under licence in Durban with Israeli assistance.

Developed from the earlier *Saar* Class, which had been constructed in a French shipyard, the *Reshefs* were the first warships to be built in Israel. The impetus for this 'home-grown' development stemmed from fears of a possible French arms embargo under pressure from the United Nations, which was in fact confirmed in 1969, the year after the *Reshef* Class was ordered.

The *Reshef* design, known at first as the *Saar III,* was based on a much larger hull than the earlier boats. With 13 m (42 ft 8 in) more length and almost double the displacement, there is a considerable improvement both in seakeeping and endurance. The emphasis on endurance at the expense of high-speed performance can be seen in the reduction from 14 000 hp in the 40-knot *Saars* to a mere 10 680 hp for a maximum speed of 32 knots in the *Reshefs*, power being provided by four MTU diesels each with a downrated output.

The increase in hull-size also enables them to carry a heavier armament than their predecessors, although the weapons themselves are largely the same. Single OTO-Melara 76-mm (3-in) dual-purpose guns are mounted fore and aft, and six Gabriel surface-to-surface missile launchers are carried. These are arranged with two fixed pairs angled outboard port and starboard forward of the after 76-mm gun, and two fixed single launchers just aft of the superstructure. It is reported that four longer-range Harpoon missiles of US manufacture were added in early 1978 and the original Gabriel missiles were likely to be replaced shortly afterwards by a new version with double the range. Two machine-guns are mounted in the bridge wings and four depth charges are carried. The search and fire-control radars are of Israeli manufacture and design, unlike those of the *Saar* Class which are French.

The *Reshef* Class appear to be very successful ships, well designed for their area of operation. The first two ships, *Reshef* and *Keshet*, were completed in time for the Middle East war of October 1973, and acquitted themselves well in engagements with the Styx-armed 'Komar' and 'Osa' Class boats of the Egyptian and Syrian navies. Their endurance enabled the Israelis to provide cover for shipping approaching their coasts out to 640 km (400 miles). Since that time ships of the *Reshef* Class have crossed the Atlantic and sailed around the Cape.

Tarshish and *Yaffo*, which are fitted with sonar, are based in the Mediterranean while the others operate in the Red Sea.

Displacement: 415 tons (standard), 950 tons (full load) *Length:* 58 m (190 ft 3 in) oa *Beam:* 7.6 m (24 ft 11 in) *Draught:* 2.4 m (7 ft 10 in) *Machinery:* 4 MBU diesels, 10 680 hp=32 knots *Armament:* 6 Gabriel surface-to-surface missiles (2×1, 2×2); 2 OTO-Melara 76-mm (3-in) dual-purpose guns (2×1); 2 machine-guns; 4 mines *Crew:* 45

Resolution

British nuclear-powered ballistic-missile submarine class. At the 1962 conference between the British prime minister and the US president at Nassau it was agreed that the technology for the Polaris missile would be made available for the construction of British nuclear submarines. An order for four boats was announced in May 1963. Vickers-Armstrongs, Barrow, would build two boats and be the lead yard for the design, while Cammell Laird would build the other two. Construction proceeded to a tight schedule, and *Resolution* was accepted into service at the end of 1967, the other three boats completing during the next two years.

Although the hulls and machinery of the class are of British design there are unmistakable external similarities with the US *Lafayette* and *Benjamin Franklin* Classes completed between 1963-67. Length and beam are identical, although there is a slight increase in draught and displacement. The RN boats are slower under water, although the surface speed of 20 knots is the same. The only significant difference in external appearance is the position of the diving planes, which are mounted close to the bow on the British boats, not on the fin.

Sixteen Polaris A-3 ballistic missiles with a range of 4630 km (2880 miles) are housed in paired launching tubes aft of the fin, with six bow tubes for 21-in (53-cm) torpedoes making up their conventional armament. They are fitted with a large sonar array and a short-range surveillance radar for surface and air warning.

Two crews are allocated to each ship to enable almost continuous patrol between refits. The four *Resolution* Class boats make up the 10th Submarine Squadron, based at Faslane. One or two boats are on patrol at any time, with the others undergoing maintenance at Faslane or refit at Rosyth naval dockyard. It seems unlikely that any further submarines of this class will be built, although the existing ships may be equipped with an improved A-3 missile incorporating multiple warheads.

Displacement: 7500/8400 tons (surfaced/submerged) *Length:* 129.5 m (425 ft) oa *Beam:* 10.1 m (33 ft 2 in) *Draught:* 9.1 m (29 ft 10 in) *Machinery:* 1 pressurized water-cooled nuclear reactor, 1-shaft steam turbines=20/25 knots (surfaced/submerged) *Armament:* 16 Polaris A-3 missiles; 6 21-in (53-cm) torpedo tubes (bow) *Crew:* 141

Restigouche

Canadian destroyer escort class, built 1952-59. The design was a repeat of the *St Laurent* Class, with almost identical dimensions and armament. A twin 76-mm (3-in)/70-cal enclosed mounting was carried forward and there was a twin 76-mm/50-cal open mounting aft of the superstructure. In the centre of the long, flat quarterdeck was a large well with a weatherproof cover which housed two Limbo A/S mortars. The above-water sensors were an SPS-12 air-search scanner and an SPS-10 surface-search scanner, both mounted on the enclosed foremast. A variety of hull sonars gave them a useful capability in their primary role of ASW. Like the *St Laurent* Class they were designed for good seakeeping and for easy production.

Their antisubmarine weapons were soon found to be inadequate to deal with the new threat from nuclear-powered submarines and in the mid-1960s it was decided that they should undergo conversion. Only four ships were converted, and in 1974 the three unconverted ships, *Chaudière, Columbia* and *St Croix* were placed in reserve. *Terra Nova* completed her refit in 1968, followed by *Gatineau* in 1969, and *Kootenay* and *Restigouche* in 1970. Unlike the *St Laurent* Class, which were given a Sea King helicopter complete with hangar and flight deck, *Restigouche* and her three sisters were given a less drastic conversion involving the replacement of the after 76-mm mounting and one of the Limbos by an Asroc launcher and replacement of the enclosed mast by a tall lattice mast similar to that fitted to the later *Iroquois* Class. The new mast facilitated improvements in communications and ECM. The dual SQS-505 sonar system (consisting of one hull-mounted and one towed sonar) of the *Iroquois* Class was also fitted, resulting in a 1.6-m (5 ft 3 in) lengthening of the stern. A small Canadian-designed launcher for Sea Sparrow missiles was mounted on a small deckhouse above the Asroc launcher. The four converted ships were still in active service in 1978.

Displacement: 2390 tons (standard), 2880 tons (full load) *Length:* 111.5 m (365 ft 9 in) oa *Beam:* 12.8 m (42 ft) *Draught:* 4.1 m (13 ft 6 in) *Machinery:* 2-shaft steam turbines, 30 000 shp=28 knots *Armament:* 2 76-mm (3-in)/70-cal (1×2); 2 76-mm/50-cal (1×2); 2 Limbo triple A/S mortars; (After conversion) 2 76-mm/70-cal (1×2); 8 Asroc launchers (1×8); Sea Sparrow launcher; 1 Limbo triple A/S mortar *Crew:* 248

No and name	laid down	launched	completed	builder
235 *Chaudière*	7/53	11/57	11/59	Halifax Shipyards
236 *Gatineau*	4/53	6/57	2/59	Davie Shipbuilding
256 *St Croix*	10/54	11/57	10/58	Marine Industries
257 *Restigouche*	7/53	11/54	6/58	Canadian Vickers
258 *Kootenay*	8/52	6/54	3/59	Burrard Dry Dock
259 *Terra Nova*	11/52	6/55	6/59	Victoria Machinery
260 *Columbia*	6/53	11/56	11/59	Burrard Dry Dock

Below: HMCS *Terra Nova*, a Canadian destroyer launched in June 1955 and the first ship to be refitted and improved in the *Restigouche* Class in 1968. She has received new A/S equipment including sonar and an Asroc launcher in place of one of her Limbos

Canadian Armed Forces

Richelieu

French battleship class, built 1935-49. In 1930 France refused to ratify the London Naval Agreement which aimed at continuing the restrictions on battleship building imposed by the Washington Treaty of 1922. She was anxious to maintain her position as a naval power, and this resulted in the laying down of the *Dunkerque* and *Strasbourg*, 26 000-ton battlecruisers authorized in 1931-34. *Richelieu* and her sister *Jean Bart* were both authorized in 1935 as improved and enlarged versions of *Dunkerque*. The forward armament was similar to *Dunkerque* in that they carried two four-gun turrets with an internal sloping belt, but they had five triple 152-mm (6-in) turrets placed amidships and aft instead of the two-and four-gun secondary turrets of *Richelieu*. The centreline 152-mm (6-in) turret aft was placed above the hangar, and there were two aircraft catapults on the quarterdeck right aft. Although intended to have a similar profile to the *Dunkerque*, this was found to be impractical and the funnel had to be sloped backwards to stop smoke fouling the bridge and conning tower. The bridge had a very large and distinctive superstructure.

The engines were four-shaft Parsons single-reduction turbines using steam from six Indret-Sural boilers. It was claimed that *Richelieu* exceeded her designed power of 150 000 shp and reached 179 000 shp; *Jean Bart* achieved 162 855 shp, still almost 13 000 shp more than she was designed for.

Richelieu was built in Brest arsenal. When France fell in 1940 she was almost finished and was running her preliminary sea trials. She assisted in the defence of Dakar against the British and Free French forces, but in 1942 she joined the Allies and in 1943 went to the United States to be refitted. The aircraft and catapults were removed and the close-range AA was replaced by 14 quadruple 40-mm (1.57-in) Bofors mountings and 48 single 20-mm (0.79-in) Oerlikons. She was also given bunkerage for 500 tons more fuel, and in all her displacement rose by 3000 tons. She subsequently served the British Pacific Fleet and was finally scrapped in 1968.

Jean Bart took part in the war very briefly, but was badly damaged in 1942. She was not repaired until after the war. *Clemenceau* was started in 1939 but her incomplete hull was captured by the Germans and then sunk by United States forces in 1944. A fourth ship, *Gascogne*, was to be of modified design, but with the second quadruple turret aft. She was never laid down, although material had been assembled by June 1940.

Displacement: 43 293 tons (normal), 47 548 tons (full load) *Length:* 247.9 m (813 ft 4 in) oa *Beam:* 33 m (108 ft 3 in) *Draught:* 9.7 m (31 ft 10 in) *Machinery:* 4-shaft geared steam turbines, 150 000 shp=30 knots *Protection:* 343 mm (13.5 in) belt, 171-51 mm (6.73-2 in) deck, 445-267 mm (17.5-10.5 in) turrets *Armament:* 8 381-mm (15-in); 9 152-mm (6-in) DP; 12 100-mm (3.9-in) AA; 16 37-mm (1.46-in) AA *Crew:* 1550

'Riga'

Soviet escort class. The first ships were laid down at Kaliningrad and Nikolaiev in 1951-52 and rapid series production followed, with more than 60 ships being completed between 1955-58. Known names of the 43 ships in service with the Soviet navy in 1978 are: *Arkhangelsky Komsomolets, Astrakhansky Komsomolets, Barsuk, Buivol, Byk, Gepard, Giena, Kobchik, Komsomolets Grusy, Leopard, Lev, Lisa, Medved, Pantera, Rysl, Shakal, Tigr, Tuman*, and *Volk*.

Intended as successors to the 'Kola' Class, the 'Rigas' were smaller and simpler vessels, and particular attention was paid to improving the seakeeping characteristics of the earlier class. While length was reduced from 96 m (315 ft) to 91.5 m (300 ft 2 in), beam remained the same. The hull was given considerable sheer forward and the bridge structure was moved further aft, giving more lift to the bow in rough seas. Speed was reduced by 2 knots compared with their predecessors, indicating that reliability rather than high performance was a priority.

The main armament was reduced by one gun to three single 100-mm (3.9-in) mounts in narrow shields, two forward and one aft, controlled by the same Wasphead director mounted on the contemporary 'Kotlin' Class destroyers. A triple mount for 53-cm (21-in) torpedoes was generally fitted, although some units had only a twin mount. Light AA comprised two twin 37-mm (1.46-in) mountings on a platform above the after 100-mm gun. Some ships have since had two 25-mm (1-in) guns added, and *Kobchik* has had two 23-mm (0.91-in) 'Gatlings' fitted on specially constructed platforms on either side of the funnel.

Newer four-, five-, and 16-barrelled hand-loaded A/S mortars have superseded (or have been added to) the original depth-charge mortars, and these are mounted on either side of B gun.

At first a tripod mast similar to that of the 'Kola' Class was fitted, but when more modern search radars became available in the late 1950s a stubby quadruped lattice mast replaced it. A few ships have been given a small lattice mast on the after superstructure with additional ECM equipment. They have no A/S launchers, and can be easily distinguished from other ships of the class by their prominent funnel cowling.

During the late 1950s four 'Riga' Class ships were built at Shanghai for China, names being *Ch'eng Tu, Kuei Lin, Kuei Yang, K'un Ming*. These ships have since been fitted with two launchers for Styx surface-to-surface missiles. In addition the following transfers of Soviet 'Rigas' have taken place: two in 1957-58 to Bulgaria, renamed *Druzki* and *Smely*; five in 1957-58 to East Germany, renamed *Ernst Thälmann, Karl Marx, Friedrich Engels* and *Karl Liebnecht* (the fifth ship was reportedly gutted by fire soon after her transfer); eight to Indonesia in 1962-64, renamed *Jos Sudarso, Slamet Rijaja, Nuku, Lambung, Maagurat, Hang Tuah, Kakiali*, and *Ngurah Rai*; and two in 1964 to Finland, renamed *Uusimaa* and *Hämeenmaa*. Two of the East German ships and four of the Indonesian ships were discarded in the 1970s.

Although now regarded as obsolescent because of their outdated equipment, the 'Riga' Class were certainly regarded as successful ships when completed, and since that time they have seen wide deployment, often in arduous sea conditions.

Displacement: 1250 tons (standard), 1600 tons (full load) *Length:* 91.5 m (300 ft 2 in) oa *Beam:* 10 m (32 ft 10 in) *Draught:* 3.4 m (11 ft 2 in) *Machinery:* 2-shaft steam turbines, 20 000 shp=28 knots *Armament:* 3 100-mm (3.9-in) guns (3×1); 4 37-mm (1.46-in) AA (2×2); 4 25-mm (1-in) AA (2×2) (some ships); 3 53-cm (21-in) torpedo tubes (1×3); 2 groups of A/S rocket launchers; depth-charge projectors and racks *Crew:* 180

RO 35-56, 70-99, 211-227

Japanese submarine class. Under the 4th and 5th Replenishment Laws of 1940-42 a large class of medium-sized submarines was ordered to a standard design known as Type K6. They were based on the *RO 33* Class, and retained their good seakeeping qualities but were larger and stronger, with a rather higher surface speed. Fuel capacity was increased and the radius of action rose to 11 000 nautical miles at 12 knots.

The design introduced the Type 95 torpedo but did not provide for any gun armament. During construction a 3-in (76-mm) gun was fitted, and light armament was improved by fitting a twin 25-mm (1-in) AA. During 1942-43 a number of boats had their conning towers rebuilt with sloping sides in the hope that the sloping surface would deflect radar pulses. The boats handled very well and were considered by many to be the most successful of the Japanese designs.

RO 35-38, 40-41, 43, 45-46, 48—built by Mitsubishi, Kobe
RO 39, 42—built by Sasebo navy yard
RO 44, 47, 49-50, 55-56—built by Tamano

The boats entered service between March 1943 and November 1944. *RO 51-54, 70-74, 76-99* and *RO 200-227* were cancelled in 1943 as materials for construction became scarce.

RO 35-42, RO 44-45, RO 47-49 and *RO 55-56* were all sunk by US destroyers. *RO 43* was sunk by US naval aircraft from the escort carrier *Anzio*. *RO 46* was sunk by the submarine *Sea Owl*. Only *RO 50* survived the war, and was subsequently scuttled by the US Navy.

Displacement: 1115/1447 tons (surfaced/submerged) *Length:* 80.5 m (264 ft) oa *Beam:* 7 m (23 ft) *Draught:* 4.1 m (13 ft 6 in) *Machinery:* 2-shaft diesels/2 electric motors, 4200/1200 hp=19.75/8 knots (surfaced/submerged) *Armament:* 1 3-in (76-mm); 2 25-mm (1-in); 4 21-in (53-cm) torpedo tubes (bow), 10 torpedoes *Crew:* 54

RO 100-117

Japanese submarine class. Nine submarines of Type KS were ordered under the Additional Programme of 1940, together with a further nine under the 1941 Emergency War Programme. They were really coastal submarines, resembling the British 'U' and 'V' Classes, and were much smaller than the previous Japanese medium submarines with RO designations. A further nine vessels of this class were planned under the 5th Replenishment Programme of 1942, but these were cancelled in favour of midget, supply and suicide types.

The design requirement for this class specified that they should be capable of carrying out patrols around the Pacific island bases, with an endurance of 21 days and a surfaced radius of action of 3500 nautical miles at 12 knots. The maximum diving depth was 75 m (245 ft). The vessels were completed with a 3-in (76-mm) high-angle deck gun instead of the two 25-mm (1-in) weapons originally specified. They carried only four torpedo tubes, mounted in the bow, and only one spare torpedo per tube.

The small size of these submarines made them less liable to detection by radar and sonar. They proved to be very manoeuvrable under water, and could dive rapidly. Nevertheless they were all lost during the war. *RO 103* and *RO 100* were mined on July 28 and November 25, 1943. The US destroyer *England* sank no less than five submarines of this class: *RO 104* (May 23, 1944), *RO 105* (May 31, 1944), *RO 106* (May 22, 1944), *RO 108* (May 26, 1944), and *RO 116* (May 24, 1944). US aircraft sank *RO 117* on June 17, 1944. The US submarine *Batfish* sank *RO 112* and *RO 113* on February 11 and 12, 1945. *RO 110* was sunk by the Indian sloop *Jumna* and the Australian vessels *Ipswich* and *Launceston* on February 11, 1944. US torpedo boats sank *RO 102* on May 14, 1943. *RO 101* was sunk by the US destroyer *Saufley* on September 15, 1943. The US destroyer *Taylor* sank *RO 107* on July 12, 1943, and *RO 111* on June 11, 1944. *RO 109* was sunk by the US high-speed transport *Horace Bass* on April 25, 1945. US destroyers *Melvin* and *Wadleigh* sank *RO 114* on June 17, 1944. US destroyers *Bell, O'Bannon, Jenkins* and *Ulvert Moore* sank *RO 115* on January 31, 1945.

Displacement: 601/782 tons (surfaced/submerged) *Length:* 61 m (200 ft) oa *Beam:* 5.9 m (19 ft 5 in) *Draught:* 3.5 m (11 ft 6 in) *Machinery:* 2-shaft diesels/2 electric motors, 1000/760 hp=14.25/8 knots (surfaced/submerged) *Armament:* 1 3-in (76-mm); 4 21-in (53-cm) torpedo tubes (bow), 8 torpedoes *Crew:* 38

Romeo

Soviet submarine class. The first of the 20 boats of this class believed to exist is thought to have been laid down at Leningrad in 1958 and completed in 1961. The last boat was completed in 1963. No names are known. Following the large ocean-going boats of the *Zulu* and *Foxtrot* Classes, the *Romeo* Class marks a return to the smaller *Whisky* design to which about 200 boats were built in the early 1950s. Dimensions, displacement, speed and range were slightly increased, and the *Romeo* Class have a more streamlined hull than their predecessors. The latter feature and their size suggests that they are hunter-killers. It is believed that over 500 of the class were originally planned, but that the programme was drastically curtailed following the development of the high-speed nuclear submarine, against which they would have had only limited capabilities.

The boats are armed with six bow tubes for a total of 18 53-cm (21-in) torpedoes or 36 mines. Sonar provision is on a par with the larger *Foxtrot* Class. The *Romeos* can easily be distinguished from other Soviet submarines by a 3-m (10-ft) high elliptical pipe which rises from the top of the fin and is thought to provide protection for the snorkel at high speeds.

Six *Romeo* Class submarines were transferred to Egypt, five in 1966 and another in 1969, and two to Bulgaria, as *Pobeda* and *Slava*, in 1972.

Displacement: 1460/1600 tons (surfaced/submerged) *Length:* 75 m (246 ft) oa *Beam:* 7 m (23 ft) *Draught:* 4.3 m (14 ft 1 in) *Machinery:* 2 diesels/2 electric motors, 4000/4000 hp=19/16 knots (surfaced/submerged) *Armament:* 6 53-cm (21-in) torpedo tubes (bow) *Crew:* 65

Rother

British frigate class. The *Rother* or 'River' Class was designed during 1941 to meet the need for a large number of ocean-going escort vessels. The only other escort ships being constructed at the time were the *Gladiolus* Class corvettes which had never been intended as ocean-going vessels and had insufficient endurance, speed and seakeeping ability to serve efficiently in the Atlantic. The *Rother* design was cast around a 91-m (300-ft) hull, which was considered to be the minimum to cope adequately with the Atlantic swell. The design was kept as simple as possible and mercantile construction practice was adopted to allow the ships to be built at yards which did not normally undertake warship work. The machinery was the same as that in the *Gladiolus* Class except that a twin-screw installation of twice the power was provided for a speed of 20 knots. The first 24 ships of the class were provided with an oil-fuel stowage of 440 tons, which gave an endurance of 7500 nautical miles at 10 knots. All subsequent vessels had bunkerage increased to 650 tons which added 2000 nautical miles to the above figure. In service the ships proved very successful, being good seaboats ideally suited to their intended service. The 'frigate' designation, adopted in 1942, had not been used since the days of the sailing ships, and was not particularly appropriate to the new craft as the old frigates were the equivalent of the modern cruiser.

In all, 151 vessels of the *Rother* Class were constructed during 1941-44. Of these 57 were built in British yards. *Annan, Monnow, Ribble (2), Nadder, Nene, Teme, Ettrick* and *Meon* were manned by the Royal Canadian Navy during 1944-45, who also received 72 built in Canadian yards. The Royal Australian Navy received 12 built in Australian yards. Ten of the Canadian vessels were transferred to the US after she entered the war, but the US shipbuilding industry fulfilled their country's needs so efficiently that only *Adur* and *Annan* were actually taken over and served as *PF. 1* and *PF. 2*. *Shiel* went to the Royal Navy under Lend-Lease, and seven (*Barle, Cuckmere, Evenlode, Findhorn, Inver, Lossie* and *Parret*) served with the Royal Canadian Navy. They were eventually transferred to the US in 1946 and subsequently scrapped. A further 13 were transferred but remained under Admiralty control until the end of the war; only *Teviot* and *Test* were returned.

Standard armament consisted of two 4-in (102-mm) low-angle guns, one forward and one aft, four 20-mm (0.79-in) AA guns (later six-eight) a Hedgehog A/S mortar on the forecastle, and eight depth-charge throwers and two racks on the quarterdeck. Early Australian units carried 4-in (102-mm) AA

The *Rother* Class RCN frigate *New Waterford* seen from the deck of an escort carrier during convoy duty in the Second World War

IWM

ROTHER CLASS NAVAL SALES AND TRANSFERS

Name	new name	date of transfer	notes
To Free French			
Windrush	*Decouverte*	1944	French navy 1945, renamed *Lucifer* 1967
Strule	*Croix de Lorraine*	1944	French navy 1945, scrapped 1961
Braid	*L'Aventure*	1944	French navy 1945, scrapped 1962
Frome	*L'Escarmouche*	1944	French navy 1945, renamed *Ailette* 1957, scrapped 1961
Moyola	*Tonkinois*	1944	French navy 1945, renamed *La Confiance* 1953, scrapped 1961
Torridge	*La Surprise*	1944	French navy 1945, renamed *El Maduma* 1964
To Royal Indian Navy			
Bann	*Tir*	1945	training ship 1948
Test	*Neza*	1944	returned to RN 1946
Nadder	*Shamsher*	1944	to Royal Pakistan Navy (RPN), 1948, scrapped 1960
Trent	*Khukri*	1945	survey vessel *Investigator* 1951
Deveron	*Dhanush*	1945	to RPN 1948 as *Zulfiquar,* converted to survey ship
To South African Navy			
Teviot	unchanged	1944	returned to RN 1946
To Royal Netherlands Navy			
Ribble (1)	*Johan Maurits Van Nassau*	1943	sold 1959
To Norway			
Prestonian	*Troll*	1956	renamed *Horten* 1956
Toronto	*Garm*	1956	renamed *Valkyrien* 1964
Penetang	*Draug*	1956	sold 1966
To Denmark			
Annan	*Niels Ebbesen*	1945	scrapped 1963
Monnow	*Holger Danske*	1946	sold 1959
To Burma			
Fal	*Mayu*	1947	in service 1978
To Israel			
Strathadam	*Misgav*	1950	sold 1959 to Ceylon, renamed *Gajabahu*
To Portugal			
Avon	*Nuno Tristã*	1949	sold 1970
Awe	*Diego Gomes*	1949	sold 1969
To Egypt			
Nith	*Domiat*	1948	sunk by HMS *Newfoundland* during Suez campaign 3/10/56
Spey	*Rashid*	1948	

Usk	*Abikir*	1948	scuttled at Suez 1956, salvaged and scrapped 1957
To Dominica			
Carlplace	*Presidente Trujillo*	1946	renamed *Mella* 1962
USS *PF.2*	*Juan Pablo Duarte*	1948	sold 1957
To Peru			
Poundmaker	*Teniene Ferre*	1947	renamed *Ferré* 1953, sold 1966
St Pierre	*Teniente Palacios*	1947	renamed *Palacios* 1953, sold 1966
To Chile			
Joliette	*Iquique*	1946	sold 1968
Glace Bay	*Esmeralda*	1946	renamed *Baquedano* 1952, sold 1968
Sea Cliff	*Covadonga*	1946	sold 1968
To Argentina			
USS *PF.1*	*Hercules*	1946	transferred coastguard 1963

guns, in place of the low-angle weapons, and eight 20-mm (0.79-in) AA. Later Australian units (*Condamine, Culgoa, Murchison* and *Shoalhaven*) carried two twin 4-in HA/LA guns in place of the singles, a twin 40-mm (1.57-in) AA mount, eight 20-mm and an HA/LA director; to compensate for the added topweight the superstructure was cut down and the 4-in guns mounted lower. *Antigonish, Kokannee, La Hulloise, New Waterford, Penetang* and *Swansea* of the Royal Canadian Navy carried a twin 4-in HA/LA mounting forward and a single 3-in (76-mm) AA aft in place of the single 4-in, and six 20-mm (2×2, 2×1). The two US vessels were fitted with standard US weapons and carried three single 3-in AA, two twin 40-mm AA, four single 20-mm and the US version of Hedgehog. Six of the British-built vessels, *Chelmer, Ettrick, Tweed, Halladale, Helmsdale* and *Cam*, were fitted experimentally with geared steam turbines of 6500 shp, but the restricted production capacity for this type of machinery prevented its general use.

Five of the class were sunk by torpedoes from submarines: *Itchen* by *U 666* off Iceland on September 23, 1943; *Tweed* by *U 305* off Ireland on January 7, 1944; *Valleyfield* by *U 548* off Cape Race on May 7, 1944; *Mourne* by *U 767* in the English Channel on June 15, 1944. *Chebogue* was torpedoed on October 4, 1944, by *U 1277*, foundered off Swansea five days later, and was raised and scrapped during 1947-48. *Lagan, Teme, Cuckmere* and *Magog* were damaged beyond repair after being torpedoed by U-Boats; *Cam* was damaged beyond repair after striking a mine. All these vessels were sold for scrapping during 1945-46. On December 20, 1946, *Aire* was wrecked on a reef off Bombay. *Plym* was used as the platform for the first British atomic bomb, which was exploded at Monte Bello on October 3, 1952.

During the decade following the war most of the class was sold either to foreign navies or for scrap. A few were sold into merchant service of which two, *Hallowell* and *Orkney*, eventually found their way back into naval

MOD

***Above:* HMS *Towy*, a British-built *Rother* Class frigate, in October 1943. She has standard features but two 20-mm Oerlikon antiaircraft guns have been added to the bridge wings**

MOD

HMS *Fal* in July 1943. A British-built *Rother* Class frigate, she was transferred to Burma in 1947 and renamed *Mayu*. In 1978 she was still in service, one of the last remaining

service when purchased by Israel in 1952.

Twenty-one of the Canadian vessels were modernized during 1953-58, of which three were transferred to Norway; all remained in service until the late 1960s before being sold for scrap. Alterations included extending the forecastle deck to the stern, fitting a new bridge structure, increasing the height of the funnel and fitting a new tripod foremast. The armament was altered to a twin 4-in forward, two single 40-mm AA in the bridge wings, a twin 40-mm AA amidships and two Squid A/S mortars aft. With the exception of *Lachlan*, which was transferred to New Zealand in 1950, the Australian vessels remained in service until the early 1960s when all except *Barcoo, Diamantina* and *Gascoyne* were sold for scrap. The three survivors and *Lachlan* were converted to survey vessels.

(British built) *Aire, Awe, Exe, Itchen, Dovey*—built by Fleming and Ferguson
Annan, Helford, Lochy, Tees, Test, Teviot—built by Hall Russell
Avon, Bann, Jed, Monnow, Taff, Tavy, Trent—built by C Hill
Ballinderry, Dart, Ribble (2), Frome, Torridge—built by Blyth
Braid, Ribble (1)—built by Simons
Cam, Chelmer—built by G Brown
Derg, Ness, Nith, Strule, Windrush, Rye—built by H Robb
Deveron, Fal, Lagan, Mourne, Moyola, Nadder, Nene, Odzani, Plym, Rother, Spey, Swale, Tay, Teme, Towy, Usk, Waveney, Wear—built by Smiths Dock
Ettrick—built by J Crown
Halladale, Helmdale, Kale, Meon, Tweed—built by Inglis

(Australian built) *Barwon, Barcoo*—built by Cockatoo dockyard
Burdekin, Diamantina, Shoalhaven—built by Walkers
Condamine—built by Newcastle dockyard
Macquarie, Gascoyne, Hawkesbury, Lachlan—built by Morts Dock
Culgoa—built by Williamstown dockyard
Murchison—built by Evans Deakin

(Canadian built) *Adur, Buckingham, Annan, Barle, Cuckmere, Eastview, Evenlode, Findhorn, Grou, Hallowell, Inver, La Hulloise, Lanark, Longueuil, Lossie, Magog, Matane, Montreal, Parret, Poundmaker, Runnymede, St John, Shiel, Stettler, Stonetown, Matane*—built by Vickers, Canada
Antigonish, Beacon Hill, Capilano, Chebogue, Kokanee, New Glasgow, New Waterford, Orkney, Port Colborne, Prince Rupert, St Catherines, St Stephen, Springhill, Strathadam, Swansea, Waskesiu, Wentworth—built by Yarrow, Canada
Prestonian, Carlplace, Coaticook, Toronto, Inch Arran, La Salle, Sea Cliffe, Buckingham, Penetang, St Pierre, St Therese, Sussexvale—built by Davie Shipbuilding
Cap de La Madeleine, Cape Breton, Joliette, Outremont, Kirkland Lake, Thetford, Valleyfield, Dunver—built by Morton
Charlottetown, Lauzon, Jonquiere, Fort Erie, Glace Bay, Levis, Victoriaville—built by G T Davie

Displacement: 1370 tons (standard), 1865 tons (full load) *Length:* 91.8 m (301 ft 3 in) oa *Beam:* 11.1 m (36 ft 6 in) *Draught:* 2.1 m (7 ft) *Machinery:* 2-shaft triple-expansion, 5500 ihp=20 knots *Armament:* 2 4-in (102-mm) (2×1); 4 20-mm (0.79-in) AA (4×1); 1 Hedgehog A/S mortar *Crew:* 140

HMS *Rothesay* fitted with Type 993 radar. She was built at Yarrow and launched in 1957

HMS *Rhyl* was completed on October 31, 1960, and underwent a major conversion after 1968

HMS *Plymouth,* like her sisters in the *Rothesay* Class, has two Babcock and Wilcox boilers

Rothesay

British antisubmarine frigate class. Twelve ships of the class were laid down between 1956-1959. The last three, *Fowey, Hastings,* and *Weymouth* were compiled as the first ships of the *Leander* Class, and the remaining nine ships were completed in 1960-61. The design followed on directly from the six *Whitby* Class frigates and received the designation Modified Type 12. Displacement, dimensions and the propulsion system were identical, the *Whitby* Class having proved remarkably successful in their excellent seakeeping characteristics, for which the hull form with its high freeboard and 'broken nose' was largely responsible. A few minor modifications in layout between decks were made following extensive experience with the earlier ships, and there were certain changes in the external appearance. The *Rothesay* Class were fitted with a thicker, raked funnel with a prominent black cap, and a large deckhouse was built up aft with a view to fitting the Seacat short-range surface-to-air missile. As a short-term measure a single 40-

mm (1.57-in) Bofors was carried, as in *Lincoln* of the *Salisbury* Class, replacing the twin 40-mm mounting of the *Whitby* Class.

Otherwise armament and sensors remained the same: a twin 114-mm (4.5-in) Mk 6 dual-purpose mounting in front of the bridge, controlled by a Mk 6M director; two Limbo A/S mortars aft. Type 293 air-search and Type 978 navigation radars were mounted side by side atop the lattice foremast, and a Type 277 height-finder was fitted between the foremast and the director.

The success of the *Rothesay* Class was soon overshadowed by the superior anti-submarine qualities of the *Leander* Class, especially their Wasp helicopter. In a major conversion programme the deckhouse aft was therefore replaced by a helicopter hangar, above which a quadruple Seacat launcher and a GWS-20 director were mounted. A small enclosed mainmast carried the IFF antenna. Only the after Limbo was retained, the forward part of the well being plated over to provide a deck for the helicopter. The bridge remained unmodified, but the Mk 6 director above it was replaced by the lighter MRS-3. The lattice foremast was replaced by a taller enclosed mast, on top of which a Type 993 'quarter-cheese' air-search scanner replaced the older Type 293 model. The Type 978 navigation radar was angled out on a platform as on the later *Leander* Class ships, in order to assist helicopter operations. Other improvements included full air-conditioning, modernized operations room, and better communications facilities. *Rothesay* herself was converted in Rosyth naval dockyard between 1966-68. She was followed by *Yarmouth, Plymouth, Londonderry, Lowestoft, Falmouth, Berwick, Rhyl* and *Brighton.*

Since conversion the *Rothesay* Class,

HMS *Lowestoft* with her Wasp A/S helicopter which was added after her conversion and is armed with homing torpedoes. It is housed in a hangar built on the after deck and though this has necessitated the removal of one of the A/S mortars the helicopter has greatly extended the range of modernised *Rothesay* frigates

PPL

No and name	laid down	launched	completed	builder
F.101 ***Yarmouth***	11/57	3/59	3/60	John Brown
F.103 ***Lowestoft***	6/58	6/60	10/61	Stephen
F.106 ***Brighton***	7/57	10/59	9/61	Yarrow
F.107 ***Rothesay***	11/56	12/57	4/60	Yarrow
F.108 ***Londonderry***	11/56	5/58	7/60	White
F.113 ***Falmouth***	11/57	12/59	7/61	Swan Hunter
F.115 ***Berwick***	6/58	12/59	6/61	Harland & Wolff
F.126 ***Plymouth***	7/58	7/59	5/61	Devonport dockyard
F.129 ***Rhyl***	1/58	4/59	10/60	Portsmouth dockyard

along with the *Leanders*, have formed the backbone of the Royal Navy frigate squadrons and have seen wide deployment. In 1977 *Lowestoft* was fitted with a large prototype towed sonar array for trials.

(As built) *Displacement:* 2150 tons (standard) 2560 tons (full load) *Length:* 113 m (370 ft 9 in) oa *Beam:* 12.5 m (41 ft) *Draught:* 5.3 m (17 ft 5 in) *Machinery:* 2-shaft steam turbines, 30 000 shp=30 knots *Armament:* 2 114-mm (4.5-in) Mk 6 (1×2); 1 40-mm (1.57-in) AA; 2 Limbo triple A/S mortars *Crew:* 200

(As converted) *Displacement:* 2380 tons (standard) 2800 tons (full load) *Dimensions and machinery:* as built *Armament:* 2 114-mm (1×2) 2 20-mm (0.79-in) (2×1); 1 Limbo triple A/S mortar; 1 Wasp helicopter *Crew:* 235

Rudderow

US destroyer escort class, built 1943-45. These were the last of the six types of DEs developed during the Second World War, and they were a 5-in (127-mm) gunned version of the turbo-electric *Buckley* type. The main changes were the addition of a twin 40-mm (1.57-in) Bofors AA mounting forward and the reduction of the height of the bridge and funnel.

Construction of the *Rudderow* Class began in the last quarter of 1943, and 71 had been launched by the end of 1944. Orders were given for 268 but eventually only 81 were completed, the rest being cancelled before launch. Builders included Philadelphia navy yard, Charleston navy yard, Bethlehem (Hingham), Bethlehem (Quincy) and Defoe (Bay City, Michigan). Only 22 were completed as destroyer escorts:
Rudderow (DE.224), *Day* (DE.225), *Chaffee* (DE.230), *Hodges* (DE.231), *Riley* (DE.579), *Leslie L B Knox* (DE.580), *McNulty* (DE.581), *Metivier* (DE.582), *George A Johnson* (DE.583), *Charles J Kimmel* (DE.584), *Daniel A Joy* (DE.585), *Lough* (DE.586), *Thomas F Nickel* (DE.587), *Peiffer* (DE.588), *Tinsman* (DE.589), *De Long* (DE.684), *Coates* (DE.685), *Eugene E Elmore* (DE.686), *Holt* (DE.706), *Jobb* (DE.707), *Parle* (DE.708), *Bray* (DE.709). *DE.226-229, 232-237, 281-283, 590-606, 674, 687-692* and *710-722* became high-speed transports (APDs).

The 5-in guns carried necessitated the lowering of the funnel and bridge heights to reduce topweight. The large number of close-range guns mounted in these ships was part of a general trend in US vessels towards the end of the war, and a reflection of the demand for increased firepower in the Pacific theatre.

The APD conversions were likewise the result of the exigencies of the Pacific war, where they were needed to augment the supply of landing craft. The conversion involved installation of two landing-craft on davits on each side of the ship, and the construction of decks for 162 troops. A lattice mainmast was also fitted to operate cargo booms.

Most *Rudderows* served in the Pacific during the war and none were lost. *Chaffee* was scrapped in 1948; *Riley* became the Taiwan *Tai Yuan* in 1969; *Holt* became the South Korean *Chung Nam* in 1963. The remainder have been disposed of since the mid-1960s.

Displacement: 1450 tons (standard), 1780 tons (full load) *Length:* 93.3 m (306 ft) oa *Beam:* 11.3 m (37 ft) *Draught:* 3 m (9 ft 9 in) *Machinery:* 2-shaft General Electric turbo-electric, 12 000 shp=24 knots *Armament:* 2 5-in (127-mm)/38-cal (2×1); 10 40-mm (1.57-in) Bofors; 6 20-mm (0.79-in) Oerlikon; 1 Hedgehog A/S mortar; 8 depth-charge throwers *Crew:* 220

S.41-60

West German missile patrol boat class. Ordered in 1970 from Constructions Méchaniques de Normandie, Cherbourg, the first boat, *S.41* (P6141) was launched and completed in 1972; *S.42-47* (P6142-6147) were completed in 1973; *S.48-54* (P6148-6154) in 1974; and *S.55-60* (P6155-6160) in 1975. Eight of the hulls (the even-numbered boats from P6146 to P6160) were contracted to Lürssen Werft but all 20 were fitted out in France.

Known as the Type 148, the class was intended to replace the first twenty of the ageing *Jaguar* Class (Type 140 and Type 141). They are basically of the *la Combattante II* design, with steel hulls and lightweight superstructure. The propulsion machinery comprises four MTU diesels each of 3000 bhp on four shafts for a maximum speed of 35.5 knots. The armament shows a considerable advance on that of the boats they are replacing. They are armed with an OTO-Melara 76-mm (3-in) gun forward, with four Exocet missile launchers in two pairs angled out to port and starboard aft of the bridge, and a single 40-mm (1.57-in) Bofors mounted on the stern. The latter weapon will eventually be replaced by eight mines. The search and tracker radars are of French origin.

S.41-50 make up the Third Squadron of S-Boats, and *S.51-60* the Fifth Squadron.

Displacement: 234 tons (standard), 265 tons (full load) *Length:* 47 m (154 ft 2 in) oa *Beam:* 7 m (23 ft) *Draught:* 2 m (6 ft 7 in) *Machinery:* 4-shaft, 4 MTU diesels, 12 000 bhp=35.5 knots *Armament:* 1 76-mm (3-in) OTO-Melara DP; 1 40-mm (1.57-in) Bofors; 4 Exocet launchers *Crew:* 30

S.61-70

West German missile patrol boat class. Known as the Type 143, the class was ordered in 1972 as a replacement for the last ten boats of the *Jaguar* Class. *S.61* (P6111) was laid down in late 1972 and ran trials from December 1974. *S.62-67* (P6112-6117) were completed in 1976 and *S.68-70* (P1118-1120) in 1977. AEG Telefunken, an electronics company, was the prime contractor, with Lürssen Werft and Kröger Werft as subcontractors. This reflects the emphasis placed by the navy on a well integrated weapon system, although 'platform' design has by no means been neglected. Using the traditional expertise of the two shipyards a large wooden hull has been designed with a view to improved seakeeping. The frames and the superstructure are of aluminium, with steel floors to take the weight of the main engines, perpetuating the 'composite' construction of the *Jaguar* Class. *S.65, S.67* and *S.69* were built by Kröger at Rendsburg, the remaining seven boats by Lürssen at Vegesack.

Four MTU diesels each rated at 4000 bhp drive four shafts for a maximum speed of 38 knots, and their endurance is double that of the French-built Type 148. With an increase of 10 m (33 ft) in length and 100 tons in displacement the boats carry an even more comprehensive armament than the Type 148. An OTO-Melara 76-mm (3-in) mounting is fitted in front of the bridge, with two pairs of Exocet surface-to-surface missile launchers aft of it. The 40-mm (1.57-in) Bofors of the Type 148 has been replaced on the stern by a second OTO 76-mm gun, and 53-cm (21-in) wire-guided torpedoes of the Seal type are mounted on either side of it. Search and tracking functions are combined in a Dutch HSA WM 27 radar comprising separate antennae mounted above and below a common platform fitted above the bridge and covered by a distinctive radome. The tall mainmast which rises from the after end of the superstructure carries elaborate ESM antennae to monitor enemy radar emissions, and communications antennae to enable the boats to coordinate their attacks. All sensor data is coordinated in a computer-equipped Combat Information Centre.

S.61-70 make up the Second Squadron of S-Boats. Following the cancellation of the Type 162 hydrofoil project it is thought that ten boats of an improved Type 143 will be ordered to replace the *Zobel* Class at the end of the 1970s.

Displacement: 378 tons (full load) *Length:* 57 m (187 ft) oa *Beam:* 7.8 m (25 ft 7 in) *Draught:* 2.4 m (7 ft 10 in) *Machinery:* 4 shafts, 4 MTU diesels, 16 000 bhp=38 knots *Armament:* 2 76-mm (3-in) OTO-Melara DP (2×1); 4 Exocet launchers; 2 53-cm (21-in) torpedo tubes *Crew:* 40

Saam

Iranian fast destroyer class. Developed from the Vosper Mk 5 design, construction was shared between the Southampton yard of Vosper Thornycroft and the Newcastle and Barrow yards of Vickers-Armstrongs, the order being announced in August 1966. *Rostam*, launched at Newcastle, was transferred to Barrow for completion. The Mk 5 design evolved in the mid-1960s in response to a requirement from smaller navies for modern high-performance vessels which would be simple to operate and would not make heavy demands on skilled manpower. The technological developments that made this possible were the advent of marine gas turbines with power in excess of 20 000 hp and the miniaturization of electrical components. Efficient maintenance of both propulsion and electronics could be achieved by unit replacement, enabling repairs to be carried out at support bases. This allowed the crew to be reduced to 125 men, with less space consequently required for accommodation.

Two Olympus gas turbines give a maximum speed of 40 knots, while Paxman diesels give economic cruising at 17.5 knots. The machinery installation is operated from a centralized control room with full instrumentation.

The armament chosen for the *Saam* Class is primarily offensive, the main weapon against shipping being the Italian Sea Killer missile, for which a quintuple launcher is mounted on the quarterdeck. The missiles are backed up by a single 114-mm (4.5-in) DP forward. *Rostam* and *Faramarz* were fitted with the Mk 8 model on completion but *Saam* and *Zaal* were initially fitted with the Mk 5 mounting until refitted in 1976-77. AA weapons consist of a lightweight triple Seacat launcher forward of the bridge and an Oerlikon-Bührle twin 35-mm (1.38-in) automatic on the stern. A Limbo A/S mortar is fitted in a well in the quarterdeck. Air search is provided by a Plessey AWS-2 scanner mounted on a pedestal just forward of the squat funnel, while fire control is performed by two Italian Sea Hunter directors on and below the foremast. The sonar retracts into the hull and is covered by doors to protect it at high speeds. Sensor data and weapons control are coordinated in a computerized operations room.

No and name	laid down	launched	completed	builder
71 (ex-DE 12) *Saam*	5/67	7/68	2/71	Vosper Thornycroft
72 (ex-DE 14) *Zaal*	3/68	3/69	3/71	Vickers, Barrow
73 (ex-DE 13) *Faramarz*	7/68	7/69	2/72	Vosper Thornycroft
74 (ex-DE 15) *Rostam*	12/67	3/69	3/72	Vickers, Newcastle

Displacement: 1110 tons (standard), 1290 tons (full load) *Length:* 94.4 m (309 ft 9 in) oa *Beam:* 10.4 m (34 ft) *Draught:* 3.4 m (11 ft 3 in) *Machinery:* 2 Olympus gas turbines, 48 000 hp=40 knots; 2 Paxman diesels, 3800 hp=17.5 knots (CODOG arrangement on 2 shafts) *Armament:* 1 114-mm (4.5-in) Mk 8 DP; 2 35-mm (1.38-in) AA (1×2); 1 Sea Killer launcher; 1 Seacat launcher; 1 Limbo A/S mortar *Crew:* 125

Saar

Israeli missile patrol boat class. Although designed by Lürssen Werft, political considerations meant that they could not be built in Germany. The order was therefore placed with Constructions Méchaniques de Normandie, Cherbourg. *Mivtach* (311), *Miznach* (312), and *Misgav* (313) were launched in 1967 and completed 1968, and *Eilat* (321), *Haifa* (322), and *Akko* (323) were launched and completed in 1968. The second group of six boats, *Saar* (331), *Soufa* (332), *Gaasch* (333), *Herev* (341), *Hanit* (342) and *Hetz* (343), were all launched and completed in 1969. Five of these were dramatically hijacked by the Israelis when almost complete, following the imposition of an arms embargo by France.

The class was ordered to counter the Styx-armed 'Komar' Class FPBs transferred to Egypt and Syria by the USSR in the early 1960s. Vessels of this size were seen as ideal for the coast-defence role and the advent of a new generation of advanced and compact weapon systems would give them more hitting power than the second-hand destroyers on which Israel had previously relied. For their own protection they rely heavily on their high speed: four Maybach fast-running diesels each of 3500 bhp drive four shafts to give them a maximum speed of over 40 knots. The armament varies between individual boats. That of the first group has included an arrangement with three single 40-mm (1.57-in) guns and two 53-cm (21-in) torpedoes, and one with a single 40-mm forward of the bridge, two single fixed launchers for Gabriel surface-to-surface missiles on either side of it, and two triple trainable Gabriel launchers aft of the bridge. The second group mount an OTO-Melara 76-mm (3-in) gun forward. Aft of the bridge two triple trainable launchers are fitted. The search and tracker radars are of French origin. The first group are also fitted with sonar.

A *Saar* Class fast missile attack craft of the Israeli navy. They saw considerable action during the Middle East war of 1973

Israeli navy

Excellent seakeeping qualities and good endurance are ascribed to the class, and they performed extremely well in the Middle East war of October 1973. In skirmishes off Latakia and the Nile Delta three Syrian and four Egyptian Soviet-built boats were claimed sunk by the Gabriel missile, which has a range of 20 km (12.5 miles), little more than half that of the Styx. The *Saar* Class also took part in bombardments of enemy coast and the protection of shipping.

Displacement: 220 tons (standard), 250 tons (full load) *Length:* 45 m (147 ft 8 in) oa *Beam:* 7 m (23 ft) *Draught:* 1.8 m (6 ft) *Machinery:* 4 shafts, 4 Maybach diesels, 14 000 bhp=40 knots *Armament:* (First group) 3 40-mm (1.57-in) (3×1); 2 53-cm (21-in) torpedo tubes; (First group, alternative scheme) 1 40-mm; 8 Gabriel launchers (2×3, 2×1); (Second group) 1 76-mm (3-in) OTO-Melara; 6 Gabriel SSM launchers (2×3); *Crew:* 35-40

Sailfish

US submarine class. When ordered in 1952 these two boats, built at Portsmouth navy yard, were the largest non-nuclear submarines to be built for the US Navy since *Narwhal* (SS.167) and *Nautilus* (SS.168), completed in 1930. *Sailfish* was laid down in December 1953, launched in September 1955 and completed in April 1956. *Salmon* was laid down in March 1954, launched in February 1956 and completed in August 1956.

Designed as radar picket submarines they were given the classification SSR. It was intended that they should surface ahead of carrier task forces to give advanced warning of air attack, being less vulnerable in this role than destroyers which had suffered heavy losses when serving as radar pickets in the war against Japan. They therefore had a retractable air-search scanner mounted on the conning tower, a large height-finding aerial abaft the conning tower and an elaborate air control centre. Speed when surfaced was much higher than when submerged.

In 1959 *Salmon* was modified as a missile-guidance submarine to act as a relay for long-range surface-to-surface missiles. Following the abandonment of the SSR concept both ships underwent FRAM II conversion. They emerged minus their radars but with three fin-shaped PUFF sonar domes for the BQG-4 passive fire-control sonar just aft of the conning tower and close to the stern. Both boats were reclassified SS in March 1961. In 1968 *Salmon* was reclassified AGSS to serve

Canadian Armed Forces

From left to right HMCS *Fraser* (233), HMCS *Saguenay* (206), HMCS *Skeena* (207) and HMCS *Margaree*, *St Laurent* Class frigates of the Royal Canadian Navy during an exercise in 1972. They are light but have excellent seakeeping qualities with their high freeboard

No and name	laid down	launched	completed	builder
DDH.205 *St Laurent*	11/50	11/51	10/55	Canadian Vickers
DDH.206 *Saguenay*	4/51	7/53	12/56	Halifax shipyards
DDH.207 *Skeena*	6/51	8/52	3/57	Burrard
DDH.229 *Ottawa*	6/51	4/53	11/56	Canadian Vickers
DDH.230 *Margaree*	9/51	3/56	10/57	Halifax Shipyards
DDH.233 *Fraser*	12/51	2/53	6/57	Burrard (completed Yarrow, Esquimalt)
DDH.234 *Assiniboine*	5/52	2/54	8/56	Marine Industries

USS *Sailfish* (below) and her sister *Salmon*, the largest conventionally powered submarines built for the US Navy in over 20 years, were originally completed as radar picket vessels but later converted to the attack role, with an armament of six bow torpedo tubes

US Navy

as a test-bed for the US Navy's deep-submergence rescue vehicle (DSRV) programme, but she reverted to SS designation the following year when the programme was abandoned. *Salmon* paid off at the end of 1977, with her sister due to pay off a year later.

Displacement: 2625/3168 tons (surfaced/submerged) *Length:* 106.8 m (350 ft 6 in) oa *Beam:* 8.8 m (29 ft) *Draught:* 5.5 m (18 ft) *Machinery:* 4 diesels/2 electric motors, 6000 bhp/8200 hp=19.5/14 knots (surfaced/submerged) *Armament:* 6 53-cm (21-in) torpedo tubes (bow) *Crew:* 95

St Laurent

Canadian destroyer escort class. Design work was begun in 1949 but construction was delayed because plans had to be constantly revised with the development of high-speed submarines. The *St Laurent* Class were the first major warships designed and built in Canada and extensive prefabrication was used with a view to rapid production in an emergency. A flush deck with high freeboard gave them excellent seakeeping qualities, and extensive use of aluminium was made in superstructure and fittings to keep topweight to a minimum.

Canada relied heavily on British and US technical assistance in the construction of the class. Yarrow supplied Canadian Vickers with a complete set of machinery for the name-ship, machinery for the others being manufactured under licence in Canada. The weapons and sensors were largely of US origin. Originally two twin 76-mm (3-in)/50-cal were fitted in open mounts fore and aft, but the forward mounting was later enclosed in a fibreglass shield to give more protection in rough weather. Two single 40-mm (1.57-in) AA were mounted on a deckhouse abaft the single funnel, and the armament was completed by two British Limbo A/S mortars, housed in a quarterdeck well with a weatherproof cover. Unlike later classes based on this design they had no gunnery director. The SPS-12 air-search and SPS-10 surface-search radars are of US origin, and two hull-mounted sonars were fitted at completion. In 1961 *St Laurent* had her stern cut away for an SQS-504 towed sonar. This was installed in the other ships when they and *St Laurent* herself underwent a major conversion between 1963 and 1966 to enable them to operate a Sea King A/S helicopter—the first destroyer-sized ships to carry a helicopter of this size. The conversion involved the construction of a flight deck in place of the after AA guns and one of the Limbo mortars, with a large hangar extended forward. The size of the hangar necessitated dividing the funnel into twin uptakes. At a later date triple Mk 32 tubes for antisubmarine homing torpedoes were added beneath the flight deck at upper-deck level. After their conversion the *St Laurent* Class were reclassified from DDE to DDH.

St Laurent was discarded in 1974, but *Fraser*, *Ottawa* and *Skeena* began major refits in 1977.

Displacement: 2260 tons (standard), 2800 tons (full load) *Length:* 115.5 m (379 ft) oa *Beam:* 12.8 m (42 ft) *Draught:* 4 m (13 ft) *Machinery:* 2-shaft steam turbines, 30000 shp=28 knots *Armament:* (As built) 4 76-mm (3-in)/50-cal AA (2×2); 2 40-mm (1.57-in) Bofors AA (2×1); 2 Limbo A/S mortars; (After conversion) 2 76-mm/50-cal (1×2); 1 Limbo A/S mortar; 6 Mk 32 A/S torpedo tubes (2×3); 1 Sea King helicopter *Crew:* 250

Salisbury

British frigate class. In addition to the four ships completed, a fifth, *Exeter*, ordered in 1956, was cancelled the following year for economy reasons; a sixth ship, *Coventry*, was completed as *Penelope* of the *Leander* Class; and a seventh projected vessel, *Gloucester*, was never built. Known as the Type 61, the *Salisbury* Class had the same hull and propulsion machinery as the Type 41 antiaircraft frigates of the *Leopard* Class which were built in parallel with them. Construction was all-welded and largely prefabricated with a view to rapid production in wartime. The hull form was a shorter version of the Type 12 hull which was to prove successful in the *Whitby* Class antisubmarine frigates. Both the Type 41 and the Type 61 were designed primarily for convoy escort duties. Endurance was therefore of greater importance than high speed, leading to a novel choice of propulsion system in the form of the Admiralty Standard Range 1 diesel. Four of these were linked to each shaft to give a maximum speed of 24 knots and a range of 7500 nautical miles at 16 knots. The uptakes were initially led up inside the lattice masts, giving the ships a distinctive appearance.

The role of the Type 61 was the direction of carrier-borne and shore-based aircraft. To equip the ship for this role one twin 114-mm (4.5-in) mounting was discarded in favour of additional air-search and height-finding equipment. The armament therefore comprised a twin 114-mm mounting forward, controlled by a Mk 6M director, a twin 40-mm (1.57-in) mounting aft and a Squid A/S mortar. *Lincoln*, the fourth ship, was completed with a large deckhouse aft intended for the Seacat short-range surface-to-air missile, and a single 40-mm Bofors was mounted as a temporary measure, as in the *Rothesay* Class. Apart from the standard Type 293 air search and Type 978 navigation radars a Type 277 Heightfinder was fitted between the foremast and the Mk 6 director with a Type 282 aerial aft.

In 1962 the after funnel and lattice mast were replaced in *Salisbury* by a new mack (mast/stack) topped by a Type 965 'double bedstead' air-search radar. *Chichester* was taken in hand in 1964 and refitted with macks fore and aft, with the additional replacement of the Type 293 by the Type 993. The Type 282 aerial was also raised in height. These modifications were extended to *Llandaff* in 1966 and *Lincoln* in 1968. *Lincoln* also had her 40-mm gun replaced by a quadruple Seacat launcher with a GWS-20 director. *Salisbury* was then taken in hand again, her foremast was modified on the same pattern as the other three ships, and she too was fitted with Seacat. Both *Lincoln* and *Salisbury* were given two single 20-mm (0.79-in) guns.

Lincoln went into reserve in the early

No and name	laid down	launched	completed	builder
F.32 *Salisbury*	1/52	6/53	2/57	Devonport dockyard
F.59 *Chichester*	1/53	4/55	5/58	Fairfield
F.61 *Llandaff*	8/53	11/55	4/58	Hawthorn Leslie
F.99 *Lincoln*	5/55	4/59	7/60	Fairfield

HMS *Llandaff*, a *Salisbury* Class frigate, showing her mack (mast/stack) with Type 95 'double bedstead' air-search radar

PPL

1970s, emerging briefly in 1976 to take part in skirmishes over fishing rights in Icelandic waters. *Chichester* served as Hong Kong guardship (minus her 'double bedstead') from 1973 until she decommissioned in 1976. *Llandaff* was sold to Bangladesh in 1976 as the *Oomar Farouq*, and *Salisbury* was sold to Egypt in 1978.

Displacement: 2170 tons (standard), 2408 tons (full load) *Length:* 106.6 m (349 ft 9 in) oa *Beam:* 12.2 m (40 ft) *Draught:* 4.7 m (15 ft 6 in) *Machinery:* 2 shafts, 8 ASR 1 diesels, 14 400 bhp=24 knots *Armament:* 2 114-mm (4.5-in) Mk 6 DP (1×2); 2 40-mm (1.57-in) (1×2) (*Chichester* and *Llandaff*); 2 20-mm (0.79-in) (2×1) (*Lincoln* and *Salisbury*); 1 Seacat launcher *Crew:* 237

San Luis

Argentine submarine class, launched 1972-73. *Salta* and *San Luis* have been built to the Type 209 design of Ingenieurkontor, Lübeck. This is a single-hull design with two main ballast tanks and trim tanks fore and aft. Snort gear and remotely controlled machinery are fitted. The batteries are of high capacity and the propulsion systems drive a slow-turning single screw. Both active and passive sonar are fitted, together with the usual radar, periscopes and Omega receiver.

Both ships were built in sections at Howaldtswerke Deutsche Werft of Kiel. *Salta* was launched in November 1972 and *San Luis* was launched in May 1973. The sections were shipped to Tanador, Buenos Aires for final assembly, and both ships were completed in May 1974.

Two more submarines to the same design have been projected for the Argentine navy, while two (*Pijao* and *Tayrona*) are in service with Colombia, two (*Shyri* and *Huancavilea*) have been built for Ecuador, four (*Glavkos, Nereus, Triton* and *Proteus*) have been completed for Greece, and six have been completed or are under construction for Peru. A further four Type 209 units have been built for the Turkish navy (*Atilay, Saldiray, Batiray* and *Yildiray*). Four are also under construction, or have been completed, for Venezuela. Though none of the type is in service with the West German navy it has been a most successful export design.

Displacement: 1180/1230 tons (surfaced/submerged) *Length:* 55.9 m (183 ft 5 in) oa *Beam:* 6.25 m (20 ft 6 in) *Draught:* 5.5 m (18 ft) *Machinery:* 1-shaft diesel-electric, 5000 hp=10/22 knots (surfaced/submerged) *Armament:* 8 53-cm (21-in) torpedo tubes (bow) *Crew:* 32

Savage

British destroyer class. The eight *Savage* or 'S' Class destroyers ordered in January 1941 formed the 5th Flotilla of the Emergency War Programme. They were laid down in 1941, launched during 1942-43 and completed in 1943 (*Shark* 1944). They were repeats of the 3rd and 4th Flotillas (*Quilliam* and *Rotherham* Classes) except that they adopted a modified bow form and an improved gun armament.

The bow was altered to resemble that in the *Afridi* Class destroyers which suffered less from spray and wetness forward than the *Javelin* Class, whose hull form was being employed in the emergency flotillas. This change involved providing a steeper rake to the stem and increased the overall length by 1.4 m (4 ft 6 in). The alterations to the armament were mainly concerned with improving AA defence. They retained the four 4.7-in (120-mm) Mk IX guns but these were fitted in new Mk XXII mountings which provided 55° elevation, instead of 40° as in the earlier ships. For the close-range armament it was decided to substitute a twin 40-mm (1.57-in) Bofors mounting for the quadruple pom-pom and to fit this on the platform between the torpedo tubes, where it had a wide arc of fire, instead of abaft the funnel. They were also to have carried four single 20-mm (0.79-in) Oerlikons, but twin 20-mm mountings were substituted for these prior to completion, two being fitted in the bridge wings and two abaft the funnel. Five of the class were complete with this armament, but *Scorpion* carried a quad pom-pom and *Swift* and *Savage* two extra twin 20-mm mountings in place of the twin 40-mm which was in short supply. *Savage* also differed in carrying a prototype of the twin HA/LA 4.5-in (114-mm) turret mounting (subsequently fitted in the *Battle* Class) in A position instead of her forward 4.7-in guns, and to avoid complications in ammunition supply and control her after 4.7-in were also replaced by single 4.5-in guns. Subsequently *Savage* was fitted with two single 20-mm on B gun deck, while in 1945 *Saumarez* had all her 20-mm guns removed and four single 40-mm Bofors fitted on the platform abaft the funnel. The class was also fitted with the usual outfit of radar equipment and all were fitted with lattice foremasts either prior to completion or shortly afterwards, except for *Savage* which carried a tripod to the end of her career.

On completion *Shark* and *Success* were transferred to the Norwegian navy and renamed *Svenner* and *Stord* respectively, but remained under Admiralty control for the remainder of the war. All eight ships of the class joined the Home Fleet, and in December 1943 were formed into the 23rd Destroyer Flotilla. In this same month *Scorpion, Stord, Saumarez* and *Savage* took part in the Battle of North Cape during which the German battlecruiser *Scharnhorst* was sunk. Their contribution was a torpedo attack resulting in four hits which slowed down the enemy ship and prevented her escaping from the battleship *Duke of York* and other units of the Home Fleet.

In 1944 the 23rd Flotilla was transferred to the Channel to cover the invasion of Normandy, and during this operation two of the class were lost. *Svenner* was torpedoed and sunk by an E-Boat off Le Havre on D-Day (June 6, 1944), and *Swift* hit a mine and sank off the beachhead on June 24. The surviving vessels remained in Home Waters until the end of the war, except *Saumarez* which transferred to the Eastern Fleet where she became leader of the 26th Flotilla. On the night of May 16, 1945, in the Straits of Malacca, she and her flotilla of 'V' Class destroyers sank the Japanese cruiser *Haguro* with eight torpedoes. *Saumarez* was hit by three 8-in (203-mm) shells, receiving heavy damage but surprisingly had only two casualties.

In 1945 *Scorpion, Scourge* and *Serapis* were transferred to the Royal Netherlands Navy and renamed *Kortenaer, Evertsen* and *Piet Hein*; they were sold for scrapping in 1962-63. *Saumarez* was sold for scrapping in 1950, with *Stord* (which was retained by the Norwegian navy) following in 1959 and *Savage* in 1962.

Saumarez, Savage—built by Hawthorn Leslie
Scorpion, Scourge—built by Cammell Laird
Serapis, Shark—built by Scotts
Success, Swift—built by White

Displacement: 1710 tons (standard), 2430 tons (full load) *Length:* 110.6 m (362 ft 9 in) oa *Beam*, 10.87 m (35 ft 8 in) *Draught:* 3.05 m (10 ft) *Machinery:* 2-shaft geared steam turbines, 40 000 shp=36 knots *Armament:* 4 4.7-in (120-mm) (4×1); 2 40-mm (1.57-in) (1×2); 8 20-mm (0.79-in) (4×2); 8 21-in (53-cm) torpedo tubes (2×4) *Crew:* 170

Seawolf

US nuclear-powered submarine. USS *Seawolf*, the world's second nuclear submarine, was laid down on September 15, 1953, at the Groton, Connecticut yard of the Electric Boat company. She was to be very similar to her predecessor, *Nautilus*, but was slightly larger with more emphasis on antisubmarine capability, reflecting the new concept of using a submarine to hunt hostile submarines. Her nuclear reactor used liquid sodium as a coolant and heat exchanger, making it smaller, and therefore lighter for the same power output than the pressurized-water reactor installed in *Nautilus*. Technical problems with the liquid sodium delayed the completion of *Seawolf*, and indeed limited her to 80% of designed power throughout her first commission. It was not until March 30, 1957, that Commander R B Laning formally commissioned her as a unit of the US Navy.

Seawolf's initial shake-down cruise was of eight week's duration in the Bermuda area, and later in the same year she was sent to take part in a NATO exercise in the eastern Atlantic area. The following year she established a 60-day record for underwater operations, proving that a submarine crew could operate efficiently for long periods regardless of the outside environment, and showing that the submarine could remain submerged throughout a potential war patrol.

Late in 1958 it was decided to replace the liquid-sodium reactor with a pressurized-water reactor. Spare parts already stocked for *Nautilus*'s reactor were used in this programme, enabling the work to be completed in only 20 months. During this first period in commission *Seawolf* had logged a total of 70 000 nautical miles, over 71% of them while dived. On her new reactor she logged 161 000 nautical miles before having to be recored. The fire control is a Mk 101 Mod 8, linked to a BQS-4 passive sonar.

In January 1961 *Seawolf* located the Portuguese liner *Santa Maria*, which had been seized by pirates, and followed her to Recife where she surrendered to the Brazilian authorities. In 1965 during a deployment to the Mediterranean *Seawolf* formed part of the world's first all-nuclear task group, formed with the aircraft carrier *Enterprise*, the cruiser *Long Beach* and the destroyer

The destroyer HMS *Sheffield* and her sisters have the distinction of being the smallest ships in the world to be fitted with an area-defence system against antiship missiles

Bainbridge. Seawolf has been employed on research and trials projects since 1969.

Displacement: 3720/4280 tons (surfaced/submerged) *Length:* 102.9 m (337 ft 6 in) oa *Beam:* 8.5 m (27 ft 9 in) *Draught:* 6.7 m (22 ft) *Machinery:* S2G nuclear reactor, 2-shaft geared steam turbines, 15 000 shp=19/20 knots (surfaced/submerged); S2Wa reactor from 1960 *Armament:* 6 21-in (53-cm) torpedo tubes (bow) *Crew:* 120

Seehund

German two-man midget submarine class. The Seehund (seal) also known as the U-Boat type XXVIIb, was developed from the unsuccessful and unpopular Hecht type. The craft was 11.9 m (39 ft) long and displaced just under 12.5 tons surfaced and 15 tons submerged. It was powered by the traditional diesel engine for surface use and electric motors when dived. The submerged endurance at 5 knots was only four hours. The craft was armed with two underslung G7e electric torpedoes. U-Boat numbers *5001-6351* were allocated.

The first boats were handed over to their crews in September 1944 at Neustadt in the Baltic. After a period of intensive training all the boats were moved to Ijmuiden in the Netherlands, which was to be the future operational base; no operations are thought to have been carried out from the Baltic bases against the USSR. The first operation was carried out on December 31, 1944, when 18 boats were sent out to attack Allied shipping in the southern North Sea. Like all midgets, their operational potential was greatly reduced in the open sea, and on this occasion the attacking craft ran into a howling gale which sent 16 of them to the bottom.

From January to the end of April 1945 the Seehunds made many sorties to attack shipping, mainly in the River Scheldt approaches to Antwerp, off Ostend and in the Thames estuary. Although they had some successes they failed to interfere seriously with the flow of supplies. On April 9, in one of their last operations, one boat sank a small US tanker off Ostend. Another boat attacked a convoy in the English Channel, four nautical miles north-east of Dungeness, sinking one ship and leaving another crippled. This attack represented the deepest penetration of the Channel by the Seehunds. Other operations included the transport of vital supplies to the German garrison cut off in the port of Dunkerque.

A total of about 250 Seehunds were completed, and many more were abandoned incomplete as the Allied armies advanced into Germany in the closing days of the war. In addition to the many boats which were lost by accident during training or on account of the weather, it is believed that Allied action accounted for 61 of these craft. Several served in the French navy after the war.

Displacement: 15 tons *Length:* 11.9 m (39 ft) *Beam:* 1.7 m (5 ft 6 in) *Draught:* 1.5 m (5 ft) *Machinery:* 1-shaft diesel/electric, 60 bhp/25 shp=7.75/6 knots (surfaced/submerged) *Armament:* 2 53-cm (21-in) torpedoes *Crew:* 2

Sheffield

British missile destroyer class. Known as the Type 42, the *Sheffield* Class is a scaled-down version of the *Bristol* (Type 82) design. The Type 82 had proved too expensive for series production, especially in view of the cancellation of the aircraft carriers she was designed to protect.

The reduction in length reflects in part some reduction in capabilities (notably a smaller number of Sea Dart missile reloads),

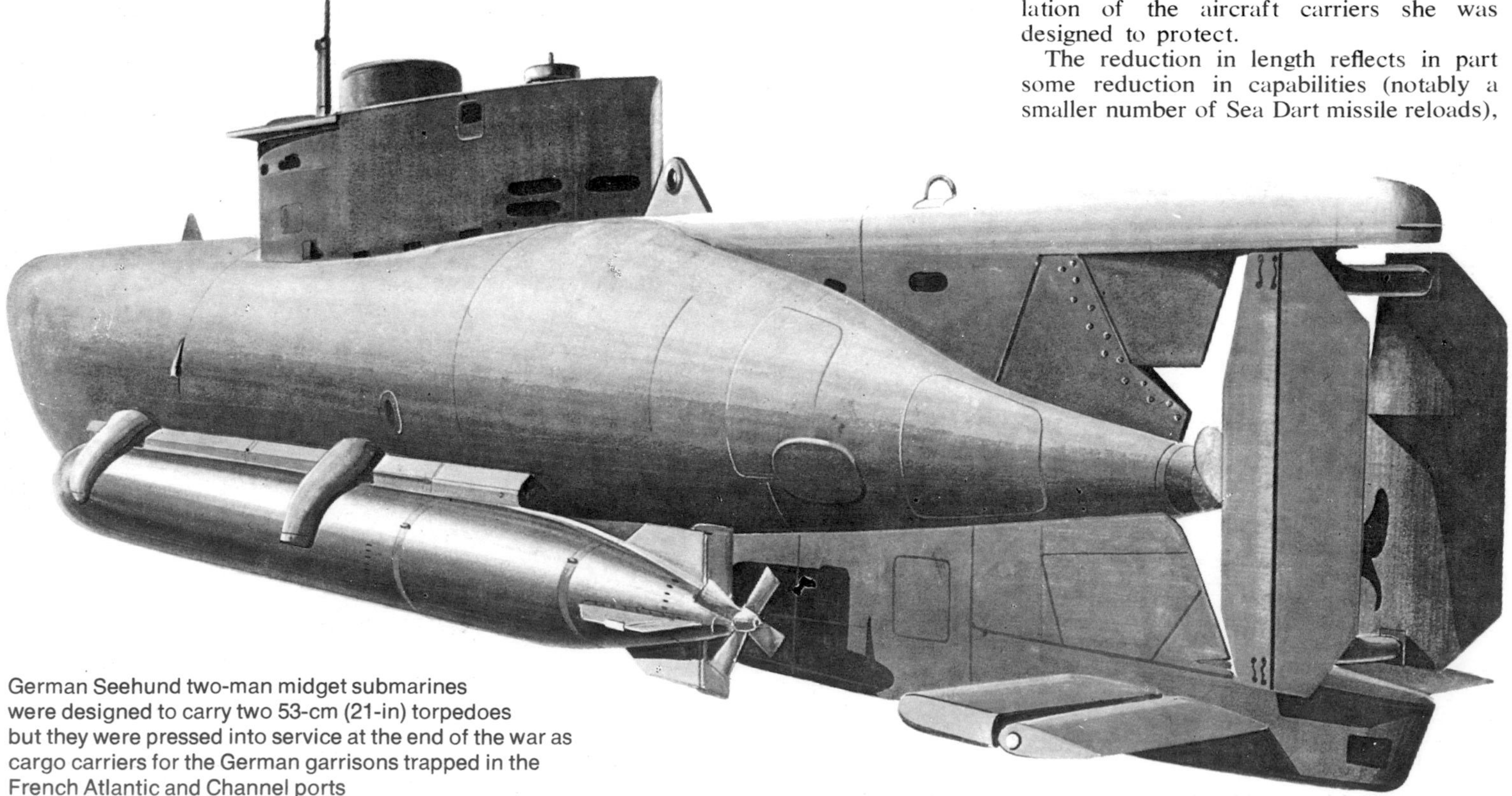
German Seehund two-man midget submarines were designed to carry two 53-cm (21-in) torpedoes but they were pressed into service at the end of the war as cargo carriers for the German garrisons trapped in the French Atlantic and Channel ports

but resulted mainly from technological advances, with considerable savings in weight and complement. The twin-arm Sea Dart launcher for area-defence missiles is a lightweight version of the Mod 0 aboard *Bristol*. The type 909 guidance radars mounted fore and aft are usually covered by fibreglass domes. The launcher itself is mounted on the forecastle, freeing the quarterdeck for a helicopter platform with the hangar forward of it. A Lynx A/S helicopter is carried, replacing Ikara as the main ASW system. At shorter ranges submarines are engaged by the Plessey STWS-1 system comprising two triple 12.75-in (32.4-cm) torpedo tubes mounted at shelter-deck level amidships. (*Sheffield* herself is not fitted with this system.)

The conventional armament, identical to that of *Bristol* (as refitted), comprises a single 4.5-in (114-mm) Mk 8 and two single 20-mm (0.79-in) Oerlikons. Two Corvus chaff dispensers are fitted, and twin SCOT satellite communication terminals can be carried in the upper wings of the bridge structure.

The above-water sensors are also the same as in *Bristol*: a Type 965 air-search 'double bedstead', a Type 992Q general-purpose search radar and a Type 1006 navigation radar. Variations in ECM provision account for minor changes in the shape of the mainmast between the ships of the class. Sensor data is coordinated by an action data automation weapon system similar to *Bristol*'s.

US Navy

A Soviet 'Shershen' fast patrol boat. It is armed with four 53-cm (21-in) torpedoes and may be intended to operate with Styx missile-armed *Osa* FTPs in a joint missile and torpedo attack

MOD

HMS *Sheffield* at sea off Portland during running-up trials in April 1975 after her completion

No and name	laid down	launched	completed	builder
D.80 *Sheffield*	1/70	6/71	2/75	Vickers
D.86 *Birmingham*	3/72	7/73	12/76	Cammell Laird
D.118 *Coventry*	3/72	6/74	11/78	Cammell Laird
D.108 *Cardiff*	11/72	2/74	—	Vickers (fitted out Swan Hunter)
D.87 *Newcastle*	2/73	4/75	3/78	Swan Hunter
D.88 *Glasgow*	3/74	4/76	—	Swan Hunter
Exeter	1976	—	—	Swan Hunter
Southampton	10/76	—	—	Vosper
Manchester	1978	—	—	Vosper
Liverpool	—	—	—	Cammell Laird
Argentine ships				
Hercules	6/71	10/72	5/76	Vickers
Santissima Trinidad	10/71	11/74	—	AFNE, Rio Santiago

The major advance over the Type 82 lies in the compact COGOG machinery arrangement, which involves less complex gearing, easier maintenance and reductions in complement. Boost for two Tyne cruise gas turbines housed in the after engine room is provided by two Olympus gas turbines in the forward room. Control and surveillance of the machinery is carried out in a centralized control room, and the compactness of the machinery layout allows a single broad funnel. *Sheffield* and the Argentine *Hercules* were completed with large circular vents protruding from the funnel sides to take the hot exhaust gases clear of the sensors, but they were found to be unnecessary and were due to be removed at the ships' first refit.

The *Sheffield* Class have had the distinction of being the smallest ships in the world to carry an area-defence system, although the design will have to be enlarged to incorporate future modifications. The second series will be larger and beamier to improve seakeeping and allow more internal space and topweight.

(Series I) *Displacement:* 3150 tons (standard), 3500 tons (full load) *Length:* 125 m (410 ft) oa *Beam:* 14.3 m (46 ft 11 in) *Draught:* 5 m (16 ft 5 in) *Machinery:* 2 Olympus gas turbines, 54 400 hp=30 knots, 2 Tyne gas turbines, 8200 hp=18 knots *Armament:* 1 4.5-in (114-mm) Mk 8 DP; 2 20-mm (0.79-in) (2×1); 2 Sea Dart launchers (1×2); 6 A/S torpedo tubes (2×3); 1 Lynx helicopter *Crew:* 312

'Shershen'

Soviet fast patrol boat class. The first boat of the class was laid down in 1962 and completed in 1965. No information is available as to the builders, but it seems likely that most of the 90-odd boats completed by the end of the 1960s were built in Baltic or Black Sea yards. In size and armament the 'Shershen' Class bears a strong resemblance to the German *Jaguar* Class FPBs built during 1957-64, which would certainly have been regarded as potential opponents. They appear to have been developed from the 'Osa' Class missile FPBs in view of their similar hull form and diesel propulsion system. They have the twin 30-mm (1.18-in) automatic AA mountings and Drum Tilt fire-control director of the 'Osa' Class. Instead of the Styx missiles of the latter, however, they are equipped with four 53-cm (21-in) torpedo tubes. The domed radar which tops the lattice mast is a surface-search radar. It is thought that the 'Shershen' and 'Osa' Classes may be intended to operate together, with the 'Shershen' Class delivering torpedo attacks from close range after the missiles have been fired from the 'Osa' Class boats.

Forty-five of the class have been built for or transferred to foreign navies, leaving an estimated 49 in service with the Soviet navy. During 1966-71, 16 boats were transferred to Yugoslavia. From 1967 onwards Egypt received six, some of which had their torpedo tubes and fire-control radar replaced by artillery rocket-launcher groups. Fifteen boats went to East Germany between 1968-74, four to Bulgaria in 1971 and four to North Korea in 1973-74.

Displacement: 145 tons (standard), 160 tons (full load) *Length:* 36 m (118 ft) oa *Beam:* 7.7 m (25 ft 3 in) *Draught:* 1.75 m (5 ft 9 in) *Machinery:* 3-shaft diesels, 13 200 bhp=38 knots *Armament:* 4 53-cm (21-in) torpedo tubes; 4 30-mm (1.18-in) AA (2×2); 2 depth-charge racks *Crew:* 16

Shimakaze

Japanese destroyer. *Shimakaze* was an experimental destroyer known as the Type C, ordered under the 1939 Programme. She was laid down at Maizuru navy yard, on August 8, 1941, launched on July 18, 1942, and completed on May 19, 1943. She was to be the prototype for large new fleet destroyers with high speed and a very powerful armament. Her new boilers and turbines were designed to develop nearly 50% more power than previous turbines and were to be a possible prototype for future destroyer classes. The outbreak of war slowed down development work on new designs and equipment, but work on the new boilers and turbines was completed in time for *Shimakaze* to run trials in 1943. On a displacement of 3048 tons the boilers developed a pressure of 570 psi at a temperature of 400°C giving 76 010 shp and a recorded speed of 39.9 knots – nearly 3 knots faster than the US *Fletcher* Class destroyers. *Shimakaze* later exceeded these figures recording 79 240 shp on a displacement of 2894 tons to give a speed of 40.9 knots.

Shimakaze was designed to carry a very heavy armament of three quintuple 24-in (61-cm) torpedo tubes and six 5-in (127-mm)/50-cal dual-purpose guns in totally enclosed turrets. With three banks of quintuple torpedo tubes ready for immediate action it was argued that some of the reload torpedoes could be dispensed with. Hence one set of reloads only was carried for the after bank of torpedo tubes.

During 1943-44 X gun was removed and two triple 25-mm (1-in) mounts added in its place to give *Shimakaze* a total of 14 25-mm. During 1944 the torpedo reload facilities were removed and the AA further increased to 28 25-mm, together with four 13-mm (0.51-in). Air- and surface-warning radar was also added.

Shimakaze had an uneventful career, and was sunk by US carrier aircraft off Cebu on November 11, 1944.

As it appeared that the *Shimakaze* design would be successful, 16 destroyers were projected to the design under the 1942 Programme. However, they were never ordered, for that programme was eventually cancelled in favour of another which concentrated on the construction of escorts and destroyers of a more simple design.

Displacement: 2567 tons (light) *Length:* 126.5 m (415 ft) oa *Beam:* 11.2 m (36 ft 9 in) *Draught:* 4.1 m (13 ft 6 in) *Machinery:* 2-shaft geared turbines, 75 000 shp=39 knots *Armament:* 6 5-in (127-mm) (3×2); 4 25-mm (1-in) (2×2); 15 24-in (61-cm) (3×5) torpedo tubes, 20 torpedoes; 2 depth-charge throwers, 18 depth charges *Crew:* not known

Shinano

Japanese aircraft carrier. On May 8, 1940, *Shinano*, the third unit of the *Yamato* Class of 18-in (46-cm) gun battleships, was laid down in a purpose-built dry dock at the Yokosuka navy yard. Construction was suspended in the autumn of 1941 in order to release men and materials for more urgent work in preparation for the forthcoming war. In June 1942, after losing five carriers in the space of a month, the Imperial Japanese Navy urgently considered ways of providing replacements. A number of ships were earmarked for conversion to carriers and the decision was taken to complete the third vessel in the *Yamato* Class as a carrier rather than as a battleship.

The 266 m (872 ft 9 in) hull of the battleship was left unchanged, apart from the removal of the armoured turret barbettes and the omission of the outer layer of the armoured belt: even then, the belt was still 205 mm (8.1 in) thick, while the main armoured deck over the magazines and machinery was up to 195 mm (7.7 in) thick. The single hangar deck was fitted out on the original flush upper deck, the forward area being devoted to maintenance and storage, while the portion aft was used by the carrier's own operational aircraft. The hangar sides were unarmoured, but the flight deck between the two lifts (at the ends of the hangar) was armoured to a thickness of 80 mm (3.15 in)—a feature hitherto seen only in British Fleet carriers and the Japanese *Taiho*. No catapults were fitted, but the 256-m (840-ft) flight deck was long enough to enable any aircraft, in service or planned, to take off with ease at maximum weight.

The standard 16-gun (406-mm [16-in]) heavy AA armament seen in other modern Japanese large carriers was fitted, the twin 12.7-cm (5-in) mountings being installed in individual sponsons around the deck edge. Close-range weapons consisted of 33 triple 25-mm (1-in) AA mountings and 12 multiple rocket launchers, intended specifically for use against dive-bombing attacks. Type 1-3 warning and the Type 2-1 aircraft control radars were fitted.

The battleship machinery was retained and the uptakes from the boilers led to one tall funnel which was canted outboard from the top of the large starboard-side island—an arrangement first employed, with complete success, in the *Junyo* Class.

Shinano was intended to operate as a support carrier, in the rear area, to provide replacement aircraft, workshop facilities, ordnance and aviation fuel (she had a capacity of 718 300 litres/158 000 Imp gal) for the front-line ships. Her own aircraft complement was to have been only 47, for the defence of herself and her consorts.

Floated out of the dock on October 8, 1944, she commissioned on November 18 and was made ready for passage to Kure under her own steam, to complete fitting out away from the Tokyo area, soon to come under heavy air attack.

She left Yokosuka early on the morning of November 28 escorted by the destroyers *Hamakaze, Isokaze* and *Yukikaze* and in the early hours of the next morning, while steaming towards the eastern entrance to the Inland Sea, she was hit by four torpedoes from the USS *Archerfish*. The internal watertight subdivision was not yet complete, not all the pumps needed for counter-flooding and evacuation were installed and the crew was still unfamiliar with the ship.

She continued to steam at 18 knots, but due to a combination of the disadvantage of incomplete work, an inexperienced crew and a number of watertight doors being left open, all power failed when the boiler rooms flooded and five hours after the attack *Shinano*, the biggest carrier to be completed before 1954 (when USS *Forrestal* appeared) capsized and sank.

Displacement: 64 800 tons (standard), approx 72 000 tons (full load) *Length:* 266 m (872 ft 9 in) oa *Beam:* 36.3 m (119 ft) wl, 40 m (131 ft 3 in) flight deck *Draught:* 10.4 m (34 ft 2 in) *Machinery:* 4-shaft geared turbines, 150 000 shp=27 knots (designed) *Aircraft:* 47+reserves *Armament:* 8 12.7-cm (5-in) DP; up to 155 25-mm (1-in) AA; 12 28 12-cm (4.7-in) AA rocket launchers *Crew:* 2400 approx

Shinyo

Japanese escort carrier. The outbreak of war in Europe in September 1939 found the Nord-Deutscher-Lloyd liner *Scharnhorst* in the Far East. She took refuge at Yokohama, where she was still lying when purchased by the Imperial Japanese Navy on February 7, 1942, for conversion as an escort carrier. Within a few months, the German navy was to be considering the conversion of her sister-ship *Gneisenau* for the same role.

The 18 000-grt *Scharnhorst* was the largest merchant ship to be converted for the auxiliary, as opposed to Fleet, role, being 27.4-m (90-ft) longer than the US *Sangamon*. Already propelled by steam turbines, she was capable of 21 knots and did not require re-engining along the lines of *Kaiyo*, whose conversion began at the end of 1942.

The liner was taken in hand at the Kure navy yard in September 1942 in the dock recently vacated by the converted *Chuyo* to which she was to appear very similar, except that external bulges were added to the hull in an attempt to improve stability. The superstructure was raised above the level of the original upper deck and a hangar box erected in its place, topped with a 179.8-m (590-ft) steel flight deck. The steel for the conversion came from the incomplete hull of the fourth *Yamato* Class battleship, construction of which had been abandoned in March 1942.

The flight deck was completely flush, the navigating bridge being located in a 'conservatory' at the forward end of the hangar structure, under the flight deck overhang, and the flying control position occupying an open sponson at the deck edge. The single funnel was in the usual starboard-side location, exhausting downwards. Four twin 12.7-cm (0.5-in) gun mountings were installed below flight deck level, abreast the after lift and slightly abaft the forward lift. Ten triple 25-mm (1-in) AA guns made up the original armament, later additions totalled an extra 20 barrels, in single and twin mountings.

The carrier was renamed *Shinyo* (condor) when she commissioned on December 15, 1943. Allocated to the General Escort Command a month later, after trials and training, she was not used in a combat role to any great extent, seeing most of her service as an aircraft transport and, in the months leading up to the Battle of the Philippine Sea, as a deck-landing training ship. The only operational sorties by her aircraft were while she was on passage, either with convoys or alone.

In mid-November 1944, having been fitted with a further eight 25 mm AA to take her total of that calibre to 50, she joined a convoy taking army aircraft and troops to Manila from Japan. A US submarine wolf-pack intercepted the convoy on November 15 and that night *Shinyo* was narrowly missed by *Barb*'s torpedoes. Two nights later, in the Yellow Sea, she was not so fortunate and was sunk in shallow water by torpedoes from the *Spadefish*.

Displacement: 17 500 tons (standard), 22 600 tons (full load) *Length:* 196 m (643 ft) oa *Beam:* 25.6 m (84 ft) wl, 35.7 m (117 ft) over sponsons *Draught:* 8.2 m (27 ft) *Machinery:* 2-shaft geared turbines, 26 000 shp=21 knots *Aircraft:* 33 *Armament:* 8 12.7-cm (5-in) DP (4×2); 50 25-mm (1-in) AA *Crew:* 942

Shokaku

Japanese fleet carriers. The experience gained with their first operational fleet carriers, *Akagi* and *Kaga*, gave the Imperial Japanese Navy's aviators and constructors a very clear idea of the ideal aircraft carrier. Treaty limitations on tonnage, however, meant that the first two custom-built fleet carriers, *Soryu* and *Hiryu*, were rather smaller and lighter than considered desirable, which meant that they could not carry as many aircraft as experience dictated. The Japanese withdrawal from the restraints of the naval treaties, effective from January 1, 1937, permitted the ordering, in that year, the first 'unlimited' class of carriers—the *Shokaku* Class.

The largest carriers laid down up to the time (1939), they were similar in appearance and internal layout to *Soryu*, but were considerably larger, being 28 m (92 ft) longer and 4.6 m (15 ft) wider at the waterline, besides displacing 10 000 tons more. The additional tonnage included armour protection on a greater scale than in any other ship designed from the outset as a carrier, with 170 mm (6.7 in) over the vitals and a maximum of 215 mm (8.5 in) on the waterline. The flight deck was unarmoured, so that there was no overhead protection for the two hangar decks, as there was in contemporary British fleet carriers, but the real 'Achilles' Heel'—common to all Japanese carriers—was the aviation-fuel system: not only were the bulk stowage tanks insufficiently isolated, the fuel distribution lines were inadequately shock-proofed, being liable to rupture as the result of shock from a hit on the ship away from their vicinity.

The ships were fast, attaining over 34 knots on trials. They were among the most powerfully engined vessels afloat, being rivalled elsewhere only by the new French and German battleships, and they also featured a bulbous forefoot which improved the hydrodynamic qualities of the hull, giving greater speed and, at cruising power, radius of action.

Seventy-two aircraft could be stowed on the two hangar decks, both of which were connected with the flight deck by three large electric lifts. The flight deck was wood-planked, except in the vicinity of the two downward-curving funnels on the starboard side. Arrester wires were provided at both ends of the deck, those forward for use in emergency or to provide a tactical freedom (which never proved to be necessary) to operate aircraft with the wind from astern. No catapults were installed.

The island in both ships of the class was located on the starboard side of the deck, the port-side location in *Akagi* and *Hiryu* having proved to be an unhelpful temporary aberration. Gun armament comprised 16 12.7-cm (5-in)/40-cal Type 89 dual-purpose guns in twin mountings, located in four-gun batteries below the level of the flight deck. The starboard after battery was in enclosed, gas-tight shields to enable the crew to work the guns in spite of the fumes from the adjacent funnels. Two of the 14 triple 25-mm (1-in) AA mountings were similarly protected—during the course of the war, more 25-mm were added, for a total of 70 barrels in *Shokaku* in June 1944 and no less than 96 in *Zuikaku* in October 1944. Multiple AA rocket launchers were also added to the latter. *Shokaku* was fitted with an early radar in September 1942 and in the following year both ships received the standard Type 2-1 warning set.

Shokaku (heaven-bound crane) and *Zuikaku* (lucky crane) were launched in June and November 1939, at, respectively, the Yokosuka navy yard and the commercial Kawasaki yard at Kobe. The name-ship was completed on August 8, 1941, and was allocated to the Carrier Division 5 on August 23 after initial trials. *Zuikaku* was not completed for another month and joined her sister-ship to work up to October 8.

Although most of the pilots allocated to fly Carrier Division 5's 36 Mitsubishi Zero fighters, 54 Aichi Val dive-bombers and 54 Nakajima Kate torpedo-bombers had already seen active service over China, insufficient time was available to work up the attack teams in all roles before the ships left the Inland Sea on November 19 to join the Pearl Harbor striking force at Hittokappu Bay, Kurile Islands. In consequence, the two waves of Carrier Division 5's strike—27 Vals and six Zeros from each ship in the first and 27 Kates and six fighters in the second—took no part in the attack on the US Pacific Fleet on December 7, concentrating on the four major airfields in Oahu, on which they released nearly 20 tons of bombs. The only Carrier Division 5 casualty was a dive-bomber from the first wave.

After operations in Ceylon, the *Shokaku*s were detached from the main carrier fleet and proceeded to Truk while the other carriers returned to Japan to prepare for the Midway operation. Carrier Division 5 sailed from Truk to cover the invasion of Port Moresby, New Guinea, on May 1.

The two Japanese carriers, the Rabaul invasion force and two US carriers intent on interception did not make contact with one another until May 7. On that day, *Yorktown*'s aircraft destroyed the Japanese light carrier *Shoho*, with the invasion force, while Carrier Division 5 sent 24 Kates, armed with bombs, and 36 Vals to sink an oiler and a destroyer misidentified as a carrier and a cruiser. In the evening, only four out of 27 strike aircraft returned from an attempted attack on the real US carriers, ten of these falling to fighters and the others being unable to find the Japanese carriers on return. The main exchange of the Battle of the Coral Sea came on May 8 when the two carrier forces struck at one another within 30 minutes. *Shokaku* was attacked and seriously damaged by *Yorktown*'s aircraft—*Zuikaku* was hidden in a squall—and missed by *Lexington*'s. Both US carriers were hit by bombs and *Lexington*, also hit by torpedoes, was lost as the result of an aviation-fuel explosion. *Shokaku* had also caught fire and was saved only with difficulty. Apart from her damage, the operation had cost Carrier Division 5 86 aircraft and most of their crews, so that *Zuikaku* was unable to join the Midway force.

On July 14, when *Shokaku* became operational, Carrier Division 5 was dissolved and the two big carriers, with the light carrier *Zuiho*, formed the Carrier Division 1. A month later, they left for Truk to challenge the Allied Fleet in the Solomons area. The air group had been adjusted so that each ship had an official complement of 27 fighters, 27 dive-bombers and 18 torpedo-bombers; *Shokaku* was actually carrying only 24 Vals, but had two Yokosuka Judy (D4Y-1S) reconnaissance aircraft aboard.

On August 24, in the Battle of the Eastern Solomons, the small *Ryujo* drew off the US carriers' main strike and Carrier Division 1 came under attack only from reconnaissance aircraft. Aircraft from *Shokaku* and *Zuikaku* damaged the USS *Enterprise* but 38 of their number failed to return. Two months later, on October 26, the two big carriers managed to launch two strikes against *Enterprise* and *Hornet* before dive-bombers from the latter broke through to score six direct hits with 454-kg (1000-lb) bombs on *Shokaku* but she again reached Japan under her own steam.

On August 10, 1944, *Zuikaku* was transferred to Carrier Division 3 and began training yet another generation of aircrew. This was interrupted by the US invasion of Leyte and on October 20, 1944, the ships of Carrier Division 3—*Zuikaku*, *Zuiho*, *Chitose* and *Chiyoda*—embarked 116 aircraft of 601st and 653rd Air Groups from Oita and sailed for the last carrier battle. The force to which the carriers was attached was to act as a decoy, drawing the attention of the US Third Fleet from the battleships and cruisers of the main striking force. On October 24, all but 40 of the aircraft were launched against a US carrier task group—none returned but attention had been drawn to the decoy force. US aircraft shadowed the Japanese carriers through the night and attacks on the next day sank all four ships of Carrier Division 3; *Zuikaku* was the prime target off Cape Engano and it took six torpedoes and seven 454-kg (1000-lb) bombs to finish her off.

Displacement: 25 675 tons (standard), approx 32 000 tons (full load) *Length:* 257.5 m (844 ft 10 in) oa *Beam:* 26 m (85 ft 4 in) wl, 29 m (95 ft 2 in) flight deck *Draught:* 8.9 m (29 ft) *Machinery:* 4-shaft geared turbines, 160 000 shp=34.2 knots *Aircraft:* 72-75 *Armament:* 8 2 12.7-cm (5-in) DP; 42 (*Zuikaku* 96) 25-mm AA; 6 28 12-cm (4.7-in) AA rocket launchers (*Zuikaku* only) *Crew:* 1660

Shumushu

Japanese escort class. By the 1930s the Japanese admiralty had recognized the need for some form of modern general-purpose escort. The requirement was for a smaller type of vessel capable of acting in support of less important coastal operations where large fleet destroyers would be unsuitable and vulnerable. The vessels, it was argued, should be able to carry out minelaying, minesweeping, antisubmarine duties, and to provide limited gunfire support. For this they would be fitted with a fairly extensive range of mine-warfare equipment, a primitive form of submarine-detection device together with a few depth charges. The design for the new escorts was completed by the mid-1930s, the ships being armed with three 4.7-in (120-mm), a 3-in (76-mm) A/S mortar and six depth charges.

Since escorts were considered to be a defensive weapons system, which at that time did not enter Japanese strategic thinking, only four vessels were ordered. Known as the Type A escorts (indicating that the Japanese were considering the possibility of developing the small escort concept) these vessels were ordered under the 1937 Programme. Work on both the design and the vessels proceeded slowly but the design was felt to be moderately successful and four more vessels were planned under the 1942 Programme, though these were never ordered as that programme was cancelled. In accordance with their low priority they were fitted with much equipment regarded as surplus to requirements, and diesels were fitted so as not to delay construction of other turbine-powered warships.

During mid-1942 the mine-warfare equipment round the stern was removed and the A/S capability somewhat improved by giving the ships six extra depth charges. Towards the end of 1942 the A/S capability was further enhanced when the ships were equipped with more modern hydrophones, and the following year saw the light AA augmented by five triple 25-mm (1-in) AA, the original twin 25-mm AA being removed. The depth charge capacity was increased to 60 and the ships were also equipped with air-warning radar.

Ishigaki was sunk by the US submarine *Herring* off the Kuriles on May 31, 1944. *Shumushu* suffered severe damage from a torpedo on November 25, 1944, and was subsequently repaired and fitted with a new bow with a straight stem and a new funnel. She was surrendered at the end of the war and transferred to the USSR as war reparations. *Hachijo* and *Kunashiri* were also surrendered, *Hachijo* being scrapped in 1947 while *Kunashiri* was wrecked on June 4, 1946.

Name	laid down	launched	completed	builder
Hachijo	1939	4/40	3/41	Sasebo navy yard
Ishigaki	1939	9/40	2/41	Mitsui
Kunashiri	1939	5/40	10/40	Asano
Shumushu	11/38	12/39	6/40	Mitsui

Displacement: 860 tons (standard), 1020 tons (full load) *Length:* 77.7 m (255 ft) oa *Beam:* 10 m (32 ft 6 in) *Draught:* 3 m (10 ft) *Machinery:* 2-shaft diesels, 4200 bhp=19.75 knots *Armament:* 3 4.7-in (120-mm) (3×1); 4 25-mm (1-in) (2×2); 1 3-in (76-mm) A/S trench mortar; 6 depth charges *Crew:* 147

Silny

Soviet destroyer class, built 1936-42. The realization that the Italian design of the Type VII or *Gordy* Class were too lightly built for operating in the Arctic led to the Type VIIU (*uluschonny,* improved), and the 20th and 30th units, *Silny* and *Storozhevoi* were altered while on the stocks. The redesign included the provision of unit machinery, and so there were two widely spaced funnels instead of the single trunked one. The hull was strengthened and the opportunity was taken to increase power slightly. The excessive vibration in the turbines which plagued the Type VII was apparently cured in this class. They were altogether a great improvement and were used as the basis for future development.

Storozhevoi, Silny, Surovy, Serdity, Strashny, Spokoiny, Skory, Statny, Svirepy, Strogy, Stroiny—built by Zhdanov yard, Leningrad
Smely (ex-*Letuchy*), *Stoiky* (ex-*Lilkhoi*), *Slavny*—built by Ordzonikidze yard, Leningrad
Smyshleny, Soobrazitelny—built by 61 Kommunar yard, Nikolaiev
Sposobny, Sovershenny—built by Sevastopol dockyard
Svobodny—built by Marti yard, Nikolaiev

On June 27, 1941, *Storozhevoi* had her bow blown off by a torpedo from a German S-Boat in the Irben Straits. She was rebuilt with a bow from an incomplete *Ognevoi* Class and recommissioned in 1943. *Serdity* and *Smely* were sunk in July 1941, the former by bombing near Ösel and the latter by mine in the Gulf of Riga. *Statny* also went down after striking a mine off Ösel on August 18, while *Skory* was lost from the same cause off Cape Juminda. *Sovershenny* struck a mine while running trials in the Black Sea and while undergoing repairs in dock at Sevastopol was hit by a bomb and capsized; after being righted she was destroyed by shellfire in April 1942.

Surovy was another victim of a mine, off Hangö in Finland in November 1941, while *Smyshleny* was mined in the Kerch Straits in March 1942. German aircraft accounted for *Svobodny* in Sevastopol in June 1942 and the *Sposobny* off the Crimean coast in October 1943. The *Soobrazitelny* made a number of runs into beleagured Sevastopol with the flotilla leader *Tashkent,* and rescued the latter's survivors when she was sunk by air attack. The existence of the *Spokoiny* is uncertain; she was towed from Leningrad to the Arctic and then to Molotovsk but disappeared subsequently, and was lost, probably in 1944-45.

Stoiky was renamed *Vitse-Admiral Drozd* in 1943. Like most of the survivors she was scrapped in the late 1950s, as the class had seen very arduous war service. The only survivor is the heroic *Soobrazitelny,* which was decommissioned in 1966 and preserved as a permanent museum ship to commemorate the deeds of the Black Sea Fleet. She is moored at Nikolaiev.

Displacement: 1686 tons (standard), 2246 tons (full load) *Length:* 112.9 m (370 ft 3 in) oa *Beam:* 10.2 m (33 ft 6 in) *Draught:* 4 m (13 ft 3 in) *Machinery:* 2-shaft geared steam turbines, 48 000-54 000 shp=36 knots *Armament:* 4 130-mm (5.1-in); 2/3 76-mm (3-in) AA (2/3×1); 6 37-mm (1.46-in) AA (6×1); 4 12.7-mm (0.5-in) machine-guns AA (2×2); 6 53-cm (21-in) torpedo tubes (2×3) *Crew:* 207

Sjöormen

Swedish submarine class, built 1965-69. Five units were built to design A-11B: *Sjöormen, Sjölejonet* and *Sjöhunden* by Kockums at Malmö and *Sjöbjornen* and *Sjöhasten* by Karlskronavarvet. The two Karlskrona boats were towed to Kockums to complete fitting out. The design resembles the US *Barbel* type, with a short *Albacore*-type hull, a single screw, and diving planes on the fin. Special X-form aft diving planes and rudders were introduced in this class and are claimed to give much greater manoeuvrability than the conventional cruciform arrangement.

The hull is divided into seven compartments and two deck levels: sonar room with ballast tank below; forward accommodation with torpedo-room below; main control room with torpedo-reloads below; auxiliary machinery spaces and galley, etc., and main battery below; after accommodation with another battery compartment below; machinery control room with diesel generators below; and the electric motor room. Torpedoes are loaded abaft the fin, through an inclined hatch down to the lower deck level. There are six torpedo tubes forward, four firing TP 61 wire-guided antiship torpedoes and two firing TP 42 antisubmarine torpedoes. Mines can also be laid from these tubes. The propulsion is by Hedemora-Pielstick diesels generating current for Asea electric motors. A proposal to use fuel cells was dropped because of delays in development. Recognition letters are: Sör, Sle, Shu, Sbj and Shä.

Displacement: 800/1125 tons (surfaced/submerged) *Length:* 51 m (167 ft 4 in) oa *Beam:* 6.1 m (20 ft) *Draught:* 5.1 m (16 ft 9 in) *Machinery:* 1-shaft diesel-electric, 3500 shp=15/20 knots (surfaced/submerged) *Armament:* 6 53-cm (21-in) torpedo tubes *Crew:* 23

Skate

US nuclear-powered submarine class. Based on the successful *Nautilus*, the *Skate* Class was the first production class of nuclear-powered submarines. They were somewhat shorter and heavier than *Nautilus*, and had an improved pressurized water-cooled reactor which was less complex and thus easier to maintain. The S3W reactor in *Skate* and *Swordfish* required a shielded tunnel for through fore-and-aft access, but the other two boats had a shielded deck with the more compact S4W reactor below.

By the end of July 1958 *Skate* was ready to commence her first sortie to the Arctic where she operated under the ice for ten days, steaming 400 nautical miles and surfacing nine times through the ice. Early the following year she again headed for the Arctic to exercise in conditions of extreme cold and maximum ice thickness. On May 17 she became the first vessel to surface at the Pole itself, and scattered the ashes of the explorer Sir Herbert Wilkins. *Skate*'s first overhaul started in January 1961 after she had steamed a total of 120 862 nautical miles.

In January 1960 *Swordfish* became the first nuclear-powered submarine to operate in the south-west Pacific, and in January 1962 she became the first nuclear vessel to refit on the Pacific coast. After *Seadragon* spent her shakedown cruise in the Caribbean, she sailed for duty in the Pacific via the infamous North-West Passage. Proceeding via the Parry Channel and using Edward Parry's 1819 journal as a guide she entered the Beaufort Sea on August 21, 1960.

No and name	completed	builder
SSN.578 ***Skate***	12/57	General Dynamics (Electric Boat)
SSN.579 ***Swordfish***	9/58	Portsmouth navy yard
SSN.583 ***Sargo***	10/58	Mare Island navy yard
SSN.584 ***Seadragon***	12/59	Portsmouth navy yard

Displacement: 2580/2861 tons (surfaced/submerged) *Length:* 81.5 m (267 ft 6 in) oa *Beam:* 7.6 m (25 ft) *Draught:* 6.9 m (22 ft 6 in) *Machinery:* pressurized-water reactor, 2-shaft steam turbine, 15 000 shp=15.5/20 knots (surfaced-/submerged) *Armament:* 8 21-in (53-cm) torpedo tubes (6 bow, 2 stern) *Crew:* 108

Skipjack

US nuclear submarine class. The *Skipjack* Class design married the tear-drop hull form of the *Albacore* design to a nuclear reactor to produce a smaller vessel than the first nuclear submarines. Unlike the earlier nuclear boats the reactor powered only a single turbine and propeller. A Mk 101 fire-control system is provided for the torpedoes (Mod 20 in *Skipjack*, Mod 17 in others), with a BQS-4 (modified) passive sonar.

USS *Skipjack* was funded in Fiscal Year 1956 and finally commissioned on April 15, 1959. During her initial shakedown cruise she became the first nuclear-powered vessel to pass through the Straits of Gibraltar and operate in the Mediterranean. *Scamp* and *Sculpin* both saw service in the Pacific, the former earning three Battle Stars for service in the Vietnam war.

Scorpion was actually laid down twice, the first hull laid down in November 1957 having been taken over to speed up the Polaris programme: it was cut in half and a section was added, and became USS *George Washington*. In 1962 the second *Scorpion* shattered *Seawolf*'s record for submerged operations by logging 70 days shut off from the outside environment. While returning home from a subsequent operation in the Mediterranean she was lost some time after May 21, 1966, some 400 nautical miles south-west of the Azores. Despite extensive enquiries no cause for this presumably accidental sinking has been determined.

Sargo, a _Skate_ Class submarine, at the North Pole in 1960. On May 17, 1958 USS _Skate_ became the first vessel to surface at the North Pole

US Navy

Commissioned in 1959, the USS *Skipjack* introduced the tear-drop hull to nuclear submarines, improving manoeuvrability and speed. She was the first nuclear-powered vessel to operate in the Mediterranean

Displacement: 3075/3500 tons (surfaced/submerged) *Length:* 76.7 m (251 ft 9 in) oa *Beam:* 9.6 m (31 ft 6 in) *Draught:* 8.5 m (28 ft) *Machinery:* S5W nuclear reactor, 1-shaft geared steam turbine 15 000 shp=20/30 knots (surfaced/submerged) *Armament:* 6 21-in (53-cm) torpedo tubes *Crew:* 112

No and name	laid down	launched	completed	built by
SSN.585 *Skipjack*	5/56	5/58	4/59	General Dynamics (Electric Boat)
SSN.588 *Scamp*	1/59	10/60	6/61	Mare Island navy yard
SSN.589 *Scorpion*	8/58	12/59	6/60	General Dynamics (Electric Boat)
SSN.590 *Sculpin*	2/58	3/60	2/61	Ingalls
SSN.591 *Shark*	2/58	3/60	2/61	Newport News Shipbuilding
SSN.592 *Snook*	4/58	10/60	11/61	Ingalls

Sleipner

Norwegian torpedo boat class, built 1935-40. Six light destroyers or torpedo boats were ordered from 1935 onwards: *Sleipner, Aeger, Gyller, Odin* and *Balder* from Horten naval yard, and *Tor* from Frederikstad Mekaniske Verkstad.

When Norway was invaded in 1940 *Sleipner* escaped to England, where she served in the reconstituted Royal Norwegian Navy. *Aeger* was sunk by bombers at Stavanger on April 9, 1940, and *Balder, Gyller, Odin* and *Tor* all fell into German hands, the first-named being still incomplete at Horten. They were partially rearmed and were renamed *Leopard, Löwe, Panther* and *Tiger.* They retained one of the 100-mm (3.9-in) Bofors in Y position but the ones in A and X positions were replaced by 20-mm (0.79-in) AA guns, and the 40-mm (1.57-in) Bofors AA was suppressed. Towards the end of the war the torpedo tubes were removed.

In 1945 the German boats were ceded back to Norwegian ownership and were given their original names. With the *Sleipner* they served in the postwar navy. *Sleipner* was scrapped in the late 1950s but the other four were refitted as frigates (pendant numbers *F.301-304*), with three single US Navy 3-in (76-mm) AA, two 40-mm Bofors AA and a Hedgehog ASW weapon.

Displacement: 597 tons (standard), 708 tons (full load) *Length:* 74.1 m (243 ft 9 in) oa *Beam:* 7.8 m (25 ft 6 in) *Draught:* 3.7 m (12 ft) max *Machinery:* 2-shaft geared steam turbines, 25 000 shp=30 knots *Armament:* (in German service) 1 100-mm (3.9-in) DP; 2/4 20-mm (0.79-in) Flak 38 (2/4×1); 2 8-mm (0.315-in) MG 34 machine-guns (2×1); 2 53-cm (21-in) torpedo tubes (1×2) *Crew:* 72

'Soldati'

Italian destroyer class, built 1934-42. A series of big destroyers based on the *Alfredo Oriani* Class was started in 1937, known as the 'Soldati' Class because they were named after warriors ancient and modern. The first group comprised 12 ships:

Alpino, Fuciliere—built by Cantieri Navali Riuniti, Ancona
Artigliere, Ascari, Aviere, Camicia Nera, Corazziere, Geniere—built by Odero-Terni-Orlando, Livorno
Bersagliere, Granatiere—built by Cantieri Navali Riuniti, Palermo
Carabiniere, Lanciere—built by Cantieri dell Tirreno, Riva Trigoso

They were big, handsome ships with a single wide funnel. All had twin 120-mm (4.7-in) guns forward and aft but *Carabiniere, Camicia Nera, Geniere* and *Lanciere* mounted a fifth single gun amidships. They were also provided with a 120-mm/15-cal howitzer for firing starshell, a feature unique to Italian ships of this period. The ships of this group were all completed in 1938-39.

A second group was started in 1940-41:

Bombardiere, Mitragliere—built by Cantieri Navali Riuniti, Ancona
Carrista, Corsaro, Legionàrio, Squadrista, Velite—built by Ordero-Terni-Orlando, Livorno

The hull was the same, and all were completed with the fifth gun amidships except *Velite*, which had four. Like the first group many had a set of torpedo tubes replaced by two additional 37-mm (1.46-in) AA and eight to ten 20-mm (0.79-in) AA guns were mounted on completion in 1942-43.

As with the rest of the Italian navy war losses were heavy. *Alpino* was sunk by bombing at La Spezia on September 19, 1943. *Artigliere* was sunk by British surface forces on October 12, 1940. *Ascari* was mined on March 24, 1943. *Aviere* was torpedoed by HM Submarine *Splendid* on December 17, 1942. *Bersagliere* was sunk by bombs in Palermo on January 7, 1943. *Corazziere* was scuttled at Genoa on September 9, 1943, and although refloated by the Germans was sunk again on September 4, 1944. *Geniere* was sunk by bombs in Palermo on March 1, 1943. *Lanciere* foundered in a storm on March 23, 1942. *Bombardiere* was torpedoed by HM Submarine *United* on January 17, 1943. *Corsaro* sank after hitting two mines on January 9, 1943. *Squadrista* was renamed *Corsaro* in July 1943, fell into German hands on September 1943 and was sunk by bombing on September 9, 1944. The incomplete *Carrista* had her bow cut off to repair the damaged *Carabiniere* and her stern cut off to repair *Velite*; the hull named *TA.34* was scrapped by the Germans.

Seven of the class survived. *Camicia Nera* (blackshirt) had been renamed *Artigliere* after the downfall of Mussolini, and was ceded to the USSR in February 1949; as *Z.12* she served in the Black Sea until about 1958. *Fuciliere* went to the USSR as the *Z.20* in January 1950 and was scrapped about the same time as her sister. *Legionario, Mitragliere* and *Velite* were ceded to France in 1948 and renamed *Du Chaffault, Jurien de la Graviere* and *Duperre*; they served until 1954-61. *Carabiniere* and *Granatiere* were retained in the postwar Italian navy and were reclassified as frigates in 1957. *Granatiere* was stricken in 1958 but her sister was used to test new weapons.

Displacement: 1715-1846 tonnes (normal), 2290-2550 tonnes (full load) *Length:* 106.74 m (350 ft 2 in) oa *Beam:* 10.15 m (33 ft 4 in) *Draught:* 3.58 m (11 ft 9 in) *Machinery:* 2-shaft geared steam turbines, 50 000 shp=25 knots *Armament:* 4/5 120-mm (4.7-in)/50-cal (2×2, 1×1); 1 120-mm/15-cal howitzer; 1 37-mm (1.46-in)/54-cal AA; 8/12 20-mm (0.79-in)/65- or 70-cal AA (8/12×1); 6 53-cm (21-in) torpedo tubes (2×3) *Crew:* 216-219

Southampton

British cruiser class. The London Naval Treaty of 1930 restricted the total cruiser tonnage allowed to the major naval powers, and the maximum gun calibre in such ships to 6.1-in (155-mm). These limitations, which were in large part instigated by the British,

Aldo Fraccaroli

***Fuciliere* and *Alpino*, two 'Soldati' Class destroyers of the Italian navy during the early years of the Second World War**

PPL

HMS *Glasgow*, a *Southampton* Class cruiser during the Second World War. She first saw action in the Norwegian campaign when she evacuated King Haakon following the German invasion

were intended to bring a halt to the construction of the large 8-in (203-mm) gun cruiser type which the Admiralty had found to be too expensive to construct in sufficient numbers to meet the needs of the Fleet. Thus in the early 1930s the British began to construct small 6-in (152-mm) gun cruisers (*Leander* and *Arethusa* Classes) which were intended to provide the maximum number of ships possible within the overall treaty limit. The Japanese approached the problem in a completely different way, and instead of constructing small cruisers produced the *Mogami* design which carried 15 6.1-in guns on a displacement of 11 000 tons. The Japanese actually reported the displacement as 8500 tons which caused something of a stir and, despite the assurance from the Admiralty's design department that this was impossible, it seems that some were willing to believe that this figure was correct. The United States quickly reacted to the Japanese ships in producing the design for the *Brooklyn* Class (15 6-in guns, 10 000 tons) and the British soon felt compelled to follow suit.

The Admiralty's answer to the *Mogami* was the *Southampton* or 'Town' Class cruisers in which a smaller armament of 12 6-in guns was accepted, partly because of the ever-present need to produce numbers of ships, which necessitated a restriction in size, and partly because more guns than this was considered unnecessary. The new ships were given sufficient armour to provide defence against 6-in shells, a speed of 32 knots and displaced 9100 tons standard. The design was based on that of the Modified *Leander (Sydney)* Class and like those ships incorporated unit machinery but the increased size and markedly different profile with raked masts and funnels gave little indication of a connection. They were the first British cruisers to be designed with integral aircraft hangars (one being fitted on each side of the forefunnel) and a fixed cross-deck catapult—an indication of the increasing sophistication of naval aircraft. The main armament was mounted in the new triple Mk XXII turret, two forward and two aft, the guns having a designed rate of fire of 12 rds/min. In practice the rate of fire was about half this figure but it still gave the ships the capability of smothering a target with about 70 6-in shells per minute, and it was hoped that this would enable them to counter not only enemy 6-in gun cruisers but also the slower firing 8-in gun ships. The secondary armament consisted of four twin 4-in (102-mm) dual-purpose gun mountings fitted abreast the after superstructure while close-range AA defence was provided by a quadruple 2-pdr pom-pom mounted on the roof of each hangar and two quadruple 0.5-in (12.7-mm) machine-gun mountings fitted on the after superstructure. The main armament director was fitted above the bridge, a secondary emergency control position aft and an HA/LA director on each side of the bridge.

Two of the class (*Southampton* and *Newcastle*) were provided under the 1933 Programme and three more under the 1934 Programme. These five were laid down during 1934/35, launched in 1936 and completed in 1937. Another three, of slightly modified design (*Liverpool, Manchester* and *Gloucester*) were added under the 1935 Programme, laid down in 1936, launched in 1937 and

USS *South Dakota* at sea in August 1943. After seeing extensive action in the South Pacific during the Second World War she was scrapped in 1962

completed in 1938. The last three were fitted with improved fire-control gear which included the addition of a second main-armament director aft, a new streamlined bridge with rounded front and machinery of 82 500 shp. They were also 300 tons heavier than the original ships and had 8 cm (3 in) more beam.

During the Second World War they saw extensive front-line service principally with the Home and Mediterranean Fleets, and they proved to be one of the best cruiser designs of the prewar period. *Southampton*, *Gloucester* and *Manchester* were lost. *Southampton* was heavily damaged and set afire during an air attack while escorting a Malta convoy on January 10, 1941. She had to be abandoned on the following day and was sunk by torpedoes from the cruisers *Gloucester* and *Orion*. On May 22, 1941, *Gloucester* was hit by four bombs and near-missed by three more during the battle for Crete and subsequently capsized and sank. *Manchester* was torpedoed by E-Boats during the night of August 12/13, 1942 while escorting the Malta convoy Pedestal. Extensive flooding was caused and she was rendered immobile and, as she was in enemy waters, the ship was abandoned and sunk with scuttling charges. Besides these losses *Liverpool* was out of action for a large part of the war owing to action damage. On October 14, 1940, while operating off Leros, she was hit in the bow by an aircraft torpedo. Extensive damage was caused by the detonation but worse was to follow. The torpedo explosion had damaged the aviation-spirit tank, positioned at the extreme forward end below water, and the bow structure was permeated with gasoline fumes. A short while after being hit these fumes were ignited by an electrical short circuit and the resulting detonation completely wrecked the fore end of the ship and left the remnants of the bow hanging into the sea. She was taken in tow by the cruiser *Orion* but progress was extremely slow until the bow finally broke away and sank. She was under repair until March 1942 but on June 14, 1942, she was again torpedoed while covering a Malta convoy. The torpedo struck abreast the after engine room, caused extensive flooding and put her machinery and steering gear out of action. She was eventually towed back to Gibraltar but on passage her damage was further increased by a number of near-miss bombs. Her repairs were completed by July 1943 but, presumably due to the manpower shortage, she was not commissioned and did not re-enter service until the war was over.

Early war modifications included the addi-

USS *Alabama* in 1945. Like her sisters, she supported US Navy carrier attacks on Japanese land targets during task force operations in the Pacific. At the end of the war she was decommissioned and handed over to Alabama as a state memorial. Since 1964 she has been anchored near Mobile

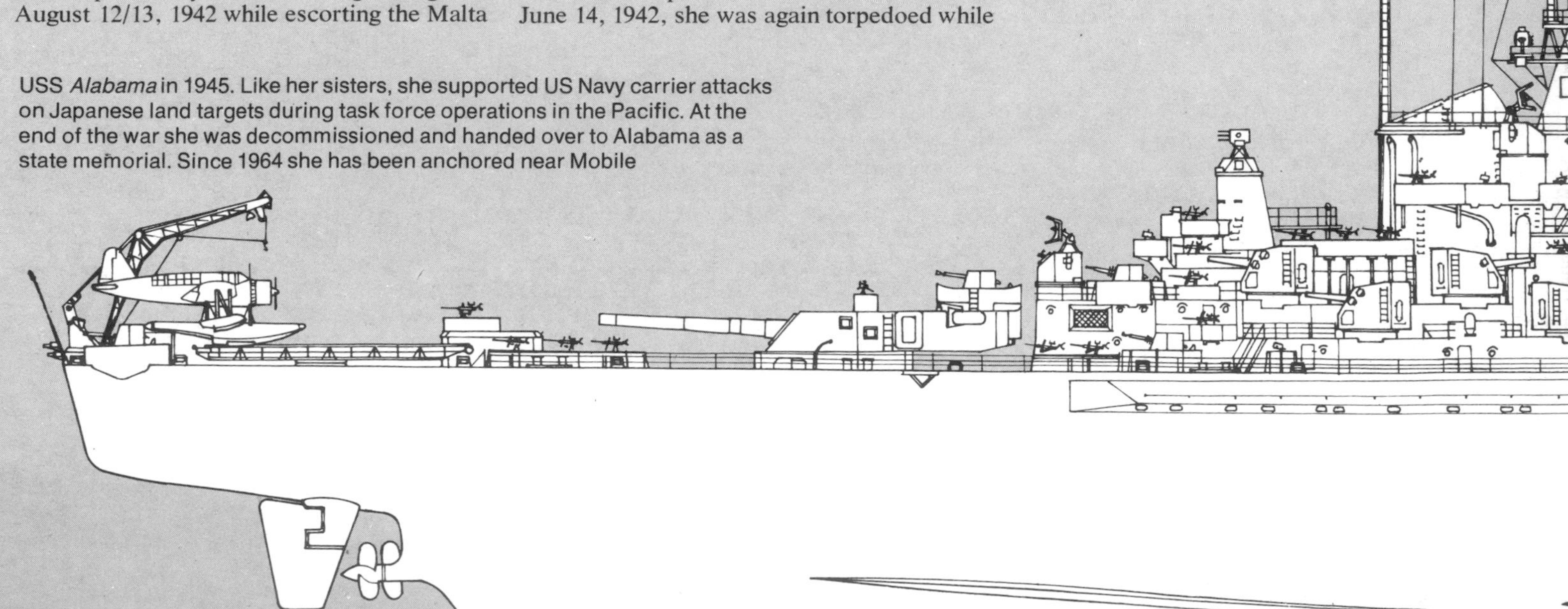

tion of between 6 and 9 20-mm (0.79-in) AA guns and the usual outfit of radar equipment for gunnery, air- and sea-warning (*Sheffield* became one of the first ships to be equipped with radar when she was fitted with an experimental air-warning set in 1938). During 1942-43 the 0.5-in (12.7-mm) guns were removed, and a number of twin 20-mm mountings substituted for some of the singles. In 1944 the need to still further improve the AA defence resulted in the removal of the aircraft equipment and X turret to provide the necessary space and weight. *Newcastle, Birmingham* and *Sheffield* received two extra and *Glasgow* and *Liverpool* four extra four-barrel pom-pom mountings while *Birmingham* and *Sheffield* also received two four-barrel 40-mm (1.57-in) Bofors. In addition the 20-mm armament was increased to between 11 and 18 guns per ship.

In most cases postwar service was limited to short periods and the class spent most of their time in reserve until sold for scrap during 1958-60. *Sheffield*, however, was extensively refitted during 1956-57 and was fitted with a lattice foremast, a uniform close-range armament of 18 40-mm (8×2, 2×1) and new AA directors. She therefore survived somewhat longer than her sisters and was not sold for scrapping until 1967.

Southampton—built by John Brown
Newcastle, Sheffield—built by Vickers-Armstrongs
Glasgow—built by Scotts
Birmingham, Gloucester—built by Devonport dockyard
Liverpool—built by Fairfield
Manchester—built by Hawthorn Leslie

Displacement: 9100 tons (load), 11 350 tons (full load) *Length:* 180.3 m (591 ft 6 in) oa *Beam:* 18.9 m (62 ft) *Draught:* 5.2 m (17 ft) *Machinery:* 4-shaft Parsons geared steam turbines 75 000 shp=32 knots *Protection:* 114 mm (4.5 in) sides, 52-25 mm (2-1 in) turrets, 38-25 mm (1.5-1 in) decks *Armament:* 12 6-in (152-mm) (4×3); 8 4-in (102-mm) (4×2); 8 2-pdr AA (2×4); 8 0.5-in (12.7-mm) AA (2×4); 6 21-in (53-cm) torpedo tubes (2×3) *Crew:* 750

South Dakota

US battleship class, built 1939-42. The design of this class was evolved in parallel with that of the *Washington* Class, as the 1939 battleships. Unlike the latter, they were intended to be protected against 16-in (406-mm) shellfire; but as they were under the constraints imposed by international treaty it was difficult to increase the weight of armour while retaining the same 28 knots speed and the nine 16-in guns of the *Washingtons*. The waterline length could be reduced to save weight, but improved protection demanded a beamier hull, and this in turn would need more power to achieve the same speed as before. The size of the machinery spaces was successfully reduced, saving weight by having a shorter citadel. The shorter hull made for improved handling and manoeuvrability. The weight saved was used to increase armour protection and internal subdivision against torpedoes. In many ways the *South Dakotas* turned out to be the most cost-effective battleships built under the Washington Treaty limits, combining heavy armour, maximum armament and a reasonable turn of speed. Their main disadvantage was that they were too slow to work with the fast carriers, but this could not have been foreseen at the time of their design.

South Dakota (BB.57) was laid down at the Camden yard of New York Shipbuilding in July 1939; she was launched on June 7, 1941, and commissioned in March 1942. *Indiana* (BB.58) was laid down the following November at Newport News, was launched on November 21, 1941, and commissioned in April 1942. *Massachusetts* (BB.59) was laid down in July 1939 by Bethlehem at Fore River, launched on September 23, 1941, and commissioned in May 1942. *Alabama* (BB.60) was laid down at Norfolk navy yard on February 1940, launched on February 16, 1942, and commissioned in August 1942.

South Dakota was sent to the Pacific soon after completing her shakedown, but grounded on a coral reef at Tangarebu in August 1942. Repairs were completed in time for her to take part in the Battle of Santa Cruz. On October 26, 1942, she claimed a record number of 26 aircraft shot down on the first occasion that proximity-fuzed shells were used at sea.

Her next action was the Battle of Guadalcanal on the night of November 14-15. She suffered a total loss of electrical power soon after the action started, when the blast of a 5-in (127-mm) gun mounting blew the ring main. Deprived of her radar, fire control and lighting, she blundered towards the Japanese battleline, and was soon engaged by the Japanese battleship *Kirishima* and the heavy cruisers *Takao* and *Atago*. She was saved by *Washington*, which fired steadily and extinguished the Japanese searchlights, allowing *South Dakota* to restore partial power and to fight back. She was hit 27 times by one 14-in (356-mm), 18 8-in (203-mm), six 6-in (152-mm), one 5-in and one of unknown calibre, but although damage was extensive it was superficial. She had 38 men killed and 60 wounded, and the damage took 62 days to repair. In 1943 she served in the North Atlantic with the British Home Fleet. On her return to the Pacific she took part in the operations against the Philippines, Okinawa and Iwo Jima, and bombarded the Japanese homeland.

Indiana replaced her damaged sister after the Battle of Guadalcanal, and covered the landings on Tarawa in 1943. In February 1944 she was badly damaged in a collision with *Washington*, and had to return to Pearl Harbor for repairs. She returned in time for the campaign against Hollandia and took part in the Marianas landings and the bombardment of Truk. With her sisters she was in action at the Battle of the Philippine Sea in June 1944, and in 1945 covered the landings on Iwo Jima and operations against the home islands.

Massachusetts was involved in the Allied invasion of North Africa (Operation Torch), during which she engaged the French battleship *Jean Bart*. After a refit she went to the Pacific in 1943, taking part in operations against the Gilberts, Kwajalein, Truk, the Carolines and Okinawa. She also took part in the Battles of the Philippine Sea and Leyte Gulf.

Alabama, like *South Dakota*, served with the British Home Fleet in 1943 before being sent to the Pacific. In February 1944 during an engagement against Japanese aircraft one of her 5-in gun mountings inadvertently fired into the back of another one, causing several casualties. Like her sisters she took part in the Philippine Sea and Leyte Gulf battles, and covered operations in the Marianas and against the Japanese mainland.

The four ships were decommissioned early in 1947. In July 1954 a study was initiated to find ways of increasing the speed of the *South Dakotas* and the *Washingtons*. The proposal was to remove the after triple 16-in gun turret to provide space for additional

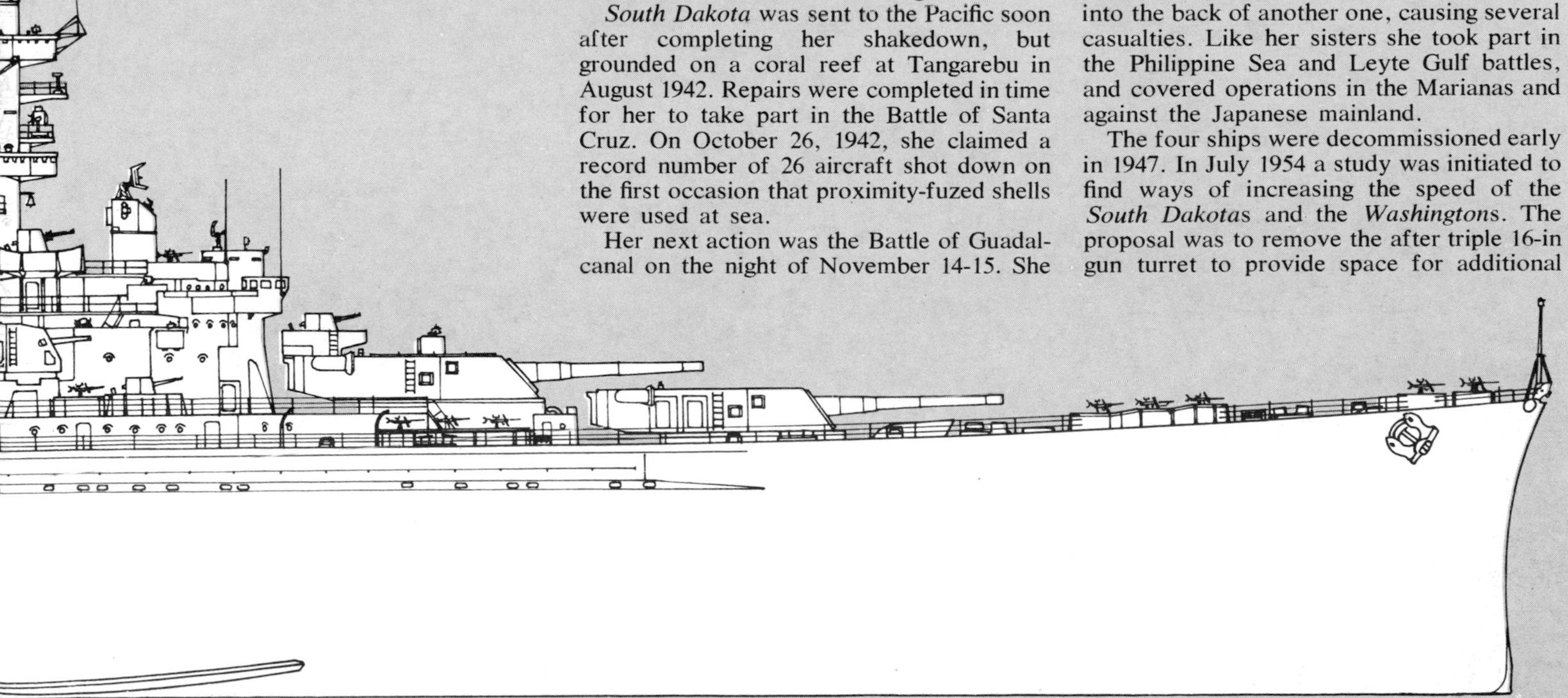

boilers. It was reported that 256 000 shp would be needed to boost speed to 31 knots, but in addition a major redesign of the after hull, rudders and propellers would have been needed. As this would cost an estimated $40 million, excluding any updating of electronics or other systems on board, the project proceeded no further. All four were stricken in 1962; parts of *South Dakota* were salvaged for a war memorial, *Alabama* was preserved as a war memorial for the state of Alabama, *Massachusetts* was similarly saved by her name-state, but the other two were scrapped.

Displacement: 38 000 tons (standard), 44 000-45 000 tons (full load) *Length:* 207.3 m (680 ft) oa *Beam:* 33 m (108 ft 3 in) *Draught:* 11.1 m (36 ft 3 in) max *Machinery:* 4-shaft geared steam turbines, 130 000 shp=28 knots *Protection:* 311 mm (12.25 in) belt, 127-38 mm (5-1.5 in) decks, 457 mm (18 in) turrets *Armament:* 9 16-in (406-mm)/45-cal Mk 6 (3×3); 16/20 5-in (127-mm)/38-cal DP Mk 12 (8/10×2); 48/68 40-mm (1.57-in) Bofors AA (12/17×4); 40/52 20-mm (0.79-in) Oerlikon AA (40/52×1); 2 Kingfisher floatplanes, 2 catapults *Crew:* 2384

Sparviero

Italian hydrofoil class. The contract for the name-vessel of this class was placed in October 1970 and it commenced trials in May 1973. The design is closely based on that of the US *Tucumcari.* The design requirement was for a vessel capable of operating in a wide variety of environments on both offensive and defensive missions. The fully submerged foil system is used. When not in use the after foils fold back against the side of the hull. The bow foil retracts forwards into a recess in the bow to preserve the hull lines. With the fully submerged canard foil arrangement almost two-thirds of the dynamic lift is provided by the two after foils with the remainder by the bow foil.

The vessel is equipped with a fully automatic control system incorporating aircraft-type gyros to sense pitch and roll, and yaw, with accelerometers measuring heave or vertical motion. An ultrasonic height detector ensures that the craft maintains flying height above the water. All data from the sensors is fed to a computer which automatically controls the foil attitudes.

When foil-borne the ship is propelled by a powerful water jet powered by a Rolls-Royce Proteus gas turbine. The pump sucks in water through inlets on the noses of the after foils and expels it through twin nozzles beneath the hull under the pump. While hull-borne, propulsion is provided by a diesel engine which powers a retractable, steerable, fixed-pitch propeller outdrive unit mounted on the centreline of the transom. Trials have shown the craft to be easily capable of meeting performance and design requirements.

Sparviero is armed with an OTO-Melara 76-mm (3-in) gun forward and Otomat surface-to-surface missiles aft. Fire control is by an Elsag NA-10 system incorporating the Orion RTN-10X radar. The radius of action is 15 400 nautical miles.

Six sister-ships are due to be completed by Cantieri Navale Riuniti between 1979-81.

Displacement: 62.5 tons *Length:* 22.9 m (75 ft 2 in) *Beam:* 7 m (23 ft) *Draught:* 4.4 m (14 ft 5 in), 1.5 m (4 ft 11 in) foil-borne *Machinery:* 1 Rolls-Royce Proteus gas turbine, 5000 hp=50 knots; 1 General Motors diesel, 160 hp *Armament:* 1 3-in (76-mm); 2 Otomat launchers *Crew:* 10

Spica

Swedish fast patrol boat class, built 1962-66. Under the *Marinplan* for 1960 six gas-turbine driven torpedo boats were ordered for the Royal Swedish Navy. *Spica* (T.121), *Sirius* (T.122) and *Capella* (T.123) were built by Gotaverken at Gothenburg, while *Castor* (T.124), *Vega* (T.125) and *Virgo* (T.126) were built by Karlskronavarvet at Karlskrona. New methods of production were developed for the class by Gotaverken. Sheet-metal jigs and a system of subassemblies were used to permit welding under cover. Each subassembly was about 7 m (23 ft) long, and was lifted onto a special building berth; the finished hull was then 'launched' by crane. The boats were powered by three Rolls-Royce (Bristol) Marine Proteus gas turbines developing 4100 shp each, to give fast starting and to save space.

The armament comprised six 53-cm (21-in) torpedo tubes firing TP 61 hydrogen peroxide torpedoes with wire guidance, backed up by a single Bofors 57-mm (2.24-in) gun forward. The gun is controlled by a Hollandse Signaalapparaten M22 fire-control system, with its distinctive radome above the bridge. Four 103-mm (4.1-in) rocket flare launchers are positioned on the sides of the wheelhouse.

The Italian hydrofoil *Sparviero* at speed. *Sparviero* is capable of 50 knots and carries an armament of a single OTO-Melara 76-mm (3-in) gun with two Otomat surface-to-surface missiles. The Italian navy plan a fleet of eight craft, six of which were due for completion in the late 1970s

Italian Navy

Karlskronavarvet

Lulea, a *Spica* Class fast patrol boat of the Royal Swedish Navy. *Spicas* are armed with six wire-guided torpedoes with a radar-controlled Bofors 57-mm (2.24-in) gun and flare launchers

and six 57-mm flare-launchers are mounted on the gun shield.

In 1970-76 a further 12 modified vessels were built by Karlskronavarvet: *Norrköping* (T.131), *Nynäshamn* (T.132), *Norrtälje* (T.133), *Varberg* (T.134), *Västeräs* (T.135), *Västervik* (T.136), *Umeä* (T.137), *Pitea* (T.138), *Lulea* (T.139), *Halmstad* (T.140), *Stromstad* (T.141) and *Ystad* (T.142). They differ from the original *Spicas* in having the Swedish-designed Philips 9LV200 fire control, which is much lighter and more compact, and its associated I-Band radar. They also have the latest model Bofors 57-mm gun, with a rate of fire of 200 rds/min, firing prefragmented proximity-fuzed ammunition to achieve a high kill rate against aircraft and missiles.

Displacement: 200-230 tons (standard), 230-260 tons (full load) *Length:* 41 m (134 ft 6 in) wl *Beam:* 7.1 m (23 ft 4 in) *Draught:* 1.6 m (5 ft 3 in) *Machinery:* 3-shaft gas turbines, 12 900 shp=40 knots *Armament:* 1 57-mm (2.24-in) DP L/70; 6 53-cm (21-in) torpedo tubes (6×1) *Crew:* 28

Split

Yugoslav destroyer, built 1939-58. A large destroyer or flotilla leader was ordered from Chantiers de la Loire in October 1938 and laid down at Split shipyard in July 1939. She was launched and named *Spalato* in 1940, but work stopped when the Germans invaded Yugoslavia in 1941. The original design was to include five 138.6-mm (5.46-in) guns, six 55-cm (21.7-in) torpedo tubes and five twin 40-mm (1.57-in) Bofors guns. She would have resembled the *Fantasque* Class, but with less powerful machinery.

When work resumed after the war, the ship was renamed *Split* and the design was completely recast. The US supplied 5-in (127-mm)/38-cal single guns, fire control and radar, and the uptakes were trunked into a single funnel. Although the original long forecastle was retained, a continuous deckhouse replaced the torpedo tubes on the main deck to provide shelter for personnel and offices for the new equipment. A quintuple set of torpedo tubes of US Navy pattern was mounted a deck higher. Mk 37 fire control is provided for the 5-in guns, with Mk 12 and Mk 22 radars, while SC and SG-1 radars are provided on the tripod mast. She started her trials in July 1958.

Despite her age *Split* presents a modern profile, with a raked bow and a prominent funnel cap. At the end of 1977 she was still serving as flagship of the Torpedo Boat 'Brigade' or Division.

Displacement: 2400 tons (standard), 3000 tons (full load) *Length:* 120 m (393 ft 8 in) oa *Beam:* 11.1 m (36 ft 5 in) *Draught:* 3.8 m (12 ft 6 in) *Machinery:* 2-shaft geared steam turbines, 50 000 shp=34 knots *Armament:* (as completed) 4 5-in (127-mm)/38-cal DP (4×1); 12 40-mm (1.57-in)/60-cal Bofors (12×1); 5 21-in (53-cm) torpedo tubes (1×5) *Crew:* 240

Spruance

US destroyer class, begun in 1972. These vessels are built in a specially designed shipbuilding facility employing modular construction methods at the Ingalls division of Litton Industries, Pascagoula. *Spruance* (DD.963) was completed in 1975, followed by *Paul F Foster* (DD.964), *Kinkaid* (DD.965), *Hewitt* (DD.966), *Elliott* (DD.967), *Arthur W Radford* (DD.968), *Peterson* (DD.969), *Caron* (DD.970), *David R Ray* (DD.971), *Oldendorf* (DD.972), *John Young* (DD.973), *Comte de Grasse* (DD.974), and *O'Brien* (DD.975). Other ships under construction in early 1979 were *Merrill* (DD.976), *Briscoe* (DD.977), *Stump* (DD.978), *Conolly* (DD.979), *Moosbrugger* (DD.980), *John Hancock* (DD.981), *Nicholson* (DD.982), *John Rodgers* (DD.983), *Leftwich* (DD.984), *Cushing* (DD.985), *Harry W Hill* (DD.986), *O'Bannon* (DD.987), *Thorn* (DD.988), *Deyo* (DD.989), *Ingersoll* (DD.990), *Fife* (DD.991), and *Fletcher* (DD.992). The last of the 30 ships should complete in 1981.

The class is intended to fill the gap left by the disposal of Second World War construction. Seen by the US Navy primarily as ASW ships with the ability to operate as part of a fast carrier task force, the *Spruance* Class attracted considerable criticism because of their light armament. These cruiser-sized ships have, however, been specially designed to have sufficient weight and space in reserve to accommodate future developments in weapons technology. The first ships emerged with only two single light 5-in (127-mm)/54-cal guns fore and aft for surface or aerial engagement, but by 1979 some ships were fitted with two quadruple launchers for Harpoon surface-to-surface missiles just aft of

The Yugoslav destroyer *Split* in May 1959. She was begun in July 1939 but construction was halted in 1940. She was still in service in 1977 as a flagship

Aldo Fraccaroli

the first funnel, and an eight-cell launcher for NATO Sea Sparrow short-range surface-to-air missiles above the after 5-in gun. It was also planned eventually to replace the forward gun by the 8-in (203-mm) lightweight mounting under development in the late 1970s, and to add two 20-mm (0.79-in) Vulcan Phalanx close-in weapon systems. The only above-water sensors fitted by 1979 were SPS-40 air-search radar and the new Mk 86 fire-control system, but the massive lattice masts have ample space for later developments.

The *Spruance* Class are the first large US ships to have all-gas-turbine propulsion. Four LM-2500 turbines, each rated at 20 000 shp, are paired en echelon to drive twin shafts with controllable-pitch propellers. The engine rooms are separated by no less than three bulkheads to minimize action damage. The generators, too, are gas-turbine driven, making the operation of the ships exceptionally quiet. This makes them difficult for submarines to detect and minimizes interference with the large SQS-53 bow sonar. The ASW weapons are an Asroc eight-cell launcher, with a large reload magazine beneath, and triple Mk 32 torpedo tubes concealed behind sliding doors in the hull beneath the flight deck. The capacious hangar houses either two Seasprite ASW helicopters or a single Sea King.

In 1978 two modified *Spruance* designs received Congressional approval. The DDG.47 design, intended to provide area-defence cover for fast carrier task forces, has twin-arm Mk 26 launchers for Standard SM-2 missiles, operating in conjunction with the advanced Aegis weapon control system; 16 ships are projected in addition to four (DD.993-996) which were laid down in 1978 for Iran, to be named *Kouroosh, Daryush, Ardeshir* and *Nader*. They have a similar armament to the DDG.47 design but have conventional sensors. DDH.997 is a single-ship design in which the hangar has been enlarged to carry four ASW helicopters.

Displacement: 7810 tons (full load) *Length:* 171 m (561 ft) *Beam:* 17.6 m (57 ft 9 in) *Draught:* 8.8 m (28 ft 11 in) *Machinery:* 4 LM-2500 gas turbines, 80 000 hp=33 knots *Armament:* 2 5-in (127-mm)/54-cal Mk 45 DP (2×1); 1 Asroc launcher; 6 Mk 32 torpedo tubes (2×3); 8 Harpoon SSM launchers (2×4); 8 Sea Sparrow SAM launchers (1×8); 2 SH-2 LAMPS helicopters or 1 SH-3 Sea King *Crew:* 296

'Stenka'/'Osa'

Soviet patrol boats, built during the 1960s. Both classes stem from the same basic design, which was developed to facilitate mass production of the various types of patrol boat needed for operations in coastal waters. The 'Osa' Class guided-missile patrol craft began building in 1959-60, the first being completed in 1961. Series production continued throughout the 1960s resulting in a total of 200, of which about 100 remained operational with the Soviet navy in 1978. Known names are *Brestsky Komsomolets, Kirovsky Komsomolets, Michurinsky Komsomolets, Tambovsky Komsomolets.* The 'Stenka' Class, which were armed as submarine-chasers, were laid down from 1967 onwards, the first being completed in 1968. A total of 67 boats are thought to have been built, all of which serve in the Soviet navy. No names are known and, like the 'Osa' Class, it is not known in which shipyards they were built.

The steel hulls of the two classes are of identical dimensions, the slightly greater overall length of the 'Stenka' being accounted for by the bulwark added to the bow. Propulsion of both types is by diesel engines on three shafts. Those installed in the 'Stenka' develop only two-thirds of the power of the 'Osa' Class, giving them a speed of 30-32 knots which is sufficient for antisubmarine duties but not for the high-speed strikes demanded of the 36-knot missile boats. The superstructure of both types is similar. The long deckhouse running aft from the bridge contains all equipment for com-

USS *Spruance* during builder's trials in 1975. Although designed for the ASW role, the destroyers of this class also carry Sea Sparrow SAMs and two 5-in (127-mm) guns

A Soviet 'Stenka' Class fast patrol boat. The 'Stenkas' are armed as submarine-chasers while their 'Osa' Class sisters mount four SS-N-2 surface-to-surface missiles in angled launchers

Norwegian *Storm* Class fast patrol boats. They carry a gun and Penguin missile armament

mand and control of operations, weapons control, and quarters for the crew. This enables the boats to be 'closed down' in the event of CBW warfare. At either end of the boats is a twin 30-mm (1.18-in) AA mounting, and the prominent Drum Tilt director is carried on a pedestal at the after end of the superstructure.

The 'Osa' Class are equipped with four launchers for SS-N-2 surface-to-surface missiles, a weapon first carried by the 'Komar' Class FPBs on which it did not prove particularly successful owing to the vessels' small size. The launchers on the 'Osa' Class, unlike those fitted to their predecessors, are completely enclosed. The forward launcher is angled upwards at 12°, while the second launcher is angled at 15° and fires above it. Shields behind each launcher deflect the blast outwards. The bulky launchers of the first boats were superseded on later boats by smaller, cylindrical launchers fixed at the same angles. The two types are known as the 'Osa-I' and 'Osa-II' respectively.

The 'Stenka' Class have four single tubes for 40-cm (15.7-in) homing torpedoes angled out alongside the after part of the superstructure. There are also two depth-charge launchers fitted to the stern.

'Osa-I' Class boats have been transferred to Romania (five boats from 1961), East Germany (15 from 1964), China (one in 1965), Yugoslavia (ten in 1965 and 1969), Egypt (ten in 1966), Algeria (three in 1967), North Korea (eight), Sudan (one), Syria (eight), Saudi Arabia (three), Bulgaria (three in 1970-71), India (eight in 1971), Iraq (six in 1972-73), Cuba (five in 1972-74), and Finland (four in 1974). In addition to these, 'Osa-II' Class boats have been transferred to Iraq (four in 1975) and Morocco (six in 1976). Two Syrian and four Egyptian boats were sunk in the 1973 Middle East war.

('Osa' Class) *Displacement:* 165 tons (standard), 205 tons (full load) *Length:* 37.5 m (123 ft) oa *Beam:* 8.5 m (27 ft 11 in) *Draught:* 1.8 m (5 ft 11 in) *Machinery:* 3-shaft diesel, 9900 bhp=36 knots *Armament:* 4 SS-N-2 missile launchers; 4 30-mm (1.18-in) AA mountings (2×2) *Crew:* 39

('Stenka' Class) *Displacement:* 185 tons (standard), 225 tons (full load) *Length:* 38 m (124 ft 8 in) oa *Beam* and *Draught:* as 'Osa' *Machinery:* 3-shaft diesel, 6600 bhp=30-32 knots *Armament:* 4 40-cm (15.7-in) torpedo tubes (4×1); 4 30-mm (1.18-in) AA mountings *Crew:* 40

Storm

Norwegian missile-armed fast strike vessel class, built 1961-71. Under a five-year modernization programme announced in July 1959 the Royal Norwegian Navy planned to build 23 motor gunboats. This was later cut back to 20, but the prototype, *Storm* (P. 960), was completed by Bergens Mekaniska Verksted in May 1963. She was largely experimental and was eventually scrapped after evaluation, and the first series production boat was *Blink* (P.961), from the same yard. She was followed by *Glimt, Skjold, Trygg, Kjekk, Djerv, Skudd, Arg, Steil, Brann, Tross, Hvass, Traust, Brott, Odd, Pil, Brask, Rokk* and *Gnist*, bearing pendant numbers P.961-979. A replacement was also built for *Storm*. It was given the same number, P.960, and was the last of the class to enter service, being commissioned along with *Gnist* and *Rokk* in 1968.

The original armament of the class was a Bofors 76-mm (3-in) gun in an automatic enclosed turret on the forecastle and a 40-mm (1.57-in) gun aft. The 76-mm L/50 gun weighs 6500 kg (14 330 lb) and uses electro-hydraulic remote control. Although no longer in production it is a useful weapon for small craft. The 40-mm gun is the standard Bofors L/70 single. In 1965 the class was rerated as gunboats, but in 1970 they started to receive the first Penguin surface-to-surface infrared homing missiles, with six launchers aft.

Six repeat editions were ordered from Bätservice at Mandal in 1968, to replace the *Rapp* Class. They had the same hull but carried four 21-in (53-cm) torpedo tubes, a single 40-mm gun forward and four Penguin missiles. Their names are *Snögg* (ex-*Lyr*) (P.980), *Rapp* (P.981), *Snar* (P.982), *Rask* (P.983), *Kvikk* (P.984) and *Kjapp* (P.985). The first of the class came into service in 1970.

Displacement: 100 tons (standard), 125 tons (full load) *Length:* 36.5 m (119 ft 9 in) oa *Beam:* 6.2 m (20 ft 4 in) *Draught:* 1.5 m (4 ft 11 in) *Machinery:* 2-shaft diesel, 7200 bhp=32 knots *Armament:* (*Storm* Group) 1 76-mm (3-in) L/50 Bofors; 1 40-mm (1.57-in) L/70 Bofors; 6 Penguin SSM-launchers; (*Snögg* Group) 1 40-mm L/70 Bofors; 4 53-cm (21-in) torpedo tubes; 4 Penguin SSM-launchers *Crew:* 22

Sturgeon

US nuclear-powered submarine class, built 1963-75. In 1962 Congress authorized the construction of the first three of a new class of nuclear-powered attack submarines. *Sturgeon* and her sisters were based on the earlier *Thresher* Class, the more visible changes being that they were slightly longer, with a taller sail and forward diving planes on the sail fitted lower down to improve control at periscope depth. The forward hydroplanes could be rotated to a vertical position to assist in surfacing through the Arctic ice. As with the *Thresher* Class, the four torpedo tubes were fitted amidships and were capable of firing the Subroc antisubmarine missile. The last nine boats, commencing with *Archerfish*, were modified to allow for fitting an improved type of sonar, which increased the length of these boats by 3 m (10 ft).

Later submarines of the class participated in the trials of the new antiship missile Sub-Harpoon. *Hawkbill* has been modified as mother ship for a deep submergence rescue vessel (DSRV), a small submarine 15.2 m (50 ft) long which she carries on the after deck. The DSRV is designed to rescue the crew of other submarines in difficulties in water too deep for the usual submarine rescue methods.

While in the fitting-out basin *Guitarro* sank in 11 m (35 ft) of water as a result of errors by the shipyard. This accident delayed her completion by over two years and cost some $25 million.

No and name	laid down	launched	completed	builder
SSN.637 ***Sturgeon***	10/63	2/66	3/67	General Dynamics (Electric Boat)
SSN.638 ***Whale***	5/64	10/66	10/68	General Dynamics, Quincey
SSN.639 ***Tautog***	1/64	4/67	8/68	Ingalls
SSN.646 ***Grayling***	5/64	6/67	10/69	Portsmouth navy yard
SSN.647 ***Pogy***	5/64	6/67	5/71	Ingalls
SSN.648 ***Aspro***	10/64	11/67	2/69	Ingalls
SSN.649 ***Sunfish***	1/65	10/66	3/69	General Dynamics, Quincy
SSN.650 ***Pargo***	6/64	9/66	1/68	General Dynamics (Electric Boat)
SSN.651 ***Queenfish***	5/65	2/66	12/66	Newport News shipbuilding
SSN.652 ***Puffer***	2/65	3/68	8/69	Ingalls
SSN.653 ***Ray***	4/65	6/66	4/67	Newport News shipbuilding
SSN.660 ***Sand Lance***	1/65	11/69	9/71	Portsmouth navy yard
SSN.661 ***Lapon***	7/65	12/66	12/67	Newport News shipbuilding
SSN.662 ***Gurnard***	12/64	5/67	12/68	Mare Island navy yard
SSN.663 ***Hammerhead***	11/65	4/67	6/68	Newport News shipbuilding
SSN.664 ***Sea Devil***	4/66	10/67	1/69	Newport News shipbuilding
SSN.665 ***Guitarro***	12/65	7/68	9/72	Mare Island navy yard
SSN.666 ***Hawkbill***	9/66	4/69	2/71	Mare Island navy yard
SSN.667 ***Bergall***	4/66	2/68	6/69	General Dynamics (Electric Boat)
SSN.668 ***Spadefish***	12/66	5/68	8/69	Newport News shipbuilding
SSN.669 ***Seahorse***	8/66	6/68	9/69	General Dynamics (Electric Boat)
SSN.670 ***Finback***	6/67	12/68	2/70	Newport News shipbuilding
SSN.672 ***Pintado***	10/67	8/69	9/71	Mare Island navy yard
SSN.673 ***Flying Fish***	6/67	5/69	4/70	General Dynamics (Electric Boat)
SSN.674 ***Trepang***	10/67	9/69	8/70	General Dynamics (Electric Boat)
SSN.675 ***Bluefish***	3/68	1/70	1/71	General Dynamics (Electric Boat)

Displacement: 3860/4630 tons (surfaced/submerged) *Length:* 89.2 m (292 ft 6 in) oa *Beam:* 9.7 m (31 ft 8 in) *Draught:* 9 m (29 ft 5 in) *Machinery:* nuclear reactor, 1-shaft steam turbine, 15000 shp=20/30 knots (surfaced/submerged) *Armament:* 4 21-in (53-cm) torpedo tubes *Crew:* 120

Suffren

French guided-missile destroyer class, built 1962-64. Under the 1960 Programme two *frégates* were ordered, *Suffren* from Lorient dockyard, and the *Duquesne* from Brest dockyard. They were to be big ocean-going fleet escorts capable of providing area defence, and were the first French ships built from the keel up armed with the Masurca SAM system. Although rated as frigates they carry pendant numbers D.602 and D.603.

A new hull form was adopted, with the forecastle deck carried aft almost to the quarterdeck, a distinctive 'flattened nose' to permit A gun to fire at zero elevation, and a wide shallow transom stern to accommodate a big towed sonar. Other unusual features are the huge 'golf-ball' dome weather-proofing the DRBI-23 three-dimensional radar (which provides air-surveillance and target designation for the SAMs) and a tall mack nearly amidships. The Masurca missiles are launched from a twin-arm launcher aft, with two DRBR-51 fire-control radars on the after superstructure.

A single launcher for the Malafon antisubmarine missile system is positioned abaft the mack, and since 1977 *Suffren* has carried four MM-38 Exocet SSM launchers on the deckhouse immediately abaft this launcher. Her sister completed similar modification in 1978, and both ships surrendered their twin 30-mm (1.18-in) guns to compensate for the weight. The SENIT 1 action data automation system is fitted.

The ships are reported to be exceptionally good seaboats, with little vibration. They have three pairs of gyroscopically controlled non-retractable stabilizers. Accommodation and working spaces are air-conditioned.

Displacement: 5090 tonnes (normal), 6090 tonnes (full load) *Length:* 157.6 m (517 ft 1 in) oa *Beam:* 15.5 m (50 ft 10 in) *Draught:* 6.1 m (20 ft) *Machinery:* 2-shaft geared steam turbines, 72500 shp=34 knots *Armament:* 2 100-mm (3.9-in)/55-cal DP Model 53 (2×1); 2 20-mm (0.79-in) Oerlikon (2×1); 1 Masurca SAM launcher, 48 Mk 3 Mod 2 and Mod 3 missiles; 1 Malafon launcher, 13 missiles; 4 MM-38 Exocet launchers; 5 L5 A/S torpedo tubes *Crew:* 350

Surcouf

French destroyer class. The first group of 12 large destroyers was authorized under the 1949 to 1952 Programmes. Named *Surcouf, Chevalier Paul, Cassard, Bouvet, Du Chayla, Dupetit Thouars, Kersaint, D'Estrées, Maillé Brézé, Vauquelin, Casabianca,* and *Guépratte,* they were laid down 1951-53, launched 1953-54, and completed 1955-57. A further five were authorized in 1953, named *Duperré, La Bourdonnais, Jauréguiberry, Tartu* and *Forbin*; they were laid down in 1954, launched in 1955 and completed 1957-58. The eighteenth ship, *La Galissonnière,* was built to a different design, and was not

ECP Armées

The *Duquesne*, a *Suffren* Class guided-missile destroyer, with DRBI-23 three-dimensional radar

laid down until 1958, being launched in 1960 and completed in 1962.

In conception the *Surcouf* Class followed on from the large French *contre-torpilleurs* built during the prewar period, except that the experience of the Second World War led to a much-improved capability against aircraft (they were in fact first to be designated antiaircraft escorts). The main armament of the first 17 (as built) comprised a twin 127-mm (5-in) dual-purpose mounting forward and a further two aft. The calibre was chosen to permit them to fire standard US 5-in (127-mm) ammunition, previous ships of this size having been armed with 130-mm (5.1-in) guns. In B position was a twin 57-mm (2.24-in) AA gun, and two other twin mountings were sited side by side just aft of the second funnel. The first 12 ships, designated the T47 type, also had two triple side-mounted torpedo tubes for surface action, and a further pair of triple tubes for antisubmarine homing torpedoes. The second group, designated the T53 R type, had only the after sets of tubes, and could fire either sort of torpedo. They were also equipped with additional air-search and height-finding radars for aircraft direction, and a Bofors A/S mortar fitted forward of X mounting.

The final ship of the class, *La Galissonnière,* designated the T56 type, was designed as a squadron escort and flotilla leader, and unlike her sisters was equipped primarily for an antisubmarine mission. When she finally commissioned in 1962 she was the first ship equipped with a missile system of French origin, the antisubmarine Malafon, the launcher for which was mounted aft. She also carried a helicopter aft on a raised flight deck with a collapsible hangar, and bow and towed sonars were fitted. The armament was completed by two of the new single 100-mm (3.9-in) automatic guns forward, and two triple banks of tubes for A/S homing torpedoes. She served for some time as a trials ship for the new ASW weapons and sensors with which she was fitted.

In the early 1960s the remainder of the class began to fragment. *Surcouf, Chevalier Paul,* and *Cassard* were converted to command ships, which involved removal of the forward 57-mm mounting to enable the bridge structure to be extended forward, and removal of the after set of torpedo tubes. *Bouvet, Du Chayla, Dupetit Thouars* and *Kersaint* were then rearmed with the US Tartar surface-to-air missile. The conversion involved the removal of the after 127-mm turrets, which were replaced by a cylindrical magazine topped by a single-arm Mk 13 launcher. Two SPG-51 tracker/illuminators were raised on pedestals just forward of the launcher. The system was completed by a US SPS-39 height-finding radar atop the mainmast, later to be replaced by the planar SPS-52. Only the forward set of torpedo tubes was retained. During 1968-70 *D'Estrées, Maillé Brézé, Vauquelin, Casabianca* and *Guépratte* underwent a major conversion influenced by the success of *La Galissonnière* as an antisubmarine vessel. Malafon was installed aft, but no helicopter was carried, its place being taken by a single 100-mm gun. A second 100-mm mounting replaced A turret, while B position was occupied by a Bofors

ECP Armées

The French destroyer *Forbin*, one of the *Surcouf* Class laid down and launched in the mid-1950s

SSN.676 *Billfish*	9/68	5/70	3/71	General Dynamics (Electric Boat)
SSN.677 *Drum*	8/68	5/70	4/72	Mare Island navy yard
SSN.678 *Archerfish*	6/69	1/71	12/71	General Dynamics (Electric Boat)
SSN.679 *Silversides*	10/69	6/71	5/72	General Dynamics (Electric Boat)
SSN.680 *William H Bates*	8/69	12/71	5/73	Ingalls
SSN.681 *Batfish*	2/70	10/71	9/72	General Dynamics (Electric Boat)
SSN.682 *Tunny*	5/70	6/72	1/74	Ingalls
SSN.683 *Parche*	12/70	1/73	8/74	Ingalls
SSN.684 *Cavalla*	6/70	2/72	2/73	General Dynamics (Electric Boat)
SSN.686 *L Mendel Rivers*	6/71	6/72	2/75	Newport News shipbuilding
SSN.687 *Richard B Russell*	10/71	1/74	8/75	Newport News shipbuilding

MOD

The Soviet cruiser *Sverdlov*, photographed by a Royal Navy Sea King helicopter in July 1976

A/S rocket launcher. As in the other conversions only the forward set of torpedo tubes was retained. A complete new sensor outfit was installed similar to that of *La Galissonnière.* The final conversion was that of *Duperré* of the T53 type, which after serving as a trials ship from 1967 was converted to an antisubmarine destroyer from 1972-74. The conversion was once again on the lines of *La Galissonnière,* but only a single 100-mm mounting was fitted forward, and she had a 'permanent' hangar with a flight deck extending aft of it in place of Malafon. Four launchers for Exocet surface-to-surface missiles were angled out on either side of the forefunnel, and a new sensor outfit was installed.

Surcouf lost her bow in a collision in the Mediterranean in 1971 and was subsequently scrapped. Of the four unconverted ships of the T53 group, *La Bourdonnais* paid off in 1976, *Jauréguiberry* in 1977 and *Tartu* in 1978. *Forbin* is presently being used as a training ship.

(T47 and T53 types) *Displacement:* 2750 tons (standard), 3750 tons (full load) *Length:* 128.4 m (421 ft 3 in) oa *Beam:* 13 m (42 ft 8 in) *Draught:* 5.6 m (18 ft 5 in) *Machinery:* 2-shaft steam turbines, 63 000 shp=34 knots *Armament:* 6 127-mm (5-in) DP (3×2); 6 57-mm (2.24-in) AA (3×2); 6 20-mm (0.79-in) AA (6×1); 12 (T53, 6) 55-cm (21.7-in) torpedo tubes (4/2×3) *Crew:* 347

(T56 type) *Displacement:* as above *Length:* 132.8 m (435 ft 8 in) oa *Beam, Draught* and *Machinery:* as above *Armament:* 2 100-mm (3.9-in) AA (2×1); 1 Malafon A/S missile-launcher; 6 55-cm (21.7-in) torpedo tubes (2×3); 1 A/S helicopter *Crew:* 333

Sverdlov

Soviet cruiser class. Of the 24 vessels thought to have been projected, 20 were laid down from 1948 onwards. The class did not find favour with Kruschev, who thought the cruiser an obsolescent type, and only 17 were launched and of these 14 were completed. These ships are thought to have been laid down 1948-53, launched 1951-54 and completed 1952-58, and are named *Sverdlov, Molotovsk* (later renamed *Oktyabrskaya Revolutsiya*), *Admiral Nakhimov, Admiral Senyavin, Zhdanov, Dzerzhinski, Ordzhonikidze, Admiral Lazarev, Admiral Ushakov, Alexandr Nevski, Alexandr Suvorov, Murmansk, Mikhail Kutusov, Dmitri Pozharski.* Builders were the Baltic and Marti yards, Leningrad; Yard 402 at Severodvinsk; Nosenko yard, Nikolaiev; and Amur yard, Komsomolsk.

The natural successors to the war-built *Chapaev* Class, the *Sverdlov* Class nevertheless reflected some of the lessons learned in the Second World War, and in particular moved away from the Italian influence of earlier cruiser construction in favour of technology transferred by the Germans under the 1939 agreement or copied from German ships which fell into Soviet hands in 1945. The forecastle deck was extended aft for improved seakeeping, the transom stern (well-suited to minelaying) abandoned, and electric welding introduced.

The main armament comprised the 12 152-mm (6-in) guns in triple mountings introduced by the *Chapaev* Class. Originally intended as the secondary armament of the battleships under construction at the start of the Second World War, it did not become operational until after the war. The gun is not automatic, but thanks to an elevation of about 50° can be used as an AA weapon. German influence can be seen both in the AA armament of the ships and in the hemispherical HA directors which closely resemble those of the German battleships and cruisers. The 100-mm (3.9-in)/60-cal turrets, of which three are mounted on either side of the ship at upper-deck level, closely resemble the C-38 antiaircraft gunhouses of the wartime German navy. The turret is fully stabilized, allowing it to be tilted 25° about its axis. The AA armament is completed by 32 37-mm (1.46-in) AA in twin mounts, divided equally between the forward and after superstructures. Mine rails with an estimated capacity of 100 mines run the full length of the quarterdeck. *Sverdlov, Ordzhonikidze, Zhdanov, Admiral Ushakov* and *Admiral Nakhimov* were also fitted with two quintuple banks of torpedo tubes amidships. The first three also have a high deckhouse surrounding the forefunnel which distinguishes them from the others.

The steam propulsion plant is a conservative one, the USSR having rejected the high-pressure superheated boilers developed by the Germans because of operating and maintenance problems experienced with their war prizes.

From 1960 to 1962 the Black Sea-built *Dzerzhinski* underwent a major conversion involving the removal of X turret and its replacement by a missile magazine for long-range SA-N-2 surface-to-air missiles with a twin-arm launcher mounted on top of it. Forward of the launcher, a blast deflector extends almost to the deck-edges. The after 37-mm AA guns were also removed and in their place is a large missile-guidance radar mounted on a pedestal. A distinctive height-finding aerial was installed aft of the first funnel, and an air-search radar on the mainmast. The conversion does not seem to have been a success and no further ships were converted.

A conversion of a different nature was undertaken in the early 1970s involving the *Zhdanov* and *Admiral Senyavin.* It began at Nikolaiev in 1970 and was completed 1973-74. *Zhdanov* had X turret replaced by a tall deckhouse containing a bin for the short-range SA-N-4 SAM pop-up launcher. The director for this is mounted on a new lattice mast which is topped by two V-Cone antennae for long-range communications. The superstructure around the forefunnel was extended to accommodate four twin 30-mm (1.18-in) AA mountings and their directors, and the torpedo tubes were removed. The conversion of *Admiral Senyavin* was similar, except that both her after turrets were removed and replaced by a large hangar which can accommodate two helicopters and on which four extra twin 30-mm mountings with their directors are mounted in addition to the SA-N-4 bin.

Both of these conversions now serve as command cruisers, but the remaining ships of the class have been little altered except for the provision of modern radars. They are presumably retained mainly for shore bombardment, although they are frequently employed as force flagships. *Admiral Nakhimov,* which was rumoured to have undergone conversion to carry SS-N-1 surface-to-surface missiles about 1960, was discarded in 1969. *Ordzhonikidze* was sold to Indonesia in 1962 and renamed *Irian*. She was discarded in the early 1970s.

Displacement: 15 450 tons (standard), 19 200 tons (full load) *Length:* 210 m (689 ft) oa *Beam:* 20 m (65 ft 7 in) *Draught:* 7 m (23 ft) *Machinery:* 2-shaft steam turbines, 110 000 shp=34 knots *Armament:* 12 (*Dzerzhinski* and *Zhdanov* 9, *Senyavin* 6) 152-mm (6-in) (4/3/2×3); 12 100-mm (3.9-in) AA (6×2); 32 (*Dzerzhinski* 16, *Pozharski* 24) 37-mm (1.46-in) AA (16/8/12×2); 100 mines (unconverted ships only); 2 SA-N-2 launchers (1×2) (*Dzerzhinski* only); 2 SA-N-4 launchers (1×2) (*Zhdanov* and *Senyavin* only); 8 (*Senyavin* 16) 30-mm (1.18-in) AA (4/8×2); 2 helicopters (*Senyavin* only) *Crew:* 1000

Swiftsure

British nuclear-powered submarine class. *Swiftsure*, the first of an improved *Valiant* Class of submarine was ordered in November 1967. The *Swiftsure* Class are 4 m (13 ft) shorter than their predecessors and have their diving planes fitted slightly lower on the hull; they are fitted with improved sonar and other electronic equipment. Armament is reduced from six to five torpedo tubes, but these tubes are capable of firing the new Tigerfish torpedoes as well as the old and well-tried Mark 8**. Power is provided by a Rolls-Royce pressurized water-cooled reactor and English Electric geared turbines. As is usual with all but the very early US nuclear-powered boats there is only one propeller shaft, with a seven-bladed propeller made of special anticavitating alloy. The entire class was built by Vickers, Barrow.

Displacement: 3500/4500 tons (surfaced/submerged) *Length:* 82.9 m (272 ft) *Beam:* 9.8 m (32 ft 3 in) *Draught:* 8.2 m (27 ft) *Machinery:* 1 pressurized water-cooled reactor, 1-shaft geared steam turbine, 15 000 shp=20/30 knots (surfaced/submerged) *Armament:* 5 21-in (53-cm) torpedo tubes (bow), to be fitted with Sub-Harpoon missiles *Crew:* 97

No and name	laid down	launched	commissioned
S.104 *Sceptre*	10/73	11/76	1978
S.108 *Sovereign*	9/70	2/73	7/74
S.109 *Superb*	3/72	10/74	11/76
S.111 *Spartan*	1974	—	—
S.112 *Severn*	1976	—	—
S.126 *Swiftsure*	4/69	9/71	4/73

HMS *Superb* leaving Barrow-in-Furness to join the Second Submarine Squadron in 1976. She is a *Swiftsure* Class submarine and the ninth British warship to bear the name *Superb*

Vickers

T.61

German torpedo-boat class, built 1941-45. Twelve large torpedo-boats were ordered late in 1940 from Dutch shipyards. The design differed considerably from the contemporary *T.1*, *T.13* and *T.22* Classes in having a raised forecastle, and had to be tailored to materials available in the Netherlands. The layout was that of a conventional destroyer, with two gun positions forward and two aft, and uptakes from three boilers trunked into a single capped funnel. The armament comprised single 12.7-cm (5-in) SK C/34 guns in single C/34 mountings, and two quadruple torpedo tubes firing G7a torpedoes. Antiaircraft defence was provided by two twin 3.7-cm (1.46-in) SK C/30 AA mountings and four 20-mm (0.79-in) Flak 38 Vierlings, two abreast on the midships searchlight platform and two in the bridge wing.

Assiduous sabotage by the Dutch Resistance coupled with a lack of materials meant that only eight had been laid down by 1942. The orders were divided between Wilton-Fijenoord *(T.61-62, T.67-68)*, Rotterdam dry dock *(T.63-64, T.69-70)* and de Schelde *(T.65-66, T.71-72)*. Only three were launched, *T.61*, *T.63* and *T.65*, of which *T.61* capsized on taking to the water. She was salved but later sunk by Allied air attack while in tow. *T.67-68* and *T.71-72* were never laid down, and the others were destroyed on the slip. *T.63* and *T.65* reached Kiel but were scuttled there in May 1945.

Displacement: 1960 tons (standard), 2604 tons (full load) *Length:* 114 m (374 ft) oa *Beam:* 11.3 m (37 ft) *Draught:* 3.8 m (12 ft 6 in) *Machinery:* 2-shaft geared steam turbines, 49 500 shp=35 knots *Armament:* 4 12.7-cm (5-in) SK C/34 (4×1); 4 3.7-cm (1.46-in) SK C/30 (2×2); 16 20-mm (0.79-in) Flak 38 AA (4×4); 8 53-cm (21-in) torpedo tubes (2×4) *Crew:* 224

Taiho

Japanese armoured fleet carrier. In 1939, influenced by the knowledge that the Royal Navy was building a class of carriers with an armoured flight deck, the Imperial Japanese Navy took the radical decision to follow suit. By the time that *Taiho* (great phoenix) was laid down in 1941, both HMS *Illustrious* and HMS *Formidable* had proved the value of the armour, and two more ships of the class were ordered in 1942, followed by five more in a supplementary programme in the same year. None of the later ships was laid down.

Unlike the British, in whose armoured carriers the hangar was a protected box, with sides and ends at least as thick as the top, the Japanese provided only the last—an armoured flight deck with a thickness of 75-80 mm (2.9-3.1 in) between the two lifts (an amidships lift would have reduced the strength of the deck). Two hangar decks were incorporated, the lower deck being of 32-mm (1.3-in) armour, all machinery, magazines and gasoline stowages being within the length covered by the armour. Waterline belt armour was 152 mm (6 in) abreast the magazines and 55 mm (2.2 in) outside the machinery spaces.

In an attempt to preserve stability, in spite of carrying so much armour high up, the designers gave a total of just over four decks' depth to the hull above the full-load waterline, so that the lower hangar deck was just above the waterline and the bottom of the lift wells were actually below it. A large island, with a canted funnel, increased the resemblance to British Fleet carriers, and for the first time the Japanese also gave the ship an enclosed bow to improve seaworthiness and the airflow over the flight deck. The machinery was the most powerful ever installed in a Japanese warship, producing 180 000 shp on trials, to give the ship a speed of 33.34 knots at a displacement of 28 300 tons.

The main gun armament also marked a departure from Japanese practice, the long-established 127-mm (5-in) Type 88 gun giving way to the excellent high-velocity 100-mm (3.9-in)/65-cal Type 98 dual-purpose guns, in twin enclosed mountings, three of which were fitted on each deck edge. Fifteen triple 25-mm (1-in) AA guns initially and an additional 26 barrels, in triple and single mountings, were provided later. Air-warning radar was fitted on the island, one antenna ahead of the funnel and the other abaft.

The intended aircraft capacity was 84, but shortage of trained aircrew reduced this number. Thirty Yokosuka Judy non-folding dive-bombers, (including three of the reconnaissance variant), 27 Mitsubishi Zero Model 52 fighters and 18 Nakajima Jill torpedo-bombers were embarked.

Built by Kawasaki at Kobe, *Taiho* was launched on April 7, 1943, and completed exactly 11 months later. She was immediately allocated to Carrier Division 1, together with *Shokaku and Zuikaku*, and despatched to the Singapore area to work up. The air unit allocated to the division was designated the 601st Air Group on May 5, shortly before the carriers sailed to join the 1st Mobile Fleet at Tawi Tawi in the southern Philippines. The fleet lay at this anchorage, awaiting the US Pacific Fleet's next move, from May 16 until June 13, when it became evident that the Marianas were the objective.

Taiho launched just one full deck-load as her contribution to Carrier Division 1's 130-aircraft first strike on June 19. These were forming up when the submarine USS *Albacore* fired six torpedoes at *Taiho*, scoring one hit right forward, almost in line with the forward lift, which fell 2 m (6 ft 6 in) and jammed. The forward aviation fuel tanks ruptured and the ship went down about 1.2 m (4 ft) by the bow. Some flooding occurred, filling the lift wells with a mixture of water and gasoline. Speed was reduced by only about one knot and *Taiho* remained in formation, and with the foward lift aperture planked over, looked set to continue operating. But inflammable vapour from the spilled gasoline spread fumes throughout the ship, and it ignited some five hours after the hit with shattering effect. The armoured flight deck was split down the centre, the hangar sides blew out and, apparently, so did a large proportion of the ship's bottom. The huge fires, fed from the ruptured gasoline tanks, were beyond all control and less than 500 of her crew were able to get clear. *Taiho* sank about 90 minutes after the explosion, taking with her over 1000 men and the 13 aircraft which she still had on board.

Displacement: 29300 tons (standard), 37270 tons (full load) *Length:* 260.5 m (854 ft 8 in) oa *Beam:* 27.7 m (91 ft) wl, 33.6 m (110 ft 3 in) oa *Draught:* 9.6 m (31 ft 6 in) *Machinery:* 4-shaft geared steam turbines, 180000 shp=33.3 knots *Aircraft:* 75 *Armament:* 12 10-cm (3.9-in) AA; 71 25-mm (1-in) AA *Crew:* 1751

Taiyo

Japanese escort carrier class. In late 1940 both the Royal Navy and the Imperial Japanese Navy initiated conversion of merchant ships into auxiliary aircraft carriers intended for trade protection. In Britain this took the form of the simple addition of a flight deck in place of the superstructure on a 5500-ton diesel freighter, which commissioned as HMS *Audacity* in June 1941. (USS *Long Island*, also commissioned in June 1941, was the US Navy's response to a British request for *Audacity* type conversions.) The Japanese, short of shipbuilding capacity and raw materials, decided quite independently to undertake even more elaborate conversions of bigger, faster ships.

A class of three 17100-grt, 22-knot NYK Line passenger liners, all built by Mitsubishi, Nagasaki, was selected of which two were already in service. The third, *Kasuga Maru*, had been launched on September 19, 1940, and she was towed to the Sasebo navy yard on May 1, 1941, and there converted as a flush-deck carrier, commissioning under the same name on September 15, 1941. Shortly afterwards, *Yawata Maru* (launched October 31, 1939) was taken in hand at the Kure navy yard and when she was commissioned (again under her original name) on May 31, 1942, her place was taken at Kure by *Nitta Maru* (launched May 20, 1939).

A 91-m (300-ft) hangar was erected one deck above the original upper deck, two centreline lifts being installed at the ends of the hangar; at the forward end of the 'box' under the flight-deck overhang were communications offices and the navigating bridge. The wooden flight deck was over 171 m (560 ft) long and was equipped with eight arrester wires and a barrier, but no catapult. A large aircraft crane was located on the port side of the flight deck amidships, but the deck was otherwise uncluttered. The original two-shaft steam turbine machinery was retained, the boiler uptakes being routed across to the starboard side to exhaust downwards from the deck edge through a single funnel. All three ships could attain 21 knots and had the high cruising speed of 18 knots.

Armament in the first ship, *Kasuga Maru*, comprised six single 120-mm (4.7-in) AA guns, three on each side; in the later ships, *Yawata Maru* and *Nitta Maru*, the two mountings on the forecastle were omitted, and those further aft were replaced by twin 127-mm (5-in) dual-purpose mountings, giving a total of four guns on each broadside. Light AA armament consisted initially of four twin 25-mm (1-in) AA mountings, but this was later increased to between 22-64 25-mm and five-ten 13.2-mm (0.52-in) AA machine-guns were added.

Kasuga Maru's first operation was to have been in support of the Luzon landings in December 1941, for which she, *Ryujo* and *Zuiho* were to have embarked the Tainan Air Group's Mitsubishi Zero fighters. Fuel-consumption trials showed that the fighters were capable of reaching the Philippines from Formosa and the carriers' contribution was therefore cancelled and the newly completed escort carrier began what was to be her main task, ferrying aircraft. As early as March 1942, *Kasuga Maru* transported Zeros to Rabaul, and as the New Guinea and, later, the Solomons campaigns intensified, so she and *Yawata Maru* became more essential in this role, bringing short-range aircraft forward from Truk or the Philippines to the combat zone and delivering them to the airfields. As the Japanese navy experienced between 20% and 30% losses on long-distance ferry flights overseas, the use of the carriers represented a considerable saving in aircraft and pilots.

Kasuga Maru and *Yawata Maru* were renamed *Taiyo* (great falcon) and *Unyo* (falcon of the clouds) on August 31, 1942. On September 28 *Taiyo* was torpedoed and damaged 64 km (40 miles) off Truk by USS *Trout*. By the time that she was repaired, the third ship was operational, *Chuyo* (ocean falcon) (ex-*Nitta Maru*) having commissioned on November 20, 1942.

Throughout 1943, the three carriers transported not only navy but also army aircraft between Japan and Truk. Although allocated to the General Escort Command in December 1943, their task remained the same and they did not operate on trade protection duties. *Chuyo* did not survive to join the new Command, for on December 4, 1943, six days before allocation, she was torpedoed and sunk off Hachijojima by USS *Sailfish*, going down with all hands after a brilliant attack in a storm by the US submarine.

Just over a month later, USS *Haddock* damaged *Unyo* as she was ferrying aircraft to Saipan. The carrier was badly damaged and had to be towed back to Japan for repairs. During the passage, two submarines made unsuccessful attacks on her. *Taiyo*, with *Shinyo* and *Kaiyo*, supported the build-up for the decisive Marianas campaign during the spring of 1944, but on August 18 she was attacked while in a convoy off Luzon by USS *Rasher*, which scored two hits. *Taiyo* caught fire, burned for 20 minutes and then blew up violently.

A month later, on September 16, 1944, *Unyo* was found in convoy in the South China Sea by USS *Barb*. The submarine fired a six-torpedo salvo which sank a 10000-dwt tanker and scored three hits on the carrier. *Unyo* sank in less than three minutes, following a huge explosion.

The *Taiyo* Class was undoubtedly usefully employed throughout their careers, but had they been used for convoy protection, in the manner so effectively demonstrated by the Allies, they might well have been able to check the activities of the daring US submarine commanders who, in the end, were responsible for the sinking of all three.

Displacement: 17830 tons (standard) *Length:* 180.14 m (591 ft) oa *Beam:* 22.5 m (73 ft 10 in) wl, 35.7 m (117 ft) oa *Draught:* 7.8 m (25 ft 6 in); (*Taiyo* 8 m [26 ft]) *Machinery:* 2-shaft geared steam turbines, 25200 shp=21.4 knots (*Taiyo* 21.1 knots) *Aircraft:* 27 *Armament:* (*Unyo* and *Chuyo*) 8 127-mm (5-in) DP (4×2); 8-24 25-mm (1-in) AA; 5-10 13.2-mm (0.52-in) AA; *(Taiyo)* 6 120-mm (4.7-in) AA (6×1); 8 25-mm AA; 10 13.2-mm AA *Crew:* 850 (*Taiyo* 747)

Takatsuki

Japanese destroyer class. *Takatsuki*, the first of the four destroyers of this class, was ordered under the 1963 Programme. They are designed for A/S duties, and at the time of completion were the largest warships in the Japanese Maritime Self-Defence Force. They are well-armed vessels carrying an extensive range of antisubmarine weapons which include an eight-barrelled Asroc launcher mounted immediately in front of the slab-sided bridge. Amidships, on either beam and just aft of the forefunnel, are two triple Mk32 A/S torpedo tube mountings with homing torpedoes. There is also a four-barrelled A/S rocket launcher mounted right forward on the forecastle. Aft on the quarterdeck is a clear space for operating the three DASH helicopters, and their hangar is forward of this and just aft of the 5-in (127-mm) gun. The DASH helicopters were removed during 1977 and replaced by two HSS-2 A/S helicopters.

The ships carry a comprehensive array of radar and sonar equipment; in 1979 SQS-35

(J) variable-depth sonar was carried only by *Takatsuki* and *Kikuzuki*, but it was planned to equip the other two vessels with VDS at their next major refit. The hull-mounted sonars are SQS-23 and OQS-3. Air-warning radar is an OPS-11, surface-warning an OPS-17 and fire-control is by a US Mk 35 radar. The gunfire-control system is the US Mk 56. The vessels are equipped with Mitsubishi machinery and the radius of action is 7000 nautical miles at 20 knots.

Displacement: 3100 tons *Length:* 136 m (446 ft 2 in) oa *Beam:* 13.4 m (44 ft) *Draught:* 4.4 m (14 ft 6 in) *Machinery:* 2-shaft geared steam turbines, 60 000 shp=32 knots *Armament:* 2 5-in (127-mm); 1 8-barrel Asroc launcher; 1 4-barrel A/S rocket launcher; 6 21-in (53-cm) torpedo tubes; 2 helicopters *Crew:* 270

No and name	completed	builder
DD.164 ***Takatsuki***	3/67	Ishikawajima
DD.165 ***Kikuzuki***	3/68	Mitsubishi
DD.166 ***Mochizuki***	3/69	Ishikawajima
DD.167 ***Nagatsuki***	2/70	Mitsubishi

Taksin

Italian cruiser class, built 1939-43. In 1938 the Royal Thai Navy ordered a pair of small cruisers from the Cantieri Riuniti dell' Adriatico shipyard, Trieste, to be named *Taksin* and *Naresuan*. They would have been single-funnelled ships with one twin 152-mm (6-in) turret forward and two aft, and a catapult between the funnel and the main-mast.

Work stopped on both ships in December 1941, but the following August the Italian navy took them over and renamed them *Etna* and *Vesuvio* respectively. *Naresuan* had been launched on August 6, 1941, and *Etna* was launched on May 28, 1942. They were redesigned as antiaircraft ships, but also capable of transporting a number of troops and stores. As recast they would have had twin 135-mm (5.3-in) dual-purpose guns, no catapult and a close-range AA armament of 65-mm (2.56-in) and 20-mm (0.79-in) guns. The funnel would have been faired into the forward bridgework and given a pronounced rake, and the pole mainmast would have been reduced to a stump.

Work proceeded very slowly for lack of steel and labour, and when the armistice was negotiated in September 1943, *Etna* and *Vesuvio* were only 60% complete. Both hulls fell into German hands but nothing was done to complete them, and they were scuttled in Zaule Bay near Trieste at the end of the war. Although refloated in 1946 they were scrapped in 1949.

Displacement: 5500 tons (standard) (increased to 6000 tons as revised) *Length:* 153.8 m (504 ft 7 in) *Beam:* 14.47 m (47 ft 6 in) *Draught:* 5.25 m (17 ft 3 in) (increased to 5.95 m [19 ft 6 in] as revised) *Machinery:* 2-shaft geared steam turbines, 45 000 shp=30 knots *Protection:* 60 mm (2.4 in) belt, 30 mm (1.2 in) deck *Armament:* (As designed) 6 152-mm (6-in) (3×2); 6 76-mm (3-in) AA (6×1); 4 40-mm (1.57-in) AA (4×1); 6 45-cm (17.7-in) torpedo tubes; 2 aircraft, 1 catapult (As AA cruisers) 6 135-mm (5.3-in)/45-cal DP (3×2); 10 65-mm (2.56-in)/45-cal AA (10×1); 20 20-mm (0.79-in)/65-cal AA (20×1); 2 aircraft, 1 catapult *Crew:* not known

Tambor

US submarine class. This class of 12 submarines was very similar to the previous *Salmon* Class. The main differences between the two classes concerned the machinery and torpedo armament, the latter being increased to six bow tubes. This class reintroduced the direct-drive propulsion system with the diesel engines arranged in tandem. This arrangement led to difficulties in coupling the engines together, and were used more than the forward diesels and consequently wore out more quickly. This meant that only half the power was normally available on one shaft for recharging the batteries.

The vessels were modified during the Second World War, and the conning tower was rebuilt so that two single 20-mm (0.79-in) mounts could be fitted forward and aft of it. In addition the 3-in (76-mm) gun was removed and a 5-in (127-mm) weapon mounted instead.

The 12 submarines were all launched in the space of just over one year, between December 1939 and January 1941.

Triton, Trent, Grayling, Grenadier—built by Portsmouth navy yard
Tambor, Tautog, Thresher, Gar, Grampus, Grayback—built by Electric Boat
Tuna, Gudgeon—built by Mare Island navy yard

Tuna was scuttled as a target off San Francisco on September 25, 1948.

The remaining vessels were all war casualties. *Triton* was sunk by three Japanese destroyers on March 15, 1943. *Trout* was sunk on February 29, 1944. *Grampus* was probably sunk by the destroyers *Minegumo* and *Murasame* on March 6, 1945. *Grayback* was sunk in collision with the Japanese freighter *Hokuan Maru* on September 9, 1943. *Grenadier* was sunk by Japanese aircraft on April 20-21, 1943. *Gudgeon* was lost some time between April and May 1944. Four ships survived the war to be sold for scrap: *Thresher* (1948), *Tambor* and *Gar* (1959), and *Tautog* (1960). *Tuna* was sunk as a target on September 25, 1948.

Displacement: 1475/2370 tons (surfaced/submerged) *Length:* 93.8 m (307 ft 9 in) oa *Beam:* 8.3 m (27 ft 3 in) *Draught:* 4.2 m (13 ft 9 in) *Machinery:* 2 shafts, 4 direct-drive diesels/2 electric motors, 5400 bhp/2740 hp=20/8.75 knots (surfaced/submerged) *Armament:* 1 3-in (76-mm); 4 machine-guns; 10 21-in (53-cm) torpedo tubes (6 bow, 4 stern), 24 torpedoes *Crew:* 85

Tang

US submarine class, built 1949-52. The design of these six submarines was based largely on information derived from captured war records and German Second World War submarines. They were designed to have a high submerged speed and the propulsion machinery consisted of a vertically mounted 16-cylinder four-row radial diesel which was half the weight and two-thirds the size of engines previously used to power submarines. Under operational conditions they did not prove satisfactory and the boats were re-engined with a lightweight horizontally mounted diesel during the 1950s. This involved cutting the boats in half and adding a 2.7-m (9-ft) section to accommodate the new diesels. The vessels were further modernized during the 1960s when another extra section was added to house improved electronics and other equipment. The final length was 87.5 m (287 ft).

The *Tang* Class were the first postwar submarines to be designed and built for the US Navy, and *Gudgeon* was the first US submarine to circumnavigate the earth. The submarines were equipped with the BQG-4 PUFFS (passive underwater fire-control feasibility system) fire-control sonar used as an A/S targeting system. This was housed in small fin-like structures on top of the deck casing.

Trigger and *Harder* were transferred to Italy in 1973-74 and renamed *Livio Piomarta* and *Romeo Romei*. *Tang* was used on acoustic research during the late 1970s.

USS *Tang* off the coast of Oahu, Hawaii in February 1961. She was launched in June 1951

US Navy

No and name	laid down	launched	completed	builder
SS.563 *Tang*	4/49	6/51	10/51	Portsmouth navy yard
SS.564 *Trigger*	2/49	6/51	3/52	Electric Boat, Groton
SS.565 *Wahoo*	10/49	10/51	5/52	Portsmouth navy yard
SS.566 *Trout*	12/49	8/51	6/52	Electric Boat, Groton
SS.567 *Gudgeon*	5/50	6/52	11/52	Portsmouth navy yard
SS.568 *Harder*	6/50	12/51	8/52	Electric Boat, Groton

(As modernized) *Displacement:* 2050/2700 tons (surfaced/submerged) *Length:* 87.5 m (287 ft) oa *Beam:* 8.3 m (27 ft 4 in) *Draught:* 5.8 m (19 ft) *Machinery:* 2-shaft diesels (3 mounted)/2 electric motors, 4500 bhp/5600 hp=15.5/16 knots (surfaced/submerged) *Armament:* 8 21-in (53-cm) torpedo tubes (6 bow, 2 stern) *Crew:* 83

'Tango'

Soviet submarine class. The first of the class took part in the Navy Day review at Sevastopol in July 1973, since which time a further three boats of the class have been completed. It is possible that the 'Tango' Class may succeed the 'Foxtrot' Class as the standard Soviet conventionally powered submarine. Length is identical to that of the earlier boats, although there has been a slight increase in beam. The propulsion plant is thought to be of similar power and performance, with the slight increase in speed probably the result of a more streamlined hull form. Like the 'Foxtrot' Class they are equipped with six bow tubes for 53-cm (21-in) torpedoes, although the stern tubes of the latter have been omitted. There has been a significant reduction in complement from 78 to 62, indicating increased automation.

The major external difference from their predecessors lies in the raised bow section, which is about 1 m (3 ft) higher forward of the conning tower than it is aft of it.

Displacement: 2100/2500 tons (surfaced/submerged) *Length:* 90.5 m (297 ft) oa *Beam:* 8.6 m (28 ft 3 in) *Draught:* 6.4 m (21 ft) *Machinery:* 3-shaft diesel/3 electric motors, 6000 bhp= 20/16 knots (surfaced/submerged) *Armament:* 6 53-cm (21-in) torpedo tubes (bow) *Crew:* 62

A Soviet 'Tango' Class submarine. 'Tangos' are conventionally powered and have a crew of 62

MOD

Tarawa

US amphibious assault ship class. Five ships were laid down between 1969-71, but four further ships were cancelled in 1973. Cancellation led to compensation being paid to the builders, the Ingalls Shipbuilding division of Litton Industries, as the original contract price was based on nine ships being built using modular construction methods at the company's specially built facility at Pascagoula.

No and name	launched	commissioned
LHA.1 *Tarawa*	12/73	5/76
LHA.2 *Saipan*	7/74	1977
LHA.3 *Belleau Wood*	1977	1978
LHA.4 *Nassau*	1978	1979
LHA.5 *Da Nang*	1978	1980

The *Tarawa* Class, designated LHA, were intended to combine the features of an amphibious assault ship (LPH), amphibious cargo ship (LKA), and amphibious transport dock (LPD) into a single hull. The ships therefore have a full-length flight deck, with a half-length hangar deck beneath that runs from amidships aft. The latter is connected to the flight deck by a port-side elevator and a large stern lift, an arrangement which gives them maximum hangar space for up to 26 troop-carrying helicopters or marine AV-8 Harrier V/STOL aircraft. The forward half of the ship is taken up by vehicle storage and maintenance facilities for tanks, trucks and jeeps. Cargo can be moved automatically by conveyors and there are seven further lifts for the movement of cargo and vehicles. Beneath the hangar deck is a docking well capable of accommodating four of the large LCU-1610 type landing craft. The ships have sophisticated internal and external communications. In addition to the main propulsion system, a bow thruster is provided for holding position while the landing craft are being floated out.

On either side of the bow and on the port side of the stern three single 127-mm (5-in)/54-cal lightweight guns are carried just

The USS *Tarawa*, one of five amphibious assault ships in service or building for the US Navy

US Navy

below flight-deck level. The director for these is the Mk 86 fire-control system, which is carried on the foremast. On the starboard side of the stern and on the forward end of the large block-like superstructure are two octuple launchers for the Basic Point Defense Missile System (BPDMS). Target data for this is provided by an SPS-52 three-dimensional planar radar on the mainmast. Surface-search is provided by an SPS-10 scanner, and aircraft-navigation by a dome-covered SPN-35 radar fitted above the flight deck on the after corner of the superstructure.

Extensive automation has resulted in considerable manpower savings, enabling a marine battalion landing team of 1800 men and all their equipment to be carried.

In January 1975 *Saipan* was damaged during a storm and grounded, delaying her completion. Labour and construction problems have resulted in further delays in the building programme.

Displacement: 39300 tons (full load) *Length:* 250 m (820 ft) oa *Beam:* 32.3 m (106 ft) *Draught:* 7.9 m (26 ft) *Machinery:* 2-shaft steam turbines, 70000 shp=24 knots *Armament:* 16 CH-46 helicopters; 6 CH-53 helicopters; 4 UH-1E helicopters or AV-8 Harrier V/STOL aircraft (in place of some helicopters); 3 127-mm (5-in)/54-cal (3×1); 16 BPDMS Sea Sparrow launchers (2×8) *Crew:* 902

Tenacious

British frigate class. In the late 1940s the Admiralty began an extensive programme of converting wartime destroyers to fast antisubmarine frigates to counter the postwar development of high-speed submarines. As originally planned these Type 15 (*Rapid* Class) conversions were fairly extensive, but in 1951 it was decided that some ships should receive the minimum of modifications for their new role: the limited conversions were designated Type 16. Although not as effective as the Type 15s, they had the advantage of being cheaper and quicker and allowed for the available finance to be extended to include more ships. The prototype for the Type 16 was the *Tumult* Class destroyer *Tenacious* which was converted at Rosyth dockyard during 1951-52. In effect the conversion involved rearmament rather than reconstruction, combined with a general refit and the addition of improved sonar, radar, direction-finding and communication equipment. Unlike the Type 15s the superstructure of *Tenacious* was not altered, and although this meant accepting restricted space for accommodation and control and operations rooms it also allowed for an improvement in the AA armament giving her limited value as a dual-purpose A/S and AA escort. The original armament was removed completely, except for the after bank of torpedo tubes which were retained for use with A/S homing torpedoes, and replaced by a twin 4-in (102-mm) DP gun mounting in B position, five single 40-mm (1.57-in) Bofors AA, mounted in the bridge wings (two), abaft the funnel (two) and on the quarterdeck (one), a twin 40-mm Bofors Mk V mount on the platform amidships and two three-barrelled Squid A/S mortars on the after superstructure.

The remainder of the *Tumult* Class destroyers, except *Troubridge* which was given the full conversion, were similarly modified during 1952-55 but four, *Teazer, Termagant, Terpsichore* and *Tumult*, were given the added sophistication of a new enclosed bridge somewhat smaller than the original. The remaining pair, *Tuscan* and *Tyrian*, were altered as *Tenacious*, retaining their original bridges. In addition to the 'T' Class vessels one 'O' Class destroyer, *Orwell*, and two 'P' Class destroyers, *Paladin* and *Petard*, were converted to Type 16s during 1952-55, and two more 'O' Class destroyers, transferred to Pakistan in 1949-50, the *Tippu Sultan* and *Tughril* (ex-*Onslow* and *Onslaught*) were also converted in 1957-59. Most of these refits followed the pattern set by *Tenacious*, but the two Pakistani ships did not mount the two single 40-mm guns abaft the funnel and several other vessels of the class had either these or the mountings in the bridge wings removed during the late 1950s. *Paladin* was converted to a minelayer during 1957 and had all her single 40-mm guns and her torpedo tubes removed to compensate for the added weight of 30 mines and the laying gear. In 1962-66 the South African *Sunar vand del Stel* underwent a similar conversion, but with a flight deck and hangars aft for two Wasp A/S helicopters.

The conversion programme was never more than a means of providing the navy with a reasonable A/S force until such time as new-construction ships entered service, and as the Type 16s were the least satisfactory of the two types they were the first to go to the scrapyard. The 'T' Class ships were sold during 1965-66, *Paladin* in 1962, *Orwell* in 1965 and *Petard* in 1967. By 1978 the two Pakistani ships were serving as static training ships and only one of the South African ships was still in service.

('T' Class) *Displacement:* 2000 tons (standard), 2530 tons (full load) *Length:* 110.6 m (362 ft 9 in) oa *Beam:* 10.9 m (35 ft 8 in) *Draught:* 4 m (13 ft) *Machinery:* 2-shaft geared steam turbines, 40000 shp=36.75 knots *Armament:* 2 4-in (102-mm) (1×2); 7 40-mm (1.57-in) (5×1, 1×2); 4 21-in (53-cm) torpedo tubes (1×4); 2 triple Squid A/S mortars *Crew:* 175

Tenacity

British patrol craft, built 1968-73. The builders, Vosper Thornycroft, built this patrol craft as a private venture to demonstrate their ability to build light craft with significantly heavier armament and range than before. Although never mounted, the fits proposed included a twin Oerlikon 35-mm (1.38-in) power-operated mounting, an Oerlikon twin 30-mm (1.18-in), a Bofors 57-mm (2.24-in) L/70 or an OTO-Melara 76-mm (3-in) Compact, with four Contraves Sea Killer surface-to-surface missiles aft.

After some time spent as a demonstration vessel with dummy missiles aft and a mockup of a gun-mounting forward with twin broom handles, *Tenacity* was bought by the Royal Navy in January 1972 and refitted for service as a patrol craft. This involved fitting davits for Gemini inflatable boats on the forecastle, two machine-guns and a navigation radar. She now serves on fishery-protection duties in coastal waters in place of *Brave Borderer* and *Brave Swordsman*, with pendant number P.276.

Displacement: 165 tons (standard), 220 tons (full load) *Length:* 44 m (144 ft 6 in) oa *Beam:* 8.1 m (26 ft 6 in) *Draught:* 2.3 m (7 ft 8 in) *Machinery:* 3-shaft Proteus gas turbines and cruising diesels on wing shafts, 12750 shp=40 knots *Armament:* 2 7.62-mm (0.30-in) mgs (2×1) *Crew:* 32

Tench

US submarine class. These submarines were basically an extension of the *Balao* Class, dimensions remaining the same but displacement being increased by some 50 tons. In other respects the vessels remained the same, except for slight variations in the machinery

No and name	launched	fate
SS.417 *Tench*	7/44	to Peru for spares 1976
SS.418 *Thornback*	7/44	Turkish *Uluc Ali Reis* 1971
SS.419 *Tigrone*	7/44	stricken 6/75
SS.420 *Tirante*	8/44	—
SS.421 *Trutta* (ex-*Tomatate*)	8/44	stricken 7/72
SS.422 *Toro*	8/44	stricken 3/65
SS.423 *Torsk*	9/44	stricken 12/71
SS.424 *Quillback* (ex-*Trembler*)	10/44	stricken 3/73
SS.425 *Trumpetfish*	5/45	stricken 10/73
SS.426 *Tusk*	7/45	Taiwanese *Hai Pao* 10/73
SS.435 *Corsair*	5/46	stricken 1963
SS.436 *Unicorn*	8/46	stricken 6/58

No and name	launched	fate
SS.437 *Walrus*	9/46	stricken 6/58
SS.475 *Argonaut*	10/44	Canadian *Rainbow* 1968
SS.476 *Runner*	10/44	stricken 12/71
SS.477 *Conger*	10/44	stricken 8/63
SS.478 *Cutlass*	11/44	Taiwanese *Hai Shih* 4/73
SS.479 *Diablo*	12/44	Pakistani *Ghazi* 1964, lost 12/71
SS.480 *Medregal*	12/44	scuttled 8/70
SS.481 *Requin*	1/45	stricken 12/71
SS.482 *Irex*	1/45	stricken 11/69
SS.483 *Sea Leopard*	3/45	Brazilian *Bahia* 3/73
SS.484 *Odax*	4/45	Brazilian *Rio de Janeiro*
SS.485 *Sirago*	5/45	stricken 6/72
SS.486 *Pomodon*	6/45	stricken 8/70
SS.487 *Remora*	7/45	Greek *Katsonis* 10/73
SS.488 *Sarda*	8/45	stricken 3/65
SS.489 *Spinax*	11/45	stricken 10/69
SS.490 *Volador*	1/46	Italian *Primo Longobardo* 1972
SS.522 *Amberjack*	12/44	Brazilian *Ceara* 10/73
SS.523 *Grampus*	12/44	Brazilian *Rio Grandedo Sul* 5/72
SS.524 *Pickerel*	12/44	Italian *Gianfranco Gazzana Priaroggia* 1972
SS.525 *Grenadier*	12/44	stricken 5/73

fitted.

The original design provided for a 5-in (127-mm) gun to be carried forward of the conning tower, but as in the previous *Balao* and *Gato* Classes this was subsequently moved to a position aft of the conning tower. The original design also provided for a 40-mm (1.57-in) forward and a 20-mm (0.79-in) aft on the conning tower. This too was altered, a 40-mm replacing the 20-mm while some units had an extra 5-in weapon added in front of the conning tower.

SS.417-424 and SS.475-490 were built by Portsmouth navy yard, SS.425 and 426 by Cramp, Philadelphia, SS.435-437 by the Electric Boat company, Groton, and SS.522-525 by Boston navy yard. The following were cancelled in 1944-45: SS.427-434, SS.438-474, SS.491-521 and SS.526-562.

Construction of SS.436 and 437 was suspended in 1946, and the incomplete SS.427 (*Turbot*) and 428 (*Ulua*) were used for test purposes. *Toro* was sunk as a sonar target during the search for the lost *Thresher* off Cape Cod in 1963. *Tigrone, Requin* and *Spinax* were converted to radar picket submarines from 1948. The least sophisticated of such conversions, they served as prototypes for the subsequent conversion of large numbers of *Balao* and *Gato* Class boats.

See also GUPPY.

Displacement: 1570/2428 tons (surfaced/submerged) *Length:* 95 m (311 ft 9 in) *Beam:* 8.3 m (27 ft 3 in) *Draught:* 4.6 m (15 ft 3 in) *Machinery:* 2-shaft diesels/2 electric motors, 5400 bhp/2740 hp=20.25/8.85 knots (surfaced/submerged) *Armament:* 1 5-in (127-mm); 1 20-mm (0.79-in); 1 40-mm (1.57-in); 10 21-in (53-cm) torpedo tubes (6 bow, 4 stern), 24 torpedoes *Crew:* 80

Thresher

US nuclear-powered submarine class, built 1959-68. Developed from the *Skipjack* Class and *Tullibee* the *Thresher* hunter-killer class was authorized in 1957. They were designed to be quieter and dive deeper than previous nuclear-powered submarines. *Thresher* was laid down in May 1959, launched bow-first on July 9, 1960, and completed in July 1960. *Gato* was the last of the class to commission on January 25, 1968.

Permit (SSN.594), *Plunger* (SSN.595, ex-*Pollack*)—built by Mare Island navy yard
Thresher (SSN.593), *Jack* (SSN.605), *Timosa* (SSN.606)—built by Portsmouth navy yard
Barb (SSN.596, ex-*Pollack,* ex-*Plunger*), *Dace* (SSN.60), *Haddock* (SSN.621)—built by Ingalls
Pollack (SSN.603, ex-*Barb*), *Haddo* (SSN.604), *Guardfish* (SSN.612)—built by New York shipbuilding
Flasher (SSN.613), *Greenling* (SSN.614), *Gato* (SSN.615)—built by General Dynamics (Electric Boat)

On April 9, 1963, *Thresher* left harbour after an extensive refit to undergo sea trials. All went well with the first day's trials, but at 0913 the following day a garbled message was received from her while she was performing a test dive. Nothing more was heard from her, and she was later located lying in 2650 m (8400 ft) of water; her crew, which consisted of 107 officers and men, and the 17 civilian observers on board were all lost in this mysterious accident.

Jack was built to test a modified powerplant designed to reduce still further the operating noise of the submarine. This involved fitting two contrarotating turbines without reduction gearing, driving two different-sized propellers driven by coaxial shafts. *Jack* is 5.5 m (18 ft) longer than her sisters, an extra 3 m (10 ft) being required in the turbine room alone.

Flasher, Gato and *Greenling* were also modified during construction and are longer and displace more than others of the class. They are fitted with improved Subsafe rescue equipment, heavier and more robust turbines and have a taller sail. *Gato* and *Greenling* had already been launched when it was decided to incorporate these modifications, and so they were towed from the Electric Boat company's yard at Groton, Connecticut, to Quincy in Massachusetts for completion, a process which included adding an additional section to the hull.

Displacement: 3750/4300 tons (surfaced/submerged) *Length:* 84.9 m (278 ft 6 in) *Beam:* 9.7 m (31 ft 9 in) *Draught:* 7.7 m (25 ft 2 in) *Machinery:* 1 S5W pressurized water-cooled reactor, 15 000 shp=20/30 knots (surfaced/submerged) *Armament:* 4 21-in (53-cm) torpedo tubes (amidships); Sub-Harpoon and Tomahawk missiles *Crew:* 103

(Jack) Displacement: 3750/4470 tons (surfaced/submerged) *Length:* 90.4 m (296 ft 6 in) (Other specifications as above)

(Flasher group) *Displacement:* 3800/4242 tons (surfaced/submerged) *Length:* 89.1 m (292 ft 2 in) (Other specifications as above)

Tiger

British cruiser class. The three ships of the *Tiger* Class, *Tiger* (built by John Brown), *Blake* (built by Fairfield) and *Lion* (built by Scotts), were originally authorized in 1941 as *Minotaur* (modified *Fiji*) Class cruisers. *Tiger* was laid down in 1941 and her two sisters in the following year, but their construction was not pressed and by the end of the war only *Lion,* launched in September 1944, had entered the water. *Tiger* and *Blake* were progressed sufficiently to allow their launch at the end of 1945 in order to clear their building slips, and all three were subsequently laid up until sufficient funds became available for their completion. In the meantime the opportunity was taken to completely redesign the ships as fully as possible to incorporate the lessons of the war together with the latest advances in armament, fire

C & S Taylor

HMS *Tiger*. Refitted in the late 1960s she was nicknamed 'Liger' since equipment from HMS *Lion* was used by Devonport dockyard in the refit

control, radar, etc. Postwar austerity seriously hampered the development of this latter equipment which, combined with the general run-down in design facilities and available finance, delayed the completion of the design until well into the 1950s; it was not until 1955 that work on the three ships was recommenced. *Tiger* was finally completed in 1959, *Lion* in 1960 (by Swan Hunter) and the *Blake* in 1961, by which time their value had considerably diminished. In place of the original armament of three triple 6-in (152-mm) and five twin 4-in (102-mm) mountings they carried two twin 6-in, one in A position and one in X, and three twin 3-in (76-mm), one in B position and one on each side amidships. The design of these guns originated from the latter years of the war and although they would have been very advanced weapons in the late 1940s, when they should have appeared, they were nearing obsolescence by the early 1960s. Both the 6-in and 3-in were fully automatic dual-purpose weapons with a rate of fire of 20 rds/min and 80 rds/min respectively, requiring very large magazines. Each mounting was provided with its own fully stabilized radar-controlled

USS *Tigrone*, one of three *Tench* Class submarines converted to the radar picket role. The *Tench* Class conversions were given a large air-search scanner on the conning tower, a height finder abaft it and a surface-search scanner on a stub mast

US Navy

Foto Drüppel

The German battleship *Tirpitz* with her guns elevated to port. She was attacked by the Fleet Air Arm, Royal Navy and RAF and finally capsized by RAF Lancasters in Tromsö Fjord

director, two being fitted on the bridge, two abreast the funnels and one aft. Other variations from original design included slightly more powerful machinery which compensated for an 800-ton increase in weight, a completely new superstructure with a large fully enclosed bridge, lattice masts and funnel caps and the provision of defences against nuclear and biological attack. At the time of their completion they were criticized for their comparatively small armament, but their volume of fire was such that another 6-in turret would only have served to empty the magazines more quickly. In any case the whole design was very space- and weight-critical, and such an addition would not have been possible without accepting a serious loss in efficiency.

Their primary roles were originally envisaged as providing defence against aircraft and surface vessels for convoys and aircraft carriers, and shore support for amphibious landings. But they were not ships of the missile age and it was clear that their value in the former role would rapidly diminish unless they were re-equipped, although for the latter they were among the few modern vessels in the fleet big enough to provide adequate command facilities. Within a few years of their completion it was therefore decided to convert all three ships to command/helicopter cruisers. Apart from the usual modernization of electronic equipment, this involved replacing the after turret and superstructure with a large hangar and raised flight deck to accommodate four A/S helicopters. In addition, the beam 3-in mountings were replaced by two quadruple Seacat missile launchers and, to provide the steadiest possible flight deck, stabilizers were also fitted. The resultant ships, although still dated, can provide command, A/S and AA facilities either at sea or off a beachhead while their helicopters can also be employed to carry troops or stores ashore in support of amphibious landings. The conversion of *Blake* was carried out during 1965-68 and that of *Tiger* during 1969-72. *Lion* was to have followed, but her refit was cancelled and she has been scrapped.

Displacement: 9630 tons (standard), 11 700 tons (full load) *Length:* 169.3 m (555 ft 6 in) oa *Beam:* 19.5 m (64 ft) *Draught:* 6.2 m (20 ft 6 in) *Machinery:* 4-shaft geared steam turbines, 80 000 shp=31.5 knots *Protection:* 89 mm (3.5 in) side, 51-32 mm (2-1.25 in) decks, 76-38 mm (3-1.5 in) turrets *Armament:* 4 6-in (152-mm) (2×2); 6 3-in (76-mm) (3×2) *Crew:* 716

Tirpitz

German battleship. Identical in most respects to her sister-ship *Bismarck*, the career of *Tirpitz* was, to all intents and purposes, as long and unadventurous as her sister's was brief and glorious. But this would ignore the practical achievements of the two ships, one of which stimulated a ten-day convulsion in the Royal Navy in Home and Atlantic Waters. It ended in the exchange of one old and unmodernized battlecruiser for a brand-new battlecruiser, while the other forced the Royal Navy to keep two battleships, a carrier and supporting fleet units in waters where they were not otherwise needed for a period of nearly three years, simply by occupying threatening positions in Norwegian fjords.

Tirpitz was laid down at the Wilhelmshaven Marinewerft in October 1936, launched on April 1, 1937, and completed for sea trials on February 25, 1941. She differed from her sister-ship in minor ways, such as her aircraft hangar and crane arrangements and the addition of two quadruple torpedo-tube mountings for use against merchant ships. Trials and work-up in the Baltic, with defect rectification at Kiel, occupied seven months and not until September 20, 1941, was she declared to be operational.

She was almost immediately despatched on her first mission—an uneventful cruise off the Aland Islands, at the mouth of the Gulf of Finland, between September 26-29, to guard against a possible break-out by the Soviet fleet from Leningrad. Thereafter, *Tirpitz* remained in the Baltic, exercising, until January 12, 1942, when she left Kiel to proceed to Trondheim via the Kiel Canal. Like her sister ship, she was never to return to Germany.

Tirpitz' prime role was to disrupt Allied sea communications with north Russia, by direct action or by the threat of interception of the convoys bound for Murmansk and Archangel. Her only full sortie for this purpose began on March 6, 1942, when she left Trondheim to intercept the Murmansk-bound convoy PQ 12. Sighted and reported by British submarines shortly after leaving her base, the German battleship and her three screening destroyers failed to find the convoy, which had been diverted by the Admiralty away from its planned route. Tracked

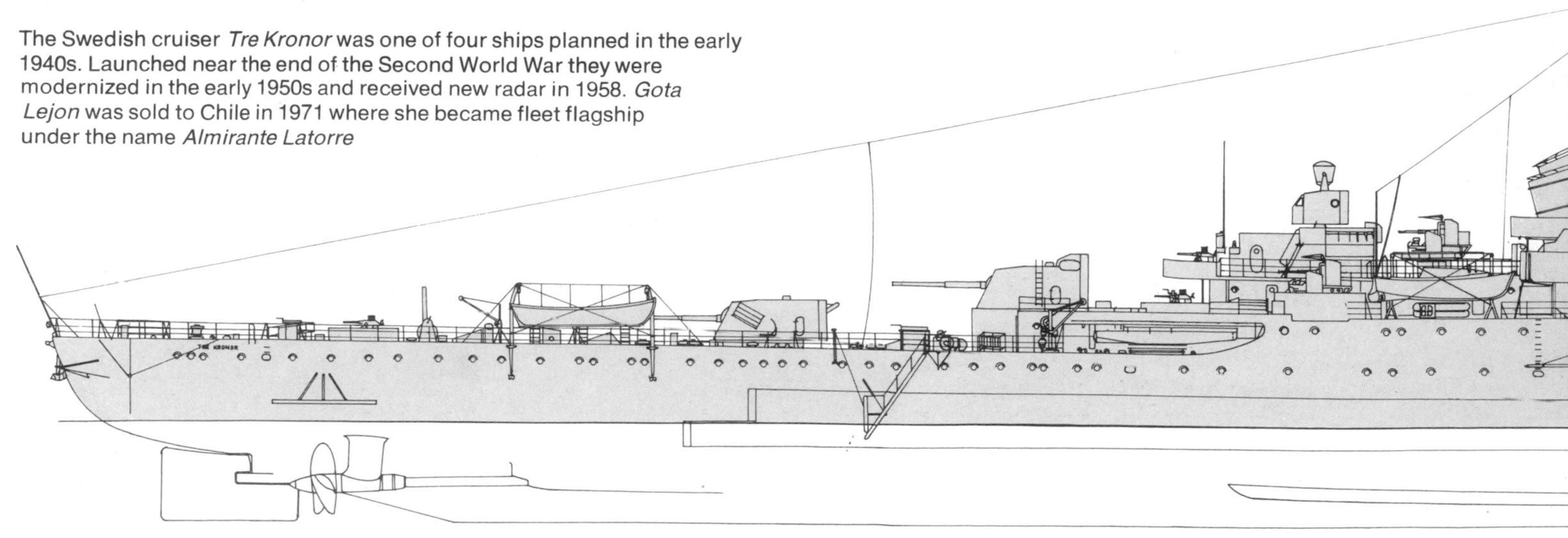

The Swedish cruiser *Tre Kronor* was one of four ships planned in the early 1940s. Launched near the end of the Second World War they were modernized in the early 1950s and received new radar in 1958. *Gota Lejon* was sold to Chile in 1971 where she became fleet flagship under the name *Almirante Latorre*

intermittently by means of decoded radio signals, *Tirpitz* was attacked and only narrowly missed by aircraft from the carrier *Victorious*, off Narvik on March 9.

Tirpitz achieved her major success against the convoys in early July 1942, simply by moving from Trondheim to Altenfjord, in the far north of Norway, where her presence close to the route of convoy PQ 17 led to the Admiralty's order to scatter the merchant ships on July 4. *Tirpitz* did not sail until July 5 and was reported three times and attacked once by a Soviet submarine during a sortie which lasted less than 12 hours: she had no direct part in the sinking of the 24 Allied ships lost from the convoy.

Although she never again stirred to attack a convoy, the threat of her intervention obliged the Royal Navy to maintain at least two capital ships and a fleet carrier in Home Waters, to protect the convoys and to guard against a foray into the North Atlantic. In October 1942, an attempt to attack her at Trondheim using human torpedoes (Chariots) came to nothing with the accidental loss of the weapons within 8 km (5 miles) of *Tirpitz*' berth, where she was at that time refitting.

Tirpitz became operational once again at the end of January 1943 and in March she was moved to Altenfjord which became her permanent base for the next 19 months. Here she was joined by *Scharnhorst* and the pocket-battleship *Lützow*: great events were afoot elsewhere during the spring and summer of 1943 and the Home Fleet 'heavies' were detached to the Mediterranean, so that the sailing of the Soviet convoys was suspended until November 1943, leaving the powerful German squadron with no targets. At last, in early September, *Tirpitz* and *Scharnhorst* were found employment, although the bombardment of almost-defenceless Spitzbergen was hardly a worthy task for these fine ships. They were at sea from September 6-9, and this fifth offensive sortie was to be *Tirpitz*' last, for on September 22, two British midget submarines laid explosive charges which caused extensive shock damage to the main machinery and gunnery systems.

Repairs were undertaken in situ—a remarkable engineering achievement—but as she was getting underway to begin trials on April 3, 1944, she was attacked by 40 Home Fleet Barracuda dive-bombers and extensively damaged. Further attacks in July and August, by which time she had been repaired again, inflicted only minor damage.

The Royal Air Force had made unsuccessful attacks on *Tirpitz* at Kiel in 1941 and at Trondheim in March and April 1942, but not until the autumn of 1944 did Bomber Command have the right combination of aircraft (Avro Lancaster), weapon (5443-kg [12000-lb] Tallboy bomb) and stabilized automatic bomb sight to make a raid at such a distance a profitable undertaking. On September 15, 27 Lancasters took off from a Soviet airfield and scored one direct hit with a 12000-pdr which hit right forward and caused extensive damage over the 36-m (118-ft) section abaft the bows.

Repairs to such severe damage were impossible in Norway and on October 15 and 16, *Tirpitz* proceeded under her own steam to an anchorage near Tromsö, where she was to form part of the fixed defences, as a floating battery. Tromsö was within range of bombers based in northern Scotland and she was attacked by 32 Lancasters on October 29, this attack achieving only one near-miss. The end came on November 12, 1944: 29 Lancasters obtained three hits and a very near miss between B and C turrets, opening the midships port side from the keel to the waterline and causing *Tirpitz* to capsize 11 minutes after the first bomb had been released. Over 1000 of her crew were lost with her.

Displacement: 41700 tons (standard), 53500 tons (full load) *Length:* 250.5 m (821 ft 10 in) oa *Beam:* 36 m (118 ft 1 in) *Draught:* 11 m (36 ft 1 in) *Machinery:* 3-shaft geared turbines, 163000 shp=31.1 knots *Armament:* 8 38-cm (15-in) (4×2); 12 15-cm (5.9-in) (6×2); 16 10.5-cm (4.1-in) AA (8×2); 16 3.7-cm (1.46-in) AA (16×1); 16 2-cm (0.8-in) AA (16×1); 64 2-cm AA (16×4) (added 1942-43); 8 53.3-cm (21-in) torpedo tubes; 4 aircraft *Crew:* 1905

Tourville

French antisubmarine escort class, built 1970-76. Three Type C67A corvettes were authorized in 1970, but in 1971 they were rerated as frigates (Type F67) and finally appeared with D numbers like destroyers. *Tourville* (D.610), *Duguay Trouin* (D.611) and *De Grasse* (D.612) were all built by DCAN Lorient.

The design is a diminutive of *Suffren*, with a double helicopter hangar aft in place of antiaircraft missiles. They have a big bow sonar and a variable-depth version of the same set, the Thomson-CSF DUBV-23/43. The antisubmarine weapons are a single Malafon launcher and 13 missiles amidships, and two launchers for L5 torpedoes in the after superstructure. Since 1976 they have been armed with six MM-38 Exocet surface-to-surface missiles and the after 100-mm (3.9-in) gun has been removed. In 1978 *Duguay Trouin* was fitted with the Crotale close-range AA missile system in the position above the hangar formerly occupied by the third 100-mm gun.

In appearance they resemble the *Suffren* Class, with two 100-mm Model '68 DP guns forward, a prominent mack amidships and the characteristic 'droop snout' of modern French warships. They are fitted with SENIT 3 action data automation and have DRBV 26, DRBV 51 and DRBC 32D radars for surveillance and weapon control. Two WG13 Lynx helicopters are carried.

Displacement: 4580 tonnes (standard), 5800 tonnes (full load) *Length:* 152.8 m (501 ft 4 in) *Beam:* 15.3 m (50 ft 2 in) *Draught:* 5.7 m (18 ft 8 in) *Machinery:* 2-shaft geared steam turbines, 54400 shp=31 knots *Armament:* 3 100-mm (3.9-in) Model '68 DP (3×1); 6 MM-38 Exocet SSMs; 1 Malafon A/S missile launcher; 2 torpedo tubes for A/S torpedoes; 2 Lynx helicopters *Crew:* 283

Tre Kronor

Swedish cruiser class, built 1943-47. In 1940 four ships were planned, light cruisers with nine 15-cm (5.9-in) guns, two to be laid down in 1940 and two more in 1943, for completion in 1943-45. The layout was unusual, with one triple turret forward and two aft.

The outbreak of the Second World War caused the deferment of the programme and allowed improvements to be incorporated. The sketch design published in 1940 showed a single tall capped funnel with paired AA guns on the centreline forward and abaft the

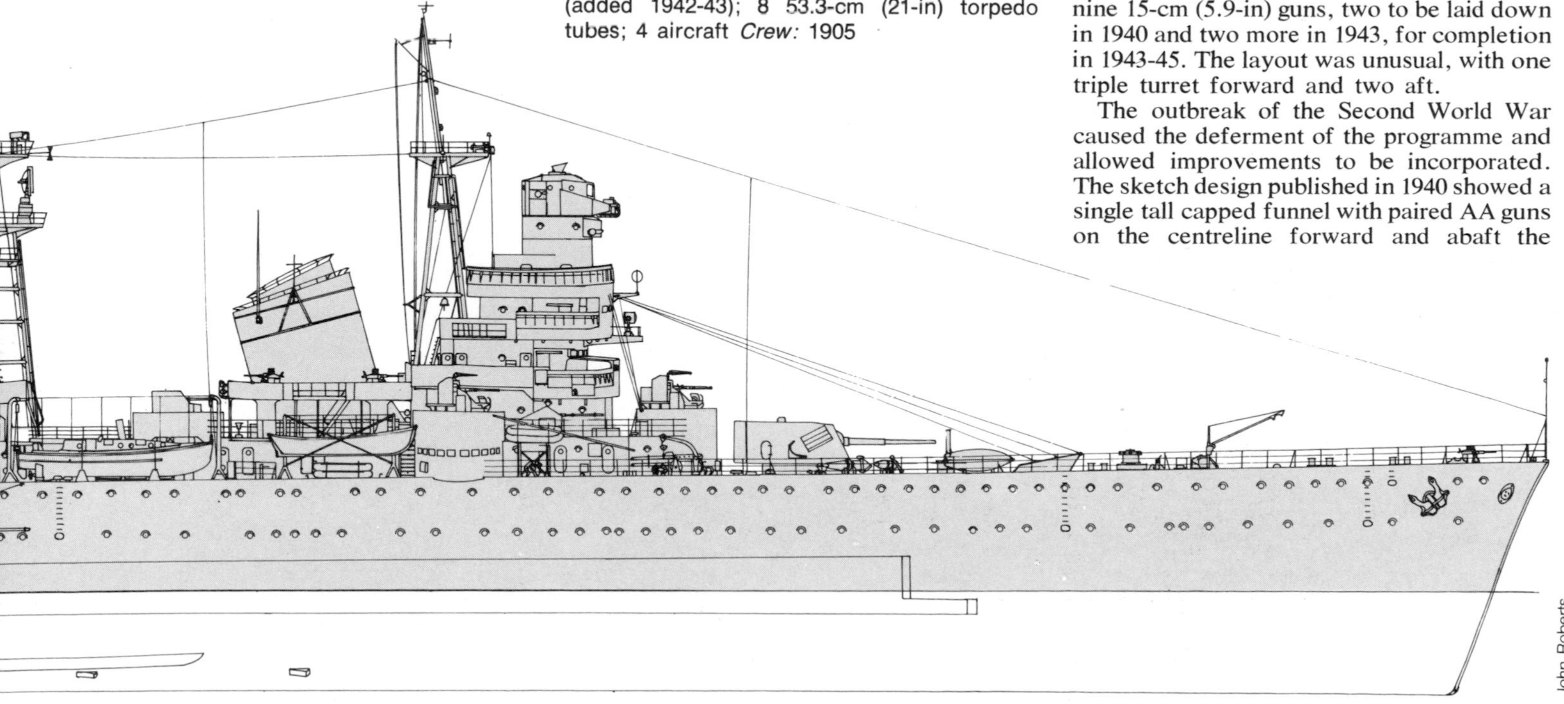

John Roberts

superstructure. In 1942 a new design was drawn up to make use of the gun mountings available from the Dutch *Eendracht* and *De Zeven Provincien*, with a triple turret forward, two twins aft and two raked funnels. The final design was powerful, well-balanced, with twin 40-mm (1.57-in) AA amidships and 25-mm (1-in) mountings forward and aft.

Contracts were signed in February 1943 for two ships, *Tre Kronor* from Götaverken, Göteborg and *Gota Lejon* from Eriksberg Mekaniska Verkstad, also of Göteborg. The ships were launched on December 16, 1944 and November 17, 1945 respectively, and both were completed late in 1947. The radar and communications were of British pattern, with Type 275 gunnery radar and Type 277 height-finder and Type 293 target indication.

In 1951-52 both ships were modernized, with enlarged bridgework and seven single 40-mm Bofors AA guns in place of the nine 25-mm mountings. In 1958 further modernization followed, with a Dutch HSA LW 03 air-warning radar on the foremast and four 57-mm (2.24-in) AA guns amidships.

Tre Kronor was paid off for scrapping in January 1964, and in July 1971 *Gota Lejon* was sold to Chile. She recommissioned as *Almirante Latorre* in September that year, and was still in commission in 1979.

Displacement: 8200 tons (standard), 9200 tons (full load) *Length:* 182 m (597 ft) oa *Beam:* 16.5 m (54 ft 1 in) *Draught:* 6.6 m (21 ft 8 in) *Machinery:* 2-shaft geared steam turbines, 100 000 shp=33 knots *Protection:* 125-75 mm (4.9-2.95 in) belt *Armament:* (As built) 7 15-cm (5.9-in)/53-cal (1×3, 2×2); 20 40-mm (1.57-in) Bofors AA (10×2); 9 25-mm (1-in) AA; 6 53-cm (21-in) torpedo tubes (2×3); (As modernized) 7 15-cm/53-cal; 4 57-mm (2.24-in) AA (4×1); 11 40-mm AA (11×1); 6 53-cm TT *Crew:* 455

Triton

British submarine class. The *Triton* or 'T' Class were designed in the early 1930s as replacements for the old boats of the 'L' Class and were intended for service as ocean-going patrol submarines like the earlier *Odin*, *Perseus* and *Rainbow* Classes. In order to build a reasonable number within the restriction placed on overall submarine tonnage by the current international treaty limitations, the displacement was restricted to 1090 tons compared with 1475 tons in the *Rainbow* Class. This was achieved by accepting a lower surface speed, which allowed for a reduction in the diesel plant and therefore the hull structure. However, the *Triton* Class were also of improved construction, with a stronger hull and greater diving speed, and were more heavily armed, having ten tubes instead of eight. All were arranged to fire forward, eight being mounted in the bows, six internally and two in the casing, and two amidships, angled out from the casing abreast the bridge. Only the internal tubes were provided with reload torpedoes.

The first of the class, *Triton*, was ordered under the 1935 Programme, a further 14 being authorized during 1936-38. The war programmes added another 47 to the class but four of these were subsequently reordered as *Amphion* Class submarines and another six, still under construction at the end of the war, were cancelled. (Three of these had been launched, and the incomplete hulls were sold for scrap during 1945-46). The early boats completed with a bulbous casing around the external bow tubes, but this was found to create a bow wave when running at periscope depth which impaired vision, and the casing was given a finer form in later vessels while the earlier units were modified during refits. The vessels ordered from 1939 onwards were fitted with an additional external tube in the casing aft and their midship tubes were moved to a position abaft the conning tower and arranged to fire aft instead of forward. Some of the prewar vessels also had the stern tube added but their midship tubes were not altered. During the middle years of the war a single 20-mm (0.79-in) AA gun was mounted at the rear of the conning tower, and air-warning radar was fitted in the majority of the class. Units under construction were similarly modified. All the 1942 and some of the 1941 Programme ships were of all-welded construction while the majority of the earlier wartime vessels were part-welded. The all-welded hulls provided the advantage of allowing oil to be carried in the ballast tanks to give a greatly extended operational range and most of those all-welded boats which completed before the end of the war were sent to the Pacific and Far East where the great distances involved made such a feature essential.

The *Triton* Class together with the smaller *Swordfish* and *Undine* Class boats provided the bulk of Britain's submarine force during the Second World War, and the earlier vessels saw extensive service in Home Waters, the Mediterranean and the Far East. Fifteen of the class were sunk of which 13 were lost in the Mediterranean. In 1940 *Triad* was lost due to unknown cause, and *Triton* was sunk by the Italian torpedo boat *Clio*. In 1941 *Tetrarch* was lost due to unknown cause. In 1942 *Tempest* and *Thorn* were sunk by the Italian torpedo boats *Circe* and *Pegaro* respectively, and *Talisman*, *Traveller* and *Triumph* were lost due to unknown cause. In 1943 *Turbulent* and *Thunderbolt* were sunk by Italian MA/SBs and the corvette *Cicogna* respectively; the *P.91* and *Trooper* were probably mined; and *Tigris* was lost due to unknown cause. The remaining pair were both lost in Home Waters in April 1940: *Tarpon* was sunk by the German minesweeper *M.6* in the North Sea and *Thistle* was torpedoed by the submarine *U4* off Norway. *Thetis* accidentally sank while on acceptance trials in Liverpool bay in 1939 but was later raised, repaired and commissioned as HMS *Thunderbolt*. *Terrapin* was extensively damaged by Japanese depth charging while operating in the South Pacific in May 1945 and, with the war almost over, she was declared a constructive total loss.

In 1940 the names *Triad, Tigris, Truant, Tetrarch, Talisman, Torbay* and *Tuna* were given to *N.53, N.63, N.68, N.77, N.79* and *N.94* respectively. The 1939 and 1940 Programme ships were initially given the numbers *P.91-99* and the majority entered service with these, but in 1943 all were given full names, except *P.91* which had been lost. *Tasman* was renamed *Talent* in 1945, to

HM Submarine *Thunderbolt*, better known as *Thetis* but renamed after she was lost in Liverpool bay in June 1939. She was recommissioned with a new name but finally lost in action in the Mediterranean in 1943 when she was attacked by an Italian corvette off Sicily

replace the original boat of that name.

The original *Talent* and *Tarn* were transferred to the Royal Netherlands Navy in 1944-45, being renamed *Zwaardfisch* and *Tijgerhaai* respectively, and during 1945-55 ten of the class were sold for scrap. *Templar* and *Tantivy* were expended as A/S targets during 1950-51 and *Truculent* was sunk in collision with a merchant vessel in January 1950 (all three were later raised and scrapped). *Taurus* and *Tapir* were temporarily loaned to the Netherlands in 1948 and operated as *Dolfijn* and *Zeehond* respectively until returned in 1953.

During 1951-56 a number of the all-welded boats, *Tabard, Taciturn, Thermopylae, Tiptoe, Totem, Trump, Truncheon* and *Turpin,* underwent major modernization. This involved lengthening the hull by adding a new 6.1-m (20-ft) section (*Taciturn* 4.3 m [14 ft], and *Thermopylae* and *Turpin* 3.7 m [12 ft]) amidships to accommodate a second pair of electric motors and more batteries. In addition the batteries were changed to the new high-capacity type, the external torpedo tubes were removed and the casing and conning tower were streamlined. The overall effect was to increase the displacement by about 200 tons and greatly improve their submerged performance in endurance, quiet running and in speed, which was raised to 15 knots. During 1955-60 *Talent, Tireless* and *Token* were given a similar but less extensive modernization in which they were streamlined and given high-capacity batteries but, being riveted vessels, not lengthened. The remaining unmodernized vessels, including the two Dutch boats, were sold for scrap during 1961-66 but the modernized vessels survived into the 1970s. Of these *Totem, Turpin* and *Truncheon* were transferred to Israel during 1967-68 and renamed *Dakar, Leviathan* and *Dolphin* respectively. *Dakar* was lost due to unknown cause in January 1968. *Leviathan* was sold for scrap in the mid-1970s and the *Dolphin,* serving as a training vessel, was the only surviving member of the class in 1978.

Triton (ordered under 1935 Programme), *Triumph* (1936), *Thistle* (1937), *Triad* (1937), *Truant* (1937), *Tetrach* (1939), *Trusty* (1939 Emergency War Programme), *Turbulent* (1939 EW), *Trespasser* (ex-*P92*) (1940), *Taurus* (ex-*P93*) (1940), *Tactician* (ex-*P94*) (1940), *Truculent* (ex-*P95*) (1940), *Templar* (ex-*P96*) (1940), *Tally Ho* (ex-*P97*) (1940), *Tantalus* (1940), *Tantivy* (1940), *Telemachus* (1941), *Talent* (1941), *Terrapin* (1941), *Thorough* (1941), *Tiptoe* (1941), *Trump* (1941), *Taciturn* (1941), *Tapir* (1941), *Tarn* (1941), *Tasman* (1941), *P91* (1940)—built by Vickers-Armstrongs
Tigris (1937), *Torbay* (1939), *Tradewind* (1941), *Trenchant* (1941)—built by Chatham dockyard
Tuna (1937), *Traveller* (1939 EW), *Trooper* (1939 EW), *Tabard* (1942)—built by Scotts
Thunderbolt (ex-*Thetis*) (1939), *Trident* (1936), *Taku* (1937), *Talisman* (1939), *Tempest* (1939 EW), *Thorn* (1939 EW), *Thrasher* (1939 EW)—built by Cammell Laird
Thule (ex-*P325*) (1941), *Tudor* (ex-*P326*) (1941), *Totem* (1942), *Truncheon* (1942)—built by Devonport dockyard
Tireless (1941), *Token* (1941), *Turpin* (1942), *Thermopylae* (1942)—built by Portsmouth dockyard

No and name	laid down	launched	completed	builder
Danish vessels				
F.344 *Bellona*	1954	1/55	1/57	Naval Meccanica, Castellammare
F.345 *Diana*	—	12/54	7/55	Cantieri del Tirreno, Riva Trigoso
F.346 *Flora*	1953	6/55	8/56	Cantieri del Tirreno, Riva Trigoso
F.347 *Triton*	1953	9/54	8/55	Cantiere Navali, Taranto
Indonesian vessels				
801 *Pattimura*	1956	7/56	1/58	Ansaldo, Livorno
802 *Sultan Hasanudin*	1957	3/57	3/58	Ansaldo, Livorno
Italian vessels				
F.542 *Aquila* (ex-*Lynx*)	1953	7/54	10/56	Breda Marghera, Venice
F.543 *Albatros*	1953	7/54	6/55	Naval Meccanica, Castellammare
F.544 *Alcione*	1953	9/54	10/55	Naval Meccanica, Castellammare
F.545 *Airone*	1953	11/54	12/55	Naval Meccanica, Castellammare

Triton was launched in 1937. The 1936 Programme boats were launched in 1938; the 1937 boats were launched in 1938-40; the 1939 boats were launched in 1939-40, and the Emergency War Programme boats were launched in 1940-42; the 1940 boats were launched in 1942; the 1941 boats were launched in 1942-45; and the 1942 boats were launched in 1943-45.

Displacement: 1090/1570 tons (surfaced/submerged) *Length:* 74.8 m (245 ft 6 in) pp *Beam:* 8.1 m (26 ft 6 in) *Draught:* 3.7 m (12 ft) *Machinery:* 2-shaft diesel/2 electric motors, 2500 bhp/1450 shp=15/9 knots (surfaced/submerged) *Armament:* 10 (later 11) 21-in (53-cm) torpedo tubes; 1 4-in (102-mm) *Crew:* 60

Triton

Danish corvette class, built 1953-58. The four Danish corvettes of the *Triton* Class were built to an Italian design in Italy for the Royal Danish Navy. Three similar ships were built for the Italian navy and one, *Lynx,* was laid down for the Royal Netherlands Navy but was subsequently transferred back to the Italian navy in 1961 and renamed *Aquila.* A further two vessels were laid down in Italy for the Indonesian navy where they are known as the *Pattimura* Class.

All the vessels have been built under the provisions of the US 'Offshore' Mutual Defense Aid Program (MDAP). Although all the vessels have been built to the same basic design they all vary in details of armament, radar, etc, as well as having slight differences in dimensions. The Italian boats originally mounted two 76-mm (3-in) guns carried fore and aft, but in 1963 these were replaced by two single Bofors 40-mm (1.57-in). It was planned that the vessels should eventually be armed with OTO-Melara 76-mm guns, but this has never been implemented. The Italian vessels were designed primarily for A/S duties, and apart from the two triple US Mk 32 A/S torpedo tubes, the Italian vessels were equipped with two Hedgehogs, two depth-charge throwers and a depth-charge rack. The combined search and navigation radar is a single SMA/SPQ-2 model and the hull mounted a sonar QCU-2 set. The radius of action of the Italian ships is quoted as 3000 nautical miles at 18 knots with a bunkerage of 100 tons of diesel fuel.

The three Danish vessels displace some 40 tons less than the Italian boats, dimensions being the same. The armament shows that the role finally chosen for the Danish corvettes is somewhat different from that of the Italian boats, and they have been armed to operate in the restricted coastal waters around the Danish coastline. They have thus retained the 76-mm guns fore and aft, and in addition carry a single Bofors 40-mm mounted on the deckhouse just forward of the after 76-mm guns. They are not very well suited for A/S duties, being fitted with four obsolete depth-charge throwers and two Hedgehogs. The sonar is the same as that in the Italian vessels, but the search radar is the British Plessey AWS-1. The ships were originally rated as corvettes but are now generally regarded as frigates, having an F pennant number.

The two Indonesian boats are somewhat

larger than the Italian and Danish boats, displacing some 150 tons more than the Italian boats and being some 6.1 m (20 ft) longer. This was to some extent necessitated by the Indonesian staff requirement that they should have a higher speed than the Italian and Danish boats. They are equipped with three diesels driving three shafts, compared with the two-shaft diesels in the other ships. The Indonesians have retained the two 76-mm and in addition are armed with a twin 70-cal 30-mm (1.18-in) gun aft. Antisubmarine armament is identical to that of the Danish boats. Bunkerage is the same as the other vessels, but with three diesels the radius of action has been reduced to 2400 nautical miles.

These ships are now considered to be obsolete, and the Danish *Diana* was finally decommissioned for scrap in 1974, and the Indonesian ship *Sultan Hasanudin* (802) is in reserve.

(Danish vessels) *Displacement:* 760 tons (standard) *Length:* 76.3 m (250 ft 4 in) oa *Beam:* 9.6 m (31 ft 6 in) *Draught:* 2.7 m (8 ft 10 in) *Machinery:* 2-shaft Fiat 409T diesels, 4400 bhp=20 knots *Armament:* 2 76-mm (3-in); 1 40-mm (1.57-in); 2 Hedgehogs; 4 depth-charge throwers *Crew:* 100-110

(Indonesian vessels) *Displacement:* 950 tons (standard) *Length:* 82.4 m (270 ft 4 in) oa *Beam:* 10.4 m (34 ft 2 in) *Draught:* 2.7 m (8 ft 10 in) *Machinery:* 3-shaft Fiat diesels, 6900 bhp=22 knots *Armament:* as Danish vessels *Crew:* 100-110

(Italian vessels) *Displacement:* 800 tons (standard) *Dimensions* and *machinery:* as Danish vessels *Armament:* 2 76-mm (3-in); 1 40-mm (1.57-in); 2 Hedgehogs; 6 Mk 32 A/S torpedo tubes (2×3) *Crew:* 100-110

Triton

US nuclear-powered radar picket submarine. *Triton* was laid down on May 29, 1956, by General Dynamics (Electric Boat) at Groton, launched August 19, 1958, and completed November 10, 1959. She was designed and constructed as a radar picket submarine (SSRN) to provide early warning of aircraft attacks against a carrier task force, submerging when she herself was in danger of attack. A large, retractable air-search antenna was housed in the conning tower, and she was provided with a Combat Information Center and extensive communications. She was fitted with four bow torpedo tubes and two stern tubes.

Because of her size the *Triton* was to have two specially designed S4G pressurized water-cooled nuclear reactors, two steam turbines and two propeller shafts. To test these reactors a prototype reactor (S3G) was specially built ashore by the Atomic Energy Commission. At an overall length of 136.4 m (447 ft 6 in) she was the largest submarine ever built until the *Ohio* Class SSBNs, the first of which was launched in 1977. But, because of her size, there were problems during construction. While on the building slip her bow blocked the railway through the shipyard; a portion had to be cut away to allow the trains to pass, and was replaced just prior to launch. Her stern projected too far out into the river, and the last 15 m (50 ft) of stern section was constructed on an adjacent ship, being joined to the main hull only days before launch. The sail was too high to pass under the shipyard cranes during the launch and the top 3.7 m (12 ft) had to be cut away to be replaced later.

The nuclear-powered radar picket submarine USS *Triton* (SSRN 586) under way in 1959

Triton's two reactors give her a maximum of 34 000 shp to produce the high surface speed necessary for operations in conjunction with fast carrier task forces. Her conventional hull configuration gives her excellent seagoing qualities, though submerged speed is a mere 20 knots.

In March 1961 the radar picket programme was abandoned and *Triton* was reclassified as an attack submarine (SSN 586). Subsequently it was proposed that she be operated as an underwater national command post afloat, a role for which her size, nuclear propulsion and large combat information center admirably suited her, but no funds for such a conversion were approved. She was therefore decommissioned May 3, 1969, only ten years after her completion, thus becoming the first nuclear-powered submarine to be placed in reserve.

Displacement: 5940/6670 tons (surfaced/submerged) *Length:* 136.4 m (447 ft 6 in) *Beam:* 11.3 m (37 ft) *Draught:* 7.3 m (24 ft) *Machinery:* 2 pressurized water-cooled S4G nuclear reactors, 2-shaft steam turbines, 34 000 shp=27/20 knots (surfaced/submerged) *Armament:* 6 21-in (53-cm) torpedo tubes (4 bow, 2 stern) *Crew:* 172 as radar picket

Tromp

Dutch guided-missile destroyer class. *Tromp* (F.801) was laid down on August 4, 1971, launched May 2, 1973, and completed May 10, 1975. *De Ruyter* (F.806) was laid down December 22, 1971, launched March 9, 1974, and completed in June 1976. Both ships were built by De Schelde, Flushing. Designed to replace the aging cruisers of the *De Ruyter* Class, they were built as flagships for the ASW frigate squadrons, and a flush deck with high freeboard was selected for good seakeeping in the North Sea and eastern Atlantic waters in which they are expected to operate.

The COGOG propulsion system is similar to that of the British Type 42 destroyers, with two Olympus gas turbines for boost and two Tyne gas turbines for cruise; the gearing is of Dutch design and manufacture. The large twin uptakes are angled out in order to keep the hot gases clear of the radars.

A twin automatic 120-mm (4.7-in) mounting, removed from one of the older *Holland* Class destroyers, is fitted forward of the bridge, with an octuple launcher for NATO Sea Sparrow missiles above it to provide short-range air defence. Both of these weapons are controlled by the HSA WM 25 director mounted above the launcher. Aft of the tall mainmast is a US Mk 13 Tartar launcher for Standard SM-1 missiles, providing area defence, with two SPG-51 tracker/illuminators. Quadruple launchers for US Harpoon SSMs have recently been fitted on the superstructure immediately forward of the funnel uptakes. Three-dimensional air search and tracking for both these weapons are combined in the massive radome which gives the ships their distinctive appearance. Inside the dome HSA radars of Dutch manufacture are mounted back to back above and below a common platform. For antisubmarine operations they carry a helicopter. A Wasp was carried initially but this will eventually be replaced by a Lynx with its own hangar and maintenance facilities. Two triple banks of Mk 32 torpedo tubes are fitted at upper-deck level amidships. The sonars are of British and US manufacture.

Three ships of the *Tromp* Class were originally projected, but in view of the high cost of the first two ships it was decided to replace the third by an area-defence version of the Standard frigate.

Displacement: 3665 tons (standard), 4300 tons (full load) *Length:* 138.6 m (454 ft 9 in) oa *Beam:* 14.8 m (48 ft 6 in) *Draught:* 4.6 m (15 ft) *Machinery:* 2 Olympus gas turbines, 44 000 hp=28 knots; 2 Tyne gas turbines, 8200 hp=18 knots *Armament:* 2 120-mm (4.7-in) DP (1×2); 1 Standard SM-1 Mk 13 launcher; 1 Sea Sparrow octuple launcher; 2 Harpoon SSM quadruple launchers; 6 Mk 32 A/S torpedo tubes; 1 helicopter *Crew:* 306

Truxtun

US nuclear-powered guided-missile cruiser. The US Navy requested seven oil-burning frigates in the FY 1962 programme; six of them were completed as *Belknap* Class vessels but Congress stipulated that one unit be nuclear-propelled. This was ordered in 1962 as DLGN.35 from New York Shipbuilding, laid down on June 17, 1963, launched as

Koninkluke Marine

The Dutch guided-missile destroyer *Tromp*. Vessels in her class are readily recognizable by the distinctive all-weather protective dome which houses complex Dutch-designed HSA radars

Truxtun on December 19, 1964, and completed on May 27, 1967. *Truxtun* carried an identical armament to that of her *Belknap* Class contemporaries, but there was one major difference in layout: the single 127-mm (5-in) Mk 45 gun was fitted forward, with its Mk 68 director above the bridge, and the twin Mk 10 launchers aft, with the two SPG-55 guidance radars above the hangar—the reverse of the placing of these two systems on *Belknap*. As on the latter, the magazine for the Mk 10 launcher could hold Terrier surface-to-surface missiles and Asroc antisubmarine missiles. Two single 76-mm (3-in)/50-cal guns were mounted in tubs projecting from the superstructure amidships. Beneath the tubs were two single Mk 32 torpedo tubes port and starboard housed in the superstructure. Two Mk 25 tubes were also built into the stern but have not been used. The armament was completed by a DASH (drone antisubmarine helicopter) with its own hangar. This was later replaced, as on the *Belknap* Class, by a manned Seasprite helicopter (LAMPS I).

The sensor outfit was even more advanced than that of the *Belknap* Class. In addition to the large SQS-26 bow sonar, *Truxtun* was fitted with an SPS-40 air-search radar and the new SPS-48 three-dimensional planar radar, with a smaller SPS-10 for surface surveillance. The latter three aerials are mounted on top of tall quadruped lattice masts, which combine with the absence of funnels to give the ship a distinctive appearance.

The propulsion system is identical to that of *Bainbridge*. The turbines give her less power and a lower speed than the *Belknap* Class, but this is more than compensated by the increase in endurance.

The Terrier missile has been superseded by the extended-range Standard missile, which has improved performance. It seems likely that the 76-mm guns may also be replaced by quadruple launchers for Harpoon surface-to-surface missiles in the near future. *Truxtun* has served in the Pacific Fleet since completion. She was redesignated CGN in 1975.

Displacement: 8200 tons (standard), 9200 tons (full load) *Length:* 118 m (387 ft 3 in) *Beam:* 17.7 m (58 ft) *Draught:* 9.4 m (30 ft 9 in) *Machinery:* 2 DG2 nuclear reactors, 2-shaft steam turbines, 60 000 shp=30 knots *Armament:* 1 twin Mk 10 launcher, Standard ER SAMs and Asroc A/S missiles; 1 127-mm (5-in)/54-cal Mk 42 DP; 2 76-mm (3-in) AA; 4 32.4-cm (12.75-in) torpedo tubes, Mk 32 A/S torpedoes; 1 Seasprite helicopter *Crew:* 510

Tucumcari

US hydrofoil. The hydrofoil *Tucumcari* was launched by Boeing Aerospace on July 15, 1967, and commissioned on March 7, 1968. She was built to test the feasibility of developing hydrofoils for military use. She was ordered in 1966 and was designed with a fully submerged foil system with a canard configuration. The two after foils supported about 70% of the displacement, while the bow foil supported 30%. When foil-borne, steering was accomplished by the forward foil rotating on its strut about a vertical axis. To maintain the hull at a constant height above the water a wave-height sensing system is used.

A water-jet propulsion system was used in which a powerful pump developed the thrust needed to propel the vessel by ejecting a considerable mass of water at high speed. When foil-borne, sea water was sucked in through openings in the foils and carried in ducts to the pump inlet. Power for the pump was provided by a Rolls-Royce Proteus gas turbine. When hull-borne another water-jet pump, driven by a General Motors diesel, provided propulsion.

The military potential of *Tucumcari* was tested in 1969-70. She carried out a number of coastal patrols off Vietnam which proved that the hydrofoil was capable of operating in rough weather conditions. The following year *Tucumcari* carried out a number of trials for various NATO navies. It was generally felt that she was rather too small to meet a practical NATO requirement, but nevertheless proved the principle and capability of the hydrofoil. As a result of these trials the Italians designed their own slightly larger hydrofoil, *Sparviero*, which was completed in May 1973, while the US designed the 230-ton *Pegasus*.

During the numerous trials carried out with *Tucumcari* she was found to suffer from a lack of lateral stability but the addition of ventilation fences to the surface-piercing struts of the foils overcame this problem. The machine-guns and mortar were removed in 1971 and a 20-mm (0.79-in) gun added. On November 15, 1972, *Tucumcari* ran aground and was severely damaged. The cost of repairs was prohibitive and the ship was scrapped in October 1973.

Displacement: 58 tons *Length:* 22.7 m (74 ft 6 in) *Beam:* 5.9 m (19 ft 6 in) *Draught:* 1.4 m (4 ft 6 in) hull-borne *Machinery:* 1 gas turbine, 3100 hp=40+ knots (foil-borne); 1 General Motors diesel, 150 hp (hull-borne) *Armament:* 1 40-mm (1.57-in); 4 machine-guns; 1 80-mm (3.1-in) mortar *Crew:* 13

Tullibee

US nuclear-powered submarine. The USS *Tullibee* (SSN.597) was originally planned as a 1000-ton submarine for antisubmarine operations, with good manoeuvrability rather than high speed. A modified *Albacore*-type teardrop hull was used, but the need to increase the size to accommodate the reactor and its shielding led to a submarine over twice the planned size. A new type of pressurized-water reactor, the S2C, with turbo-electric drive was used to power the boat, giving a higher silent speed than in the earlier boats. The whole of the bow was used to house sonar equipment for detecting and tracking enemy submarines, and the four torpedo tubes were therefore fitted amidships position, angled out at 10° from either side of the hull.

Tullibee was laid down on May 26, 1958, launched on April 27, 1960 and commissioned on November 10, 1960. Experience gained with *Tullibee* was incorporated in the later *Thresher* Class, and no further submarines were built to this design.

Displacement: 2317/2640 tons (surfaced/submerged) *Length:* 83.2 m (273 ft) oa *Beam:* 7.2 m (23 ft 6 in) *Draught:* 6.4 m (21 ft) *Machinery:* 1-shaft S2C nuclear reactor, 1-shaft turbo-electric, 2500 shp=15/15 knots (surfaced/submerged) *Armament:* 4 21-in (53-cm) torpedo tubes *Crew:* 87

Tumult

British destroyer class. The vessels of the *Tumult* Class formed the 6th Destroyer Flotilla of the Emergency War Programme and were of identical design to the previous *Savage* Class except that they were not fitted for Arctic service. They were laid down in 1941, launched in 1942 and completed in 1943. The designed AA armament consisted of a twin 40-mm (1.57-in) mounting amidships and four twin 20-mm (0.79-in) mountings, two abaft the funnels and one in each of the bridge wings. At the time of completion the twin 40-mm was in short supply, so *Tyrian, Tuscan, Tumult* and *Troubridge* carried two single 20-mm and *Tenacious* two twin 20-mm mountings in its place. These weapons were later replaced by the proper mounting. In addition *Tumult* was completed with an experimental arrangement of two fixed torpedo tubes, mounted on the upper deck abreast the funnel, instead of her forward bank of revolving tubes. After trials these were removed and the ship reverted to the standard tube outfit.

On completion the class were formed into the 24th Destroyer Flotilla and sent to the Mediterranean where they operated until late in 1944 when they were earmarked for the British Eastern Fleet. Before being transferred they were refitted to improve their AA defence and had their twin 20-mm mountings replaced by four or five 40-mm or 2-pdr singles, except *Tyrian* which retained the 20-mm guns in her bridge wings. Early in 1945 they sailed for the Indian Ocean where instead of joining the Eastern Fleet they were attached to the newly formed British Pacific Fleet with which they operated until after the war.

In 1946 the class was placed in reserve except for the *Troubridge*, which served as leader to the 3rd Destroyer Flotilla, Mediterranean, during 1946-49. During the 1950s the entire class was converted into fast antisubmarine frigates which extended their lives until the late 1960s when the majority were sold for scrap.

See also *Rapid* and *Tenacious*.

Teazer, Tenacious—built by Cammell Laird
Termagant, Terpsichore—built by Denny
Troubridge, Tumult—built by John Brown
Tuscan, Tyrian—built by Swan Hunter

Displacement: 1800 tons (standard), 2500 tons (full load) *Length:* 110.6 m (362 ft 9 in) oa *Beam:* 10.9 m (35 ft 9 in) *Draught:* 3.05 m (10 ft) *Machinery:* 2-shaft geared turbines, 40 000 shp=36 knots *Armament:* 4 4.7-in (120-mm); 2 40-mm (1.57-in); 8 20-mm (0.79-in) (4×2) ; 8 21-in (53-cm) torpedo tubes (2×4) *Crew:* 179

Turunmaa

Finnish corvette class. Ordered in 1966 from the Wärtsila shipyard, Helsinki, both ships were laid down in March 1967. *Turunmaa* was launched on July 11, 1967, and completed on August 29, 1968. *Karjala* was launched on August 16, 1967, and completed October 21, 1968. Small and compact, with a low flush-decked hull, topped by a tall superstructure with an enclosed bridge, the *Turunmaa* Class were designed primarily for trade protection. The requirement for good endurance at cruising speed combined with a capability for bursts of high speed resulted in a novel propulsion system. Three small Mercedes-Benz diesels, each with a rating of 1330 bhp, drive three shafts for a cruising speed of 17 knots. On the centre shaft aft of the diesel is an Olympus gas turbine with a rating of 22 000 hp which is used to boost speed to 35 knots. This was only the second installation of the Olympus turbine (the first was on HMS *Exmouth*), and the ships were apparently still running in 1979 with the original turbines.

The armament is conventional. A single 120-mm (4.7-in) Bofors dual-purpose gun, with an elevation of 80° and a rate of fire of 80 rds/min is mounted forward of the bridge. Two single 40-mm (1.57-in) Bofors AA guns are carried, one on the after end of the superstructure and the other on the stern, and there is also a twin 30-mm (1.18-in) mounting aft of the single mast. For fire control against ships or aircraft a Dutch HSA M-22 radome is fitted above the bridge. The armament is completed by two depth-charge projectors. To counteract the considerable topweight Vosper Thornycroft fin stabilizers are fitted.

Displacement: 660 tons (standard), 770 tons (full load) *Length:* 74.1 m (243 ft) oa *Beam:* 7.8 m (25 ft 6 in) *Draught:* 2.6 m (8 ft 6 in) *Machinery:* 1-shaft Olympus gas turbine, 22 000 hp=35 knots, 3-shaft Mercedes-Benz diesels, 3990 bhp=17 knots *Armament:* 1 120-mm (4.7-in) DP; 2 40-mm (1.57-in) AA (2×1); 1 30-mm (1.18-in) AA (1×2); 2 depth-charge projectors *Crew:* 70

'Turya'

Soviet hydrofoil class. These hydrofoils, of which it is estimated that about 30 are in service, have been developed from the basic 'Osa' patrol boats, large numbers of which are in service. Dimensions are the same as the 'Osas' but displacement has been increased by some 35 tons. They appear to be a hydrofoil version of the standard 'Stenka' displacement-hull patrol craft, also developed from the 'Osa'.

The 'Turya' Class have been developed from the outset as a military hydrofoil, whereas the earlier 'Pchela' Class were developed for use by the frontier guard. They carry a fairly standard armament for an older type of patrol boat of four torpedo tubes and guns. They do show one unusual feature in that there appears to be a form of VDS fitted on the transom stern. Although the hydrofoils are fitted with sonar they appear to lack any form of antisubmarine armament. They would probably be able to co-operate with shore-based helicopters in an A/S role. It is possible that the 16-in (41-cm) A/S torpedo will replace the 21-in (53-cm). The main search radar is a Pot Drum and fire control is exercised through Drum Tilt. The 'Turya' Class vessels began to enter service in 1973, and production is estimated at about 4-5 a year.

Displacement: 200 tons (standard), 230 tons (full load) *Length:* 39.2 m (128 ft 8 in) *Beam:* 7.6 m (25 ft) *Draught:* 1.8 m (5 ft 10 in) *Machinery:* 3 diesels, 14 000 hp=40 knots *Armament:* 2 57-mm (2.24-in) (1×2); 2 25-mm (1-in) (1×2); 4 21-in (53-cm) torpedo tubes *Crew:* 30

U-Boats

German submarines. Under the terms of the Treaty of Versailles Germany was not allowed to retain or build any submarines so that at the outbreak of war in 1939 the German U-Boat fleet was comparatively modern, all the vessels having been built since 1935. Between 1919 and 1934 German submarine technicians had not been idle, and among those submarines built in various European shipyards to German design and with German technical assistance were *Gür* built in 1932 for the Turkish navy, and *Vesikko* built in 1933 for Finland. *Gür* was 72.4 m (237 ft 6 in) long and displaced 750 tons (surfaced) and 960 tons (submerged), and was armed with six torpedo tubes (four bow and two stern) and one 4-in (102-mm) gun. *Vesikko* was a smaller boat of only 250 tons (surfaced) and 300 tons (submerged); it was 40.8 m (134 ft) long, and armed with three bow 53-cm (21-in) torpedo tubes and a small gun.

Thus *Gür* provided a prototype for an ocean-going submarine, while *Vesikko* was the forerunner of the coastal submarines. In order to get the building programme under way as rapidly as possible to fulfil the need to have submarines at sea and to train future crews, it was the coastal submarines of Type II, as they were to be known, that were the first to be laid down. The first such boat for the German navy, called *U 1*, was launched in Kiel in June 1935, the remainder following shortly afterwards. Types IIB and IIC were similar, but were larger and carried additional fuel to increase their range. Type IID boats were introduced in 1940; they were still larger; and were fitted with saddle tanks to increase their range further. Although used for operations early in the war these boats were soon relegated to training duties, an essential part of the enormous expansion programme that the U-Boat arm was to undertake.

Meanwhile the Type I, of which only two boats were built, gave the German navy a capability of operations in the Atlantic. Basically the same design and performance as *Gür*, these two boats in turn were to become the prototype, with the *UB48* Class of 1917, of a new series of ocean-going submarines, the Type VII. This type, with its several variants, was undoubtedly the mainstay of the German submarine fleet throughout the war. The variants retained many structural characteristics of the original Type VII but

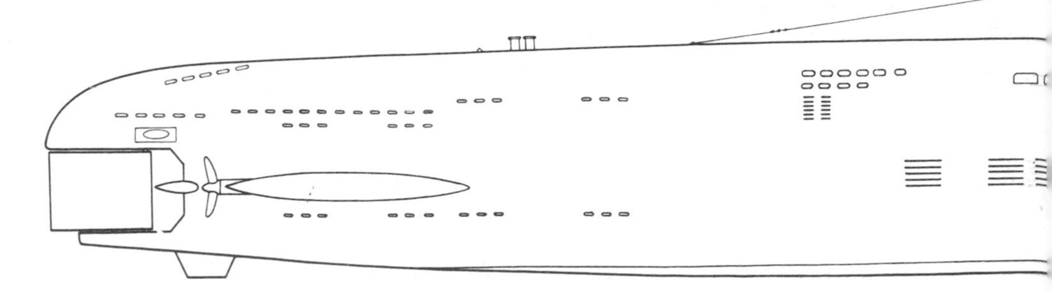

TYPES I and II

Type	IA	IIA	IIB	IIC	IID
Numbers	*U 25, 26*	*U 1-6*	*U 7-24, 120, 121* (ex-Yugoslav)	*U 56-63*	*U 137-152*
Displacement (tons) (surfaced/submerged)	862/983	254/303	279/329	291/341	314/364
Length (m/ft)	72.5/238	41.1/135	42.7/140	44.2/145	44.2/145
Beam (m/ft)	6.2/20.3	4.1/13.5	4.1/13.5	4.1/13.5	4.9/16
Draught (m/ft)	4.3/14	3.8/12.5	3.9/12.8	3.8/12.75	3.9/12.8
Speed (knots) (surfaced/submerged)	18.5/8.25	13/7	13/7	12/7	13/7
Fuel (tons)	96	12	21	23	38
Range (nautical miles)/ at speed (knots)	7900/10	1500/10	2700/10	2900/10	4400/10
Torpedo tubes/ no of torpedoes	4 bow, 2 stern/14*	3 bow/5 (normal), 6 (max)*	3 bow/5 or 6*	3 bow/5 or 6*	3 bow/5 or 6*
Guns	1 10.5-cm (4.1-in); 1 20-mm (0.79-in) AA	1 20-mm (0.79-in) AA	2/3 20-mm (0.79-in) AA	2 20-mm (0.79-in) AA	1 20-mm (0.79-in) AA

For notes see page overleaf

were designed either for better performance or for more specialized roles. The first Type VIIA was *U27*, launched in 1936, designed for operations in the Atlantic. It had good seakeeping qualities and easy handling both on the surface and submerged, and carried the best possible torpedo armament that could be fitted into a submarine of less than 65 m (213 ft) in length and only 626 tons surfaced displacement. Inevitably this was achieved at the expense of other factors, and habitability was spartan, to say the least. The Type VIIAs are distinguished by their single external torpedo tube aft. *U30*, a boat of this type, was responsible for sinking the liner *Athenia* early in the war.

U45, the first Type VIIB, was launched in April 1938. The type had increased size and displacement to accommodate higher-performance engines and more fuel. The stern torpedo tube was made internal with the hull. The *U47* commanded by Korvetten-Kapitän Günther Prien entered Scapa Flow in 1939 and sank *Royal Oak*, and later was to sink many thousands of tons of Allied shipping in the Atlantic.

The Type VIIC, introduced in 1940, had a further increase in displacement and fuel capacity, more torpedo reloads, and a better AA armament. Contracts were placed for 688 boats of this type, though later some of these were cancelled and others were destroyed by enemy action during construction. The Type VIIC-41 differed only in that it had a stronger hull to give a greater diving depth. Eight boats of this type were to have been completed for the Italian navy, but they were taken into commission by the Germans themselves following the Italian surrender. *U573* was interned in Spain at Cartagena after being badly damaged by depth charges dropped from an RAF aircraft in 1942. The following year she was sold to Spain and renumbered *G.7*. *U570* surrendered after being damaged by an RAF aircraft south of Iceland, and later was commissioned as HMS *Graph*. Orders for a second variant, the Type VIIC-42, were cancelled to allow production to concentrate on newer types. Had it entered service it would have had increased range and an even greater diving depth.

A minelaying variant, the Type VIID, was introduced in 1942. The six boats of this type had a 9.8-m (32 ft 2-in) section added into the hull aft of the conning tower to take five free-flooding mine chutes carrying a total of 15 moored mines similar to those carried by surface minelayers. In the Type VIIF this extra section was adapted to carry 25 torpedoes to replenish other submarines already on patrol. Four boats of this type were built, and they carried additional fuel to increase their range. In addition to the replenishment torpedoes for other boats they had their own establishment of torpedoes to carry out their own operations.

A total of 705 boats of the Type VII variants had entered service by the time of the surrender in 1945, and of these, 437 were lost in action. The *U977* (Type VIIC) left Norway rather than surrender, and after a

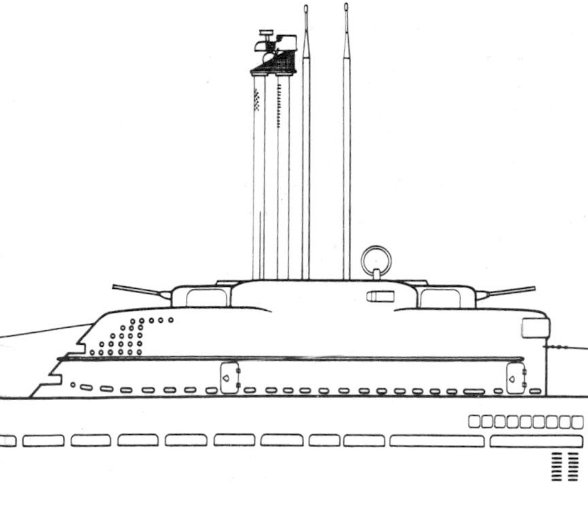
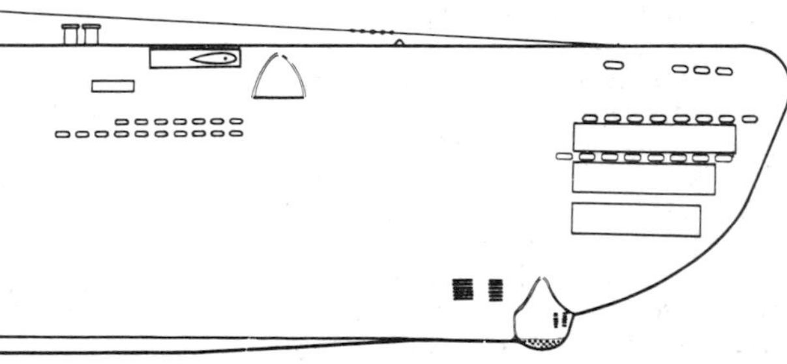

The German Type XXI U-Boat, produced too late to see service in significant numbers

TYPE VII

Type	VIIA	VIIB	VIIC	VIIC-41	VIIC-42	VIID	VIIF
Numbers	*U 27-36*	*U 45-55, 73-76, 83-87, 99-102*	*U 69-72, 77-82, 88-98, 132-136, 201-212, 221-232, 235-458, 465-486, 551-683, 701-779, 821-836, 901-908, 921-930, 951-1058, 1063-1065*	*U 1101-1220, 1271-1279, 1301-1308*	Cancelled	*U 213-218*	*U 1059-1062*
Displacement (tons) (surfaced/submerged)	626/745	753/857	769/871	769/871	990/1050	965/1080	1084/1181
Length (m/ft)	64.9/213	66.9/219.5	67.5/221.5	67.5/221.5	68.7/225.7	77/252.6	78/256
Beam (m/ft)	5.9/19.4	6.2/20.3	6.2/20.3	6.2/20.3	6.2/20.3	6.4/21	7.3/24
Draught (m/ft)	4.4/14.4	4.7/15.4	4.7/15.4	4.7/15.4		5/16.4	5.2/17
Speed (knots) (surfaced/submerged)	17/8	18/8	17.75/7.5	17.75/7.5	Est 18.5 max	16.75/7.25	17.5/8
Fuel (tons)	67	108	114	114	Planned 180	170	199
Range (nautical miles)/ at speed (knots)	4300/12	6500/12	6500/12; 8850/10		About 12 600	8100/12	9500/12
Torpedo tubes/ no of torpedoes	4 bow, 1 stern/11**	4 bow, 1 stern/14**	4 bow, 1 stern/14**	4 bow, 1 stern/14**	/12**	4 bow, 1 stern/12**; 15 mine chutes/ 15 mines	4 bow, 1 stern/39
Guns	1 3.5-in (89-mm); 1 20-mm (0.79-in)	1 37-mm (1.46-in); 2 20-mm	1 37-mm; 2 20-mm***	1 37-mm; 2 20-mm		1 37-mm; 2 20-mm	1 37-mm; 2 20-mm

continuous submerged passage of 66 days reached Argentina on August 17, 1945, where her crew were interned.

The big sister of the Type VII was the Type IX which had a greater range and better habitability. It was designed for operations in distant waters and possessed good seakeeping qualities. The first boat, *U 37*, was commissioned in August 1938 only three months after being launched. The Type IXB built shortly afterwards carried an extra 11 tons of fuel. The Types IXC and IXC-40, which differed only slightly from each other, again increased the fuel capacity and range of the boats. Contracts for some of these boats were cancelled in 1944 in order to concentrate production on the new Type XXI. *U 511* was handed over to Japan in 1943 and became the *RO 500*; U 1224 similarly became *RO 501* in 1944, but was sunk north-west of the Cape Verde Islands by a US destroyer while on passage to Japan.

As the Allied blockade on Germany tightened there arose a requirement for a submarine to carry small cargoes of vital materials from the Far East to Germany. The Type IXC design was therefore modified by being lengthened by 7.6 m (25 ft) and given a cargo capacity of 252 tons. The Type IXD 41 which resulted sacrificed all its own torpedo armament and some of its battery capacity to achieve this while a later version, the Type IXD-42, reverted to having its own torpedo armament. This last series of boats may be regarded as the final series of the conventional submarine to join the German navy. Apart from its ability to carry vital cargo from the Far East it also had the greatest range of any German submarine of over 31 500 nautical miles. *U 195* was transferred to Japan as *I 506*, while *U 181* and *U 862* became the *I 501* and the *I 502*.

A small number of Type XB submarines

U 236, a German Type VII submarine, one of the standard designs during the Second World War. *U 236* was one of the Type VIIC submarines, the third version, and entered service in January 1943. Damaged in an attack at the end of the war she had to be scuttled by her crew

TYPE IX

Type	IX	IXB	IXC	IXC-40	IXD-41	IXD-42
Numbers	*U 37-44*	*U 64-65, 103-111, 122-124*	*U 66-68, 125-131, 153-166, 171-176, 501-524, 841-846, 853-858, 865-870, 877-881, 889, 1221-1238*	*U 167-170, 183-194, 525-550, 801-806*	*U 180, 195*	*U 177-179, 181, 182, 196-200, 847-852, 859-864, 871-876*
Displacement (tons) (surfaced/submerged)	1032/1153	1051/1178	1120/1232	1144/1257	1610/1799	1616/1804
Length (m/ft)	77/252.6	77/252.6	72.2/237	72.2/237	88/289	88/289
Beam (m/ft)	6.6/21.6	6.9/22.6	6.9/22.6	6.9/22.6	7.5/24.60	7.5/24.60
Draught (m/ft)	4.7/15.5	4.7/15.5	4.7/15.5	4.7/15.5	5.6/18.37	5.6/18.37
Speed (knots) (surfaced/submerged)	18.25/7.75	18.25/7.25	18.25/7.25	18.25/7.25	16.5/7	19.25/7
Fuel (tons)	154	166	208	214	203	442
Range (nautical miles)/ at speed (knots)	10 500/10	12 000/10	13 450/10	13 850/10	12 750/10	23 700/12; 31 500/10
Torpedo tubes/ no of torpedoes	4 bow, 2 stern 22*	4 bow, 2 stern/22*	4 bow, 2 stern/22*	4 bow, 2 stern/22*	nil; 252 tons cargo	4 bow, 2 stern/24*
Guns	1 10.5-cm; 1 37-mm AA; 1 20-mm AA***	1 37-mm AA; 4 20-mm AA****	1 37-mm AA; 4 20-mm AA****	1 37-mm AA; 4 20-mm AA****	1 37-mm AA; 4 20-mm AA	1 37-mm AA; 20-mm AA****

TYPES X and XIV

Type	XB	XIV
Numbers	*U 116-119, 219, 220, 233, 234*	*U 459-464, 487-490*
Displacement (tons) (surfaced/submerged)	1763/2177	1688/1932
Length (m/ft)	90.4/296.6	67.5/221.5
Beam (m/ft)	9.3/30.6	9.4/30.84
Draught (m/ft)	4.7/15.4	6.6/21.7
Speed (knots) (surfaced/submerged)	17/7	15/6
Fuel (tons)	368	203 plus 517 as cargo
Range (nautical miles)/ at speed (knots)	14 450/12	12 350/10; 9300/12
Torpedo tubes/ no of torpedoes	2 stern/15*; 30 mine chutes/66 mines	nil, 4 as cargo
Guns	1 37-mm AA; 4 20-mm AA	2 37-mm AA; 2 20-mm AA

were built as large ocean-going minelayers, the Type XA never having left the drawing board. The mines were stowed in six internal mine chutes aft of the forward torpedo tubes, three mines in each chute, and two mines in each of 24 external chutes arranged either side of the boat amidships. Torpedo reloads were stowed both internally and externally. The boats had a range in excess of 14 000 nautical miles, and they were later increasingly used for cargo-carrying missions. *U 219* was in Penang at the time of the German surrender and was captured by the Japanese who renumbered her *I 505*.

The Type XIV were tanker U-Boats derived from the Type VIIC. They were used to supply fuel to other submarines to increase their time on patrol, and for this purpose they carried an additional 203 tons of fuel. They had no torpedo tubes of their own though they carried four torpedoes for transfer to other boats.

From the early stages of the war the German naval staff were interested in producing a 'true submarine' able to travel fast underwater and needing no more than the very minimum time on the surface. This became increasingly important as Allied air power made it increasingly unsafe for German submarines to remain on the surface. One answer was to fit *Schnorkel* (snorkel) tubes to all new construction, and also to

* Indicates that mines could be carried in lieu of some or all of the torpedoes
** Indicates that the torpedo load could be varied so that a mixture of torpedoes and mines could be carried, the mines being launched through the torpedo tubes and carried at the expense of the torpedo armament
*** Some boats carried up to 8 20-mm
**** Indicates that the armament varied with time

EXPERIMENTAL and TURBINE-POWERED

Type Numbers	*V 80*	*V 300* *U 791* (not completed)	XXVIIA *U 792-795*	XXVIIB *U 1405, 1406, 1407*	XXVIIG None	XXVIIK *U 798* (not completed)
Displacement (tons) (surfaced/submerged)	80	655/725	236/259	312/357		
Length (m/ft)	26/85.30	52.1/171	34/111.5	41.5/136.15	39.5/129.6	40.7/133.5
Beam (m/ft)	2.6/8.5	4/13	3.4/11.15	3.4/11.15	3.4/11.15	3.4/11.15
Draught (m/ft)	7.25	18/59	15/49.2	14/46	14/46	16/52.5
Speed (knots) (surfaced/submerged)	not known	19 planned	26	21.5	21.5	14/16
Fuel (tons)	not known	Perhydrol 98	Perhydrol 40; O.F. 14	Perhydrol 55; O.F. 20	Perhydrol 55	Ingolin 55; O.F. 26
Range (nautical miles)/ at speed (knots)	not known	205/19	80/26	114/20	not known	114/20
Torpedo tubes/ no of torpedoes	none	2 bow/6	2 bow/4	2 bow/4	2 bow/4	none
Guns	none	none	none	none	none	none

existing boats. The snorkel was a prewar Dutch idea for ventilating the submarine and was adapted by the Germans to enable the submarine to use its diesel engines while dived. It consisted of a long tube hinged at the bottom so that it would fit flush with the deck when not in use, but when raised would project above water while the submarine was at periscope depth. The head of the tube had a float valve which closed when it was dipped below the surface or covered by a wave. The alternative was some form of closed-cycle engine, and in this direction the most promising development was the turbine designed by Professor Walter and fitted in the submarine *V 80* in 1940. The system relied on the breakdown of a high concentration of hydrogen peroxide (perhydrol) in a catalyst chamber to form oxygen and steam. The oxygen was then used to ignite fuel oil which was mixed with it, and the resulting high-pressure gas mixture was able to drive a turbine. The greatest difficulties lay in the manufacture and storage of the hydrogen peroxide, which decomposes, sometimes violently, in the presence of the slightest impurities. *V 80*, a small submarine of only 80 tons, was designed to test the feasibility of the system. A larger design, based on a Type VIIC hull, was numbered *V 300* (later *U 791*) and carried torpedo tubes. She never completed and was scrapped in 1944. A further design, *V 301*, was based on a new hull shape but never got further than the drawing board.

The next stage was the construction of four small Type XVIIA submarines which were launched in 1943. They were used initially to test out the system, and it was hoped that they would later become operational. As armament they were fitted with two bow torpedo tubes. They had one shaft with two Walter geared turbines which it was hoped would give a submerged speed of around 26 knots. They also had standard diesel-electric drive for normal propulsion. Two variants, Types XVIIB and XVIIG, had only one of the Walter turbines, but this still gave a designed maximum speed of a little over 20 knots. None of the Type XVIIGs were completed, and though other boats of this Type carried out extensive trials they never became operational. *U 1407* (Type XVIIB) was taken over by the Royal Navy at the end of the war. She commissioned as *Meteorite* and carried out further development trials before being scrapped in 1950. These postwar trials led in turn to the building of the two submarines of the *Explorer* Class for the RN using the same propulsion techniques.

Because of the slow development of the Walter turbine the Type XVIIK was planned to give the necessary fast underwater speed and some immunity from air attack. This would have had the Type XVIIB hull with a closed-cycle diesel engine. Cylinders of compressed air to give the boat adequate endurance took up too much space, and in the first instance the boats were purely experimental and no torpedo armament was fitted. A speed of about 16 knots was expected, but none of the boats was completed.

The Type XXI was a fundamentally new sort of submarine with a very streamlined hull and high-capacity batteries to give great submerged speed and endurance. The design was suggested at a conference in Paris in November 1942 as an alternative to the Walter turbine boats which were taking so long to develop, and by June 1943 the preliminary design work was complete. The planned submerged speed was 18 knots for 90 minutes, a tremendous advance on any existing submarine's performance and one that would have caused formidable problems to

One of the 14 Type IXB ocean-going submarines built during the war. They had superior endurance compared to the Type VII but had a longer building time. They sank, on average, as high a tonnage as U-Boats operating nearer to Britain

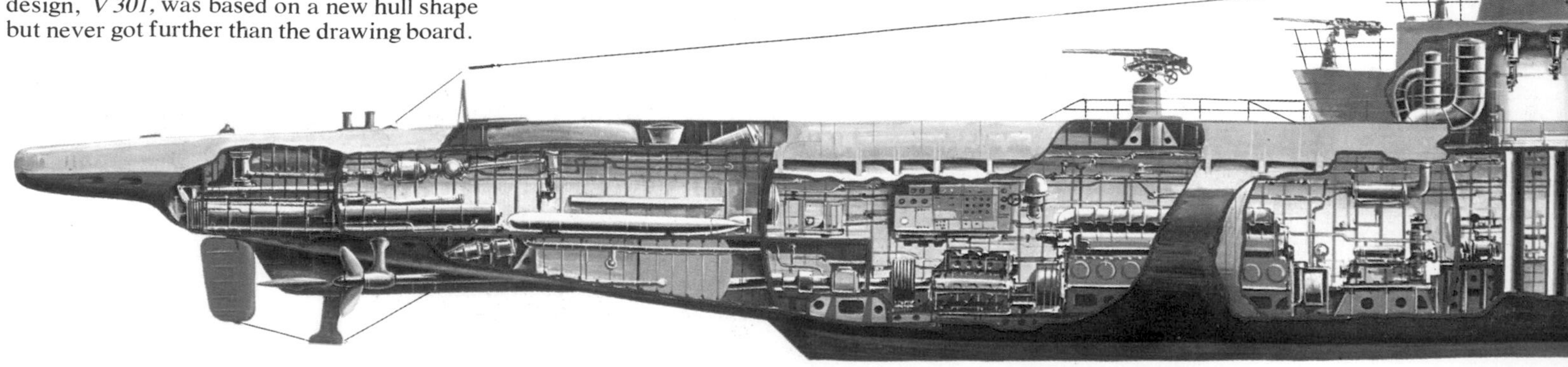

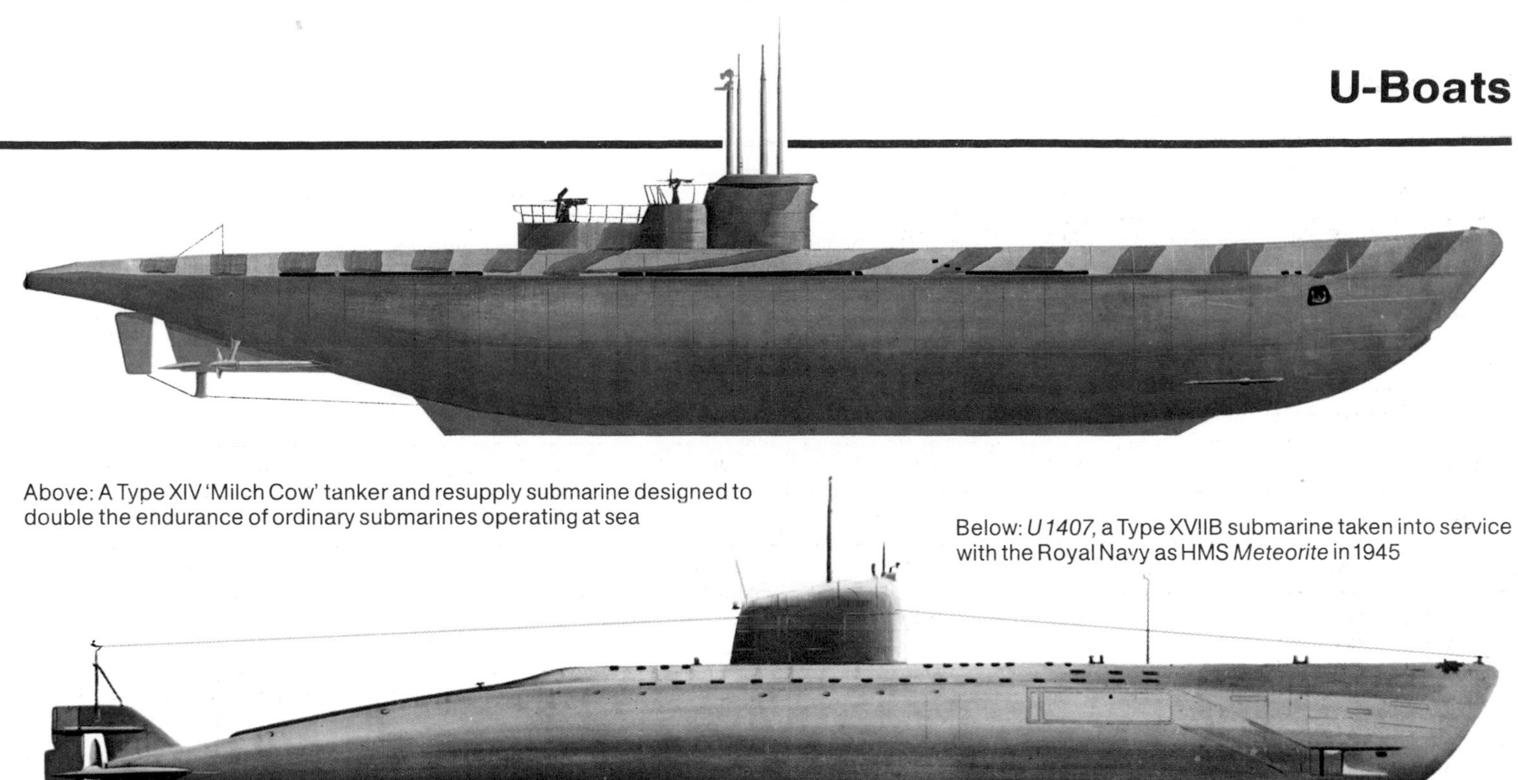

Above: A Type XIV 'Milch Cow' tanker and resupply submarine designed to double the endurance of ordinary submarines operating at sea

Below: *U 1407*, a Type XVIIB submarine taken into service with the Royal Navy as HMS *Meteorite* in 1945

the Allied navies had the Type XXI become operational in any numbers earlier in the war. Additional advantages of this type of U-Boat were a deep-diving capability, a fast silent speed and rapid torpedo reloading. The underwater armament was six bow tubes with 23 torpedoes. It was planned to give these boats a defensive AA armament of a quadruple 30-mm (1.18-in) gun of a new design, but because of production problems few were fitted and most boats had the standard 20-mm (0.79-in) weapon. To speed production the hull was prefabricated in eight all-welded sections in different shipyards away from the main bombing targets of the Allied forces. After transporting the sections to the launching slip they could be welded together rapidly and the boat launched, after spending a minimum time on a vulnerable launching slip.

The size of the Type XXI made it unsuitable for operations in the North Sea or English Channel. The Type XXIII was evolved incorporating many of the ideas of the Type XXI but with coastal characteristics and prefabricated in only four sections. The armament consisted of only two torpedo tubes. In order to maintain a clean streamlined hull shape the conventional deck casing was dispensed with.

In August 1943 the Types XXI and XXIII were ordered and to give them due priority the contracts for the Type VIIC-42 were cancelled. Despite the dispersal of the prefabrication yards, production delays and the Allied bombing combined to defer the operational dates for both types. Fourteen Type XXIs alone, some of which were almost ready for operations after long workup and crew training, were destroyed in Bremen, Hamburg and Kiel between mid-February and mid-April 1945. The first and only Type XXI to become operational was the *U 2511*

TYPES XXI and XXIII

Type	XXIA	XXIII
Numbers	*U 2501-2564, 3001-3060, 3501-3542*	*U 2321-2371, 4701-4712*
Displacement (tons) (surfaced/submerged)	1621/1819	232/256
Length (m/ft)	72.2/237	34.9/114.5
Beam (m/ft)	6.6/21.77	3/10
Draught (m/ft)	6.2/20.3	3.7/12
Speed (knots) (surfaced/submerged)	15.5/17	9.75/12.5
Fuel (tons)	250	18
Range (nautical miles)/ at speed (knots)	15 500/10	4300/6
Torpedo tubes/ no of torpedoes	6 bow/20	2 bow/2
Guns	2 30-mm (1.18-in) AA	none

which sailed from Hamburg on March 18, 1945. She was then delayed with defects, and it was not until April 30 that she left her Norwegian base to commence operations. She was ordered to return to her base on May 4 for the surrender without having made any attacks on shipping.

The first Type XXIII, *U2321*, was launched in Hamburg in April 1944, but it was January 31 and February 6, 1945, before the *U2324* and *U2322* respectively left their base at Kristiansand for the first operational patrols. In all five boats carried out eight patrols, and although they only had limited success it showed the great potential of these boats, and the commanding officers were most enthusiastic about their performance. There is no doubt that had they become operational earlier in the war they would have been able to cause enormous damage and provided enormous problems for Allied escort forces.

Two variants of the Type XXI were designed in 1944, both increasing the number of torpedo tubes fitted. The Type XXIB had a second torpedo compartment fitted forward in the boat with the tubes firing astern angled out at 10° from the centreline. The Type XXIC had even more tubes fitted. None were built, and other variants were still in the design stage when the war ended. The Type XXI *U2518*, survived the war and served as *Roland Morillot* in the French navy, whilst *U2540* became the *Wilhelm Bauer* in 1960 in a reformed West German navy.

A number of other types and variants had been considered since 1935, but for various reasons were not proceeded with. These ranged from the Type III, which would have carried two MTBs in a special hangar aft of the conning tower, to the large Type XX transports. A Walter turbine version of the Type XXI was to be the Type XVIII; the Type XXXVI was to be a large ocean-going boat with a closed-cycle diesel engine.

Ukuru

Japanese escort class. The steadily increasing losses of her merchant fleet to US submarines forced Japan into convoying what was left of the fleet. The prewar attitude of ignoring the possibility of Japan being on the defensive had left the navy without an adequate escort force. Consequently, under the 1941 War Programme, designs were prepared for a new class of escorts, the largest to be ordered at that time. Eight of them, known as the Modified Type B, were ordered under the 1942-43 Estimates, with another 34 under the 1942 Modified Programme (1943-44 Estimates). Of these 34, a total of 18 were cancelled in the autumn of 1944 before they had been laid down. Under the 1943-44 War Programme (1944-45 Estimates) another 21 were planned, but 12 of these were also cancelled in the autumn of 1944. Under the 1944-45 War Programme 79 units were planned, but none was laid down before 1945.

These escorts were very similar to the *Mikura* Class, displacement and dimensions remaining the same. The hull form, however, was much plainer with flare, curves and sheer almost completely eliminated; with a much more basic hull form it was hoped that production could be speeded up. The hulls were prefabricated and by eliminating all but essential items the average construction time for units was reduced to four-five months. The bridge was enlarged to accommodate extra personnel for manning the radar and sonar equipment. The radar consisted of a Type 22 surface-warning set on the foremast and a Type 13 air-warning set on the mainmast. Armament was the same as in *Mikura* except that the light AA was increased to 16 25-mm (1-in) mounted as two triple mounts abreast the bridge, one mount aft of the mainmast and two triple mounts abreast the hexagonal funnel. On a bandstand in front of the bridge was mounted a single 25-mm gun superimposed over the mortar. A number of units were given in addition four single 25-mm mounts on the quarterdeck. Some early units were equipped with a paravane, but this was subsequently removed as it impeded the operation of the depth-charge throwers. The stowage of depth charges varied between units but was generally about 120. An electric lift from the depth-charge magazine carried the charges to the deck where some units were fitted with up to 16 depth-charge throwers.

Aguni, Amami, Okinawa, Ukuru—built by Tsurumi
Chikubu, Hodaka, Ikara, Ikino, Kozu, Murotsu, Shinnan, Urumi, Yaku—built by Uraga
Daito, Habuto, Hiburi, Ikuma, Kume, Mokuto, Otsu, Sakito, Shiskaka, Shonan, Tomoshiri—built by Hitachi
Habushi, Inagi, Kanawa, Oga, Takane—built by Mitsui
Iwo, Kuga, Shiga, Uku—built by Sasebo

Four of these were still under construction at the end of the war. *Murotsu, Otsu* and *Urumi* were very nearly complete, but work had only just begun on *Tomoshiri.* The remainder were all completed between June 1944 and the end of the war.

The following survived the war: *Aguni, Amami, Chikubu* (recommissioned into the new Japanese Self-Defence Force in 1948, renamed *Atsumi* in 1955), *Habushi, Habuto, Hodaka, Ikino, Ikuna* (as *Chikubu*, renamed *Ojika* in 1955), *Iwo, Kanawa, Kogu* (to USSR), *Kuga, Sakito, Shiga* (as *Chikubu*, renamed *Tusgaru* 1955), *Shisaka* (to China 1947), *Takane, Uku* (as *Chikubu*, renamed *Satsuma* 1955). Five were sunk by submarines: *Hiburi* (by *Harder* 8/44), *Kume* (by *Spadefish* 1/45, *Oga* (by *Springer* 5/45), *Shonan* (by *Hoe* 2/45), *Yaku* (by *Hammerhead* 2/45). Three were mined: *Daito* (11/45), *Ikara* (8/45), *Mokuto* (4/45). Two were sunk by aircraft: *Inagi* (8/45), *Okinawa* (7/45)

Displacement: 940 tons (standard) *Length:* 78 m (256 ft) oa *Beam:* 9 m (29 ft 6 in) *Draught:* 3 m (10 ft) *Machinery:* 2-shaft diesels, 4200 bhp=19.5 knots *Armament:* 3 4.7-in (120-mm) (1×1, 1×2); 16 25-mm (1-in); 1 3-in (76-mm) A/S mortar; 120 depth charges *Crew:* 150

Ulster

British destroyer class. The *Ulster* or 'U' Class destroyers were ordered in June 1941 as the 7th Flotilla of the Emergency War Programme. They were laid down during 1941-42, launched during 1942-43 and completed during 1943-44. In design they were repeats of the *Savage* or 'S' Class from which they differed in minor detail only. All completed with their designed armament, except *Undine* and *Urchin* which carried two twin 20-mm (0.79-in) mountings in place of their twin 40-mm (1.57-in) mounts which were not available at the time; *Undine* later received her twin 40-mm but *Urchin* did not. *Ulster* and *Grenville* completed with tripod foremasts, as designed, but these were later replaced by lattice masts while the rest of the class were similarly modified before entering service. Late in 1944 the four twin 20-mm mountings and the 44-in searchlight amidships were replaced by single 40-mm guns except in *Ulster*, which remained unaltered, and *Urania*, which had her 20-mm guns replaced by the 40-mm weapons but retained the searchlight.

On completion *Grenville* and *Ulster* joined the Home Fleet but soon afterwards they were loaned to the Plymouth Command. In November both were damaged in action with German destroyers off the French coast. After repairs they transferred to the Mediterranean where they were joined by *Undine* and *Urchin*, the remainder of the class going to the Home Fleet. After covering the landings at Anzio, the Mediterranean vessels returned home and the entire class was brought together to cover the Normandy landings. In July 1944 *Urchin, Undaunted, Ulster* and *Undine* returned to the Mediterranean where they covered the landings in the south of France. At the end of 1944 all eight sailed for the Far East where they joined the British Pacific Fleet with which they operated until the end of the war. During the assault on Okinawa in April 1945 *Ulster* suffered a near miss by a kamikaze aircraft, and the explosion blew a hole 7.6 m (25 ft) long and 3.7 m (12 ft) deep in her side amidships causing extensive flooding. She was towed to Leyte, temporarily repaired by the US Navy and then taken home for full repairs between October 1945 and February 1946. In 1946 all except *Ulster*, which served as a training vessel until 1952, were placed in reserve. During the 1950s all eight were converted to Type 15 fast antisubmarine frigates and some survived into the early 1970s before being placed on the disposal list, the first to go being *Ulysses*, in 1962, and the last of the class, *Undaunted*, being sunk as a target in 1978.

See also *Rapid.*

Grenville, Ulster—built by Swan Hunter
Ulysses, Undaunted—built Cammell Laird
Undine, Ursa—built by Thornycroft
Urania, Urchin—built by Vickers-Armstrongs

Displacement: 1780 tons (standard), 2510 tons (full load) *Length:* 110.6 m (362 ft 9 in) oa *Beam:* 10.9 m (35 ft 8 in) *Draught:* 2.9 m (9 ft 6 in) *Machinery:* 2-shaft geared steam turbines, 40 000 shp=36 knots *Armament:* 4 4.7-in (120-mm) (4×1); 2 40-mm (1.57-in) (1×2); 8 20-mm (0.79-in) (4×2); 8 21-in (53-cm) torpedo tubes (2×4) *Crew:* 179

Undine

British submarine class. The 1937 Programme provided for the construction of three small submarines, *Undine, Unity* and

Ursula, which were intended to serve as training vessels for submarine crews and to provide targets for A/S training. In wartime they were expected to undertake short patrols, but this was very much a secondary consideration. The three boats carried six bow tubes (four internal and two external) but only *Ursula* was fitted with a gun—a single 12-pdr. They were driven exclusively by electric motors, current being supplied by the batteries when submerged or by diesel-driven generators when surfaced. After the outbreak of war it was realized that these small vessels could be useful in the shallow waters of the North Sea where endurance was not a major problem, and as they could be built quickly 12 were ordered under the 1939 Emergency War Programme followed by another 22 under the 1940 Programme. The entry of Italy into the War gave the class another ideal area of operations in the Mediterranean, and a further 20 were ordered under the 1941 Programme and 34 under the 1942 Programme. Up to 1941 these vessels were repeats of the original trio except that they carried a 3-in (76-mm) gun and omitted the external bow tubes *(Unique, Upholder, Upright* and *Utmost* were fitted with six tubes like the originals) but the 1942 Programme boats were modified to part-welded construction which enabled them to dive to 91 m (300 ft) compared with 61 m (200 ft) in the earlier vessels. These latter boats were designated the 'V' Class although both the 'U' and 'V' Groups employed names beginning with both letters.

Despite their limited range and armament the class gave sterling service during the war and accounted for many thousands of tons of enemy shipping. In many ways their small size was an advantage as they were more manoeuvrable than larger boats, and the fact that they were available in large numbers made up for their individual inferiority. Seventy-two of the class entered service at regular intervals between 1941 and 1945, but after the end of hostilities in the Mediterranean their value diminished considerably and 20 of the 'V' Class ships were cancelled in 1944. All but two of the class *(Umpire* and *Una* constructed by Chatham dockyard) were built by Vickers-Armstrongs, a remarkable achievement although hardly comparable to German U-Boat production. The war-construction vessels, except for the 1939 Programme boats, were originally given numbers but those surviving until 1943 were given full 'U' or 'V' names.

As might be expected, war losses were heavy, particularly among the early units of the class. Eight were sunk by depth charging; *Undine* in 1940 in the North Sea, and *Union, Upholder, Urge, Utmost, P.38, P.48* and *Usurper* during 1941-43 in the Mediterranean. Also lost in the Mediterranean during this period were *Usk, P.32* and *P.33* which were mined, *P.36* and *P.39* which were bombed, and *Uredd* and *Undaunted* due to unknown cause. Four were lost by accident in Home Waters: *Unity, Umpire, Vandal* and *P.58,* but the last named was salvaged and re-entered service as *Vitality* in 1943. In addition to these, *Unique* disappeared in the Atlantic west of Gibraltar in 1942, and *Unbeaten* was accidentally sunk by RAF bombers in the Bay of Biscay in the same year. Several of the class were transferred to foreign navies both during and after the war. Most of the remaining vessels had been sold for scrap by 1950.

'U' Class
Undine, Unity, Ursula—1937 Programme
Umpire, Una, Unbeaten, Undaunted, Union, Unique, Upholder, Upright, Urchin, Urge, Usk, Utmost—1939 Programme
Uproar, P.32, P.33, Ultimatum, Umbra, P.36, Unbending, P.38, P.39, Uredd, Unbroken, Unison, United, Unrivalled, Unruffled, P.47, P.48, Unruly, Unseen, P.52, Ultor, Unshaken—1940 Programme
Unsparing, Usurper, Universal, Untamed, Untiring, Varangian, Uther, Unswerving, Vandal, Upstart, Varne, Vox—1941 Programme

'V' Class
Venturer, Viking, Veldt, Vampire, Vox, Vigorous, Virtue, Visigoth, Vivid, Voracious, Vulpine, Varne, Upshot, Urtica, Vineyard, Variance, Vengeful, Vortex, Virulent, Volatile, Vagabond, Votary—1942 Programme

Ursula, Unbroken and *Unison* were transferred to the USSR in 1944 and renamed *B.4, B.2* and *B.3.* They were returned 1949. *Urchin* and *P.52* transferred to Poland in 1941 and 1942 respectively and renamed *Sokol* and *Dzik.* They were returned 1946. *Uredd* transferred to Norway in 1941 and was replaced by *Ula* when lost in 1943; *Variance* transferred 1944 and was renamed *Utsira.* Norway also received *Venturer, Viking* and *Votary* in 1946 (renamed *Utstein, Uttaer* and *Utsira*); all these vessels were retained by the Norwegian navy. *Untiring, Upstart, Veldt, Vengeful, Virulent* and *Volatile* transferred to Greece during 1944-46 and renamed *Xifias, Amfitriti, Pipinos, Delfin, Argonaftis* and *Trianian* respectively. The first pair were returned in 1952 and the remainder during 1957-58. *Vox, Vineyard, Vortex* transferred to France during 1943-44 and renamed *Curie, Doris* and *Morse*; they were returned 1946-47. The Netherlands received *P.47* in 1942, *Dzik* (ex-*P.52*) in 1943 and *Vulpine* and *Morse* (ex-*Vortex*) in 1947. *P.47* was renamed *Dolfyn* in 1953; the *Dzik* became *U 1* on transfer then *Springeren* in 1948, while the last pair were renamed *Storen* and *Saelen* respectively.

Displacement: 545/735 tons (surfaced/submerged) *Length:* 60 m (196 ft 9 in) oa, ('V' Class) 62.3 m (204 ft 6 in) *Beam:* 4.9 m (16 ft) *Draught:* 3.9 m (12 ft 9 in) *Machinery:* 2-shaft diesel-electric 618 bhp ('V' Class, 800 bhp)/ 825 shp=11.75 (12.75)/9 knots (surfaced/submerged) *Armament:* 1 3-in (76-mm); 4 21-in (53-cm) torpedo tubes *Crew:* 33

Unryu

Japanese fleet carrier class. In 1941, well before the outbreak of the Pacific War, the Imperial Japanese Navy decided to order six 17 000-ton fast carriers for the mobile fleet. The basic design chosen was that of the *Hiryu,* the principal differences being the positioning of the island on the conventional starboard side of the deck and the elimination of the third lift, amidships. The magazines were protected by 150-mm (5.9-in) belt armour but a deck only 55 mm (2.2 in) thick, so that the ships were no better protected against bombing attack than *Soryu.* The lower hangar was nearly 13 m (43 ft) shorter than *Hiryu*'s, so that aircraft complement was reduced from 64 to 57.

Three ships were laid down shortly after the outbreak of war; *Unryu* was built by Yokosuka navy yard, *Katsuraoi* and *Aso* by Kure navy yard, *Amagi* and *Kasagi* by Mitsubishi, Nagasaki, and *Ikoma* by Kawasaki, Kobe. *Unryu* and *Amagi* were built with the intended 152 000-shp cruiser-type machinery, but the Japanese turbine industry could not provide a third installation in the time scale and so *Katsuragi* had to be fitted with two sets of destroyer turbines, with an output of 104 000 shp. The maximum speed was not lowered appreciably, for on trials *Katsuragi* made 32.7 knots—only slightly less than the 34-knot more powerful units.

Lack of shipyard capacity delayed the start of construction of the second batch of three until 1943, by which time 'Supplementary Programmes' had added another 11 ships of the class to the list of orders which could never hope to be fulfilled within the likely time-scale of this war, given Japan's acute lack of steel. The three ships laid down in 1943, *Kasagi, Ikoma* and *Aso,* were launched in late 1944, the last named being powered like *Katsuragi,* but none was completed before the end of the war, fitting-out being suspended during the spring of 1945.

Unryu and *Amagi* were completed on August 6 and 11, 1944 respectively. Both were allocated to the Carrier Division 1 and began to work up a new air group to replace the losses sustained two months earlier in the 'Marianas Turkey Shoot'. It was anticipated that they, and possibly the nearly complete *Katsuragi,* would be ready for action by mid-November but this plan was shattered by the opening moves in the Leyte campaign, a full month before the Japanese had expected the next US assault. The aircraft Carrier Division 1 were flown ashore to Formosa on October 10, 1944, where they were virtually wiped out four days later. Ironically, *Katsuragi* commissioned on the latter date.

The three carriers were used to ferry aircraft between Japan, China and Luzon during the remainder of 1944. While engaged on this duty, *Unryu* was attacked by the submarine USS *Redfish* on the night of December 19; one hit was scored from the first salvo, setting the carrier on fire and stopping her. *Redfish* reloaded and hit *Unryu* again with a torpedo which caused a huge explosion, following which the ship sank rapidly, leaving few survivors.

Amagi and *Katsuragi* were restricted to home waters after the end of 1944: not only were there no aircrew available for training, but Japan was very short of oil fuel. After April 20, 1945, when Carrier Division 1 was disbanded, only *Katsuragi,* of all the Japanese carriers, remained in full commission, although still inactive. On July 24, both ships were hit by bombs in Kure harbour during a US Navy carrier strike: *Katsuragi*'s midship superstructure, including the flight deck, was wrecked by explosions in the hangars—*Amagi* sustained similar damage but was also holed below the waterline, causing her to flood and eventually capsize in shallow water.

The three incomplete ships, *Kasagi* (flight

deck complete, armament not installed), *Aso* and *Ikoma* (complete only as far as the lower hangar deck), were also attacked and damaged; *Aso* had previously been used as a trials platform for shaped-charge warhead development. All three, and *Amagi*, were scrapped in 1947, the only work on them subsequent to August 1945 being concerned with salvage. *Katsuragi* was patched up to make her hangars weatherproof, but was decommissioned on November 11, 1946, and broken up at Osaka.

Displacement: 17460 tons (standard), 22800 tons (full load), (*Katsuragi* and *Aso*) 17 260 tons (standard), 22535 tons (full load) *Length:* 227.4 m (746 ft) oa *Beam:* 21.9 m (72 ft) wl, 27 m (88 ft 6 in) flight deck *Draught:* 7.8 m (25 ft 9 in), (*Katsuragi* and *Aso*) 7.8 m (25 ft 6 in) *Machinery:* 4-shaft geared turbines, 152000 shp=34 knots, (*Katsuragi* and *Aso*) 104000 shp=32.7 knots *Aircraft:* 57 *Armament:* 12 127-mm (5-in) DP; 89 25-mm (1-in) AA; 168 12-cm (4.7-in) AA rocket launchers (6×28) *Crew:* 1595 (*Katsuragi* and *Aso*) 1500

Uzushio

Japanese submarine class. Eight of these double-hulled submarines have been completed since 1971 for the Japanese navy. The hull is of teardrop design and constructed of high-tensile steel to enable a greater diving depth to be achieved. They are being refitted with a new bow sonar.

The last two vessels are of an enlarged and improved design. Displacement has been increased to 2200 tons and overall length by some 4 m (13 ft) and beam 0.9 m (3 ft). These improved submarines are expected to have much greater diving depth capabilities than the earlier *Uzushio* boats.

Displacement: 1850 tons (standard) *Length:* 72 m (236 ft 3 in) *Beam:* 9 m (29 ft 6 in) *Draught:* 7.5 m (24 ft 7 in) *Machinery:* 1 shaft, 2 Kawasaki-MAN diesels/1 electric motor, 3400 bhp/7200 hp=12/20 knots (surfaced/submerged) *Armament:* 6 21-in (53-cm) torpedo tubes (bow) *Crew:* 80

No and name	laid down	launched	completed	builder
SS.566 *Uzushio*	9/68	3/70	1/71	Kawasaki
SS.567 *Makishio*	6/69	1/71	2/72	Mitsubishi
SS.568 *Isoshio*	7/70	3/72	11/72	Kawasaki
SS.569 *Narushio*	5/71	11/72	9/73	Mitsubishi
SS.570 *Kuroshio*	7/72	2/74	11/74	Kawasaki
SS.571 *Takashio*	7/73	6/75	1/76	Mitsubishi
SS.572 *Yaeshio*	4/75	5/77	3/78	Kawasaki
SS.573	12/76	3/78	1979	Mitsubishi

Valentine

British destroyer class. The *Valentine* or 'V' Class destroyers ordered in September 1941 were the 8th Flotilla of the Emergency War Programme. In design they were repeats of the *Savage* Class except in a few minor details. They were laid down in 1942, launched during 1942-43 and completed during 1943-44. All completed with lattice foremasts except *Venus*, which retained the original tripod mast, while *Volage* also differed from her sisters in having a quadruple pom-pom mounting amidships instead of the specified twin 40-mm (1.57-in). On completion *Valentine* and *Vixen* were transferred to the Royal Canadian Navy and renamed *Algonquin* and *Sioux* respectively.

The new ships were formed into the 25th Flotilla for service with the Home Fleet, the early units being employed mainly as escorts for Arctic convoys. *Virago* saw action very soon after completion when she took part in the sinking of the German battlecruiser *Scharnhorst* in December 1944. In the following month however the flotilla's leader, *Hardy*, had to be sunk by *Venus* after being seriously damaged by an acoustic torpedo, fired by the German submarine *U 278*. At the time *Hardy* was escorting the Arctic convoy JW56B.

In June 1944 all the remaining ships of the class, except *Volage*, formed part of the covering force for the Normandy landings. At the end of 1944 the class, with the exception of the two RCN ships, was refitted for service with the Eastern Fleet. The main alterations were the addition of four 40-mm AA guns and the removal of the twin 20-mm (0.79-in) mountings (two of these were retained in *Verulam*), improvements in the radar and other electronic equipment and modifications to make them more suitable for a tropical climate. They sailed for the Far East early in 1945 together with the 'S' Class leader *Saumarez* as a replacement for *Hardy*. On the night of May 16, 1945, they became involved in their most famous exploit when *Saumarez*, *Verulam*, *Vigilant*, *Venus* and *Virago* intercepted the Japanese cruiser *Haguro* in the Straits of Malacca. In a perfectly executed night torpedo attack they scored no less than eight hits on the enemy ship which later sank. The only loss to the British vessels was superficial damage and two casualties in *Saumarez* which had been little more than grazed by three 8-in (203-mm) shells.

At the end of the war the class served for a short period in the Mediterranean, where *Volage* had her bows blown off by a mine in October 1946, and was then placed in reserve. During the 1950s all, including the RCN vessels, were converted into *Rapid* Class fast anti-submarine frigates, which extended their lives into the late 1960s/early 1970s.

The attractive lines of HMS *Vanguard*, the Royal Navy's last battleship. She was known as the only British battleship that did not fire its guns in anger, for though she was launched in 1944 she did not complete until 1946. However, she was the most efficient and seaworthy vessel of her type to be produced

Hardy, Valentine—built by John Brown
Venus, Verulam—built by Fairfield
Vigilant, Virago—built by Swan Hunter
Vixen, Volage—built by White

Displacement: 1800 tons (standard), 2530 tons (full load) *Length:* 110.6 m (362 ft 9 in) oa *Beam:* 10.9 m (35 ft 9 in) *Draught:* 3 m (10 ft) *Machinery:* 2-shaft geared steam turbines, 40 000 shp=36 knots *Armament:* 4 4.7-in (120-mm) (4×1); 2 40-mm (1.57-in) (1×2); 8 20-mm (0.79-in) (4×2); 8 21-in (53-cm) torpedo tubes (2×4) *Crew:* 180

Valiant

British submarine class. The Royal Navy's first nuclear-powered submarine, HMS *Dreadnought*, was virtually the seventh submarine of the US *Skipjack* Class, and included a US reactor. When it was announced on August 31, 1960, that a second nuclear submarine was to be built by Vickers at Barrow it was also stated that this would be of all-British design and would include a British reactor built by Rolls-Royce. *Valiant* and her four sisters (*Warspite, Churchill, Conqueror*, and *Courageous*) are similar to *Dreadnought*, though they are slightly larger and much quieter in operation. With powerful sonar for detecting and tracking other submarines they are armed with six 21-in (53-cm) bow torpedo tubes.

Displacement: 4400/4900 tons (surface/submerged) *Length:* 86.7 m (285 ft) *Beam:* 10.1 m (33 ft 3 in) *Draught:* 8.2 m (27 ft) *Machinery:* 1 Rolls-Royce pressurized water-cooled reactor, 1-shaft geared steam turbine=28 knots *Armament:* 6 21-in (53-cm) torpedo tubes (bow) *Crew:* 103

Vanguard

British battleship. When naval rearmament began in 1937 one of the major problems encountered was that the ordnance manufacturing industry had become seriously run down. As warship guns, particularly those for battleships, took as long to produce as the ships themselves this seriously hampered the rate at which new ships could be built. Early in 1939 it was suggested that a new battleship might be built by utilizing four spare twin 15-in (381-mm) mountings originally manufactured for *Courageous* and *Glorious* during the First World War. From this suggestion a design for a 40 000-ton battleship was produced in which the weight saved by utilizing a comparatively light main armament was used to provide a speed of 30 knots. It was intended that the new ship should form the nucleus for a Far East Fleet, where her high speed and armament would be an ideal match for Japanese ships. Work on the design ceased on the outbreak of war but was resurrected soon after by the new First Lord of the Admiralty, Winston Churchill, and in February 1940 the design was continued. However, progress was slow owing to the heavy demands placed upon the available design facilities during 1940-41 and the ship was not ordered until March 1941. She was laid down at John Brown's yard, Clydebank, in October 1941. It was hoped she would complete in 1944, but with the shipbuilding industry already overloaded, mainly with escort vessels and merchant ships, this proved impossible. She was named *Vanguard* when launched in November 1944 and did not complete until April 1946. This long period of construction allowed for a continual revision of the details of the design in the light of war experience.

The main armament was both of the same design and the same layout as that of the *Queen Elizabeth* Class, designed in 1912, but prior to fitting in the ship the mountings were 'modernized', increasing the elevation of the guns to 30° and providing remote power control for training. Although the guns were of old pattern they were also one of the most efficient heavy ordnance types ever produced and this combined with new, modified ammunition, left them only marginally inferior in performance to more modern weapons. The rest of the ship was generally an enlarged and improved version of *King George V* with much the same secondary armament, armour arrangement and hull structure. The machinery was of higher power, to give 3 knots more speed, and as the *King George V* Class had proved very wet in heavy weather the sheer forward was substantially increased. The oil-fuel stowage was increased to improve endurance, which the war had demonstrated to be insufficient in existing British capital ships. The designed close-range AA armament was constantly changed while the ship was under construction, and she finally completed with a very modern uniform AA battery of 40-mm (1.57-in) Bofors, most of which were fitted in the new six-barrelled Mk VI mounting. She also carried a twin 40-mm on the roof of B turret and a few single 40-mm. The completed ship was very impressive with heavy well-balanced superstructure and capped funnels but she paid the price of having so many additions made during building by being overweight and overcrowded. Nevertheless she was easily the best of Britain's battleships and was one of the most efficient and seaworthy vessels of her type ever produced. On trials she achieved 31.57 knots with 136 000 shp on a displacement of 45 720 tons.

Vanguard arrived too late to be of any practical use. She became known as the only British battleship that had never fired its guns in anger, and was employed on various duties until 1949 when she became a seagoing training ship, with occasional spells of service as a flagship. She was placed in reserve in the mid-1950s and sold for scrap in 1960.

Displacement: 44 500 tons (standard), 51 420 tons (full load) *Length:* 243.8 m (799 ft 11 in) oa *Beam:* 32.9 m (108 ft) *Draught:* 9.2 m (30 ft 3 in) *Machinery:* 4-shaft geared steam turbines, 130 000 shp=30 knots *Protection:* 356-330 mm (14-13 in) sides, 305 mm (12 in) bulkheads, 330-279 mm (13-11 in) barbettes, 330-178 mm (13-7 in) turrets, 152-127 mm (6-5 in) decks *Armament:* 8 15-in (381-mm) (4×2); 16 5.25-in (133-mm) (8×2); 73 40-mm (1.57-in) AA (10×6, 1×2, 11×1) *Crew:* 1893 (2000 as flagship)

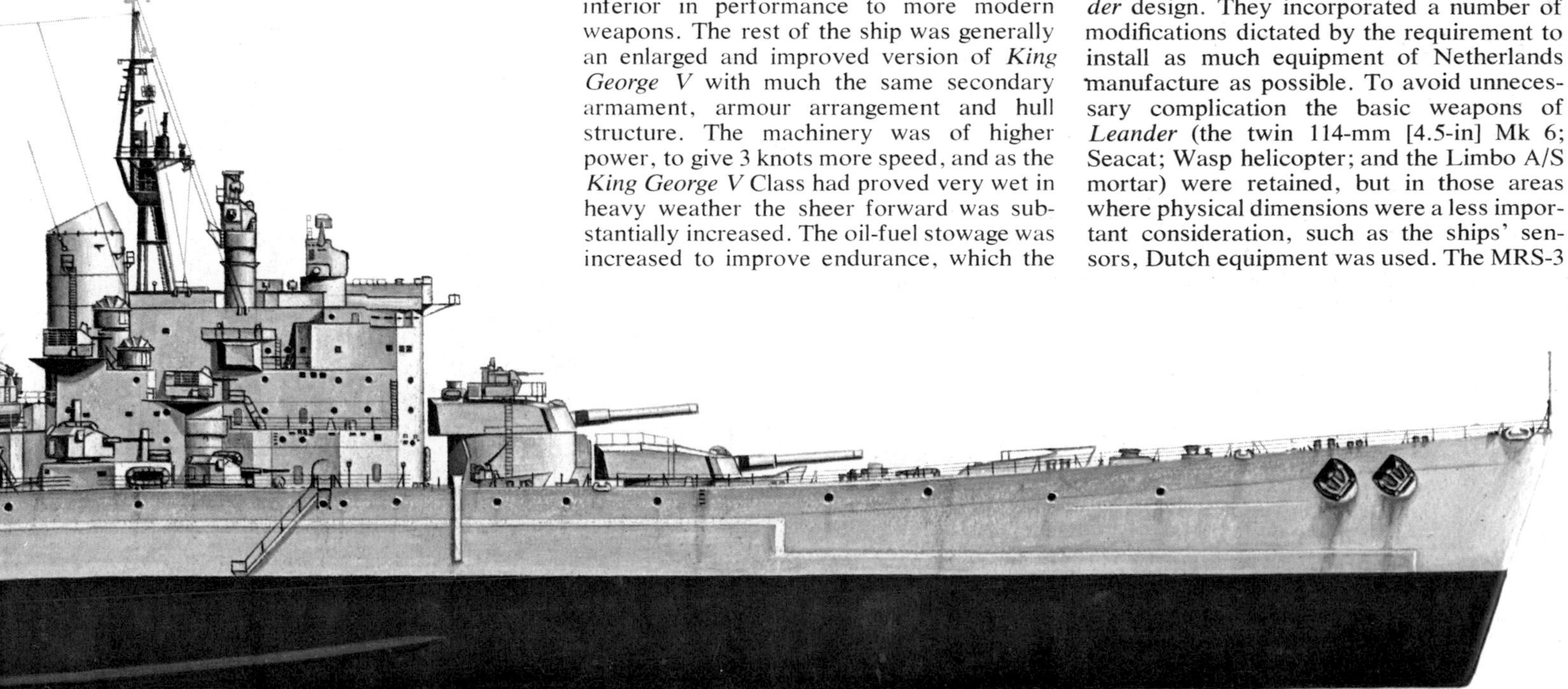

Van Speijk

Dutch frigate class. Four ships were ordered in 1962 (F.802-805) and two in 1964 (F.814-815).

Built to replace the six frigates of the *Van Amstel* Class (ex-US *Cannon* Class) the *Van Speijk* Class were based on the British *Leander* design. They incorporated a number of modifications dictated by the requirement to install as much equipment of Netherlands manufacture as possible. To avoid unnecessary complication the basic weapons of *Leander* (the twin 114-mm [4.5-in] Mk 6; Seacat; Wasp helicopter; and the Limbo A/S mortar) were retained, but in those areas where physical dimensions were a less important consideration, such as the ships' sensors, Dutch equipment was used. The MRS-3

No and name	laid down	launched	commissioned	builder
F.802 *Van Speijk*	10/63	3/65	2/67	Nederlandse DSM, Amsterdam
F.803 *Van Galen*	7/63	3/66	8/67	KM DeSchelde, Flushing
F.804 *Tjerk Hiddes*	6/64	12/65	8/67	Nederlandse DSM, Amsterdam
F.805 *Van Nes*	7/63	3/66	8/67	KM DeSchelde, Flushing
F.814 *Isaac Sweers*	5/65	3/67	5/68	Nederlandse DSM, Amsterdam
F.815 *Evertsen*	7/65	6/66	12/67	KM DeSchelde, Flushing

director of *Leander* was therefore replaced by an HSA M-45, while the Seacat director was the similar M-44. The small size and low weight of the latter enabled a second Seacat launcher and a second director to be worked in. Air search was provided by an LW-03 scanner, which replaced the Type 965 on the mainmast, and surface surveillance by a DA-02 antenna, mounted atop the foremast. The navigation radar platform which projects from the foremast is on the centreline, as in the earlier British *Leanders*. *Van Nes* and *Evertsen* are fitted with an HF/DF mast which is topped by a cone-shaped ECM jammer, similar to that on HMS *Apollo*. The other four units have a much taller version of the mast fitted to the middle *Leanders*. The sonars are a mixture of British and Dutch models.

In the mid-1970s it was decided that all six of the class should undergo 18-month refits; the first, that of *Van Speijk* herself, began in January 1977. It is intended to replace the 11-mm mounting by a single OTO-Melara 76-mm (3-in) gun and to install two quadruple launchers for Harpoon surface-to-surface missiles between the funnel and the mainmast. Two triple torpedo mountings will be fitted, and the Limbo A/S mortar will be removed, the well being plated over to provide an enlarged flight deck for a Lynx helicopter. In order to accommodate the latter a telescopic extension will be built into the hangar. New electronics and improved communications will be provided and the operations room updated. Increased automation is planned, and this will reduce the complement from 253 to 235.

Displacement: 2200 tons (standard), 2850 tons (full load) *Length:* 113.4 m (372 ft) oa *Beam:* 12.5 m (41 ft) *Draught:* 4.6 m (15 ft) *Machinery:* 2-shaft steam turbines, 30 000 shp=30 knots *Armament:* 2 114-mm (4.5-in) Mk 6 DP (1×2); 2 Seacat SAM quadruple launchers; 1 Limbo triple A/S mortar; 1 Wasp helicopter *Crew:* 253

'Victor'

Soviet nuclear-powered attack submarine class. The first boat was laid down in 1965 and was completed in 1968. By 1979 15 further boats had been completed to this design at the Admiralty yard, Leningrad, at a rate of about two per year. The only known name is *50 Letya SSSR*.

The first 'Victor' Class boat appeared at about the same time as the first of the 'Charlie' Class, to which they bear a close resemblance. They have the same teardrop hull form and streamlined conning tower, and dimensions (at first thought to be very different) have turned out to be identical. The only distinguishing features externally are the gently sloping bow, the angled front of the conning tower (compared with the vertical front in the 'Charlie' Class), and its proximity to the bow. Whereas the 'Charlie' Class carry antiship missiles, the *Victor* Class appear to have been designed as hunter-killer submarines, a role in which they succeed the 'November' Class. Improvements over the latter include a much quieter propulsion system, a more streamlined hull form, and more horsepower in a hull which is a full 15 m (50 ft) shorter, giving them five knots more speed surfaced or submerged. Unlike the 'November' Class, all eight 53-cm (21-in) torpedo tubes are in the bow; 64 mines can be carried in place of the torpedoes. The 'Victor' Class are thought to have acquired the SS-N-15 antisubmarine missile which, like the equivalent US Subroc missile, can be fired from torpedo tubes.

In 1973 a new submarine type was observed in the waters of the Northern Fleet. It was at first given the code name 'Uniform', but because of its resemblance to the 'Victor' Class was redesignated 'Victor II', the earlier boats being reclassified 'Victor I'. Two further boats of this type are known to have been completed. Apart from a slight increase in length, displacement and speed there is little to distinguish the two versions in shape or performance.

('Victor I') *Displacement:* 4300/5100 tons (surfaced/submerged) *Length:* 94 m (308 ft 6 in) oa *Beam:* 10 m (32 ft 9 in) *Draught:* 8 m (26 ft 3 in) *Machinery:* 1 pressurized water-cooled reactor, 2-shaft steam turbines, 24 000 shp=26/30 knots (surfaced/submerged) *Armament:* 8 53-cm (21-in) torpedo tubes; mines; SS-N-15 SSMs *Crew:* 100

('Victor II') *Displacement:* 4700/6000 tons (surfaced/submerged) *Length:* 88.5 m (290 ft 4 in) oa *Machinery:* 30 000 shp=33 knots (submerged) (Other specifications as for 'Victor I')

Vikrant

Indian navy light fleet carrier. Laid down as a *Majestic* Class light fleet carrier at the Tyneside yard of Vickers-Armstrongs, in October 1943, and launched on September 22, 1945 as HMS *Hercules*, the ship which was to become the Indian navy's first aircraft carrier was purchased on January 1, 1957. At this time she was structurally complete and fitted out, apart from armament, electronics and internal communications, having been laid up since May 1946, when construction

A Soviet 'Victor' Class nuclear-powered attack submarine photographed by the RN in 1975

MOD

had been suspended.

Renamed *Vikrant*, she was taken in hand in April 1957 at Belfast and completed by Harland & Wolff. The work involved the replacement of the original hydraulic catapult by a longer, more powerful steam catapult, more modern arrester gear, improved air conditioning in living spaces and extended aircraft-control facilities. An angled deck was, of course, featured, necessitating an extension of the flight deck on the port side, abreast the island. As completed, she closely resembled HMAS *Melbourne*.

Vikrant was accepted by the Indian navy on March 4, 1961, the conversion having taken an inordinately long time, for reasons which are not clear. She worked up in British waters with an air group which included ex-Royal Navy Hawker Sea Hawks and new-built Breguet Br.1050 Alizé antisubmarine aircraft; these continued to serve aboard her until 1979, with the number of types of potential fixed-wing aircraft available to replace them limited by the carrier's small size and relatively slow speed. The Indian navy was given a demonstration of VTOL operations and a Hawker-Siddeley Harrier flew to and from *Vikrant*'s deck in 1972.

Vikrant was based at Cochin, near the Indian navy's main air station. Her one combat operation was in 1973, during the second Indo-Pakistan war: she served in the Bay of Bengal, where her aircraft effectively blockaded the East Pakistan coast between Chittagong and Cox's Bazaar, the Sea Hawks undertaking successful strikes against naval and military targets.

Displacement: 16 000 tons (standard), 19 500 tons (full load) *Length:* 213.4 m (700 ft) oa *Beam:* 24.4 m (80 ft) wl, 39 m (128 ft) over sponsons *Draught:* 7.3 m (24 ft) *Machinery:* 2-shaft geared turbines, 40 000 shp=23 knots approx *Aircraft:* 23 *Armament:* 17 40-mm (1.57-in) Bofors *Crew:* 1400 approx

Virginia

US nuclear-powered guided-missile cruiser class. Early planning called for at least 11 of this class to provide, in conjunction with earlier classes of DLGN and CGN, four escorts for each of the four nuclear-powered carriers projected. But by 1978 only four ships had been authorized, a fifth having been rejected by Congress in 1976.

Developed from the *California* Class, to which they bear a close resemblance, the *Virginia* Class introduced a number of major improvements in capabilities. The most important of these was the substitution of the Mk 26 twin-arm launcher, capable of firing Harpoon SSMs and Asroc A/S missiles in addition to Standard MR (medium range) surface-to-air missiles, for the Mk 13 Tartar launchers of *California*. This eliminated the need for a separate Asroc launcher, enabling length to be reduced by 4 m (13 ft) compared with their predecessors. The other major difference is that they can operate two helicopters, for which a separate hangar with a telescoping cover is provided below the flight deck marked out on the fantail. The hangar is served by an electro-mechanical lift. Two lightweight 127-mm (5-in) Mk 45 mountings are fitted, as in the *California* Class, but unlike the latter they have their Mk 32 torpedo tubes in trainable triple banks abreast the after superstructure. As with their predecessors, the major above-water sensors are carried on two massive towers amidships. An SPS-48 three-dimensional planar radar and the SPS-55 surface-surveillance scanner are mounted on the forward tower, and an SPS-40 air-search scanner on the after one. The Mk 86 fire-control system for the 127-mm guns is fitted to the forward tower, but the *Virginias* have only two SPG-51 tracker/illuminators for the missiles (compared with four on the *California* Class) and these are mounted on the after superstructure. The SQS-53 sonar is linked to the Mk 116 underwater fire-control system and the Combat Information Center (CIC).

All four ships of the class were built by Newport News. *Virginia* and *Texas* have served in the Atlantic Fleet since completion.

Displacement: 11 000 tons (full load) *Length:* 178.3 m (585 ft) oa *Beam:* 19.2 m (63 ft) *Draught:* 9 m (29 ft 6 in) *Machinery:* 2 DG2 pressurized nuclear reactors, 2-shaft steam turbines=30 knots *Armament:* 2 twin Mk 26 launchers for Standard MR SAMs or Asroc A/S missiles; 2 127-mm (5-in)/54-cal Mk 45 DP (2×1); Mk 32 A/S torpedo tubes (2×3); 2 Seasprite helicopters *Crew:* 442

No and name	commissioned
CGN.38 *Virginia*	9/76
CGN.39 *Texas*	9/77
CGN.40 *Mississippi*	—
CGN.41 *Arkansas*	—

Vittorio Veneto

Italian helicopter cruiser. *Vittorio Veneto* was laid down at the yard of Navalmeccanica Castellamare di Stabia on June 10, 1965, launched February 5, 1967, and completed April 30, 1969. Developed from the *Andrea Doria* Class, the first Italian helicopter cruisers, *Vittorio Veneto* carried a similar gun and missile armament but more than twice the number of helicopters. This was achieved by an increase in size from 5000 tons (standard) to 7500 tons, combined with a completely different hangar arrangement. Whereas the *Doria* had a conventional cruiser/destroyer arrangement with the hangar forming the after superstructure and leading directly onto the flight deck, the after part of *Vittorio Veneto* was raised to enable a large hangar to be located beneath the flight deck, on the lines of the French *Jeanne d'Arc* and the Soviet *Moskva*, with a lift at the forward end to connect the two. Nine of the tiny Agusta 204B helicopters can be accommodated, with four Sea Kings as an alternative complement. The AB 204B helicopters operate in pairs for antisubmarine operations, one helicopter carrying ASW sensors while the other carries homing torpedoes.

A US Mk 10 twin-arm launcher for Terrier surface-to-surface missiles and Asroc A/S missiles is mounted on the forecastle, and two SPG-55 tracker/illuminators for the Terrier missiles are fitted above the bridge. Air-search and three-dimensional tracking is provided by two radars of US manufacture, the SPS-52 and the SPS-40. These are carried on two tall macks, which give *Vittorio Veneto* a much more 'American' look than her immediate predecessors. For close-range air defence there are eight single 76-mm (3-in) AA guns, two of which are mounted forward of the bridge, two on either side of the ship, and the remaining two aft. These are controlled by four Argo directors of Italian manufacture—one above the bridge with two in the wings, and a further installation aft below the second mack. The armament is completed by two triple Mk 32 torpedo mountings, fitted at forecastle-deck level on either side of the bridge. The sonar is an SQS-23 of US manufacture.

Displacement: 7500 tons (standard), 8850 tons (full load) *Length:* 170 m (557 ft 9 in) oa *Beam:* 19.4 m (63 ft 8 in) *Draught:* 5.2 m (17 ft) *Machinery:* 2-shaft steam turbines, 73 000 shp=32 knots *Armament:* 1 twin Mk 10 launcher for Terrier SAMs or Asroc A/S missiles; 8 76-mm (3-in)/62-cal AA (8×1); 6 Mk 32 homing-torpedo tubes (2×3); 9 AB 204B or 4 Sea King A/S helicopters *Crew:* 530

Wager

British destroyer class. The eight destroyers of the *Wager*, or 'W', Class formed the 9th Flotilla of the Emergency War Programme. They were ordered in December 1941, laid down in 1942, launched in 1943 and completed in 1944 except for the leader, *Kempenfelt*, which completed in 1943. They were the last of the emergency group to follow, strictly, the design of the *Savage* Class and the last British destroyers to be fitted with 4.7-in (120-mm) guns. They did, however, differ from the earlier ships in having a combined HA/LA director on the bridge. On completion the ships joined the Home Fleet and were eventually formed into the 27th Destroyer Flotilla.

At the end of 1944 all eight were refitted for service in the Far East. Modifications included the fitting of between one and five 40-mm AA guns, the ships with two or more losing part or all of their 20-mm (0.79-in) guns. In January 1945 the entire flotilla joined the British Pacific Fleet and during March to May *Whelp, Whirlwind, Wager* and *Kempenfelt* took part in the assault on Okinawa. They were placed in reserve in the late 1940s. Four of the class were subsequently sold to foreign navies, *Wessex* and *Whelp* to South Africa in 1950 and 1953 and *Kempenfelt* and *Wager* to Yugoslavia in 1958, and renamed *Jan van Riebeeck, Simon van der Stel, Kotar* and *Pula*. The remaining four were converted to fast A/S frigates during 1952-55. *Wrangler* was sold to South Africa as *Vrystaat* in 1957.

See also *Rapid*.

Kempenfelt, Wager—built by John Brown; *Wakeful, Wessex*—built by Fairfield; *Whelp, Whirlwind*—built by Hawthorn Leslie; *Wizard, Wrangler*—built by Vickers-Armstrongs

Displacement: 1870 tons (standard), 2510 tons (full load) *Length:* 110.6 m (362 ft 9 in) oa *Beam:* 10.9 m (35 ft 9 in) *Draught:* 3 m (10 ft) *Machinery:* 2-shaft geared steam turbines, 40 000 shp=

36 knots *Armament:* 4 4.7-in (120-mm) (4×1); 2 40-mm (1.57-in) AA (1×2); 8 20-mm (0.79-in) AA (4×2); 8 21-in (53-cm) torpedo tubes (2×4) *Crew:* 179

Wagner

US radar picket escort class. *Wagner* and *Valdivier*, two members of the *John C Butler* Class, were laid down on November 8, 1943, at the Boston navy yard; they were launched on December 27, 1943, but construction was suspended in August 1946. Work resumed in 1954 to a revised design, and they were completed as radar picket escort ships, *Wagner* (DER.539) commissioning on December 31, 1955, and *Valdivier* (DER.540) on December 1, 1955.

They retained the main armament of the *John C Butler* Class, but the 40-mm (1.57-in) AA was discarded and the centre part of the ships redesigned to incorporate the necessary radars. The hull was built up amidships to shelter-deck level and a large modern bridge fitted. The single pole mast of the DEs was replaced by a tripod, on which an SPS-29 air-search radar was mounted. Aft of the single funnel was a second tripod mast topped by a tactical air navigation (TACAN) radome. On a new deckhouse aft of this was an SPS-8 height-finding radar. An elaborate combat information centre was installed.

During the 1950s and 1960s these ships were employed as part of a seaward radar picket barrier. This concept was abandoned in 1965 and soon afterwards the *Wagner* Class were placed in reserve. They were scrapped in the early 1970s.

Displacement: 1745 tons (standard), 2100 tons (full load) *Length:* 93.3 m (306 ft) *Beam:* 11.2 m (36 ft 9 in) *Draught:* 3.4 m (11 ft 3 in) *Machinery:* 2-shaft steam turbines, 12 000 shp=24 knots *Armament:* 2 127-mm (5-in)/38-cal DP (2×1); 1 Hedgehog A/S mortar *Crew:* 187

Washington

US battleship class, built 1937-42. These were the first capital ships to be built for the US Navy since the Washington Treaty, and were limited to 35 000 tons. Design work had started as early as 1929, but after much discussion the characteristics of the 'Battleship 1937' design were settled as 12 14-in (356-mm)/50-cal guns in three quadruple turrets, protection against 14-in shells, a dual-purpose secondary armament, and a speed of 27 knots. The specification was thus very similar to that of the British *King George V* Class, for both navies were bound by the 1936 London Naval Treaty, which had reduced gun calibre to 14 in. But unlike Britain, the US delayed ordering the heavy gun mountings until it became clear that Japan would not ratify the treaty and that both the Italians and the French were building 15-in (380-mm) gunned ships. On June 21, 1937, permission was given to change the armament of the new battleships to three triple 16-in (406-mm)/45 cal mountings, after the first keel had been laid. Fortunately the weight of a triple 16-in was roughly the same as that of a quadruple 14-in, and so only minor alterations had to be made to the barbettes and turntables. The Mk 6 16-in/45-cal had a maximum elevation of 45° and fired a 1225-kg (2700-lb) shell with a muzzle velocity of 700 m/sec (2300 ft/sec), giving a maximum range of 33 740 m (36 900 yards).

North Carolina (BB.55) was laid down at New York navy yard in October 1937 and she commissioned on April 9, 1941. Her sister *Washington* (BB.56) was laid down at Philadelphia navy yard in June 1938 and she commissioned on May 15, 1941. They set a new standard for appearance in US capital ships, with a flush deck and two thin funnels set well back. The protection comprised a flat armoured deck across the top of the main belt, which was inclined behind a prominent antitorpedo bulge at an angle of 15°. As in the case of other US capital ships of the period the published figures of armour thicknesses were exaggerated, and it was reported that the *North Carolina* had 152-mm (6-in) decks and 406-mm (16-in) belts. In fact the maximum thickness of deck was 140 mm (5.5 in), including the supporting mild-steel deck, and the belt did not exceed 305 mm (12 in).

The most radical feature of the new design was the big increase in speed from 21 to 27 knots. In service both ships achieved their designed speed but suffered badly from vibration. They were, however, economical steamers, good for 13 500 nautical miles at 15 knots or 3400 nautical miles at 27 knots.

North Carolina was the only battleship involved in the invasion of Guadalcanal in August 1942 as she was escorting the fast carriers *Saratoga*, *Wasp* and *Enterprise.* She fought in the battle of the eastern Solomons and claimed seven Japanese aircraft. On September 15, she was torpedoed by the Japanese submarine *I 15* on the port side opposite the forward turrets. Despite the hit and a hole of 9.5×5.5 m (32×18 ft) she managed to control the flooding and even reached 25 knots for a while; she took three months to repair, and returned to the Solomons by the end of 1942.

After a refit in 1943 to replace her 1.1-in (28-mm) AA guns with 40-mm (1.57-in) Bofors she joined first Task Force 50 and later TF 58. She took part in most of the bombardments covering the landings across the Pacific, but was only damaged once more. On April 6, 1945, while fighting off an air attack off Okinawa, she was hit underneath a 5-in gun director by a shell from a nearby 'friendly' ship. In September 1945 she was present at Tokyo Bay for the surrender of Japan, and then returned to the US. After less than two years she was put into reserve and never recommissioned, but after being stricken in June 1960 she was bought by the state of North Carolina and towed to Wilmington, NC to serve as a war memorial.

Washington served for a while with the British Home Fleet in 1942, and covered several convoys to Murmansk. On May 1, 1942, she sustained some damage from exploding depth charges when HMS *King George V* cut the destroyer *Punjabi* in two, dead ahead of her. In September 1942 she joined Task Force 17 for the Solomons campaign, and two months later played a major role in the Battle of Guadalcanal. About an hour before midnight on November 13 *Washington* and *South Dakota* were stalking a Japanese force on radar, but as soon as the two battleships opened fire a short circuit in one of the *South Dakota*'s 5-in gun mountings caused a total loss of electrical power. She blundered towards the Japanese line and was illuminated by searchlights at 4600 m (5000 yards). The captain of *Washington* wisely kept his searchlights switched off, and while the Japanese concentrated on *South Dakota*, closed to within 1800 m (2000 yards) before opening fire. In a seven-minute engagement she fired 75 16-in and hundreds of 5-in shells, hitting the fast battleship *Kirishima* with nine 16-in and 40 5-in, without sustaining a single hit herself.

Like her sister, *Washington* served in most of the landings across the Pacific, but without doing more than bombard shore targets and defend the fast carriers against air attack. On February 1, 1944, she was seriously damaged in a collision with the battleship *Indiana* while operating off the Marshall Islands. Her bow was badly damaged, and repairs took three months, but she was back in time for the Marianas campaign in June. Her last operation was against Okinawa in March-April 1945 as she returned to the US for refit. After VJ-Day she repatriated troops from Europe, and was finally decommissioned in June 1947. She was never brought out of reserve, and was stricken in 1960 and scrapped.

Displacement: 36 900 tons (standard), 44 800 tons (full load) *Length:* (Washington) 222.1 m (728 ft 9 in); (North Carolina) 222.2 m (729 ft) oa *Beam:* 33 m (108 ft 3 in) *Draught:* 10.8 m (35 ft 6 in) *Machinery:* 4-shaft geared steam turbines, 121 000 shp=27 knots *Protection:* 305-165 mm (12-6.5 in) belt, 140-38 mm (5.5-1.5 in) decks, 406-178 mm (16-7 in) turrets *Armament:* 9 16-in (406-mm)/45-cal Mk 6 (3×3); 20 5-in (127-mm)/38-cal DP Mk 12 (10×2); 16 1.1-in (28-in) AA (4×4); 12 0.5-in (12.7-mm) machine-guns (12×1); 3 floatplanes, 2 catapults *Crew:* 1880

Wellington/Winchester

British hovercraft. These two major types of hovercraft were developed by the British Hovercraft Corporation at Cowes, Isle of Wight, to meet an anticipated military market. The first to be developed was the SR.N6 Winchester which was adapted to a military role from the civilian transport version. The first military Winchester was modified for radar duties, carrying radar and communications equipment. This craft was purchased by the Royal Navy for its Hovercraft Trials Unit formed in 1974. The craft has been extensively tested in the amphibious assault role carrying up to 30 fully equipped troops or 3 tons of cargo at speeds up to 70 knots up to a range of 200 nautical miles.

Since the initial converted SR.N6 a number of military versions have been developed around the basic SR.N6 design. The Mk 2/3 has a roof loading-hatch and strengthened side decks for carrying loads up to 0.5 tons and operates in a logistic-support role. The Mk 4 version has been supplied to the Iranian navy. The Mk 5 is a support and amphibious-assault version. There are various versions of the Mk 6; the 6A fast patrol craft, 6B logistic and 6C general-purpose and command vehicle. The Mk 6 has greatly increased manoeuvrability over the earlier Marks, which it derives from the twin propellers aft.

The *Wellington* BH.7 is a fast amphibious craft designed from the outset for a military role. Iran operates six BH.7s. The Royal

Navy also operates a BH.7 and this craft has carried out numerous trials in the MCM role. Various versions are available including a logistics (Mk 4) which has a bow loading door and can carry 170 fully equipped troops or two scout cars, a fast patrol craft armed with two single 20-mm (0.79-in) cannon (Mk 5A) and a projected strike craft version armed with surface-to-surface guided missiles and a 76-mm (3-in) gun.

Weight: 10-17 tons *Length:* 16.2-19.2 m (53-63 ft) *Beam:* 7-7.9 m (23-26 ft) *Height:* 4.6-6.6 m (15-21 ft 8 in) *Machinery:* 1 Rolls-Royce Marine Gnome gas turbine, 1000 hp (1400 hp in Mks 5A and 6)=50+ knots *Crew:* 3

(BH.7) *Weight:* 45-55 tons *Length:* 23.9 m (78 ft 4 in) *Beam:* 13.9 m (45 ft 6 in) *Height:* 10-10.4 m (33-34 ft) *Machinery:* 1 Rolls-Royce Marine Proteus gas turbine, 4250 hp=65 knots *Crew:* 3

C & S Taylor

HMS *Torquay*, a *Whitby* Class frigate built by Harland and Wolff and converted as a trainer

'Whiskey'

Soviet submarine class. The first 'Whiskey' Class boat is thought to have been laid down in 1950 and completed in 1951. Some 200 boats followed, out of a possible construction programme of nearly 350. The class was first designed in 1944 as a successor to the 'S' Class, but eventually incorporated a number of lessons learned from the German Type XXI. Surfaced and submerged speed was on a par with the slightly larger German boats, and they were fitted with four bow and two stern tubes, for 18 torpedoes or 24 mines. Early boats, like those of the contemporary 'Zulu' Class, carried twin 25-mm (1-in) AA guns in extensions forward of the conning tower, and some were fitted with a single 57-mm (2.24-in) or 76-mm (3-in) gun aft of the conning tower ('Whiskey I', 'II' and 'IV' and variations). Eventually, however, the 'Whiskey V' configuration, with a vertical face to the conning tower, became standard. In the 1950s two 'Whiskey' Class submarines were fitted out to carry out oceanographic research under the names *Severyanka* and *Slavyanka*. Of the others only 87 boats remained operational with the Soviet navy in 1979, and these were expected to decommission in the near future. Eight boats were transferred to Egypt in 1957-62, two to Bulgaria in 1958, 14 to Indonesia in 1959-62, four to North Korea and four to Poland in 1962-69; four were left to Albania in 1961 when the USSR evacuated its base at Saseno.

Beginning in 1960, five or six boats were converted as radar picket submarines. They were fitted with the specially designed Boat Sail air-search antenna, which can be folded and retracted into the large conning tower. Only four of this type, designated 'Whiskey Canvas Bag', remain in service.

In 1956 an experimental installation of a single SS-N-3 Shaddock cruise missile in a cylindrical launcher was made aft of the conning tower of a 'Whiskey' Class submarine. Beginning in 1959, a further five boats were fitted with two SS-N-3 launchers side by side. These two types were designated 'Whiskey Single Cylinder' and 'Whiskey Twin Cylinder'. The launchers can be elevated to about 20° and fire aft. Only the 'Whiskey Twin Cylinder' boats remain.

The third SS-N-3 conversion, begun in Leningrad in 1961, was undertaken to counteract the effects of bottlenecks in the production of raisable launchers which were causing delays in the construction of the 'Juliet' Class. The six boats converted were cut apart amidships and an extra 10-m (33-ft) section was inserted. The conning tower was completely rebuilt to incorporate four fixed launchers, elevated to about 15° and firing forward. The missile exhaust escapes through vents in the after end of the conning tower. The bow torpedo tubes are retained.

('Whiskey') *Displacement:* 1350/1600 tons (surfaced/submerged) *Length:* 73 m (239 ft 6 in) oa *Beam:* 6.5 m (21 ft 4 in) *Draught:* 4.2 m (13 ft 9 in) *Machinery:* 2-shaft diesels/2 electric motors, 4000 bhp/2700 hp=17/15 knots (surfaced/submerged) *Armament:* 6 53-cm (21-in) torpedo tubes (4 bow, 2 stern) *Crew:* 65

Whitby

British frigate class. The six ships of the *Whitby* Class, *Blackpool, Torquay, Eastbourne, Scarborough, Tenby* and *Whitby*, ordered in 1951 formed part of the Royal Navy's first postwar new construction programme. Designated Type 12, A/S frigates, these vessels were designed to meet the requirements of high speed, manoeuvrability and good seaworthiness which were necessary to counter the latest types of submarine which had very high submerged speeds. To obtain the first named feature, within a hull of reasonable size, a small high-power steam turbine plant was adopted which utilized double reduction gearing to obtain the maximum level of efficiency from both the turbines and propellers. Geared cruising turbines were also fitted for economy at low powers but these were disconnected when running at high speeds. The hull form was kept reasonably fine (to assist in obtaining the designed 30 knots) and given a high freeboard with raised forecastle which presented a unique profile. The result was, however, extremely satisfactory as the ships proved to be exceptionally fine seaboats which were steady, dry and comfortable in almost any weather and the general form provided a basic pattern for the subsequent British frigates of the *Rothesay* and *Leander* Classes.

Manoeuvrability was also very good, largely due to the adoption of twin rudders, and the Type 12 became extremely popular, not least because the standard of crew comfort and accommodation was high compared with earlier vessels (mostly war construction ships overcrowded by alterations and additions). The whole design exploited both the fund of knowledge gained during the war and the continued development of that knowledge in postwar equipment. The hull was of partly prefabricated all-welded construction and served to provide data for future use, particularly mass production in time of war. The armament consisted of a twin 4.5-in (114-mm) dual-purpose gun mounting fitted forward of the bridge remotely controlled by an HA/LA, radar-linked, director forward of the mainmast. Further aft a twin 40-mm (1.57-in) Mk V mounting, controlled by a small AA director on a raised structure just forward of it, provided a somewhat less sophisticated defence against aircraft over the after arcs. The main weapons of the ships were however two three-barrelled Limbo 10 A/S mortars mounted in a well aft and four single fixed, and one revolving twin, torpedo tube in each side for use with A/S homing torpedoes. However, the latter were subsequently removed possibly because they proved unsuccessful or perhaps to reduce topweight.

The six Royal Navy ships, which were constructed during 1952-58, were followed by two more constructed for the Indian navy. These vessels, *Trishul* and *Talwar*, were laid down in 1957 and completed during 1959-60. They differed from the RN vessels in mounting an additional single 40-mm AA gun on each side amidships and in omitting the torpedo tubes from completion. During the late 1960s the RN vessels had the twin 40-mm gun mounting, and its associate director, removed and a single 40-mm mounted in its place. In the early 1970s *Torquay* and *Eastbourne* were converted to training ships, the former vessels having a large deckhouse added aft and the 40-mm guns removed and the latter being disarmed completely. *Torquay* was also used for trials purposes and when converted became the first seagoing ship to be fitted with CAAIS (computer-assisted action information system). *Scarborough* and *Tenby* were sold to Pakistan in 1974 and the remaining Royal Navy ships were placed on the disposal list during 1975-78.

See also *Rothesay.*

Blackpool, Torquay, Trishul (RIN)—built by Harland and Wolff
Eastbourne, Scarborough—built by Vickers-Armstrongs,
Tenby, Whitby, Talwar(RIN)—built by Cammell Laird

Displacement: 2150 tons (standard), 2560 tons (full load) *Length:* 112.8 m (370 ft) oa *Beam:* 12.5 m (41 ft) *Draught:* 3.4 m (11 ft 3 in) *Machinery:* 2-shaft geared steam turbines, 30000 shp=31 knots *Armament:* 2 4.5-in (114-mm) DP (1×2); 2 40-mm (1.57-in) (1×2); 2 Limbo A/S mortars *Crew:* 220

Worcester

US light cruiser class. *Worcester* (CL. 144) was laid down on January 25, 1945, launched on February 4, 1947, and completed June 25, 1948; *Roanoke* (CL.145) was laid down on May 15, 1945, launched on June 16, 1947, and completed on April 4, 1948. Both were built by New York shipbuilding .Two further vessels, *Vallejo* (CL.146) and *Gary* (CL.147), were cancelled in August 1945, while six other units (CL.154-159) were cancelled in March of the same year.

The *Worcester* Class departed from the *Cleveland* line of light cruiser development, and were rather an expansion of the *Oakland* Class of antiaircraft cruisers, incorporating the lessons of wartime experience. In place of the 5-in (127-mm) guns of the latter they were equipped with a new twin 6-in (152-mm) semiautomatic dual-purpose mounting, of which three were carried fore and aft. This gave them a formidable antiship capability that their predecessors lacked. Another major improvement over the *Oakland* Class lay in the provision of four HA/LA directors for the main armament in addition to two LA DCTs. In place of the standard wartime 40-mm (1.57-in) AA they were fitted with the new rapid-fire 3-in (76-mm) gun in five twin mountings on either side amidships, a further twin mounting above the bow and two single mountings on the stern, controlled by local RDF-fitted directors.

Protection was generally more thorough, with a deeper, thicker belt extended to enclose the bases of the end turrets. The aircraft and catapult were never shipped.

The penalties paid for these improvements in terms of size—they were more than twice the displacement of the *Oakland* Class—cost and manpower were, however, too high for the continuation of this line of development. After a minor updating of sensors in the mid-1950s both ships were placed in reserve in 1958-59.

Displacement: 14700 tons (standard), 18000 tons (full load) *Length:* 207.3 m (680 ft) oa *Beam:* 21.6 m (70 ft 9 in) *Draught:* 7.6 m (25 ft) *Machinery:* 4-shaft steam turbines, 120000 shp=33 knots *Protection:* 152-76 mm (6-3 in) belt, 76-51 mm (3-2 in) deck, 102 mm (4 in) turrets, 165 mm (6.5 in) conning tower *Armament:* 12 6-in (152-mm)/47-cal DP (6×2); 24 3-in (76-mm)/50-cal AA (11×2, 2×1); 1 helicopter *Crew:* 1401

X.3

British midget submarine class. The staff requirement for a British midget submarine was conceived from a need to find some means of attacking enemy warships in heavily protected ports and anchorages beyond the range of land-based aircraft. When the requirement was first discussed in 1940, carrier aircraft could not carry bombs large enough to damage well-armoured warships seriously.

The design requirement was for a small submersible of limited radius which could be towed to its area of operations where it would slip the tow and proceed under its own power to the target. Once under the target the small submarine would release high-explosive charges which would detonate by a time mechanism.

By the time the Admiralty were ready to proceed, a private-venture midget submarine was already under construction. This was taken over by the Admiralty and a second craft to an identical design was ordered. Known as *X.3* and *X.4,* these two prototype midget submarines carried out numerous tests and trials to test the feasibility of the project. The design was basically a miniature version of one of the large submarines with a central control room, a wet and dry compartment fitted with pumping facilities to enable a diver to enter and leave the submarine while submerged, a battery compartment and the engine room. Only one set of hydroplanes, mounted aft, was fitted, and the craft carried two large explosive charges clamped to their sides.

Trials with *X.3* and *X.4* showed that the best means of getting the midget to its target area was to tow it behind another submarine (usually one of the 'S' or 'T' Classes). The 'X' craft negotiated the passage to its operational area submerged.

The midgets suffered from a serious operational hazard resulting from the very low freeboard. This meant that the hatch could not be left open when the boat was surfaced and so a long air mast had to be fitted to ventilate the boat, the hatches remaining closed. The air mast was also used for safety for the officer conning the boat when it was surfaced. To prevent him being washed overboard, a fate that befell *X.4* during the early days of trials, the conning officer was strapped to the air mast.

With trials completed, series production began and between December 1942 and April 1944 12 craft numbered *X.5-10* and *X.20-25* were built. These production craft differed from *X.3* and *X.4* in that both the battery and wet and dry compartments were forward, the control room remained amidships and the engine room aft.

The 'X' craft carried out a number of operations in European waters and achieved a large measure of success. The most notable operation was that carried out by *X.5-10* against the German battleship *Tirpitz* in September 1943. The force of six midgets suffered a staggering 100% loss but managed to damage the hull of the *Tirpitz* seriously, her machinery being thrown completely out of alignment by the explosion. The surviving 'X' craft were all scrapped in 1945.

Displacement: 27/30 tons (surfaced/submerged) *Length:* 15.6 m (51 ft 3 in) *Beam:* 1.75 m (5 ft 9 in) *Draught:* 1.75 m (5 ft 9 in) *Machinery:* 1-shaft diesel/1 electric motor, 42 bhp/30 hp=6.5/5.5 knots (surfaced/submerged) *Armament:* 2 2-ton Amatol explosive charges *Crew:* 4

XE.1-12

British midget submarine class. The success of the midgets in northern waters prompted the Admiralty to consider the possibility of using midgets in the Far East theatre of operations. Climatic conditions in the Far East were vastly different to those in northern Europe, and the distances to be covered much greater. It was therefore decided to retain the basic internal layout of the 'X' craft, but make them slightly larger and provide them with some refinements. The most important of these new features was the provision of air-conditioning, a necessity for operations in the Far East. Externally the two classes differed slightly. In the 'XE' craft the casing was extended flush right up to the bows which provided extra stowage space which had also been found to be necessary. They were also fitted with two spring-loaded legs forward and one aft. These, together with a slightly positive buoyancy, enabled the midget to come to rest directly under the target which thus meant that the explosive charges could be much more accurately placed under the target.

The midget *XE.3* carried out a successful operation on July 31, 1945 when she laid charges under the Japanese cruiser *Takao* which sank at her moorings in the Jahore Straits off Singapore.

Of a total of 12 craft ordered only five were completed (*XE.7-9, XE.11-12*), the others being cancelled. Of those completed *XE.11* was lost in a collision in March 1945 and the wreck scrapped. The remaining craft were all scrapped in 1952.

Displacement: 30.25/33.5 tons (surfaced/submerged) *Length:* 16.2 m (53 ft 3 in) oa *Beam:* 1.75 m (5 ft 9 in) *Draught:* 1.75 m (5 ft 9 in) *Machinery:* 1-shaft diesel/1 electric motor, 42 bhp/30 hp=6.5/5.5 knots (surfaced/submerged) *Armament:* 2 2-ton Amatol explosive charges *Crew:* 5

Yamagumo

Japanese destroyer class. The six destroyers of this class are characterized by their high freeboard, which is much greater than other destroyers. Like other Japanese destroyers built since the mid-1960s they have a pronounced sheer forward with knuckle at the bow. This design feature does much to cut down the amount of water shipped over the forecastle area in the rough seas of the Pacific.

The staff requirement for these vessels stipulated that they should concentrate on the A/S role and only minimal gun armament of two twin 3-in (76-mm) mounts is carried for self-defence. Antisubmarine armament consists of an eight-barrelled Asroc launcher sited amidships between the two funnels, a four-barrelled A/S rocket launcher in B position in front of the bridge and two triple A/S torpedo tubes sited high up abreast the after funnel. A variety of sonars are carried: DD113-115 carrying an SQS-23 set, DD119-

121 an OQS-3 VDS set. In addition DD113, 114, 120 and 121 are equipped with an SQS-35(J) set.

The 3-in guns are due to be replaced by OTO-Melara 76-mm (3-in) weapons as the vessels enter dockyards for refit. Gunnery control is exercised by US Mk 56 and Mk 63 systems. The radar outfit comprises an OPS-11 air-warning set, an OPS-17 surface-warning set and a US Mk 35 set for gunnery control.

The last unit, *Yuugumo*, was to have been the leadship of an improved *Yamagumo* design being slightly larger and fitted with a CODOG propulsion system, which would have given an increased speed up to 32 knots. However, the staff requirement was altered and the ship completed to a standard *Yamagumo* design.

No and name	completed	builder
DD113 *Yamagumo*	1/66	Mitsui
DD114 *Makigumo*	3/66	Uraga
DD115 *Asagumo*	8/67	Maizuru
DD119 *Aokumo*	11/72	Sumitomo
DD120 *Akigumo*	7/74	Sumitomo
DD121 *Yuugumo*	3/78	Sumitomo

Displacement: 2100 tons *Length:* 114.9 m (377 ft) *Beam:* 11.8 m (38 ft 8 in) *Draught:* 4 m (13 ft 1 in) *Machinery:* 2-shaft diesels (a total of 6 are mounted), 26 500 hp=27 knots *Armament:* 4 3-in (76-mm) (2×2); 1 8-barrel Asroc; 1 4-barrel A/S launcher; 6 Mk 32 A/S tubes (2×3) *Crew:* 210

Yamato

Japanese battleship class. Work on the super-battleships of the *Yamato* Class began in 1934, in direct contravention of the Washington Treaty limits. The Japanese realized they had not the industrial capacity to match the United States should war break out between the two countries. The design requirement therefore was to provide a class of ships which would outclass any other battleship then known to be under construction, and to maintain their superiority for a number of years. These ships were to outclass in speed, range, armament, and protection any ship that might be built in the near future and to be capable of engaging on equal terms other groups of warships. Experiments carried out on the hull of the incomplete *Tosa* provided much valuable information on which to base the design. A new bridge layout and fire-control direction was tested in *Hiei*.

The design excelled in all that the Japanese set out to achieve. The main armament was unmatched, the 18-in (457-mm) guns mounted having been originally designed for a class previously cancelled under the terms of the Washington Treaty. The increasing growth of carrier air forces, not the least the experiments and trials being conducted in Japan, led the designers to specify what was at the time an exceptionally heavy AA armament.

The initial plan drawn up in 1935 provided for a ship of 69 500 tons displacement, a length of 294.1 m (965 ft) and beam of 41.1 m (135 ft) with nine 18-in guns in triple turrets all mounted forward of the bridge as in the British *Nelson* Class. Secondary armament consisted of 12 6-in (152-mm) (guns which had originally been mounted on the *Mogami* Class cruisers), 12 5-in (127-mm) AA and 24 25-mm (1-in) AA. Turbines producing 200 000 shaft horsepower were specified to develop a speed of 31 knots and a radius of 8000 nautical miles at 18 knots. To mislead foreign intelligence the ships were stated to carry 16-in (406-mm) guns.

The design, however, proved to be beyond the engineering capabilities of the Japanese, turbines of such power not being available, and in the time specified for construction it was unlikely that such powerful turbines could be developed. The requirements were therefore modified and a maximum speed of 27 knots was then specified.

Following the redefined staff requirement a further 21 plans incorporating various modifications on the original plan were drawn up. The final plan as accepted provided for a smaller ship of 62 000 tons with a mixed propulsion plant of two turbine-driven shafts developing a total of 75 000 shp and two diesel-driven shafts developing a total of 60 000 bhp. Armament remained the same as in the original design but was sited on a conventional layout of A, B and Y turrets for the main armament with the secondary and light AA centred amidships.

The diesels chosen were of the two-cycle double-acting type, but similar diesels mounted in other vessels had given problems and as protection around the engine room was to be of 203-mm (8-in) armour plate it would be impossible to remove defective engines. It was therefore decided to replace the two diesels with two turbines identical to those already planned. This would then theoretically give the ships a total of 150 000 shaft horsepower.

This design was finally passed in March 1939, just two years and five months after the initial request for the design had been placed.

As soon as the design was passed an order for two ships (*Yamato* and *Musashi*) was placed with the Kure navy yard and Mitsubishi of Nagasaki, respectively, under the 3rd Reinforcement Programme of 1937. Under the 4th Reinforcement Programme of 1939 two more battleships were ordered, the *Shinano* from the Yokosuka navy yard and hull No 111 from the Kure navy yard. Work on the first two battleships proceeded quickly, *Yamato* being laid down on November 4, 1937, launched August 8, 1940 and completed on December 16, 1941. *Musashi* was laid down on March 29, 1938, launched on November 1, 1940 and completed on August 5, 1942.

To improve seakeeping qualities and assist in maintaining high speeds great use was made of streamlining. The ships were given a very graceful sheer line as one turret was well depressed into the hull. The sinking of A gun very low down together with the sheer caused a pronounced rise in the hull of almost one deck level just under the bridge. The ships were completed with a large bulbous bow while, to aid steering, an auxiliary rudder was mounted just forward of the main rudder.

To aid damage control, the maintenance of watertight integrity in the event of the armour belt being breached and to localize damage to machinery, all boilers, turbines, generators and ancillary machinery were placed in separate compartments. A total of 1147 watertight compartments were provided of which 1065 were below the armour deck. The deck armour was designed to withstand hits from 500-kg (1100-lb) bombs and 18-in (457-mm) shells. Abreast the main magazines an additional lower belt was fitted which joined with a lower armour deck extending the full beam of the ships below the magazines to give added protection against torpedo damage. New types of armour plate were developed for the ships of a very high quality.

On the outbreak of war work on the *Shinano* and hull No 111 ceased. Following the heavy carrier losses at the Battle of Midway in June 1942 *Shinano* was redesigned as a carrier while No 111 was cancelled and the assembled material dismantled.

Shinano was to have been completed to a modified design as a battleship with 3.9-in (100-mm) guns replacing the 5-in. Under the 1942 Programme an improved *Shinano*, No 787 was planned with extra 3.9-in guns replacing the 6.1-in (155-mm). Under the same programme two other battleships, *798* and 799, were projected to a similar design. These ships were to have mounted six 19.7-in (500-mm) guns in twin turrets. The 1942 Programme was cancelled with no further mention of 787, 798 and 799.

Yamato and *Musashi* received continuous alterations to their armament during the war. In the autumn of 1943 the beam 6.1-in turrets were removed. They were replaced in what was hoped to be a temporary measure by 12 25-mm, the intention being to replace these by six twin 5-in turrets. *Yamato* received these in February 1944 when undergoing repair after being torpedoed by the US submarine *Skate* in December 1943. Both vessels carried varying outfits of light AA, at the Battle of Leyte Gulf in October 1944 *Musashi* having 12 5-in and 115 25-mm.

Musashi was finally sunk at the Battle of Leyte Gulf after being hit by a total of 20 torpedoes and 17 bombs. *Yamato* also received a number of hits during the battle and suffered some flooding. She returned home for repairs when she was given more 25-mm guns to give her a total of 146 25-mm. *Yamato* was sailed on a final suicide mission in April 1945, the plan being for her to run herself aground on the island of Okinawa to bombard US positions. Before she reached Okinawa, *Yamato* was sunk on April 7 by US naval aircraft after being hit by 11 torpedoes and seven bombs.

Displacement: 64 000 tons (standard) *Length:* 263 m (863 ft) oa *Beam:* 38.9 m (127 ft 9 in) *Draught:* 10.4 m (34 ft 3 in) *Machinery:* 4-shaft geared turbines, 147 948 shp=27 knots *Protection:* 406-102 mm (16-4 in) main belt, 229-197 mm (9-7.75 in) deck, 648-191 mm (25.5-7.5 in) turrets, 502-76 mm (19.75-3 in) conning tower *Armament:* 9 18.1-in (460-mm) (3×3); 12 6.1-in (155-mm) (4×3); 12 5-in (127-mm) (6×2); 24 25-mm (1-in) (8×3); 4 13-mm (0.512-in) (2×2); 6 aircraft *Crew:* 2500

Yankee

Soviet nuclear-powered ballistic-missile sub-

The Soviet *Yankee* Class nuclear-powered ballistic missile submarines are similar in design to the US Polaris SSBNs and carry 16 missiles

marine class. The first *Yankee* is thought to have been completed in late 1967, and by 1975 34 of the class were completed at Severodvinsk at a rate of about five per year—an indication of the high priority given to the programme. The *Yankee* Class were the first Soviet SSBNs built to the same design as the US Polaris boats, the earliest of which preceded them by seven years. Previously Soviet ballistic missile submarines had carried only two or three missiles, and the tubes for these had been built into the conning tower. The *Yankee* Class, however, had eight pairs of missile tubes aft of the conning tower. These contained the new SS-N-6 missile which had twice the range of its immediate predecessor, the SS-N-5, but still little more than half that of the contemporary Polaris A-3. Six bow torpedo tubes were fitted, with a reload capacity of 18 torpedoes or 36 mines.

The high installed horsepower, reckoned by some to be as much as 40 000 hp, provides an interesting comparison with comparable US boats. The *Yankee* Class have two shafts compared with one for their US counterparts, indicating that the USSR places a high premium on speed and manoeuvrability in these boats, since the relatively short range of the SS-N-6 missile would compel them to operate close to a hostile shore line. A further difference from US practice is that the *Yankees* do not operate on a two-crew basis. This places severe restrictions on the number of boats on patrol at any one time. Most units of the *Yankee* Class are in the Northern Fleet, with about eight boats in the Pacific.

Displacement: 8300/9000 tons (surfaced/submerged) *Length:* 129.5 m (424 ft 9 in) oa *Beam:* 8.5 m (28 ft) *Draught:* 9 m (29 ft 6 in) *Machinery:* 1 pressurized-water reactor, 2-shaft steam turbines, 40 000+ shp=25/30 knots (surfaced/submerged) *Armament:* 16 SS-N-6 ballistic missiles; 6 53-cm torpedo tubes (bow) *Crew:* 120

Yastreb

Soviet torpedo boat or light destroyer class, built 1939-44. A class intended to remedy the deficiencies of the *Shtorm* Class was started four years after the completion of that class. Known as the *Ptitsi* (birds) Class, they were diminutives of the contemporary *Silny* Class destroyers, but the first or *Yastreb* Group had to sacrifice the torpedo tubes and one gun to reduce topweight. *Yastreb, Oryol, Berkut, Gryf, Sokol* and *Voron* were built by Zhdanov yard, Leningrad (the builder of *Kondor* is not known, and one other was built at Zhdanov). It is not known how many of these were completed, but German sources claim that three were completed by 1944. A further eight were ordered for the Far East and Black Sea. *Albatross, Krechet, Chaika, Fregat* and *Ortolan* were built at Nikolaiev and then shipped to the Far East. Six unnamed vessels were laid down at the 61 Kommunar Yard, Nikolaiev (reported to be *Tigr, Leopard, Yaguar, Rys, Kuguar* and *Pantera*).

Albatross is known to have commissioned in 1944, but the dates of the *Chaika* and *Krechet* are not certain, and their hulls were captured by the Germans at Nikolaiev in 1941. In *Albatross* the torpedo armament was retained but she was completed with only two boilers, and so could make only 25 knots. As no 100-mm (3.9-in) guns were available she was armed with three 85-mm (3.35-in) guns, and had only four machine-guns as AA armament. However, it is believed that she received her full armament after the war. *Yastreb* was scrapped at Libau (now Liepaja) in about 1959.

Displacement: 840-920 tons (normal), 1250-1330 tons (full load) *Length:* 85-87 m (279 ft-285 ft 6 in) oa *Beam:* 8.3-8.4 m (27 ft 3 in-27 ft 6 in) *Draught:* 3 m (9 ft 9 in) *Machinery:* 2-shaft geared steam turbines, 23 000 shp=30 knots *Armament:* 3 100-mm (3.9-in)/51-cal (3×1); 4 37-mm (1.46-in) AA (4×1); 8 machine-guns; 3 53-cm (21-in) torpedo tubes (1×3) (removed from *Yastreb* Group); 20 mines *Crew:* 84-92

YU 1

Japanese submarine class. Finding it was unable to rely on the navy ships to keep its island garrisons supplied the Japanese army decided to build its own transport submarines for running supplies. The extremely simple design was based to some extent on *Ha 101* and production began in 1943 at the Kasado Iron Works, Hitachi shipbuilding company and Kudamatsu.

They had no offensive capability and only a minimal gun armament for self-defence. They had a cargo capacity of 40 tons. Radius of action was 1500 nautical miles at 8 knots surfaced, and 32 nautical miles at 4 knots submerged. They were manned entirely by army personnel and only *YU 10* and *YU 12* survived the war to be subsequently scrapped after sinking in a storm.

Displacement: 273/370 tons (surfaced/submerged) *Length:* 40.8 m (134 ft) oa *Beam:* 4.1 m (13 ft 6 in) *Draught:* 2.7 m (9 ft) *Machinery:* 1 shaft, 2 diesels/1 electric motor, 400 bhp/75 hp=10/5 knots (surfaced/submerged) *Armament:* 1 37-mm (1.46-in) *Crew:* 13

YU 1001

Japanese submarine class. With the completion of the *YU 1* Class the Japanese army embarked on the design of a rather larger transport submarine to be used to transport supplies along the coast in Korea. Displacement was increased by some 20 tons and length by about 7.9 m (26 ft). The same basic design was retained but more powerful diesels were fitted to give 700 hp and a slightly higher surfaced speed. Cargo capacity and radius of action were the same as the *YU 1* Class.

Construction of the 14 boats in this class began in November 1944 at Jinsen in Korea, well away, it was hoped, from the attention of US strategic bombers. Most of the class were sunk during the war, only *YU 1007, 1011, 1013* and *1017* surrendering to be scrapped after the war.

Displacement: 392 tons (surfaced) *Length:* 49 m (160 ft 9 in) oa *Beam:* 5 m (16 ft 6 in) *Draught:* 2.6 m (8 ft 6 in) *Machinery:* 1-shaft, 2 diesels/1 electric motor, 700 bhp/75 hp=12/5 knots (surfaced/submerged) *Crew:* not known

Yugumo

Japanese destroyer class. This class of destroyers was basically an extension of the *Kagero* Class with only minor modifications. The length was increased by about 0.6 m (2 ft) while displacement rose by some 44 tons. There were slight differences in the armament resulting from a requirement to increase the AA capability of fleet destroyers. A new model 5-in (127-mm) gun with a maximum elevation of 75° was fitted. Many units in the class were completed with radar, which necessitated a new-style foremast to support the weight of the aerial. Early units were later refitted with radar during the war. The bridge differed slightly from that in the *Kagero*'s, being more streamlined to lessen wind resistance.

During 1943-44 many units had X turret replaced by two triple 25-mm (1-in) and one set of reload torpedoes removed. Light AA at this stage in the war averaged 15 25-mm and after June 1944 surviving vessels carried up to 28 25-mm.

The destroyers were ordered under the 1939 (12 units), 1941 (16 units, eight of which were cancelled) and Modified 1942 Programme (eight units all cancelled). Cancelled vessels of the 1941 Programme were *Kawagiri, Kiyokaze, Murakaze, Satokaze, Taekaze, Tanigiri, Umigiri* and *Yamagiri*.

Akigumo, Kazegumo, Kishinami, Kiyonami, Kiyoshimo, Suzunami, Takanami—built by Uraga
Akishimo, Asashimo, Fujinami, Makigumo, Naganami, Onami, Tamanami—built by Fujinagata
Hamanami, Hayanami, Hayashimo, Makinami, Okinami, Yugumo—built by Maizuru navy yard.

They all entered service between September 1941-May 1944. None of the class survived the war, losses being recorded as follows:

Akishimo (November 13, 1944), *Asashimo* (April 7, 1945), *Fujinami* (October 27, 1944), *Hamanami* (November 11, 1944), *Hayashimo* (October 26, 1944), *Kiyonami* (July 20, 1943), *Kiyoshimo* (December 26, 1944), *Naganami* (November 11, 1944), *Okinami* (November 13, 1944), *Suzunami* (November 11, 1943) were sunk by US naval aircraft.

Makinami (November 25, 1943), *Onami* (November 25, 1943), *Takanami* (December 1, 1942), *Yugumo* (October 7, 1943) were sunk by US surface forces.

Makigumo (February 1, 1943) was sunk by mine.

Akigumo was sunk by USS *Redfin* (April 11, 1944), *Hayanami* was sunk by USS

Harder (June 7, 1944), *Kazegumo* was sunk by USS *Hake* (June 8, 1944), *Kishinami* was sunk by USS *Flasher* (December 4, 1944), and *Tamanami* by USS *Mingo* (July 7, 1944).

Displacement: 2077 tons (standard) *Length:* 119.2 m (391 ft 1 in) oa *Beam:* 10.8 m (35 ft 5 in) *Draught:* 3.7 m (12 ft 2 in) *Machinery:* 2-shaft geared turbines, 52000 shp=35 knots *Armament:* 6 5-in (127-mm) (3×2); 4 25-mm (1-in); 8 24-in (61-cm) torpedo tubes (2×4), 16 torpedoes; 36 depth charges *Crew:* 228

Z.23

German destroyer class built 1939-41. In 1936, at the same time as the design was finalized for the *von Roeder* Class, work began on a Type 1936A armed with 15-cm (5.9-in) guns. The rationale is curious, for experience with cruiser-calibre guns in the *S.113* in 1918 had shown that they were too clumsy and slow-firing for destroyers. The explanation is probably that the Germans hoped to offset the Royal Navy's overwhelming superiority in destroyers and light cruisers by somehow bridging the gap. The other reasons were probably psychological; the Japanese, French and Italians had all built large destroyers and Germany would not want to be left behind.

The clipper bow introduced in *Karl Galster* was retained, but the machinery was no more successful and it was a standing joke in the Kriegsmarine that these destroyers suffered from rickets. The layout was similar, but with a twin mounting forward. Eight ships were ordered from AG Weser, Bremen, but no names were allocated and the ships were merely numbered *Z.23-30.*

Production of the C38 twin 15-cm mounting was delayed and so all ships were completed with a single C36 15-cm gun on the forecastle. All except *Z.26* received the proper mounting in 1942-43, but *Z.28* was fitted as a flotilla leader and as she had a deckhouse in place of No 3 gun aft she was completed with two single guns forward, as in the *von Roeder* Class. The AA armament was heavily modified after 1941, with twin and single 3.7-cm (1.46-in) guns, a quadruple 20-mm (0.79-in) Vierling on the after superstructure and single 20-mm guns.

Z.26 was sunk by gunfire from the British cruiser *Trinidad* and the destroyer *Eclipse* during an attack on a Murmansk convoy on March 29, 1942. *Z.27* was sunk by the British cruisers *Glasgow* and *Enterprise* in the Bay of Biscay on December 28, 1943. *Z.23* was scuttled at La Pallice near Rochefort on August 21, 1944, after damage by RAF bombers, and four days later *Z.24* was driven ashore by rocket fire from aircraft near Le Verdon. *Z.28* was sunk by bombs at Sassnitz on March 6, 1945, and the surviving three fell into Allied hands in May. *Z.25* became the French *Hoche* in 1946 and served until 1957. *Z.29* was ceded to the United States but scuttled in the Skagerrak in 1946; *Z.30* was used by the Royal Navy for various tests and was finally sunk as a target in 1948.

In September 1939 a repeat order was placed for seven more ships of a slightly modified 1936A (Mob) Type; *Z.31-34* from AG Weser and *Z.37-39* from Germania, Kiel. They were similar in general appearance, but only *Z.31* was completed with the single C36 15-cm gun forward. After battle damage she was rearmed at the beginning of 1945 with a single 10.5-cm (4.1-in) AA gun forward.

Z.32 was driven ashore by the gunfire of the Canadian destroyers *Haida* and *Huron* off Ushant on June 9, 1944. *Z.37* was scuttled at Bordeaux on August 24, 1944. The survivors fell into Allied hands in 1945: *Z.31* was the French *Marceau* from 1946 to 1956; *Z.33* was the Soviet *Provorny* for about the same time; *Z.38* became HMS *Nonsuch* and served in the Royal Navy until 1949. *Z.34* was scuttled by the US Navy in the Skagerrak in March 1946 but *Z.39* was taken over as *DD.939*, cannibalized for spares for the French ex-German destroyers and finally used as a floating pier.

Displacement: 2630 tons (standard), 3600 tons (full load) *Length:* 127 m (416 ft 9 in) oa *Beam:* 12 m (39 ft 3 in) *Draught:* 4.6 m (15 ft) *Machinery:* 2-shaft geared steam turbines, 70000 shp=38 knots *Armament:* 4/5 15-cm L/50 (4/5×1; or 1×2, 3×1; or 1×2, 2×1); 6 37-mm (1.46-in) AA (3×2); 7/8 20-mm (0.79 in) AA (2×4, or 1×2, 5×1); 8 53-cm (21-in) torpedo tubes, 16 torpedoes; 60 mines *Crew:* 333

Z.35

German destroyer class, built 1941-44. The 15-cm (5.9-in) C38 twin turret had been a failure in the *Z.23* Class, partly because it took up too much internal space and partly because at 100 tons it put too much weight too far forward for good seakeeping. Accordingly the following 1936B type returned to the single 12.7-cm (5-in) gun as in the *von Roeder* Class. In any case the growing need to find space for AA would have meant a reduction in the number of 15-cm guns. Eight ships were authorized, but *Z.40-42* ordered from Germania were cancelled in March 1940 and replaced by the three scout cruisers *Sp.1-3. Z.35-36* and *Z.43-45* were built by AG Weser.

Z.35 and *Z.36* were both mined in the Gulf of Finland on December 12, 1944. *Z.43* was scuttled in Geltinger Bight on May 3, 1945, after being damaged by a mine and then bombed; her wreck was raised and scrapped in 1953. The incomplete *Z.44* was bombed at Bremen while fitting out, and the hull was scuttled by the Allies in July 1946 along with her incomplete sister *Z.45.*

Displacement: 2527 tons (standard), 3507 tons (full load) *Length:* 127 m (416 ft 9 in) oa *Beam:* 12 m (39 ft 3 in) *Draught:* 4.3 m (14 ft) *Machinery:* 2-shaft geared steam turbines, 70000 shp=38 knots *Armament:* 5 12.7-cm (5-in) L/45 (5×1); 6 37-mm (1.46-in) AA (2×2, 2×1); 13 20-mm (0.79-in) AA (3×4, 1×1); 8 53-cm (21-in) torpedo tubes; 76 mines *Crew:* 333

Z.46

German destroyer class. After the re-introduction of the 12.7-cm (5-in) gun in the 1936B Type a new 12.8-cm (5.1-in) C41 twin dual-purpose gun mounting was introduced for the 1936C Type. These would have been disposed in one mounting forward and two aft, with a radar-controlled director above the bridge and on the after superstructure. In other respects the design was a repeat of the earlier *Z.23* and *Z.35* Classes. Five ships, *Z.46-50*, were ordered from AG Weser but *Z.48-50* were never laid down. Both *Z.46* and *Z.47* were hit by bombs while under construction and had to be scrapped on the slipway.

Displacement: 2574 tons (standard), 3594 tons (full load) *Length:* 126 m (413 ft 6 in) oa *Beam:* 12.2 m (40 ft) *Draught:* 4.4 m (14 ft 6 in) max *Machinery:* 2-shaft geared steam turbines, 70000 shp=37.5 knots *Armament:* 6 12.8-cm (5.1-in)/45-cal (3×2); 8 20-mm (0.79-in) AA (4×2); 8 53-cm (21-in) torpedo tubes, 16 torpedoes; 60 mines *Crew:* 320

Z.51

German destroyer of 1943. The ultimate development of German destroyers was this prototype for a diesel-driven destroyer with greatly increased range. The hull was based on the 1938B project, but with a forecastle for improved seakeeping. A new 13.4-cm (5.3-in) dual-purpose single mounting was available and a new quadruple 3.7-cm (1.46-in). The most advanced feature of the design was the use of high-speed MAN V12Z 32/44 diesels, on each wing shaft and four on the centre shaft. An endurance of 13 500 nautical miles was expected at the cruising speed of 19 knots, but tests on the engines showed that little more than 5500 nautical miles would have been achieved in practice. *T.51* was laid down by AG Weser in 1943 but was bombed during construction and had to be abandoned. The production ships *Z.52-56* were ordered but never laid down.

Displacement: 2070 tons (standard), 2675 tons (full load) *Length:* 114 m (374 ft) oa *Beam:* 11 m (36 ft) *Draught:* 4.4 m (14 ft 6 in) maximum *Machinery:* 3-shaft diesel, 57100 bhp=36 knots *Armament:* 4 134-mm (5.3-in) DP (4×1); 8 3.7-cm (1.5-in) AA (2×4); 12 20-mm (0.79-in) AA (4×3); 6 53-cm (21-in) torpedo tubes (2×3); 50 mines *Crew:* 247

Zambesi

British destroyer class. The *Zambesi* or 'Z' Class destroyers were the 10th Flotilla of the Emergency War Programme. They were ordered and laid down in 1942, launched during 1943-44 and completed during June-December 1944. Like the five previous flotillas they were repeats of the 'S' Class except in the matter of armament. In May 1942 it was approved to fit them with 4.5-in (114-mm) instead of 4.7-in (120-mm) guns, a change resulting from a decision to fit all future destroyers with this weapon following the provision of twin 4.5-in mountings in the *Battle* Class destroyers. Although of smaller calibre the 4.5 fired a 25-kg (55-lb) shell, 2.3 kg (5 lb) heavier than that of the 4.7-in and in most respects it was considered superior. The mounting was simply a slightly modified version of the 4.7-in 55° single fitted in the 'S' to 'W' Classes. In addition to this alteration the 'Z' Class were fitted with a new HA/LA director on the bridge—the K tower—a fully stabilized control platform which provided remote power operation. Unfortunately the K tower was not successful as it was complex and prone to breakdowns, and was rather too heavy for use in a small ship. The equipment was also late in delivery which delayed the commissioning of several of the 'Z' Class. To compensate in part for the added topweight two single 20-mm (0.79-in) guns were fitted abaft the funnel instead of twins, as in the earlier classes, except in the *Zambesi.* During 1945 several of the class had these weapons replaced by single 2-pdr pom-poms, while *Zenith* had all her 20-mm guns replaced by four 2-pdr (4×1) and *Myngs* also had a single 40-mm (1.57-in) Bofors fitted in place of her searchlight.

Like the 'S' Class they were fitted for Arctic service and were mainly employed during the last year of the war as escorts to Soviet convoys. They continued in commission for a short time after the war but by the late 1940s most of the class was in reserve. In 1955 *Myngs* and *Zenith* were sold to Egypt and renamed *El Qaher* and *El Fateh* respectively and, to maintain the status quo, *Zealous* and *Zodiac* were sold to Israel and renamed *Elath* and *Yaffa.* On October 7, 1967, *Elath* was sunk by three Styx missiles fired from Port Said. Of the remainder *Zambesi, Zebra* and *Zephyr* were sold for scrap during 1958-59 while *Zest* was converted to a fast A/S frigate during the early 1950s.

Myngs, Zephyr—built by Vickers-Armstrongs
Zambesi, Zealous—built by Cammell Laird
Zebra, Zenith—built by Denny
Zest, Zodiac—built by Thornycroft

Displacement: 1830 tons (standard), 2560 tons (full load) *Length:* 19.1 m (62 ft 9 in) oa *Beam:* 10.9 m (35 ft 9 in) *Draught:* 3 m (10 ft) *Machinery:* 2-shaft geared steam turbines, 40 000 shp=36 knots *Armament:* 4 4.5-in (114-mm) (4×1); 2 40-mm (1.57-in) (1×2); 6 20-mm (0.79-in) (2×2, 2×1); 8 21-in (53-cm) torpedo tubes (2×4) *Crew:* 179

'Zulu'

Soviet attack submarine class. The first 'Zulu' Class boat was laid down about 1950 and completed in 1951; 36 of the class were projected, but only 32 were completed. They were built in the Sudomekh yard, Leningrad, and Yard 402, Severodvinsk. The 'Zulu' Class had nearly twice the displacement of the more numerous 'Whiskey' Class boats, which were laid down at about the same time, and were even more heavily influenced than the latter by the German Type XXI. It appears that a number of the earlier boats were fitted with the closed-cycle Walther propulsion system on the outer shafts, but the Soviet designers were no more able to solve the problems with this system than the Germans, and the original turbines were replaced by diesel-electric engines. These problems caused considerable delays in the construction programme, and the 'Zulu' Class boats did not become operational until the mid-1950s. The early boats also had one or two pairs of 25-mm (1-in) AA guns built into the after end of the conning tower, following German practice in the Type XXI, and some even had a single 100-mm (3.9-in) gun fitted forward of the conning tower (the 'Zulu I' variation). All guns were removed, but differences persisted in the conning tower, dividing the class into 'Zulu II', 'III' and 'IV' variations.

Speed when surfaced is higher than that of the Type XXI, while submerged speed is about the same. The 'Zulus' are fitted with six bow tubes and four stern tubes, with a capacity of 22 torpedoes or 44 mines.

In the mid-1950s seven further 'Zulu' Class hulls were taken over and converted to become the USSR's first ballistic missile submarines. The first boat was completed about 1958 and the last about 1961. The conversion, which took place at Severodvinsk, involved enlargement of the conning tower to accommodate two SS-N-4 Sark ballistic missiles, with a range of 350 nautical miles. The launch tubes descend from the conning tower into the hull. This group became known as the 'Zulu V' Class.

Of the original 32 boats of the 'Zulu I-IV' Class only 22 remained operational in 1978. Of the seven 'Zulu-V' conversions, six had been decommissioned, three of them having been fitted out for oceanographic research and renamed *Lira, Orion* and *Vega.*

Displacement: 2500/2900 tons (surfaced/submerged) *Length:* 90 m (295 ft 3 in) *Beam:* 7.5 m (24 ft 6 in) *Draught:* 6 m (19 ft 9 in) *Machinery:* 3-shaft diesels/3 electric motors, 10 000 bhp/3500 hp=18/15 knots (surfaced/submerged) *Armament:* SS-N-4 Sark missiles (*Zulu V* only) 10 53-cm (21-in) torpedo tubes (6 bow, 4 stern), 22 torpedoes *Crew:* 70 (*Zulu V,* 74)

Index

An italic page number indicates that the entry is illustrated.
Aircraft carriers include escort carriers, seaplane carriers and commando carriers.
Capital ships include battleships and battlecruisers.
Cruisers include scouts.
Destroyers include torpedo boats, torpedo boat destroyers and destroyer escorts.
Escorts include sloops, frigates and corvettes.
Motor torpedo boats include motor gunboats, fast patrol boats, fast attack craft, hydrofoils, etc.
Ships of the same type, name and nationality are differentiated by date of launch unless otherwise specified.

(Arg) Argentina
(Aus) Australia
(Br) Britain
(Braz) Brazil
(Bulg) Bulgaria
(Can) Canada
(Col) Colombia
(Den) Denmark
(Ec) Ecuador
(Fin) Finland
(Fr) France
(Ger) Germany
(Gr) Greece
(In) India
(Indon) Indonesia
(Isr) Israel
(It) Italy
(Jap) Japan
(Mal) Malaysia
(Mex) Mexico
(Neth) Holland
(Nig) Nigeria
(Nor) Norway
(NZ) New Zealand
(Pak) Pakistan
(Pol) Poland
(Port) Portugal
(SA) South Africa
(S Kor) South Korea
(Sp) Spain
(Swe) Sweden
(Taiw) Taiwan
(Thai) Thailand
(Tur) Turkey
(US) United States
(USSR) Soviet Union
(Ven) Venezuela
(Yug) Yugoslavia
The names of Burma, Chile, China, Egypt, Ghana, Iran and Peru are given in full.

Aircraft Carriers

Amphibious Assault Ships, Gunboats and Monitors

Capital Ships

Cruisers

Destroyers

Escorts

Minelayers and Minesweepers

Motor Torpedo Boats

Submarines